JAMES BOND

IAN FLEMING'S

JAMES BOND

MOONRAKER

FROM RUSSIA, WITH LOVE

DR NO

GOLDFINGER

THUNDERBALL

ON HER MAJESTY'S SECRET SERVICE

CHANCELLOR PRESS

Moonraker first published in Great Britain in 1955
by Jonathan Cape Limited
From Russia, With Love first published in Great Britain in 1957
by Jonathan Cape Limited
Dr No first published in Great Britain in 1958
by Jonathan Cape Limited
Goldfinger first published in Great Britain in 1959
by Jonathan Cape Limited
Thunderball first published in Great Britain in 1961
by Jonathan Cape Limited
On Her Majesty's Secret Service first published in Great Britain in 1963
by Jonathan Cape Limited

This collected volume first published in Great Britain in 1994 by
Chancellor Press an imprint of
Reed Consumer Books Limited
Michelin House
81 Fulham Road
London SW3 6RB
and Auckland, Melbourne, Singapore and Toronto

ISBN 1 85152 587 4

A CIP catalogue record for this title is available at the British Library

Printed in Great Britain by The Bath Press, Avon

IAN FLEMING'S

JAMES BOND

MOONRAKER

PART ONE

Monday

Chapter One

Secret Paper-work

The two thirty-eights roared simultaneously.

The walls of the underground room took the crash of sound and batted it to and fro between them until there was silence. James Bond watched the smoke being sucked from each end of the room towards the central Ventaxia fan. The memory in his right hand of how he had drawn and fired with one sweep from the left made him confident. He broke the chamber sideways out of the Colt Detective Special and waited, his gun pointing at the floor, while the Instructor walked the twenty yards towards him through the half-light of the gallery.

Bond saw that the Instructor was grinning. 'I don't believe it,' he said. 'I got you that time.'

The Instructor came up with him. 'I'm in hospital, but you're dead, sir,' he said. In one hand he held the silhouette target of the upper body of a man. In the other a polaroid film, postcard size. He handed this to Bond and they turned to a table behind them on which there was a green-shaded desk-light and a large magnifying glass.

Bond picked up the glass and bent over the photograph. It was a flash-light photograph of him. Around his right hand there was a blurred burst of white flame. He focused the glass carefully on the left side of his dark jacket. In the centre of his heart there was a tiny pinpoint of light.

Without speaking, the Instructor laid the big white man-shaped target under the lamp. Its heart was a black bullseye, about three inches across. Just below and half an inch to the right was the rent made by Bond's bullet.

'Through the left wall of the stomach and out at the back,' said the Instructor, with satisfaction. He took out a pencil and scribbled an addition on the side of the target. 'Twenty rounds and I make it you owe me seven-and-six, sir,' he said impassively.

Bond laughed. He counted out some silver. 'Double the stakes next Monday,' he said.

'That's all right with me,' said the Instructor. 'But you can't beat the machine, sir. And if you want to get into the team for the Dewar Trophy we ought to give the thirty-eights a rest and spend some time on the Remington. That new long twenty-two cartridge they've just brought out is going to mean at least 7,900 out of a possible 8,000 to win. Most of your bullets have got to be in the X-ring and that's only as big as a shilling when it's under your nose. At a hundred yards it isn't there at all.'

'To hell with the Dewar Trophy,' said Bond. 'It's your money I'm after.' He shook the unfired bullets in the chamber of his gun into his cupped hand

and laid them and the gun on the table. 'See you Monday. Same time?'

'Ten o'clock'll be fine, sir,' said the Instructor, jerking down the two handles on the iron door. He smiled at Bond's back as it disappeared up the steep concrete stairs leading to the ground floor. He was pleased with Bond's shooting, but he wouldn't have thought of telling him that he was the best shot in the Service. Only M was allowed to know that, and his Chief of Staff, who would be told to enter the scores of that day's shoot on Bond's Confidential Record.

Bond pushed through the green baize door at the top of the basement steps and walked over to the lift that would take him up to the eighth floor of the tall, grey building near Regent's Park that is the headquarters of the Secret Service. He was satisfied with his score but not proud of it. His trigger finger twitched in his pocket as he wondered how to conjure up that little extra flash of speed that would beat the machine, the complicated box of tricks that sprung the target for just three seconds, fired back at him with a blank ·38, and shot a pencil of light at him and photographed it as he stood and fired from the circle of chalk on the floor.

The lift doors sighed open and Bond got in. The liftman could smell the cordite on him. They always smelled like that when they came up from the shooting gallery. He liked it. It reminded him of the Army. He pressed the button for the eighth and rested the stump of his left arm against the control handle.

If only the light was better thought Bond. But M insisted that all shooting should be done in averagely bad conditions. A dim light and a target that shot back at you was as close as he could get to copying the real thing. 'Shooting hell out of a piece of cardboard doesn't prove anything' was his single-line introduction to the Small-arms Defence Manual.

The lift eased to a stop and as Bond stepped out into the drab Ministry-of-Works-green corridor and into the bustling world of girls carrying files, doors opening and shutting, and muted telephone bells, he emptied his mind of all thoughts of his shoot and prepared himself for the normal business of a routine day at Headquarters.

He walked along to the end door on the right. It was as anonymous as all the others he had passed. No numbers. If you had any business on the eighth floor, and your office was not on that floor, someone would come and fetch you to the room you needed and see you back into the lift when you were through.

Bond knocked and waited. He looked at his watch. Eleven o'clock. Mondays were hell. Two days of dockets and files to plough through. And week-ends were generally busy times abroad. Empty flats got burgled. People were photographed in compromising positions. Motor-car 'accidents' looked better, got more cursory handling, amidst the week-end slaughter on the roads. The weekly bags from Washington, Istanbul, and Tokyo would have come in and been sorted. They might hold something for him.

The door opened and he had his daily moment of pleasure at having a beautiful secretary. 'Morning Lil,' he said.

The careful warmth of her smile of welcome dropped about ten degrees.

'Give me that coat,' she said. 'It stinks of cordite. And don't call me Lil. You know I hate it.'

Bond took off his coat and handed it to her. 'Anyone who gets christened

Loelia Ponsonby ought to get used to pet names.'

He stood beside her desk in the little anteroom which she had somehow made to seem a little more human than an office and watched her hang his coat on the iron frame of the open window.

She was tall and dark with a reserved, unbroken beauty to which the war and five years in the Service had lent a touch of sternness. Unless she married soon, Bond thought for the hundredth time, or had a lover, her cool air of authority might easily become spinsterish and she would join the army of women who had married a career.

Bond had told her as much, often, and he and the two other members of the OO Section had at various times made determined assaults on her virtue. She had handled them all with the same cool motherliness (which, to salve their egos, they privately defined as frigidity) and, the day after, she treated them with small attentions and kindnesses to show that it was really all her fault and that she forgave them.

What they didn't know was that she worried herself almost to death when they were in danger and that she loved them equally; but that she had no intention of becoming emotionally involved with any man who might be dead next week. And it was true that an appointment in the Secret Service was a form of peonage. If you were a woman there wasn't much of you left for other relationships. It was easier for the men. They had an excuse for fragmentary affairs. For them marriage and children and a home were out of the question if they were to be of any use 'in the field' as it was cosily termed. But, for the women, an affair outside the Service automatically made you a 'security risk' and in the last analysis you had a choice of resignation from the Service and a normal life, or of perpetual concubinage to your King and Country.

Loelia Ponsonby knew that she had almost reached the time for decision and all her instincts told her to get out. But every day the drama and romance of her Cavell-Nightingale world locked her more securely into the company of the other girls at Headquarters and every day it seemed more difficult to betray by resignation the father-figure which The Service had become.

Meanwhile she was one of the most envied girls in the building and a member of the small company of Principal Secretaries who had access to the innermost secrets of the Service–'The Pearls and Twin-set' as they were called behind their backs by the other girls, with ironical reference to their supposedly 'County' and 'Kensington' backgrounds–and, so far as the Personnel Branch was concerned, her destiny in twenty years' time would be that single golden line right at the end of a New Year's Honours List, among the medals for officials of the Fishery Board, of the Post Office, of the Women's Institute, towards the bottom of the O.B.E.s: 'Miss Loelia Ponsonby, Principal Secretary in the Ministry of Defence.'

She turned away from the window. She was dressed in a sugar-pink and white striped shirt and a plain dark blue skirt.

Bond smiled into her grey eyes. 'I only call you Lil on Mondays,' he said. 'Miss Ponsonby the rest of the week. But I'll never call you Loelia. It sounds like somebody in an indecent limerick. Any messages?'

'No,' she said shortly. She relented. 'But there's piles of stuff on your desk. Nothing urgent. But there's an awful lot of it. Oh, and the powder-vine says that 008's got out. He's in Berlin, resting. Isn't it wonderful!'

Bond looked quickly at her. 'When did you hear that?'

'About half an hour ago,' she said.

Bond opened the inner door to the big office with the three desks and shut it behind him. He went and stood by the window, looking out at the late spring green of the trees in Regent's Park. So Bill had made it after all. Peenemunde and back. Resting in Berlin sounded bad. Must be in pretty poor shape. Well, he'd just have to wait for news from the only leak in the building–the girls' rest-room, known to the impotent fury of the Security staff as 'The powder-vine.'

Bond sighed and sat down at his desk, pulling towards him the tray of brown folders bearing the top-secret red star. And what about 0011? It was two months since he had vanished into the 'Dirty Half-mile' in Singapore. Not a word since. While he, Bond, No. 007, the senior of the three men in the Service who had earned the double 0 number, sat at his comfortable desk doing paper-work and flirting with their secretary.

He shrugged his shoulders and resolutely opened the top folder. Inside there was a detailed map of southern Poland and north-eastern Germany. Its feature was a straggling red line connecting Warsaw and Berlin. There was also a long typewritten memorandum headed *Mainline: A well-established Escape Route from East to West.*

Bond took out his black gunmetal cigarette-box and his black-oxidized Ronson lighter and put them on the desk beside him. He lit a cigarette, one of the Macedonian blend with the three gold rings round the butt that Morlands of Grosvenor Street made for him, then he settled himself forward in the padded swivel chair and began to read.

It was the beginning of a typical routine day for Bond. It was only two or three times a year that an assignment came along requiring his particular abilities. For the rest of the year he had the duties of an easy-going senior civil servant–elastic office hours from around ten to six; lunch, generally in the canteen; evenings spent playing cards in the company of a few close friends, or at Crockford's; or making love, with rather cold passion, to one of three similarly disposed married women; week-ends playing golf for high stakes at one of the clubs near London.

He took no holidays, but was generally given a fortnight's leave at the end of each assignment–in addition to any sick-leave that might be necessary. He earned £1,500 a year, the salary of a Principal Officer in the Civil Service, and he had a thousand a year free of tax of his own. When he was on a job he could spend as much as he liked, so for the other months of the year he could live very well on his £2,000 a year net.

He had a small but comfortable flat off the King's Road, an elderly Scottish housekeeper–a treasure called May–and a 1930 4½-litre Bentley coupé, supercharged, which he kept expertly tuned so that he could do a hundred when he wanted to.

On these things he spent all his money and it was his ambition to have as little as possible in his banking account when he was killed, as, when he was depressed he knew he would be, before the statutory age of forty-five.

Eight years to go before he was automatically taken off the OO list and given a staff job at Headquarters. At least eight tough assignments. Probably sixteen. Perhaps twenty-four. Too many.

There were five cigarette-ends in the big glass ashtray by the time Bond had finished memorizing the details of 'Mainline'. He picked up a red pencil and ran his eye down the distribution list on the cover. The list started with

'M', then 'C.o.S.', then a dozen or so letters and numbers and then, at the end 'oo'. Against this he put a neat tick, signed it with the figure 7, and tossed the file into his OUT tray.

It was twelve o'clock. Bond took the next folder off the pile and opened it. It was from the Radio Intelligence Division of N.A.T.O., 'For Information Only' and it was headed 'Radio Signatures'.

Bond pulled the rest of the pile towards him and glanced at the first page of each. These were their titles:

The Inspectoscope–a machine for the detection of contraband.
Philopon–A Japanese murder-drug.
Possible points of concealment on trains. No. II. Germany.
The methods of Smersh. No. 6. Kidnapping.
Route Five to Pekin.
Vladivostock. A Photographic Reconnaissance by U.S. Thunderjet.

Bond was not surprised by the curious mixture he was supposed to digest. The OO Section of the Secret Service was not concerned with the current operations of other sections and stations, only with background information which might be useful or instructive to the only three men in the Service whose duties included assassination–who might be ordered to kill. There was no urgency about these files. No action was required by him or by his two colleagues except that each of them jotted down the numbers of dockets which he considered the other two should also read when they were next attached to Headquarters. When the OO Section had finished with this lot they would go down to their final destination in 'Records'.

Bond turned back to the N.A.T.O. paper.

'The almost inevitable manner', he read, 'in which individuality is revealed by minute patterns of behaviour, is demonstrated by the indelible characteristics of the "fist" of each radio operator. This "fist", or manner of tapping out messages, is distinctive and recognizable by those who are practised in receiving messages. It can also be measured by very sensitive mechanisms. To illustrate, in 1943 the United States Radio Intelligence Bureau made use of this fact in tracing an enemy station in Chile operated by "Pedro", a young German. When the Chilean police closed in on the station, "Pedro" escaped. A year later, expert listeners spotted a new illegal transmitter and were able to recognize "Pedro" as the operator. In order to disguise his "fist" he was transmitting left-handed, but the disguise was not effective and he was captured.

'N.A.T.O. Radio Research has recently been experimenting with a form of "scrambler" which can be attached to the wrist of operators with the object of interfering minutely with the nerve centres which control the muscles of the hand. However . . .'

There were three telephones on Bond's desk. A black one for outside calls, a green office telephone, and a red one which went only to M and his Chief of Staff. It was the familiar burr of the red one that broke the silence of the room.

It was M's Chief of Staff.

'Can you come up?' asked the pleasant voice.

'M?' asked Bond.

'Yes.'

'Any clue?'

'Simply said if you were about he'd like to see you.'

'Right,' said Bond, and put down the receiver.

He collected his coat, told his secretary he would be with M and not to wait for him, left his office and walked along the corridor to the lift.

While he waited for it, he thought of those other times, when, in the middle of an empty day, the red telephone had suddenly broken the silence and taken him out of one world and set him down in another. He shrugged his shoulders–Monday! He might have expected trouble.

The lift came. 'Ninth,' said Bond, and stepped in.

Chapter Two

The Columbite King

The ninth was the top floor of the building. Most of it was occupied by Communications, the hand-picked inter-services team of operators whose only interest was the world of microwaves, sunspots, and the Heaviside Layer. Above them, on the flat roof, were the three squat masts of one of the most powerful transmitters in England, explained on the bold bronze list of occupants in the entrance hall of the building by the words 'Radio Tests Ltd.' The other tenants were declared to be 'Universal Export Co.', 'Delaney Bros. (1940) Ltd.', 'The Omnium Corporation', and 'Enquiries (Miss E. Twining, O.B.E.)'.

Miss Twining was a real person. Forty years earlier she had been a Loelia Ponsonby. Now, in retirement, she sat in a small office on the ground floor and spent her days tearing up circulars, paying the rates and taxes of her ghostly tenants, and politely brushing off salesmen and people who wanted to export something or have their radios mended.

It was always very quiet on the ninth floor. As Bond turned to the left outside the lift and walked along the softly carpeted corridor to the green baize door that led to the offices of M and his personal staff, the only sound he heard was a thin high-pitched whine that was so faint that you almost had to listen for it.

Without knocking he pushed through the green door and walked into the last room but one along the passage.

Miss Moneypenny, M's private secretary, looked up from her typewriter and smiled at him. They liked each other and she knew that Bond admired her looks. She was wearing the same model shirt as his own secretary, but with blue stripes.

'New uniform, Penny?' said Bond.

She laughed. 'Loelia and I share the same little woman,' she said. 'We tossed and I got blue.'

A snort came through the open door of the adjoining room. The Chief of Staff, a man of about Bond's age, came out, a sardonic grin on his pale, overworked face.

'Break it up,' he said. 'M's waiting. Lunch afterwards?'

'Fine,' said Bond. He turned to the door beside Miss Moneypenny, walked through and shut it after him. Above it, a green light went on. Miss Moneypenny raised her eyebrows at the Chief of Staff. He shook his head.

'I don't think it's business, Penny,' he said. 'Just sent for him out of the blue.' He went back into his own room and got on with the day's work.

When Bond came through the door, M was sitting at his broad desk, lighting a pipe. He made a vague gesture with the lighted match towards the chair on the other side of the desk and Bond walked over and sat down. M glanced at him sharply through the smoke and then threw the box of matches on to the empty expanse of red leather in front of him.

'Have a good leave?' he asked abruptly.

'Yes, thank you, sir,' said Bond.

'Still sunburned, I see.' M looked his disapproval. He didn't really begrudge Bond a holiday which had been partly convalescence. The hint of criticism came from the puritan and the jesuit who live in all leaders of men.

'Yes, sir,' said Bond noncommittally. 'It's very hot near the equator.'

'Quite,' said M. 'Well-deserved rest.' He screwed up his eyes without humour. 'Hope the colour won't last too long. Always suspicious of sunburned men in England. Either they've not got a job of work to do or they put it on with a sun-lamp.' He dismissed the subject with a short sideways jerk of his pipe.

He put the pipe back in his mouth and pulled at it absent-mindedly. It had gone out. He reached for the matches and wasted some time getting it going again.

'Looks as if we'll get that gold after all,' he said finally. 'There's been some talk of the Hague Court, but Ashenheim's a fine lawyer.'*

'Good,' said Bond.

There was silence for a moment. M gazed into the bowl of his pipe. Through the open windows came the distant roar of London's traffic. A pigeon landed on one of the window-sills with a clatter of wings and quickly took off again.

Bond tried to read something in the weatherbeaten face he knew so well and which held so much of his loyalty But the grey eyes were quiet and the little pulse that always beat high up on the right temple when M was tense showed no sign of life.

Suddenly Bond suspected that M was embarrassed. He had the feeling that M didn't know where to begin. Bond wanted to help. He shifted in his chair and took his eyes off M. He looked down at his hands and idly picked at a rough nail.

M lifted his eyes from his pipe and cleared his throat.

'Got anything particular on at the moment, James?' he asked in a neutral voice.

'James.' That was unusual. It was rare for M to use a Christian name in this room.

'Only paperwork and the usual courses,' said Bond. 'Anything you want me for, sir?'

'As a matter of fact there is,' said M. He frowned at Bond. 'But it's really got nothing to do with the Service. Almost a personal matter. Thought you might give me a hand.'

'Of course, sir,' said Bond. He was relieved for M's sake that the ice had

* This refers to Bond's previous assignment; described in *Live and Let Die* by the same author.

been broken. Probably one of the old man's relations had got into trouble and M didn't want to ask a favour of Scotland Yard. Blackmail, perhaps. Or drugs. He was pleased that M should have chosen him. Of course he would take care of it. M was such a desperate stickler about Government property and personnel. Using Bond on a personal matter must have seemed to him like stealing the Government's money.

'Thought you'd say so,' said M, gruffly. 'Won't take up much of your time. An evening ought to be enough.' He paused. Well now, you've heard of this man Sir Hugo Drax?'

'Of course, sir,' said Bond, surprised at the name. 'You can't open a paper without reading something about him. *Sunday Express* is running his life. Extraordinary story.'

'I know,' said M shortly. 'Just give me the facts as you see them. I'd like to know if your version tallies with mine.'

Bond gazed out of the window for a moment to marshal his thoughts. M didn't like haphazard talk. He liked a fully detailed story with no um-ing and er-ing. No afterthoughts or hedging.

'Well, sir,' said Bond finally. 'For one thing the man's a national hero. The public have taken to him. I suppose he's in much the same class as Jack Hobbs or Gordon Richards. They've got a real feeling for him. They consider he's one of them, but a glorified version. A sort of superman. He's not much to look at, with all those scars from his war injuries, and he's a bit loud-mouthed and ostentatious. But they rather like that. Makes him a sort of Lonsdale figure, but more in their class. They like his friends calling him "Hugger" Drax. It makes him a bit of a card and I expect it gives the women a thrill. And then when you think what he's doing for the country, out of his own pocket and far beyond what any government seems to be able to do, it's really extraordinary that they don't insist on making him Prime Minister.'

Bond saw the cold eyes getting chillier, but he was determined not to let his admiration for Drax's achievements be dampened by the older man. 'After all, sir,' he continued reasonably, 'it looks as if he's made this country safe from war for years. And he can't be much over forty. I feel the same as most people about him. And then there's all this mystery about his real identity. I'm not surprised people feel rather sorry for him, although he is a multi-millionaire. He seems to be a lonely sort of man in spite of his gay life.'

M smiled drily. 'All that sounds rather like a trailer for the *Express* story. He's certainly an extraordinary man. But what's your version of the facts? I don't expect I know much more than you do. Probably less. Don't read the papers very carefully, and there are no files on him except at the War Office and they're not very illuminating. Now then. What's the gist of this *Express* story?'

'Sorry, sir,' said Bond. 'But the facts are pretty slim. Well,' he looked out of the window again and concentrated, 'in the German break-through in the Ardennes in the winter of '44, the Germans made a lot of use of guerrillas and saboteurs. Gave them the rather spooky name of Werewolves. They did quite a lot of damage of one sort or another. Very good at camouflage and stay-behind tricks of all sorts and some of them went on operating long after Ardennes had failed and we had crossed the Rhine. They were supposed to carry on even when we had overrun the country. But they packed up pretty quickly when things got really bad.

'One of their best coups was to blow up one of the rear liaison H.Q.s between the American and British armies. Reinforcement Holding Units I think they're called. It was a mixed affair, all kinds of Allied personnel–American signals, British ambulance drivers–a rather shifting group from every sort of unit. The Werewolves somehow managed to mine the mess-hall and, when it blew, it took with it quite a lot of the field hospital as well. Killed or wounded over a hundred. Sorting out all the bodies was the hell of a business. One of the English bodies was Drax. Half his face blown away. Total amnesia that lasted a year and at the end of that time they didn't know who he was and nor did he. There were about twenty-five other unidentified bodies that neither we nor the Americans could sort out. Either not enough bits, or perhaps people in transit, or there without authorization. It was that sort of a unit. Two commanding officers, of course. Sloppy staff work. Lousy records. So after a year in various hospitals they took Drax through the War Office file of Missing Men. When they came to the papers of a no-next-of-kin called Hugo Drax, an orphan who had been working in the Liverpool docks before the war, he showed signs of interest, and the photograph and physical description seemed to tally more or less with what our man must have looked like before he was blown up. From that time he began to mend. He started to talk a bit about simple things he remembered, and the doctors got very proud of him. The War Office found a man who had served in the same Pioneer unit as this "Hugo Drax" and he came along to the hospital and said he was sure the man was Drax. That settled it. Advertising didn't produce another Hugo Drax and he was finally discharged late in 1945 in that name with back pay and a full disability pension.'

'But he still says he doesn't really know who he is,' interrupted M. 'He's a member of Blades. I've often played cards with him and talked to him afterwards at dinner. He says he sometimes gets a strong feeling of "having been there before". Often goes to Liverpool to try and hunt up his past. Anyway, what else?'

Bond's eyes were turned inwards, remembering. 'He seems to have disappeared for about three years after the war,' he said. 'Then the City started to hear about him from all over the world. The Metal Market heard about him first. Seems he'd cornered a very valuable ore called Columbite. Everybody was wanting the stuff. It's got an extraordinarily high melting point. Jet engines can't be made without it. There's very little of it in the world, only a few thousand tons are produced every year, mostly as a by-product of the Nigerian tin mines. Drax must have looked at the Jet Age and somehow put his finger on its main scarcity. He must have got hold of about £10,000 from somewhere because the *Express* says that in 1946 he'd bought three tons of Columbite, which cost him around £3,000 a ton. He got a £5,000 premium on this lot from an American aircraft firm who wanted it in a hurry. Then he started buying futures in the stuff, six months, nine months, a year forward. In three years he'd made a corner. Anyone who wanted Columbite went to Drax Metals for it. All this time he'd been playing about with futures in other small commodities–Shellac, Sisal, Black Pepper–anything where you could build up a big position on margin. Of course he gambled on a rising commodity market but he had the guts to keep his foot right down on the pedal even when the pace got hot as hell. And whenever he took a profit he ploughed the money back again. For instance, he was one of the first men to buy up used ore-dumps in South Africa. Now they're being re-mined for their uranium content. Another fortune there.'

M's quiet eyes were fixed on Bond. He puffed at his pipe, listening.

'Of course,' continued Bond, lost in his story, 'all this made the City wonder what the hell was going on. The commodity brokers kept on coming across the name of Drax. Whatever they wanted Drax had got it and was holding out for a much higher price than they were prepared to pay. He operated from Tangier–free port, no taxes, no currency restrictions. By 1950 he was a multi-millionaire. Then he came back to England and started spending it. He simply threw it about. Best houses, best cars, best women. Boxes at the Opera, at Goodwood. Prize-winning Jersey herds. Prize-winning carnations. Prize-winning two-year-olds. Two yachts; money for the Walker Cup team; £100,000 for the Flood Disaster Fund; Coronation Ball for Nurses at the Albert Hall–there wasn't a week when he wasn't hitting the headlines with some splash or other. And all the time he went on getting richer and the people simply loved it. It was the Arabian Nights. It lit up their lives. If a wounded soldier from Liverpool could get there in five years, why shouldn't they or their sons? It sounded almost as easy as winning a gigantic football pool.

'And then came his astonishing letter to the Queen: "Your Majesty, may I have the temerity . . ." and the typical genius of the single banner-line across the *Express* next day: "TEMERITY DRAX", and the story of how he had given to Britain his entire holding in Columbite to build a super atomic rocket with a range that would cover nearly every capital in Europe–the immediate answer to anyone who tried to atom-bomb London. £10,000,000 he was going to put up out of his own pocket, and he had the design of the thing and was prepared to find the staff to build it.

'And then there were months of delay and everyone got impatient. Questions in the House. The Opposition nearly forced a vote of Confidence. And then the announcement by the Prime Minister that the design had been approved by the Woomera Range experts of the Ministry of Supply, and that the Queen had been graciously pleased to accept the gift on behalf of the people of Britain and had conferred a knighthood on the donor.'

Bond paused, almost carried away by the story of this extraordinary man.

'Yes,' said M. '"Peace in Our Time–This Time". I remember the headline. A year ago. And now the rocket's nearly ready. "The Moonraker". And from all I hear it really should do what he says. It's very odd.' He relapsed into silence, gazing out of the window.

He turned back and faced Bond across the desk.

'That's about it,' he said slowly. 'I don't know much more than you do. A wonderful story. Extraordinary man.' He paused, reflecting. 'There's only one thing. . .' M tapped the stem of his pipe against his teeth.

'What's that, sir?' asked Bond.

M seemed to make up his mind. He looked mildly across at Bond.

'Sir Hugo Drax cheats at cards.'

Chapter Three

'Belly Strippers', etc.

'Cheats at cards?'

M frowned. 'That's what I said,' he commented drily.

'It doesn't seem to you odd that a multi-millionaire should cheat at cards?'

Bond grinned apologetically. 'Not as odd as all that, sir,' he said. 'I've known very rich people cheat themselves at Patience. But it just didn't fit in with my picture of Drax. Bit of an anti-climax.'

'That's the point,' said M. 'Why does he do it? And don't forget that cheating at cards can still smash a man. In so-called "Society", it's about the only crime that can still finish you, whoever you are. Drax does it so well that nobody's caught him yet. As a matter of fact I doubt if anyone has begun to suspect him except Basildon. He's the Chairman of Blades. He came to me. He's got a vague idea I've got something to do with Intelligence and I've given him a hand over over one or two little troubles in the past. Asked my advice. Said he didn't want a fuss at the club, of course, but above all he wants to save Drax from making a fool of himself. He admires him as much as we all do and he's terrified of an incident. You couldn't stop a scandal like that getting out. A lot of M.P.s are members and it would soon get talked about in the Lobby. Then the gossip-writers would get hold of it. Drax would have to resign from Blades and the next thing there'd be a libel action brought in his defence by one of his friends. Tranby Croft all over again. At least, that's how Basildon's mind is working and I must say I can see it that way too. Anyway, said M with finality, 'I've agreed to help and', he looked levelly at Bond, 'that's where you come in. You're the best card-player in the Service, or' he smiled ironically, 'you should be after the casino jobs you've been on, and I remembered that we'd spent quite a lot of money putting you through a course in card-sharping before you went after those Roumanians in Monte Carlo before the war.'

Bond smiled grimly. 'Steffi Esposito,' he said softly. 'That was the chap. American. Made me work ten hours a day for a week learning a thing called the Riffle Stack and how to deal Seconds and Bottoms and Middles. I wrote a long report about it at the time. Must be buried in Records. He knew every trick in the game. How to wax the aces so that the pack will break at them; Edge Work and Line Work with a razor on the backs of the high cards; Trimming; Arm Pressure Holdouts–mechanical gadgets up your sleeve that feed you cards. Belly Strippers–trimming a whole pack less than a millimetre down both sides, but leaving a slight belly on the cards you're interested in–the aces, for instance. Shiners, tiny mirrors built into rings, or fitted into the bottom of a pipe-bowl. Actually,' Bond admitted, 'it was his tip about "Luminous Readers" that helped me on that Monte Carlo job. A croupier was using an invisible ink the team could pick out with special glasses. But Steffi was a wonderful chap. Scotland Yard found him for us.

He could shuffle the pack once and then cut the four aces out of it. Absolute magic.'

'Sounds a bit too professional for our man,' commented M. 'That sort of work needs hours of practice every day, or an accomplice, and I can't believe he'd find that at Blades. No, there's nothing sensational about his cheating and for all I know it might be a fantastic run of luck. It's odd. He's not a particularly good player–he only plays bridge by the way–but quite often he brings off bids or doubles or finesses that are absolutely phenomenal–quite against the odds. Or the conventions. But they come off. He's always a big winner and they play high at Blades. He hasn't lost on a weekly settlement since he joined a year ago. We've got two or three of the finest players in the world in the Club and none of them has ever had a record like that over twelve months. It's getting talked about in a sort of joking way and I think Basildon's right to do something about it. What system do you suppose Drax has got?'

Bond was longing for his lunch. The Chief of Staff must have given him up half an hour ago. He could have talked to M about cheating for hours, and M who never seemed to be interested in food or sleep, would have listened to everything and remembered it afterwards. But Bond was hungry.

'Assuming he's not a professional, sir, and can't doctor the cards in any way, there are only two answers. He's either looking, or else he's got a system of signals with his partner. Does he often play with the same man?'

'We always cut for partners after each rubber,' said M. 'Unless there's a challenge. And on guest nights, Mondays and Thursdays, you stick to your guest. Drax nearly always brings a man called Meyer, his metal broker. Nice chap. Jew. Very fine player.'

'I might be able to tell if I watched,' said Bond.

'That's what I was going to say,' said M. 'How about coming along tonight? At any rate you'll get a good dinner. Meet me there about six. I'll take some money off you at piquet and we'll watch the bridge for a little. After dinner we'll have a rubber or two with Drax and his friend. They're always there on Monday. All right? Sure I'm not taking you away from your work?'

'No, sir,' said Bond with a grin. 'And I'd like to come very much. Bit of a busman's holiday. And if Drax is cheating, I'll show him I've spotted it and that should be enough to warn him off. I wouldn't like to see him get into a mess. That all, sir?'

'Yes, James,' said M. 'And thank you for your help. Drax must be a bloody fool. Obviously a bit of a crank. But it isn't the man I'm worried about. I wouldn't like to chance anything going wrong with this rocket of his. And Drax more or less *is* the Moonraker. Well, see you at six. Don't bother about dressing. Some of us do for dinner and some of us don't. Tonight we won't. Better go along now and sandpaper your fingertips or whatever you sharpers do.'

Bond smiled back at M and got to his feet. It sounded a promising evening. As he walked over to the door and let himself out he reflected that here at last was an interview with M that didn't cast a shadow.

M's secretary was still at her desk. There was a plate of sandwiches and a glass of milk beside her typewriter. She looked sharply at Bond, but there was nothing to be read in his expression.

'I suppose he gave up,' said Bond.

'Nearly an hour ago,' said Miss Moneypenny reproachfully. 'It's half-past two. He'll be back any minute now.'

'I'll go down to the canteen before it closes,' he said. 'Tell him I'll pay for his lunch next time.' He smiled at her and walked out into the corridor and along to the lift.

There were only a few people left in the officers' canteen. Bond sat by himself and ate a grilled sole, a large mixed salad with his own dressing laced with mustard, some Brie cheese and toast, and half a carafe of white Bordeaux. He had two cups of black coffee and was back in his office by three. With half his mind preoccupied with M's problem, he hurried through the rest of the N.A.T.O. file, said goodbye to his secretary after telling her where he would be that evening, and at four-thirty was collecting his car from the staff garage at the back of the building.

'Supercharger's whining a bit, sir,' said the ex-R.A.F. mechanic who regarded Bond's Bentley as his own property. 'Take it down tomorrow if you won't be needing her at lunch-time.'

'Thanks,' said Bond, 'that'll be fine.' He took the car quietly out into the park and over to Baker Street, the two-inch exhaust bubbling fatly in his wake.

He was home in fifteen minutes. He left the car under the plane trees in the little square and let himself into the ground floor flat of the converted Regency house, went into the book-lined sitting-room and, after a moment's search, pulled *Scarne on Cards* out of its shelf and dropped it on the ornate Empire desk near the broad window.

He walked through into the smallish bedroom with the white and gold Cole wallpaper and the deep red curtains, undressed and threw his clothes, more or less tidily, on the dark blue counterpane of the double bed. Then he went into the bathroom and had a quick shower. Before leaving the bathroom he examined his face in the glass and decided that he had no intention of sacrificing a lifetime prejudice by shaving twice in one day.

In the glass, the grey-blue eyes looked back at him with the extra light they held when his mind was focused on a problem that interested him. The lean, hard face had a hungry, competitive edge to it. There was something swift and intent in the way he ran his fingers along his jaw and in the impatient stroke of the hairbrush to put back the comma of black hair that fell down an inch above his right eyebrow. It crossed his mind that, with the fading of his sunburn, the scar down the right cheek that had shown so white was beginning to be less prominent, and automatically he glanced down his naked body and registered that the almost indecent white area left by his bathing trunks was less sharply defined. He smiled at some memory and went through into the bedroom.

Ten minutes later, in a heavy white silk shirt, dark blue trousers of Navy serge, dark blue socks, and well-polished black moccasin shoes, he was sitting at his desk with a pack of cards in one hand and Scarne's wonderful guide to cheating open in front of him.

For half an hour, as he ran quickly through the section on Methods, he practised the vital Mechanic's Grip (three fingers curled round the long edge of the cards, and the index finger at the short upper edge away from him), Palming, and Nullifying the Cut. His hands worked automatically at these basic manoeuvres while his eyes read, and he was glad to find that his fingers were supple and assured and that there was no noise from the cards even with the very difficult single-handed Annulment.

At five-thirty he slapped the cards on the table and shut the book.

He went into his bedroom, filled the wide black case with cigarettes and slipped it into his hip pocket, put on a black knitted silk tie and his coat and verified that his cheque book was in his notecase.

He stood for a moment, thinking. Then he selected two white silk handkerchiefs, carefully rumpled them, and put one into each side-pocket of his coat.

He lit a cigarette and walked back into the sitting-room and sat down at his desk again and relaxed for ten minutes, gazing out of the window at the empty square and thinking about the evening that was just going to begin and about Blades, probably the most famous private card club in the world.

The exact date of the foundation of Blades is uncertain. The second half of the eighteenth century saw the opening of many coffee houses and gaming rooms, and premises and proprietors shifted often with changing fashions and fortunes. Whites was founded in 1755, Almacks in 1764, and Brooks's in 1774, and it was in that year that the Scavoir Vivre, which was to be the cradle of Blades, opened its doors on to Park Street, a quiet backwater off St James's.

The Scavoir Vivre was too exclusive to live and it black-balled itself to death within a year. Then, in 1776, Horace Walpole wrote: 'A new club is opened off St James's Street that piques itself in surpassing all its predecessors' and in 1778 'Blades' first occurs in a letter from Gibbon, the historian, who coupled it with the name of its founder, a German called Longchamp at that time conducting the Jockey Club at Newmarket.

From the outset Blades seems to have been a success, and in 1782 we find the Duke of Wirtemberg writing excitedly home to his younger brother: 'This is indeed the "Ace of Clubs"! There have been four or five quinze tables going in the room at the same time, with whist and piquet, after which a full Hazard table. I have known two at the same time. Two chests each containing 4000 guinea rouleaus were scarce sufficient for the night's circulation.'

Mention of Hazard perhaps provides a clue to the club's prosperity. Permission to play this dangerous but popular game must have been given by the Committee in contravention of its own rules which laid down that 'No game is to be admitted to the House of the Society but Chess, Whist, Picket, Cribbage, Quadrille, Ombre and Tredville'.

In any event the club continued to flourish and remains to this day the home of some of the highest 'polite' gambling in the world. It is not as aristocratic as it was, the redistribution of wealth has seen to that, but it is still the most exclusive club in London. The membership is restricted to two hundred and each candidate must have two qualifications for election: he must behave like a gentleman and he must be able to 'show' £100,000 in cash or gilt-edged securities.

The amenities of Blades, apart from the gambling, are so desirable that the Committee has had to rule that every member is required to win or lose £500 a year on the club premises, or pay an annual fine of £250. The food and wine are the best in London and no bills are presented, the cost of all meals being deducted at the end of each week *pro rata* from the profits of the winners. Seeing that about £5,000 changes hands each week at the tables the impost is not too painful and the losers have the satisfaction of saving something from the wreck; and the custom explains the fairness of the levy on infrequent gamblers.

Club servants are the making or breaking of any club and the servants of Blades have no equal. The half-dozen waitresses in the dining-room are of such a high standard of beauty that some of the younger members have been known to smuggle them undetected into débutante balls, and if, at night, one or another of the girls is persuaded to stray into one of the twelve members' bedrooms at the back of the club, that is regarded as the member's private concern.

There are one or two other small refinements which contribute to the luxury of the place. Only brand-new currency notes and silver are paid out on the premises and, if a member is staying overnight, his notes and small change are taken away by the valet who brings the early morning tea and *The Times* and are replaced with new money. No newspaper comes to the reading room before it has been ironed. Floris provides the soaps and lotions in the lavatories and bedrooms; there is a direct wire to Ladbroke's from the porter's lodge; the club has the finest tents and boxes at the principal race-meetings, at Lords, Henley, and Wimbledon, and members travelling abroad have automatic membership of the leading club in every foreign capital.

In short, membership of Blades, in return for the £100 entrance fee and the £50 a year subscription, provides the standard of luxury of the Victorian age together with the opportunity to win or lose, in great comfort, anything up to £20,000 a year.

Bond, reflecting on all this, decided that he was going to enjoy his evening. He had played at Blades only a dozen times in his life, and on the last occasion he had burnt his fingers badly in a high poker game, but the prospect of some expensive bridge and of the swing of a few, to him, not unimportant hundred pounds made his muscles taut with anticipation.

And then, of course, there was the little business of Sir Hugo Drax, which might bring an additional touch of drama to the evening.

He was not even disturbed by a curious portent he encountered while he was driving along King's Road into Sloane Square with half his mind on the traffic and the other half exploring the evening ahead.

It was a few minutes to six and there was thunder about. The sky threatened rain and it had become suddenly dark. Across the square from him, high up in the air, a bold electric sign started to flash on and off. The fading light-waves had caused the cathode tube to start the mechanism which would keep the sign flashing through the dark hours until, around six in the morning, the early light of day would again sensitize the tube and cause the circuit to close.

Startled at the great crimson words, Bond pulled in to the curb, got out of the car and crossed to the other side of the street to get a better view of the big skysign.

Ah! That was it. Some of the letters had been hidden by a neighbouring building. It was only one of those Shell advertisements. 'SUMMER SHELL IS HERE' was what it said.

Bond smiled to himself and walked back to his car and drove on.

When he had first seen the sign, half-hidden by the building, great crimson letters across the evening sky had flashed a different message.

They had said: 'HELL IS HERE . . . HELL IS HERE . . . HELL IS HERE.'

Chapter Four

The 'Shiner'

Bond left the Bentley outside Brooks's and walked round the corner into Park Street.

The Adam frontage of Blades, recessed a yard or so back from its neighbours, was elegant in the soft dusk. The dark red curtains had been drawn across the ground floor bow-windows on either side of the entrance and a liveried servant showed for a moment as he drew them across the three windows of the floor above. In the centre of the three, Bond could see the heads and shoulders of two men bent over a game, probably backgammon he thought, and he caught a glimpse of the spangled fire of one of the three great chandeliers that illuminate the famous gambling room.

Bond pushed through the swing-doors and walked up to the old-fashioned porter's lodge ruled over by Brevett, the guardian of Blades and the counsellor and family friend of half the members.

'Evening, Brevett. Is the Admiral in?'

'Good evening, sir,' said Brevett, who knew Bond as an occasional guest at the club. 'The Admiral's waiting for you in the card-room. Page, take Commander Bond up to the Admiral. Lively now!'

As Bond followed the liveried page boy across the worn black and white marble floor of the hall and up the wide staircase with its fine mahogany balustrade, he remembered the story of how, at one election, nine blackballs had been found in the box when there were only eight members of the committee present. Brevett, who had handed the box from member to member, was said to have confessed to the Chairman that he was so afraid the candidate would be elected that he put in a blackball himself. No one had objected. The committee would rather have lost its chairman than the porter whose family had held the same post at Blades for a hundred years.

The page pushed open one wing of the tall doors at the top of the stairs and held it for Bond to go through. The long room was not crowded and Bond saw M sitting by himself playing patience in the alcove formed by the left hand of the three bow windows. He dismissed the page and walked across the heavy carpet, noticing the rich background smell of cigar-smoke, the quiet voices that came from the three tables of bridge, and the sharp rattle of dice across an unseen backgammon board.

'There you are,' said M as Bond came up. He waved to the chair that faced him across the card-table. 'Just let me finish this. I haven't cracked this man Canfield for months. Drink?'

'No, thanks,' said Bond. He sat down and lit a cigarette and watched with amusement the concentration M was putting into his game.

'Admiral Sir M★★★★ M★★★★★★★–something at the Ministry of Defence.' M looked like any member of any of the clubs in St James's Street. Dark grey suit, stiff white collar, the favourite dark blue bow-tie with white spots, rather loosely tied, the thin black cord of the rimless eyeglass that M seemed only to use to read menus, the keen sailor's face, with the clear, sharp sailor's eyes. It was difficult to believe that an hour before he had been playing with a thousand live chessmen against the enemies of England; that there might be, this evening, fresh blood on his hands, or a successful burglary, or the hideous knowledge of a disgusting blackmail case.

And what could the casual observer think of him, 'Commander James Bond, C.M.G., R.N.V.S.R.', also 'something at the Ministry of Defence', the rather saturnine young man in his middle thirties sitting opposite the Admiral? Something a bit cold and dangerous in that face. Looks pretty fit. May have been attached to Templer in Malaya. Or Nairobi. Mau Mau work. Tough-looking customer. Doesn't look the sort of chap one usually sees in Blades.

Bond knew that there was something alien and un-English about himself. He knew that he was a difficult man to cover up. Particularly in England. He shrugged his shoulders. Abroad was what mattered. He would never have a job to do in England. Outside the jurisdiction of the Service. Anyway, he didn't need a cover this evening. This was recreation.

M snorted and threw his cards down. Bond automatically gathered in the pack and as automatically gave it the Scarne shuffle, marrying the two halves with the quick downward riffle that never brings the cards off the table. He squared off the pack and pushed it away.

M beckoned to a passing waiter. 'Piquet cards, please, Tanner,' he said.

The waiter went away and came back a moment later with the two thin packs. He stripped off the wrapping and placed them, with two markers, on the table. He stood waiting.

'Bring me a whisky and soda,' said M. 'Sure you won't have anything?'

Bond looked at his watch. It was half-past six. 'Could I have a dry Martini?' he said. 'Made with Vodka. Large slice of lemon-peel.'

'Rot-gut,' commented M briefly as the waiter went away. 'Now I'll just take a pound or two off you and then we'll go and have a look at the bridge. Our friend hasn't turned up yet.'

For half an hour they played the game at which the expert player can nearly always win even with the cards running slightly against him. At the end of the game Bond laughed and counted out three pound notes.

'One of these days I'm going to take some trouble and really learn piquet,' he said. 'I've never won against you yet.'

'It's all memory and playing the odds,' said M with satisfaction. He finished his whisky and soda. 'Let's go over and see what's going on at the bridge. Our man's playing at Basildon's table. Came in about ten minutes ago. If you notice anything, just give me a nod and we'll go downstairs and talk about it.'

He stood up and Bond followed suit.

The far end of the room had begun to fill up and half a dozen tables of bridge were going. At the round poker table under the centre chandelier three players were counting chips into five stacks, waiting for two more players to come in. The kidney-shaped baccarat table was still shrouded and would probably remain so after dinner, when it would be used for chemin-de-fer.

Bond followed M out of their alcove, relishing the scene down the long room, the oases of green, the tinkle of glasses as the waiters moved amongst the tables, the hum of talk punctuated by sudden exclamations and warm laughter, the haze of blue smoke rising up through the dark red lamp-shades that hung over the centre of each table. His pulses quickened with the smell of it all and his nostrils flared slightly as the two men came down the long room and joined the company.

M, with Bond beside him, wandered casually from table to table, exchanging greetings with the players until they reached the last table beneath the fine Lawrence of Beau Brummel over the wide Adam fireplace.

'Double, damn you,' said the loud, cheerful voice of the player with his back to Bond. Bond thoughtfully noted the head of tight reddish hair that was all he could see of the speaker, then he looked to the left at the rather studious profile of Lord Basildon. The Chairman of Blades was leaning back, looking critically down his nose at the hand of cards which was held out and away from him as if it were a rare object.

'My hand is so exquisite that I am forced to redouble, my dear Drax,' he said. He looked across at his partner. 'Tommy,' he said. 'Charge this to me if it goes wrong.'

'Rot,' said his partner. 'Meyer? Better take Drax out.'

'Too frightened,' said the middle-aged florid man who was playing with Drax. 'No bid.' He picked up his cigar from the brass ashtray and put it carefully into the middle of his mouth.

'No bid here,' said Basildon's partner.

'And nothing here,' came Drax's voice.

'Five clubs redoubled,' said Basildon. 'Your lead, Meyer.'

Bond looked over Drax's shoulder. Drax had the ace of spades and the ace of hearts. He promptly made them both and led another heart which Basildon took on the table with the king.

'Well,' said Basildon. 'There are four trumps against me including the queen. I shall play Drax to have her.' He finessed against Drax. Meyer took the trick with the queen.

'Hell and damnation,' said Basildon. 'What's the queen doing in Meyer's hand? Well I'm damned. Anyway the rest are mine.' He fanned his cards down on the table. He looked defensively at his partner. 'Can you beat it, Tommy? Drax doubles and Meyer has the queen.' There was not more than a natural exasperation in his voice.

Drax chuckled. 'Didn't expect my partner to have a Yarborough did you?' he said cheerfully to Basildon. 'Well that's just the four hundred above the line. Your deal.' He cut the cards to Basildon and the game went on.

So it had been Drax's deal the hand before. That might be important. Bond lit a cigarette and reflectively examined the back of Drax's head.

M's voice cut in on Bond's thoughts. 'You remember my friend Commander Bond, Basil? Thought we'd come along and play some cards this evening.'

Basildon smiled up at Bond. 'Evening,' he said. He waved a hand round the table from left to right. 'Meyer, Dangerfield, Drax.' The three men looked up briefly and Bond nodded a greeting to the table in general. 'You all know the Admiral,' added the Chairman, starting to deal.

Drax half turned in his chair. 'Ah, the Admiral,' he said boisterously. 'Glad to have you aboard Admiral. Drink?'

'No thanks,' said M with a thin smile. 'Just had one.'

Drax turned and glanced up at Bond, who caught a glimpse of a tuft of reddish moustache and a rather chilly blue eye. 'What about you?' asked Drax perfunctorily.

'No, thanks,' said Bond.

Drax swivelled back to the table and picked up his cards. Bond watched the big blunt hands sort them.

Then he moved round the table with a second clue to ponder.

Drax didn't sort his cards into suits as most players do, but only into reds and blacks, ungraded, making his hand very difficult to kibitz and almost impossible for one his neighbours, if they were so inclined, to decipher.

Bond knew it for the way people hold their hands who are very careful card-players indeed.

Bond went and stood beside the chimneypiece. He took out a cigarette and lit it at the flame from a small gas-jet enclosed in a silver grille–a relic of the days before the use of matches–that protruded from the wall beside him.

From where he stood he could see the hand of Meyer, and by moving a pace to the right, of Basildon. His view of Sir Hugo Drax was uninterrupted and he inspected him carefully while appearing to interest himself only in the game.

Drax gave the impression of being a little larger than life. He was physically big–about six foot tall, Bond guessed–and his shoulders were exceptionally broad. He had a big square head and the tight reddish hair was parted in the middle. On either side of the parting the hair dipped down in a curve towards the temples with the object, Bond assumed, of hiding as much as possible of the tissue of shining puckered skin that covered most of the right half of his face. Other relics of plastic surgery could be detected in the man's right ear, which was not a perfect match with its companion on the left, and the right eye, which had been a surgical failure. It was considerably larger than the left eye, because of a contraction of the borrowed skin used to rebuild the upper and lower eyelids, and it looked painfully bloodshot. Bond doubted if it was capable of closing completely and he guessed that Drax covered it with a patch at night.

To conceal as much as possible of the unsightly taut skin that covered half his face, Drax had grown a bushy reddish moustache and had allowed his whiskers to grow down to the level of the lobes of his ears. He also had patches of hair on his cheek-bones.

The heavy moustache served another purpose. It helped to hide a naturally prognathous upper jaw and a marked protrusion of the upper row of teeth. Bond reflected that this was probably due to sucking his thumb as a child, and it had resulted in an ugly splaying, or diastema, of what Bond had heard his dentist call 'the centrals'. The moustache helped to hide these 'ogre's teeth' and it was only when Drax uttered, as he frequently did, his short braying laugh that the splay could be seen.

The general effect of the face–the riot of red-brown hair, the powerful nose and jaw, the florid skin–was flamboyant. It put Bond in mind of a ring-master at a circus. The contrasting sharpness and coldness of the left eye supported the likeness.

A bullying, boorish, loud-mouthed vulgarian. That would have been Bond's verdict if he had not known something of Drax's abilities. As it was, it crossed his mind that much of the effect might be Drax's idea of a latter-day Regency buck–the harmless disguise of a man with a smashed face who was also a snob.

Looking for further clues, Bond noticed that Drax was sweating rather freely. Despite the occasional growl of thunder outside it was a cool evening, and yet Drax was constantly mopping his face and neck with a huge bandana handkerchief. He smoked incessantly, stubbing out the cork-tipped Virginian cigarettes after a dozen lungfuls of smoke and almost immediately lighting another from a box of fifty in his coat pocket. His big hands, their backs thickly covered with reddish hair, were always on the move, fiddling with his cards, handling the cigarette lighter that stood beside a plain flat silver cigarette-case in front of him, twisting a lock of hair on the side of his head, using the handkerchief on his face and neck. Occasionally he put a finger greedily to his mouth and worried a nail. Even at a distance Bond could see that every finger-nail was bitten down to the quick.

The hands themselves were strong and capable but the thumbs had something ungainly about them which it took Bond a moment or two to define. He finally detected that they were unnaturally long and reached level with the top joint of the index finger.

Bond concluded his inspection with Drax's clothes which were expensive and in excellent taste–a dark blue pin-stripe in lightweight flannel, double-breasted with turn-back cuffs, a heavy white silk shirt with a stiff collar, an unobtrusive tie with a small grey and white check, modest cuff-links, which looked like Cartier, and a plain gold Patek Philippe watch with a black leather strap.

Bond lit another cigarette and concentrated on the game, leaving his subconscious to digest the details of Drax's appearance and manner that had seemed to him significant and that might help to explain the riddle of his cheating, the nature of which had still to be discovered.

Half an hour later the cards had completed the circle.

'My deal,' said Drax with authority. 'Game all and we have a satisfactory inflation above the line. Now then, Max, see if you can't pick up a few aces. I'm tired of doing all the work.' He dealt smoothly and slowly round the table, keeping up a running fire of rather heavy-handed banter with the company. 'Long rubber,' he said to M who was sitting smoking his pipe between Drax and Basildon. 'Sorry to have kept you out so long. How about a challenge after dinner? Max and I'll take on you and Commander Thingummy. What did you say his name was? Good player?'

'Bond,' said M. 'James Bond. Yes, I think we'd like that very much. What do you say, James?'

Bond's eyes were glued to the bent head and slowly moving hands of the dealer. Yes, that was it! Got you, you bastard. A Shiner. A simple, bloody Shiner that wouldn't have lasted five minutes in a pro's game. M saw the glint of assurance in Bond's eyes as they met his across the table.

'Fine,' said Bond cheerfully. 'Couldn't be better.'

He made an imperceptible movement of the head. 'How about showing me the Betting Book before dinner? You always say it'll amuse me.'

M nodded. 'Yes. Come along. It's in the Secretary's office. Then Basildon can come down and give us a cocktail and tell us the result of this death-struggle.' He got up.

'Order what you want,' said Basildon with a sharp glance at M. 'I'll be down directly we've polished them off.'

'Around nine then,' said Drax, glancing from M to Bond. 'Show him the bet about the girl in the balloon.' He picked up his hand. 'Looks like I shall have the Casino's money to play with,' he said after a rapid glance at his cards. 'Three No Trumps.' He shot a triumphant glance at Basildon. 'Put that in your pipe and smoke it.'

Bond, following M out of the room, missed Basildon's reply.

They walked down the stairs and along to the Secretary's office in silence. The room was in darkness. M switched on the light and went and sat down in the swivel chair in front of the busy-looking desk. He turned the chair to face Bond who had walked over to the empty fireplace and was taking out a cigarette.

'Any luck?' he asked looking up at him.

'Yes,' said Bond. 'He cheats all right.'

'Ah,' said M unemotionally. 'How does he do it?'

'Only on the deal,' said Bond. 'You know that silver cigarette-case he has in front of him, with his lighter? He never takes cigarettes from it. Doesn't want to get fingermarks on the surface. It's plain silver and very highly polished. When he deals, it's almost concealed by the cards and his big hands. And he doesn't move his hands away from it. Deals four piles quite close to him. Every card is reflected in the top of the case. It's just as good as a mirror although it looks perfectly innocent lying there. As he's such a good businessman it would be normal for him to have a first-class memory. You remember I told you about "Shiners"? Well, that's just a version of one. No wonder he brings off these miraculous finesses every once in a while. That double we watched was easy. He knew his partner had the guarded queen. With his two aces the double was a certainty. The rest of the time he just plays his average game. But knowing all the cards on every fourth deal is a terrific edge. It's not surprising he always shows a profit.'

'But one doesn't notice him doing it,' protested M.

'It's quite natural to look down when one's dealing,' said Bond. 'Everybody does. And he covers up with a lot of banter, much more than he produces when someone else is dealing. I expect he's got very good peripheral vision–the thing they mark us so highly for when we take our medical for the Service. Very wide angle of sight.'

The door opened and Basildon came in. He was bristling. He shut the door behind him.' That dam' shut-out bid of Drax's,' he exploded. 'Tommy and I could have made four hearts if we could have got around to bidding it. Between them they had the ace of hearts, six club tricks, and the ace, king of diamonds and a bare guard in spades. Made nine tricks straight off. How he had the face to open Three No Trumps I can't imagine.' He calmed down a little. 'Well, Miles,' he said, 'has your friend got the answer?'

M gestured to Bond, who repeated what he had told M.

Lord Basildon's face got angrier as Bond talked.

'Damn the man,' he exploded when Bond had finished. 'What the hell does he want to do that for? Bloody millionaire. Rolling in money. Fine scandal we're in for. I'll simply have to tell the Committee. Haven't had a cheating case since the 'fourteen-eighteen war.' He paced up and down the room. The club was quickly forgotten as he remembered the significance of Drax himself. 'And they say this rocket of his is going to be ready before long. Only comes up here once or twice a week for a bit of relaxation. Why, the man's a public hero! This is terrible.'

Basildon's anger was chilled by the thought of his responsibility. He turned to M for help. 'Now, Miles, what am I to do? He's won thousands of pounds in this club and others have lost it. Take this evening. It doesn't matter about my losses, of course. But what about Dangerfield? I happen to know he's been having a bad time on the stock market lately. I don't see how I can avoid telling the Committee. Can't shirk it–whoever Drax is. And you know what that'll mean. There are ten on the Committee. Bound to be a leak. And then look at the scandal. They tell me the Moonraker can't exist without Drax and the papers say the whole future of the country depends on the thing. This is a damned serious business.' He paused and shot a hopeful glance at M and then at Bond. 'Is there any alternative?'

Bond stubbed out his cigarette. 'He could be stopped,' he said quietly. 'That is,' he added with a thin smile, 'if you don't mind paying him out in his own coin.'

'Do anything you bloody well like,' said Basildon emphatically. 'What are you thinking of?' Hope dawned in his eyes at Bond's assurance.

'Well,' said Bond. 'I could show him I'd spotted him and at the same time flay the hide off him at his own game. Of course Meyer'd get hurt in the process. Might lose a lot of money as Drax's partner. Would that matter?'

'Serve him right,' said Basildon, overcome with relief and ready to grasp at any solution. 'He's been riding along on Drax's back. Making plenty of money playing with him. You don't think . . .'

'No,' said Bond. 'I'm sure he doesn't know what's going on. Although some of Drax's bids must come as a bit of a shock. Well,' he turned to M, 'is it all right with you, sir?'

M reflected. He looked at Basildon. There was no doubt of his view.

He looked at Bond. 'All right,' he said. 'What must be, must be. Don't like the idea, but I can see Basildon's point. So long as you can bring it off and,' he smiled, 'as long as you don't want me to palm any cards or anything of that sort. No talent for it.'

'No,' said Bond. He put his hands in his coat pockets and touched the two silk handkerchiefs. 'And I think it should work. All I need is a couple of packs of used cards, one of each colour, and ten minutes in here alone.'

Chapter Five

Dinner at Blades

It was eight o'clock as Bond followed M through the tall doors, across the well of the staircase from the card room, that opened into the beautiful white and gold Regency dining-room of Blades.

M chose not to hear a call from Basildon who was presiding over the big centre table where there were still two places vacant. Instead, he walked firmly across the room to the end one of a row of six smaller tables, waved Bond into the comfortable armed chair that faced outwards into the room, and himself took the one on Bond's left so that his back was to the company.

The head steward was already behind Bond's chair. He placed a broad menu card beside his plate and handed another to M. 'Blades' was written in fine gold script across the top. Below there was a forest of print.

'Don't bother to read through all that,' said M, 'unless you've got no ideas. One of the first rules of the club, and one of the best, was that any member may speak for any dish, cheap or dear, but he must pay for it. The same's true today, only the odds are one doesn't have to pay for it. Just order what you feel like.' He looked up at the steward. 'Any of that Beluga caviar left, Porterfield?'

'Yes, sir. There was a new delivery last week.'

'Well,' said M. 'Caviar for me. Devilled kidney and a slice of your excellent bacon. Peas and new potatoes. Strawberries in kirsch. What about you, James?'

'I've got a mania for really good smoked salmon,' said Bond. Then he pointed down the menu, 'Lamb cutlets. The same vegetables as you, as it's May. Asparagus with Hollandaise sauce sounds wonderful. And perhaps a slice of pineapple.' He sat back and pushed the menu away.

'Thank heavens for a man who makes up his mind,' said M. He looked up at the steward. 'Have you got all that, Porterfield?'

'Yes, sir.' The steward smiled. 'You wouldn't care for a marrow bone after the strawberries, sir? We got half a dozen in today from the country, and I'd specially kept one in case you came in.'

'Of course. You know I can't resist them. Bad for me but it can't be helped. God knows what I'm celebrating this evening. But it doesn't often happen. Ask Grimley to come over, would you.'

'He's here now, sir,' said the steward, making way for the wine-waiter.

'Ah, Grimley, some Vodka please.' He turned to Bond. 'Not the stuff you had in your cocktail. This is real pre-war Wolfschmidt from Riga. Like some with your smoked salmon?'

'Very much,' said Bond.

'Then what?' asked M. 'Champagne? Personally I'm going to have a half-bottle of claret. The Mouton Rothschild '34, please, Grimley. But don't pay any attention to me, James. I'm an old man. Champagne's no good for me. We've got some good champagnes, haven't we, Grimley? None of that stuff you're always telling me about, I'm afraid, James. Don't often see it in England. Taittinger, wasn't it?'

Bond smiled at M's memory. 'Yes,' he said, 'but it's only a fad of mine. As a matter of fact, for various reasons I believe I would like to drink champagne this evening. Perhaps I could leave it to Grimley.

The wine-waiter was pleased. 'If I may suggest it, sir, the Dom Perignon '46. I understand that France only sells it for dollars, sir, so you don't often see it in London. I believe it was a gift from the Regency Club in New York, sir. I have some on ice at the moment. It's the Chairman's favourite and he's told me to have it ready every evening in case he needs it.'

Bond smiled his agreement.

'So be it, Grimley,' said M. 'The Dom Perignon. Bring it straight away, would you?'

A waitress appeared and put racks of fresh toast on the table and a silver dish of Jersey butter. As she bent over the table her black skirt brushed Bond's arm and he looked up into two pert, sparkling eyes under a soft fringe of hair. The eyes held his for a fraction of a second and then she whisked away. Bond's eyes followed the white bow at her waist and the starched collar and cuffs of her uniform as she went down the long room. His eyes narrowed. He recalled a pre-war establishment in Paris where the girls were dressed with the same exciting severity. Until they turned round and showed their backs.

He smiled to himself. The *Marthe Richards* law had changed all that.

M turned from studying their neighbours behind him. 'Why were you so cryptic about drinking champagne?'

'Well, if you don't mind, sir,' Bond explained, 'I've got to get a bit tight tonight. I'll have to seem very drunk when the time comes. It's not an easy thing to act unless you do it with a good deal of conviction. I hope you won't get worried if I seem to get frayed at the edges later on.'

M shrugged his shoulders. 'You've got a head like a rock, James,' he said. 'Drink as much as you like if it's going to help. Ah, here's the Vodka.'

When M poured him three fingers from the frosted carafe Bond took a pinch of black pepper and dropped it on the surface of the Vodka. The pepper slowly settled to the bottom of the glass leaving a few grains on the surface which Bond dabbed up with the tip of a finger. Then he tossed the cold liquor well to the back of his throat and put his glass, with the dregs of the pepper at the bottom, back on the table.

M gave him a glance of rather ironical inquiry.

'It's a trick the Russians taught me that time you attached me to the Embassy in Moscow,' apologized Bond. 'There's often quite a lot of fusel oil on the surface of this stuff–at least there used to be when it was badly distilled. Poisonous. In Russia, where you get a lot of bath-tub liquor, it's an understood thing to sprinkle a little pepper in your glass. It takes the fusel oil to the bottom. I got to like the taste and now it's a habit. But I shouldn't have insulted the club Wolfschmidt,' he added with a grin.

M grunted. 'So long as you don't put pepper in Basildon's favourite champagne,' he said drily.

A harsh bray of laughter came from a table at the far end of the room. M looked over his shoulder and then turned back to his caviar.

'What do you think of this man Drax?' he said through a mouthful of buttered toast.

Bond helped himself to another slice of smoked salmon from the silver dish beside him. It had the delicate glutinous texture only achieved by the Highland curers–very different from the desiccated products of Scandinavia. He rolled a wafer-thin slice of brown bread-and-butter into a cylinder and contemplated it thoughtfully.

'One can't like his manner much. At first I was rather surprised that you tolerate him here.' He glanced at M, who shrugged his shoulders. 'But that's none of my business and anyway clubs would be very dull without a sprinkling of eccentrics. And in any case he's a national hero and a millionaire and obviously an adequate card-player. Even when he isn't helping himself to the odds,' he added. 'But I can see he's the sort of man I always imagined. Full-blooded, ruthless, shrewd. Plenty of guts. I'm not surprised he's managed to get where he is. What I don't understand is why he should be quite happy to throw it all away. This cheating of his. It's really beyond belief. What's he trying to prove with it? That he can beat everyone at everything? He seems to put so much passion into his cards–as if it wasn't a game at all, but some sort of trial of strength. You've only got to look at his fingernails. Bitten to the quick. And he sweats too much. There's a lot of tension there somewhere. It comes out in those ghastly jokes of his. They're harsh. There's no light touch about them. He seemed to want to squash Basildon like a fly. Hope I shall be able to keep my temper. That manner of his is pretty riling. He even treats his partner as if he was muck. He hasn't quite got under my skin, but I shan't at all mind sticking a very sharp pin into him tonight.' He smiled at M. 'If it comes off, that is.'

'I know what you mean,' said M. 'But you may be being a bit hard on the man. After all, it's a big step from the Liverpool docks, or wherever he came from, to where he is now. And he's one of those people who was born with naturally hairy heels. Nothing to do with snobbery. I expect his mates in Liverpool found him just as loud-mouthed as Blades does. As for his cheating, there's probably a crooked streak in him somewhere. I dare say he took plenty of short cuts on his way up. Somebody said that to become very rich you have to be helped by a combination of remarkable circumstances and an unbroken run of luck. It certainly isn't only the qualities of people that make them rich. At least that's my experience. At the beginning, getting together the first ten thousand, or the first hundred thousand, things have got to go damn right. And in that commodity business after the war, with all the regulations and restrictions, I expect it was often a case of being able to drop a thousand pounds in the right pocket. Officials. The ones who understood nothing but addition, division–and silence. The useful ones.'

M paused while the next course came. With it arrived the champagne in a silver ice-bucket, and the small Waterford decanter containing M's half-bottle of claret.

The wine-steward waited until they had delivered a favourable judgment on the wines and then moved away. As he did so a page came up to their table. 'Commander Bond?' he asked.

Bond took the envelope that was handed to him and slit it open. He took out a thin paper packet and carefully opened it under the level of the table. It contained a white powder. He took a silver fruit knife off the table and dipped the tip of the blade into the packet so that about half its contents were transferred to the knife. He reached for his glass of champagne and tipped the powder into it.

'Now what?' said M with a trace of impatience.

There was no hint of apology in Bond's face. It wasn't M who was going to have to do the work that evening. Bond knew what he was doing. Whenever he had a job of work to do he would take infinite pains beforehand and leave as little as possible to chance. Then if something went wrong it was the unforeseeable. For that he accepted no responsibility.

'Benzedrine,' he said. 'I rang up my secretary before dinner and asked her to wangle some out of the surgery at Headquarters. It's what I shall need if I'm going to keep my wits about me tonight. It's apt to make one a bit over-confident, but that'll be a help too.' He stirred the champagne with a scrap of toast so that the white powder whirled among the bubbles. Then he drank the mixture down with one long swallow. 'It doesn't taste,' said Bond, 'and the champagne is quite excellent.'

M smiled at him indulgently. 'It's your funeral,' he said.–'Now we'd better get on with our dinner. How were the cutlets?'

'Superb,' said Bond. 'I could cut them with a fork. The best English cooking is the best in the world–particularly at this time of the year. By the way, what stakes will we be playing for this evening? I don't mind very much. We ought to end up the winners. But I'd like to know how much it will cost Drax.'

'Drax likes to play for what he calls "One and One",' said M, helping himself from the strawberries that had just been put on the table. 'Modest sounding stake, if you don't know what it stands for. In fact it's one tenner a hundred and one hundred pounds on the rubber.'

'Oh,' said Bond, respectfully. 'I see.'

'But he's perfectly happy to play for Two and Two or even Three and Three. Mounts up at those figures. The average rubber of bridge at Blades is about ten points. That's £200 at One and One. And the bridge here makes for big rubbers. There are no conventions so there's plenty of gambling and bluffing. Sometimes it's more like poker. They're a mixed lot of players. Some of them are the best in England, but others are terribly wild. Don't seem to mind how much they lose. General Bealey, just behind us,' M made a gesture with his head, 'doesn't know the reds from the blacks. Nearly always a few hundred down at the end of the week. Doesn't seem to care. Bad heart. No dependants. Stacks of money from jute. But Duff Sutherland, the scruffy-looking chap next to the Chairman, is an absolute killer. Makes a regular ten thousand a year out of the club. Nice chap. Wonderful card manners. Used to play chess for England.'

M was interrupted by the arrival of his marrow bone. It was placed upright in a spotless lace napkin on the silver plate. An ornate silver marrow-scoop was laid beside it.

After the asparagus, Bond had little appetite for the thin slivers of pineapple. He tipped the last of the ice-cold champagne into his glass. He felt wonderful. The effects of the benzedrine and champagne had more than offset the splendour of the food. For the first time he took his mind away from the dinner and his conversation with M and glanced round the room.

It was a sparkling scene. There were perhaps fifty men in the room, the majority in dinner jackets, all at ease with themselves and their surroundings, all stimulated by the peerless food and drink, all animated by a common interest–the prospect of high gambling, the grand slam, the ace pot, the key-throw in a 64 game at backgammon. There might be cheats or possible cheats amongst them, men who beat their wives, men with perverse instincts, greedy men, cowardly men, lying men; but the elegance of the room invested each one with a kind of aristocracy.

At the far end, above the cold table, laden with lobsters, pies, joints, and delicacies in aspic, Romney's unfinished full-length portrait of Mrs Fitzherbert gazed provocatively across at Fragonard's *Jeu de Cartes*, the broad conversation-piece which half-filled the opposite wall above the Adam fireplace. Along the lateral walls, in the centre of each gilt-edged panel, was one of the rare engravings of the Hell-Fire Club in which each figure is shown making a minute gesture of scatological or magical significance. Above, marrying the walls into the ceiling, ran a frieze in plaster relief of carved urns and swags interrupted at intervals by the capitals of the fluted pilasters which framed the windows and the tall double doors, the latter delicately carved with a design showing the Tudor Rose interwoven with a ribbon effect.

The central chandelier, a cascade of crystal ropes terminating in a broad basket of strung quartz, sparkled warmly above the white damask tablecloths and George IV silver. Below, in the centre of each table, branched candlesticks distributed the golden light of three candles, each surmounted by a red silk shade, so that the faces of the diners shone with a convivial warmth which glossed over the occasional chill of an eye or cruel twist of a mouth.

Even as Bond drank in the warm elegance of the scene, some of the groups began to break up. There was a drift towards the door accompanied by an exchange of challenges, side-bets, and exhortations to hurry up and get down to business. Sir Hugo Drax, his hairy red face shining with cheerful anticipation, came towards them with Meyer in his wake.

'Well, gentlemen,' he said jovially as he reached their table. 'Are the lambs ready for the slaughter and the geese for the plucking?' He grinned and in a wolfish pantomime drew a finger across his throat. 'We'll go ahead and lay out the axe and the basket. Made your wills?'

'Be with you in a moment,' said M edgily. 'You go along and stack the cards.'

Drax laughed. 'We shan't need any artificial aids,' he said. 'Don't be long.' He turned and made for the door. Meyer enveloped them in an uncertain smile and followed him.

M grunted. 'We'll have coffee and brandy in the card-room,' he said to Bond. 'Can't smoke here. Now then. Any final plans?'

'I'll have to fatten him up for the kill, so please don't worry if I seem to be betting high,' said Bond. 'We'll just have to play our normal game till the time comes. When it's his deal, we'll have to be careful. Of course, he can't alter the cards and there's no reason why he shouldn't deal us good hands, but he's bound to bring off some pretty remarkable coups. Do you mind if I sit on his left?'

'No,' said M. 'Anything else?'

Bond reflected for a moment. 'Only one thing, sir,' he said. 'When the times comes, I shall take a white handkerchief out of my coat pocket. That will mean that you are about to be dealt a Yarborough. Would you please leave the bidding of that hand to me?'

Chapter Six

Cards with a Stranger

Drax and Meyer were waiting for them. They were leaning back in their chairs, smoking Cabinet Havanas.

On the small tables beside them there was coffee and large balloons of brandy. As M and Bond came up, Drax was tearing the paper cover off a new pack of cards. The other pack was fanned out across the green baize in front of him.

'Ah, there you are,' said Drax. He leant forward and cut a card. They all followed suit. Drax won the cut and elected to stay where he was and take the red cards.

Bond sat down on Drax's left.

M beckoned to a passing waiter. 'Coffee and the club brandy,' he said. He took out a thin black cheroot and offered one to Bond who accepted it. Then he picked up the red cards and started to shuffle them.

'Stakes?' asked Drax, looking at M. 'One and One? Or more? I'll be glad to accommodate you up to Five and Five.'

'One and One'll be enough for me,' said M. 'James?'

Drax cut in, 'I suppose your guest knows what he's in for?' he asked sharply.

Bond answered for M. 'Yes,' he said briefly. He smiled at Drax. 'And I feel rather generous tonight. What would you like to take off me?'

'Every penny you've got,' said Drax cheerfully. 'How much can you afford?'

'I'll tell you when there's none left,' said Bond. He suddenly decided to be ruthless. 'I'm told that Five and Five is your limit. Let's play for that.'

Almost before the words were out of his mouth he regretted them. £50 a hundred! £500 side-bets! Four bad rubbers would be double his income for a year. If something went wrong he'd look pretty stupid. Have to borrow from M. And M wasn't a particularly rich man. Suddenly he saw that this ridiculous game might end in a very nasty mess. He felt the prickle of sweat on his forehead. That damned benzedrine. And, for him of all people to allow himself to be needled by a blustering loud-mouthed bastard like Drax, And he wasn't even on a job. The whole evening was a bit of social pantomime that meant less than nothing to him. Even M had only been dragged into it by chance. And all of a sudden he'd let himself be swept up into a duel with this multi-millionaire, into a gamble for literally all Bond possessed, for the simple reason that the man had got filthy manners and he'd wanted to teach him a lesson. And supposing the lesson didn't come off? Bond cursed himself for an impulse that earlier in the day would have seemed unthinkable. Champagne and Benzedrine! Never again.

Drax was looking at him in sarcastic disbelief. He turned to M who was still unconcernedly shuffling the cards. 'I suppose your guest is good for his commitments,' he said. Unforgivably.

Bond saw the blood rush up M's neck and into his face. M paused for an instant in his shuffling. When he continued Bond noticed that his hands were quite calm. M looked up and took the cheroot very deliberately out from between his teeth. His voice was perfectly controlled. 'If you mean "Am I good for my guest's commitments",' he said coldly, 'the answer is yes.'

He cut the cards to Drax with his left hand and with his right knocked the ash off his cheroot into the copper ashtray in the corner of the table. Bond heard the faint hiss as the burning ash hit the water.

Drax squinted sideways at M. He picked up the cards. 'Of course, of course,' he said hastily. 'I didn't mean . . .' He left the sentence unfinished and turned to Bond. 'Right, then,' he said, looking rather curiously at Bond. 'Five and Five it is. Meyer,' he turned to his partner, 'how much would you like to take? There's Six and Six to cut up.'

'One and One's enough for me, Hugger,' said Meyer apologetically. 'Unless you'd like me to take some more.' He looked anxiously at his partner.

'Of course not,' said Drax. 'I like a high game. Never get enough on generally. Now then,' he started to deal. 'Off we go.'

And suddenly Bond didn't care about the high stakes. Suddenly all he wanted to do was to give this hairy ape the lesson of his life, give him a shock which would make him remember this evening for ever, remember Bond, remember M, remember the last time he would cheat at Blades, remember the time of day, the weather outside, what he had had for dinner.

For all its importance, Bond had forgotten the Moonraker. This was a private affair between two men.

As he watched the casual downward glance at the cigarette-case between the two hands and felt the cool memory ticking up the card values as they passed over its surface, Bond cleared his mind of all regrets, absolved himself of all blame for what was about to happen, and focused his attention on the game. He settled himself more comfortably into his chair and rested his hands on the padded leather arms. Then he took the thin cheroot from between his teeth, laid it on the burnished copper surround of the ashtray beside him and reached for his coffee. It was very black and strong. He emptied the cup and picked up the balloon glass with its fat measure of pale brandy. As he sipped it and then drank again, more deeply, he looked over the rim at M. M met his eye and smiled briefly.

'Hope you like it,' he said. 'Comes from one of the Rothschild estates at Cognac. About a hundred years ago one of the family bequeathed us a barrel of it every year in perpetuity. During the war they hid a barrel for us every year and then sent us over the whole lot in 1945. Ever since then we've been drinking doubles. And,' he gathered up his cards, 'now we shall have to concentrate.'

Bond picked up his hand. It was average. A bare two-and-a-half quick tricks, the suits evenly distributed. He reached for his cheroot and gave it a final draw then killed it in the ashtray.

'Three clubs,' said Drax.

No bid from Bond.

Four clubs from Meyer.

No bid from M.

Hm, thought Bond. He's not quite got the cards for a game call this time. Shut-out call–knows that his partner has got a bare raise. M may have got a perfectly good bid. We may have all the hearts between us, for instance. But M never gets a bid. Presumably they'll make four clubs.

They did, with the help of one finesse through Bond. M turned out not to have had hearts, but a long string of diamonds, missing only the king, which was in Meyer's hand and would have been caught. Drax didn't have nearly enough length for a three call. Meyer had the rest of the clubs.

Anyway, thought Bond as he dealt the next hand, we were lucky to escape without a game call.

Their good luck continued. Bond opened a No Trump, was put up to three by M, and they made it with an overtrick. On Meyer's deal they went one down in five diamonds, but on the next hand M opened four spades and Bond's three small trumps and an outside king, queen were all M needed for the contract.

First rubber to M and Bond. Drax looked annoyed. He had lost £900 on the rubber and the cards seemed to be running against them.

'Shall we go straight on?' he asked. 'No point in cutting.'

M smiled across at Bond. The same thought was in both their minds. So Drax wanted to keep the deal. Bond shrugged his shoulders.

'No objection,' said M. 'These seats seem to be doing their best for us.'

'Up to now,' said Drax, looking more cheerful.

And with reason. On the next hand he and Meyer bid and made a small slam in spades that required two hair-raising finesses, both of which Drax, after a good deal of pantomime and hemming and hawing, negotiated smoothly, each time commenting loudly on his good fortune.

'Hugger, you're wonderful,' said Meyer fulsomely. 'How the devil do you do it?'

Bond thought it time to sow a tiny seed. 'Memory,' he said.

Drax looked at him, sharply. 'What do you mean, memory?' he said. 'What's that got to do with taking a finesse?'

'I was going to add "and card sense",' said Bond smoothly. 'They're the two qualities that make great card-players.'

'Oh,' said Drax slowly. 'Yes, I see.' He cut the cards to Bond and as Bond dealt he felt the other man's eyes examining him carefully.

The game proceeded at an even pace. The cards refused to get hot and no one seemed inclined to take chances. M doubled Meyer in an incautious four-spade bid and got him two down vulnerable, but on the next hand Drax went out with a laydown three No Trumps. Bond's win on the first rubber was wiped out and a bit more besides.

'Anyone care for a drink?' asked M as he cut the cards to Drax for the third rubber. 'James. A little more champagne. The second bottle always tastes better.'

'I'd like that very much,' said Bond.

The waiter came. The others ordered whiskies and sodas.

Drax turned to Bond. 'This game needs livening up,' he said. 'A hundred we win this hand.' He had completed the deal and the cards lay in neat piles in the centre of the table.

Bond looked at him. The damaged eye glared at him redly. The other was cold and hard and scornful. There were beads of sweat on either side of the large, beaky nose.

Bond wondered if he was having a fly thrown over him to see if he was suspicious of the deal. He decided to leave the man in doubt. It was a hundred down the drain, but it would give him an excuse for increasing the stakes later.

'On your deal?' he said with a smile. 'Well,' he weighed imaginary chances. 'Yes. All right.' An idea seemed to come to him. 'And the same on the next hand. If you like,' he added.

'All right, all right,' said Drax impatiently. 'If you want to throw good money after bad.'

'You seem very certain about this hand,' said Bond indifferently, picking up his cards. They were a poor lot and he had no answer to Drax's opening No Trump except to double it. The bluff had no effect on Drax's partner. Meyer said 'Two No Trumps' and Bond was relieved when M, with no long suit, said 'No bid'. Drax left it in two No Trumps and made the contract.

'Thanks,' he said with relish, and wrote carefully on his score. 'Now let's see if you can get it back.'

Much to his annoyance, Bond couldn't. The cards still ran for Meyer and Drax and they made three hearts and the game.

Drax was pleased with himself. He took a long swallow at his whisky and soda and wiped down his face with his bandana handkerchief.

'God is with the big battalions,' he said jovially. 'Got to have the cards as well as play them. Coming back for more or had enough?'

Bond's champagne had come and was standing beside him in its silver bucket. There was a glass goblet three-quarters full beside it on the side table. Bond picked it up and drained it, as if to give himself Dutch courage. Then he filled it again.

'All right,' he said thickly, 'a hundred on the next two hands.'

And promptly lost them both, and the rubber.

Bond suddenly realized that he was nearly £1,500 down. He drank another glass of champagne. 'Save trouble if we just double the stakes on this rubber,' he said rather wildly. 'All right with you?'

Drax had dealt and was looking at his cards. His lips were wet with anticipation. He looked at Bond who seemed to be having difficulty lighting his cigarette. 'Taken,' he said quickly. 'A hundred pounds a hundred and a thousand on the rubber.' Then he felt he could risk a touch of sportsmanship. Bond could hardly cancel the bet now. 'But I seem to have got some good tickets here,' he added. 'Are you still on?'

'Of course, of course,' said Bond, clumsily picking up his hand. 'I made the bet, didn't I?'

'All right then,' said Drax with satisfaction. 'Three No Trumps here.'

He made four.

Then, to Bond's relief, the cards turned. Bond bid and made a small slam in hearts and on the next hand M ran out in three No Trumps.

Bond grinned cheerfully into the sweating face. Drax was picking angrily at his nails. 'Big battalions,' said Bond, rubbing it in.

Drax growled something and busied himself with the score.

Bond looked across at M, who was putting a match, with evident satisfaction at the way the game had gone, to his second cheroot of the evening, an almost unheard of indulgence.

''Fraid this'll have to be my last rubber,' said Bond. 'Got to get up early. Hope you'll forgive me.'

M looked at his watch. 'It's past midnight,' he said. 'What about you, Meyer?'

Meyer, who had been a silent passenger for most of the evening and who had the look of a man caught in a cage with a couple of tigers, seemed relieved at being offered a chance of making his escape. He leapt at the idea of getting back to his quiet flat in Albany and the soothing companionship of his collection of Battersea snuff-boxes.

'Quite all right with me, Admiral,' he said quickly. 'What about you, Hugger? Nearly ready for bed?'

Drax ignored him. He looked up from his score-sheet at Bond. He noticed the signs of intoxication. The moist forehead, the black comma of hair that hung untidily over the right eyebrow, the sheen of alcohol in the grey-blue eyes.

'Pretty miserable balance so far,' he said. 'I make it you win a couple of hundred or so. Of course if you want to run out of the game you can. But how about some fireworks to finish up with? Treble the stakes on the last rubber? Fifteen and fifteen? Historic match. Am I on?'

Bond looked up at him. He paused before answering. He wanted Drax to remember every detail of this last rubber, every word that had been spoken, every gesture.

'Well,' said Drax impatiently. 'What about it?'

Bond looked into the cold left eye in the flushed face. He spoke to it alone. 'One hundred and fifty pounds a hundred, and fifteen hundred pounds on the rubber,' he said distinctly. 'You're on.'

Chapter Seven

The Quickness of the Hand

There was a moment's silence at the table. It was broken by the agitated voice of Meyer.

'Here I say,' he said anxiously. 'Don't include me in on this, Hugger.' He knew it was a private bet with Bond, but he wanted to show Drax that he was thoroughly nervous about the whole affair. He saw himself making some ghastly mistake that would cost his partner a lot of money.

'Don't be ridiculous, Max,' said Drax harshly. 'You play your hand. This is nothing to do with you. Just an enjoyable little bet with our rash friend here. Come along, come along. My deal, Admiral.'

M cut the cards and the game began.

Bond lit a cigarette with hands that had suddenly become quite steady. His mind was clear. He knew exactly what he had to do, and when, and he was glad that the moment of decision had come.

He sat back in his chair and for a moment he had the impression that there was a crowd behind him at each elbow, and that faces were peering over his shoulder, waiting to see his cards. He somehow felt that the ghosts were friendly, that they approved of the rough justice that was about to be done.

He smiled as he caught himself sending this company of dead gamblers a message, that they should see that all went well.

The background noise of the famous gaming room broke in on his thoughts. He looked round. In the middle of the long room, under the central chandelier, there were several onlookers round the poker game. 'Raise you a hundred.' 'And a hundred.' 'And a hundred.' 'Damn you. I'll look', and a shout of triumph followed by a hubbub of comment. In the distance he could hear the rattle of a croupier's rake against the counters at the Shemmy game. Nearer at hand, at his end of the room, there were three other tables of bridge over which the smoke of cigars and cigarettes rose towards the barrelled ceiling.

Nearly every night for more than a hundred and fifty years there had been just such a scene, he reflected, in this famous room. The same cries of victory and defeat, the same dedicated faces, the same smell of tobacco and drama. For Bond, who loved gambling, it was the most exciting spectacle in the world. He gave it a last glance to fix it all in his mind and then he turned back to his table.

He picked up his cards and his eyes glittered. For once, on Drax's deal, he had a cast-iron game hand; seven spades with the four top honours, the ace of hearts, and the ace, king of diamonds. He looked at Drax. Had he and Meyer got the clubs? Even so Bond could overbid. Would Drax try and force him too high and risk a double? Bond waited.

'No bid,' said Drax, unable to keep the bitterness of his private knowledge of Bond's hand out of his voice.

'Four spades,' said Bond.

No bid from Meyer; from M; reluctantly from Drax.

M provided some help, and they made five.

One hundred and fifty points below the line. A hundred above for honours.

'Humph,' said a voice at Bond's elbow. He looked up. It was Basildon. His game had finished and he had strolled over to see what was happening on this separate battlefield.

He picked up Bond's score-sheet and looked at it.

'That was a bit of a beetle-crusher,' he said cheerfully. 'Seems you're holding the champions. What are the stakes?'

Bond left the answer to Drax. He was glad of the diversion. It could not have been better timed. Drax had cut the blue cards to him. He married the two halves and put the pack just in front of him, near the edge of the table.

'Fifteen and fifteen. On my left,' said Drax.

Bond heard Basildon draw in his breath.

'Chap seemed to want to gamble, so I accommodated him. Now he goes and gets all the cards . . .'

Drax grumbled on.

Across the table, M saw a white handkerchief materialize in Bond's right hand. M's eyes narrowed. Bond seemed to wipe his face with it. M saw him glance sharply at Drax and Meyer then the handkerchief was back in his pocket.

A blue pack was in Bond's hands and he had started to deal.

'That's the hell of a stake,' said Basildon. 'We once had a thousand-pound side-bet on a game of bridge. But that was in the rubber boom before the 'fourteen-eighteen war. Hope nobody's going to get hurt.' He meant it. Very high stakes in a private game generally led to trouble. He walked round and stood between M and Drax.

Bond completed the deal. With a touch of anxiety he picked up his cards.

He had nothing but five clubs to the ace, queen, ten, and eight small diamonds to the queen.

It was all right. The trap was set.

He almost felt Drax stiffen as the big man thumbed through his cards, and then, unbelieving, thumbed them through again. Bond knew that Drax had an incredibly good hand. Ten certain tricks, the ace, king of diamonds, the four top honours in spades, the four top honours in hearts, and the king, knave, nine of clubs.

Bond had dealt them to him–in the Secretary's room before dinner.

Bond waited, wondering how Drax would react to the huge hand. He took an almost cruel interest in watching the greedy fish come to the lure.

Drax exceeded his expectations.

Casually he folded his hand and laid it on the table. Nonchalantly he took the flat carton out of his pocket, selected a cigarette and lit it. He didn't look at Bond. He glanced up at Basildon.

'Yes,' he said, continuing the conversation about their stakes. 'It's a high game, but not the highest I've ever played. Once played for two thousand a rubber in Cairo. At the Mahomet Ali as a matter of fact. They've really got guts there. Often bet on every trick as well as on the game and rubber. Now,' he picked up his hand and looked slyly at Bond. 'I've got some good tickets here. I'll admit it. But then you may have too, for all I know.' (Unlikely, you old shark, thought Bond, with three of the ace-kings in your own hand.) 'Care to have something extra just on this hand?'

Bond made a show of studying his cards with the minuteness of someone who is nearly very drunk. 'I've got a promising lot too,' he said thickly. 'If my partner fits and the cards lie right I might make a lot of tricks myself. What are you suggesting?'

'Sounds as if we're pretty evenly matched,' lied Drax. 'What do you say to a hundred a trick on the side? From what you say that shouldn't be too painful.'

Bond looked thoughtful and rather fuddled. He took another careful look at his hand, running through the cards one by one. 'All right,' he said. 'You're on. And frankly you've made me gamble. You've obviously got a big hand, so I must shut you out and chance it.'

Bond looked blearily across at M. 'Pay your losses on this one, partner,' he said. 'Here we go. Er–seven clubs.'

In the dead silence that followed, Basildon, who had seen Drax's hand, was so startled that he dropped his whisky and soda on the floor. He looked dazedly down at the broken glass and let it lie.

Drax said 'What?' in a startled voice and hastily ran through his cards again for reassurance.

'Did you say grand slam in clubs?' he asked, looking curiously at his obviously drunken opponent. 'Well, it's your funeral. What do you say, Max?'

'No bid,' said Meyer, feeling in the air the electricity of just that crisis he had hoped to avoid. Why the hell hadn't he gone home before this last rubber? He groaned inwardly.

'No bid,' said M, apparently unperturbed.

'Double.' The word came viciously out of Drax's mouth. He put down his hand and looked cruelly, scornfully at this tipsy oaf who had at last, inexplicably, fallen into his hands.

'That mean you double the side bets too?' asked Bond.

'Yes,' said Drax greedily. 'Yes. That's what I meant.'

'All right,' said Bond. He paused. He looked at Drax and not at his hand. 'Redouble. The contract and the side-bets. £400 a trick on the side.'

It was at that moment that the first hint of a dreadful, incredible doubt entered Drax's mind. But again he looked at his hand, and again he was reassured. At the very worst he couldn't fail to make two tricks.

A muttered 'No bid' from Meyer. A rather strangled 'No bid' from M. An impatient shake of the head from Drax.

Basildon stood, his face very pale, looking intently across the table at Bond.

Then he walked slowly round the table, scrutinizing all the hands. What he saw was this:

BOND

♢ Queen, 8, 7, 6, 5, 4, 3, 2
♣ Ace, queen, 10, 8, 4

DRAX

♠ Ace, king, queen, knave
♡ Ace, king, queen, knave
♢ Ace, king
♣ King, knave, 9

MEYER

♠ 6, 5, 4, 3, 2
♡ 10, 9, 8, 7, 2
♢ Knave, 10, 9

M

♠ 10, 9, 8, 7
♡ 6, 5, 4, 3
♣ 7, 6, 5, 3, 2

And suddenly Basildon understood. It was a laydown Grand Slam for Bond against any defence. Whatever Meyer led, Bond must get in with a trump in his own hand or on the table. Then, in between clearing trumps, finessing of course against Drax, he would play two rounds of diamonds, trumping them in dummy and catching Drax's ace and king in the process. After five plays he would be left with the remaining trumps and six winning diamonds. Drax's aces and kings would be totally valueless.

It was sheer murder.

Basildon, almost in a trance, continued round the table and stood between M and Meyer so that he could watch Drax's face, and Bond's. His own face was impassive, but his hands, which he had stuffed into his trouser pockets so that they would not betray him, were sweating. He waited, almost fearfully, for the terrible punishment that Drax was about to receive–thirteen separate lashes whose scars no card-player would ever lose.

'Come along, come along,' said Drax impatiently. 'Lead something, Max. Can't be here all night.'

You poor fool, thought Basildon. In ten minutes you'll wish that Meyer had died in his chair before he could pull out that first card.

In fact, Meyer looked as if at any moment he might have a stroke. He was deathly pale, and the perspiration was dropping off his chin on to his shirt front. For all he knew, his first card might be a disaster.

At last, reasoning that Bond might be void in his own long suits, spades and hearts, he led the knave of diamonds.

It made no difference what he led, but when M's hand went down showing chicane in diamonds, Drax snarled across at his partner. 'Haven't you got anything else, you dam' fool? Want to hand it to him on a plate? Whose side are you on, anyway?'

Meyer cringed into his clothes. 'Best I could do, Hugger,' he said miserably, wiping his face with his handkerchief.

But by this time Drax had got his own worries.

Bond trumped on the table, catching Drax's king of diamonds, and promptly led a club. Drax put up his nine. Bond took it with his ten and led a diamond, trumping it on the table. Drax's ace fell. Another club from the table, catching Drax's knave.

Then the ace of clubs.

As Drax surrendered his king, for the first time he saw what might be happening. His eyes squinted anxiously at Bond, waiting fearfully for the next card. Had Bond got the diamonds? Hadn't Meyer got them guarded? After all, he had opened with them. Drax waited, his cards slippery with sweat.

Morphy, the great chess player, had a terrible habit. He would never raise his eyes from the game until he knew his opponent could not escape defeat. Then he would slowly lift his great head and gaze curiously at the man across the board. His opponent would feel the gaze and would slowly, humbly raise his eyes to meet Morphy's. At that moment he would know that it was no good continuing the game. The eyes of Morphy said so. There was nothing left but surrender.

Now, like Morphy, Bond lifted his head and looked straight into Drax's eyes. Then he slowly drew out the queen of diamonds and placed it on the table. Without waiting for Meyer to play he followed it, deliberately, with the 8, 7, 6, 5, 4, and the two winning clubs.

Then he spoke. 'That's all, Drax,' he said quietly, and sat slowly back in his chair.

Drax's first reaction was to lurch forward and tear Meyer's cards out of his hand. He faced them on the table, scrabbling feverishly among them for a possible winner.

Then he flung them back across the baize.

His face was dead white, but his eyes blazed redly at Bond. Suddenly he raised one clenched fist and crashed it on the table among the pile of impotent aces and kings and queens in front of him.

Very low, he spat the words at Bond. 'You're a che . . .'

'That's enough, Drax.' Basildon's voice came across the table like a whiplash. 'None of that talk here. I've been watching the whole game. Settle up. If you've got any complaints, put them in writing to the Committee.'

Drax got slowly to his feet. He stood away from his chair and ran a hand through his wet red hair. The colour came slowly back into his face and with it an expression of cunning. He glanced down at Bond and there was in his good eye a contemptuous triumph which Bond found curiously disturbing.

He turned to the table. 'Good-night, gentlemen,' he said, looking at each of them with the same oddly scornful expression. 'I owe about £15,000. I will accept Meyer's addition.'

He leant forward and picked up his cigarette-case and lighter.

Then he looked again at Bond and spoke very quietly, the red moustache lifting slowly from the splayed upper teeth.

'I should spend the money quickly, Commander Bond,' he said.

Then he turned away from the table and walked swiftly out of the room.

PART TWO

Tuesday, Wednesday

Chapter Eight

The Red Telephone

Although he had not got to bed until two, Bond walked into his headquarters punctually at ten the next morning. He was feeling dreadful. As well as acidity and liver as a result of drinking nearly two whole bottles of champagne, he had a touch of the melancholy, and the spiritual deflation that were partly the after-effects of the benzedrine and partly reaction to the drama of the night before.

When he went up in the lift towards another routine day, the bitter taste of the midnight hours was still with him.

After Meyer had scuttled thankfully off to bed, Bond had taken the two packs of cards out of the pockets of his coat and had put them on the table in front of Basildon and M. One was the blue pack that Drax had cut to him and that he had pocketed, substituting instead, under cover of his handkerchief, the stacked blue pack in his right-hand pocket. The other was the stacked red pack in his left-hand pocket which had not been needed.

He fanned the red pack out on the table and showed M and Basildon that it would have produced the same freak grand slam that had defeated Drax.

'It's a famous Culbertson hand,' he explained. 'He used it to spoof his own quick-trick conventions. I had to doctor a red and a blue pack. Couldn't know which colour I would be dealing with.'

'Well, it certainly went with a bang,' said Basildon gratefully. 'I expect he'll put two and two together and either stay away or play straight in future. Expensive evening for him. Don't let's have any argument about your winnings,' he added. 'You've done everyone–and particularly Drax–a good turn tonight. Things might have gone wrong. Then it would have been your fingers that would have got burned. Cheque will reach you on Saturday.'

They had said good-night and Bond, in a mood of anticlimax, had gone off to bed. He had taken a mild sleeping pill to try and clear his mind of the bizarre events of the evening and prepare himself for the morning and the office. Before he slept he reflected, as he had often reflected in other moments of triumph at the card table, that the gain to the winner is, in some odd way, always less than the loss to the loser.

When he closed the door behind him Loelia Ponsonby looked curiously at the dark shadows under his eyes. He noticed the glance, as she had intended.

He grinned. 'Partly work and partly play,' he explained. 'In strictly masculine company,' he added. 'And thanks very much for the benzedrine. It really was badly needed. Hope I didn't interfere with your evening?'

'Of course not,' she said, thinking of the dinner and the library book she had abandoned when Bond telephoned. She looked down at her shorthand pad. 'The Chief of Staff telephoned half an hour ago. He said that M would be wanting you today. He couldn't say when. I told him that you've got Unarmed Combat at three and he said to cancel it. That's all, except the dockets left over from yesterday.'

'Thank heavens,' said Bond. 'I couldn't have stood being thrown about by that dam' Commando chap today. Any news of 008?'

'Yes,' she said. 'They say he's all right. He's been moved to the military hospital at Wahnerheide. Apparently it's only shock.'

Bond knew what 'shock' might mean in his profession. 'Good,' he said without conviction. He smiled at her and went into his office and closed the door.

He walked decisively round his desk to the chair, sat down, and pulled the top file towards him. Monday was gone. This was Tuesday. A new day. Closing his mind to his headache and to thoughts about the night, he lit a cigarette and opened the brown folder with the Top Secret red star on it. It was a memorandum from the Office of the Chief Preventive Officer of the United States Customs Branch and it was headed *The Inspectoscope*.

He focused his eyes. 'The Inspectoscope', he read, 'is an instrument using fluoroscopic principles for the detection of contraband. It is manufactured by the Sicular Inspectoscope Company of San Francisco and is widely used in American prisons for the secret detection of metal objects concealed in the clothing or on the person of criminals and prison visitors. It is also used in the detection of I.D.B. (Illicit Diamond Buying) and diamond smuggling in the diamond fields of Africa and Brazil. The instrument costs seven thousand dollars, is approximately eight feet long by seven feet high and weighs nearly three tons. It requires two trained operators. Experiments have been made with this instrument in the customs hall of the International Airport at Idlewild with the following results . . .'

Bond skipped two pages containing details of a number of petty smuggling cases and studied the 'Summary of Conclusions' from which he deduced, with some irritation, that he would have to think of some place other than his armpit for carrying his ·25 Beretta the next time he travelled abroad. He made a mental note to discuss the problem with the Technical Devices Section.

He ticked and initialled the distribution slip and automatically reached for the next folder entitled *Philopon. A Japanese murder-drug*.

'Philopon', his mind was trying to wander and he dragged it sharply back to the typewritten pages, 'Philopon is the chief factor in the increase in crime in Japan. According to the Welfare Ministry there are now 1,500,000 addicts in the country, of whom one million are under the age of 20, and the Tokyo Metropolitan Police attribute 70% of juvenile crime to the influences of the drug.

'Addiction, as in the case of marijuana in the United States, begins with one "shot". The effect is "stimulating" and the drug is habit-forming. It is also cheap–about ten yen (sixpence) a shot–and the addict rapidly increases his shots to the neighbourhood of one hundred a day. In these quantities the addiction becomes expensive and the victim automatically turns to crime to pay for the drug. That the crime often includes physical assault and murder is due to a peculiar property of the drug. It induces an acute persecution complex in the addict who becomes prey to the illusion that people want to kill him and that he is always being followed with harmful intent. He will turn with his feet and fists, or with a razor, on a stranger in the streets who he thinks has scrutinized him offensively. Less advanced addicts tend to avoid an old friend who has reached the one hundred shots a day dosage, and this of course merely increases his feeling of persecution.

'In this way murder becomes an act of self-defence, virtuous and justified, and it will readily be seen what a dangerous weapon it can become in the handling and direction of organized crime by a "master-mind".

'Philopon has been traced as the motive power behind the notorious Bar Mecca murder case and as a result of that unpleasant affair the police rounded up more than 5,000 *purveyors* of the drug in a matter of weeks.

'As usual Korean nationals are being blamed . . .'

Suddenly Bond rebelled. What the hell was he doing reading all this stuff? When would he conceivably require to know about a Japanese murder-drug called Philopon?

Inattentively he skimmed through the remaining pages, ticked himself off the distribution slip, and threw the docket into his out-tray.

His headache was still sitting over his right eye as if it had been nailed there. He opened one of the drawers of his desk and took out a bottle of Phensic. He considered asking his secretary for a glass of water, but he disliked being cossetted. With distaste he crunched two tablets between his teeth and swallowed down the harsh powder.

Then he lit a cigarette and got up and stood by the window. He looked across the green panorama far below him and, without seeing it, let his eyes wander aimlessly along the jagged horizon of London while his mind focused on the strange events of the night before.

And the more he thought about it, the stranger it all seemed.

Why should Drax, a millionaire, a public hero, a man with a unique position in the country, why should this remarkable man cheat at cards? What could he achieve by it? What could he prove to himself? Did he think that he was so much a law unto himself, so far above the common herd and their puny canons of behaviour that he could spit in the face of public opinion?

Bond's mind paused. Spit in their faces. That just about described his manner at Blades. The combination of superiority and scorn. As if he was dealing with human muck so far beneath contempt that there was no need to put up even a pretence of decent behaviour in its company.

Presumably Drax enjoyed gambling. Perhaps it eased the tensions in him, the tensions that showed in his harsh voice, his nail-biting, the constant sweating. But he mustn't lose. It would be contemptible to lose to these inferior people. So, at whatever risk, he must cheat his way to victory. As for the possibility of detection, presumably he thought that he could bluster his way out of any corner. If he thought about it at all. And people with obsessions, reflected Bond, were blind to danger. They even courted it in a perverse way. Kleptomaniacs would try to steal more and more difficult objects. Sex maniacs would parade their importunities as if they were longing to be arrested. Pyromaniacs often made no attempt to avoid being linked with their fire-raising.

But what obsession was it that was consuming this man? What was the origin of the compulsive urge that was driving him down the steep hill into the sea?

All the signs pointed to paranoia. Delusions of grandeur and, behind that, of persecution. The contempt in his face. The bullying voice. The expression of secret triumph with which he had met defeat after a moment of bitter collapse. The triumph of the maniac who knows that whatever the facts may say he is right. Whoever may try to thwart him he can overcome. For him there is no defeat because of his secret power. He knows how to make gold. He can fly like a bird. He is almighty–the man in the padded cell who is God.

Yes, thought Bond, gazing blindly out over Regent's Park. That is the solution. Sir Hugo Drax is a raving paranoiac. That is the power which has driven him on, by devious routes, to make his millions. That is the mainspring of the gift to England of this giant rocket that will annihilate our enemies. Thanks to the all-powerful Drax.

But who can tell how near to breaking-point this man is? Who has penetrated behind that bluster, behind all that red hair on his face, who has read the signs as more than the effect of his humble origins or of sensitivity about his war wounds?

Apparently no one. Then was he, Bond, right in his analysis? What was it based on? Was this glimpse through a shuttered window into a man's soul sufficient evidence? Perhaps others had caught such a glimpse. Perhaps there had been other moments of supreme tension in Singapore, Hong Kong, Nigeria, Tangier, when some merchant sitting across a table from Drax had noticed the sweat and the bitten nails and the red blaze of the eyes in the face from which all the blood had suddenly been drained.

If one had time, thought Bond, one ought to seek those people out, if they existed, and really find out about this man, perhaps get him in the killing-bottle before it was too late.

Too late? Bond smiled to himself. What was he being so dramatic about? What had this man done to him? Made him a present of £15,000. Bond shrugged. It was none of his business anyway. But that last remark of his 'Spend it quickly, Commander Bond'. What had he meant by that? It must be those words, Bond reflected, that had stayed in the back of his mind and made him ponder so carefully over the problem of Drax.

Bond turned brusquely away from the window. To hell with it, he thought. I'm getting obsessed myself. Now then. Fifteen thousand pounds. A miraculous windfall. All right then, he *would* spend it quickly. He sat down at his desk and picked up a pencil. He thought for a moment and then wrote carefully on a memorandum pad headed 'Top Secret':

(1) Rolls-Bentley Convertible, say £5,000.

(2) Three diamond clips at £250 each, £750.

He paused. That still left nearly £10,000. Some clothes, paint the flat, a set of the new Henry Cotton irons, a few dozen of the Taittinger champagne. But those could wait. He would go that afternoon and buy the clips and talk to Bentley's. Put all the rest into gold shares. Make a fortune. Retire.

In angry protest the red telephone splintered the silence.

'Can you come up? M wants you.' It was the Chief of Staff, speaking urgently.

'Coming,' said Bond, suddenly alert. 'Any clue?'

'Search me,' said the Chief of Staff. 'Hasn't touched his signals yet. Been over at the Yard and the Ministry of Supply all the morning.'

He rang off.

Chapter Nine

Take it from here

A few minutes later Bond was walking through the familiar door and the green light had gone on over the entrance.

M looked sharply at him. 'You look pretty dreadful, 007,' he said. 'Sit down.'

It's business, thought Bond, his pulse quickening. No Christian names today. He sat down. M was studying some pencilled notes on a scratch-pad. He looked up. His eyes were no longer interested in Bond.

'Trouble down at Drax's plant last night,' he said. 'Double killing. Police tried to get hold of Drax. Didn't think of Blades apparently. Caught up with him when he got back to the Ritz about half-past one this morning. Two men from the Moonraker got shot in a public house near the plant. Both dead. Drax told the police he couldn't care less and then hung up. Typical of the man. He's down there now. Taking the thing a bit more seriously, I gather.'

'Curious coincidence,' said Bond thoughtfully. 'But where do we come in, sir? Isn't it a police job?'

'Partly,' said M, 'but it happens that we're responsible for a lot of the key personnel down there. Germans,' he added. 'I'd better explain.' He looked down at his pad. 'It's an R.A.F. establishment and the cover-plan is that it's part of the big radar network along the East Coast. The R.A.F. are responsible for guarding the perimeter and the Ministry of Supply only has authority at the centre where the work is going on. It's on the edge of the cliffs between Dover and Deal. The whole area covers about a thousand acres, but the site itself is about two hundred. On the site there are only Drax and fifty-two others left. All the construction team have gone.'

Pack of cards and a joker, reflected Bond.

'Fifty of these are Germans,' continued M, 'More or less all the guided missile experts the Russians didn't get. Drax paid for them to come over here and work on the Moonraker. Nobody was very happy with the arrangement but there was no alternative. The Ministry of Supply couldn't spare any of their experts from Woomera. Drax had to find his men where he could. To strengthen the R.A.F. security people, the Ministry appointed their own security officer to live on the site. Man called Major Tallon.'

M paused and looked up at the ceiling.

'He was one of the two who got killed last night. Shot by one of the Germans, who then shot himself.'

M lowered his eyes and looked at Bond. Bond said nothing, waiting for the rest of the story.

'It happened in a public house near the site. Plenty of witnesses. Apparently it's an inn on the edge of the site that is in bounds to the men. Must have somewhere to go to, I suppose.' M paused. He kept his eyes on Bond. 'Now you asked where we come in on all this. We come in because we cleared this particular German, and all the others, before they were allowed to come over here. We've got the dossiers of all of them. So when this happened the first thing R.A.F. Security and Scotland Yard wanted was the dossier of the dead man. They got on to the Duty Officer last night and he dug the papers out of Records and sent them over to the Yard. Routine job. He noted it in the log. When I got here this morning and saw this entry in the log I suddenly got interested.' M spoke quietly. 'After spending the evening with Drax, it was, as you remarked, a curious coincidence.'

'Very curious, sir,' said Bond, still waiting.

'And there's one more thing,' concluded M. 'And this is the real reason why I've let myself get involved instead of keeping clear of the whole business. This has got to take priority over everything. M's voice was very quiet. They're going to fire the Moonraker on Friday. Less than four days' time. Practice shoot.'

M paused and reached for his pipe and busied himself lighting it.

Bond said nothing. He still couldn't see what all this had to do with the Secret Service whose jurisdiction runs only outside the United Kingdom. It seemed a job for the Special Branch of Scotland Yard, or conceivably for M.I.5. He waited. He looked at his watch. It was noon.

M got his pipe going and continued.

'But quite apart from that,' said M, 'I got interested because last night I got interested in Drax.'

'So did I, sir,' said Bond.

'So when I read the log,' said M, ignoring Bond's comment, 'I telephoned Vallance at the Yard and asked him what it was all about. He was rather worried and asked me to come over. I said I didn't want to tread on Five's corns but he said he had already spoken to them. They maintained it was a matter between my department and the police since it was we who had cleared the German who did the killing. So I went along.'

M paused and looked down at his notes.

'The place is on the coast about three miles north of Dover,' he said. 'There's this inn near by on the main coast road, the "World without Want", and the men from the site go there in the evening. Last night, about seven-thirty, the Security man from the Ministry, this man Tallon, went along there and was having a whisky and soda and chatting away with some of the Germans when the murderer, if you like to call him that, came in and walked straight up to Tallon. He pulled a Luger–no serial numbers by the way–out of his shirt and said,' M looked up, '"I love Gala Brand. You shall not have her." Then he shot Tallon through the heart and put the smoking gun in his own mouth and pulled the trigger.'

'What a ghastly business,' said Bond. He could see every detail of the shambles in the crowded taproom of a typical English public house. 'Who's the girl?'

'That's another complication,' said M. 'She's an agent of the Special Branch. Bilingual in German. One of Vallance's best girls. She and Tallon were the only two non-Germans Drax had with him on the site. Vallance is a suspicious chap. Has to be. This Moonraker plan is obviously the most important thing happening in England. Without telling anyone and acting more or less on instinct, he planted this Brand girl on Drax and somehow fixed for her to be taken on as his private secretary. Been on the site since the beginning. She's had absolutely nothing to report. Says that Drax is an excellent chief, except for his manners, and drives his men like hell. Apparently he started by making passes at her, even after she'd spun the usual yarn about being engaged, but after she'd shown she could defend herself, which of course she can, he gave up and she says they're perfectly good friends. Naturally she knew Tallon, but he was old enough to be her father, besides being happily married with four children, and she told Vallance's man who got a word with her this morning that he's taken her to the cinema in a paternal sort of way twice in eighteen months. As for the killer, man called Egon Bartsch, he was an electronics expert whom she barely knew by sight.'

'What do his friends say about all this?' asked Bond.

'The man who shared his room with him backs up Bartsch. Says he was madly in love with the Brand woman and put his whole lack of success down to "The Englishman". He says Bartsch had been getting very moody and reserved lately and that he wasn't a bit surprised to hear of the shooting.'

'Sounds pretty corroborative,' said Bond. 'Somehow one can see the picture. One of those highly strung nervous chaps with the usual German chip on the shoulder. What does Vallance think?'

'He's not sure,' said M. 'He's mainly concerned with protecting his girl from the Press and seeing that her cover doesn't get blown. All the papers are on to it of course. It'll be in the midday editions. And they're all howling for a picture of the girl. Vallance is having one cooked up and got down to her that'll look more or less like any girl, but just sufficiently like her. She'll send it out this evening. Fortunately the reporters can't get near the place. She's refusing to talk and Vallance is praying that some friend or relation won't blow the gaff. They're holding the inquest today and Vallance is hoping that the case will be officially closed by this evening and that the papers will have to let it die for lack of material.'

'What about this practice shoot?' asked Bond.

'They're sticking to the schedule,' said M. 'Noon on Friday. They're using a dummy warhead and firing her vertically with only three-quarter tanks. They're clearing about a hundred square miles of the North Sea from about Latitude 52 up. That's north of a line joining the Hague and the Wash. Full details are going to be given out by the P.M. on Thursday night.'

M stopped talking. He swivelled his chair round so that he could look out of the window. Bond heard a distant clock chime the four quarters. One o'clock. Was he going to miss his lunch again. If M would stop ferreting about in the business of other Departments he could have a quick lunch and get round to Bentley's. Bond shifted slightly in his chair.

M turned back and faced him again across the desk.

'The people who are most worried about all this,' he said, 'are the Ministry of Supply. Tallon was one of their best men. His reports had been completely negative all along. Then he suddenly rang up the Assistant Under-Secretary yesterday afternoon and said he thought something fishy was going on at the site and he asked to see the Minister personally at ten o'clock this morning. Wouldn't say anything more on the telephone. And a few hours later he gets shot. Another funny coincidence, wasn't it?'

'Very funny,' said Bond. 'But why don't they close down the site and have a wholesale inquiry? After all, this thing's too big to take a chance on.'

'The Cabinet met early this morning,' said M, 'and the Prime Minister asked the obvious question. What evidence was there of any attempt, or even of any intention, to sabotage the Moonraker? The answer was none. There were only fears which had been brought to the surface in the last twenty-four hours by Tallon's vague message and the double murder. Everyone agreed that unless there was a grain of evidence, which so far hasn't turned up, both these incidents could be put down to the terrific nervous tension on the site. The way things are in the world at the moment it was decided that the sooner the Moonraker could give us an independent say in world affairs the better for us and,' M shrugged his shoulders, 'quite possibly for the world. And it was agreed that for a thousand reasons why the Moonraker should be fired the reasons against didn't stand up. The Minister of Supply had to agree, but he knows as well as you or I that, whatever the facts, it would be a colossal victory for the Russians to sabotage the Moonraker on the eve of her practice shoot. If they did it well enough they might easily get the whole project shelved. There are fifty Germans working on the thing. Any one of them could have relatives still being held in Russia whose lives could be used as a lever.' M paused. He looked up at the ceiling. Then his eyes came down and rested thoughtfully on Bond.

'The Minister asked me to go and see him after the Cabinet. He said that the least he could do was replace Tallon at once. The new man must be bilingual in German, a sabotage expert, and have had plenty of experience of our Russian friends. M.I.5 have put up three candidates. They're all on cases at the moment, but they could be extricated in a few hours. But then the Minister asked my opinion. I gave it. He talked to the Prime Minister and a lot of red tape got cut very quickly.'

Bond looked sharply, resentfully, into the grey, uncompromising eyes.

'So,' said M flatly, 'Sir Hugo Drax has been notified of your appointment and he expects you down at his headquarters in time for dinner this evening.'

Chapter Ten

Special Branch Agent

At six o'clock that Tuesday evening towards the end of May, James Bond was thrashing the big Bentley down the Dover road along the straight stretch that runs into Maidstone.

Although he was driving fast and with concentration, part of his mind was going back over his movements since he had left M's office four and a half hours earlier.

After giving a brief outline of the case to his secretary and eating a quick lunch at a table to himself in the canteen, he had told the garage for God's sake to hurry up with his car and deliver it, filled up, to his flat not later than four o'clock. Then he had taken a taxi down to Scotland Yard where he had an appointment with Assistant Commissioner Vallance at a quarter to three.

The courtyards and cul-de-sacs of the Yard had reminded him as usual of a prison without roofs. The overhead strip lighting in the cold corridor took the colour out of the cheeks of the police sergeant who asked his business and watched him sign the apple-green chit. It did the same for the face of the constable who led him up the short steps and along the bleak passage between the rows of anonymous doors to the waiting-room.

A quiet, middle-aged woman with the resigned eyes of someone who had seen everything came in and said the Assistant Commissioner would be free in five minutes. Bond had gone to the window and had looked out into the grey courtyard below. A constable, looking naked without his helmet, had come out of a building and walked across the yard munching a split roll with something pink between the two halves. It had been very quiet and the noise of the traffic on Whitehall and on the Embankment had sounded far away. Bond had felt dispirited. He was getting tangled up with strange departments. He would be out of touch with his own people and his own Service routines. Already, in this waiting-room, he felt out of his element. Only criminals or informers came and waited here, or influential people vainly trying to get out of a dangerous driving charge or desperately hoping to persuade Vallance that their sons were not really homosexuals. You could not be in the waiting-room of the Special Branch for any innocent purpose. You were either prosecuting or defending.

At last the woman came for him. He stubbed out his cigarette in the top of the Player's cigarette tin that serves as an ashtray in the waiting-rooms of government departments, and followed her across the corridor.

After the gloom of the waiting-room the unseasonable fire on the hearth of the large cheerful room had seemed like a trick, like the cigarette offered you by the Gestapo.

It had taken Bond a full five minutes to shake off his depression and realize that Ronnie Vallance was relieved to see him, that he was not interested in inter-departmental jealousies and that he was only looking to Bond to protect the Moonraker and get one of his best officers out of what might be a bad mess.

Vallance was a man of great tact. For the first few minutes he had spoken only of M. And he had spoken with inside knowledge and with sincerity. Without even mentioning the case he had gained Bond's friendship and co-operation.

As Bond swung the Bentley through the crowded streets of Maidstone he reflected that Vallance's gift had come from twenty years of avoiding the corns of M.I.5, of working in with the uniformed branch of the police, and of handling ignorant politicians and affronted foreign diplomats.

When Bond had left him after a quarter of an hour's hard talking, each man knew that he had acquired an ally. Vallance had sized up Bond and knew that Gala Brand would get all Bond's help and whatever protection she needed. He also respected Bond's professional approach to the assignment and his absence of departmental rivalry with the Special Branch. As for Bond, he was full of admiration for what he had learned about Vallance's agent, and he felt that he was no longer naked and that he had Vallance and the whole of Vallance's department behind him.

Bond had left Scotland Yard with the feeling that he had achieved Clausewitz's first principle. He had made his base secure.

His visit to the Ministry of Supply had added nothing to his knowledge of the case. He had studied Tallon's record and his reports. The former was quite straightforward – a lifetime in Army Intelligence and Field Security – and the latter painted a picture of a very lively and well-managed technical establishment–one or two cases of drunkenness, one of petty theft, several personal vendettas leading to fights and mild bloodshed, but otherwise a loyal and hardworking team of men.

Then he had had an inadequate half-hour in the Operations Room of the Ministry with Professor Train, a fat, scruffy, undistinguished-looking man who had been runner-up for the Physics Division of the Nobel Prize the year before and who was one of the greatest experts on guided missiles in the world.

Professor Train had walked up to a row of huge wall maps and had pulled down the cord of one of them. Bond was faced with a ten-foot horizontal scale diagram of something that looked like a V2 with big fins.

'Now,' said Professor Train, 'you know nothing about rockets so I'm going to put this in simple terms and not fill you up with a lot of stuff about Nozzle Expansion Ratios, Exhaust Velocity, and the Keplerian Ellipse. The Moonraker, as Drax chooses to call it, is a single-stage rocket. It uses up all its fuel shooting itself into the air and then it homes on to the objective. The V2's trajectory was more like a shell fired from a gun. At the top of its 200-mile flight it had climbed to about 70 miles. It was fuelled with a very combustible mixture of alcohol and liquid oxygen which was watered down so as not to burn out the mild steel which was all they were allocated for the engine. There are far more powerful fuels available but until now we hadn't been able to achieve very much with them for the same reason, their combustion temperature is so high that they would burn out the toughest engine.'

The Professor paused and stuck a finger in Bond's chest. 'All you, my dear sir, have to remember about this rocket is that, thanks to Drax's Columbite which has a melting point of about 3,500 degrees Centigrade, compared with 1,300 in the V2 engines, we can use one of the super fuels without burning out the engine. In fact,' he looked at Bond as if Bond should be impressed, 'we are using fluorine and hydrogen.'

'Oh, really,' said Bond reverently.

The Professor looked at him sharply. 'So we hope to achieve a speed in the neighbourhood of 15,000 miles an hour and a vertical range of about 1,000 miles. This should produce an operational range of about 4,000 miles, bringing every European capital within reach of England. Very useful,' he added drily, 'in certain circumstances. But, for the scientists, chiefly desirable as a step towards escape from the earth. Any questions?'

'How does it work?' asked Bond dutifully.

The Professor gestured brusquely towards the diagram. 'Let's start from the nose,' he said. 'First comes the warhead. For the practice shoot this will contain upper-atmosphere instruments, radar and suchlike. Then the gyro compasses to make it fly straight–pitch-and-yaw gyro and roll gyro. Then various minor instruments, servo motors, power supply. And then the big fuel tanks–30,000 pounds of the stuff.

'At the stern you get two small tanks to drive the turbine. Four hundred pounds of hydrogen peroxide mixes with forty pounds of potassium permanganate and makes steam which drives the turbines underneath them. These drive a set of centrifugal pumps which force the main fuel into the rocket motor. Under terrific pressure. Do you follow me?' He cocked a dubious eyebrow at Bond.

'Sounds much the same principle as a jet plane,' said Bond.

The Professor seemed pleased. 'More or less,' he said, 'but the rocket carries all its fuel inside it, instead of sucking in oxygen from outside like the Comet. Well then,' he continued, 'the fuel gets ignited in the motor and squirts out at the end in a continuous blast. Rather like a continuous recoil from a gun. And this blast forces the rocket into the air like any other firework. Of course it's at the stern that the Columbite comes in. It's allowed us to make a motor that won't be melted by the fantastic heat. And then,' he pointed, 'those are the tail fins to keep it steady at the beginning of its flight. Also made of Columbite alloy or they'd break away with the colossal air pressure. Anything else?'

'How can you be certain it'll come down where you mean it to?' asked Bond. 'What's to prevent it falling on The Hague next Monday?'

'The gyros will see to that. But as a matter of fact we're taking no chances on Monday and we're using a radar homing device on a raft in the middle of the sea. There'll be a radar transmitter in the nose of the rocket which will pick up an echo from our gadget in the sea and home on to it automatically. Of course,' the Professor grinned, 'if we ever had to use the thing in wartime it would be a great help to have a homing device transmitting energy from the middle of Moscow or Warsaw or Prague or Monte Carlo or wherever we might be shooting at. It'll probably be up to you chaps to get one there. Good luck to you.'

Bond smiled non-committally. 'One more question,' he said. 'If you wanted to sabotage the rocket what would be the easiest way?'

'Any number,' said the Professor cheerfully. 'Sand in the fuel. Grit in the pumps. A small hole anywhere on the fuselage or the fins. With that power and at those speeds the smallest fault would finish it.'

'Thanks very much,' said Bond. 'It seems you've got fewer worries about the Moonraker than I have.'

'It's a wonderful machine,' said the Professor. 'She'll fly all right if nobody interferes with her. Drax has done a sound job. Wonderful organizer. That's a brilliant team he put together. And they'll do anything for him. We've got a lot to thank him for.'

Bond did a racing change and swung the big car left at the Charing fork, preferring the clear road by Chilham and Canterbury to the bottlenecks of Ashford and Folkestone. The car howled up to eighty in third and he held it in the same gear to negotiate the hairpin at the top of the long gradient leading up to the Molash road.

And, he wondered, going back into top and listening with satisfaction to the relaxed thunder of the exhaust, and what about Drax? What sort of a reception was Drax going to give him this evening? According to M, when his name had been suggested over the telephone, Drax had paused for a moment and then said, 'Oh yes. I know the fellow. Didn't know he was mixed up in that racket. I'd be interested to have another look at him. Send him along. I'll expect him in time for dinner.' Then he had rung off.

The people at the Ministry had their own view of Drax. In their dealings with him they had found him a dedicated man, completely bound up in the Moonraker, living for nothing but its success, driving his men to the limit, fighting for priorities in material with other departments, goading the Ministry of Supply into clearing his requirements at Cabinet level. They disliked his hectoring manners but they respected him for his know-how and his drive and his dedication. And, like the rest of England, they considered him a possible saviour of the country.

Well, thought Bond, accelerating down the straight stretch of road past Chilham Castle, he could see that picture too and if he was going to work with the man he must adjust himself to the heroic version. If Drax was willing, he would put the whole affair at Blades out of his mind and concentrate on protecting Drax and his wonderful project from their country's enemies. There were only about three days to go. The security precautions were already minute and Drax might resent suggestions for increasing them. It was not going to be easy and a great deal of tact would have to be used. Tact. Not Bond's long suit and not, he reflected, connected in any way with what he knew of Drax's character.

Bond took the short cut out of Canterbury by the Old Dover road and looked at his watch. It was six-thirty. Another fifteen minutes to Dover and then another ten minutes along the Deal road. Were there any other plans to be made? The double killing was out of his hands, thank heaven. 'Murder and suicide while of unsound mind' had been the coroner's verdict. The girl had not even been called. He would stop for a drink at the World without Want and have a quick word with the innkeeper. The next day he would have to try and smell out the 'something fishy' that Tallon had wanted to see the Minister about. No clue about that. Nothing had been found in Tallon's room, which presumably he would now be taking over. Well, at any rate that would give him plenty of leisure to go through Tallon's papers.

Bond concentrated on his driving as he coasted down into Dover. He kept left and was soon climbing out of the town again past the wonderful cardboard castle.

There was a patch of low cloud on top of the hill and a spit of rain on his windshield. There was a cold breeze coming in from the sea. The visibility was bad and he switched on his lights as he motored slowly along the coast-road, the ruby-spangled masts of the Swingate radar station rising like petrified Roman candles on his right.

The girl? He would have to be careful how he contacted her and careful not to upset her. He wondered if she would be any use to him. After a year on the site she would have had all the opportunities of a private secretary to 'The Chief' to get under the skin of the whole project–and of Drax. And she had a mind trained to his own particular craft. But he would have to be prepared for her to be suspicious of the new broom and perhaps resentful. He wondered what she was really like. The photograph on her record-sheet at the Yard had shown an attractive but rather severe girl and any hint of seductiveness had been abstracted by the cheerless jacket of her policewoman's uniform.

Hair: Auburn. Eyes: Blue. Height: 5 ft. 7. Weight: 9 stone. Hips: 38. Waist: 26. Bust: 38. Distinguishing marks: Mole on upper curvature of right breast.

Hm! thought Bond.

He put the statistics out of his mind as he came to the turning to the right. There was a signpost that said Kingsdown, and the lights of a small inn.

He pulled up and switched off the engine. Above his head a sign which said 'World without Want' in faded gold lettering groaned in the salt breeze that came over the cliffs half a mile away. He got out, stretched and walked over to the door of the public bar. It was locked. Closed for cleaning? He tried the next door, which opened and gave access to the small private bar.

Behind the bar a stolid-looking man in shirt-sleeves was reading an evening paper.

He looked up as Bond entered, and put his paper down. 'Evening, sir,' he said, evidently relieved to see a customer.

'Evening,' said Bond. 'Large whisky and soda, please.' He sat up at the bar and waited while the man poured two measures of Black and White and put the glass in front of him with a syphon of soda.

Bond filled the glass with soda and drank. 'Bad business you had here last night,' he said, putting the glass down.

'Terrible, sir,' said the man. 'And bad for trade. Would you be from the Press, sir? Had nothing but reporters and policemen in and out of the house all day long.'

'No,' said Bond. 'I've come to take over the job of the fellow who got shot. Major Tallon. Was he one of your regular customers?'

'Never came here but the once, sir, and that was the end of him. Now I've been put out of bounds for a week and the public has got to be painted from top to bottom. But I will say that Sir Hugo has been very decent about it. Sent me fifty quid this afternoon to pay for the damage. He must be a fine gentleman that. Made himself well liked in these parts. Always very generous and a cheery word for one and all.'

'Yes. Fine man,' said Bond. 'Did you see it all happen?'

'Didn't see the first shot, sir. Serving a pint at the time. Then of course I looked up. Dropped the ruddy pint on the floor.'

'What happened then?'

'Well, everybody's standing back of course. Nothing but Germans in the place. About a dozen of them. There's the body on the floor and the chap with the gun looking down at him. Then suddenly he stands to attention and sticks his left arm up in the air. "Eil?" he shouts like the silly bastards used to do during the war. Then he puts the end of the gun in his mouth. Next thing,' the man made a grimace, 'he's all over my ruddy ceiling.'

'That was all he said after the shot?' asked Bond. 'Just "Heil"?'

'That's all, sir. Don't seem to be able to forget the bloody word, do they?'

'No,' said Bond thoughtfully, 'they certainly don't.'

Chapter Eleven

Policewoman Brand

Five minutes later Bond was showing his Ministry pass to the uniformed guard on duty at the gate in the high wire fence.

The R.A.F. sergeant handed it back to him and saluted. 'Sir Hugo's expecting you, sir. It's the big house up in the woods there.' He pointed to some lights a hundred yards further on towards the cliffs.

Bond heard him telephoning to the next guard point. He motored slowly along the new tarmac road that had been laid across the fields behind Kingsdown. He could hear the distant boom of the sea at the foot of the tall cliffs and from somewhere closer at hand there was a high-pitched whine of machinery which grew louder as he approached the trees.

He was stopped again by a plain-clothes guard at a second wire fence through which a five-bar gate gave access to the interior of the wood, and as he was waved through he heard the distant baying of police dogs which suggested some form of night patrol. All these precautions seemed efficient. Bond decided that he wouldn't have to worry himself with problems of external security.

Once through the trees the car was running over a flat concrete apron the limits of which, in the bad light, were out of range even of the huge twin beams of his Marchal headlamps. A hundred yards to his left, on the edge of the trees, there were the lights of a large house half-hidden behind a wall six feet thick, that rose straight up off the surface of the concrete almost to the height of the house. Bond slowed the car down to walking pace and turned its bonnet away from the house towards the sea and towards a dark shape that suddenly glinted white in the revolving beams of the South Goodwin Lightship far out in the Channel. His lights cut a path down the apron to where, almost on the edge of the cliff and at least half a mile away, a squat dome surged up about fifty feet out of the concrete. It looked like the top of an observatory and Bond could distinguish the flange of a joint running east and west across the surface of the dome.

He turned the car back and slowly ran it up between what he now assumed to be a blast-wall and the front of the house. As he pulled up outside the house the door opened and a manservant in a white jacket came out. He smartly opened the door of the car.

'Good evening, sir. This way please.'

He spoke woodenly and with a trace of accent. Bond followed him into the house and across a comfortable hall to a door on which the butler knocked.

'In.'

Bond smiled to himself at the harsh tone of the well-remembered voice and at the note of command in the single monosyllable.

At the far end of the long, bright, chintzy living-room Drax was standing with his back to an empty grate, a huge figure in a plum-coloured velvet smoking-jacket that clashed with the reddish hair on his face. There were three other people standing near him, two men and a woman.

'Ah, my dear fellow,' said Drax boisterously, striding forward to meet him and shaking him cordially by the hand. 'So we meet again. And so soon. Didn't realize you were a ruddy spy for my Ministry or I'd have been more careful about playing cards against you. Spent that money yet?' he asked, leading him towards the fire.

'Not yet,' smiled Bond. 'Haven't seen the colour of it.'

'Of course. Settlement on Saturday. Probably get the cheque just in time to celebrate our little firework display, what? Now let's see.' He led Bond up to the woman. 'This is my secretary, Miss Brand.'

Bond looked into a pair of very level blue eyes.

'Good evening.' He gave her a friendly smile.

There was no answering smile in the eyes which looked calmly into his. No answering pressure of her hand. 'How do you do,' she said indifferently, almost, Bond sensed, with hostility.

It crossed Bond's mind that she had been well-chosen. Another Loelia

Ponsonby. Reserved, efficient, loyal, virginal. Thank heavens, he thought. A professional.

'My right-hand man, Dr Walter.' The thin elderly man with a pair of angry eyes under a shock of black hair seemed not to notice Bond's outstretched hand. He sprang to attention and gave a quick nod of the head. 'Valter,' said the thin mouth above the black imperial, correcting Drax's pronounciation.

'And my–what shall I say–my dogsbody. What you might call my A.D.C., Willy Krebs.' There was the touch of a slightly damp hand. 'Ferry pleased to meet you,' said an ingratiating voice and Bond looked into a pale round unhealthy face now split in a stage smile which died almost as Bond noticed it. Bond looked into his eyes. They were like two restless black buttons and they twisted away from Bond's gaze.

Both men wore spotless white overalls with plastic zip fasteners at the sleeves and ankles and down the back. Their hair was close-cropped so that the skin shone through and they would have looked like people from another planet but for the untidy black moustache and imperial of Dr Walter and the pale wispy moustache of Krebs. They were both caricatures–a mad scientist and a youthful version of Peter Lorre.

The colourful ogreish figure of Drax was a pleasant contrast in this chilly company and Bond was grateful to him for the cheerful roughness of his welcome and for his apparent wish to bury the hatchet and make the best of his new security officer.

Drax was very much the host. He rubbed his hands together. 'Now, Willy,' he said, 'how about making one of your excellent dry Martinis for us? Except, of course, for the Doctor. Doesn't drink or smoke,' he explained to Bond, returning to his place by the mantelpiece. 'Hardly breathes.' He barked out a short laugh. 'Thinks of nothing but the rocket. Do you, my friend?'

The Doctor looked stonily in front of him. 'You are pleased to joke,' he said.

'Now, now,' said Drax, as if to a child. 'We will go back to those leading edges later. Everybody's quite happy about them except you.' He turned to Bond. 'The good Doctor is always frightening us,' he explained indulgently. 'He's always having nightmares about something. Now it's the leading edges of the fins. They're already as sharp as razor blades–hardly any wind resistance at all. And he suddenly gets it into his head that they're going to melt. Friction of the air. Of course everything's possible, but they've been tested at over 3,000 degrees and, as I tell him, if they're going to melt then the whole rocket will melt. And that's just not going to happen,' he added with a grim smile.

Krebs came up with a silver tray with four full glasses and a frosted shaker. The Martini was excellent and Bond said so.

'You are ferry kind,' said Krebs with a smirk of satisfaction. 'Sir Hugo is ferry exacting.'

'Fill up his glass,' said Drax, 'and then perhaps our friend would like to wash. We dine at eight sharp.'

As he spoke, there came the muffled wail of a siren and almost immediately the sound of a body of men running in strict unison across the concrete apron outside.

'That's the first night shift,' explained Drax. 'Barracks are just behind the house. Must be eight o'clock. We do everything at the double here,' he added with a gleam of satisfaction in his eye. 'Precision. Lot of scientists about, but we try to run the place like a military establishment. Willy, look after the Commander. We'll go ahead. Come along, my dear.'

As Bond followed Krebs to the door through which he had entered, he saw the other two with Drax in the lead make for the double doors at the end of the room which had opened as Drax finished speaking. The manservant in the white coat stood in the entrance. As Bond went out into the hall it crossed his mind that Drax would certainly go into the dining-room ahead of Miss Brand. Forceful personality. Treated his staff like children. Obviously a born leader. Where had he got it from? The Army? Or did it grow on one with millions of money? Bond followed the slug-like neck of Krebs and wondered.

The dinner was excellent. Drax was a genial host and at his own table his manners were faultless. Most of his conversation consisted in drawing out Dr Walter for the benefit of Bond, and it covered a wide range of technical matters which Drax took pains to explain briefly after each topic had been exhausted. Bond was impressed by the confidence with which Drax handled each abstruse problem as it was raised, and by his immense grasp of detail. A genuine admiration for the man gradually developed in him and overshadowed much of his previous dislike. He felt more than ever inclined to forget the Blades affair now that he was faced with the other Drax, the creator and inspired leader of a remarkable enterprise.

Bond sat between his host and Miss Brand. He made several attempts to engage her in conversation. He failed completely. She answered with polite monosyllables and would hardly meet his eye. Bond became mildly irritated. He found her physically very attractive and it annoyed him to be unable to extract the smallest response. He felt that her frigid indifference was overacted and that security would have been far better met with an easy, friendly approach instead of this exaggerated reticence. He felt a strong urge to give her a sharp kick on the ankle. The idea entertained him and he found himself observing her with a fresh eye–as a girl and not as an official colleague. As a start, and under cover of a long argument between Drax and Walter, in which she was required to join, about the collation of weather reports from the Air Ministry and from Europe, he began to add up his impressions of her.

She was far more attractive than her photograph had suggested and it was difficult to see traces of the severe competence of a policewoman in the seductive girl beside him. There was authority in the definite line of the profile, but the long black eyelashes over the dark blue eyes and the rather wide mouth might have been painted by Marie Laurencin. Yet the lips were too full for a Laurencin and the dark brown hair that curved inwards at the base of the neck was of a different fashion. There was a hint of northern blood in the high cheekbones and in the very slight upward slant of the eyes, but the warmth of her skin was entirely English. There was too much poise and authority in her gestures and in the carriage of her head for her to be a very convincing portrait of a secretary. In fact she seemed almost a member of Drax's team, and Bond noticed that the men listened with attention as she answered Drax's questions.

Her rather severe evening dress was in charcoal black grosgrain with full sleeves that came below the elbow. The wrap-over bodice just showed the swell of her breasts, which were as splendid as Bond had guessed from the measurements on her record sheet. At the point of the vee there was a bright blue cameo brooch, a Tassie intaglio, Bond guessed, cheap but imaginative. She wore no other jewellery except a half-hoop of small diamonds on her engagement finger. Apart from the warm rouge on her lips, she wore no make-up and her nails were square cut with a natural polish.

Altogether, Bond decided, she was a very lovely girl and, beneath her reserve, a very passionate one. And, he reflected, she might be a policewoman and an expert at jujitsu, but she also had a mole on her right breast.

With this comforting thought Bond turned the whole of his attention to the conversation between Drax and Walter and made no further attempts to make friends with the girl.

Dinner ended at nine. 'Now we will go over and introduce you to the Moonraker,' said Drax, rising abruptly from the table. 'Walter will accompany us. He has much to do. Come along my dear Bond.'

Without a word to Krebs or the girl he strode out of the room. Bond and Walter followed him.

They left the house and walked across the concrete towards the distant shape on the edge of the cliff. The moon had risen and in the distance the squat dome shone palely in its light.

A hundred yards from the site Drax stopped. 'I will explain the geography,' he said. 'Walter, you go ahead. They will be waiting for you to have another look at those fins. Don't worry about them, my dear fellow. Those people at High Duty Alloys know what they're doing. Now,' he turned to Bond and gestured towards the milk-white dome, 'in there is the Moonraker. What you see is the lid of a wide shaft that has been cut about forty foot down into the chalk. The two halves of the dome are opened hydraulically and fold back flush with that twenty-foot wall. If they were open now, you would see the nose of the Moonraker just protruding above the level of the wall. Over there,' he pointed to a square shape that was almost out of sight in the direction of Deal, 'is the firing point. Concrete blockhouse. Full of radar tracking gadgets–Doppler velocity radar and flight-path radar, for instance. Information is fed to them by twenty telemetering channels in the nose of the rocket. There's a big television screen in there too so that you can watch the behaviour of the rocket inside the shaft after the pumps have been started. Another television set to follow the beginning of its climb. Alongside the blockhouse there's a hoist down the face of the cliff. Quite a lot of gear has been brought to the site by sea and then sent up on the hoist. That whine you hear is from the power house over there,' he gestured vaguely in the direction of Dover. 'The men's barracks and the house are protected by the blast-wall, but when we fire there won't be anyone within a mile of the site, except the Ministry experts and the B.B.C. team who are going to be in the firing point. Hope it'll stand up to the blast. Walter says that the site and a lot of the concrete apron will be melted by the heat. That's all. Nothing else you need to know about until we get inside. Come along.'

Bond noted again the abrupt tone of command. He followed in silence across the moonlit expanse until they came to the supporting wall of the dome. A naked red bulb glowed over a steel-plated door in the wall. It illuminated a bold sign which said in English and German: MORTAL DANGER.

ENTRY FORBIDDEN WHEN RED LAMP SHOWS. RING AND WAIT.

Drax pressed a button beneath the notice and there was the muffled clang of an alarm bell. 'Might be somebody working with oxy-acetylene or doing some other delicate job,' he explained. 'Take his mind off his job for a split second as someone comes in and you could have an expensive mistake. Everybody downs tools when the bell rings and then starts up again when they see what it is.' Drax stood away from the door and pointed upwards to a row of four-foot wide gratings just below the top of the wall. 'Ventilator shafts,' he explained. 'Air-conditioning inside to 70 degrees.'

The door was opened by a man with a truncheon in his hand and a revolver at his hip. Bond followed Drax through into a small anteroom. It contained nothing but a bench and a neat row of felt slippers.

'Have to put these on,' said Drax sitting down and kicking off his shoes. 'Might slip and knock into someone. Better leave your coats here too. Seventy degrees is quite warm.'

'Thanks,' said Bond remembering the Beretta at his armpit. 'As a matter of fact I don't feel the heat.'

Feeling like a visitor to an operating theatre, Bond followed Drax through a communicating door out on to an iron catwalk and into a blaze of spotlights that made him automatically put a hand up to his eyes as he grasped the guard-rail in front of him.

When he took his hand away he was greeted by a scene of such splendour that for several minutes he stood speechless, his eyes dazzled by the terrible beauty of the greatest weapon on earth.

Chapter Twelve

The Moonraker

It was like being inside the polished barrel of a huge gun. From the floor, forty feet below, rose circular walls of polished metal near the top of which he and Drax clung like two flies. Up through the centre of the shaft, which was about thirty feet wide, soared a pencil of glistening chromium, whose point, tapering to a needle-sharp antenna, seemed to graze the roof twenty feet above their heads.

The shimmering projectile rested on a blunt cone of latticed steel which rose from the floor between the tips of three severely back-swept delta fins that looked as sharp as surgeons' scalpels. But otherwise nothing marred the silken sheen of the fifty feet of polished chrome steel except the spidery fingers of two light gantries which stood out from the walls and clasped the waist of the rocket between thick pads of foam-rubber.

Where they touched the rocket, small access doors stood open in the steel skin and, as Bond looked down, a man crawled out of one door on to the narrow platform of the gantry and closed the door behind him with a gloved hand. He walked gingerly along the narrow bridge to the wall and turned a handle. There was the sharp whine of machinery and the gantry took its padded hand off the rocket and held it poised in the air, like the forelegs of a praying mantis. The whine altered to a deeper tone and the gantry slowly telescoped in on itself. Then it reached out again and seized the rocket ten feet lower down. Its operator crawled out along its arm and opened another small access door and disappeared inside.

'Probably checking the fuel-feed from the after tanks,' said Drax. 'Gravity feed. Tricky bit of design. What do you think of her?' He looked with pleasure at Bond's rapt expression.

'One of the most beautiful things I've ever seen,' said Bond. It was easy to talk. There was hardly a sound in the great steel shaft and the voices of the men clustered below under the tail of the rocket were no more than a murmur.

Drax pointed upwards. 'Warhead,' he explained. 'Experimental one now. Full of instruments. Telemeters and so forth. Then the gyros just opposite us here. Then mostly fuel tanks all the way down until you get to the turbines near the tail. Driven by superheated steam, made by decomposing hydrogen peroxide. The fuel, fluorine and hydrogen' (he glanced sharply at Bond. 'That's top-secret by the way') 'falls down the feed tubes and gets ignited as soon as it's forced into the motor. Sort of controlled explosion which shoots the rocket into the air. That steel floor under the rocket slides away. There's a big exhaust pit underneath. Comes out at the base of the cliff. You'll see it tomorrow. Looks like a huge cave. When we ran a static test the other day the chalk melted and ran out into the sea like water. Hope we don't burn down the famous white cliffs when we come to the real thing. Like to come and have a look at the works?'

Bond followed silently as Drax led the way down the steep iron ladder that curved down the side of the steel wall. He felt a glow of admiration and almost of reverence for this man and his majestic achievement. How could he ever have been put off by Drax's childish behaviour at the card-table? Even the greatest men have their weaknesses. Drax must need an outlet for the tension of the fantastic responsibility he was carrying. It was clear from the conversation at dinner that he couldn't shed much on to the shoulders of his highly-strung deputy. From him alone had to spring the vitality and confidence to buoy up his whole team. Even in such a small thing as winning at cards it must be important to him to be constantly reassuring himself, constantly searching out omens of good fortune and success, even to the point of creating these omens for himself. Who, Bond asked himself, wouldn't sweat and bite his nails when so much had been dared, when so much was at stake?

As they filed down the long curve of the stairway, their figures grotesquely reflected back at them by the mirror of the rocket's chromium skin, Bond almost felt the man-in-the-street's affection for the man whom, only a few hours previously, he had been dissecting without pity, almost with loathing.

When they reached the steel-plated floor of the shaft, Drax paused and looked up. Bond followed his eyes. Seen from that angle it seemed as if they were gazing up a thin straight shaft of light into the blazing heaven of the arcs, a shaft of light that was not pure white but a shot mother-of-pearl satin. There were shimmers of red in it picked up from the crimson canisters of a giant foam fire-extinguisher that stood near them, a man in an asbestos suit beside it aiming its nozzle at the base of the rocket. There was a streak of violet whose origin was a violet bulb on the board of an instrument panel in the wall, which controlled the steel cover over the exhaust pit. And there was a whisper of emerald green from the shaded light over a plain deal table at which a man sat and wrote down figures as they were called to him from the group gathered directly beneath the Moonraker's tail.

Gazing up this pastel column, so incredibly slim and graceful, it seemed unthinkable that anything so delicate could withstand the pressures which it had been designed to meet on Friday–the howling stream of the most powerful controlled explosion that had ever been attempted; the impact of the sound barrier; the unknown pressures of the atmosphere at 15,000 miles an hour; the terrible shock as it plunged back from a thousand miles up and hit the atmospheric envelope of the earth.

Drax seemed to read his thoughts. He turned to Bond. 'It will be like committing murder,' he said. Then surprisingly, he burst into a braying laugh. 'Walter,' he called to the group of men. 'Come here.' Walter detached himself and came over. 'Walter. I was saying to our friend the Commander that when we fire the Moonraker it will be like committing murder.'

Bond was not surprised to see a look of puzzled incredulity come over the Doctor's face.

Drax said irritably, 'Child murder. Murder of our child,' he gestured at the rocket. 'Wake up. Wake up. What's the matter with you?'

Walter's face cleared. Frostily he beamed his appreciation of the simile. 'Murder. Yes, that is good. Ha! ha! And now, Sir Hugo. The graphite slats in the exhaust vent. The Ministry is quite happy about their melting-point? They do not feel that . . .' Still talking, Walter led Drax under the tail of the rocket. Bond followed.

The faces of the ten men were turned towards them as they came up. Drax introduced him with a wave of the hand. 'Commander Bond, our new security officer,' he said briefly.

The group eyed Bond in silence. There was no move to greet him and the ten pairs of eyes were incurious.

'Now then, what's all this fuss about the graphite? . . .' The group closed round Drax and Walter. Bond was left standing alone.

He was not surprised by the coolness of his reception. He would have regarded the intrusion of an amateur into the secrets of his own department with much the same indifference mixed with resentment. And he sympathized with these hand-picked technicians who had lived for months among the highest realms of astronautics and were now on the threshold of the final arbitration. And yet, he reminded himself, the innocent among them must know that Bond had his own duty to perform, his own vital part in this project. Supposing one pair of those uncommunicative eyes concealed a man within a man, an enemy, perhaps at this very moment exulting in his knowledge that the graphite which Walter seemed to mistrust was indeed under-strength. It was true that they had the look of a well-knit team, almost of a brotherhood, as they stood round Drax and Walter, hanging on their words, their eyes intent on the mouths of the two men. But was part of one brain moving within the privacy of some secret orbit, ticking off its hidden calculus like the stealthy mechanism of an infernal machine?

Bond moved casually up and down the triangle made by the three points of the fins as they rested in their rubber-lined cavities in the steel floor, interesting himself in whatever met his eyes, but every now and then focusing the group of men from a new angle.

With the exception of Drax they all wore the same tight nylon overalls fastened with plastic zips. There was nowhere a hint of metal and none wore spectacles. As in the case of Walter and Krebs their heads were close-shaved, presumably, Bond would have thought, to prevent a loose hair falling into the mechanism. And yet, and this struck Bond as a most bizarre characteristic of the team, each man sported a luxuriant moustache to whose culture it was clear that a great deal of attention had been devoted. They were in all shapes and tints: fair or mousy or dark; handlebar, walrus, Kaiser, Hitler–each face bore its own hairy badge amongst which the rank, reddish growth of Drax's facial hair blazed like the official stamp of their paramount chief.

Why, wondered Bond, should every man on the site wear a moustache? He had never liked the things, but combined with these shaven heads, there was something positively obscene about this crop of hairy tufts. It would have been just bearable if they had all been cut to the same pattern, but this range of individual fashions, this riot of personalized growth, had something particularly horrible about it against the background of the naked round heads.

There was nothing else to notice; the men were of average height and they were all on the slim side–tailored, Bond supposed, more or less to the requirements of their work. Agility would be needed on the gantries, and compactness for manoeuvring through the access doors and around the tiny compartments in the rocket. Their hands looked relaxed and spotlessly clean, and their feet in the felt slippers were motionless with concentration. He never once caught any of them glancing in his direction and, as for penetrating their minds or weighing up their loyalties, he admitted to himself that the task of unmasking the thoughts of fifty of these robot-like Germans in three days was quite hopeless. Then he remembered. It was fifty no longer. Only forty-nine. One of these robots had blown his top (apt expression, reflected Bond). And what had come out of Bartsch's secret thoughts? Lust for a woman and a Heil Hitler. Would he be far wrong, wondered Bond, if he guessed that, forgetting the Moonraker, those were also the dominant thoughts inside the other forty-nine heads?

'Doctor Walter! That is an order.' Drax's voice of controlled anger broke in on Bond's thoughts as he stood fingering the sharp leading edge of the tail of one of the Columbite fins. 'Back to work. We have wasted enough time.'

The men scattered smartly about their duties and Drax came up to where Bond was standing, leaving Walter hanging about indecisively beneath the exhaust vent of the rocket.

Drax's face was thunderous. 'Damn fool. Always seeing trouble,' he muttered. And then abruptly, as if he wanted to clear his deputy out of his mind, 'Come along to my office. Show you the flight plan. Then we'll go off to bed.'

Bond followed him across the floor. Drax turned a small handle flush with the steel wall and a narrow door opened with a soft hiss. Three feet inside there was another steel door and Bond noticed that they were both edged with rubber. Air-lock. Before closing the outer door Drax paused on the threshold and pointed along the circular wall to a number of similar inconspicuous flat knobs in the wall. 'Workshops,' he said. 'Electricians, generators, fuelling control, washrooms, stores.' He pointed to the adjoining door. 'My secretary's room.' He closed the outer door before he opened the second and walked into his office and shut the inner door behind Bond.

It was a severe room painted pale grey, containing a broad desk and several chairs of tubular metal and dark blue canvas. The floor was carpeted in grey. There were two green filing cabinets and a large metal radio set. A half-open door showed part of a tiled bathroom. The desk faced a wide blank wall which seemed to be made of opaque glass. Drax walked up to the wall and snapped down two switches on its extreme right. The whole wall lit up and Bond was faced with two maps each about six feet square traced on the back of the glass.

The left-hand map showed the eastern quarter of England from Portsmouth to Hull and the adjoining waters from Latitude 50 to 55. From the red dot near Dover which was the site of the Moonraker, arcs showing the range in ten-mile intervals had been drawn up the map. At a point eighty miles from the site, between the Friesian Islands and Hull, there was a red diamond in the middle of the ocean.

Drax waved towards the dense mathematical tables and columns of compass readings which filled the right-hand side of the map. 'Wind velocities, atmospheric pressure, ready-reckoner for the gyro settings,' he said. 'All worked out using the rocket's velocity and range as constants. We get the weather every day from the Air Ministry and readings from the upper atmosphere every time the R.A.F. jet can get up there. When he's at maximum altitude he releases helium balloons that can get up still further. The earth's atmosphere reaches about fifty miles up. After twenty there's hardly any density to affect the Moonraker. It'll coast up almost in a vacuum. Getting through the first twenty miles is the problem. The gravity pull's another worry. Walter can explain all those things if you're interested. There'll be continuous weather reports during the last few hours on Friday. And we'll set the gyros just before the take-off. For the time being, Miss Brand gets together the data every morning and keeps a table of gyro settings in case they're wanted.'

Drax pointed at the second of the two maps. This was a diagram of the rocket's flight ellipse from firing point to target. There were more columns of figures. 'Speed of the earth and its effect on the rocket's trajectory,' explained Drax. 'The earth will be turning to the east while the rocket's in flight. That factor has to be married in with the figures on the other map. Complicated business. Fortunately you don't have to understand it. Leave it to Miss Brand. Now then,' he switched off the lights and the wall went blank, 'any particular questions about your job? Don't think there'll be much for you to do. You can see that the place is already riddled with security. The Ministry's insisted on it from the beginning.'

'Everything looks all right,' said Bond. He examined Drax's face. The good eye was looking at him sharply. Bond paused. 'Do you think there was anything between your secretary and Major Tallon?' he asked. It was an obvious question and he might just as well ask it now.

'Could have been,' said Drax easily. 'Attractive girl. They were thrown together a lot down here. At any rate she seems to have got under Bartsch's skin.'

'I hear Bartsch saluted and shouted "Heil Hitler" before he put the gun in his mouth,' said Bond.

'So they tell me,' said Drax evenly. 'What of it?'

'Why do all the men wear moustaches?' asked Bond, ignoring Drax's question. Again he had the impression that his question had nettled the other man.

Drax gave one of his short barking laughs. 'My idea,' he said. 'They're difficult to recognize in those white overalls and with their heads shaved. So I told them all to grow moustaches. The thing's become quite a fetish with them. Like in the R.A.F. during the war. See anything wrong with it?'

'Of course not,' said Bond. 'Rather startling at first. I would have thought that large numbers on their suits with a different colour for each shift would have been more effective.'

'Well,' said Drax, turning away towards the door as if to end the conversation, 'I decided on moustaches.'

Chapter Thirteen

Dead Reckoning

On Wednesday morning Bond woke early in the dead man's bed.

He had slept little. Drax had said nothing on their way back to the house and had bidden him a curt good-night at the foot of the stairs. Bond had walked along the carpeted corridor to where light shone from an open door and had found his things neatly laid out in a comfortable bedroom. The room was furnished in the same expensive taste as the ground floor and there were biscuits and a bottle of Vichy (not a Vichy bottle of tap-water, Bond established) beside the Heal bed.

There were no signs of the previous occupant except a leather case containing binoculars on the dressing-table and a metal filing cabinet which was locked. Bond knew about filing cabinets. He tilted it against the wall, reached underneath, and found the bottom end of the bar-lock which protrudes downwards when the top section has been locked. Upwards pressure released the drawers one by one and he softly lowered the edge of the cabinet back on to the floor with the unkind reflection that Major Tallon would not have survived very long in the Secret Service.

The top drawer contained scale maps of the site and its component buildings and Admiralty Chart No. 1895 of the Straits of Dover. Bond laid each sheet on the bed and examined them minutely. There were traces of cigarette ash in the folds of the Admiralty chart.

Bond fetched his tool-box–a square leather case that stood beside the dressing-table. He examined the numbers on the wheels of the combination lock and, satisfied that they had not been disturbed, turned them to the code number. The box was closely fitted with instruments. Bond selected a fingerprint powder-spray and a large magnifying glass. He puffed the fine greyish powder foot by foot over the whole expanse of the chart. A forest of fingerprints showed. By going over these with the magnifying glass he established that they belonged to two people. He isolated two of the best sets, took a Leica with a flashbulb attachment out of the leather case and photographed them. Then he carefully examined through his glass two minute furrows in the paper which the powder had brought to light.

These appeared to be two lines drawn out from the coast to form a cross-bearing in the sea. It was a very narrow bearing, and both lines seemed to originate from the house where Bond was. In fact, thought Bond, they might indicate observations of some object in the sea made from each wing of the house.

The two lines were drawn not with a pencil, but, presumably to avoid detection, with a stylus which had barely furrowed the paper.

At the point where they met there was the trace of a question mark, and this point was on the twelve-fathom line about fifty yards from the cliff on a direct bearing from the house to the South Goodwin Lightship.

There was nothing else to be gathered from the chart. Bond glanced at his watch. Twenty minutes to one. He heard distant footsteps in the hall and the click of a light being extinguished. On an impulse he rose and softly switched off the lights in his room, leaving only the shaded reading-light beside the bed.

He heard the heavy footsteps of Drax approaching up the stairs. There was the click of another switch and then silence. Bond could imagine the great hairy face turned down the corridor, looking, listening. Then there was a creak and the sound of a door being softly opened and as softly closed. Bond waited, visualizing the motions of the man as he prepared for bed. There was the muffled sound of a window being thrown open and the distant trumpet of a nose being blown. Then silence.

Bond gave Drax another five minutes then he went over to the filing cabinet and softly pulled out the other drawers. There was nothing in the second and third, but the bottom one was solid with files arranged under index letters. They were the dossiers of all the men working on the site. Bond pulled out the 'A' section and went back to the bed and started to read.

In each case the formula was the same: full name, address, date of birth, description, distinguishing marks, profession or trade since the war, war record, political record and present sympathies, criminal record, health, next of kin. Some of the men had wives and children whose particulars were noted, and with each dossier there were photographs, full face and profile, and the fingerprints of both hands.

Two hours and ten cigarettes later he had worked through all of them and had discovered two points of general interest. First, that every one of the fifty men appeared to have led a blameless life without a breath of political or criminal odium. This seemed so unlikely that he decided to refer every single dossier back to Station D for a thorough recheck at the first opportunity.

The second point was that none of the faces in the photographs bore a moustache. Despite Drax's explanation, this fact raised a second tiny question mark in Bond's mind.

Bond got up from the bed and locked everything away, putting the Admiralty Chart and one of the files in his leather case. He turned the wheels of the combination lock and thrust the case far under his bed so that it rested directly beneath his pillow at the inside angle of the wall. Then he quietly washed and cleaned his teeth in the adjoining bathroom and eased the window wide open.

The moon was still shining: as it must have shone, Bond thought, when, aroused perhaps by some unusual noise, Tallon had climbed up to the roof, maybe only a couple of nights before, and had seen, out at sea, what he had seen. He would have had his glasses with him and Bond, remembering, turned back from the window and picked them up. They were a very powerful German pair, booty perhaps from the war, and the 7 × 50 on the top plates told Bond that they were night glasses. And then the careful Tallon must have walked softly (but not softly enough?) to the other end of the roof and had raised his glasses again, estimating the distance from the edge of the cliff to the object in the sea, and from the object to the Goodwin Lightship. Then he would have come back the way he had gone and softly re-entered his room.

Bond saw Tallon, perhaps for the first time since he had been in the house, carefully lock the door and walk over to the filing cabinet and take out the chart which he had hardly glanced at till then and on it softly mark the lines of his rough bearing. Perhaps he looked at it for a long while before putting the minute question mark beside it.

And what had the unknown object been? Impossible to say. A boat? A light? A noise?

Whatever it was Tallon had not been supposed to see it. And somebody had heard him. Somebody had guessed he had seen it and had waited until Tallon had left his room next morning. Then that man had come into his room and had searched it. Probably the chart had revealed nothing, but there were the night glasses by the window.

That had been enough. And that night Tallon had died.

Bond pulled himself up. He was going too fast, building up a case on the flimsiest evidence. Bartsch had killed Tallon and Bartsch was not the man who had heard the noise, the man who had left his fingerprints on the chart, the man whose dossier Bond had put away in his leather case.

That man had been the oily A.D.C., Krebs, the man with the neck like a white slug. They were his prints on the chart. For a quarter of an hour Bond had compared the impressions on the chart with the prints on Kreb's dossier. But who said Krebs had heard a noise or done anything about it if he had? Well, to begin with, he looked a natural snooper. He had the eyes of a petty thief. And those prints of his had definitely been made on the chart after Tallon had studied it. Krebs's fingers overlaid Tallon's at several points.

But how could Krebs possibly be involved, with Drax's eye constantly on him? The confidential assistant. But what about Cicero, the trusted valet of the British Ambassador in Ankara during the war? The hand in the pocket of the striped trousers hanging over the back of the chair. The Ambassador's keys. The safe. The secrets. This picture looked very much the same.

Bond shivered. He suddenly realized that he had been standing for a long time in front of the open windows and that it was time to get some sleep.

Before he got into bed he took his shoulder-holster from the chair where it hung beside his discarded clothes and removed the Beretta with the skeleton grip and slipped it under his pillow. As a defence against whom? Bond didn't know, but his intuition told him quite definitely that there was danger about. The smell of it was insistent although it was still imprecise and lingered only on the threshold of his sub-conscious. In fact he knew his feelings were based on a number of tiny question-marks which had materialized during the past twenty-four hours–the riddle of Drax; Bartsch's 'Heil Hitler'; the bizarre moustaches; the fifty worthy Germans; the chart; the night glasses; Krebs.

First he must pass on his suspicions to Vallance. Then explore the possibilities of Krebs. Then look to the defences of the Moonraker–the seaward side for instance. And then get together with this Brand girl and agree on a plan for the next two days. There wasn't much time to lose.

While he forced sleep to come into his teeming mind, Bond visualized the figure seven on the dial of a clock and left it to the hidden cells of his memory to wake him. He wanted to be out of the house and on the telephone to Vallance as early as possible. If his actions aroused suspicion he would not be dismayed. One of his objects was to attract into his orbit the same forces that had concerned themselves with Tallon, for of one thing he felt reasonably certain, Major Tallon had not died because he loved Gala Brand.

The extra-sensory alarm clock did not fail him. Punctually at seven, his mouth dry with too many cigarettes the night before, he forced himself out of bed and into a cold bath. He had shaved, gargled with a sharp mouthwash, and now, in a battered black and white dogtooth suit, dark blue Sea Island cotton shirt and black silk knitted tie, he was walking softly, but not surreptitiously, along the corridor to the head of the stairs, the square leather case in his left hand.

He found the garage at the back of the house and the big engine of the Bentley answered with the first pressure on the starter. He motored slowly across the concrete apron beneath the indifferent gaze of the curtained windows of the house and pulled up, the engine idling in neutral, at the edge of the trees. His eyes travelled back to the house and confirmed his calculation that a man standing on its roof would be able to see over the top of the blast-wall and get a view of the edge of the cliff and of the sea beyond.

There was no sign of life round the domed emplacement of the Moonraker, and the concrete, already beginning to shimmer in the early morning sun, stretched emptily away towards Deal. It looked like a newly laid aerodrome or rather, he thought, with its three disparate concrete 'things', the beehive dome, the flat-iron blast-wall, and the distant cube of the firing point, each casting black pools of shadow towards him in the early sun, like a Dali desert landscape on which three *objets trouvés* reposed at carefully calculated random.

Out at sea, in the early mist that promised a hot day, the South Goodwin Lightship could just be seen, a dim red barque married for ever to the same compass point and condemned, like a property ship on the stage of Drury Lane, to watch the diorama of the waves and clouds sail busily into the wings while, without papers or passengers or cargo, it lay anchored for ever to the departure point which was also its destination.

At thirty seconds' interval it blared its sad complaint into the mist, a long double trumpet note on a falling cadence. A siren song, Bond reflected, to repel instead of to seduce. He wondered how the seven men of its crew were now supporting the noise as they munched their pork and beans. Did they flinch as it punctuated the Housewife's Choice coming at full strength from the radio in the narrow mess? But a secure life,* Bond decided, although anchored to the gates of a graveyard.

He made a mental note to find out if those seven men had seen or heard the thing that Tallon had marked on the chart, then he drove quickly on through the guard posts.

* Bond was wrong: Friday, November 26th 1954. R.I.P.

In Dover, Bond pulled up at the Café Royal, a modest little restaurant with a modest kitchen but capable, as he knew of old, of turning out excellent fish and egg dishes. The Italian-Swiss mother and son who ran it welcomed him as an old friend and he asked for a plate of scrambled eggs and bacon and plenty of coffee to be ready in half an hour. Then he drove on to the police station and put in a call to Vallance through the Scotland Yard switchboard. Vallance was at home having breakfast. He listened without comment to Bond's guarded talk, but he expressed surprise that Bond had not had an opportunity to have a talk with Gala Brand. 'She's a bright girl, that,' he said. 'If Mr K. is up to something she's sure to have an idea what it is. And if T heard a noise on Sunday night, she may have heard it too. Though I'll admit she's said nothing about it.'

Bond said nothing about the reception he had had from Vallance's agent. 'Going to talk to her this morning,' he said, 'and I'll send up the chart and the Leica film for you to have a look at. I'll give them to the Inspector. Perhaps one of his road patrols could bring them up. By the way, where did T telephone from when he rang up his employer on Monday?'

'I'll have the call traced and let you know,' said Vallance. 'And I'll have Trinity House ask the South Goodwins and the Coastguards if they can help. Anything else?'

'No,' said Bond. The line went through too many switchboards. Perhaps if it had been M he would have hinted more. It seemed ridiculous to talk to Vallance about moustaches and the creep of danger he had felt the night before and which the daylight had dissipated. These policemen wanted hard facts. They were better, he decided, at solving crimes than at anticipating them. 'No. That's all.' He hung up.

He felt more cheerful after an excellent breakfast. He read the *Express* and *The Times* and found a bare report of the inquest on Tallon. The *Express* had made a big play with the girl's photograph and he was amused to see what a neutral likeness Vallance had managed to produce. He decided that he must try and work with her. He would take her completely into his confidence whether she was receptive or not. Perhaps she also had her suspicions and intuitions which were so vague that she was keeping them to herself.

Bond drove back fast to the house. It was just nine o'clock and as he came through the trees on to the concrete there was the wail of a siren and from the woods behind the house a double file of twelve men appeared running, in purposeful unison, towards the launching dome. They marked time while one of their number rang the bell, then the door opened and they filed through and out of sight.

Scratch a German and you find precision, thought Bond.

Chapter Fourteen

Itching Fingers

Half an hour before, Gala Brand had stubbed out her breakfast cigarette, swallowed the remains of her coffee, left her bedroom and walked across to the site, looking very much the private secretary in a spotless white shirt and dark blue pleated skirt.

Punctually at eight-thirty she was in her office. There was a sheaf of Air Ministry teleprints on her desk and her first action was to transfer a digest of their contents on to a weather map and walk through the communicating door into Drax's office and pin the map to the board that hung in the angle of the wall beside the blank glass wall. Then she pressed the switch that illuminated the wall map, made some calculations based on the columns of figures revealed by the light, and entered the results on the diagram she had pinned to the board.

She had done this, with Air Ministry figures that became more and more precise as the practice shoot drew nearer, every day since the site was completed and the building of the rocket had begun inside it, and she had become so expert that she now carried in her head the gyro settings for almost every variation in the weather at the different altitudes.

So it irritated her all the more that Drax did not seem to accept her figures. Every day when, punctually at nine, the warning bells clanged and he came down the steep iron stairway and into his office, his first action was to call for the insufferable Dr Walter and together they would work out all her figures afresh and transfer the results to the thin black notebook that Drax always carried in the hip pocket of his trousers. She knew that this was an invariable routine and she had become tired of watching it through an inconspicuous hole she had drilled, so as to be able to send Vallance a weekly record of Drax's visitors, in the thin wall between the two offices. The method was amateurish but effective and she had slowly built up a complete picture of the daily routine she came to find so irritating. It was irritating for two reasons. It meant that Drax didn't trust her figures, and it undermined her chance of having some part, however modest, in the final launching of the rocket.

It was natural that over the months she should have become as immersed in her disguise as she was in her real profession. It was fundamental to the thoroughness of her cover that her personality should be as truly split as possible. And now, while she spied and probed and sniffed the wind around Drax for her Chief in London, she was passionately concerned with the success of the Moonraker and had become as dedicated to its service as anyone else on the site.

And the rest of her duties as Drax's private secretary were insufferably dull. Every day there was a big post addressed to Drax in London and forwarded down by the Ministry, and that morning she had found the usual batch of about fifty letters waiting on her desk. They would be of three kinds. Begging letters, letters from rocket cranks, and business letters from Drax's stockbroker and from other commercial agents. To these Drax would dictate brief replies and the rest of her day would be occupied with typing and filing.

So it was natural that her one duty connected with the operation of the rocket should bulk very large in the dull round, and that morning, as she checked and rechecked her flight-plan, she was more than ever determined that her figures should be accepted on The Day. And yet, as she often reminded herself, perhaps there was no question but that they would be. Perhaps the daily calculations of Drax and Walter for entry in the little black book were nothing but a recheck of her own figures. Certainly Drax had never queried either her weather plan or the gyro settings she calculated from them. And when one day she had asked straight out whether her figures were correct he had replied with evident sincerity, 'Excellent, my dear. Most valuable. Couldn't manage without them.'

Gala Brand walked back into her own office and started slitting open the letters. Only two more flight plans, for Thursday and Friday and then, on her figures or on a different set, the set in Drax's pocket, the gyros would be finally adjusted and the switch would be pulled in the firing point.

She absentmindedly looked at her finger-nails and then stretched her two hands out with their backs towards her. How often in the course of her training at the Police College had she been sent out among the other pupils and told not to come back without a pocketbook, a vanity case, a fountain pen, even a wristwatch? How often during the courses had the hand of her instructor whipped round and caught her wrist with a 'Now, now, Miss. That won't do at all. Might have been an elephant looking for sugar in the keeper's pocket. Try again.'

Coolly she flexed her fingers and then, her mind made up, turned back to the pile of letters.

At a few minutes to nine the alarm bells rang and she heard Drax arrive in the office. A moment later she heard him open the double doors again and call for Walter. Then came the usual mumble of voices whose words were drowned by the soft whirr of the ventilators.

She arranged the letters in their three piles and sat forward relaxed, her elbows resting on the desk and her chin in her left hand.

Commander Bond. James Bond. Clearly a conceited young man like so many of them in the Secret Service. And why had he been sent down instead of somebody she could work with, one of her friends from the Special Branch, or even somebody from M.I.5? The message from the Assistant Commissioner had said that there was no one else available at short notice, that this was one of the stars of the Secret Service who had the complete confidence of the Special Branch and the blessings of M.I.5. Even the Prime Minister had had to give permission for him to operate, for just this one assignment, inside England. But what use could he be in the short time that was left? He could probably shoot all right and talk foreign languages and do a lot of tricks that might be useful abroad. But what good could he do down here without any beautiful spies to make love to. Because he was certainly good-looking. (Gala Brand automatically reached into her bag for her vanity case. She examined herself in the little mirror and dabbed at her nose with a powder puff.) Rather like Hoagy Carmichael in a way. That black hair falling down over the right eyebrow. Much the same bones. But there was something a bit cruel in the mouth, and the eyes were cold. Were they grey or blue? It had been difficult to say last night. Well, at any rate she had put him in his place and shown him that she wasn't impressed by dashing young men from the Secret Service, however romantic they might look. There were just as good-looking men in the Special Branch, and they were real detectives, not just people that Phillips Oppenheim had dreamed up with fast cars and special cigarettes with gold bands on them and shoulder-holsters. Oh, she had spotted that all right and had even brushed against him to make sure. Ah well, she supposed she would have to make some sort of show of working along with him, though in what direction heaven only knew. If she had been down there ever since the place had been built without spotting anything, what could this Bond man hope to discover in a couple of days? And what was there to find out? Of course there were one or two things she couldn't understand. Should she tell him about Krebs for instance? The first thing was to see that he didn't blow her cover by doing something stupid. She would have to be cool and firm and extremely careful. But that didn't mean, she decided, as the buzzer went and she collected the letters and her shorthand book, that she couldn't be friendly. Entirely on her own terms, of course.

Her second decision made, she opened the communicating door and walked into the office of Sir Hugo Drax.

When she came back into her room half an hour later she found Bond sitting back in her chair with Whitaker's *Almanack* open on the desk in front of him. She pursed her lips as Bond got up and wished her a cheerful good morning. She nodded briefly and walked round her desk and sat down. She moved the Whitaker's carefully aside and put her letters and notebook in its place.

'You might have a spare chair for visitors,' said Bond with a grin which she defined as impertinent, 'and somthing better to read than reference books.'

She ignored him. 'Sir Hugo wants you,' she said. 'I was just going to see if you had got up yet.'

'Liar,' said Bond. 'You heard me go by at half-past seven. I saw you peering out between the curtains.'

'I did nothing of the sort,' she said indignantly. 'Why should I be interested in a car going by?'

'I told you you heard the car,' said Bond. He pressed home his advantage. 'And by the way,' he said, 'you shouldn't scratch your head with the blunt end of the pencil when you're taking dictation. None of the best private secretaries do.'

Bond glanced significantly at a point against the jamb of the communicating door. He shrugged his shoulders.

Gala's defences dropped. Damn the man, she thought. She gave him a reluctant smile. 'Oh, well,' she said. 'Come on. I can't spend all the morning playing guessing games. He wants both of us and he doesn't like being kept waiting.' She rose and walked over to the communicating door and opened it. Bond followed her through and shut the door behind him.

Drax was standing looking at the illuminated wall map. He turned as they came in. 'Ah, there you are,' he said with a sharp glance at Bond. 'Thought you might have left us. Guards reported you out at seven-thirty this morning.'

'I had to make a telephone call,' said Bond. 'I hope I didn't disturb anyone.'

'There's a telephone in my study,' Drax said curtly. 'Tallon found it good enough.'

'Ah, poor Tallon,' said Bond non-committally. There was a hectoring note in Drax's voice that he particularly disliked and that made him instinctively want to deflate the man. On this occasion he was successful.

Drax shot him a hard glance which he covered up with a short barking laugh and a shrug of the shoulders. 'Do as you please,' he said. 'You've got your job to do. So long as you don't upset the routines down here. You must remember,' he added more reasonably, 'all my men are nervous as kittens just now and I can't have them upset by mysterious goings-on. I hope you're not wanting to ask them a lot of questions today. I'd rather they didn't have anything more to worry about. They haven't recovered from Monday yet. Miss Brand here can tell you all about them, and I believe all their files are in Tallon's room. Have you had a look at them yet?'

'No key to the filing cabinet,' said Bond truthfully.

'Sorry, my fault,' said Drax. He went to his desk and opened a drawer from which he took a small bunch of keys and handed them to Bond. 'Should have given you these last night. The Inspector chap on the case asked me to hand them over to you. Sorry.'

'Thanks very much,' said Bond. He paused. 'By the way, how long have you had Krebs?' He asked the question on an impulse. There was a moment's quiet in the room.

'Krebs?' repeated Drax thoughtfully. He walked over to his desk and sat down. He reached into his trouser pocket and pulled out a packet of his cork-tipped cigarettes. His blunt fingers scrabbled with its cellophane wrapping. He extracted a cigarette and stuffed it into his mouth under the fringe of his reddish moustache and lit it.

Bond was surprised. 'I didn't realize one could smoke down here,' he said, taking out his own case.

Drax's cigarette, a tiny white faggot in the middle of the big red face, waggled up and down as he answered without taking it out of his mouth. 'Quite all right in here,' he said. 'These rooms are air-tight. Doors lined with rubber. Separate ventilation. Have to keep the workshops and generators separate from the shaft and anyway,' his lips grinned round the cigarette, 'I have to be able to smoke.'

Drax took the cigarette out of his mouth and looked at it. He seemed to make up his mind. 'You were asking about Krebs,' he said. 'Well,' he looked meaningly up at Bond, 'just between ourselves I don't entirely trust the fellow.' He held up an admonitory hand. 'Nothing definite, of course, or I'd have had him put away, but I've found him snooping about the house and once I caught him in my study going through my private papers. He had a perfectly good explanation and I let him off with a warning. But quite honestly I have my suspicions of the man. Of course, he can't do any harm. He's part of the household staff and none of them is allowed in here but,' he looked candidly into Bond's eyes, 'I would have said you ought to concentrate on him. Bright of you to have bowled him out so quickly,' he added with respect. 'What put you on to him?'

'Oh, nothing much,' said Bond. 'He's got a shifty look. But what you say's interesting and I'll certainly keep an eye on him.'

He turned to Gala Brand who had remained silent ever since they had entered the room.

'And what do you think of Krebs, Miss Brand?' he asked politely.

The girl spoke to Drax. 'I don't know much about these things, Sir Hugo,' she said with a modesty and a touch of impulsiveness which Bond admired. 'But I don't trust the man at all. I hadn't meant to tell you, but he's been poking around my room, opening letters and so forth. I know he has.'

Drax was shocked. 'Has he indeed?' he said. He bashed his cigarette out in the ashtray and killed the glowing fragments one by one. 'So much for Krebs,' he said, without looking up.

Chapter Fifteen

Rough Justice

There was a moment's silence in the room during which Bond reflected how odd it was that suspicions should have fallen so suddenly and so unanimously on one man. And did that automatically clear all the others? Might not Krebs be the inside man of a gang? Or was he working on his own and, if so, with what object? And what did his snooping have to do with the death of Tallon and Bartsch?

Drax broke the silence. 'Well, that seems to settle it,' he said, looking to Bond for confirmation. Bond gave a non-committal nod. 'Just have to leave him to you. At all events, we must see he is kept well away from the site. As a matter of fact I shall be taking him to London tomorrow. Last-minute details to be settled with the Ministry and Walter can't be spared. Krebs is the only man I've got who can do the work of an A.D.C. That'll keep him out of trouble. We'll all have to keep an eye on him until then. Unless of course you want to put him under lock and key straight away. I'd prefer not,' he said candidly. 'Don't want to upset the team any more.'

'It shouldn't be necessary,' said Bond. 'Has he got any particular friends among the other men?'

'Never seen him speak to any of them except Walter and the household,' said Drax. 'Daresay he considers himself a cut above the others. Personally I don't believe there's much harm in the chap or I wouldn't have kept him. He's left alone in that house all day long and I expect he's one of those people who like playing the detective and prying into other people's affairs. What do you say? Perhaps we could leave it like that?'

Bond nodded, keeping his thoughts to himself.

'Well, then,' said Drax, obviously glad to leave a distasteful subject and get back to business, 'we've got other things to talk about. Two more days to go and I'd better tell you the programme.' He got up from his chair and paced heavily up and down the room behind his desk. 'Today is Wednesday,' he said. 'At one o'clock the site will be closed for fuelling. This will be supervised by Dr Walter and myself and two men from the Ministry. Just in case anything goes wrong a television camera will record everything we do. Then, if there is an explosion, our successors will know better next time,' he barked a short laugh. 'Weather permitting, the roof will be opened tonight to allow the fumes to clear. My men will stand guard in watches at ten-yard intervals a hundred yards from the site. There will be three armed men on the beach opposite the exhaust hole in the cliff. Tomorrow morning the site will be opened again until midday for a final check and from that moment, except for the gyro settings, the Moonraker will be ready to go. The guards will be permanently on duty round the site. On Friday morning I shall personally supervise the gyro settings. The men from the Ministry will take over the firing point and the R.A.F. will man the radar. The B.B.C. will set up their vans behind the firing point and will begin their running commentary at eleven-forty-five. At midday exactly I shall press the plunger, a radio beam will break an electric circuit and,' he smiled broadly, 'we shall see what we shall see.' He paused, fingering his chin. 'Now what else? Well now. Shipping will be cleared from the target area from midnight on Thursday. The Navy will provide a patrol of the boundaries of the area all through the morning. There will be a B.B.C. commentator in one of the ships. The Ministry of Supply experts will be in a salvage ship with deep-sea television and after the rocket has landed they will try to bring up the remains. You may be interested to know,' continued Drax, rubbing his hands with almost childish pleasure, 'that a messenger from the Prime Minister has brought me the very welcome news that not only will there be a special Cabinet Meeting to listen to the broadcast, but the Palace will also be listening in to the launching.'

'Splendid,' said Bond, pleased for the man's sake.

'Thank you,' said Drax. 'Now I want to be quite certain that you are satisfied with my security arrangements on the site itself. I don't think we need worry about what goes on outside. The R.A.F. and the police seem to be doing a very thorough job.'

'Everything seems to have been taken care of,' said Bond. 'There doesn't seem to be very much for me to do in the time that's left.'

'Nothing that I can think of,' agreed Drax, 'except our friend Krebs. This afternoon he will be in the television van taking notes, so he will be out of trouble. Why don't you have a look at the beach and the bottom of the cliff while he's out of action? That's the only weak spot I can think of. I've often thought that if someone wanted to get into the site he would try the exhaust pit. Take Miss Brand with you. Two pairs of eyes, and so forth, and she won't be able to use her office until tomorrow morning.'

'Good,' said Bond. 'I'd certainly like to have a look at the seaward side after lunch, and if Miss Brand's got nothing better to do . . .' He turned towards her with his eyebrows raised.

Gala Brand looked down her nose. 'Certainly, if Sir Hugo wishes,' she said without enthusiasm.

Drax rubbed his hands together. 'Then that's settled,' he said. 'And now I must get down to work. Miss Brand, would you ask Dr Walter to come along if he's free. See you at lunch,' he said to Bond, on a note of dismissal.

Bond nodded. 'I think I'll walk over and have a look at the firing point,' he said, not quite knowing why he lied. He turned and followed Gala Brand out through the double doors into the base of the shaft.

A huge black snake of rubber piping meandered over the shining steel floor and Bond watched the girl pick her way among its coils to where Walter was standing alone. He was gazing up at the mouth of the fuel pipe being hoist to where a gantry, outstretched to the threshold of an access door halfway up the rocket, indicated the main fuel tanks.

She said something to Walter and then stood beside him looking upwards as the pipe was delicately manhandled through into the interior of the rocket.

Bond thought she looked very innocent standing there with her brown hair falling back from her head and the curve of her ivory throat sweeping down into the plain white shirt. With her hands clasped behind her back, gazing raptly upwards at the glittering fifty feet of the Moonraker, she might have been a schoolgirl looking at a Christmas tree–except for the impudent pride of the jutting breasts, swept up by the thrown-back head and shoulders.

Bond smiled to himself as he walked to the foot of the iron stairway and started to climb. That innocent, desirable girl, he reminded himself, is an extremely efficient policewoman. She knows how to kick, and where; she can break my arm probably more easily and quickly than I can break hers, and at least half of her belongs to the Special Branch of Scotland Yard. Of course, he reflected, looking down just in time to see her follow Dr Walter into Drax's office, there is always the other half.

Outside, the brilliant May sunshine seemed particularly golden after the blue-white of the arcs and Bond could feel it hot on his back as he walked purposefully across the concrete towards the house. The foghorn from the Goodwins was silent and the morning was so quiet that he could hear the rhythmic thump of a ship's engines as a coaster negotiated the Inner Leads, between the Goodwins and the shore, on its way northwards.

He approached the house under cover of the wide blast-wall and then quickly crossed the few yards to the front door, the crepe rubber soles of his shoes making no noise. He eased open the door and left it ajar and walked softly into the hall and stood listening. There was the early summer noise of a bumble-bee fussing against the pane of one of the windows and a distant clatter from the barracks behind the house. Otherwise the silence was deep and warm and reassuring.

Bond walked carefully across the hall and up the stairs, placing his feet flat on the ground and using the extreme edges of the steps where the boards would be less likely to creak. There was no noise in the corridor but Bond saw that his door at the far end was wide open. He took his gun from under his armpit and walked swiftly down the carpeted passage.

Krebs had his back to him. He was kneeling forward in the middle of the floor with his elbows on the ground. His hands were at the wheels of the combination lock of Bond's leather case. His whole attention was focused on the click of the tumblers in the lock.

The target was tempting and Bond didn't hesitate. His teeth showing in a hard smile, he took two quick paces into the room and his foot lashed out.

All his force was behind the point of his shoe and his balance and timing were perfect.

The scream of a jay was driven out of Krebs as, like the caricature of a leaping frog, he hurtled over Bond's case, across a yard or so of carpet, and into the front of the mahogany dressing-table. His head hit the middle of it so hard that the heavy piece of furniture rocked on its base. The scream was abruptly cut off and he crashed in an inert spreadeagle on the floor and lay still.

Bond stood looking at him and listening for the sound of hurrying footsteps, but there was still silence in the house. He walked over to the sprawling figure and bent down and heaved it over on its back. The face around the smudge of yellow moustache was pale and some blood had oozed down over the forehead from a cut in the top of the skull. The eyes were closed and the breathing was laboured.

Bond knelt down on one knee and went carefully through every pocket of Kreb's neat grey pinstripe suit, laying the disappointingly meagre contents on the carpet beside the body. There was no pocketbook and no papers. The only objects of interest were a bunch of skeleton keys, a spring knife with a well-sharpened stiletto blade, and an obscene little truss-shaped black leather cosh. Bond pocketed these and then went to his bedside and fetched the untouched bottle of Vichy water.

It took five minutes to revive Krebs and get him into a sitting position with his back to the dressing-table and another five for him to be capable of speaking. Gradually the colour came back to his face and the craftiness to his eyes.

'I answer no questions except to Sir Hugo,' he said as Bond started the interrogation. 'You have no right to question me. I was doing my duty.' His voice was surly and assured.

Bond took the empty Vichy bottle by the neck. 'Think again,' he said. 'Or I'll beat the daylights out of you until this breaks and then use the neck for some plastic surgery. Who told you to go over my room?'

'*Leck mich am Arsch.*' Krebs spat the obscene insult at him.

Bond bent down and cracked him sharply across the shins.

Kreb's body cringed, but, as Bond raised his arm again, he suddenly shot up from the floor and dived under the descending bottle. The blow caught him hard on the shoulder, but it didn't check his momentum and he was out of the door and halfway down the corridor before Bond started in pursuit.

Bond stopped outside the door and watched the flying figure swerve down the stairs and out of sight. Then, as he heard the scurrying squeak of the rubber-soled shoes as they fled down the stairs and across the hall, he laughed abruptly to himself and went back into his room and locked the door. Short of beating the man's brains out it hadn't looked as if he would get much out of Krebs. He had given him something to think about. Crafty little brute. His injuries couldn't have been so bad after all. Well, it would be up to Drax to punish him.

Unless, of course, Krebs had been carrying out Drax's orders.

Bond cleaned up the mess in his room and sat down on his bed and gazed at the opposite wall with unseeing eyes.

It had not been only instinct that had made him tell Drax he was going to the firing point instead of to the house. It had seriously crossed his mind that the snooping of Krebs was on Drax's orders, and that Drax ran his own security system. And yet how did that tally with the deaths of Tallon and Bartsch? Or had the double killing been a coincidence unrelated to the marks on the chart and the fingerprints of Krebs?

As if summoned by his thoughts, there came a knock on the door and the butler came in. He was followed by a police sergeant in road patrol uniform who saluted and handed Bond a telegram. Bond took it over to the window.

It was signed Baxter, which meant Vallance, and it read:

FIRSTLY CALL WAS FROM HOUSE SECONDLY FOG REQUIRED OPERATION OF FOGHORN SO SHIP HEARD COMMA OBSERVED NOTHING THIRDLY YOUR COMPASS RECKONING TOO NEAR SHORE THUS OUT OF SIGHT OF SAINT MARGARETS OR DEAL COASTGUARDS ENDS.

'Thank you,' said Bond. 'No answer.'

When the door was closed Bond put his lighter to the telegram and dropped it in the fireplace, scuffing the charred remains into powder with the sole of his shoe.

Nothing much there except that Tallon's call to the Ministry might indeed have been heard by someone in the house, which might have resulted in the search of his room, which might have resulted in his death. But what about Bartsch? If all this was part of something much bigger how could it be linked up with an attempt to sabotage the rocket? Wasn't it much simpler to conclude that Krebs was a natural snooper, or more likely that he was operating for Drax, who seemed to be meticulously security-conscious and who might want to be sure of the loyalty of his secretary, of Tallon, and certainly, after their encounter at Blades, of Bond? Wasn't he just acting like the chief (and Bond had known many of them who would fit the picture) of some super-secret project during the war who had reinforced official security with his own private spy system?

If that theory was correct there only remained the double killing. Now that Bond had caught the magic and the tension of the Moonraker the facts of the hysterical shooting seemed more reasonable. As for the mark on the chart, that might have been made any day in the past year; the night-glasses were just night-glasses and the moustaches on the men were just a lot of moustaches.

Bond sat on in the silent room, shifting the pieces in the jigsaw so that two entirely different pictures alternated in his mind. In one the sun shone and all was clear and innocent as the day outside. The other was a dark confusion of guilty motives, obscure suspicions, and nightmare queries.

When the gong sounded for lunch he still did not know which picture to choose. To shelve a decision he cleared his mind of everything but the prospect of his afternoon alone with Gala Brand.

Chapter Sixteen

A Golden Day

It was a wonderful afternoon of blue and green and gold. When they left the concrete apron through the guard-gate near the empty firing point, now connected by a thick cable with the launching site, they stopped for a moment on the edge of the great chalk cliff and stood gazing over the whole corner of England where Caesar had first landed two thousand years before.

To their left the carpet of green turf, bright with small wildflowers, sloped gradually down to the long pebble beaches of Walmer and Deal which curved off towards Sandwich and the Bay. Beyond, the cliffs of Ramsgate, showing white through the distant haze that hid the North Foreland, guarded the grey scar of Manston aerodrome above which American Thunderjets wrote their white scribbles in the sky. Then came the Isle of Thanet and, out of sight, the Mouth of the Thames.

It was low tide and the Goodwins were golden and tender in the sparkling blue of the Straits with only the smattering of masts and spars that stretched along their length to tell the true story. The white lettering on the South Goodwins Lightship was easy to read and even the name of her sister ship to the north showed white against the red of her hull.

Between the sands and the coast, along the twelve-fathom channel of the Inner Leads, there were half a dozen ships beating up through the Downs, the thud of their engines coming clearly off the quiet sea, and between the evil sands and the sharp outline of the French coast there were ships of all registries going about their business–liners, merchantmen, ungainly Dutch schuyts, and even a slim corvette hastening down south, perhaps to Portsmouth. As far as the eye could reach the Eastern Approaches of England were dotted with traffic plying towards near or distant horizons, towards a home port, or towards the other side of the world. It was a panorama full of colour and excitement and romance and the two people on the edge of the cliff were silent as they stood for a time and watched it all.

The peace was broken by two blasts on the siren from the house and they turned to gaze at the ugly concrete world that had been cleaned out of their minds. As they watched, a red flag was broken out above the dome of the launching site and two R.A.F. crash-wagons with red crosses on their sides rolled out of the trees to the edge of the blast-wall and pulled up.

'Fuelling's going to begin,' said Bond. 'Let's get on with our walk. There'll be nothing to see and if there happened to be something we probably wouldn't survive it at this range.'

She smiled at him. 'Yes,' she said. 'And I'm sick of the sight of all this concrete.'

They walked on down the gentle slope and were soon out of sight of the firing point and the high wire fence.

The ice of Gala's reserve melted quickly in the sunshine.

The exotic gaiety of her clothes, a black and white striped cotton shirt tucked into a wide hand-stitched black leather belt above a medium length skirt in shocking pink, seemed to have infected her, and it was impossible for Bond to recognize the chill woman of the night before in the girl who now walked beside him and laughed happily at his ignorance of the names of the wildflowers, the samphire, Viper's bugloss, and fumitory round their feet.

Triumphantly she found a bee orchis and picked it.

'You wouldn't do that if you knew that flowers scream when they are picked,' said Bond.

Gala looked at him. 'What do you mean?' she asked, suspecting a joke.

'Didn't you know?' He smiled at her reaction. 'There's an Indian called Professor Bhose, who's written a treatise on the nervous system of flowers. He measured their reaction to pain. He even recorded the scream of a rose being picked. It must be one of the most heartrending sounds in the world. I heard something like it as you picked that flower.'

'I don't believe it,' she said, looking suspiciously at the torn root.

'Anyway,' she said maliciously, 'I wouldn't have thought you were a person to get sentimental. Don't people in your section of the Service make a business of killing? And not just flowers either. People.'

'Flowers can't shoot back,' said Bond.

She looked at the orchis. 'Now you've made me feel like a murderer. It's very unkind of you. But,' she admitted reluctantly, 'I shall have to find out about this Indian and if you're right I shall never pick a flower again as long as I live. What am I going to do with this one? You make me feel it's bleeding all over my hands.'

'Give it to me,' said Bond. 'According to you, my hands are dripping with blood already. A little more won't hurt.'

She handed it to him and their hands touched. 'You can stick it in the muzzle of your revolver,' she said to cover the flash of contact.

Bond laughed. 'So the eyes aren't only for decoration,' he said. 'Anyway it's an automatic and I left it in my room.' He drew the stalk of the flower through one of the button-holes in his blue cotton shirt. 'I thought a shoulder-holster would look a bit conspicuous without a coat to cover it. And I don't think anyone will be going over my room this afternoon.'

By tacit agreement they edged away from the moment of warmth. Bond told her of his discovery of Krebs and of the scene in his bedroom.

'Serves him right,' she said. 'I've never trusted him. But what did Sir Hugo say?'

'I had a word with him before lunch,' said Bond. 'Gave him Krebs's knife and keys as proof. He was furious and went straight off to see the man, muttering with rage. When he came back he said that Krebs seemed to be in a pretty bad way and was I satisfied that he'd been punished enough? All that business about not wanting to upset the team at the last moment and so forth. So I agreed that he'd be sent back to Germany next week and that meanwhile he would consider himself under open arrest–only allowed out of his room under surveillance.'

They scrambled down a steep cliff-path to the beach and turned to the right beside the deserted small-arms range of the Royal Marine Garrison at Deal. They walked along in silence until they came to the two-mile stretch of shingle that runs at low tide beneath the towering white cliffs to St Margaret's Bay.

As they trudged slowly through the deep smooth pebbles Bond told her of all that had gone through his mind since the previous day. He held nothing back and he showed each false hare as it had been started and finally run to earth, leaving nothing but a thin scent of ill-founded suspicions and a muddle of clues that all ended in the same question mark . . . where was a pattern? Where was a plan into which the clues would fit? And always the same answer, that nothing Bond knew or suspected seemed to have any conceivable bearing on the security from sabotage of the Moonraker. And that, when all was said and done, was the only matter with which he and the girl were concerned. Not with the death of Tallon and Bartsch, not with the egregious Krebs, but only with the protection of the whole Moonraker project from its possible enemies.

'Isn't that so?' Bond concluded.

Gala stopped and stood for a moment looking out across the tumbled rocks and seaweed towards the quiet glimmering swell of the sea. She was hot and out of breath from the hard going through the shingle and she thought how wonderful it would be to bathe–to step back for a moment into those childish days beside the sea before her life had been caught up in this strange cold profession with its tensions and hollow thrills. She glanced at the ruthless brown face of the man beside her. Did he have moments of longing for the peaceful simple things of life? Of course not. He liked Paris and Berlin and New York and trains and aeroplanes and expensive food, and, yes certainly, expensive women.

'Well?' said Bond, wondering if she was going to come out with some piece of evidence that he had overlooked. 'What do you think?'

'I'm sorry,' said Gala. 'I was dreaming. No,' she answered his question, 'I think you're right. I've been down here since the beginning and although there've been odd little things from time to time, and of course the shooting, I've seen absolutely nothing wrong. Every one of the team, from Sir Hugo down, is heart and soul behind the rocket. It's all they live for and it's been wonderful to see the whole thing grow. The Germans are terrific workers–and I can quite believe that Bartsch broke under the strain–and they love being driven by Sir Hugo and he loves driving them. They worship him. And as for security, the place is solid with it and I'm sure that anyone who tried to get near the Moonraker would be torn to pieces. I agree with you about Krebs and that he was probably working under Drax's orders. It was because I believed that, that I didn't bother to report him when he went through my things. There was nothing for him to find, of course. Just private letters and so on. It would be typical of Sir Hugo to make absolutely sure. And I must say,' she said candidly, 'that I admire him for it. He's a ruthless man with deplorable manners and not a very nice face under all that red hair, but I love working for him and I'm longing for the Moonraker to be a success. Living with it for so long has made me feel just like his men do about it.'

She looked up to see his reactions.

He nodded. 'After only a day I can understand that,' he said. 'And I suppose I agree with you. There's nothing to go on except my intuition and that will have to look after itself. The main thing is that the Moonraker looks as safe as the Crown Jewels, and probably safer.' He shrugged his shoulders impatiently, dissatisfied with himself for disowning the intuitions that were so much of his trade. 'Come on,' he said, almost roughly. 'We're wasting time.'

Understanding, she smiled to herself and followed.

Round the next bend of the cliff they came up with the base of the hoist, encrusted with seaweed and barnacles. Fifty yards further on they reached the jetty, a strong tubular iron frame paved with latticed iron strips that ran out over the rocks and beyond.

Between the two, and perhaps twenty feet up the cliff face, yawned the wide black mouth of the exhaust tunnel which slanted up inside the cliff to the steel floor beneath the stern of the rocket. From the under-lip of the cave melted chalk drooled down like lava and there were splashes of the stuff all over the pebbles and rocks below. In his mind's eye Bond could see the blazing white shaft of flame come howling out of the face of the cliff and he could hear the sea hiss and bubble as the liquid chalk poured into the water.

He looked up at the narrow section of the launching dome that showed above the edge of the cliff two hundred feet up in the sky, and imagined the four men in their gas-masks and asbestos suits watching the gauges as the terrible liquid explosive pulsed down the black rubber tube into the stomach of the rocket. He suddenly realized that they were in range if anything went wrong with the fuelling.

'Let's get away from here,' he said to the girl.

When they had put a hundred yards between themselves and the cave Bond stopped and looked back. He imagined himself with six tough men and all the right gear, and he wondered how he would set about attacking the site from the sea–kyaks to the jetty at low tide; a ladder to the lip of the cave–and then what? Impossible to climb the polished steel walls of the exhaust tunnel. It would be a question of firing an anti-tank weapon through the steel floor beneath the rocket, following up with some phosphorus shells and hoping that something would catch fire. Untidy business, but it might be effective. Getting away afterwards would be nasty. Sitting targets from the top of the cliff. But that wouldn't worry a Russian suicide squad. It was all quite feasible.

Gala had been standing beside him watching the eyes that measured and speculated. 'It's not as easy as you might think,' she said, seeing the frown on his face. 'Even when it's high tide and very rough they have guards along the top of the cliff at night. And they've got searchlights and Brens and grenades. Their orders are to shoot and ask questions afterwards. Of course it would be better to floodlight the cliff at night. But that would only pinpoint the site. I really believe they've thought of everything.'

Bond was still frowning. 'If they had covering fire from a submarine or an X-craft a good team could still do it,' he said. 'It'll be hell, but I'm going for a swim. The Admiralty chart says there's a twelve-fathom channel out there, but I'd like to have a look. There must be plenty of water at the end of the jetty but I'll be happier when I've seen for myself.' He smiled at her. 'Why don't you have a bathe too? It's going to be dam' cold, but it would do you good after stewing inside that concrete dome all the morning.'

Gala's eyes lit up. 'Do you think I could?' she asked doubtfully. 'I'm frightfully hot. But what are we going to wear?' She blushed at the thought of her brief and almost transparent nylon pants and brassière.

'To hell with that,' said Bond airily. 'You must have got some bits and pieces on underneath and I've got pants on. We shall be perfectly respectable and there's no one to see, and I promise not to look,' he lied cheerfully, leading the way round the next bend in the cliff. 'You undress behind that rock and I'll use this one,' he said. 'Come on. Don't be a goose. It's all in the line of duty.'

Without waiting for her to answer he moved behind the tall rock, taking off his shirt as he did so.

'Oh, well,' said Gala, relieved to have the decision taken out of her hands. She went behind her rock and slowly unbuttoned her skirt.

When she peered nervously out, Bond was already halfway down the strip of coarse brown sand that led out among the pools to where the incoming tide eddied through the green and black moraine of the rocks. He looked lithe and brown. The blue pants were reassuring.

Gingerly she followed him, and then suddenly she was in the water. At once nothing else mattered but the velvet ice of the sea and the beauty of the patches of sand between the waving hair of the seaweed that she could see in the clear green depths below her as she buried her head and swam along parallel with the shore in a fast crawl.

When she was level with the jetty she stopped for a moment to get her breath. There was no sign of Bond whom she had last seen streaking along a hundred yards ahead of her. She trod water hard to keep up her circulation and then started back again, unwillingly thinking of him, thinking of the hard brown body that must be somewhere near her, among the rocks, perhaps, or diving to the sand to gauge the depth of water that would be available to an enemy.

She turned back to look for him again and it was then that he suddenly surged up from the sea beneath her. She felt the quick tight clasp of his arms round her and the swift hard impact of his lips on hers.

'Damn you,' she said furiously, but already he had dived again and by the time she had spat out a mouthful of sea-water and got her bearings he was swimming blithely twenty yards away.

She turned and swam aloofly out to sea, feeling rather ridiculous but determined to snub him. It was just as she had thought. These Secret Service people always seemed to have time for sex however important their jobs might be.

But her body obstinately tingled with the shock of the kiss and the golden day seemed to have taken on a new beauty. As she swam further out to sea and then turned back and looked along the snarling milk-white teeth of England to the distant arm of Dover and at the black and white confetti of the ravens and gulls tossed against the vivid backcloth of green fields, she decided that anything was permissible on such a day and that, just this once, she would forgive him.

Half an hour later they were lying, waiting for the sun to dry them, separated by a respectable yard of sand at the foot of the cliff.

The kiss had not been mentioned, but Gala's efforts to preserve an atmosphere of aloofness had collapsed under the excitement of examining a lobster that Bond had dived for and caught with his hands. Reluctantly they put it back into one of the rockpools and watched it scuttle backwards into the shelter of the seaweed. And now they lay, tired and exhilarated by their icy swim, and prayed that the sun would not slip behind the clifftop high above their heads before they were warm and dry enough to get back into their clothes.

But those were not Bond's only thoughts. The beautiful strapping body of the girl beside him, incredibly erotic in the tight emphasis of the clinging brassière and pants, came between him and his concern about the Moonraker. And anyway there was nothing he could do about the Moonraker for another hour. It was not yet five o'clock and the fuelling would not be finished until after six. It would only be then that he could get hold of Drax and make certain that for the next two nights the guards were strengthened on the cliff and that they had the right weapons. For he had seen for himself that there was plenty of water, even at low tide, for a submarine.

So there was at least a quarter of an hour to spare before they would have to start back.

Meanwhile this girl. The half-stripped body splayed above him on the surface as he swam up from below; the soft-hard quick kiss with his arms about her; the pointed hillocks of her breasts, so close to him, and the soft flat stomach descending into the mystery of her tightly closed thighs.

To hell with it.

He wrenched his mind out of its fever and gazed straight up into the endless blue of the sky, forcing himself to watch the soaring beauty of the herring gulls as they ranged effortlessly among the air currents that fountained up over the high cliff-top above them. But the soft down of the birds' white under-bellies seduced his thoughts back to her and gave him no rest.

'Why are you called Gala?' he said to break his hot, crouching thoughts.

She laughed. 'I was teased about it all through school,' she said, and Bond was impatient at the easy, clear voice, 'and then through the Wrens and then by half the police force of London. But my real name's even worse. It's Galatea. She was a cruiser my father was serving in when I was born. I suppose Gala's not too bad. I've almost forgotten what I'm called. I'm always having to change my name now that I'm in the Special Branch.'

'In the Special Branch.' 'In the Special Branch.' 'In the . . .'

When the bomb falls. When the pilot miscalculates and the plane hits short of the runway. When the blood leaves the heart and consciousness goes, there are thoughts in the mind, or words, or perhaps a phrase of music, which ring on for the few seconds before death like the dying clang of a bell.

Bond wasn't killed, but the words were still in his mind, several seconds later, after it had all happened.

Ever since they had lain down on the sand up against the cliff, while his thoughts had been of Gala, his eyes had been carelessly watching two gulls playing around a wisp of straw that was the edge of their nest on a small ledge about ten feet below the distant top of the cliff. They would crane and bow in their love-play, with only their heads visible to Bond against the dazzling white of the chalk, and then the male would soar out and away and at once back to the ledge to take up his love-making again.

Bond was dreamily watching them as he listened to the girl, when suddenly both gulls dashed away from the ledge with a single shrill scream of fear. At the same moment there was a puff of black smoke and a soft boom from the top of the cliff and a great section of the white chalk directly above Bond and Gala seemed to sway outwards, zigzag cracks snaking down its face.

The next thing Bond knew was that he was lying on top of Gala, his face pressed into her cheek, that the air was full of thunder, that his breath was stifled and that the sun had gone out. His back was numb and aching under a great weight and in his left ear, besides the echo of the thunder, there was the end of a choking scream.

He was barely conscious and he had to wait until his senses came halfway back to life.

The Special Branch. What was it she had said about the Special Branch?

He made frantic efforts to move. Only in his right arm, the arm nearest to the cliff, was there any play at all, but as he jerked his shoulder the arm became freer until at last, with a great backward heave, light and air reached down to them. Retching in the fog of chalk-dust, he widened the hole until his head could take its crushing weight off Gala. He felt the feeble movement as she turned her head sideways towards the light and air. A growing trickle of dust and stones into the hole he had cleared made him dig fiercely again. Gradually he enlarged the space until he could get a purchase on his right elbow and then, coughing so that he thought his lungs would burst, he heaved his right shoulder up until suddenly it and his head were free.

His first thought was that there had been an explosion in the Moonraker. He looked up at the cliff and then along the shore. No. They were a hundred yards from the site. It was only in the skyline directly above them that a great mouthful had been bitten out of the cliff.

Then he thought of their immediate danger. Gala moaned and he could feel the frantic thud of her heart against his chest, but the ghastly white mask of her face was now free to the air and he wrenched his body from side to side on top of her to try and ease the pressure on her lungs and stomach. Slowly, inch by inch, his muscles cracking under the strain, he worked his way under the pile of dust and rubble towards the cliff face where he knew the weight would be less.

And then at last his chest was free and he could snake his body into a kneeling position beside her. Blood dripped from his cut back and arms and mingled with the chalk dust that continually poured down the sides of the hole he had made, but he could feel that no bones were broken and, in the rage of the rescue work, he felt no pain.

Grunting and coughing and without a pause to take breath he heaved her up into a sitting position and with a bleeding hand wiped some of the chalk dust from her face. Then, freeing his legs from the tomb of chalk, he somehow manhandled her up on to the top of the mound with her back against the cliff.

He knelt and looked at her, at the terrible white scarecrow that minutes before had been one of the most beautiful girls he had ever seen, and as he looked at her and at the streaks of his blood down her face he prayed that her eyes would open.

When, seconds later, they did, the relief was so great that Bond turned away and was rackingly sick.

Chapter Seventeen

Wild Surmises

When the paroxysm was over he felt Gala's hand in his hair. He looked round and saw her wince at the sight of him. She tugged at his hair and pointed up the cliffs. As she did so a shower of small pieces of chalk rattled down beside them.

Weakly he got to his knees and then to his feet and together they scrambled and slid down off the mountain of chalk and away from the crater against the cliff from which they had escaped.

The harsh sand under their feet was like velvet. They both collapsed full length and lay clutching at it with their horrible white hands as if its rough gold would wash the filthy whiteness away. Then Gala too was mercifully sick and Bond crawled a few paces away to leave her alone. He hauled himself to his feet against a single lump of chalk as big as a small motor-car, and at last his bloodshot eyes took in the hell that had almost engulfed them.

Down to the beginning of the rocks, now lapped by the incoming tide, sprawled the debris of the cliff face, an avalanche of chalk blocks and shapes. The white dust of its collapse covered nearly an acre. Above it a jagged rent had appeared in the cliff and a wedge of blue sky had been bitten out of the distant top where before the line of the horizon had been almost straight. There were no longer any seabirds near them and Bond guessed that the smell of disaster would keep them away from the place for days.

The nearness of their bodies to the cliff was what had saved them, that and the slight protection of the overhang below which the sea had bitten into the base of the cliff. They had been buried by the deluge of smaller stuff. The heavier chunks, any one of which would have crushed them, had fallen outwards, the nearest missing them by a few feet. And their nearness to the cliff was the reason for Bond's right arm having been comparatively free so that they had been able to burrow out of the mound before they were stifled. Bond realized that if some reflex had not hurled him on top of Gala at the moment of the avalanche they would now both be dead.

He felt her hand on his shoulder. Without looking at her he put his arm round her waist and together they got down to the blessed sea and let their bodies fall weakly, thankfully, into the shallows.

Ten minutes later it was two comparatively human beings who walked back up the sand to the rocks where their clothes lay, a few yards away from the cliff-fall. They were both completely naked. The rags of their underclothing lay somewhere under the pile of chalk dust, torn off in their struggle to escape. But, like survivors from a shipwreck, their nakedness meant nothing. Washed clean of the cloying gritty chalk dust and with their hair and mouths scoured with the salt water, they felt weak and bedraggled, but by the time they had got their clothes on and had shared Gala's comb there was little to show what they had been through.

They sat with their backs to a rock and Bond lit a first delicious cigarette, drinking the smoke deeply into his lungs and expelling it slowly through his nostrils. When Gala had done the best she could with her powder and lipstick he lit a cigarette for her and, as he handed it to her, for the first time they looked into each other's eyes and smiled. Then they sat and looked silently out to sea, at the golden panorama that was the same and yet entirely new.

Bond broke the silence.

'Well, by God,' he said. 'That was close.'

'I still don't know what happened,' said Gala. 'Except that you saved my life.' She put her hand on his and then took it away.

'If you hadn't been there I should be dead,' said Bond. 'If I'd stayed where I was—' He shrugged his shoulders.

Then he turned and looked at her. 'I suppose you realize,' he said flatly, 'that someone pushed the cliff down on us?' She looked back at him with wide eyes. 'If we searched around in all that,' he gestured towards the avalanche of chalk, 'we would find the marks of two or three drill-holes and traces of dynamite. I saw the smoke and I heard the bang of the explosion a split second before the cliff came down. And so did the gulls,' he added.

'And what's more,' continued Bond after a pause, 'it can't have been only Krebs. It was done in full view of the site. And it was done by several people, well organized, with spies on us from the moment we went down the cliff path to the beach.'

There was comprehension in Gala's eyes and a flash of fear. 'What are we to do?' she asked anxiously. 'What's it all about?'

'They want us dead,' said Bond calmly. 'So we have to stay alive. As to what it's all about, we'll just have to find that out.'

'You see,' he went on, 'I'm afraid even Vallance isn't going to be much help. When they made up their minds we were properly buried, they'll have got away from the top of the cliff as fast as they could. They'd know that even if someone saw the cliff-fall, or heard it, they wouldn't get very excited. There are twenty miles of these cliffs and not many people come here until the summer. If the coastguards heard it they may have made a note in the log. But in the spring I expect they get plenty of falls. The winter frosts thaw out in cracks that may be hundreds of years old. So our friends would wait until we didn't turn up tonight and then get the police and coastguards to search for us. They'd keep quiet until the high tide had made porridge out of a good deal of this.' He gestured towards the shambles of fallen chalk. 'The whole scheme is admirable. And even if Vallance believes us, there's not enough evidence to make the Prime Minister interfere with the Moonraker. The damn thing's so infernally important. All the world's waiting to see if it'll work or not. And anyway, what's our story? What the hell's it all about? Some of those bloody Germans up there seem to want us dead before Friday. But what for?' He paused. It's up to us, Gala. It's a lousy business but we've simply got to solve it ourselves.'

He looked into her eyes. 'What about it?'

Gala laughed abruptly. 'Don't be ridiculous,' she said. 'It's what we're paid for. Of course we'll take them on. And I agree we'd get nowhere with London. We'd look absolutely ridiculous telephoning reports about cliffs falling on our heads. What are we doing down here anyway, fooling around without any clothes on instead of getting on with our jobs?'

Bond grinned. 'We only lay down for ten minutes to get dry,' he protested mildly. 'How do you think we ought to have spent the afternoon? Taking everybody's fingerprints all over again? That's about all you police think about.' He felt ashamed when he saw her stiffen. He held his hand up. 'I didn't really mean that,' he said. 'But can't you see what we've done this afternoon? Just what had to be done. We've made the enemy show his hand. Now we've got to take the next step and find out who the enemy is and why he wanted us out of the way. And then if we've got enough evidence that someone's trying to sabotage the Moonraker we'll have the whole place turned inside out, the practice shoot postponed, and to hell with politics.'

She jumped to her feet. 'Oh, of course you're right,' she said impatiently. 'It's just that I want to do something about it in a hurry.' She looked for a moment out to sea, away from Bond. 'You've only just come into the picture. I've been living with this rocket for more than a year and I can't bear the idea that something may happen to it. So much seems to depend on it. For all of us. I want to get back there quickly and find out who wanted to kill us. It may be nothing to do with the Moonraker, but I want to make sure.'

Bond stood up, showing nothing of the pain from the cuts and bruises on his back and legs. 'Come on,' he said, 'it's nearly six o'clock. The tide's coming in fast but we can get to St Margaret's before it catches us. We'll clean up at the Granville there and have a drink and some food and then we'll go back to the house in the middle of dinner. I shall be interested to see what sort of a reception we get. After that we'll have to concentrate on staying alive and seeing what we can see. Can you make it to St Margaret's?'

'Don't be silly,' said Gala. 'Policewomen aren't made of gossamer.' She gave a reluctant smile at Bond's ironically respectful 'Of course not', and they turned towards the distant tower of the South Foreland lighthouse and set off through the shingle.

At half-past eight the taxi from St Margaret's dropped them at the second guard gate and they showed their passes and walked quietly up through the trees on to the expanse of concrete. They both felt keyed up and in high spirits. A hot bath and an hour's rest at the accommodating Granville had been followed by two stiff brandies-and-sodas for Gala and three for Bond followed by delicious fried soles and Welsh rarebits and coffee. And now, as they confidently approached the house, it would have needed second sight to tell that they were both dead tired and that they were naked and bruised under their walking clothes.

They let themselves quietly in through the front door and stood for a moment in the lighted hall. A cheerful mumble of voices came from the dining-room. There was a pause followed by a burst of laughter which was dominated by the harsh bark of Sir Hugo Drax.

Bond's mouth twisted wryly as he led the way across the hall to the door of the dining-room. Then he fixed a cheerful smile on his face and opened the door for Gala to pass through.

Drax sat at the head of the table, festive in his plum-coloured smoking-jacket. A forkful of food, halfway to his open mouth, had stopped in mid-air as they appeared in the doorway. Unnoticed, the food slid off the fork and fell with a soft, distinct 'plep' on to the edge of the table.

Krebs had been in the act of drinking a glass of red wine and the glass, frozen against his mouth, poured a thin trickle down his chin and thence on to his brown satin tie and yellow shirt.

Dr Walter had had his back to the door and it was not until he observed the unusual behaviour of the others, the bulging eyes, the gape of the mouths, and the blood-drained faces, that he whipped his head round towards the door. His reactions, thought Bond, were slower than the others, or else his nerves were steadier. '*Ach so*,' he said softly. '*Die Engländer*.'

Drax was on his feet. 'My dear chap,' he said thickly. 'My dear chap. We were really very worried. Just wondering whether to send out a search party. Few minutes ago one of the guards came in and reported there seemed to have been a cliff-fall.' He came round towards them, his napkin in one hand and the fork still erect in the other.

With the movement the blood surged back into his face, which became first mottled and then its usual red. 'You really might have let me know,' he spoke to the girl, anger rising in his voice. 'Most extraordinary behaviour.'

'It was my fault,' said Bond, moving forward into the room so that he could keep them all in view. 'The walk was longer than I expected. I thought we might get caught by the tide so we went on to St Margaret's and had something to eat there and took a taxi. Miss Brand wanted to telephone but I thought we would be back before eight. You must put the blame on me. But please go ahead with your dinner. Perhaps I might join you for coffee and dessert. I expect Miss Brand would prefer to go to her room. She must be tired after her long day.'

Bond walked deliberately round the table and took the chair next to Krebs. Those pale eyes, he noticed, after the first shock, had been fixed firmly on his plate. As Bond came up behind him he was delighted to see a large mound of Elastoplast on the crown of Kreb's head.

'Yes, go to bed, Miss Brand. I will talk to you in the morning,' said Drax testily. Gala obediently left the room and Drax went to his chair and sat heavily down.

'Most remarkable those cliffs,' said Bond blithely. 'Quite awe-inspiring walking along wondering if they're going to choose just that moment to collapse on one. Reminded me of Russian roulette. And yet one never reads of people being killed by cliffs falling on them. The odds against getting hurt must be terrific.' He paused. 'By the way, what was that you were saying about a cliff-fall just now?'

There was a faint groan on Bond's right, followed by a crash of glass and china as Krebs's head fell forward on to the table.

Bond looked at him with polite curiosity.

'Walter,' said Drax sharply. 'Can't you see that Krebs is ill? Take the man out and put him to bed. And don't be too soft with him. The man drinks too much. Hurry up.'

Walter, his face crumpled and angry, strode round the table and jerked Kreb's head out of the debris. He took him by his coat collar and hauled him to his feet and away from his chair.

'*Du Scheusskerl*,' hissed Walter at the mottled, vacant face. '*Marsch!*' He turned him round and hustled him to the swing door into the pantry and rammed him through. There were muffled sounds of stumbling and cursing and then a door banged and there was silence.

'He must have had a heavy day,' said Bond looking at Drax.

The big man was sweating freely. He wiped his face with a circular sweep of his napkin. 'Nonsense,' he said shortly. 'He drinks.'

The butler, erect and unperturbed by thc apparition of Krebs and Walter in his pantry, brought in the coffee. Bond took some and sipped it. He waited for the pantry door to close again. Another German, he thought. He'll already have passed the news back to the barracks. Or perhaps all the team weren't involved. Perhaps there was a team within a team. And if so, did Drax know about it? His behaviour when Bond and Gala had come through the door had been inconclusive. Had part of his astonishment been affronted dignity, the shock of a vain man whose programme has been upset by a chit of a secretary? He had certainly covered up well. And all the afternoon he had been down the shaft supervising the fuelling. Bond decided to probe a little.

'How did the fuelling go?' he asked, his eyes fixed on the other man.

Drax was lighting a long cigar. He glanced up at Bond through the smoke and the flame of his match.

'Excellently.' He puffed at the cigar to get it going. 'Everything is ready now. The guards are out. An hour or two clearing up down there in the morning and then the site will be closed. By the way,' he added. 'I shall be taking Miss Brand up to London in the car tomorrow afternoon. I shall need a secretary as well as Krebs. Have you got any plans?'

'I have to go to London too,' said Bond on an impulse. 'I have my final report to make to the Ministry.'

'Oh, really?' said Drax casually. 'What about? I thought you were satisfied with the arrangements.'

'Yes,' said Bond non-committally.

'That's all right then,' said Drax breezily. 'And now if you don't mind,' he got up from the table, 'I've got some papers waiting for me in my study. So I'll say good-night.'

'Good-night,' said Bond to the already retreating back.

Bond finished his coffee and went out into the hall and up to his bedroom. It was obvious that it had been searched again. He shrugged his shoulders. There was only the leather case. Its contents would show nothing except that he had come equipped with the tools of his trade.

His Beretta in its shoulder-holster was still where he had hidden it, in the empty leather case that belonged to Tallon's night-glasses. He took the gun out and slipped it under his pillow.

He took a hot bath and used half a bottle of iodine on the cuts and bruises he could reach. Then he got into bed and turned out the light. His body hurt and he was exhausted.

For a moment he thought of Gala. He had told her to take a sleeping pill and lock her door, but otherwise not to worry about anything until the morning.

Before he emptied his mind for sleep he wondered uneasily about her trip with Drax the next day to London.

Uneasily, but not desperately. In due course many questions would have to be answered and many mysteries probed, but the basic facts seemed solid and unanswerable. This extraordinary millionaire had built this great weapon. The Ministry of Supply were pleased with it and considered it sound. The Prime Minister and Parliament thought so too. The rocket was to be fired in less than thirty-six hours under full supervision and the security arrangements were as strict as they could possibly be. Somebody, and probably several people, wanted him and the girl out of the way. Nerves were stretched down here. There was a lot of tension about. Perhaps there was jealousy. Perhaps some people actually suspected them of being saboteurs. But what would that matter so long as he and Gala kept their eyes open? Not much more than a day to go. They were right out in the open here, in May, in England, in peacetime. It was crazy to worry about a few lunatics so long as the Moonraker was out of danger.

And as for tomorrow, reflected Bond as sleep reached out for him, he would arrange to meet Gala in London and bring her back with him. Or she could even stay up in London for the night. Either way he would look after her until the Moonraker was safely fired and then, before work began on the Mark II weapon, there would have to be a very thorough clean-up indeed.

But these were treacherously comforting thoughts. There was danger about and Bond knew it.

He finally drifted into sleep with one small scene firmly fixed in his mind.

There had been something very disquieting about the dinner-table downstairs. It had been laid for only three people.

PART THREE

Thursday, Friday –

Chapter Eighteen

Beneath the Flat Stone

The Mercedes was a beautiful thing. Bond pulled his battered grey Bentley up alongside it and inspected it. It was a Type 300 S, the sports model with a disappearing hood–one of only half a dozen in England, he reflected. Left-hand drive. Probably bought in Germany. He had seen a few of them over there. One had hissed by him on the Munich Autobahn the year before when he was doing a solid ninety in the Bentley. The body, too short and heavy to be graceful, was painted white, with red leather upholstery. Garish for England, but Bond guessed that Drax had chosen white in honour of the famous Mercedes-Benz racing colours that had already swept the board again sincc the war at Le Mans and the Nurburgring.

Typical of Drax of buy a Mercedes. There was something ruthless and majestic about the cars, he decided, remembering the years from 1934 to 1939 when they had completely dominated the Grand Prix scene, children of the famous Blitzen Benz that had captured the world's speed record at 142 m.p.h. back in 1911. Bond recalled some of their famous drivers, Caracciola, Lang, Seaman, Brauchitsch, and the days when he had seen them drifting the fast sweeping bends of Tripoli at 190, or screaming along the tree-lined straight at Berne with the Auto Unions on their tails.

And yet, Bond looked across at his supercharged Bentley, nearly twenty-five years older than Drax's car and still capable of beating 100, and yet when Bentleys were racing, before Rolls had tamed them into sedate town carriages, they had whipped the blown SS-K's almost as they wished.

Bond had once dabbled on the fringe of the racing world and he was lost in his memories, hearing again the harsh scream of Caracciola's great white beast of a car as it howled past the grandstands at Le Mans, when Drax came out of the house followed by Gala Brand and Krebs.

'Fast car,' said Drax, pleased with Bond's look of admiration. He gestured towards the Bentley. 'They used to be good in the old days,' he added with a touch of patronage. 'Now they're only built for going to the theatre. Too well-mannered. Even the Continental. Now then you, get in the back.'

Krebs obediently climbed into the narrow back seat behind thc driver. He sat sideways, his mackintosh up round his ears, his eyes fixed enigmatically on Bond.

Gala Brand, smart in a dark grey tailor-made and black beret and carrying a lightweight black raincoat and gloves, climbed into the right half of the divided front seat. The wide door closed with the rich double click of a Fabergé box.

No sign passed between Bond and Gala. They had made their plans at a whispered meeting in his room before lunch–dinner in London at half-past seven and then back to the house in Bond's car. She sat demurely, her hands in her lap and her eyes to the front, as Drax climbed in, pressed the starter, and pulled the gleaming lever on the steering wheel back into third. The car surged away with hardly a purr from the exhaust and Bond watched it disappear into the trees before he climbed into the Bentley and moved off in leisurely pursuit.

In the hastening Mercedes, Gala busied herself with her thoughts. The night had been uneventful and the morning had been devoted to clearing the launching site of everything that might possibly burn when the Moonraker was fired. Drax had not referred to the events of the previous day and there had been no change in his usual manner. She had prepared her last firing plan (Drax himself was to do it on the morrow) and as usual Walter had been sent for and through her spy-hole she had seen the figures being entered in Drax's black book.

It was a hot, sunny day and Drax was driving in his shirt-sleeves. She glanced down and to the left at the top of the little book protruding from his hip-pocket. This drive might be her last chance. Since the evening before she had felt a different person. Perhaps Bond had aroused her competitive spirit, perhaps it was revulsion from playing the secretary too long, perhaps it was the shock of the cliff-fall and the zest of realizing after so many quiet months that she was playing a dangerous game. But now she felt the time had come to take risks. Discovery of the Moonraker's flight-plan was a routine affair and it would give her personal satisfaction to find out the secret of the black note-book. It would be easy.

Casually she laid her folded coat over the space between herself and Drax. At the same time she made a show of arranging herself comfortably, during the course of which she drew an inch of two nearer Drax and her hand came to rest in the folds of the coat between them. Then she settled herself to wait.

Her chance came, as she had thought it might, in the congested traffic of Maidstone. Drax, intent, was trying to beat the traffic lights at the corner of King Street and Gabriel's Hill, but the line of traffic was too slow and he was checked behind a battered family saloon. Gala could see that when the lights changed he was determined to cut in front of the car in front and teach it a lesson. He was a brilliant driver, but a vindictive and impatient one who was always anxious for any car that held him up to be given something to remember.

As the lights went green he gave a blast on his triple horns, pulled out to the right at the intersection, accelerated brutally and got by, shaking his head angrily at the driver of the saloon as he passed it.

In the middle of this harsh manoeuvre it was natural for Gala to allow herself to be thrown towards him. At the same time her left hand dived under the coat and her fingers touched, felt, and extracted the book in one flow of motion. Then the hand was back in the folds of the coat again and Drax, all his feeling in his feet and his hands, was seeing nothing but the traffic ahead and the chances of getting across the zebra outside the Royal Star without hitting two women and a boy who were nearly halfway across it.

Now it was a question of facing Drax's growl of rage as with a maidenly but urgent voice she asked if she could possibly stop for a moment to powder her nose.

A garage would be dangerous. He might decide to fill up with petrol. And perhaps he also carried his money in his hip-pocket. But was there an hotel? Yes, she remembered, the Thomas Wyatt just outside Maidstone. And it had no petrol pumps. She started to fidget slightly. She pulled the coat back on to her lap. She cleared her throat.

'Oh, excuse me, Sir Hugo,' she said in a strangled voice.

'Yes. What is it?'.

'I'm terribly sorry, Sir Hugo. But could you possibly stop for just a moment. I want, I mean, I'm terribly sorry but I'd like to powder my nose. It's terribly stupid of me. I'm so sorry.'

'Christ,' said Drax. 'Why the hell didn't you . . . Oh, yes. Well, all right. Find a place.' He grumbled on into his moustache, but brought the big car down into the fifties.

'There's a hotel just around this bend,' said Gala nervously. 'Thank you so much, Sir Hugo. It was stupid of me. I won't be a moment. Yes, here it is.'

The car swerved up to the front of the inn and stopped with a jerk. 'Hurry up. Hurry up,' said Drax as Gala, leaving the door of the car open, sped obediently across the gravel, her coat with its precious secret held tightly in front of her body.

She locked the door of the lavatory and snatched open the notebook.

There they were, just as she had thought. On each page, under the date, the neat columns of figures, the atmospheric pressure, the wind velocity, the temperature, just as she had recorded them from the Air Ministry figures. And at the foot of each page the estimated settings for the gyro compasses.

Gala frowned. At a glance she could see that they were entirely different from hers. Drax's figures simply bore no relation to hers whatsoever.

She turned to the last completed page containing the figures for that day. Why, she was wrong by nearly ninety degrees on the estimated course. If the rocket were fired on her flight plan it would land somewhere in France. She looked wildly at her face in the mirror over the washbasin. How could she have gone so monstrously wrong? And why hadn't Drax ever told her? Why, she ran quickly through the book again, every day she had been ninety degrees out, firing the Moonraker at right angles to its true course. And yet she simply couldn't have made such a mistake. Did the Ministry know these secret figures? And why should they be secret?

Suddenly her bewilderment turned to fright. She must somehow get safely, quietly to London and tell somebody. Even though she might be called a fool and a meddler.

Coldly she turned back several pages in the book, took her nail file out of her bag and, as neatly as she could, cut out a specimen page, rolled it up into a tight ball and stuffed it into the tip of a finger of one of her gloves.

She glanced at her face in the mirror. It was pale and she quickly rubbed her cheeks to bring back the colour. Then she put back the look of an apologetic secretary and hurried out and ran across the gravel to the car, clutching the note-book among the folds of her coat.

The engine of the Mercedes was turning over. Drax glowered at her impatiently as she scrambled back into her seat.

'Come on. Come on,' he said, putting the car into third and taking his foot off the clutch so that she nearly caught her ankle in the heavy door. The tyres churned up the gravel as he accelerated out of the parking place and dry-skidded into the London road.

Gala was jerked back, but she remembered to let the coat with her guilty hand in its folds fall on the seat between her and the driver.

And now the book back into the hip-pocket.

She watched the speedometer hovering in the seventies as Drax flung the heavy car along the crown of the road.

She tried to remember her lessons. Distracting pressure on some other part of the body. Distracting the attention. Distraction. The victim must not be at ease. His senses must be focused away. He must be unaware of the touch on his body. Anaesthetized by a stronger stimulus.

Like now, for instance. Drax, bent forward over the wheel, was fighting for a chance to get past a sixty-foot R.A.F. trailer, but the oncoming traffic was leaving no room on the crown of the road. There was a gap and Drax rammed the lever into second and took it, his horns braying imperiously.

Gala's hand reached to the left under the coat.

But another hand struck like a snake.

'Got you.'

Krebs was leaning half over the back of the driving seat. His hand was crushing hers into the slippery cover of the notebook under the folds of the coat.

Gala sat frozen into black ice. With all her strength she wrenched at her hand. It was no good. Krebs had all his weight on it now.

Drax had got past the trailer and the road was empty. Krebs said urgently in German, 'Please stop the car, *mein Kapitän*. Miss Brand is a spy.'

Drax gave a startled glance to his right. What he saw was enough. He put his hand quickly down to his hip-pocket, and then, slowly, deliberately, put it back on the wheel. The sharp turning to Mereworth was just coming up on his left. 'Hold her,' said Drax. He braked so that the tyres screamed, changed down and wrenched the car into the side-road. A few hundred yards down it he pulled the car into the side and stopped.

Drax looked up and down the road. It was empty. He reached over one gloved hand and wrenched Gala's face towards him.

'What is this?'

'I can explain it, Sir Hugo.' Gala tried to bluff against the horror and desperation she knew was in her face. 'It's a mistake. I didn't mean . . .'

Under cover of an angry shrug of the shoulders, her right hand moved softly behind her and the guilty pair of gloves were thrust behind the leather cushion.

'*Sehen sie her, mein Kapitän*. I saw her edging up close to you. It seemed to me strange.'

With his other hand Krebs had whipped the coat away and there were the bent white fingers of her left hand crushed into the cover of the notebook still a foot away from Drax's hip-pocket.

'So.'

The word was deadly cold and with a shivering finality.

Drax let go her chin, but her horrified eyes remained locked into his.

A kind of frozen cruelty was showing through the jolly façade of red skin and whiskers. It was a different man. The man behind the mask. The creature beneath the flat stone that Gala Brand had lifted.

Drax glanced again up and down the empty road.

Then, looking carefully into the suddenly aware blue eyes, he drew the leather driving gauntlet off his left hand and with his right whipped her as hard as he could across the face with it.

Only a short cry was forced out of Gala's constricted throat, but tears of pain ran down her cheeks. Suddenly she began to fight like a mad woman.

With all her strength she heaved and fought against the two iron arms that held her. With her free right hand she tried to reach the face that leant over her and get at the eyes. But Krebs easily moved his head out of her reach and quietly increased the pressure across her throat, hissing murderously to himself as her nails tore strips of skin off the backs of his hands, but noting with a scientist's eye as her struggles became weaker.

Drax watched carefully, with one eye on the road, as Krebs brought her under control and then he started the car and drove cautiously on along the wooded road. He grunted with satisfaction as he came upon a cart-track into the woods and he turned up it and only stopped when he was well out of sight of the road.

Gala had just realized that there was no noise from the engine when she heard Drax say 'there'. A finger touched her skull behind the left ear. Kreb's arm came away from her throat and she slumped gratefully forward, gasping for air. Then something crashed into the back of her head where the finger had touched it and there was a flash of wonderfully releasing pain and blackness.

An hour later passers-by saw a white Mercedes draw up outside a small house at the Buckingham Palace end of Ebury Street and two kind gentlemen help a sick girl out and through the front door. Those who were near could see that the poor girl's face was very pale and that her eyes were shut and that the kind gentlemen almost had to carry her up the steps. The big gentleman with the red face and whiskers was heard to say quite distinctly to the other man that poor Mildred had promised she wouldn't go out until she was quite well again. Very sad.

Gala came to herself in a large top-floor room that seemed to be full of machinery. She was tied very securely to a chair and apart from the searing pain in her head she could feel that her lips and cheek were bruised and swollen.

Heavy curtains were drawn across the window and there was a musty smell in the room as if it was rarely used. There was dust on the few pieces of conventional furniture and only the chromium and ebonite dials on the machines looked clean and new. She thought that she was probably in hospital. She closed her eyes and wondered. It was not long before she remembered. She spent several minutes controlling herself and then she opened her eyes again.

Drax, his back to her, was watching the dials on a machine that looked like a very large radio set. There were three more similar machines in her line of sight and from one of them a thin steel aerial reached up to a rough hole that had been cut for it in the plaster of the ceiling. The room was brightly lit by several tall standard lamps, each of which held a naked high wattage bulb.

To her left there was a noise of tinkering and by swivelling her half-closed eyes in their sockets, which made the pain in her head much worse, she saw the figure of Krebs bent over an electric generator on the floor. Beside it there was a small petrol engine and it was this that was giving trouble. Every now and then Krebs would grasp the starting-handle and crank it hard and a feeble stutter would come from the engine before he went back to his tinkering.

'You dam' fool,' said Drax in German, 'hurry up. I've got to go and see those bloody oafs at the Ministry.'

'At once, *mein Kapitän*,' said Krebs dutifully. He seized the handle again. This time after two or three coughs the engine started up and began to purr.

'It won't make too much noise?' asked Drax.

'No, *mein Kapitän*. The room has been soundproofed,' answered Krebs. 'Dr Walter assures me that nothing will be heard outside.'

Gala closed her eyes and decided that her only hope was to feign unconsciousness for as long as possible. Did they intend to kill her? Here in this room? And what was all this machinery? It looked like wireless, or perhaps radar. That curved glass screen above Drax's head that had given an occasional flicker as Drax fiddled with the knobs below the dials.

Slowly her mind started to work again. Why, for instance, was Drax suddenly talking perfect German? And why did Krebs address him as *Herr Kapitän*? And the figures in the black book. Why did they nearly kill her because she had seen them? What did they mean?

Ninety degrees, ninety degrees.

Lazily her mind turned the problem over.

Ninety degrees difference. Supposing her figures had been right all the time for the target eighty miles away in the North Sea. Just supposing she had been right. Then she wouldn't have been aiming the rocket into the middle of France after all. But Drax's figures? Ninety degrees to the left of her North Sea target? Somewhere in England presumably. Eighty miles from Dover. Yes, of course. That was it. Drax's figures. The firing plan in the little black book. They would drop the Moonraker just about in the middle of London.

But on London! On London!!

So one's heart really does go into one's throat. How extraordinary. Such a commonplace and yet there it is and it really does almost stop one breathing.

And now, let me see, so this is a radar homing device. How ingenious. The same as there would be on the raft in the North Sea. This would bring the rocket down within a hundred yards of Buckingham Palace. But would that matter with a warhead full of instruments?

It was probably the cruelty of Drax's blow across her face that settled it, but suddenly she knew, she KNEW that somehow it would be a real warhead, an atomic warhead, and that Drax was an enemy of England and that tomorrow at noon he was going to destroy London.

Gala made a last effort to understand.

Through this ceiling, through this chair, into the ground. The thin needle of the rocket. Dropping fast as light out of a clear sky. The crowds in the streets. The Palace. The nursemaids in the park. The birds in the trees. The great bloom of flame a mile wide. And then the mushroom cloud. And nothing left. Nothing. Nothing. Nothing.

'No. Oh, NO!'

But the scream was only in her mind and Gala, her body a twisted black potato crisp amongst a million others, had already fainted.

Chapter Nineteen

Missing Person

Bond sat at his favourite restaurant table in London, the right-hand corner table for two on the first floor, and watched the people and the traffic in Piccadilly and down the Haymarket.

It was 7.45 and his second Vodka dry Martini with a large slice of lemon peel had just been brought to him by Baker, the head waiter. He sipped it, wondering idly why Gala was late. It was not like her. She was the sort of girl who would telephone if she had been kept at the Yard. Vallance, whom he had visited at five, had said that Gala was due with him at six.

Vallance had been very anxious to see her. He was a worried man and when Bond reported briefly on the security of the Moonraker, Vallance seemed to be listening with only half his mind.

It appeared that all that day there had been heavy selling of sterling. It had started in Tangier and quickly spread to Zürich and New York. The pound had been fluctuating wildly in the money markets of the world and the arbitrage dealers had made a killing. The net result was that the pound was a whole three cents down on the day and the forward rates were still weaker. It was front-page news in the evening papers and at the close of business the Treasury had got on to Vallance and told him the extraordinary news that the selling wave had been started by Drax Metals Ltd in Tangier. The operation had begun that morning and by close of business the firm had managed to sell British currency short to the tune of twenty million pounds. This had been too much for the markets, and the Bank of England had had to step in and buy in order to stop a still sharper run. It was then that Drax Metals had come to light as the seller.

Now the Treasury wanted to know what it was all about–whether it was Drax himself selling or one of the big commodity interests who were clients of his firm. The first thing they did was to tackle Vallance. Vallance could only think that in some way the Moonraker was to be a failure and that Drax knew it and wanted to profit by his knowledge. He at once spoke to the Ministry of Supply, but they pooh-poohed the idea. There was no reason to think the Moonraker would be a failure and even if its practice flight was not successful the fact would be covered up with talk of technical hitches and so forth. In any case, whether the rocket was a success or not, there could be no possible reaction on British financial credit. No, they certainly wouldn't think of mentioning the matter to the Prime Minister. Drax Metals was a big trading organization. They were probably acting for some foreign government. The Argentine. Perhaps even Russia. Someone with big sterling balances. Anyway it was nothing to do with the Ministry, or with the Moonraker, which would be launched punctually at noon the next day.

This had made sense to Vallance, but he was still worried. He didn't like mysteries and he was glad to share his concern with Bond. Above all he wanted to ask Gala if she had seen any Tangier cables and if so whether Drax had made any comment on them.

Bond was sure Gala would have mentioned anything of the sort to him, and he said so to Vallance. They had talked some more and then Bond had left for his headquarters where M was expecting him.

M had been interested in everything, even the shaven heads and moustaches of the men. He questioned Bond minutely and when Bond finished his story with the gist of his last conversation with Vallance M sat for a long time lost in thought.

'007,' he said at last, 'I don't like any part of this. There's something going on down there but I can't for the life of me make any sense out of it. And I don't see where I can possibly interfere. All the facts are known to the Special Branch and to the Ministry and, God knows, I've got nothing to add to them. Even if I had a word with the P.M., which would be damned unfair on Vallance, what am I to tell him? What facts? What's it all about? There's nothing but the smell of it all. And it's a bad smell. And,' he added, 'a very big one, if I'm not mistaken.'

'No,' he looked across at Bond and his eyes held an unusual note of urgency. 'It looks as if it's all up to you. And that girl. You're lucky she's a good one. Anything you want? Anything I can do to help?'

'No thank you, sir,' Bond had said and he had walked out through the familiar corridors and down in the lift to his own office where he had terrified Loelia Ponsonby by giving her a kiss as he said good-night. The only times he ever did that were at Christmas, on her birthday, and just before there was something dangerous to be done.

Bond drank down the rest of his Martini and looked at his watch. Now it was eight o'clock and suddenly he shivered.

He got straight up from his table and walked out to the telephone.

The switchboard at the Yard said that the Assistant Commissioner had been trying to reach him. He had had to go to a dinner at the Mansion House. Could Commander Bond please stay by the telephone? Bond waited impatiently. All his fears surged up at him from the chunk of black bakelite. He could see the rows of polite faces. The uniformed waiter slowly edging his way round to Vallance. The quickly pulled-back chair. The unobtrusive exit. Those echoing stone lobbies. The discreet booth.

The telephone screamed at him. 'That you, Bond? Vallance here. Seen anything of Miss Brand?'

Bond's heart went cold. 'No,' he said sharply. 'She's half an hour late for dinner. Didn't she turn up at six?'

'No, and I've had a "trace" sent out and there's no sign of her at the usual address she stays at when she comes to London. None of her friends has seen her. If she left in Drax's car at two-thirty she should have been in London by half-past four. There's been no crash on the Dover road during the afternoon and the A.A. and the R.A.C. are negative.' There was a pause. 'Now listen.' There was urgent appeal in Vallance's voice, 'She's a good girl that, and I don't want anything to happen to her. Can you handle it for me? I can't put out a general call for her. The killing down there had made her news and we'd have the whole Press round our ears. It will be even worse after ten tonight. Downing Street are issuing a communiqué about the practice shoot and tomorrow's papers are going to be nothing but Moonraker. The P.M.'s going to broadcast. Her disappearance would turn the whole thing into a crime story. Tomorrow's too important for that and anyway the girl may have had a fainting fit or something. But I want her found. Well? What do you say? Can you handle it? You can have all the help you want. I'll tell the Duty Officer that he's to accept your orders.'

'Don't worry,' said Bond. 'Of course I'll look after it.' He paused, his mind racing. 'Just tell me something. What do you know about Drax's movements?'

'He wasn't expected at the Ministry until seven,' said Vallance. 'I left word . . .' There was a confused noise on the line and Bond heard Vallance say 'Thanks'. He came back on the line. 'Just got a report passed on by the City police,' he said. 'The Yard couldn't get me on the 'phone. Talking to you. Let's see,' he read, '"Sir Hugo Drax arrived Ministry 1900 left at 2000. Left message dining at Blades if wanted. Back at site 2300."' Vallance commented: 'That means he'll be leaving London about nine. Just a moment.' He read on: '"Sir Hugo stated Miss Brand felt unwell on arrival in London and at her request he left her at Victoria Station bus terminal at 16.45. Miss Brand stated she would rest with some friends, address unknown, and contact Sir Hugo at Ministry at 1900. She had not done so." And that's all,' said Vallance. 'Oh, by the way, we made the inquiry about Miss Brand on your behalf. Said you had arranged to meet her at six and she hadn't turned up.'

'Yes,' said Bond, his thoughts elsewhere. 'That doesn't seem to get us anywhere. I'll have to get busy. Just one more thing. Has Drax got a place in London, flat or anything like that?'

'He always stays at the Ritz nowadays,' said Vallance. 'Sold his house in Grosvenor Square when he moved down to Dover. But we happen to know he's got some sort of an establishment in Ebury Street. We checked there. But there was no answer to the bell and my man said the house looked unoccupied. Just behind Buckingham Palace. Some sort of hideout of his. Keeps it very quiet. Probably takes his women there. Anything else? I ought to be getting back or all this big brass will think the Crown Jewels have been stolen.'

'You go ahead,' said Bond. 'I'll do my best and if I get stuck I'll call on your men to help. Don't worry if you don't hear from me. So long.'

'So long,' said Vallance with a note of relief in his voice. 'And thanks. Best of luck.'

Bond rang off.

He picked up the receiver again and called Blades.

'This is the Ministry of Supply,' he said. 'Is Sir Hugo Drax in the club?'

'Yes, sir,' it was the friendly voice of Brevett. 'He's in the dining-room. Do you wish to speak to him?'

'No, it's all right,' said Bond. 'I just wanted to make certain he hadn't left yet.'

Without noticing what he was eating Bond wolfed down some food and left the restaurant at 8.45. His car was outside waiting for him and he said good-night to the driver from Headquarters and drove to St James's Street. He parked under cover of the central row of taxis opposite Boodle's and settled himself behind an evening paper over which he could keep his eyes on a section of Drax's Mercedes which he was relieved to see standing in Park Street, unattended.

He had not long to wait. Suddenly a broad shaft of yellow light shone out from the doorway of Blades and the big figure of Drax appeared. He wore a heavy ulster up round his ears and a cap pulled down over his eyes. He walked quickly to the white Mercedes, slammed the door, and was away across to the left-hand side of St James's Street and braking to turn opposite St James's Palace while Bond was still in third.

God the man moves quickly, thought Bond, doing a racing change round the island in the Mall with Drax already passing the statue in front of the Palace. He kept the Bentley in third and thundered in pursuit. Buckingham Palace Gate. So it looked like Ebury Street. Keeping the white car just in view, Bond made hurried plans. The lights at the corner of Lower Grosvenor Place were green for Drax and red for Bond. Bond jumped them and was just in time to see Drax swing left into the beginning of Ebury Street. Gambling on Drax making a stop at his house, Bond accelerated to the corner and pulled up just short of it. As he jumped out of the Bentley, leaving the engine ticking over, and took the few steps towards Ebury Street, he heard two short blasts on the Mercedes' horn and as he carefully edged round the corner he was in time to see Krebs helping the muffled figure of a girl across the pavement. Then the door of the Mercedes slammed and Drax was off again.

Bond ran back to his car, whipped into third, and went after him.

Thank God the Mercedes was white. There it went, its stop-lights blazing briefly at the intersections, the headlamps full on and the horn blaring at any hint of a check in the sparse traffic.

Bond set his teeth and rode his car as if she was a Lipizaner at the Spanish Riding School in Vienna. He could not use headlights or horn for fear of betraying his presence to the car in front. He just had to play on his brakes and gears and hope for the best.

The deep note of his two-inch exhaust thundered back at him from the houses on either side and his tyres screamed on the tarmac. He thanked heavens for the new set of racing Michelins that were only a week old. If only the lights would be kind. He seemed to be getting nothing but amber and red while Drax was always being swept on by the green. Chelsea Bridge. So it did look like the Dover road by the South Circular! Could he hope to keep up with the Mercedes on A20? Drax had two passengers. His car might not be tuned. But with that independent springing he could corner better than Bond. The old Bentley was a bit high off the ground for this sort of work. Bond stamped on his brakes and risked a howl on his triple klaxons as a homeward-bound taxi started to weave over to the right. It jerked back to the left and Bond heard a four-letter yell as he shot past.

Clapham Common and the flicker of the white car through the trees. Bond ran the Bentley up to eighty along the safe bit of road and saw the lights go red just in time to stop Drax at the end of it. He put the Bentley into neutral and coasted up silently. Fifty yards away. Forty, thirty, twenty. The lights changed and Drax was over the crossing and away again, but not before Bond had seen that Krebs was beside the driver and that there was no sign of Gala except the hump of a rug over the narrow back seat.

So there was no question. You don't take a sick girl for a drive like a sack of potatoes. Nor at that speed for the matter of that. So she was a prisoner. Why? What had she done? What had she discovered? What the hell, in fact, was all this about?

Each dark conjecture came and for a moment settled like a vulture on

Bond's shoulder and croaked into his ear that he had been a blind fool. Blind, blind, blind. From the moment he had sat in his office after the night at Blades and made his mind up about Drax being a dangerous man he should have been on his toes. At the first smell of trouble, the marks on the chart for instance, he should have taken action. But what action? He had passed on each clue, each fear. What could he have done except kill Drax? And get hanged for his pains? Well, then. What about the present? Should he stop and telephone the Yard? And let the car get away? For all he knew Gala was being taken for a ride and Drax planned to get rid of her on the way to Dover. And that Bond might conceivably prevent if only his car could take it.

As if to echo his thoughts the tortured rubber screamed as he left the South Circular road into A20 and took the roundabout at forty. No. He had told M that he would stay with it. He had told Vallance the same. The case had been dumped firmly into his lap and he must do what he could. At least if he kept up with the Mercedes he might shoot up its tyres and apologize afterwards. To let it get away would be criminal.

So be it, said Bond to himself.

He had to slow for some lights and he used the pause to pull a pair of goggles out of the dashboard compartment and cover his eyes with them. Then he leant over to the left and twisted the big screw on the windscreen and then eased the one beside his right hand. He pressed the narrow screen flat down on the bonnet and tightened the screws again.

Then he accelerated away from Swanley Junction and was soon doing ninety astride the cats' eyes down the Farningham by-pass, the wind howling past his ears and the shrill scream of his supercharger riding with him for company.

A mile ahead the great eyes of the Mercedes hooded themselves as they went over the crest of Wrotham Hill and disappeared down into the moonlit panorama of the Weald of Kent.

Chapter Twenty

Drax's Gambit

There were three separate sources of pain in Gala's body. The throbbing ache behind her left ear, the bite of the flex at her wrists, and the chafing of the strap round her ankles.

Every bump in the road, every swerve, every sudden pressure of Drax's foot on the brakes or the accelerator awoke one or another of these pains and rasped at her nerves. If only she had been wedged into the back seat more tightly. But there was just room enough for her body to roll a few inches on the occasional seat so that she was constantly having to twist her bruised face away from contact with the walls of shiny pig-skin.

The air she breathed was stuffy with the smell of new leather upholstery, exhaust fumes, and the occasional sharp stench of burning rubber as Drax flayed the tyres on a sharp corner.

And yet the discomfort and pain were nothing.

Krebs! Curiously enough her fear and loathing of Krebs tormented her most. The other things were too big. The mystery of Drax and his hatred of England. The riddle of his perfect command of German. The Moonraker. The secret of the atomic warhead. How to save London. These were matters which she had long ago put away in the back of her mind as insoluble.

But the afternoon alone with Krebs was present and dreadful and her mind went back and back to the details of it like a tongue to an aching tooth.

Long after Drax had gone she had kept up her pretence of unconsciousness. At first Krebs had occupied himself with the machines, talking to them in German in a cooing baby-talk. 'There, my *Liebchen*. That's better now, isn't it? A drop of oil for you my *Pupperl*? But certainly. Coming up at once. No, no lazybones. I said a thousand revolutions. Not nine hundred. Come along now. We can do better than that, can't we? Yes, my *Schatz*. That's it. Round and round we go. Up and down. Round and round. Let me wipe your pretty face for you so that we can see what the little dial is saying. *Jesu Maria, bist du ein braves Kind!*'

And so it had gone on with intervals of standing in front of Gala, picking his nose and sucking at his teeth in a horribly ruminative way. Until he stayed longer and longer in front of her, forgetting the machines, wondering, making up his mind.

And then she had felt his hand undo the top button of her dress and the automatic recoil of her body had had to be covered by a realistic groan and a pantomime of consciousness returning.

She had asked for water and he had gone into a bathroom and fetched some for her in a toothglass. Then he had pulled a kitchen chair up in front of her and had sat down astride it, his chin resting on the top rail of its back, and had gazed at her speculatively from under his pale drooping lids.

She had been the first to break the silence. 'Why have I been brought here?' she asked. 'What are all those machines?'

He licked his lips and the little pouting red mouth opened under the smudge of yellow moustache and formed itself slowly into a rhomboid-shaped smile. 'That is a lure for little birds,' he said. 'Soon it will lure a little bird into this warm nest. Then the little bird will lay an egg. Oh, such a big round egg! Such a beautiful fat egg.' The lower half of his face giggled with delight while his eyes mooned. 'And the pretty girl is here because otherwise she might frighten the little bird away. And that would be so sad, wouldn't it,' he spat out the next three words, 'filthy English bitch?'

His eyes became intent and purposeful. He hitched his chair nearer so that his face was only a foot away from hers and she was enveloped in the miasma of his breath. 'Now English bitch. Who are you working for?' He waited. 'You must answer me, you know,' he said softly. 'We are all alone here. There is no one to hear you scream.'

'Don't be stupid,' said Gala desperately. 'How could I be working for anyone except Sir Hugo?' (Krebs smiled at the name.) 'I was just curious about the flight plan . . .' she went into a rambling explanation about her figures and Drax's figures and how she had wanted to share in the success of the Moonraker.

'Try again,' whispered Krebs when she had finished. 'You must do better than that,' and suddenly his eyes had turned hot with cruelty and his hands had reached towards her from behind the back of his chair. . . .

In the rear of the hurtling Mercedes Gala ground her teeth together and whimpered at the memory of the soft crawling fingers on her body, probing, pinching, pulling, while all the time the hot vacant eyes gazed curiously into hers until finally she gathered the saliva in her mouth and spat full in his face.

He hadn't even paused to wipe his face, but suddenly he had really hurt her and she had screamed once and then mercifully fainted.

And then she had found herself being pushed into the back of the car, a rug was thrown over her, and they were hurtling through the streets of London and she could hear other cars near them, the frantic ringing of a bicycle bell, an occasional shout, the animal growl of an old klaxon, the whirring putter of a motor-scooter, a scream of brakes, and she had realized that she was back in the real world, that English people, friends, were all around her. She had struggled to get to her knees and scream but Krebs must have felt her movement because his hands were suddenly at her ankles, strapping them to the footrail along the floor, and she knew that she was lost and suddenly the tears were pouring down her cheeks and she was praying that somehow, somebody would be in time.

That had been less than an hour ago and now she could tell from the slow pace of the car and the noise of other traffic that they had reached a large town–Maidstone if she was being taken back to the site.

In the comparative silence of their progress through the town she suddenly heard Kreb's voice. There was a note of urgency in it.

'*Mein Kapitän*,' he said. 'I have been watching a car for some time. It is certainly following us. It has seldom been using its lights. It is only a hundred metres behind us now. I think it is the car of Commander Bond.'

Drax grunted with surprise and she could hear his big body shift round to get a quick look.

He swore sharply and then there was silence and she could feel the big car weaving and straining in the thin traffic. '*Ja sowas!*' said Drax finally. His voice was thoughtful. 'So that old museum-piece of his can still move. So much the better, my dear Krebs. He seems to be alone.' He laughed harshly. 'So we will give him a run for his money and if he survives it we will get him in the bag with the woman. Turn on the radio. Home Service. We will soon find out if there is a hitch.'

There was a short crackle of static and then Gala could hear the voice of the Prime Minister, the voice of all the great occasions in her life, coming through in broken fragments as Drax put the car into third and accelerated out of the town . . . weapon devised by the ingenuity of man . . . a thousand miles into the firmament . . . area patrolled by Her Majesty's ships . . . designed exclusively for the defence of our beloved island . . . a long era of peace . . . development for Man's great journey away from the confines of this planet . . . Sir Hugo Drax, that great patriot and benefactor of our country . . .'

Gala heard Drax's roar of laughter above the howling of the wind, a great scornful bray of triumph, and then the set was switched off.

'James,' whispered Gala to herself. 'There's only you left. Be careful. But make haste.'

Bond's face was a mask of dust and filthy with the blood of flies and moths that had smashed against it. Often he had had to take a cramped hand off the wheel to clear his goggles, but the Bentley was going beautifully and he felt sure of holding the Mercedes.

He was touching ninety-five on the straight just before the entrance to Leeds Castle when great lights were suddenly switched on behind him and a four-tone windhorn sounded its impudent 'pom-pim-pom-pam' almost in his ear.

The apparition of a third car in the race was almost unbelievable. Bond had hardly troubled to look in his driving mirror since he left London. No one but a racing-driver or a desperate man could have kept up with them, and his mind was in a turmoil as he automatically pulled over to the left and saw out of the corner of his eye a low, fire-engine-red car come up level with him and draw away with a good ten miles extra on its clock.

He caught a glimpse of the famous Alfa radiator and along the edge of the bonnet in bold white script the words 'Attaboy II'. Then there was the grinning face of a youth in shirt-sleeves who stuck two rude fingers in the air before he pulled away in the welter of sound which an Alfa at speed compounds from the whine of its supercharger, the Gatling crackle of its exhaust, and the thunderous howl of its transmission.

Bond grinned in admiration as he raised a hand to the driver. Alfa-Romeo supercharged straight-eight, he thought to himself. Must be nearly as old as mine. 'Thirty-two or '33 probably. And only half my c.c. Targa Florio in 1931 and did well everywhere after that. Probably a hot-rod type from one of the R.A.F. stations round here. Trying to get back from a party in time to sign in before he's put on the report. He watched affectionately as the Alfa wagged its tail in the S-bend abreast of Leeds Castle and then howled off on the long wide road towards the distant Charing fork.

Bond could imagine the grin of delight as the boy came up with Drax. 'Oh, boy. It's a Merc!' And the rage of Drax at the impudent music of the windhorn. Must be doing 105, reflected Bond. Hope the damn fool doesn't run out of road. He watched the two sets of tail lights closing up, the boy in the Alfa preparing for his trick of coming up behind and suddenly switching everything on when he could see a chance to get by.

There. Four hundred yards away the Mercedes showed white in the sudden twin shafts from the Alfa. There was a mile of clear road ahead, straight as a die. Bond could almost feel the boy's feet stamping the pedal still further into the floorboards. Attaboy!

Up front in the Mercedes Krebs had his mouth close to Drax's ear. 'Another of them,' he shouted urgently. 'Can't see his face. Coming up to pass now.'

Drax let out a harsh obscenity. His bared teeth showed white in the pale glimmer from the dashboard. 'Teach the swine a lesson,' he said, setting his shoulders and gripping the wheel tightly in the great leather gauntlets. Out of the corner of his eye he watched the nose of the Alfa creep up to starboard. 'Pom-pim-pom-pam' chirped the windhorn. Softly, delicately, Drax inched the wheel of the Mercedes to the right and, at the horrible crash of metal, whipped it back again to correct the slew of his tail.

'Bravo! Bravo!' screamed Krebs, beside himself with excitement as he knelt on the seat and looked back. 'Double somersault. Jumped the hedge upside down. I think he's burning already. Yes. There are flames.'

'That'll give our fine Mister Bond something to think about,' snarled Drax, breathing heavily.

But Bond, his face a tight mask, had hardly checked his speed and there was nothing but revenge in his mind as he hurtled on after the flying Mercedes.

He had seen it all. The grotesque flight of the red car as it turned over and over, the flying figure of the driver, his arms and legs spreadeagled as he soared out of the driving seat, and the final thunder as the car hurdled the hedge upside down and crashed into the field.

As he flashed by, noting the horrible graffiti of the black skid-marks across the tarmac, his mind recorded one final macabre touch. Somehow undamaged in the holocaust, the windhorn was still making contact and its ululations were going on up to the sky, stridently clearing imaginary roads for the passage of Attaboy II–'Pom-pim-pom-pam.' 'Pom-pim-pom-pam . . .'

So a murder had taken place in front of his eyes. Or at any rate an attempted murder. So, whatever his motives, Sir Hugo Drax had declared war and didn't mind Bond knowing it. This made a lot of things easier. It meant that Drax was a criminal and probably a maniac. Above all it meant certain danger for the Moonraker. That was enough for Bond. He reached under the dashboard and from its concealed holster drew out the long-barrelled ·45 Colt Army Special and laid it on the seat beside him. The battle was now in the open and somehow the Mercedes must be stopped.

Using the road as if it was Donnington, Bond rammed his foot down and kept it there. Gradually, with the needle twitching either side of the hundred mark, he began to narrow the gap.

Drax took the left-hand fork at Charing and hissed up the long hill. Ahead, in the giant beam of his headlights, one of Bowaters' huge eight-wheeled A.E.C. Diesel carriers was just grinding into the first bend of the hairpin, labouring under the fourteen tons of newsprint it was taking on a night run to one of the East Kent newspapers.

Drax cursed under his breath as he saw the long carrier with the twenty gigantic rolls, each containing five miles of newsprint, roped to its platform. Right in the middle of the tricky S-bend at the top of the hill.

He looked in the driving mirror and saw the Bentley coming into the fork. And then Drax had his idea.

'Krebs,' the word was a pistol shot. 'Get out your knife.'

There was a sharp click and the stiletto was in Kreb's hand. One didn't dawdle when there was that note in the master's voice.

'I am going to slow down behind this lorry. Take your shoes and socks off and climb out on to the bonnet and when I come up behind the lorry jump on to it. I shall be going at walking-pace. It will be safe. Cut the ropes that hold the rolls of paper. The left ones first. Then the right. I shall have pulled up level with the lorry and when you have cut the second lot jump into the car. Be careful you are not swept off with the paper. *Verstanden? Also. Hals und Beinbruch!*'

Drax dowsed his headlights and swept round the bend at eighty. The lorry was twenty yards ahead and Drax had to brake hard to avoid crashing into its tail. The Mercedes executed a dry skid until its radiator was almost underneath the platform of the carrier.

Drax changed down to second. 'Now!' He held the car steady as a rock as Krebs, with bare feet, went over the windscreen and scrambled along the shining bonnet, his knife in his hand.

With a leap he was up and hacking at the left-hand ropes. Drax pulled away to the right and crawled up level with the rear wheels of the Diesel, the oily smoke from its exhaust in his eyes and nostrils.

Bond's lights were just showing round the bend.

There was a series of huge thuds as the left-hand rolls poured off the back of the lorry into the road and went hurtling off into the darkness. And more thuds as the right-hand ropes parted. One roll burst as it landed and Drax heard a tearing rattle as the unwinding paper crashed back down the one-in-ten gradient.

Released of its load the lorry almost bounded forward and Drax had to accelerate a little to catch the flying figure of Krebs who landed half across Gala's back and half in the front seat. Drax stamped his foot into the floor and sped off up the hill, ignoring a shout from the lorry-driver above the clatter of the Diesel pistons as he shot ahead.

As he hurtled round the next bend he saw the shaft of two headlights curve up into the sky over the tops of the trees until they were almost vertical. They wavered there for an instant and then the beams whirled away across the sky and went out.

A great barking laugh broke out of Drax as for a split second he took his eyes off the road and raised his face triumphantly towards the stars.

Chapter Twenty-one

'The Persuader'

Krebs echoed the maniac laugh with a high giggle. 'A master-stroke, *mein Kapitän*. You should have seen them charge off down the hill. The one that burst. *Wunderschön!* Like the lavatory paper of a giant. That one will have made a pretty parcel of him. He was just coming round the bend. And the second salvo was as good as the first. Did you see the driver's face? *Zum Kotzen!* And the *Firma* Bowater! A fine paperchase they have got on their hands.'

'You did well,' said Drax briefly, his mind elsewhere.

Suddenly he pulled into the side of the road with a scream of protest from the tyres.

'*Donnerwetter*,' he said angrily, as he started to turn the car. 'But we can't leave the man there. We must get him.' The car was already hissing back down the road. 'Gun,' ordered Drax briefly.

They passed the lorry at the top of the hill. It was stopped and there was no sign of the driver. Probably telephoning to the company, thought Drax, slowing up as they went round the first bend. There were lights on in the two or three houses and a group of people were standing round one of the rolls of newsprint that lay amongst the ruins of their front gate. There were more rolls in the hedge on the right of the road. On the left a telegraph pole leant drunkenly, snapped in the middle. Then at the next bend was the beginning of a great confusion of paper stretching away down the long hill, festooning the hedges and the road like the sweeping of some elephantine fancy-dress ball.

The Bentley had nearly broken through the railings that fenced off the right of the bend from a steep bank. Amidst a puzzle of twisted iron stanchions it hung, nose down, with one wheel, still attached to the broken back axle, poised crookedly over its rump like a surrealist umbrella.

Drax pulled up and he and Krebs got out and stood quietly, listening.

There was no sound except the distant rumination of a car travelling fast on the Ashford road and the chirrup of a sleepless cricket.

With their guns out they walked cautiously over to the remains of the Bentley, their feet crunching the broken glass on the road. Deep furrows had been cut across the grass verge and there was a strong smell of petrol and burnt rubber in the air. The hot metal of the car ticked and crackled softly and steam was still fountaining from the shattered radiator.

Bond was lying face downwards at the bottom of the bank twenty feet away from the car. Krebs turned him over. His face was covered with blood but he was breathing. They searched him thoroughly and Drax pocketed the slim Beretta. Then together they hauled him across the road and wedged him into the back seat of the Mercedes, half on top of Gala.

When she realized who it was she gave a cry of horror.

'*Halt's Maul*,' snarled Drax. He got into the front seat and while he turned the car Krebs leant over from the front seat and busied himself with a long piece of flex. 'Make a good job of it,' said Drax. 'I don't want any mistakes.' He had an afterthought. 'And then go back to the wreck and get the number plates. Hurry. I will watch the road.'

Krebs pulled the rug over the two inert bodies and jumped out of the car. Using his knife as a screwdriver he was soon back with the plates, and the big car started to move just as a group of local residents appeared walking nervously down the hill shining their torches over the scene of devastation.

Krebs grinned happily to himself at the thought of the stupid English having to clean up all this mess. He settled himself back to enjoy the part of the drive he had always liked best, the spring woods full of bluebells and celandines on the way to Chilham.

They made him particularly happy at night. Lit up amongst the green torches of the young trees by the great headlamps of the Mercedes, they made him think of the beautiful forests of the Ardennes and of the devoted little band with which he had served, and of driving along in a captured American jeep with, just like tonight, his adored leader at the wheel. *Der Tag* had been a long time coming, but now it was here. With young Krebs in the van. At last the cheering crowds, the medals, the women, the flowers. He gazed out at the fleeting hosts of bluebells and felt warm and happy.

Gala could taste Bond's blood. His face was beside hers on the leather seat and she shifted to give him more room. His breathing was heavy and irregular and she wondered how badly he was hurt. Tentatively she whispered into his ear. And then louder. He groaned and his breath came faster.

'James,' she whispered urgently. 'James.'

He mumbled something and she pushed hard against him.

He uttered a string of obscenities and his body heaved.

He lay still again and she could almost feel him exploring his sensations.

'It's me, Gala.' She felt him stiffen.

'Christ,' he said. 'Hell of a mess.'

'Are you all right? Is anything broken?'

She felt him tense his arms and legs. 'Seems all right,' he said. 'Crack on the head. Am I talking sense?'

'Of course,' said Gala. 'Now listen.'

Hurriedly she told him all she knew, beginning with the notebook.

His body was as rigid as a board against her, and he hardly breathed as he listened to the incredible story.

They they were running into Canterbury and Bond put his mouth to her ear. 'Going to try and chuck myself over the back,' he whispered. 'Get to a telephone. Only hope.'

He started to heave himself up on his knees, his weight almost grinding the breath out of the girl.

There was a sharp crack and he fell back on top of her.

'Another move out of you and you're dead,' said the voice of Krebs coming softly between the front seats.

Only another twenty minutes to the site! Gala gritted her teeth and set about bringing Bond back to consciousness again.

She had only just succeeded when the car drew up at the door of the launching-dome and Krebs, a gun in his hand, was undoing the bonds round their ankles.

They had a glimpse of the familiar moonlit cement and of the semi-circle of guards some distance away before they were hustled through the door and, when their shoes had been torn off by Krebs, out on to the iron catwalk inside the launching-dome.

There the gleaming rocket stood, beautiful, innocent, like a new toy for Cyclops.

But there was a horrible smell of chemicals in the air and to Bond the Moonraker was a giant hypodermic needle ready to be plunged into the heart of England. Despite a growl from Krebs he paused on the stairway and looked up at its glittering nose. A million deaths. A million. A million. A million.

On his hands? For God's sake! On HIS hands?

With Krebs's gun prodding him, he went slowly down the steps on the heels of Gala.

As he turned through the doors of Drax's office, he pulled himself together. Suddenly his mind was clear and all the lethargy and pain had left his body. Something, anything, must be done. Somehow he would find a way. His whole body and mind became focused and sharp as a blade. His eyes were alive again and defeat sloughed off him like the skin of a snake.

Drax had gone ahead and was sitting at his desk. He had a Luger in his hand. It was pointing at a spot halfway between Bond and Gala and it was steady as a rock.

Behind him, Bond heard the double doors thud shut.

'I was one of the best shots in the Brandenburg Division,' said Drax conversationally. 'Tie her to that chair, Krebs. Then the man.'

Gala looked desperately at Bond.

'You won't shoot,' said Bond. 'You'd be afraid of touching off the fuel.' He walked slowly towards the desk.

Drax smiled cheerfully and looked along the barrel at Bond's stomach. 'Your memory is bad, Englishman,' he said flatly. 'I told you this room is cut off from the shaft by the double doors. Another step and you will have no stomach.'

Bond looked at the confident, narrowed eyes and stopped.

'Go ahead, Krebs.'

When they were both tied securely and painfully to the arms and legs of two tubular steel chairs a few feet apart beneath the glass wall-map, Krebs left the room. He came back in a moment with a mechanic's blowtorch.

He set the ugly machine on the desk, pumped air into it with a few brisk strokes of the plunger, and set a match to it. A blue flame hissed out a couple of inches into the room. He picked up the instrument and walked towards Gala. He stopped a few feet to one side of her.

'Now then,' said Drax grimly. 'Let's get this over without any fuss. The good Krebs is an artist with one of those things. We used to call him "*Der Zwangsmann*–The Persuader". I shall never forget the way he went over the last spy we caught together. Just south of the Rhine, wasn't it, Krebs?'

Bond pricked up his ears.

'Yes, *mein Kapitän*,' Krebs chuckled reminiscently. 'It was a pig of a Belgian.'

'All right then,' said Drax. 'Just remember, you two. There's no fair play down here. No jolly good sports and all that. This is business.' The voice cracked like a whip on the word. 'You,' he looked at Gala Brand, 'who are you working for?'

Gala was silent.

'Anywhere you like, Krebs.'

Krebs's mouth was half open. His tongue ran up and down his lower lip. He seemed to be having difficulty with his breathing as he took a step towards the girl.

The little flame roared greedily.

'Stop,' said Bond coldly. 'She works for Scotland Yard. So do I.' These things were pointless now. They were of no conceivable use to Drax. In any case, by tomorrow afternoon there might be no Scotland Yard.

'That's better,' said Drax. 'Now, does anybody know you are prisoners? Did you stop and telephone anyone?'

If I say yes, thought Bond, he will shoot us both and get rid of the bodies and the last chance of stopping the Moonraker will be gone. And if the Yard knows, why aren't they here already? No. Our chance may come. The Bentley will be found. Vallance may get worried when he doesn't hear from me.

'No,' he said. 'If I had, they'd be here by now.'

'True,' said Drax reflectively. 'In that case I am no longer interested in you and I congratulate you on making the interview so harmonious. It might have been more difficult if you had been alone. A girl is always useful on these occasions. Krebs, put that down. You may go. Tell the others what is necessary. They will be wondering. I shall entertain our guests for a while and then I shall come up to the house. See the car gets properly washed down. The back seat. And get rid of the marks on the right-hand side. Tell them to take the whole panel off if necessary. Or they can set fire to the dam' thing. We shan't be needing it any more,' he laughed abruptly. '*Verstanden?*'

'Yes, *mein Kapitän*.' Krebs reluctantly placed the softly roaring blowtorch on the desk beside Drax. 'In case you need it,' he said, looking hopefully at Gala and Bond. He went out through the double doors.

Drax put the Luger down on the desk in front of him. He opened a drawer and took out a cigar and lit it from a Ronson desk lighter. Then he settled himself comfortably. There was silence in the room for several minutes while Drax puffed contentedly at his cigar. Then he seemed to make up his mind. He looked benevolently at Bond.

'You don't know how I have longed for an English audience,' he said as if he was addressing a Press conference. 'You don't know how I have longed to tell my story. As a matter of fact, a full account of my operations is now in the hands of a very respectable firm of Edinburgh solicitors. I beg their pardon–Writers to the Signet. Well out of danger.' He beamed from one to the other. 'And these good folk have instructions to open the envelope on the completion of the first successful flight of the Moonraker. But you lucky people shall have a preview of what I have written and then, when tomorrow at noon you see through those open doors,' he gestured to his right, 'the first wisp of steam from the turbines and know that you are to be burnt alive in about half a second, you will have the momentary satisfaction of knowing what it is all in aid of, as,' he grinned wolfishly, 'we Englishmen say.'

'You can spare us the jokes,' said Bond roughly. 'Get on with your story, Kraut.'

Drax's eyes blazed momentarily. 'A Kraut. Yes, I am indeed a *Reichsdeutscher*'–the mouth beneath the red moustache savoured the fine word–'and even England will soon agree that they have been licked by just one single German. And then perhaps they'll stop calling us Krauts–BY ORDER!' The words were yelled out and the whole of Prussian militarism was in the parade-ground below.

Drax glowered across the desk at Bond, the great splayed teeth under the red moustache tearing nervously at one fingernail after another. Then, with an effort, he crammed his right hand into his trouser pocket, as if to put it out of temptation, and picked up his cigar with his left. He puffed at it for a moment and then, his voice still taut, he began.

Chapter Twenty-two

Pandora's Box

'My real name,' said Drax, addressing himself to Bond, 'is Graf Hugo von der Drache. My mother was English and because of her I was educated in England until I was twelve. Then I could stand this filthy country no longer and I completed my education in Berlin and Leipzig.'

Bond could imagine that the hulking bully with the ogre's teeth had not been very welcome at an English private school. And being a foreign count with a mouthful of names would not have helped much.

'When I was twenty,' Drax's eyes glowed reminiscently, 'I went to work in the family business. It was a subsidiary of the great steel combine *Rheinmetall Borsig*. Never heard of it, I suppose. Well, if you'd been hit by an 88 mm. shell during the war it would probably have been one of theirs. Our subsidiary were experts in special steels and I learned all about them and a lot about the aircraft industry. Our most exacting customers. That's when I first heard about Columbite. Worth diamonds in those days. Then I joined the party and almost immediately we were at war. A wonderful time. I was twenty-eight and a lieutenant in the 140th Panzer Regiment. And we ran through the British Army and France like a knife through butter. Intoxicating.'

For a moment Drax puffed luxuriously at his cigar and Bond guessed that he was seeing the burning villages of Belgium in the smoke.

'Those were great days, my dear Bond.' Drax reached out a long arm and tapped the ash of his cigar off on to the floor. 'But then I was picked out for the Brandenburg Division and I had to leave the girls and the champagne and go back to Germany and start training for the big water-jump to England. My English was needed in the Division. We were all going to be in English uniforms. It would have been fun, but the damned generals said it couldn't be done and I was transferred to the Foreign Intelligence Service of the S.S. The R.S.H.A. it was called, and SS *Obergruppenführer* Kaltenbrunner had just taken over the command after Heydrich was assassinated in '42. He was a good man and I was under the direct orders of a still better one, *Obersturmbannführer*,' he rolled out the delicious title with relish, 'Otto Skorzeny. His job in the R.S.H.A. was terrorism and sabotage. A pleasant interlude, my dear Bond, during which I was able to bring many an Englishman to book which,' Drax beamed coldly at Bond, 'gave me much pleasure. But then,' Drax's fist crashed down on the desk, 'Hitler was betrayed again by those swinish generals and the English and Americans were allowed to land in France.'

'Too bad,' said Bond drily.

'Yes, my dear Bond, it was indeed too bad.' Drax chose to ignore the irony. 'But for me it was the high-spot of the whole war. Skorzeny turned all his saboteurs and terrorists into SS *Jagdverbände* for use behind the enemy lines. Each *Jagdverbänd* was divided into *Streifkorps* and then into *Kommandos*, each carrying the name of its commanding officer. With the rank of *Oberleutnant*,' Drax swelled visibly, 'at the head of *Kommando* "Drache" I went right through the American lines with the famous 150 Panzer Brigade in the Ardennes breakthrough in December '44. No doubt you will remember the effect of this Brigade in its American uniforms and with its captured American tanks and vehicles. *Kolossal!* When the Brigade had to withdraw I stayed where I was and went to ground in the Forests of Ardennes, fifty miles behind the Allied lines. There were twenty of us, ten good men and ten Hitlerjugend Werewolves. In their teens, but good lads all of them. And, by a coincidence, in charge of them was a young man called Krebs who turned out to have certain gifts which qualified him for the post of executioner and "persuader" to our merry little band.' Drax chuckled pleasantly.

Bond licked his lips as he remembered the crack Krebs's head had made against the dressing-table. Had he kicked him as hard as he possibly could? Yes, his memory reassured him, with every ounce of strength he could put into his shoe.

'We stayed in those woods for six months,' continued Drax proudly, 'and all the time we reported back to the Fatherland by radio. The location vans never spotted us. Then one day disaster came.' Drax shook his head at the memory. 'There was a big farmhouse a mile away from our hideout in the forest. A lot of Nissen huts had been built round it and it was used as a rear headquarters for some sort of liaison group, English and Americans. A hopeless place. No discipline, no security, and full of hangers-on and shirkers from all over the place. We had kept an eye on it for some time and one day I decided to blow it up. It was a simple plan. In the evening, two of my men, one in American uniform and one in British, were to drive up in a captured scout car containing two tons of explosive. There was a car park–no sentries of course–near the mess hall and they were to run the car in as close to the mess hall as possible, time the fuse for the seven o'clock dinner hour, and then get away. All quite easy and I went off that morning on my own business and left the job to my second in command. I was dressed in the uniform of your Signal Corps and I set off on a captured British motor-cycle to shoot a dispatch rider from the same unit who made a daily run along a near-by road. Sure enough he came along dead on time and I went after him out of a side road. I caught up with him,' said Drax conversationally, 'and shot him in the back, took his papers and put him on top of his machine in the woods and set fire to him.'

Drax saw the fury in Bond's eyes and held up his hand. 'Not very sporting? My dear chap, the man was already dead. However, to continue. I went on my way and then what should happen? One of our planes coming back from a reconnaissance came after me down the road with his cannon. One of our planes! Blasted me right off the road. God knows how long I lay in the ditch. Some time in the afternoon I came to for a bit and had the sense to hide my cap and jacket and the dispatches. In the hedge. They're probably still there. I must go and collect them one day. Interesting souvenirs. Then I set fire to the remains of the motor-cycle and I must have fainted again because the next thing I knew I had been picked up by a British vehicle and we were driving into that damned liaison headquarters! Believe it or not! And there was the scout car, right up alongside the mess hall! It was too much for me. I was full of shell splinters and my leg was broken. Well, I fainted and when I came round there was half the hospital on top of me and I only had half a face.' He put up his hand and stroked the shiny skin on his left temple and cheek. 'After that it was a question of acting a part. They had no idea who I was. The car that had picked me up had gone or been blown to pieces. I was just an Englishman in an English shirt and trousers who was nearly dead.'

Drax paused and took out another cigar and lit it. There was silence in the room save for the soft, diminished roar of the blowtorch. Its threatening voice was quieter. Pressure running out, reflected Bond.

He turned his head and looked at Gala. For the first time he saw the ugly bruise behind her left ear. He gave her a smile of encouragement and she smiled wryly back.

Drax spoke through the cigar smoke: 'There is not much more to tell,' he said. 'During the next year that I was being pushed from one hospital to the next I made my plans down to the smallest detail. They consisted quite simply of revenge on England for what she had done to me and to my country. It gradually became an obsession. I admit it. Every day during that year of the rape and destruction of my country, my hatred and scorn for the English grew more bitter.' The veins on Drax's face started to swell and suddenly he pounded on the desk and shouted across at them, looking with bulging eyes from one to the other. 'I loathe and despise you all. You swine! Useless, idle, decadent fools, hiding behind your bloody white cliffs while other people fight your battles. Too weak to defend your colonies, toadying to America with your hats in your hands. Stinking snobs who'll do anything for money. Hah!' he was triumphant. 'I knew that all I needed was money and the façade of a gentleman. Gentleman! *Pfui Teufel!* To me a gentleman is just someone I can take advantage of. Those bloody fools in Blades for instance. Moneyed oafs. For months I took thousands of pounds off them, swindled them right under their noses until you came along and upset the apple-cart.'

Drax's eyes narrowed. 'What put you on to the cigarette-case?' he asked sharply.

Bond shrugged his shoulders. 'My eyes,' he said indifferently.

'Ah well,' said Drax, 'perhaps I was a bit careless that night. But where was I? Ah yes, in hospital. And the good doctors were so anxious to help me find out who I really was.' He let out a roar of laughter. 'It was easy. So easy.' His eyes became cunning. 'From the identities they offered me so helpfully I came upon the name of Hugo Drax. What a coincidence! From Drache to Drax! Tentatively I thought it *might* be me. They were very proud. Yes, they said, *of course* it is you. The doctors triumphantly forced me into his shoes. I put them on and walked out of the hospital in them and I walked round London looking for someone to kill and rob. And one day, in a little office high above Piccadilly, a Jewish moneylender.' (Now Drax was talking faster. The words poured excitedly from his lips. Bond watched a fleck of foam gather at one corner of his mouth and grow.) 'Ha. It was easy. Crack on his bald skull. £15,000 in the safe. And then away and out of the country. Tangier–where you could do anything, buy anything, fix anything. Columbite. Rarer than platinum and everyone would want it. The Jet Age. I knew about these things. I had not forgotten my own profession. And then by God I worked. For five years I lived for money. And I was brave as a lion. I took terrible risks. And suddenly the first million was there. Then the second. Then the fifth. Then the twentieth. I came back to England. I spent a million of it and London was in my pocket. And then I went back to Germany. I found Krebs. I found fifty of them. Loyal Germans. Brilliant technicians. All living under false names like so many others of my old comrades. I gave them their orders and they waited, peacefully, innocently. And where was I?' Drax stared across at Bond, his eyes wide. 'I was in Moscow. Moscow! A man with Columbite to sell can go anywhere. I got to the right people. They listened to my plans. They gave me Walter, the new genius of their guided missile station at Peenemunde, and the good Russians started to build the atomic warhead,' he gestured up to the ceiling, 'that is now waiting up there. Then I came back to London.' A pause. 'The Coronation. My letter to the Palace. Triumph. Hooray for Drax,' he burst into a roar of laughter. 'England at my feet. Every bloody fool in the country! And then my men come over and we start. Under the very skirts of Britannia. On top of her famous cliffs. We work like devils. We built a jetty into your English Channel. For supplies! For supplies from my good friends the Russians that came in dead on time last Monday night. But then Tallon has to hear something. The old fool. He talks to the Ministry. But Krebs is listening. There were fifty volunteers to kill the man. Lots are drawn and Bartsch dies a hero's death.' Drax paused. 'He will not be forgotten.' Then he went on. 'The new warhead is hoisted into place. It fits. A perfect piece of design. The same weight. Everything perfect, and the old one, the tin can full of the Ministry's cherished instruments, is now in Stettin–behind the Iron Curtain. And the faithful submarine is on her way back here and will soon,' he looked at his watch, 'be creeping under the waters of the English Channel to take us all off at one minute past midday tomorrow.'

Drax wiped his mouth with the back of his hand and lay back in his chair and gazed up at the ceiling, his eyes full of visions. Suddenly he chuckled and squinted quizzically down his nose at Bond.

'And do you know what we shall do first when we go on board? We shall shave off those famous moustaches you were so interested in. You smelt a mouse, my dear Bond, where you ought to have a smelt a rat. Those shaven heads and those moustaches we all cultivated so assiduously. Just a precaution, my dear fellow. Try shaving your own head and growing a big black moustache. Even your mother wouldn't recognize you. It's the combination that counts. Just a tiny refinement. Precision, my dear fellow. Precision in every detail. That has been my watchword.' He chuckled fatly and puffed away at his cigar.

Suddenly he looked sharply, suspiciously up at Bond. 'Well. Say something. Don't sit there like a dummy. What do you think of my story? Don't you think it's extraordinary, remarkable? For one man to have done all that? Come on, come on.' A hand came up to his mouth and he started tearing furiously at his nails. Then it was plunged back into his pocket and his eyes became cruel and cold. 'Or do you want me to have to send for Krebs,' he made a gesture towards the house telephone on his desk. 'The Persuader. Poor Krebs. He's like a child who's had his toys taken away from him. Or perhaps Walter. He would give you both something to remember. There's no softness in that one. Well?'

'Yes,' said Bond. He looked levelly at the great red face across the desk. 'It's a remarkable case-history. Galloping paranoia. Delusions of jealousy and persecution. Megalomaniac hatred and desire for revenge. Curiously enough,' he went on conversationally, 'it may have something to do with your teeth. Diastema, they call it. Comes from sucking your thumb when you're a child. Yes. I expect that's what the psychologists will say when they get you into the lunatic asylum. "Ogre's teeth." Being bullied at school and so on. Extraordinary the effect it has on a child. Then Nazism helped to fan the flames and then came the crack on your ugly head. The crack you engineered yourself. I expect that settled it. From then on you were really mad. Same sort of thing as people who think they're God. Extraordinary what tenacity they have. Absolute fanatics. You're almost a genius. Lombroso would have been delighted with you. As it is you're just a mad dog that'll have to be shot. Or else you'll commit suicide. Paranoiacs generally do. Too bad. Sad business.'

Bond paused and put all the scorn he could summon into his voice, 'And now let's get on with this farce, you great hairy-faced lunatic.'

It worked. With every word Drax's face had become more contorted with rage, his eyes were red with it, the sweat of fury was dripping off his jowls on to his shirt, the lips were drawn back from the gaping teeth and a string of saliva had crept out of his mouth and was hanging down from his chin. Now, at the last private-school insult that must have awoken God knows what stinging memories, he leapt up from his chair and lunged round the desk at Bond, his hairy fists flailing.

Bond gritted his teeth and took it.

When Drax had twice had to pick the chair up with Bond in it, the tornado of rage suddenly passed. He took out his silk handkerchief and wiped his face and hands. Then he walked quietly to the door and spoke across the lolling head of Bond to the girl.

'I don't think you two will give me any trouble,' he said, and his voice was quite calm and certain. 'Krebs never makes a mistake with his knots.' He gesticulated towards the bloody figure in the other chair. 'When he wakes up,' he said, 'you can tell him that these doors will open once more, just before noon tomorrow. A few minutes later there will be nothing left of either of you. Not even,' he added as he wrenched open the inner door, 'the stoppings in your teeth.'

The outer door slammed.

Bond slowly raised his head and grinned painfully at the girl with his bloodstained lips.

'Had to get him mad,' he said with difficulty. 'Didn't want to give him time to think. Had to work up a brainstorm.'

Gala looked at him uncomprehendingly, her eyes wide at the terrible mask of his face.

''S'all right,' said Bond thickly. 'Don't worry. London's okay. Got a plan.'

Over on the desk the blowtorch gave a quiet 'plop' and went out.

Chapter Twenty-three

Zero Minus

Through half-closed eyes Bond looked intently at the torch while for a few precious seconds he sat and let life creep back into his body. His head felt as if it had been used as a football, but there was nothing broken. Drax had hit him unscientifically and with the welter of blows of a drunken man.

Gala watched him anxiously. The eyes in the bloody face were almost shut, but the line of the jaw was taut with concentration and she could feel the effort of will he was making.

He gave his head a shake and when he turned towards her she could see that his eyes were feverish with triumph.

He nodded towards the desk. 'The lighter,' he said urgently. 'I had to try and make him forget it. Follow me. I'll show you.' He started to rock the light steel chair inch by inch towards the desk. 'For God's sake don't tip over or we've had it. But make it fast or the blowlamp'll get cold.'

Uncomprehendingly, and feeling almost as if they were playing some ghastly children's game, Gala carefully rocked her way across the floor in his wake.

Seconds later Bond told her to stop beside the desk while he went rocking on round to Drax's chair. Then he manoeuvred himself into position opposite his target and with a sudden lurch heaved himself and the chair forward so that his head came down.

There was a painful crack as the Ronson desk lighter connected with his teeth, but his lips held it and the top of it was in his mouth as he heaved the chair back with just enough force to prevent it spilling over. Then he started his patient journey back to where Gala was sitting at the corner of the desk on which Krebs had left the blowlamp.

He rested until his breath was steady again. 'Now we come to the difficult part,' he said grimly. 'While I try to get this torch going, you get your chair round so that your right arm is as close in front of me as possible.'

Obediently she edged herself round while Bond swayed his chair so that it leant against the edge of the desk and allowed his mouth to reach forward and grip the handle of the blow-torch between his teeth.

Then he eased the torch towards him and after minutes of patient work he had the torch and the lighter arranged to his liking at the edge of the desk.

After another rest he bent down, closed the valve of the torch with his teeth, and proceeded to get pressure back by slowly and repeatedly pulling up the plunger with his lips and pressing it back with his chin. His face could feel the warmth in the pre-heater and he could smell the remnants of gas in it. If only it hadn't cooled off too much.

He straightened up.

'Last lap, Gala,' he said, smiling crookedly at her. 'I may have to hurt you a bit. All right?'

'Of course,' said Gala.

'Then here goes,' said Bond, and he bent forward and released the safety valve on the left of the canister.

Then he quickly bent forward over the Ronson, which was standing at right angles and just below the neck of the torch, and with his two front teeth pressed down sharply on the ignition lever.

It was a horrible manoeuvre and though he whipped back his head with the speed of a snake he let out a gasp of pain as the jet of blue fire from the torch seared across his bruised cheek and the bridge of his nose.

But the vaporized paraffin was hissing out its vital tongue of flame and he shook the water out of his streaming eyes and bent his head almost at right angles and again got his teeth to the handle of the blowtorch.

He thought his jaw would break with the weight of the thing and the nerves of his front teeth screamed at him, but he swayed his chair carefully upright away from the desk and then strained his bent neck forward until the tip of blue fire from the torch was biting into the flex that bound Gala's right wrist to the arm of her chair.

He tried desperately to keep the flame steady but the breath rasped through the girl's teeth as the handle shifted between his jaws and the flame of the torch brushed her forearm.

But then it was over. Melted by the fierce heat, the copper strands parted one by one and suddenly Gala's right arm was free and she was reaching to take the torch out of Bond's mouth.

Bond's head fell back on to his shoulders and he twisted his neck luxuriously to get the blood moving in the aching muscles.

Almost before he knew it, Gala was bending over his arms and legs and he too was free.

As he sat still for a moment, his eyes closed, waiting for the life to come back into his body, he suddenly, delightedly felt Gala's soft lips on his mouth.

He opened his eyes. She was standing in front of him, her eyes shining. 'That's for what you did,' she said seriously.

'You're a wonderful girl,' he said simply.

But then, knowing what he was going to have to do, knowing that while she might conceivably survive, he had only another few minutes to live, he closed his eyes so that she should not see the hopelessness in them.

Gala saw the expression on his face and she turned away. She thought it was only exhaustion and the cumulative effect of what his body had suffered, and she suddenly remembered the peroxide in the washroom next to her office.

She went through the communicating door. How extraordinary it was to see her familiar things again. It must be someone else who had sat at that desk and typed letters and powdered her nose. She shrugged her shoulders and went into the little washroom. God what a sight and God how tired she felt! But first she took a wet towel and some peroxide and went back and spent ten minutes attending to the battlefield which was Bond's face.

He sat silent, a hand resting on her waist, and watched her gratefully. Then when she had gone back into her room and he heard her shut the door of the washroom behind her he got up, turned off the still hissing blowtorch, and walked into Drax's shower, stripped and stood for five minutes under the icy water. 'Preparing the corpse!' he reflected ruefully as he surveyed his battered face in the mirror.

He put on his clothes and went back to Drax's desk which he searched methodically. It yielded only one prize, the 'office bottle', a half-full bottle of Haig and Haig. He fetched two glasses and some water and called to Gala.

He heard the door of the washroom open. 'What is it?'

'Whisky.'

'You drink. I'll be ready in a minute.'

Bond looked at the bottle and poured himself three-quarters of a toothglass and drank it straight down in two gulps. Then he gingerly lit a blessed cigarette and sat on the edge of the desk and felt the liquor burn down through his stomach into his legs.

He picked up the bottle again and looked at it. Plenty for Gala and a whole full glass for himself before he walked out through the door. Better than nothing. It wouldn't be too bad with that inside him so long as he walked quickly out and shut the doors behind him. No looking back.

Gala came in, a transformed Gala, looking as beautiful as the night he had first seen her, except for the lines of exhaustion under the eyes that the powder could not quite conceal and the angry welts at her wrists and ankles.

Bond gave her a drink and took another one himself and their eyes smiled at each other over the rims of their glasses.

Then Bond stood up.

'Listen, Gala,' he said in a matter-of-fact voice. 'We've got to face it and get it over so I'll make it short and then we'll have another drink.' He heard her catch her breath, but he went on. 'In ten minutes or so I'm going to shut you into Drax's bathroom and put you under the shower and turn it full on.'

'James,' she cried. She stepped close to him. 'Don't go on. I know you're going to say something dreadful. Please stop, James.'

'Come on, Gala,' said Bond roughly. 'What the hell does it matter. It's a bloody miracle we've got the chance.' He moved away from her. He walked to the doors leading out into the shaft.

'And then,' he said, and he held up the precious lighter in his right hand, 'I shall walk out of here and shut the doors and go and light a last cigarette under the tail of the Moonraker.'

'God,' she whispered. 'What are you saying? You're mad.' She looked at him through eyes wide with horror.

'Don't be ridiculous,' said Bond impatiently. 'What the hell else is there to do? The explosion will be so terrific that one won't feel anything. And it's bound to work with all that fuel vapour hanging around. It's me or a million people in London. The warhead won't go off. Atom bombs don't explode like that. It'll be melted probably. There's just a chance you may get away. Most of the explosion will take the line of least resistance through the roof–and down the exhaust pit, if I can work the machinery that opens up the floor.' He smiled. 'Cheer up,' he said, walking over to her and taking one of her hands. 'The boy stood on the burning deck. I've wanted to copy him since I was five.'

Gala pulled her hand away. 'I don't care what you say,' she said angrily. 'We've got to think of something else. You don't trust me to have any ideas. You just tell me what you think we've got to do.' She walked over to the wall map and pressed down the switch. 'Of course if we have to use the lighter we have to.' She gazed at the map of the false flight plan, barely seeing it. 'But the idea of you walking in there alone and standing in the middle of all those ghastly fumes from the fuel and calmly flicking that thing and then being blown to dust . . . And anyway, if we have to do it, we'll do it together. I'd rather that than be burnt to death in here. And anyway,' she paused, 'I'd like to go with you. We're in this together.'

Bond's eyes were tender as he walked towards her and put an arm round her waist and hugged her to him. 'Gala, you're a darling,' he said simply. 'And if there's any other way we'll take it. But,' he looked at his watch, 'it's past midnight and we've got to decide quickly. At any moment it may occur to Drax to send guards down to see that we're all right, and God knows what time he'll be coming down to set the gyros.'

Gala twisted her body round like a cat. She gazed at him with her mouth open, her face taut with excitement. 'The gyros,' she whispered, 'to set the gyros.' She leant weakly back against the wall, her eyes searching Bond's face. 'Don't you SEE?' her voice was on the edge of hysteria. 'After he's gone, we could alter the gyros back, back to the old flight plan, then the rocket will simply fall into the North Sea where it's supposed to go.'

She stepped away from the wall and seized his shirt in both hands and looked imploringly at him. 'Can't we?' she said. 'Can't we?'

'Do you know the other settings?' asked Bond sharply.

'Of course I do,' she said urgently. 'I've been living with them for a year. We won't have a weather report but we'll just have to chance that. The forecast this morning said we would have the same conditions as today.'

'By God,' said Bond. 'We might do it. If only we can hide somewhere and make Drax think we've escaped. What about the exhaust pit? If I can work the machine to open the floor.'

'It's a straight hundred-foot drop,' said Gala, shaking her head. 'And the walls are polished steel. Just like glass. And there's no rope or anything down there. They cleared everything out of the workshop yesterday. And anyway there are guards on the beach.'

Bond reflected. Then his eyes brightened. 'I've got an idea,' he said. 'But first of all what about the radar, the homing device in London. Won't that pull the rocket off its course and back on to London?'

Gala shook her head. 'It's only got a range of about a hundred miles,' she said. 'The rocket won't even pick up its signal. If it's aimed into the North Sea it will get into the orbit of the transmitter on the raft. There's absolutely nothing wrong with my plan. But where can we hide?'

'One of the ventilator shafts,' said Bond. 'Come on.'

He gave a last look round the room. The lighter was in his pocket. That would still be the last resort. There was nothing else they would want. He followed Gala out into the gleaming shaft and made for the instrument panel which controlled the steel cover to the exhaust pit.

After a quick examination he threw over a heavy lever from '*Zu*' to '*Auf*'. There was a soft hiss from the hydraulic machinery behind the wall and the two semi-circles of steel opened beneath the tail of the rocket and slid back into their grooves. He walked over and looked down.

The arcs in the roof above glinted back at him from the polished walls of the wide steel funnel until they curved away out of sight towards the distant hollow boom of the sea.

Bond went back into Drax's office and pulled down the shower curtain in the bathroom. Then Gala and he tore it into strips and tied them together. He made a jagged rent at the end of the last strip so as to give an impression that the escape rope had broken. Then he tied the other end firmly round the pointed tip of one of the Moonraker's three fins and dropped the rest so that it hung down the shaft.

It was not much of a false scent, but it might gain some time.

The big round mouths of the ventilator shafts were spaced about ten yards apart and about four feet off the floor. Bond counted. There were fifty of them. He carefully opened the hinged grating that covered one of them and looked up. Forty feet away there was a faint glimmer from the moonlight outside. He decided that they were tunnelled straight up inside the wall of the site until they turned at right angles towards the gratings in the outside walls.

Bond reached up and ran his hand along the surface. It was unfinished roughcast concrete and he grunted with satisfaction as he felt first one sharp protuberance and then another. They were the jagged ends of the steel rods reinforcing the walls, cut off where the shafts had been bored.

It was going to be a painful business, but there was no doubt they could inch their way up one of these shafts, like mountaineers up a rock chimney, and, in the turn at the top, lie hidden from anything but the sort of painstaking search that would be difficult in the morning with all the officials from London round the site.

Bond knelt down and the girl climbed on to his back and started up.

An hour later, their feet and shoulders bruised and cut, they lay exhausted, squeezed tight in each other's arms, their heads inches away from the circular grating directly above the outside door, and listened to the guards restlessly shifting their feet in the darkness a hundred yards away.

Five o'clock, six, seven.

Slowly the sun came up behind the dome and the seagulls started to call in the cliffs and then suddenly there were the three figures walking towards them in the distance, passed by a fresh platoon of guards doubling, chins up, knees up, to relieve the night watch.

The figures came nearer and the squinting, exhausted eyes of the hidden couple could see every detail of Drax's blood-orange face, the lean, pale foxiness of Dr Walter, the suety, overslept puffiness of Krebs.

The three men walked like executioners, saying nothing. Drax took out his key and they silently filed through the door a few feet below the taut bodies of Bond and Gala.

Then for ten minutes there was silence except for the occasional boom of voices up the ventilator shaft as the three men moved about down on the steel floor round the exhaust pit. Bond smiled to himself at the thought of the rage and consternation on Drax's face; the miserable Krebs wilting under the lash of Drax's tongue; the bitter accusation in Walter's eyes. Then the door burst open beneath him and Krebs was calling urgently to the leader of the guards. A man detached himself from the semi-circle and ran up.

'*Die Engländer*,' Krebs's voice was almost hysterical. 'Escaped. The *Herr Kapitän* thinks they may be in one of the ventilator shafts. We are going to take a chance. The dome will be opened again and we will clear out the fumes from the fuel. And then the *Herr Doktor* will put the steam hose up each shaft. If they're there it will finish them. Choose four men. The rubber gloves and firesuits are down there. We'll take the pressure off the heating. Tell the others to listen for the screams. *Verstanden?*'

'*Zu Befehl.*' The man doubled smartly back to his troop and Krebs, the sweat of anxiety on his face, turned and disappeared back through the door.

For a moment Bond lay motionless.

There was a heavy rumble above their heads as the dome divided and swung open.

The steam hose!

He had heard of mutinies in ships being fought with it. Rioters in factories. Would it reach forty feet? Would the pressure last? How many boilers fed the heating? Among the fifty ventilator shafts, where would they choose to begin? Had Bond or Gala left any clue to the one they had climbed?

He felt that Gala was waiting for him to explain. To do something. To protect them.

Five men came doubling from the semi-circle of guards. They passed underneath and disappeared.

Bond put his mouth to Gala's ear. 'This may hurt,' he said. 'Can't say how much. Can't be helped. Just have to take it. No noise.' He felt the answering tentative pressure from her arms. 'Bring your knees up. Don't be shy. This is no time to be maidenly.'

'Shut up,' whispered Gala angrily. He felt one knee creep up until it was locked between his thighs. His own knee followed suit until it would go no further. She squirmed furiously. 'Don't be a bloody fool,' whispered Bond, pulling her head in close to his chest so that it was half covered by his open shirt.

He overlay her as much as possible. There was nothing to be done about their ankles or his hands. He pulled his shirt collar up as far over their heads as possible. They held tightly to each other.

Hot, cramped, breathless. Waiting, it suddenly occurred to Bond, like two lovers in the undergrowth. Waiting for the footsteps to go by so that they could start again. He smiled grimly to himself and listened.

There was silence down the shaft. They must be in the engine room. Walter would be watching the hose being coupled to the outlet valve. Now there were distant noises. Where would they start?

Somewhere, not far away, there was a soft, long-drawn out whisper, like the inefficient whistle of a distant train.

He drew his shirt collar back and stole a look out through the grating at the guards. Those he could see were looking straight at the launching-dome, somewhere to his left.

Again the long harsh whisper. And again.

It was getting louder. He could see the heads of the guards pivoting towards the grating in the wall which hid him and Gala. They must be watching, fascinated, as the thick white jets of steam shot out through the gratings high up in the cement wall, wondering if this one, or that one, or that one, would be accompanied by a double scream.

He could feel Gala's heart beating against his. She didn't know what was coming. She trusted him.

'It may hurt,' he whispered to her again. 'It may burn. It won't kill us. Be brave. Don't make a sound.'

'I'm all right,' she whispered angrily. But he could feel her body press closer in to his.

Whoosh. It was getting closer.

Whoosh! Two away.

WHOOSH!! Next door. A suspicion of the wet smell of steam came to him.

Hold tight, Bond said to himself. He smothered her in towards him and held his breath.

Now. Quick. Get it over, damn you.

And suddenly there was a great pressure and heat and a roaring in the ears and a moment of blazing pain.

Then dead silence, a mixture of sharp cold and fire on the ankles and hands, a feeling of soaking wet and a desperate, choking effort to get pure air into the lungs.

Their bodies automatically fought to withdraw from each other, to capture some inches of space and air for the areas of skin that were already blistering. The breath rattled in their throats and the water poured off the cement into their open mouths until they bent sideways and choked the water out to join the trickle that was oozing under their soaking bodies and along past their scalded ankles and then down the vertical walls of the shaft up which they had come.

And the howl of the steam pipe drew away from them until it became a whisper and finally stopped, and there was silence in their narrow cement prison except for their stubborn breathing and the ticking of Bond's watch.

And the two bodies lay and waited, nursing their pain.

Half an hour–half a year–later, Walter and Krebs and Drax filed out below them.

But, as a precaution, the guards had been left behind in the launching-dome.

Chapter Twenty-four

Zero

'Then we're all agreed?'

'Yes, Sir Hugo,' it was the Minister of Supply speaking. Bond recognized the dapper, assured figure. 'Those are the settings. My people have checked them independently with the Air Ministry this morning.'

'Then if you'll allow me the privilege,' Drax held up the slip of paper and made to turn towards the launching-dome.

'Hold it, Sir Hugo. Just like that, please. Arm in the air.' The flash bulbs flashed and the bank of cameras whirred and clicked for the last time and Drax turned and walked the few yards towards the dome, almost, it seemed to Bond, looking him straight in the eye through the grating above the door of the site.

The small crowd of reporters and cameramen dissolved and straggled off across the concrete apron, leaving only a nervously chatting group of officials to wait for Drax to emerge.

Bond looked at his watch. 11.45. Hurry up, damn you, he thought.

For the hundredth time he repeated to himself the figures Gala had taught him during the hours of cramped pain that had followed their ordeal by steam, and for the hundredth time he shifted his limbs to keep the circulation going.

'Get ready,' he whispered into Gala's ear. 'Are you all right?'

He could feel the girl smile. 'Fine.' She shut her mind to the thought of her blistered legs and the quick rasping descent back down the ventilator shaft.

The door clanged shut beneath them followed by the click of the lock and, preceded by the five guards, the figure of Drax appeared below striding masterfully towards the group of officials, the slip of lying figures in his hand.

Bond looked at his watch. 11.47. 'Now,' he whispered.

'Good luck,' she whispered back.

Slither, scrape, rip. His shoulders carefully expanding and contracting; blistered, bloodstained feet scrabbling for the sharp knobs of iron, Bond, his lacerated body tearing its way down the forty feet of shaft, prayed that the girl would have strength to stand it when she followed.

A last ten-foot drop that jarred his spine, a kick at the grating and he was out on the steel floor and running for the stairs, leaving a trail of red footprints and a spray of blood-drops from his raw shoulders.

The arcs had been extinguished, but the daylight streamed down through the open roof and the blue from the sky mingling with the fierce glitter of the sunshine gave Bond the impression that he was running up inside a huge sapphire.

The great deadly needle in the centre might have been made of glass.

Looking above him as he sweated and panted up the endless sweep of the iron stairway, it was difficult for him to see where its tapering nose ended and the sky began.

Behind the crouching silence that enveloped the shimmering bullet, Bond could hear a quick, deadly ticking, the hasty tripping of tiny metal feet somewhere in the body of the Moonraker. It filled the great steel chamber like the beating heart in Poe's story and Bond knew that directly Drax at the firing point pressed the switch that sent the radio beam zinging over the two hundred yards to the waiting rocket, the ticking would suddenly cease, there would be the soft whine of the lighted pinwheel, a wisp of steam from the turbines, and then the howling jet of flame on which the rocket would slowly rise and sweep majestically out on the start of its gigantic acceleration curve.

And then in front of him there was the spidery arm of the gantry folded back against the wall and Bond's hand was at the lever and the arm was slowly stretching down and out towards the square hairline on the glittering skin of the rocket that was the door of the gyro chamber.

Bond, on hands and knees, was along it even before the rubber pads came to rest against the polished chrome. There was the flush disc the size of a shilling, just as Gala had described. Press, click, and the tiny door had flicked open on its hard spring. Inside. Careful not to cut your head. The gleaming handles beneath the staring compass-roses. Turn. Twist. Steady. That's for the roll. Now the pitch and yaw. Turn. Twist, ever so gently. And steady. A last look. A glance at his watch. Four minutes to go. Don't panic. Back out. Door click. A cat-like scurry. Don't look down. Gantry up. Clang against the wall. And now for the stairs.

Tick-tick-tick-tick.

As Bond shot down he caught a glimpse of Gala's tense, white face as she stood holding open the outer door of Drax's office. God, how his body hurt! A final leap and a clumsy swerve to the right. Clang as Gala slammed the outer door. Another clang and they were across the room and into the shower and the water was hissing down on their clinging, panting bodies.

Through the noise of it, above the beating of his heart, Bond heard a sudden crackle of static and then the voice of the B.B.C. announcer coming from the big set in Drax's room a few inches away through the thin wall of the bathroom. It had been Gala again who had remembered Drax's wireless and who had found time to throw the switches while Bond was working on the gyros.

'. . . be five minutes delay,' said the breezy, excited voice. 'Sir Hugo has been persuaded to say a few words into the microphone.' Bond turned off the shower and the voice came to them more clearly. 'He looks very confident. Just saying something into the Minister's ear. They're both laughing. Wonder what it was? Ah, here's my colleague with the latest weather report from the Air Ministry. What's that? Perfect at all altitudes. Good show. It certainly is a wonderful day down below here. Haha. Those crowds in the distance by the coastguard station will be getting quite a sunburn. There must be thousands. What's that you say? Twenty thousand? Well, it certainly looks like it. And Walmer Beach is black with them too. The whole of Kent seems to be out. Terrible crick in the neck we're all going to get, I'm afraid. Worse than Wimbledon. Haha. Hullo, what's going on down there by the jetty? By jove, there's a submarine just surfaced alongside. I say, what a sight. One of our biggest I should say. And Sir

Hugo's team is down there too. Lined up on the jetty as if they were on parade. Magnificent body of men. Now they're filing on board. Perfect discipline. Must be an idea of the Admiralty's. Give them a special grandstand out in the Channel. Splendid show. Wish you could be here to see it. Now Sir Hugo is coming towards us. In a moment he'll be speaking to you. Fine figure of a man. Everyone in the firing point is giving him a cheer. I'm sure we all feel like cheering him today. He's coming into the firing point. I can see the sun glinting on the nose of the Moonraker way over there behind him. Just showing out of the top of the launching dome. Hope somebody's got a camera. Now here he is,' a pause. Sir Hugo Drax.'

Bond looked into Gala's dripping face. Soaked and bleeding they stood in each other's arms, speechless and trembling slightly with the storm of their emotions. Their eyes were blank and fathomless as they met and held each other's gaze.

'Your Majesty, men and women of England,' the voice was a velvet snarl. 'I am about to change the course of England's history.' A pause, 'In a few minutes' time the lives of all of you will be altered, in some cases, ahem, drastically, by the, er, impact of the Moonraker. I am very proud and pleased that fate has singled me out, from amongst all my fellow countrymen, to fire this great arrow of vengeance into the skies and thus to proclaim for all time, and for all the world to witness, the might of my fatherland. I hope that this occasion will be forever a warning that the fate of my country's enemies will be written in dust, in ashes, in tears, and,' a pause, 'in blood. And now thank you all for listening and I sincerely hope that those of you who are able will repeat my words to your children, if you have any, tonight.'

A rattle of rather hesitant applause sounded out of the machine and then came the breezy voice of the announcer. 'And that was Sir Hugo Drax saying a few words to you before he walks across the floor of the firing point to the switch on the wall which will fire the Moonraker. The first time he has spoken in public. Very, ahem, forthright. Doesn't mince his words. However, a lot of us will say there's no harm in that. And now it's time for me to hand over to the expert, Group Captain Tandy of the Ministry of Supply, who will describe to you the actual firing of the Moonraker. After that you will hear Peter Trimble in one of the naval security patrol, H.M.S. *Merganzer*, describe the scene in the target area. Group Captain Tandy.'

Bond glanced at his watch. 'Only a minute more,' he said to Gala. 'God, I'd like to get my hands on Drax. Here,' he reached for the cake of soap and gouged some pieces off it. 'Stuff this in your ears when the time comes. The noise is going to be terrific. I don't know about the heat. It won't last long and the steel walls may stand up to it.'

Gala looked at him. She smiled. 'If you hold me it won't be too bad,' she said.

'. . . and now Sir Hugo has his hand on the switch and he's watching the chronometer.'

'TEN,' broke in another voice, heavy and sonorous as the toll of a bell.

Bond turned on the shower and the water hissed down on their clinging bodies.

'NINE,' tolled the voice of the time-keeper.

'. . . the radar operators are watching the screens. Nothing but a mass of wavy lines. . . .'

'EIGHT.'

'. . . all wearing ear-plugs. Blockhouse should be indestructible. Concrete walls are twelve feet thick. Pyramid roof, twenty-seven feet thick at the point . . .'

'SEVEN.'

'. . . first the radio beam will stop the time mechanism alongside the turbines. Set the pinwheel going. Flaming thing like a catherine wheel. . . .'

'SIX.'

'. . . Valves will open. Liquid fuel. Secret formula. Terrific stuff. Dynamite. Pours down from the fuel tanks . . .'

'FIVE.'

'. . . ignited by the pinwheel when the fuel gets to the rocket motor. . . .'

'FOUR.'

'. . . meanwhile the peroxide and permanganate have mixed, made steam and the turbine pumps begin to turn . . .'

'THREE.'

'. . . pumping the flaming fuel through the motor out of the stern of the rocket into the exhaust pit. Gigantic heat . . . 3,500 degrees. . . .'

'TWO.'

'. . . Sir Hugo is about to press the switch. He's staring out through the slit. Perspiration on his forehead. Absolute silence in here. Terrific tension.'

'ONE.'

Nothing but the noise of the water, steadily pouring down on the two clinging bodies.

FIRE!

Bond's heart jumped into this throat at the shout. He felt Gala shudder. Silence. Nothing but the hissing of the water. . . .

'. . . Sir Hugo's left the firing point. Walking calmly over to the edge of the cliff. So confident. He's stepped on to the hoist. He's going down. Of course. He must be going out to the submarine. Television screen shows a little steam coming out of the tail of the rocket. A few more seconds. Yes, he's out on the jetty. He looked back and raised his arm in the air. Good old Sir Hu . . .'

A soft thunder came to Bond and Gala. Louder. Louder. The tiled floor began to tremble under their feet. A hurricane scream. They were being pulverized by it. The walls were quaking, steaming. Their legs began going out of control under their teetering bodies. Hold her up. Hold her up. Stop it! Stop it!! STOP THAT NOISE!!!

Christ, he was going to faint. The water was boiling. Must turn it off. Got it. No. Pipe's burst. Steam, smell, iron, paint.

Get her out! Get her out!! Get her out!!!

And then there was silence. Silence you could feel, hold, squeeze. And they were on the floor of Drax's office. Only the light in the bathroom still shining out. And the smoke's clearing. And the filthy smell of burning iron and paint. Being sucked out by the air-conditioner. And the steel wall is bent towards them like a huge blister. Gala's eyes are open and she's smiling. But the rocket. What happened. London? North Sea? The radio. Looks all right. He shook his head and the deafness slowly cleared. He remembered the soap. Gouged it out.

'. . . through the sound barrier. Travelling perfectly, right in the centre of the radar screen. A perfect launching. Afraid you couldn't hear anything because of the noise. Terrific. First of all the great sheet of flame coming out of the cliff from the exhaust pit and then you should have seen the nose slowly creep up out of the dome. And there she was like a great silver pencil. Standing upright on this huge column of flame and slowly climbing into the air and the flame splashing for hundreds of yards over the concrete. The howl of the thing must have nearly burst our microphones. Great bits have fallen off the cliff and the concrete looks like a spider's web. Terrible vibration. And then she was climbing faster and faster. A hundred miles an hour. A thousand. And,' he broke off, 'what's that you say? Really! And now she's travelling at over ten thousand miles an hour! She's three hundred miles up. Can't hear her any more, of course. We could only see her flame for a few seconds. Like a star. Sir Hugo must be a proud man. He's out there in the Channel now. The submarine went off like a rocket, haha, must be doing more than thirty knots. Throwing up a huge wake. Off the East Goodwins now. Travelling north. She'll soon be up with the patrol ships. They'll have a view of the launching and of the landing. Quite a surprise trip that. No one here had an inkling. Even the Naval authorities seem a bit mystified. C.-in-C. Nore has been on the telephone. But now that's all I can tell you from here and I'll hand you over to Peter Trimble on board H.M.S. *Merganzer* somewhere off the East Coast.'

Nothing but the pumping lungs showed that the two limp bodies in the creeping pool of water on the floor were still alive, but their battered ear-drums were desperately clinging to the crackle of static that came briefly from the blistered metal cabinet. Now for the verdict on their work.

'And this is Peter Trimble speaking. It's a beautiful morning, I mean–er–afternoon here. Just north of the Goodwin Sands. Calm as a millpond. No wind. Bright sunshine. And the target area is reported clear of shipping. Is that right, Commander Edwards? Yes, the Captain says it's quite clear. Nothing on the radar screens yet. I'm not allowed to tell you the range we shall pick her up at. Security and all that. But we shall only catch the rocket for a split second. Isn't that right, Captain? But the target's just showing on the screen. Out of sight from the bridge, of course. Must be seventy miles north of here. We could see the Moonraker going up. Terrific sight. Noise like thunder. Long flame coming out of the tail. Must have been ten miles away but you couldn't miss the light. Yes, Captain? Oh yes, I see. Well, that's very interesting. Big submarine coming up fast. Only about a mile away. Suppose it's the one they say Sir Hugo's aboard with his men. None of us here were told anything about her. Captain Edwards says she doesn't answer the Aldis lamp. Not flying colours. Very mysterious. I've got her now. Quite clear in my glasses. We've changed course to intercept her. The Captain says she isn't one of ours. Thinks she must be a foreigner. Hullo! She's broken out her colours. WHAT'S that? Good heavens. The Captain says she's a Russian. I say! And now she's hauled down her colours and she's submerging. Bang. Did you hear that? We fired a shot across her bows. But she's disappeared. What's that? The asdic operator says she's going even faster under water. Twenty-five knots. Terrific. Well, she can't see much under water. But she's right in the target area now. Twelve minutes past noon. The Moonraker must have turned and be on her way down. A thousand miles up. Coming down at ten thousand miles an hour. She'll be here any second now. Hope there's not going to be a tragedy. The Russian's well inside the danger zone. The radar operator's holding up his hand. That means she's due. She's coming. She's COMING. . . . Whew!

Not even a whisper. GOD! what's that? Look out! Look out! Terrific explosion. Black cloud going up into the air. There's a tidal wave coming at us. Great wall of water tearing down. There goes the submarine. God! Thrown out of the water upside down. It's coming. It's COMING . . .'

Chapter Twenty-five

Zero Plus

'. . . Two hundred dead so far and about the same number missing,' said M. 'Reports still coming in from the East Coast and there's bad news from Holland. Breached miles of their sea defences. Most of our losses were among the patrol craft. Two of them capsized, including the *Merganzer*. Commanding Officer missing. And that B.B.C. chap. Goodwin Lightships broke their moorings. No news from Belgium or France yet. There are going to be some pretty heavy bills to pay when everything gets sorted out.'

It was the next afternoon and Bond, a rubber-tipped stick beside his chair, was back where he had started–across the desk from the quiet man with the cold grey eyes who had invited him to dinner and a game of cards a hundred years ago.

Under his clothes Bond was latticed with surgical tape. Pain burned up his legs whenever he moved his feet. There was a vivid red streak across his left cheek and the bridge of his nose, and the tannic ointment dressing glinted in the light from the window. He held a cigarette clumsily in one gloved hand. Incredibly M had invited him to smoke.

'Any news of the submarine, sir?' he asked.

'They've located her,' said M with satisfaction. 'Lying on her side in about thirty fathoms. The salvage ship that was to look after the remains of the rocket is over her now. The divers have been down and there's no answer to signals against her hull. The Soviet Ambassador has been round at the Foreign Office this morning. I gather he says a salvage ship is on her way down from the Baltic, but we've said that we can't wait as the wreck's a danger to navigation.' M chuckled. 'So she would be I dare say if anyone happened to be navigating at thirty fathoms in the Channel. But I'm glad I'm not a member of the Cabinet,' he added drily. 'They've been in session on and off since the end of the broadcast. Vallance got hold of those Edinburgh solicitors before they'd opened Drax's message to the world. I gather it's a terrific document. Reads as if it had been written by Jehovah. Vallance took it to the Cabinet last night and stayed at No. 10 to fill in the blanks.'

'I know,' said Bond. 'He kept on telephoning me at the hospital for details until after midnight. I could hardly think straight for all the dope they'd pushed into me. What's going to happen?'

'They're going to try the biggest cover-up job in history,' said M. 'A lot of scientific twaddle about the fuel having been only half used up. Unexpectedly powerful explosion on impact. Full compensation to be paid.

Tragic loss of Sir Hugo Drax and his team. Great patriot. Tragic loss of one of H.M. submarines. Latest experimental model. Orders misunderstood. Very sad. Fortunately only a skeleton crew. Next of kin will be informed. Tragic loss of B.B.C. man. Unaccountable error in mistaking White Ensign for Soviet naval colours. Very similar design. White Ensign recovered from the wreck.'

'But what about the atomic explosion?' asked Bond. 'Radiation and atomic dust and all that. The famous mushroom-shaped cloud. Surely that's going to be a bit of a problem.'

'Apparently it's not worrying them too much,' said M. 'The cloud is going to be passed off as the normal formation after an explosion of that size. The Ministry of Supply know the whole story. Had to be told. Their men were down on the East Coast all last night with Geiger counters and there's not been a positive report yet.' M smiled coldly. 'The cloud's got to come down somewhere, of course, but by a happy chance such wind as there is is drifting it up north. Back home, as you might say.'

Bond smiled painfully, 'I see,' he said. 'How very appropriate.'

'Of course,' continued M, picking up his pipe and starting to fill it, 'there are going to be some nasty rumours. They've begun already. A lot of people saw you and Miss Brand being brought out of the site on stretchers. Then there's Bowaters' case against Drax for the loss of all that newsprint. There'll be the inquest on the young man who was killed in the Alfa Romeo. And somebody's got to explain away the remains of your car, amongst which,' he looked accusingly at Bond, 'a long-barrel Colt was found. And then there's the Ministry of Supply. Vallance had to call some more of their men yesterday to help clean out that house in Ebury Street. But those people are trained to keep secrets. You won't get a leak there. Naturally it's going to be a risky business. The big lie always is. But what's the alternative? Trouble with Germany? War with Russia? Lots of people on both sides of the Atlantic would be only too glad of an excuse.'

M paused and put a match to his pipe. 'If the story holds,' he continued reflectively, 'we shan't come out of this too badly. We've wanted one of their high-speed U-boats and we'll be glad of the clues we can pick up about their atom bombs. The Russians know that we know that their gamble failed. Malenkov's none too firmly in the saddle and this may mean another Kremlin revolt. As for the Germans. Well, we all knew there was plenty of Nazism left and this will make the Cabinet go just a bit more carefully on German rearmament. And, as a very minor consequence,' he gave a wry smile, 'it will make Vallance's security job, and mine for the matter of that, just a little bit easier in the future. These politicians can't see that the atomic age has created the most deadly saboteur in the history of the world–the little man with the heavy suitcase.'

'Will the Press wear the story?' asked Bond dubiously.

M shrugged his shoulders. 'The Prime Minister saw the editors this morning,' he said, putting another match to his pipe, 'and I gather he's got away with it so far. If the rumours get bad later on, he'll probably have to see them again and tell them some of the truth. Then they'll play all right. They always do when it's important enough. The main thing is to gain time and stave off the firebrands. For the moment everyone's so proud of the Moonraker that they're not inquiring too closely into what went wrong.'

There was a soft burr from the intercom on M's desk and a ruby light winked on and off. M picked up the single earphone and leant towards it. 'Yes?' he said. There was a pause. 'I'll take it on the Cabinet line.' He picked up the white receiver from the bank of four telephones.

'Yes,' said M. 'Speaking.' There was a pause. 'Yes, sir? Over.' M pressed down the button of his scrambler. He held the receiver close to his ear and not a sound from it reached Bond. There was a long pause during which M puffed occasionally at the pipe in his left hand. He took it out of his mouth. 'I agree, sir.' Another pause. 'I know my man would have been very proud, sir. But of course it's a rule here.' M frowned. 'If you will allow me to say so, sir, I think it would be very unwise.' A pause, then M's face cleared. 'Thank you, sir. And of course Vallance has not got the same problem. And it would be the least she deserves.' Another pause. 'I understand. That will be done.' Another pause. 'That's very kind of you, sir.'

M put the white receiver back on its cradle and the scrambler button clicked back to the *en clair* position.

For a moment M continued to look at the telephone as if in doubt about what had been said. Then he twisted his chair round away from the desk and gazed thoughtfully out of the window.

There was silence in the room and Bond shifted in his chair to ease the pain that was creeping back into his body.

The same pigeon as on Monday, or perhaps another one, came to rest on the window-sill with the same clatter of wings. It walked up and down, nodding and cooing, and then planed off towards the trees in the park. The traffic murmured sleepily in the distance.

How nearly it had come, thought Bond, to being stilled. How nearly there might be nothing now but the distant clang of the ambulance bells underneath a lurid black and orange sky, the stench of burning, the screams of people still trapped in the buildings. The softly beating heart of London silenced for a generation. And a whole generation of her people dead in the streets amongst the ruins of a civilization that might not rise again for centuries.

All that would have come about but for a man who scornfully cheated at cards to feed the fires of his maniac ego; but for the stuffy chairman of Blades who detected him; but for M who agreed to help an old friend; but for Bond's half-remembered lessons from a card-sharper; but for Vallance's precautions; but for Gala's head for figures; but for a whole pattern of tiny circumstances, a whole pattern of chance.

Whose pattern?

There was a shrill squeak as M's chair swivelled round. Bond carefully focused again on the grey eyes across the desk.

'That was the Prime Minister,' M said gruffly. 'Says he wants you and Miss Brand out of the country.' M lowered his eyes and looked stolidly into the bowl of his pipe. 'You're both to be out by tomorrow afternoon. There are too many people in this case who know your faces. Might put two and two together when they see the shape you're both in. Go anywhere you like. Unlimited expenses for both of you. Any currency you like. I'll tell the Paymaster. Stay away a month. But keep out of circulation. You'd both be gone this afternoon only the girl's got an appointment at eleven tomorrow morning. At the Palace. Immediate award of the George Cross. Won't be gazetted until the New Year of course. Like to meet her one day. Must be a good girl. As a matter of fact,' M's expression as he looked up was unreadable. 'The Prime Minister had something in mind for you. Forgotten that we don't go in for those sort of things here. So he asked me to thank you for him. Said some nice things about the Service. Very kind of him.'

M gave one of the rare smiles that lit up his face with quick brightness and warmth. Bond smiled back. They understood the things that had been left unsaid.

Bond knew it was time to go. He got up. 'Thank you very much, sir,' he said. 'And I'm glad about the girl.'

'All right then,' said M on a note of dismissal. 'Well, that's the lot. See you in a month. Oh and by the way,' he added casually. 'Call in at your office. You'll find something there from me. Little memento.'

James Bond went down in the lift and limped along the familiar corridor to his office. When he walked through the inner door he found his secretary arranging some papers on the next desk to his.

'008 coming back?' he asked.

'Yes,' she smiled happily. 'He's being flown out tonight.'

'Well I'm glad you'll have company,' said Bond. 'I'm going off again.'

'Oh,' she said. She looked quickly at his face and then away. 'You look as if you needed a bit of a rest.'

'I'm going to get one,' said Bond. 'A month's exile.' He thought of Gala. 'It's going to be pure holiday. Anything for me?'

'Your new car's downstairs. I've inspected it. The man said you'd ordered it on trial this morning. It looks lovely. Oh, and there's a parcel from M's office. Shall I unpack it?'

'Yes, do,' said Bond.

He sat down at his desk and looked at his watch. Five o'clock. He was feeling tired. He knew he was going to feel tired for several days. He always got these reactions at the end of an ugly assignment, the aftermath of days of taut nerves, tension, fear.

His secretary came back into the room with two heavy looking cardboard boxes. She put them on his desk and he opened the top one. When he saw the grease-paper he knew what to expect.

There was a card in the box. He took it out and read it. In M's green ink it said: 'You may be needing these.' There was no signature.

Bond unwrapped the grease-paper and cradled the shining new Beretta in his hand. A memento. No. A reminder. He shrugged his shoulders and slipped the gun under his coat into the empty holster. He got clumsily to his feet.

'There'll be a long-barrel Colt in the other box,' he said to his secretary. 'Keep it until I get back. Then I'll take it down to the range and fire it in.'

He walked to the door. 'So long, Lil,' he said, 'regards to 008 and tell him to be careful of you. I'll be in France. Station F will have the address. But only in an emergency.'

She smiled at him. 'How much of an emergency?' she asked.

Bond gave a short laugh. 'Any invitation to a quiet game of bridge,' he said.

He limped out and shut the door behind him.

The 1953 Mark VI had an open touring body. It was battleship grey like the old 4½ litre that had gone to its grave in a Maidstone garage, and the dark blue leather upholstery gave a luxurious hiss as he climbed awkwardly in beside the test driver.

Half an hour later the driver helped him out at the corner of Birdcage Walk and Queen Anne's Gate. 'We could get more speed out of her if you want it, sir,' he said. 'If we could have her back for a fortnight we could tune her to do well over the hundred.'

'Later,' said Bond. 'She's sold. On one condition. That you get her over to the ferry terminal at Calais by tomorrow evening.'

The test driver grinned. 'Roger,' he said. 'I'll take her over myself. See you on the pier, sir.'

'Fine,' said Bond. 'Go easy on A20. The Dover road's a dangerous place these days.'

'Don't worry, sir,' said the driver, thinking that this man must be a bit of a cissy for all that he seemed to know plenty about motor-cars. 'Piece of cake.'

'Not every day,' said Bond with a smile. 'See you at Calais.'

Without waiting for a reply, he limped off with his stick through the dusty bars of evening sunlight that filtered down through the trees in the park.

Bond sat down on one of the seats opposite the island in the lake and took out his cigarette-case and lit a cigarette. He looked at his watch. Five minutes to six. He reminded himself that she was the sort of girl who would be punctual. He had reserved the corner table for dinner. And then? But first there would be the long luxurious planning. What would she like. Where would she like to go? Where had she ever been? Germany, of course. France? Miss out Paris. They could do that on their way back. Get as far as they could the first night, away from the Pas de Calais. There was that farmhouse with the wonderful food between Montreuil and Etaples. Then the fast sweep down to the Loire. The little places near the river for a few days. Not the chateau towns. Places like Beaugency, for instance. Then slowly south, always keeping to the western roads, avoiding the five-star life. Slowly exploring. Bond pulled himself up. Exploring what? Each other? Was he getting serious about this girl?

'James.'

It was a clear, high, rather nervous voice. Not the voice he had expected.

He looked up. She was standing a few feet away from him. He noticed that she was wearing a black beret at a rakish angle and that she looked exciting and mysterious like someone you see driving by abroad, alone in an open car, someone unattainable and more desirable than anyone you have ever known. Someone who is on her way to make love to somebody else. Someone who is not for you.

He got up and they took each other's hands.

It was she who released herself. She didn't sit down.

'I wish you were going to be there tomorrow, James.' Her eyes were soft as she looked at him. Soft, but, he thought, somehow evasive.

He smiled. 'Tomorrow morning or tomorrow night?'

'Don't be ridiculous,' she laughed, blushing, 'I meant at the Palace.'

'What are you going to do afterwards?' asked Bond.

She looked at him carefully. What did the look remind him of? The Morphy look? The look he had given Drax on that last hand at Blades? No. Not quite. There was something else there. Tenderness? Regret?

She looked over his shoulder.

Bond turned round. A hundred yards away there was the tall figure of a young man with fair hair trimmed short. His back was towards them as he was idling along, killing time.

Bond turned back and Gala's eyes met his squarely.

'I'm going to marry that man,' she said quietly. 'Tomorrow afternoon.' And then, as if no other explanation was needed, 'His name's Detective-Inspector Vivian.'

'Oh,' said Bond. He smiled stiffly. 'I see.'

There was a moment of silence during which their eyes slid away from each other.

And yet why should he have expected anything else? A kiss. The contact of two frightened bodies clinging together in the midst of danger. There had been nothing more. And there had been the engagement ring to tell him. Why had he automatically assumed that it had only been worn to keep Drax at bay? Why had he imagined that she shared his desires, his plans?

And now what? wondered Bond. He shrugged his shoulders to shift the pain of failure–the pain that is so much greater than the pleasure of success. An exit line. He must get out of these two young lives and take his cold heart elsewhere. There must be no regrets. No false sentiment. He must play the role which she expected of him. The tough man of the world. The Secret Agent. The man who was only a silhouette.

She was looking at him rather nervously, waiting to be relieved of the stranger who had tried to get his foot in the door of her heart.

Bond smiled warmly at her. 'I'm jealous,' he said. 'I had other plans for you tomorrow night.'

She smiled back at him, grateful that the silence had been broken. 'What were they?' she asked.

'I was going to take you off to a farmhouse in France,' he said. 'And after a wonderful dinner I was going to see if it's true what they say about the scream of a rose.'

She laughed. 'I'm sorry I can't oblige. But there are plenty of others waiting to be picked.'

'Yes, I suppose so,' said Bond. 'Well, goodbye, Gala.' He held out his hand.

'Goodbye, James.'

He touched her for the last time and then they turned away from each other and walked off into their different lives.

FROM RUSSIA, WITH LOVE

FROM RUSSIA, WITH LOVE

Author's Note

Not that it matters, but a great deal of the background to this story is accurate.

SMERSH, a contraction of Smiert Spionam–Death to Spies–exists and remains today the most secret department of the Soviet government.

At the beginning of 1956, when this book was written, the strength of SMERSH at home and abroad was about 40,000 and General Grubozaboyschikov was its chief. My description of his appearance is correct.

Today, the headquarters of SMERSH are where, in Chapter 4, I have placed them–at No. 13 Stretenka Ulitsa, Moscow. The Conference Room is faithfully described and the Intelligence chiefs who meet round the table are real officials who are frequently summoned to that room for purposes similar to those I have recounted.

I.F.
March 1956

PART ONE

THE PLAN

Chapter One

Roseland

The naked man who lay splayed out on his face beside the swimming pool might have been dead.

He might have been drowned and fished out of the pool and laid out on the grass to dry while the police or the next-of-kin were summoned. Even the little pile of objects in the grass beside his head might have been his personal effects, meticulously assembled in full view so that no one should think that something had been stolen by his rescuers.

To judge by the glittering pile, this had been, or was, a rich man. It contained the typical membership badges of the rich man's club–a money clip, made of a Mexican fifty-dollar piece and holding a substantial wad of banknotes, a well-used gold Dunhill lighter, an oval gold cigarette case with the wavy ridges and discreet turquoise button that means Fabergé, and the sort of novel a rich man pulls out of the bookcase to take into the garden–*The Little Nugget*–an old P. G. Wodehouse. There was also a bulky gold wrist-watch on a well-used brown crocodile strap. It was a Girard-Perregaux model designed for people who like gadgets, and it had a sweep second-hand and two little windows in the face to tell the day of the month, and the month, and the phase of the moon. The story it now told was 2.30 on June 10th with the moon three-quarters full.

A blue and green dragon-fly flashed out from among the rose bushes at the end of the garden and hovered in mid-air a few inches above the base of the man's spine. It had been attracted by the golden shimmer of the June sunshine on the ridge of fine blond hairs above the coccyx. A puff of breeze came off the sea. The tiny field of hairs bent gently. The dragon-fly darted nervously sideways and hung above the man's left shoulder, looking down. The young grass below the man's open mouth stirred. A large drop of sweat rolled down the side of the fleshy nose and dropped glittering into the grass. That was enough. The dragon-fly flashed away through the roses and over the jagged glass on top of the high garden wall. It might be good food, but it moved.

The garden in which the man lay was about an acre of well-kept lawn surrounded on three sides by thickly banked rose bushes from which came the steady murmur of bees. Behind the drowsy noise of the bees the sea boomed softly at the bottom of the cliff at the end of the garden.

There was no view of the sea from the garden–no view of anything except of the sky and the clouds above the twelve-foot wall. In fact you could only see out of the property from the two upstairs bedrooms of the villa that formed the fourth side of this very private enclosure. From them you could see a great expanse of blue water in front of you and, on either side, the upper windows of neighbouring villas and the tops of the trees in their gardens–Mediterranean-type evergreen oaks, stone pines, casuarinas and an occasional palm tree.

The villa was modern–a squat elongated box without ornament. On the garden side the flat pink-washed façade was pierced by four iron-framed windows and by a central glass door leading on to a small square of pale green glazed tiles. The tiles merged into the lawn. The other side of the villa, standing back a few yards from a dusty road, was almost identical. But on this side the four windows were barred, and the central door was of oak.

The villa had two medium-sized bedrooms on the upper floor and on the ground floor a sitting-room and a kitchen, part of which was walled off into a lavatory. There was no bathroom.

The drowsy luxurious silence of early afternoon was broken by the sound of a car coming down the road. It stopped in front of the villa. There was the tinny clang of a car door being slammed and the car drove on. The door bell rang twice. The naked man beside the swimming pool did not move, but, at the noise of the bell and of the departing car, his eyes had for an instant opened very wide. It was as if the eyelids had pricked up like an animal's ears. The man immediately remembered where he was and the day of the week and the time of the day. The noises were identified. They eyelids with their fringe of shorty sandy eyelashes drooped drowsily back over the very pale blue, opaque, inward-looking eyes. The small cruel lips opened in a wide jaw-breaking yawn which brought saliva into the mouth. The man spat the saliva into the grass and waited.

A young woman carrying a small string bag and dressed in a white cotton shirt and a short, unalluring blue skirt came through the glass door and strode mannishly across the glazed tiles and the stretch of lawn towards the naked man. A few yards away from him, she dropped her string bag on the grass and sat down and took off her cheap and rather dusty shoes. Then she stood up and unbuttoned her shirt and took it off and put it, neatly folded, beside the string bag.

The girl had nothing on under the shirt. Her skin was pleasantly sunburned and her shoulders and fine breasts shone with health. When she bent her arms to undo the side-buttons of her skirt, small tufts of fair hair showed in her armpits. The impression of a healthy animal peasant girl was heightened by the chunky hips in faded blue stockinet bathing trunks and the thick short thighs and legs that were revealed when she had stripped.

The girl put the skirt neatly beside her shirt, opened the string bag, took out an old soda-water bottle containing some heavy colourless liquid and went over to the man and knelt on the grass beside him. She poured some of the liquid, a light olive oil, scented, as was everything in that part of the world, with roses, between his shoulder blades and, after flexing her fingers like a pianist, began massaging the sterno-mastoid and the trapezius muscles at the back of the man's neck.

It was hard work. The man was immensely strong and the bulging muscles at the base of the neck hardly yielded to the girl's thumbs even when the downward weight of her shoulders was behind them. By the time she was finished with the man she would be soaked in perspiration and so utterly exhausted that she would fall into the swimming pool and then lie down in the shade and sleep until the car came for her. But that wasn't what she minded as her hands worked automatically on across the man's back. It was her instinctive horror for the finest body she had ever seen.

None of this horror showed in the flat, impassive face of the masseuse, and the upward-slanting black eyes under the fringe of short coarse black hair were as empty as oil slicks, but inside her the animal whimpered and cringed and her pulse-rate, if it had occurred to her to take it, would have been high.

Once again, as so often over the past two years, she wondered why she loathed this splendid body, and once again she vaguely tried to analyse her revulsion. Perhaps this time she would get rid of feelings which she felt guiltily certain were much more unprofessional than the sexual desire some of her patients awoke in her.

To take the small things first: his hair. She looked down at the round, smallish head on the sinewy neck. It was covered with tight red-gold curls that should have reminded her pleasantly of the formalized hair in the pictures she had seen of classical statues. But the curls were somehow too tight, too thickly pressed against each other and against the skull. They set her teeth on edge like finger-nails against pile carpet. And the golden curls came down so low into the back of the neck–almost (she thought in professional terms) to the fifth cervical vertebra. And there they stopped abruptly in a straight line of small stiff golden hairs.

The girl paused to give her hands a rest and sat back on her haunches. The beautiful upper half of her body was already shining with sweat. She wiped the back of her forearm across her forehead and reached for the bottle of oil. She poured about a tablespoonful on to the small furry plateau at the base of the man's spine, flexed her fingers and bent forward again.

This embryo tail of golden down above the cleft of the buttocks–in a lover it would have been gay, exciting, but on this man it was somehow bestial. No, reptilian. But snakes had no hair. Well, she couldn't help that. It seemed reptilian to her. She shifted her hands on down to the two mounds of the gluteal muscles. Now was the time when many of her patients, particularly the young ones on the football team, would start joking with her. Then, if she was not very careful, the suggestions would come. Sometimes she could silence these by digging sharply down towards the sciatic nerve. At other times, and particularly if she found the man attractive, there would be giggling arguments, a brief wrestling-match and a quick, delicious surrender.

With this man it was different, almost uncannily different. From the very first he had been like a lump of inanimate meat. In two years he had never said a word to her. When she had done his back and it was time for him to turn over, neither his eyes nor his body had once shown the smallest interest in her. When she tapped his shoulder, he would just roll over and gaze at the sky through half-closed lids and occasionally let out one of the long shuddering yawns that were the only sign that he had human reactions at all.

The girl shifted her position and slowly worked down the right leg towards the Achilles tendon. When she came to it, she looked back up the fine body. Was her revulsion *only* physical? Was it the reddish colour of the sunburn on the naturally milk-white skin, the sort of roast meat look? Was it the texture of the skin itself, the deep, widely spaced pores in the satiny surface? The thickly scattered orange freckles on the shoulders? Or was it the asexuality of the man? The indifference of these splendid, insolently bulging muscles? Or was it spiritual–an animal instinct telling her that inside this wonderful body there was an evil person?

The masseuse got to her feet and stood, twisting her head slowly from side to side and flexing her shoulders. She stretched her arms out sideways and then upwards and held them for a moment to get the blood down out of them. She went to her string bag and took out a hand-towel and wiped the perspiration off her face and body.

When she turned back to the man, he had already rolled over and now lay, his head resting on one open hand, gazing blankly at the sky. The disengaged arm was flung out on the grass, waiting for her. She walked over and knelt on the grass behind his head. She rubbed some oil into her palms, picked up the limp half-open hand and started kneading the short thick fingers.

The girl glanced nervously sideways at the red-brown face below the crown of tight golden curls. Superficially it was all right–handsome in a butcher's-boyish way, with its full pink cheeks, upturned nose and rounded chin. But, looked at closer, there was something cruel about the thin-lipped rather pursed mouth, a pigginess about the wide nostrils in the upturned nose, and the blankness that veiled the very pale blue eyes communicated itself over the whole face and made it look drowned and morgue-like. It was, she reflected, as if someone had taken a china doll and painted its face to frighten.

The masseuse worked up the arm to the huge biceps. Where had the man got these fantastic muscles from? Was he a boxer? What did he do with his formidable body? Rumour said this was a police villa. The two men-servants were obviously guards of some sort, although they did the cooking and the housework. Regularly every month the man went away for a few days and she would be told not to come. And from time to time she would be told to stay away for a week, or two weeks, or a month. Once, after one of these absences, the man's neck and the upper part of his body had been a mass of bruises. On another occasion the red corner of a half-healed wound had shown under a foot of surgical plaster down the ribs over his heart. She had never dared to ask about him at the hospital or in the town. When she had first been sent to the house, one of the men-servants had told her that if she spoke about what she saw she would go to prison. Back at the hospital, the Chief Superintendent, who had never recognized her existence before, had sent for her and had said the same thing. She would go to prison. The girl's strong fingers gouged nervously into the big deltoid muscle on the point of the shoulder. She had always known it was a matter of State Security. Perhaps that was what revolted her about this splendid body. Perhaps it was just fear of the organization that had the body in custody. She squeezed her eyes shut at the thought of who he might be, of what he could order to be done to her. Quickly she opened them again. He might have noticed. But the eyes gazed blankly up at the sky.

Now–she reached for the oil–to do the face.

The girl's thumbs had scarcely pressed into the sockets of the man's closed eyes when the telephone in the house started ringing. The sound reached impatiently out into the quiet garden. At once the man was up on one knee like a runner waiting for the gun. But he didn't move forward. The ringing stopped. There was the mutter of a voice. The girl could not hear what it was saying, but it sounded humble, noting instructions. The voice stopped and one of the men-servants showed briefly at the door, made a gesture of summons, and went back into the house. Half way through the gesture, the naked man was already running. She watched the brown back flash through the open glass door. Better not let him find her there when he came out again–doing nothing, perhaps listening. She got to her feet, took two steps to the concrete edge of the pool and dived gracefully in.

Although it would have explained her instincts about the man whose body she massaged, it was as well for the girl's peace of mind that she did not know who he was.

His real name was Donovan Grant, or 'Red' Grant. But, for the past ten years, it had been Krassno Granitski, with the code-name of 'Granit'.

He was the Chief Executioner of SMERSH, the murder *apparat* of the M.G.B., and at this moment he was receiving his instructions on the M.G.B. direct line with Moscow.

Chapter Two

The Slaughterer

Grant put the telephone softly back on its cradle and sat looking at it.

The bullet-headed guard standing over him said, 'You had better start moving.'

'Did they give you any idea of the task?' Grant spoke Russian excellently but with a thick accent. He could have passed for a national of any of the Soviet Baltic provinces. The voice was high and flat as if it was reciting something dull from a book.

'No. Only that you are wanted in Moscow. The plane is on its way. It will be here in about an hour. Half an hour for refuelling and then three or four hours, depending on whether you come down at Kharkov. You will be in Moscow by midnight. You had better pack. I will order the car.'

Grant got nervously to his feet. 'Yes. You are right. But they didn't even say if it was an operation? One likes to know. It was a secure line. They could have given a hint. They generally do.'

'This time they didn't.'

Grant walked slowly out through the glass door on to the lawn. If he noticed the girl sitting on the far edge of the pool he made no sign. He bent and picked up his book, and the golden trophies of his profession, and walked back into the house and up the few stairs to his bedroom.

The room was bleak and furnished only with an iron bedstead, from which the rumpled sheets hung down on one side to the floor, a cane chair, an unpainted clothes cupboard and a cheap washstand with a tin basin. The floor was strewn with English and American magazines. Garish paper-backs and hard-cover thrillers were stacked against the wall below the window.

Grant bent down and pulled a battered Italian fibre suitcase from under the bed. He packed into it a selection of well-laundered cheap respectable clothes from the cupboard. Then he washed his body hurriedly with cold water, and the inevitably rose-scented soap, and dried himself on one of the sheets from the bed.

There was the noise of a car outside. Grant hastily dressed in clothes as drab and nondescript as those he had packed, put on his wrist-watch, pocketed his other belongings and picked up his suitcase and went down the stairs.

The front door was open. He could see his two guards talking to the driver of a battered ZIS saloon. 'Bloody fools,' he thought. (He still did most of his thinking in English.) 'Probably telling him to see I get on the plane all right. Probably can't imagine that a foreigner would want to live in their blasted country.' The cold eyes sneered as Grant put down his suitcase on the doorstep and hunted among the bunch of coats that hung from pegs on the kitchen door. He found his 'uniform', the drab raincoat and black cloth cap of Soviet officialdom, put them on, picked up his suitcase and went out and climbed in beside the plain-clothes driver, roughly shouldering aside one of the guards as he did so.

The two men stood back, saying nothing, but looking at him with hard eyes. The driver took his foot off the clutch, and the car, already in gear, accelerated fast away down the dusty road.

The villa was on the south-eastern coast of the Crimea, about half way between Feodosiya and Yalta. It was one of many official holiday *datchas* along the favourite stretch of mountainous coastline that is part of the Russian Riviera. Red Grant knew that he was immensely privileged to be housed there instead of in some dreary villa on the outskirts of Moscow. As the car climbed up into the mountains, he thought that they certainly treated him as well as they knew how, even if their concern for his welfare had two faces.

The forty-mile drive to the airport at Simferopol took an hour. There were no other cars on the road and the occasional cart from the vineyards quickly pulled into the ditch at the sound of their horn. As everywhere in Russia, a car meant an official, and an official could only mean danger.

There were roses all the way, fields of them alternating with the vineyards, hedges of them along the road and, at the approach to the airport, a vast circular bed planted with red and white varieties to make a red star against a white background. Grant was sick of them and he longed to get to Moscow and away from their sweet stench.

They drove past the entrance to the Civil Airport and followed a high wall for about a mile to the military side of the aerodrome. At a tall wire gate the driver showed his pass to two tommy-gunned sentries and drove through on to the tarmac. Several planes stood about, big camouflaged military transports, small twin-engined trainers and two Navy helicopters. The driver stopped to ask a man in overalls where to find Grant's plane. At once a metallic twanging came from the observant control tower and a loudspeaker barked at them: 'To the left. Far down to the left. Number V-BO.'

The driver was obediently motoring on across the tarmac when the iron voice barked again. 'Stop!'

As the driver jammed on his brakes, there sounded a deafening scream above their heads. Both men instinctively ducked as a flight of four MIG 17s came out of the setting sun and skimmed over them, their squat wind-brakes right down for the landing. The planes hit the huge runway one after the other, puffs of blue smoke spurting from their nose-tyres, and, with jets howling, taxied to the distant boundary line and turned to come back to the control tower and the hangars.

'Proceed!'

A hundred yards further on they came to a plane with the recognition letters V-BO. It was a two-engined Ilyushin 12. A small aluminium ladder hung down from the cabin door and the car stopped beside it. One of the crew appeared at the door. He came down the ladder and carefully examined the driver's pass and Grant's identity papers and then waved the driver away and gestured Grant to follow him up the ladder. He didn't offer to help with the suitcase, but Grant carried it up the ladder as if it had been no heavier than a book. The crewman pulled the ladder up after him, banged the wide hatch shut and went forward to the cockpit.

There were twenty empty seats to choose from. Grant settled into the one nearest the hatch and fastened his seat-belt. A short crackle of talk with the control tower came through the open door to the cockpit, the two engines whined and coughed and fired and the plane turned quickly as if it had been a motor car, rolled out to the start of the north-south runway, and, without any further preliminaries, hurtled down it and up into the air.

Grant unbuckled his seat-belt, lit a gold-tipped Troika cigarette and settled back to reflect comfortably on his past career and to consider the immediate future.

Donovon Grant was the result of a midnight union between a German professional weight-lifter and a Southern Irish waitress. The union lasted for a quarter of an hour on the damp grass behind a circus tent outside Belfast. Afterwards the father gave the mother half-a-crown and the mother walked happily home to her bed in the kitchen of a café near the railway station. When the baby was expected, she went to live with an aunt in the small village of Aughmacloy that straddles the border, and there, six months later, she died of puerperal fever shortly after giving birth to a twelve-pound boy. Before she died, she said that the boy was to be called Donovan (the weight-lifter had styled himself 'The Mighty O'Donovan) and Grant, which was her own name.

The boy was reluctantly cared for by the aunt and grew up healthy and extremely strong, but very quiet. He had no friends. He refused to communicate with other children and when he wanted anything from them he took it with his fists. In the local school he continued to be feared and disliked, but he made a name for himself boxing and wrestling at local fairs where the bloodthirsty fury of his attack, combined with guile, gave him victory over much older and bigger boys.

It was through his fighting that he came to the notice of the Sinn-Feiners who used Aughmacloy as a principal pipeline for their comings and goings with the north, and also of the local smugglers who used the village for the same purpose. When he left school he became a strong-arm man for both these groups. They paid him well for his work but saw as little of him as they could.

It was about this time that his body began to feel strange and violent compulsions around the time of the full moon. When, in October of his sixteenth year, he first got 'The Feelings' as he called them to himself, he went out and strangled a cat. This made him 'feel better' for a whole month. In November, it was a big sheepdog, and, for Christmas, he slit the throat of a cow, at midnight in a neighbour's shed. These actions made him 'feel good'. He had enough sense to see that the village would soon start wondering about the mysterious deaths, so he bought a bicycle and on one night every month he rode off into the countryside. Often he had to go very far to find what he wanted and, after two months of having to satisfy himself with geese and chickens, he took a chance and cut the throat of a sleeping tramp.

There were so few people abroad at night that soon he took to the roads earlier, bicycling far and wide so that he came to distant villages in the dusk when solitary people were coming home from the fields and girls were going out to their trysts.

When he killed the occasional girl he did not 'interfere' with her in any way. That side of things, which he had heard talked about, was quite incomprehensible to him. It was only the wonderful act of killing that made him 'feel better'. Nothing else.

By the end of his seventeenth year, ghastly rumours were spreading round the whole of Fermanagh, Tyrone and Armagh. When a woman was killed in broad daylight, strangled and thrust carelessly into a haystack, the rumours flared into panic. Groups of vigilantes were formed in the villages, police reinforcements were brought in with police dogs, and stories about the 'Moon Killer' brought journalists to the area. Several times Grant on his bicycle was stopped and questioned, but he had powerful protection in Aughmacloy and his story of training-spins to keep him fit for his boxing were always backed up, for he was now the pride of the village and contender for the North of Ireland light-heavyweight championship.

Again, before it was too late, instinct saved him from discovery and he left Aughmacloy and went to Belfast and put himself in the hands of a broken-down boxing promoter who wanted him to turn professional. Discipline in the sleazy gymnasium was strict. It was almost a prison and, when the blood first boiled again in Grant's veins, there was nothing for it but to half kill one of his sparring partners. After twice having to be pulled off a man in the ring, it was only by winning the championship that he was saved from being thrown out by the promoter.

Grant won the championship in 1945, on his eighteenth birthday, then they took him for National Service and he became a driver in the Royal Corps of Signals. The training period in England sobered him, or at least made him more careful when he had 'The Feelings'. Now, at the full moon, he took to drink instead. He would take a bottle of whisky into the woods round Aldershot and drink it all down as he watched his sensations, coldly, until unconsciousness came. Then, in the early hours of the morning, he would stagger back to camp, only half satisfied, but not dangerous any more. If a sentry caught him, it was only a day's C.B., because his commanding officer wanted to keep him happy for the Army championships.

But Grant's transport section was rushed to Berlin about the time of the Corridor trouble with the Russians and he missed the championships. In Berlin, the constant smell of danger intrigued him and made him even more careful and cunning. He still got dead drunk at the full moon, but all the rest of the time he was watching and plotting. He liked all he heard about the Russians, their brutality, their carelessness of human life, and their guile, and he decided to go over to them. But how? What could he bring them as a gift? What did they want?

It was the B.A.O.R. championships that finally told him to go over. By chance they took place on a night of the full moon. Grant, fighting for the Royal Corps, was warned for holding and hitting low and was disqualified in the third round for persistent foul fighting. The whole stadium hissed him as he left the ring–the loudest demonstration came from his own regiment–and the next morning the commanding officer sent for him and coldly said he was a disgrace to the Royal Corps and would be sent home with the next draft. His fellow drivers sent him to Coventry and, since no one would drive transport with him, he had to be transferred to the coveted motor cycle dispatch service.

The transfer could not have suited Grant better. He waited a few days and then, one evening when he had collected the day's out-going mail from the Military Intelligence Headquarters on the Reichskanzlerplatz, he made straight for the Russian Sector, waited with his engine running until the British control gate was opened to allow a taxi through, and then tore through the closing gate at forty and skidded to a stop beside the concrete pillbox of the Russian Frontier post.

They hauled him roughly into the guardroom. A wooden-faced officer behind a desk asked him what he wanted.

'I want the Soviet Secret Service,' said Grant flatly. 'The Head of it.'

The officer stared coldly at him. He said something in Russian. The soldiers who had brought Grant in started to drag him out again. Grant easily shook them off. One of them lifted his tommy-gun.

Grant said, speaking patiently and distinctly, 'I have a lot of secret papers. Outside. In the leather bags on the motor cycle.' He had a brainwave. 'You will get into bad trouble if they don't get to your Secret Service.'

The officer said something to the soldiers and they stood back. 'We have no Secret Service,' he said in stilted English. 'Sit down and complete this form.'

Grant sat down at the desk and filled in a long form which asked questions about anyone who wanted to visit the Eastern zone–name, address, nature of business and so forth. Meanwhile the officer spoke softly and briefly into a telephone.

By the time Grant had finished, two more soldiers, non-commissioned officers wearing drab green forage caps and with green badges of rank on their khaki uniforms, had come into the room. The frontier officer handed the form, without looking at it, to one of them and they took Grant out and put him and his motor cycle into the back of a closed van and locked the door on him. After a fast drive lasting a quarter of an hour the van stopped, and when Grant got out he found himself in the courtyard behind a large new building. He was taken into the building and up in a lift and left alone in a cell without windows. It contained nothing but one iron bench. After an hour, during which, he supposed, they went through the secret papers, he was led into a comfortable office in which an officer with three rows of decorations and the gold tabs of a full colonel was sitting behind a desk.

The desk was bare except for a bowl of roses.

Ten years later, Grant, looking out of the window of the plane at a wide cluster of lights twenty thousand feet below, which he guessed was Kharkov, grinned mirthlessly at his reflection in the Perspex window.

Roses. From that moment his life had been nothing but roses. Roses, roses, all the way.

Chapter Three

Post-Graduate Studies

'So you would like to work in the Soviet Union, Mister Grant?'

It was half an hour later and the M.G.B. colonel was bored with the interview. He thought that he had extracted from this rather unpleasant British soldier every military detail that could possibly be of interest. A few polite phrases to repay the man for the rich haul of secrets his dispatch bags had yielded, and then the man could go down to the cells and in due course be shipped off to Vorkuta or some other labour camp.

'Yes, I would like to work for you.'

'And what work could you do, Mister Grant? We have plenty of unskilled labour. We do not need truck-drivers and,' the colonel smiled fleetingly, 'if there is any boxing to be done we have plenty of men who can box. Two possible Olympic champions amongst them, incidentally.'

'I am an expert at killing people. I do it very well. I like it.'

The colonel saw the red flame that flickered for an instant behind the very pale blue eyes under the sandy lashes. He thought, the man means it. He's mad as well as unpleasant. He looked coldly at Grant, wondering if it was worth while wasting food on him at Vorkuta. Better perhaps to have him shot. Or throw him back into the British Sector and let his own people worry about him.

'You don't believe me,' said Grant impatiently. This was the wrong man, the wrong department. 'Who does the rough stuff for you here?' He was certain the Russians had some sort of a murder squad. Everybody said so. 'Let me talk to them. I'll kill somebody for them. Anybody they like. Now.'

The colonel looked at him sourly. Perhaps he had better report the matter. 'Wait here.' He got up and went out of the room, leaving the door open. A guard came and stood in the doorway and watched Grant's back, his hand on his pistol.

The colonel went into the next room. It was empty. There were three telephones on the desk. He picked up the receiver of the M.G.B. direct line to Moscow. When the military operator answered he said, 'SMERSH'. When SMERSH answered he asked for the Chief of Operations.

Ten minutes later he put the receiver back. What luck! A simple, constructive solution. Whichever way it went it would turn out well. If the Englishman succeeded, it would be splendid. If he failed, it would still cause a lot of trouble in the Western Sector–trouble for the British because Grant was their man, trouble with the Germans because the attempt would frighten a lot of their spies, trouble with the Americans because they were supplying most of the funds for the Baumgarten ring and would now think Baumgarten's security was no good. Pleased with himself, the colonel walked back into his office and sat down again opposite Grant.

'You mean what you say?'

'Of course I do.'

'Have you a good memory?'

'Yes.'

'In the British Sector there is a German called Dr Baumgarten. He lives in Flat 5 at No. 22 Kurfürstendamm. Do you know where that is?'

'Yes.'

'Tonight, with your motor cycle, you will be put back into the British Sector. Your number plates will be changed. Your people will be on the lookout for you. You will take an envelope to Dr Baumgarten. It will be marked to be delivered by hand. In your uniform, and with this envelope, you will have no difficulty. You will say that the message is so private that you must see Dr Baumgarten alone. Then you will kill him.' The colonel paused. His eyebrows lifted. 'Yes?'

'Yes,' said Grant stolidly. 'And if I do, will you give me more of this work?'

'It is possible,' said the colonel indifferently. 'First you must show what you can do. When you have completed your task and returned to the Soviet Sector, you may ask for Colonel Boris.' He rang a bell and a man in plain clothes came in. The colonel gestured towards him. 'This man will give you food. Later he will give you the envelope and a sharp knife of American manufacture. It is an excellent weapon. Good luck.'

The colonel reached and picked a rose out of the bowl and sniffed it luxuriously.

Grant got to his feet. 'Thank you, sir,' he said warmly.

The colonel did not answer or look up from the rose. Grant followed the man in plain clothes out of the room.

The plane roared on across the Heartland of Russia. They had left behind them the blast furnaces flaming far away to the east around Stalino and, to the west, the silver thread of the Dnieper branching away at Dnepropetrovsk. The splash of light around Kharkov had marked the frontier of the Ukraine, and the smaller blaze of the phosphate town of Kursk had come and gone. Now Grant knew that the solid unbroken blackness below hid the great central Steppe where the billions of tons of Russia's grain were whispering and ripening in the darkness. There would be no more oases of light until, in another hour, they would have covered the last three hundred miles to Moscow.

For by now Grant knew a lot about Russia. After the quick, neat, sensational murder of a vital West German spy, Grant had no sooner slipped back over the frontier and somehow fumbled his way to 'Colonel Boris' than he was put into plain clothes, with a flying helmet to cover his hair, hustled into an empty M.G.B. plane and flown straight to Moscow.

Then began a year of semi-prison which Grant had devoted to keeping fit and to learning Russian while people came and went around him–interrogators, stool-pigeons, doctors. Meanwhile, Soviet spies in England and Northern Ireland had painstakingly investigated his past.

At the end of the year Grant was given as clean a bill of political health as any foreigner can get in Russia. The spies had confirmed his story. The English and American stool-pigeons reported that he was totally uninterested in the politics or social customs of any country in the world, and the doctors and psychologists agreed that he was an advanced manic depressive whose periods coincided with the full moon. They added that

Grant was also a narcissist and asexual and that his tolerance of pain was high. These peculiarities apart, his physical health was superb and, though his educational standards were hopelessly low, he was as naturally cunning as a fox. Everyone agreed that Grant was an exceedingly dangerous member of society and that he should be put away.

When the dossier came before the Head of Personnel of the M.G.B., he was about to write 'Kill him' in the margin when he had second thoughts.

A great deal of killing has to be done in the U.S.S.R., not because the average Russian is a cruel man, although some of their races are among the cruellest peoples in the world, but as an instrument of policy. People who act against the State are enemies of the State, and the State has no room for enemies. There is too much to do for precious time to be allotted to them, and, if they are a persistent nuisance, they get killed. In a country with a population of 200,000,000, you can kill many thousands a year without missing them. If, as happened in the two biggest purges, a million people have to be killed in one year, that is also not a grave loss. The serious problem is the shortage of executioners. Executioners have a short 'life'. They get tired of the work. The soul sickens of it. After ten, twenty, a hundred death-rattles, the human being, however sub-human he may be, acquires, perhaps by a process of osmosis with death itself, a germ of death which enters his body and eats into him like a canker. Melancholy and drink take him, and a dreadful lassitude which brings a glaze to the eyes and slows up the movements and destroys accuracy. When the employer sees these signs he has no alternative but to execute the executioner and find another one.

The Head of Personnel of the M.G.B. was aware of the problem and of the constant search not only for the refined assassin, but also for the common butcher. And here at last was a man who appeared to be expert at both forms of killing, dedicated to his craft and indeed, if the doctors were to be believed, destined for it.

Head of Personnel wrote a short, pungent minute on Grant's papers, marked them 'SMERSH Otdyel II' and tossed them into his OUT tray.

Department 2 of SMERSH, in charge of Operations and Executions, took over the body of Donovan Grant, changed his name to Granitsky and put him on their books.

The next two years were hard for Grant. He had to go back to school and to a school that made him long for the chipped deal desks in the corrugated iron shed, full of the smell of little boys and the hum of drowsy blue-bottles, that had been his only conception of what a school was like. Now, in the Intelligence School for Foreigners outside Leningrad, squashed tightly among the ranks of Germans, Czechs, Poles, Balts, Chinese and Negroes, all with serious dedicated faces and pens that raced across their notebooks, he struggled with subjects that were pure double-dutch to him.

There were courses in 'General Politcal Knowledge', which included the history of Labour movements, of the Communist Party and the Industrial Forces of the world, and the teachings of Marx, Lenin and Stalin, all dotted with foreign names which he could barely spell. There were lessons on 'The Class-enemy we are fighting', with lectures on Capitalism and Fascism; weeks spent on 'Tactics, Agitation and Propaganda' and more weeks on the problems of minority peoples, Colonial races, the Negroes, the Jews. Every month ended with examinations during which Grant sat and wrote illiterate nonsense, interspersed with scraps of half-forgotten English history and mis-spelled Communist slogans, and inevitably had his papers torn up, on one occasion, in front of the whole class.

But he stuck it out, and when they came to 'Technical Subjects' he did better. He was quick to understand the rudiments of Codes and Ciphers, because he wanted to understand them. He was good at Communications, and immediately grasped the maze of contacts, cut-outs, couriers and post-boxes, and he got excellent marks for Fieldwork in which each student had to plan and operate dummy assignments in the suburbs and countryside around Leningrad. Finally, when it came to tests of Vigilance, Discretion, 'Safety-First', Presence of Mind, Courage and Coolness, he got top marks out of the whole school.

At the end of the year, the report that went back to SMERSH concluded 'Politcal value Nil. Operational value Excellent'–which was just what Otdyel II wanted to hear.

The next year was spent, with only two other foreign students among several hundred Russians, at the School for Terror and Diversion at Kuchino, outside Moscow. Here Grant went triumphantly through courses in judo, boxing, athletics, photography and radio under the general supervision of the famous Colonel Arkady Fotoyev, father of the modern Soviet spy, and completed his small-arms instruction at the hands of Lieutenant-Colonel Nikolai Godlovsky, the Soviet Rifle Champion.

Twice during this year, without warning, an M.G.B. car came for him on the night of the full moon and took him to one of the Moscow jails. There, with a black hood over his head, he was allowed to carry out executions with various weapons–the rope, the axe, the sub-machine gun. Electro-cardiograms, blood-pressure and various other medical tests were applied to him before, during and after these occasions, but their purpose and findings were not revealed to him.

It was a good year and he felt, and rightly, that he was giving satisfaction.

In 1949 and '50 Grant was allowed to go on minor operations with Mobile Groups or *Avanposts*, in the satellite countries. These were beatings-up and simple assassinations of Russian spies and intelligence workers suspected of treachery or other aberrations. Grant carried out these duties neatly, exactly and inconspicuously, as though he was carefully and constantly watched he never showed the smallest deviation from the standards required of him, and no weaknesses of character or technical skill. It might have been different if he had been required to kill when doing a solo task at the full-moon period, but his superiors, realizing that at that period he would be outside their control, or his own, chose safe dates for his operations. The moon period was reserved exclusively for butchery in the prisons, and from time to time this was arranged for him as a reward for a successful operation in cold blood.

In 1951 and '52 Grant's usefullness became more fully and more officially recognized. As a result of excellent work, notably in the Eastern Sector of Berlin, he was granted Soviet citizenship and increases in pay which by 1953 amounted to a handsome 5000 roubles a month. In 1953 he was given the rank of Major, with pension rights back-dated to the day of his first contact with 'Colonel Boris', and the villa in the Crimea was allotted to him. Two bodyguards were attached to him, partly to protect him and partly to guard against the outside chance of his 'going private', as defection is called in M.G.B. jargon, and, once a month, he was transported to the nearest jail and allowed as many executions as there were candidates available.

Naturally Grant had no friends. He was hated or feared or envied by everyone who came in contact with him. He did not even have any of those professional acquaintanceships that pass for friendship in the discreet and careful world of Soviet officialdom. But, if he noticed the fact, he didn't care. The only individuals he was interested in were his victims. The rest of his life was inside him. And it was richly and excitingly populated with his thoughts.

Then, of course, he had SMERSH. No one in the Soviet Union who has SMERSH on his side need worry about friends, or indeed about anything whatever except keeping the black wings of SMERSH over his head.

Grant was still thinking vaguely of how he stood with his employers when the plane started to lose altitude as it picked up the radar beam of Tushino Airport just south of the red glow that was Moscow.

He was at the top of his tree, the chief executioner of SMERSH, and therefore of the whole of the Soviet Union. What could he aim for now? Further promotion? More money? More gold nicknacks? More important targets? Better techniques?

There really didn't seem to be anything more to go for. Or was there perhaps some other man whom he had never heard of, in some other country, who would have to be set aside before absolute supremacy was his?

Chapter Four

The Moguls of Death

Smersh is the official murder organization of the Soviet government. It operates both at home and abroad and, in 1955, it employed a total of 40,000 men and women. SMERSH is a contraction of 'Smiert Spionam', which means 'Death to Spies'. It is a name used only among its staff and among Soviet officials. No sane member of the public would dream of allowing the word to pass his lips.

The headquarters of SMERSH is a very large and ugly modern building on the Sretenka Ulitsa. It is No. 13 on this wide, dull street, and pedestrians keep their eyes to the ground as they pass the two sentries with sub-machine guns who stand on either side of the broad steps leading up to the big iron double door. If they remember in time, or can do so inconspicuously, they cross the street and pass by on the other side.

The direction of SMERSH is carried out from the 2nd floor. The most important room on the 2nd floor is a very large light room painted in the pale olive green that is the common denominator of government offices all over the world. Opposite the sound-proofed door, two wide windows look over the courtyard at the back of the building. The floor is close-fitted with a colourful Caucasian carpet of the finest quality. Across the far left-hand corner of the room stands a massive oak desk. The top of the desk is covered with red velvet under a thick sheet of plate glass.

On the left side of the desk are IN and OUT baskets and on the right four telephones.

From the centre of the desk, to form a T with it, a conference table stretches diagonally out across the room. Eight straight-backed red leather chairs are drawn up to it. This table is also covered with red velvet, but without protective glass. Ash-trays are on the table, and two heavy carafes of water with glasses.

On the walls are four large pictures in gold frames. In 1955, these were a portrait of Stalin over the door, one of Lenin between the two windows and, facing each other on the other two walls, portraits of Bulganin and, where until January 13th, 1954, a portrait of Beria had hung, a portrait of Army General Ivan Aleksandrovitch Serov, Chief of the Committee of State Security.

On the left-hand wall, under the portrait of Bulganin, stands a large *Televisor*, or TV set, in a handsome polished oak cabinet. Concealed in this is a tape-recorder which can be switched on from the desk. The microphone for the recorder stretches under the whole area of the conference table and its leads are concealed in the legs of the table. Next to the *Televisor* is a small door leading into a personal lavatory and washroom and into a small projection room for showing secret films.

Under the portrait of General Serov is a bookcase containing, on the top shelves, the works of Marx, Engels, Lenin and Stalin, and more accessibly, books in all languages on espionage, counter-espionage, police methods and criminology. Next to the bookcase, against the wall, stands a long narrow table on which are a dozen large leather-bound albums with dates stamped in gold on the covers. These contain photographs of Soviet citizens and foreigners who have been assassinated by SMERSH.

About the time Grant was coming in to land at Tushino Airport, just before 11.30 at night, a tough-looking, thick-set man of about fifty was standing at this table leafing through the volume for 1954.

The Head of SMERSH, Colonel General Grubozaboyschikov, known in the building as 'G.', was dressed in a neat khaki tunic with a high collar, and dark blue cavalry trousers with two thin red stripes down the sides. The trousers ended in riding boots of soft, highly polished black leather. On the breast of the tunic were three rows of medal ribbons–two Orders of Lenin, Order of Suvorov, Order of Alexander Nevksy, Order of the Red Banner, two Orders of the Red Star, the Twenty Years Service medal and medals for the Defence of Moscow and the Capture of Berlin. At the tail of these came the rose-pink and grey ribbon of the British C.B.E. and the claret and white ribbon of the American Medal for Merit. Above the ribbons hung the gold star of a Hero of the Soviet Union.

Above the high collar of the tunic the face was narrow and sharp. There were flabby pouches under the eyes, which were round and brown and protruded like polished marbles below thick black brows. The skull was shaven clean and the tight white skin glittered in the light of the central chandelier. The mouth was broad and grim above a deeply cleft chin. It was a hard, unyielding face of formidable authority.

One of the telephones on the desk buzzed softly. The man walked with tight and precise steps to his tall chair behind the desk. He sat down and picked up the receiver of the telephone marked in white with the letters V.Ch. These letters are short for *Vysoko-chastoty*, or High Frequency. Only some fifty supreme officials are connected to the V.Ch. switchboard, and all are Ministers of State or Heads of selected Departments. It is served by a small exchange in the Kremlin operated by professional security officers. Even they cannot overhear conversations on it, but every word spoken over its lines is automatically recorded.

'Yes?'

'Serov speaking. What action has been taken since the meeting of the Praesidium this morning?'

'I have a meeting here in a few minutes' time, Comrade General–R.U.M.I.D., G.R.U. and of course M.G.B. After that, if action is agreed, I shall have a meeting with my Head of Operations and Head of Plans. In case liquidation is decided upon, I have taken the precaution of bringing the necessary operative to Moscow. This time I shall myself supervise the preparations. We do not want another Khoklov affair.'

'The devil knows we don't. Telephone me after the first meeting. I wish to report to the Praesidium tomorrow morning.'

'Certainly, Comrade General.'

General G. put back the receiver and pressed a bell under his desk. At the same time he switched on the wire-recorder. His A.D.C., an M.G.B. captain, came in.

'Have they arrived?'

'Yes, Comrade General.'

'Bring them in.'

In a few minutes six men, five of them in uniform, filed in through the door and, with hardly a glance at the man behind the desk, took their places at the conference table. They were three senior officers, heads of their departments, and each was accompanied by an A.D.C. In the Soviet Union, no man goes alone to a conference. For his own protection, and for the reassurance of his department, he invariably takes a witness so that his department can have independent versions of what went on at the conference and, above all, of what was said on its behalf. This is important in case there is a subsequent investigation. No notes are taken at the conference and decisions are passed back to departments by word of mouth.

On the far side of the table sat Lieutenant-General Slavin, head of the G.R.U., the intelligence department of the General Staff of the Army, with a full colonel beside him. At the end of the table sat Lieutenant-General Vozdvishensky of R.U.M.I.D., the Intelligence Department of the Ministry of Foreign Affairs, with a middle-aged man in plain clothes. With his back to the door, sat Colonel of State Security Nikitin, Head of Intelligence for the M.G.B., the Soviet Secret Service, with a major at his side.

'Good evening, Comrades.'

A polite, careful murmur came from the three senior officers. Each one knew, and thought he was the only one to know, that the room was wired for sound, and each one, without telling his A.D.C., had decided to utter the bare minimum of words consonant with good discipline and the needs of the State.

'Let us smoke.' General G. took out a packet of Moskwa-Volga cigarettes and lit one with an American Zippo lighter. There was a clicking of lighters round the table. General G. pinched the long cardboard tube of his cigarette so that it was almost flat and put it between his teeth on the right side of his mouth. He stretched his lips back from his teeth and started talking in short clipped sentences that came out with something of a hiss from between the teeth and the uptilted cigarette.

'Comrades, we meet under instructions from Comrade General Serov. General Serov, on behalf of the Praesidium, has ordered me to make known to you certain matters of State Policy. We are then to confer and recommend a course of action which will be in line with this Policy and assist it. We have to reach our decision quickly. But our decision will be of supreme importance to the State. It will therefore have to be a correct decision.'

General G. paused to allow the significance of his words time to sink in. One by one, he slowly examined the faces of the three senior officers at the table. Their eyes looked stolidly back at him. Inside, these extremely important men were perturbed. They were about to look through the furnace door. They were about to learn a State secret, the knowledge of which might one day have most dangerous consequences for them. Sitting in the quiet room, they felt bathed in the dreadful incandescence that shines out from the centre of all power in the Soviet Union–the High Praesidium.

The final ash fell off the end of General G.'s cigarette on to his tunic. He brushed it off and threw the cardboard butt into the basket for secret waste beside his desk. He lit another cigarette and spoke through it.

'Our recommendation concerns a conspicuous act of terrorism to be carried out in enemy territory within three months.'

Six pairs of expressionless eyes stared at the head of SMERSH, waiting.

'Comrades,' General G. leant back in his chair and his voice became expository, 'the foreign policy of the U.S.S.R. has entered a new phase. Formerly, it was a "Hard" policy–a policy [he allowed himself the joke on Stalin's name] of steel. This policy, effective as it was, built up tensions in the West, notably in America, which were becoming dangerous. The Americans are unpredictable people. They are hysterical. The reports of our Intelligence began to indicate that we were pushing America to the brink of an undeclared atomic attack on the U.S.S.R. You have read these reports and you know what I say is true. We do not want such a war. If there is to be a war, it is we who will choose the time. Certain powerful Americans, notably the Pentagon Group led by Admiral Radford, were helped in their firebrand schemes by the very successes of our "Hard" policy. So it was decided that the time had come to change our methods, while maintaining our aims. A new policy was created–the "Hard-Soft" policy. Geneva was the beginning of this policy. We were "soft". China threatens Quemoy and Matsu. We are "hard". We open our frontiers to a lot of newspaper men and actors and artists although we know many of them to be spies. Our leaders laugh and makes jokes at receptions in Moscow. In the middle of the jokes we drop the biggest test bomb of all time. Comrades Bulganin and Khrushschev and Comrade General Serov [General G. carefully included the names for the ears of the tape-recorder] visit India and the East and blackguard the English. When they get back, they have friendly discussions with the British Ambassador about their forthcoming goodwill visit to London. And so it goes on–the stick and then the carrot, the smile and then the frown. And the West is confused. Tensions are relaxed before they have time to harden. The reactions of our enemies are clumsy, their strategy disorganized. Meanwhile the common people laugh at our jokes, cheer our football teams and slobber with delight when we release a few prisoners of war whom we wish to feed no longer!'

There were smiles of pleasure and pride round the table. What a brilliant policy! What fools we are making of them in the West!

'At the same time,' continued General G., himself smiling thinly at the pleasure he had caused, 'we continue to forge everywhere stealthily ahead–revolution in Morocco, arms to Egypt, friendship with Yugoslavia, trouble in Cyprus, riots in Turkey, strikes in England, great political gains in France–there is no front in the world on which we are not quietly advancing.'

General G. saw the eyes shining greedily round the table. The men were softened up. Now it was time to be hard. Now it was time for them to feel the new policy on themselves. The Intelligence services would also have to pull their weight in this great game that was being played on their behalf. Smoothly General G. leaned forward. He planted his right elbow on the desk and raised his fist in the air.

'But Comrades,' his voice was soft, 'where has there been failure in carrying out the State Policy of the U.S.S.R.? Who has all along been soft when we wished to be hard? Who has suffered defeats while victory was going to all other departments of the State? Who, with their stupid blunders, has made the Soviet Union look foolish and weak throughout the world? WHO?'

The voice had risen almost to a scream. General G. thought how well he was delivering the denunciation demanded by the Praesidium. How splendid it would sound when the tape was played back to Serov!

He glared down the conference table at the pale, expectant faces. General G.'s fist crashed forward on to the desk.

'The whole Intelligence *apparat* of the Soviet Union, Comrades.' The voice was now a furious bellow. 'It is we who are the sluggards, the saboteurs, the traitors! It is we who are failing the Soviet Union in its great and glorious struggle! We!' His arm swept round the room. 'All of us!' The voice came back to normal, became more reasonable. 'Comrades, look at the record. *Sookin Sin* [he allowed himself the peasant obscenity], son-of-a-bitch, look at the record! First we lose Gouzenko and the whole of the Canadian *apparat* and the scientist Fuchs, then the American *apparat* is cleaned up, then we lose men like Tokaev, then comes the scandalous Khoklov affair which did great damage to our country, then Petrov and his wife in Australia–a bungled business if ever there was one! The list is endless–defeat after defeat, and the devil knows I have not mentioned the half of it.'

General G. paused. He continued in his softest voice. 'Comrades, I have to tell you that unless tonight we make a recommendation for a great Intelligence victory, and unless we act correctly on that recommendation, if it is approved, there will be trouble.'

General G. sought for a final phrase to convey the threat without defining it. He found it. 'There will be,' he paused and looked, with artificial mildness, down the table, 'displeasure.'

Chapter Five

Konspiratsia

The moujiks had received the knout. General G. gave them a few minutes to lick their wounds and recover from the shock of the official lashing that had been meted out.

No one said a word for the defence. No one spoke up for his department or mentioned the countless victories of Soviet Intelligence that could be set against the few mistakes. And no one questioned the right of the Head of SMERSH, who shared the guilt with them, to deliver this terrible denunciation. The Word had gone out from the Throne, and General G. had been chosen as the mouthpiece for the Word. It was a great compliment to General G. that he had been thus chosen, a sign of grace, a sign of coming preferment, and everyone present made a careful note of the fact that, in the Intelligence hierarchy, General G., with SMERSH behind him, had come to the top of the pile.

At the end of the table, the representative of the Foreign Ministry, Lieutenant-General Vozdvishensky of R.U.M.I.D., watched the smoke curl up from the tip of his long Kazbek cigarette and remembered how Molotov had privately told him, when Beria was dead, that General G. would go far. There had been no great foresight in this prophecy, reflected Vozdvishensky. Beria had disliked G. and had constantly hindered his advancement, side-tracking him away from the main ladder of power into one of the minor departments of the then Ministry of State Security, which, on the death of Stalin, Beria had quickly abolished as a Ministry. Until 1952, G. had been deputy to one of the heads of this Ministry. When the post was abolished, he devoted his energies to plotting the downfall of Beria, working under the secret orders of the formidable General Serov, whose record put him out of even Beria's reach.

Serov, a Hero of the Soviet Union and a veteran of the famous predecessors of the M.G.B.–the Cheka, the Ogpu, the N.K.V.D. and the M.V.D.–was in every respect a bigger man than Beria. He had been directly behind the mass executions of the 1930s when a million died, he had been *metteur en scène* of most of the great Moscow show trials, he had organized the bloody genocide in the Central Caucasus in February 1944, and it was he who had inspired the mass deportations from the Baltic States and the kidnapping of the German atom and other scientists who had given Russia her great technical leap forward after the war.

And Beria and all his court had gone to the gallows, while General G. had been given SMERSH as his reward. As for Army General Ivan Serov, he, with Bulganin and Khrushchev, now ruled Russia. One day, he might even stand on the peak, alone. But, guessed General Vozdvishensky, glancing up the table at the gleaming billiard-ball skull, probably with General G. not far behind him.

The skull lifted and the hard bulging brown eyes looked straight down the table into the eyes of General Vozdvishensky. General Vozdvishensky managed to look back calmly and even with a hint of appraisal.

That is a deep one, thought General G. Let us put the spotlight on him and see how he shows up on the sound-track.

'Comrades,' gold flashed from both corners of his mouth as he stretched his lips in a chairman's smile, 'let us not be too dismayed. Even the highest tree has an axe waiting at its foot. We have never thought that our departments were so successful as to be beyond criticism. What I have been instructed to say to you will not have come as a surprise to any of us. So let us take up the challenge with a good heart and get down to business.'

Round the table there was no answering smile to these platitudes. General G. had not expected that there would be. He lit a cigarette and continued.

'I said that we have at once to recommend an act of terrorism in the intelligence field, and one of our departments–no doubt my own–will be called upon to carry out this act.'

An inaudible sigh of relief went round the table. So at least SMERSH would be the responsible department! That was something.

'But the choice of a target will not be an easy matter, and our collective responsibility for the correct choice will be a heavy one.'

Soft-hard, hard-soft. The ball was now back with the conference.

'It is not just a question of blowing up a building or shooting a prime minister. Such bourgeois horseplay is not contemplated. Our operation must be delicate, refined and aimed at the heart of the Intelligence *apparat* of the West. It must do grave damage to the enemy *apparat*–hidden damage which the public will hear perhaps nothing of, but which will be the secret talk of government circles. But it must also cause a public scandal so devastating that the world will lick its lips and sneer at the shame and stupidity of our enemies. Naturally Governments will know that it is a Soviet *konspiratsia*. That is good. It will be a piece of "hard" policy. And the agents and spies of the West will know it, too, and they will marvel at our cleverness and they will tremble. Traitors and possible defectors will change their minds. Our own operatives will be stimulated. They will be encouraged to greater efforts by our display of strength and genius. But of course we shall deny any knowledge of the deed, whatever it may be, and it is desirable that the common people of the Soviet Union should remain in complete ignorance of our complicity.'

General G. paused and looked down the table at the representative of R.U.M.I.D., who again held his gaze impassively.

'And now to choose the organization at which we will strike, and then to decide on the specific target within that organization. Comrade Lieutenant-General Vozdvishensky, since you observe the foreign intelligence scene from a neutral standpoint [this was a jibe at the notorious jealousies that exist between the military intelligence of the G.R.U. and the Secret Service of the M.G.B.], perhaps you would survey the field for us. We wish to have your opinion of the relative importance of the Western Intelligence Services. We will then choose the one which is the most dangerous and which we would most wish to damage.'

General G. sat back in his tall chair. He rested his elbows on the arms and supported his chin on the interlaced fingers of his joined hands, like a teacher preparing to listen to a long construe.

General Vozdvishensky was not dismayed by his task. He had been in intelligence, mostly abroad, for thirty years. He had served as a 'doorman' at the Soviety Embassy in London under Litvinoff. He had worked with the Tass Agency in New York and had then gone back to London, to Amtorg, the Soviet Trade Organization. For five years he had been Military Attaché under the brilliant Madame Kollontai in the Stockholm Embassy. He had helped train Sorge, the Soviet master spy, before Sorge went to Tokyo. During the war, he had been for a while resident Director in Switzerland, or 'Schmidtland', as it had been known in the spy-jargon, and there he had helped sow the seeds of the sensationally successful but tragically misused 'Lucy' network. He had even gone several times into Germany as a courier to the 'Rote Kapelle', and had narrowly escaped being cleaned up with it. And after the war, on transfer to the Foreign Ministry, he had been on the inside of the Burgess and Maclean operation and on countless other plots to penetrate the Foreign Ministries of the West. He was a professional spy to his finger-tips and he was perfectly prepared to put on record his opinions of the rivals with whom he had been crossing swords all his life.

The A.D.C. at his side was less comfortable. He was nervous at R.U.M.I.D. being pinned down in this way, and without a full departmental briefing. He scoured his brain clear and sharpened his ears to catch every word.

'In this matter,' said General Vozdvishensky carefully, 'one must not confuse the man with the office. Every country has good spies and it is not always the biggest countries that have the most or the best. But Secret Services are expensive, and small countries cannot afford the co-ordinated effort which produces good intelligence–the forgery departments, the radio network, the record department, the digestive apparatus that evaluates and compares the reports of the agents. There are individual agents serving Norway, Holland, Belgium and even Portugal who could be a great nuisance to us if these countries knew the value of their reports or made good use of them. But they do not. Instead of passing their information on to the larger powers, they prefer to sit on it and feel important. So we need not worry with these smaller countries,' he paused, 'until we come to Sweden. There they have been spying on us for centuries. They have always had better information on the Baltic than even Finland or Germany. They are dangerous. I would like to put a stop to their activities.'

General G. interrupted. 'Comrade, they are always having spy scandals in Sweden. One more scandal would not make the world look up. Please continue.'

'Italy can be dismissed,' went on General Vozdvishensky, without appearing to notice the interruption. 'They are clever and active, but they do us no harm. They are only interested in their own backyard, the Mediterranean. The same can be said of Spain, except that their counter-intelligence is a great hindrance to the Party. We have lost many good men to these Fascists. But to mount an operation against them would probably cost us more men. And little would be achieved. They are not yet ripe for revolution. In France, while we have penetrated most of their Services, the Deuxième Bureau is still clever and dangerous. There is a man called Mathis at the head of it. A Mendès-France appointment. He would be a tempting target and it would be easy to operate in France.'

'France is looking after herself,' commented General G.

'England is another matter altogether. I think we all have respect for her Intelligence Service,' General Vozdvishensky looked round the table. There were grudging nods from everyone present, including General G. 'Their Security Service is excellent. England, being an island, has great security advantages and their so-called M.I.5 employs men with good education and good brains. Their Secret Service is still better. They have notable successes. In certain types of operation, we are constantly finding that they have been there before us. Their agents are good. They pay them little money–only a thousand or two thousand roubles a month–but they serve with devotion. Yet these agents have no special privileges in England, no relief from taxation and no special shops such as we have, from which they can buy cheap goods. Their social standing abroad is not high, and their wives have to pass as the wives of secretaries. They are rarely awarded a decoration until they retire. And yet these men and women continue to do this dangerous work. It is curious. It is perhaps the Public School and University tradition. The love of adventure. But still it is odd that they play this game so well, for they are not natural conspirators.' General Vozdvishensky felt that his remarks might be taken as too laudatory. He hastily qualified them. 'Of course, most of their strength lies in the myth–in the myth of Scotland Yard, of Sherlock Holmes, of the Secret Service. We certainly have nothing to fear from these gentlemen. But this myth is a hindrance which it would be good to set aside.'

'And the Americans?' General G. wanted to put a stop to Vozdvishensky's attempts to qualify his praise of British Intelligence. One day that bit about the Public School and University tradition would sound well in court. Next, hoped General G., he will be saying that the Pentagon is stronger than the Kremlin.

'The Americans have the biggest and richest service among our enemies. Technically, in such matters as radio and weapons and equipment, they are the best. But they have no understanding for the work. They get enthusiastic about some Balkan spy who says he has a secret army in the Ukraine. They load him with money with which to buy boots for this army. Of course he goes at once to Paris and spends the money on women. Americans try to do everything with money. Good spies will not work for money alone–only bad ones, of which the Americans have several divisions.'

'They have successes, Comrade,' said General G. silkily. 'Perhaps you underestimate them.'

General Vozdvishensky shrugged. 'They must have successes, Comrade General. You cannot sow a million seeds without reaping one potato. Personally I do not think the Americans need engage the attention of this conference.' The head of R.U.M.I.D. sat back in his chair and stolidly took out his cigarette case.

'A very interesting exposition,' said General G. coldly. 'Comrade General Slavin?'

General Slavin of the G.R.U. had no intention of committing himself on behalf of the General Staff of the Army. 'I have listened with interest to the words of Comrade General Vozdvishensky. I have nothing to add.'

Colonel of State Security Nikitin of M.G.B. felt it would do no great harm to show up the G.R.U. as being too stupid to have any ideas at all, and at the same time to make a modest recommendation that would probably tally with the inner thoughts of those present–and that was certainly on the tip of

General G.'s tongue. Colonel Nikitin also knew that, given the proposition that had been posed by the Praesidium, the Soviet Secret Service would back him up.

'I recommend the English Secret Service as the object of terrorist action,' he said decisively. 'The devil knows my department hardly finds them a worthy adversary, but they are the best of an indifferent lot.'

General G. was annoyed by the authority in the man's voice, and by having his thunder stolen, for he also had intended to sum up in favour of an operation against the British. He tapped his lighter softly on the desk to reimpose his chairmanship. 'Is it agreed then, Comrades? An act of terrorism against the British Secret Service?'

There were careful, slow nods all round the table.

'I agree. And now for the target within that organization. I remember Comrade General Vozdvishensky saying something about a myth upon which much of the alleged strength of this Secret Service depends. How can we help to destroy the myth and thus strike at the very motive force of this organization? Where does this myth reside? We cannot destroy all its personnel at one blow. Does it reside in the Head? Who is the Head of the British Secret Service?'

Colonel Nikitin's aide whispered in his ear. Colonel Nikitin decided that this was a question he could and perhaps should answer.

'He is an Admiral. He is known by the letter M. We have a *zapiska* on him, but it contains little. He does not drink very much. He is too old for women. The public does not know of his existence. It would be difficult to create a scandal round his death. And he would not be easy to kill. He rarely goes abroad. To shoot him in a London street would not be very refined.'

'There is much in what you say, Comrade,' said General G. 'But we are here to find a target who *will* fulfil our requirements. Have they no one who is a hero to the organization? Someone who is admired and whose ignominious destruction would cause dismay? Myths are built on heroic deeds and heroic people. Have they no such men?'

There was silence round the table while everyone searched his memory. So many names to remember, so many dossiers, so many operations going on every day all over the world. Who was there in the British Secret Service? Who was the man who . . . ?

It was Colonel Nikitin of the M.G.B. who broke the embarrassed silence. He said hesitantly, 'There is a man called Bond.'

Chapter Six

Death Warrant

'*Y*b**nna mat!*' The gross obscenity was a favourite with General G. His hand slapped down on the desk. 'Comrade, there certainly is "a man called Bond" as you put it.' His voice was sarcastic. 'James Bond. [He pronounced it "Shems".] And nobody, myself included, could think of this spy's name!

We are indeed forgetful. No wonder the Intelligence *apparat* is under criticism.'

General Vozdvishensky felt he should defend himself and his department. 'There are countless enemies of the Soviet Union, Comrade General,' he protested. 'If I want their names, I send to the Central Index for them. Certainly I know the name of this Bond. He has been a great trouble to us at different times. But today my mind is full of other names–names of people who are causing us trouble today, this week. I am interested in football, but I cannot remember the name of every foreigner who has scored a goal against the Dynamos.'

'You are pleased to joke, Comrade,' said General G. to underline this out-of-place comment. 'This is a serious matter. I for one admit my fault in not remembering the name of this notorious agent. Comrade Colonel Nikitin will no doubt refresh our memories further, but I recall that this Bond has at least twice frustrated the operations of SMERSH. That is,' he added, 'before I assumed control of the department. There was this affair in France, at that Casino town. The man Le Chiffre. An excellent leader of the Party in France. He foolishly got into some money troubles. But he would have got out of them if this Bond had not interfered. I recall that the Department had to act quickly and liquidate the Frenchman. The executioner should have dealt with the Englishman at the same time, but he did not. Then there was this Negro of ours in Harlem. A great man–one of the greatest foreign agents we have ever employed, and with a vast network behind him. There was some business about a treasure in the Caribbean. I forget the details. This Englishman was sent out by the Secret Service and smashed the whole organization and killed our man. It was a great reverse. Once again my predecessor should have proceeded ruthlessly against this English spy.'

Colonel Nikitin broke in. 'We had a similar experience in the case of the German, Drax, and the rocket. You will recall the matter, Comrade General. A most important *konspiratsia*. The General Staff were deeply involved. It was a matter of High Policy which could have borne decisive fruit. But again it was this Bond who frustrated the operation. The German was killed. There were grave consequences for the State. There followed a period of serious embarrassment which was only solved with difficulty.'

General Slavin of G.R.U. felt that he should say something. The rocket had been an Army operation and its failure had been laid at the door of G.R.U. Nikitin knew this perfectly well. As usual M.G.B. was trying to make trouble for G.R.U.–raking up old history in this manner. 'We asked for this man to be dealt with by your department, Comrade Colonel,' he said icily. 'I cannot recall that any action followed our request. If it had, we should not now be having to bother with him.'

Colonel Nikitin's temples throbbed with rage. He controlled himself. 'With due respect, Comrade General,' he said in a loud, sarcastic voice, 'the request of G.R.U. was not confirmed by Higher Authority. Further embarrassment with England was not desired. Perhaps that detail has slipped your memory. In any case, if such a request had reached M.G.B., it would have been referred to SMERSH for action.'

'My department received no such request,' said General G. sharply. 'Or the execution of this man would have rapidly followed. However, this is no time for historical researches. The rocket affair was three years ago. Perhaps the M.G.B. could tell us of the more recent activities of this man.'

Colonel Nikitin whispered hurriedly with his aide. He turned back to the table. 'We have very little further information, Comrade General,' he said defensively. 'We believe that he was involved in some diamond smuggling affair. That was last year. Between Africa and America. The case did not concern us. Since then we have no further news of him. Perhaps there is more recent information on his file.'

General G. nodded. He picked up the receiver of the telephone nearest to him. This was the so-called *Kommandant Telefon* of the M.G.B. All lines were direct and there was no central switchboard. He dialled a number. 'Central Index? Here General Grubozaboyschikov. The *zapiska* of "Bond"–English spy. Emergency.' He listened for the immediate 'At once, Comrade General,' and put back the receiver. He looked down the table with authority. 'Comrades, from many points of view this spy sounds an appropriate target. He appears to be a dangerous enemy of the State. His liquidation will be of benefit to all departments of our Intelligence *apparat*. Is that so?'

The conference grunted.

'Also his loss will be felt by the Secret Service. But will it do more? Will it seriously wound them? Will it help to destroy this myth about which we have been speaking? Is that man a hero to his organization and his country?'

General Vozdvishensky decided that this question was intended for him. He spoke up. 'The English are not interested in heroes unless they are footballers or cricketers or jockeys. If a man climbs a mountain or runs very fast he also is a hero to some people, but not to the masses. The Queen of England is also a hero, and Churchill. But the English are not greatly interested in military heroes. This man Bond is unknown to the public. If he was known, he would still not be a hero. In England, neither open war nor secret war is a heroic matter. They do not like to think about war, and after a war the names of their war heroes are forgotten as quickly as possible. Within the Secret Service, this man may be a local hero or he may not. It will depend on his appearance and personal characteristics. Of these I know nothing. He may be fat and greasy and unpleasant. No one makes a hero out of such a man, however successful he is.'

Nikitin broke in. 'English spies we have captured speak highly of this man. He is certainly much admired in his Service. He is said to be a lone wolf, but a good looking one.'

The internal office telephone purred softly. General G. lifted the receiver, listened briefly and said, 'Bring it in.' There was a knock on the door. The A.D.C. came in carrying a bulky file in cardboard covers. He crossed the room and placed the file on the desk in front of the General and walked out, closing the door softly behind him.

The file had a shiny black cover. A thick white stripe ran diagonally across it from top right-hand corner to bottom left. In the top left-hand space there were the letters 'S.S.' in white, and under them 'SOVERSHENNOE SEKRETNO', the equivalent of 'Top Secret'. Across the centre was neatly painted in white letters 'JAMES BOND', and underneath '*Angliski Spion*'.

General G. opened the file and took out a large envelope containing photographs which he emptied on to the glass surface of the desk. He picked them up one by one. He looked closely at them, sometimes through a magnifying glass which he took out of a drawer, and passed them across the desk to Nikitin who glanced at them and handed them on.

The first was dated 1946. It showed a dark young man sitting at a table outside a sunlit café. There was a tall glass beside him on the table and a soda-water siphon. The right forearm rested on the table and there was a cigarette between the fingers of the right hand that hung negligently down from the edge of the table. The legs were crossed in that attitude that only an Englishman adopts–with the right ankle resting on the left knee and the left hand grasping the ankle. It was a careless pose. The man didn't know that he was being photographed from a point about twenty feet away.

The next was dated 1950. It was a face and shoulders, blurred, but of the same man. It was a close-up and Bond was looking with careful, narrowed eyes at something, probably the photographer's face, just above the lens. A miniature button-hole camera, guessed General G.

The third was from 1951. Taken from the left flank, quite close, it showed the same man in a dark suit, without a hat, walking down a wide empty street. He was passing a shuttered shop whose sign said 'Charcuterie'. He looked as if he was going somewhere urgently. The clean-cut profile was pointing straight ahead and the crook of the right elbow suggested that his right hand was in the pocket of his coat. General G. reflected that it was probably taken from a car. He thought that the decisive look of the man, and the purposeful slant of his striding figure, looked dangerous, as if he was making quickly for something bad that was happening further down the street.

The fourth and last photograph was marked *Passe. 1953*. The corner of the Royal Seal and the letters '. . . REIGN OFFICE' in the segment of a circle showed in the bottom right-hand corner. The photograph, which had been blown up to cabinet size, must have been made at a frontier, or by the concierge of an hotel when Bond had surrendered his passport. General G. carefully went over the face with his magnifying glass.

It was a dark, clean-cut face, with a three-inch scar showing whitely down the sunburned skin of the right cheek. The eyes were wide and level under straight, rather long black brows. The hair was black, parted on the left, and carelessly brushed so that a thick black comma fell down over the right eyebrow. The longish straight nose ran down to a short upper lip below which was a wide and finely drawn but cruel mouth. The line of the jaw was straight and firm. A section of dark suit, white shirt and black knitted tie completed the picture.

General G. held the photograph out at arm's length. Decision, authority, ruthlessness–these qualities he could see. He didn't care what else went on inside the man. He passed the photograph down the table and turned to the file, glancing rapidly down each page and flipping brusquely on to the next.

The photographs came back to him. He kept his place with a finger and looked briefly up. 'He looks a nasty customer,' he said grimly. 'His story confirms it. I will read out some extracts. Then we must decide. It is getting late.' He turned back to the first page and began to rattle off the points that struck him.

'First name: JAMES. Height: 183 centimetres; weight: 76 kilograms; slim build, eyes: blue; hair: black; scar down right cheek and on left shoulder; signs of plastic surgery on back of right hand (see Appendix "A"); all-round athlete; expert pistol shot, boxer, knife-thrower; does not use disguises. Languages: French and German. Smokes heavily (N.B.: special cigarettes with three gold bands); vices: drink, but not to excess, and women. Not thought to accept bribes.'

General G. skipped a page and went on:

'This man is invariably armed with a ·25 Beretta automatic carried in a holster under his left arm. Magazine holds eight rounds. Has been known to carry a knife strapped to his left forearm; has used steel-capped shoes; knows the basic holds of judo. In general, fights with tenacity and has a high tolerance of pain (see Appendix "B").'

General G. riffled through more pages giving extracts from agents' reports from which this data was drawn. He came to the last page before the Appendices which gave details of the cases on which Bond had been encountered. He ran his eye to the bottom and read out: 'Conclusion. This man is a dangerous professional terrorist and spy. He has worked for the British Secret Service since 1938 and now (see Highsmith file of December 1950) holds the secret number "007" in that Service. The double o numerals signify an agent who has killed and who is privileged to kill on active service. There are believed to be only two other British agents with this authority. The fact that this spy was decorated with the C.M.G. in 1953, an award usually given only on retirement from the Secret Service, is a measure of his worth. If encountered in the field, the fact and full details to be reported to headquarters (see SMERSH, M.G.B. and G.R.U. Standing Orders 1951 onwards).'

General G. shut the file and slapped his hand decisively on the cover. 'Well, Comrades. Are we agreed?'

'Yes,' said Colonel Nikitin, loudly.

'Yes,' said General Slavin in a bored voice.

General Vozdvishensky was looking down at his fingernails. He was sick of murder. He had enjoyed his time in England. 'Yes,' he said. 'I suppose so.'

General G.'s hand went to the internal office telephone. He spoke to his A.D.C. 'Death Warrant,' he said harshly. 'Made out in the name of "James Bond".' He spelled the names out. 'Description: *Angliski Spion*. Crime: Enemy of the State.' He put the receiver back and leant forward in his chair. 'And now it will be a question of devising an appropriate *konspiratsia*. And one that cannot fail!' He smiled grimly. 'We cannot have another of those Khoklov affairs.'

The door opened and the A.D.C. came in carrying a bright yellow sheet of paper. He put it in front of General G. and went out. General G. ran his eyes down the paper and wrote the words 'To be killed. Grubozaboyschikov' at the head of the large empty space at the bottom. He passed the paper to the M.G.B. man who read it and wrote 'Kill him. Nikitin' and handed it across to the head of G.R.U. who wrote 'Kill him. Slavin'. One of the A.D.C.s passed the paper to the plain-clothes man sitting beside the representative of R.U.M.I.D. The man put it in front of General Vozdvishensky and handed him a pen.

General Vozdvishensky read the paper carefully. He raised his eyes slowly to those of General G. who was watching him and, without looking down, scribbled the 'Kill him' more or less under the other signatures and scrawled his name after it. Then he took his hands away from the paper and got to his feet.

'If that is all, Comrade General?' he pushed his chair back.

General G. was pleased. His instincts about this man had been right. He would have to put a watch on him and pass on his suspicions to General Serov. 'One moment, Comrade General,' he said. 'I have something to add to the warrant.'

The paper was handed up to him. He took out his pen and scratched out what he had written. He wrote again, speaking the words slowly as he did so.

'To be killed WITH IGNOMINY. Grubozaboyschikov.'

He looked up and smiled pleasantly to the company. 'Thank you, Comrades. That is all. I shall advise you of the decision of the Praesidium on our recommendation. Good night.'

When the conference had filed out, General G. rose to his feet and stretched and gave a loud controlled yawn. He sat down again at his desk, switched off the wire-recorder and rang for his A.D.C. The man came in and stood beside his desk.

General G. handed him the yellow paper. 'Send this over to General Serov at once. Find out where Kronsteen is and have him fetched by car. I don't care if he's in bed. He will have to come. Otdyel II will know where to find him. And I will see Colonel Klebb in ten minutes.'

'Yes, Comrade General.' The man left the room.

General G. picked up the V.Ch. receiver and asked for General Serov. He spoke quietly for five minutes. At the end he concluded: 'And I am now about to give the task to Colonel Klebb and the Planner, Kronsteen. We will discuss the outlines of a suitable *konspiratsia* and they will give me detailed proposals tomorrow. Is that in order, Comrade General?'

'Yes,' came the quiet voice of General Serov of the High Praesidium. 'Kill him. But let it be excellently accomplished. The Praesidium will ratify the decision in the morning.'

The line went dead. The inter-office telephone rang. General G. said 'Yes' into the receiver and put it back.

A moment later the A.D.C. opened the big door and stood in the entrance. 'Comrade Colonel Klebb,' he announced.

A toad-like figure in an olive green uniform which bore the single red ribbon of the Order of Lenin came into the room and walked with quick short steps over to the desk.

General G. looked up and waved to the nearest chair at the conference table. 'Good evening, Comrade.'

The squat face split into a sugary smile. 'Good evening, Comrade General.'

The Head of Otdyel II, the department of SMERSH in charge of Operations and Executions, hitched up her skirts and sat down.

Chapter Seven

The Wizard of Ice

The two faces of the double clock in the shiny, domed case looked out across the chess-board like the eyes of some huge sea monster that had peered over the edge of the table to watch the game.

The two faces of the chess clock showed different times. Kronsteen's showed twenty minutes to one. The long red pendulum that ticked off the seconds was moving in its staccato sweep across the bottom half of his clock's face, while the enemy clock was silent and its pendulum motionless down the face. But Makharov's clock said five minutes to one. He had wasted time in the middle of the game and he now had only five minutes to go. He was in bad 'time-trouble' and unless Kronsteen made some lunatic mistake, which was unthinkable, he was beaten.

Kronsteen sat motionless and erect, as malevolently inscrutable as a parrot. His elbows were on the table and his big head rested on clenched fists that pressed into his cheeks, squashing the pursed lips into a pout of hauteur and disdain. Under the wide, bulging brow the rather slanting black eyes looked down with deadly calm on his winning board. But, behind the mask, the blood was throbbing in the dynamo of his brain, and a thick worm-like vein in his right temple pulsed at a beat of over ninety. He had sweated away a pound of weight in the last two hours and ten minutes, and the spectre of a false move still had one hand at his throat. But to Makharov, and to the spectators, he was still 'The Wizard of Ice' whose game had been compared to a man eating fish. First he stripped off the skin, then he picked out the bones, then he ate the fish. Kronsteen had been Champion of Moscow two years running, was now in the final for the third time and, if he won this game, would be a contender for Grand Mastership.

In the pool of silence round the roped-off top table there was no sound except the loud tripping feet of Kronsteen's clock. The two umpires sat motionless in their raised chairs. They knew, as did Makharov, that this was certainly the kill. Kronsteen had introduced a brilliant twist into the Meran Variation of the Queen's Gambit Declined. Makharov had kept up with him until the 28th move. He had lost time on that move. Perhaps he had made a mistake there, and perhaps again on the 31st and 33rd moves. Who could say? It would be a game to be debated all over Russia for weeks to come.

There came a sigh from the crowded tiers opposite the Championship game. Kronsteen had slowly removed the right hand from his cheek and had stretched it across the board. Like the pincers of a pink crab, his thumb and forefinger had opened, then they had descended. The hand, holding a piece, moved up and sideways and down. Then the hand was slowly brought back to the face.

The spectators buzzed and whispered as they saw, on the great wall map, the 41st move duplicated with a shift of one of the three-foot placards.

R-Kt8. That must be the kill!

Kronsteen reached deliberately over and pressed down the lever at the bottom of his clock. His red pendulum went dead. His clock showed a quarter to one. At the same instant, Makharov's pendulum came to life and started its loud, inexorable beat.

Kronsteen sat back. He placed his hands flat on the table and looked coldly across at the glistening, lowered face of the man whose guts he knew, for he too had suffered defeat in his time, would be writhing in agony like an eel pierced with a spear. Makharov, Champion of Georgia. Well, tomorrow Comrade Makharov could go back to Georgia and stay there. At any rate this year he would not be moving with his family up to Moscow.

A man in plain clothes slipped under the ropes and whispered to one of the umpires. He handed him a white envelope. The umpire shook his head, pointing at Makharov's clock, which now said three minutes to one. The man in plain clothes whispered one short sentence which made the umpire sullenly bow his head. He pinged a handbell.

'There is an urgent personal message for Comrade Kronsteen,' he announced into the microphone. 'There will be a three minutes' pause.'

A mutter went round the hall. Even though Makharov now courteously raised his eyes from the board and sat immobile, gazing up into the recesses of the high, vaulted ceiling, the spectators knew that the position of the game was engraved on his brain. A three minutes' pause simply meant three extra minutes for Makharov.

Kronsteen felt the same stab of annoyance, but his face was expressionless as the umpire stepped down from his chair and handed him a plain, unaddressed envelope. Kronsteen ripped it open with his thumb and extracted the anonymous sheet of paper. It said, in the large typewritten characters he knew so well, 'YOU ARE REQUIRED THIS INSTANT'. No signature and no address.

Kronsteen folded the paper and carefully placed it in his inside breast pocket. later it would be recovered from him and destroyed. He looked up at the face of the plain-clothes man standing beside the umpire. The eyes were watching him impatiently, commandingly. To hell with these people, thought Kronsteen. He would *not* resign with only three minutes to go. It was unthinkable. It was an insult to the People's Sport. But, as he made a gesture to the umpire that the game could continue, he trembled inside, and he avoided the eyes of the plain-clothes man who remained standing, in coiled immobility, inside the ropes.

The bell pinged. 'The game proceeds.'

Makharov slowly bent down his head. The hand of his clock slipped past the hour and he was still alive.

Kronsteen continued to tremble inside. What he had done was unheard of in an employee of SMERSH, or of any other State agency. He would certainly be reported. Gross disobedience. Dereliction of duty. What might be the consequences? At the best a tongue-lashing from General G., and black mark on his *zapiska*. At the worst? Kronsteen couldn't imagine. He didn't like to think. Whatever happened, the sweets of victory had turned bitter in his mouth.

But now it was the end. With five seconds to go on his clock, Makharov raised his whipped eyes no higher than the pouting lips of his opponent and bent his head in the brief, formal bow of surrender. At the double ping of the umpire's bell, the crowded hall rose to its feet with a thunder of applause.

Kronsteen stood up and bowed to his opponent, to the umpires, and finally, deeply, to the spectators. Then, with the plain-clothes man in his wake, he ducked under the ropes and fought his way coldly and rudely through the mass of his clamouring admirers towards the main exit.

Outside the Tournament Hall, in the middle of the wide Pushkin Ulitza, with its engine running, stood the usual anonymous black ZIK saloon. Kronsteen climbed into the back and shut the door. As the plain-clothes man jumped on to the running-board and squeezed into the front seat, the driver crashed his gears and the car tore off down the street.

Kronsteen knew it would be a waste of breath to apologize to the plain-clothes guard. It would also be contrary to discipline. After all, he was Head of the Planning Department of SMERSH, with the honorary rank of full Colonel. And his brain was worth diamonds to the organization. Perhaps he could argue his way out of the mess. He gazed out of the window at the dark streets, already wet with the work of the night cleaning squad, and bent his mind to his defence. Then there came a straight street at the end of which the moon rode fast between the onion spires of the Kremlin, and they were there.

When the guard handed Kronsteen over to the A.D.C., he also handed the A.D.C. a slip of paper. The A.D.C. glanced at it and looked coldly up at Kronsteen with half-raised eyebrows. Kronsteen looked calmly back without saying anything. The A.D.C. shrugged his shoulders and picked up the office telephone and announced him.

When they went into the big room and Kronsteen had been waved to a chair and had nodded acknowledgment of the brief pursed smile of Colonel Klebb, the A.D.C. went up to General G. and handed him the piece of paper. The General read it and looked hard across at Kronsteen. While the A.D.C. walked to the door and went out, the General went on looking at Kronsteen. When the door was shut, General G. opened his mouth and said softly, 'Well, Comrade?'

Kronsteen was calm. He knew the story that would appeal. He spoke quietly and with authority. 'To the public, Comrade General, I am a professional chess player. Tonight I became Champion of Moscow for the third year in succession. If, with only three minutes to go. I had received a message that my wife was being murdered outside the door of the Tournament Hall, I would not have raised a finger to save her. My public know that. They are as dedicated to the game as myself. Tonight, if I had resigned the game and had come immediately on receipt of that message, five thousand people would have known that it could only be on the orders of such a department as this. There would have been a storm of gossip. My future goings and comings would have been watched for clues. It would have been the end of my cover. In the interests of State Security, I waited three minutes before obeying the order. Even so, my hurried departure will be the subject of much comment. I shall have to say that one of my children is gravely ill. I shall have to put a child into hospital for a week to support the story. I deeply apologize for the delay in carrying out the order. But the decision was a difficult one. I did what I thought best in the interests of the Department.'

General G. looked thoughtfully into the dark slanting eyes. The man was guilty, but the defence was good. He read the paper again as if weighing up the size of the offence, then he took out his lighter and burned it. He dropped the last burning corner on to the glass top of his desk and blew the ashes sideways on to the floor. He said nothing to reveal his thoughts, but the burning of the evidence was all that mattered to Kronsteen. Now nothing could go on his *zapiska*. He was deeply relieved and grateful. He would bend all his ingenuity to the matter on hand. The General had performed an act of great clemency. Kronsteen would repay him with the full coin of his mind.

'Pass over the photographs, Comrade Colonel,' said General G., as if the brief court-martial had not occurred. 'The matter is as follows. . . .'

So it is another death, thought Kronsteen, as the General talked and he examined the dark ruthless face that gazed levelly at him from the blown-up passport photograph. While Kronsteen listened with half his mind to what the General was saying, he picked out the salient facts–English spy. Great scandal desired. No Soviet involvement. Expert killer. Weakness for women (therefore not homosexual, thought Kronsteen). Drinks (but nothing is said about drugs). Unbribable (who knows? There is a price for every man). No expense would be spared. All equipment and personnel available from all intelligence departments. Success to be achieved within three months. Broad ideas required now. Details to be worked out later.

General G. fastened his sharp eyes on Colonel Klebb. 'What are your immediate reactions, Comrade Colonel?'

The square-cut rimless glass of the spectacles flashed in the light of the chandelier as the woman straightened from her position of bowed concentration and looked across the desk at the General. The pale moist lips below the sheen of nicotine-stained fur over the mouth parted and started moving rapidly up and down as the woman gave her views. To Kronsteen, watching the face across the table, the square, expressionless opening and shutting of the lips reminded him of the boxlike jabber of a puppet.

The voice was hoarse and flat and without emotion, '. . . resembles in some respects the case of Stolzenberg. If you remember, Comrade General, this also was a matter of destroying a reputation as well as a life. On that occasion the matter was simple. The spy was also a pervert. If you recall . . .'

Kronsteen stopped listening. He knew all these cases. He had handled the planning of most of them and they were filed away in his memory like so many chess gambits. Instead, with closed ears, he examined the face of this dreadful woman and wondered casually how much longer she would last in her job–how much longer he would have to work with her.

Dreadful? Kronsteen was not interested in human beings–not even in his own children. Nor did the categories of 'good' and 'bad' have a place in his vocabulary. To him all people were chess pieces. He was only interested in their reactions to the movements of other pieces. To foretell their reactions, which was the greater part of his job, one had to understand their individual characteristics. Their basic instincts were immutable. Self-preservation, sex and the instinct of the herd–in that order. Their temperaments could be sanguine, phlegmatic, choleric or melancholic. The temperament of an individual would largely decide the comparative strength of his emotions and his sentiments. Character would greatly depend on upbringing and, whatever Pavlov and the Behaviourists might say, to a certain extent on the character of the parents. And, of course, people's lives and behaviour would be partly conditioned by physical strengths and weaknesses.

It was with these basic classifications at the back of his mind that

Kronsteen's cold brain considered the woman across the table. It was the hundredth time he had summed her up, but now they had weeks of joint work in front of them and it was as well to refresh the memory so that a sudden intrusion of the human element in their partnership should not come as a surprise.

Of course Rosa Klebb had a strong will to survive, or she would not have become one of the most powerful women in the State, and certainly the most feared. Her rise, Kronsteen remembered, had begun with the Spanish Civil War. Then, as a double agent inside P.O.U.M.–that is, working for the O.G.P.U. in Moscow as well as for Communist Intelligence in Spain–she had been the right hand, and some sort of a mistress, they said, of her chief, the famous Andreas Nin. She had worked with him from 1935 to 1937. Then, on the orders of Moscow, he was murdered and, it was rumoured, murdered by her. Whether this was true or not, from then on she had progressed slowly but straight up the ladder of power, surviving setbacks, surviving wars, surviving, because she forged no allegiances and joined no factions, all the purges, until, in 1953, with the death of Beria, the bloodstained hands grasped the rung, so few from the very top, that was Head of the Operations Department of SMERSH.

And, reflected Kronsteen, much of her success was due to the peculiar nature of her next most important instinct, the Sex Instinct. For Rosa Klebb undoubtedly belonged to the rarest of all sexual types. She was a Neuter. Kronsteen was certain of it. The stories of men and, yes, of women, were too circumstantial to be doubted. She might enjoy the act physically, but the instrument was of no importance. For her, sex was nothing more than an itch. And this psychological and physiological neutrality of hers at once relieved her of so many human emotions and sentiments and desires. Sexual neutrality was the essence of coldness in an individual. It was a great and wonderful thing to be born with.

In her, the Herd instinct would also be dead. Her urge for power demanded that she should be a wolf and not a sheep. She was a lone operator, but never a lonely one, because the warmth of company was unnecessary to her. And, of course, temperamentally, she would be a phlegmatic–imperturbable, tolerant of pain, sluggish. Laziness would be her besetting vice, thought Kronsteen. She would be difficult to get out of her warm, hoggish bed in the morning. Her private habits would be slovenly, even dirty. It would not be pleasant, thought Kronsteen, to look into the intimate side of her life, when she relaxed, out of uniform. Kronsteen's pouting lips curled away from the thought and his mind hastened on, skipping her character, which was certainly cunning and strong, to her appearance.

Rosa Klebb would be in her late forties, he assumed, placing her by the date of the Spanish War. She was short, about five foot four, and squat, and her dumpy arms and short neck, and the calves of the thick legs in the drab khaki stockings, were very strong for a woman. The devil knows, thought Kronsteen, what her breasts were like, but the bulge of uniform that rested on the table-top looked like a badly packed sandbag, and in general her figure, with its big pear-shaped hips, could only be likened to a 'cello.

The *tricoteuses* of the French Revolution must have had faces like hers, decided Kronsteen, sitting back in his chair and tilting his head slightly to one side. The thinning orange hair scraped back to the tight, obscene bun;

the shiny yellow-brown eyes that stared so coldly at General G. through the sharp-edged squares of glass, the wedge of thickly powdered, large-pored nose; the wet trap of a mouth, that went on opening and shutting as if it was operated by wires under the chin. Those French women, as they sat and knitted and chatted while the guillotine clanged down, must have had the same pale, thick chicken's skin that scragged in little folds under the eyes and at the corners of the mouth and below the jaws, the same big peasant's ears, the same tight, hard dimpled fists, like knobkerries, that, in the case of the Russian woman, now lay tightly clenched on the red velvet table-top on either side of the big bundle of bosom. And their faces must have conveyed the same impression, concluded Kronsteen, of coldness and cruelty and strength as this, yes, he had to allow himself the emotive word, *dreadful* woman of SMERSH.

'Thank you, Comrade Colonel. Your review of the position is of value. And now, Comrade Kronsteen, have you anything to add? Please be short. It is two o'clock and we all have a heavy day before us.' General G.'s eyes, bloodshot with strain and lack of sleep, stared fixedly across the desk into the fathomless brown pools below the bulging forehead. There had been no need to tell this man to be brief. Kronsteen never had much to say, but each of his words was worth speeches from the rest of the staff.

Kronsteen had already made up his mind, or he would not have allowed his thoughts to concentrate for so long on the woman.

He slowly tilted back his head and gazed into the nothingness of the ceiling. His voice was extremely mild, but it had the authority that commands close attention.

'Comrade General, it was a Frenchman, in some respects a predecessor of yours, Fouché, who observed that it is no good killing a man unless you also destroy his reputation. It will, of course, be easy to kill this man Bond. Any paid Bulgarian assassin would do it, if properly instructed. The second part of the operation, the destruction of this man's character, is more important and more difficult. At this stage it is only clear to me that the deed must be done away from England, and in a country over whose press and radio we have influence. If you ask me how the man is to be got there, I can only say that if the bait is important enough, and its capture is open to this man alone, he will be sent to seize it from wherever he may happen to be. To avoid the appearance of a trap, I would consider giving the bait a touch of eccentricity, of the unusual. The English pride themselves on their eccentricity. They treat the eccentric proposition as a challenge. I would rely partly on this reading of their psychology to have them send this important operator after the bait.'

Kronsteen paused. He lowered his head so that he was looking just over General G.'s shoulder.

'I shall proceed to devise such a trap,' he said indifferently. 'For the present, I can only say that if the bait is successful in attracting its prey, we are then likely to require an assassin with a perfect command of the English language.'

Kronsteen's eyes moved to the red velvet table-top in front of him. Thoughtfully, as if this was the kernel of the problem, he added: 'We shall also require a reliable and extremely beautiful girl.'

Chapter Eight

The Beautiful Lure

Sitting by the window of her one room and looking out at the serene June evening, at the first pink of the sunset reflected in the windows across the street, at the distant onion spire of a church that flamed like a torch above the ragged horizon of Moscow roofs, Corporal of State Security Tatiana Romanova thought that she was happier than she had ever been before.

Her happiness was not romantic. It had nothing to do with the rapturous start to a love affair–those days and weeks before the first tiny tear-clouds appear on the horizon. It was the quiet, settled happiness of security, of being able to look forward with confidence to the future, heightened by the immediate things, a word of praise she had had that afternoon from Professor Denikin, the smell of a good supper cooking on the electric stove, her favourite prelude to *Boris Goudonov* being played by the Moscow State Orchestra on the radio, and, over all, the beauty of the fact that the long winter and short spring were past and it was June.

The room was a tiny box in the huge modern apartment building on the Sadovaya-Chernogriazskay Ulitza that is the women's barracks of the State Security Departments. Built by prison labour, and finished in 1939, the fine eight-storey building contains two thousand rooms, some, like hers on the third floor, nothing but square boxes with a telephone, hot and cold water, a single electric light and a share of the central bathrooms and lavatories, others, on the two top floors, consisting of two- and three-room flats with bathrooms. These were for high-ranking women. Graduation up the building was strictly by rank, and Corporal Romanova had to rise through Sergeant, Lieutenant, Captain, Major and Lieutenant-Colonel before she would reach the paradise of the eighth and Colonels' floor.

But heaven knew she was content enough with her present lot. A salary of 1200 roubles a month (thirty per cent more than she could have earned in any other Ministry), a room to herself; cheap food and clothes from the 'closed shops' on the ground floor of the building; a monthly allocation of at least two Ministry tickets to the Ballet or the Opera; a full two weeks' paid holiday a year. And, above all, a steady job with good prospects in Moscow–not in one of those dreary provincial towns where nothing happened month after month, and where the arrival of a new film or the visit of a travelling circus was the only thing to keep one out of bed in the evening.

Of course, you had to pay for being in the M.G.B. The uniform put you apart from the world. People were afraid, which didn't suit the nature of most girls, and you were confined to the society of other M.G.B. girls and men, one of whom, when the time came, you would have to marry in order to stay with the Ministry. And they worked like the devil–eight to six, five and a half days a week, and only forty minutes off for lunch in the canteen. But it was a good lunch, a real meal, and you could do with little supper and save up for the sable coat that would one day take the place of the well-worn Siberian fox.

At the thought of her supper, Corporal Romanova left the chair by the window and went to examine the pot of thick soup, with a few shreds of meat and some powdered mushroom, that was to be her supper. It was nearly done and smelled delicious. She turned off the electricity and let the pot simmer while she washed and tidied, as, years before, she had been taught to do before meals.

While she dried her hands, she examined herself in the big oval looking-glass over the washstand.

One of her early boy-friends had said she looked like the young Greta Garbo. What nonsense! And yet tonight she did look rather well. Fine dark brown silken hair brushed straight back from a tall brow and falling heavily down almost to the shoulders, there to curl slightly up at the ends (Garbo had once done her hair like that and Corporal Romanova admitted to herself that she had copied it), a good, soft pale skin with an ivory sheen at the cheek-bones; wide apart, level eyes of the deepest blue under straight natural brows (she closed one eye after the other. Yes, her lashes were certainly long enough!) a straight, rather imperious nose–and then the mouth. What about the mouth? Was it too broad? It must look terribly wide when she smiled. She smiled at herself in the mirror. Yes, it was wide; but then so had Garbo's been. At least the lips were full and finely etched. There was the hint of a smile at the corners. No one could say it was a cold mouth! And the oval of her face. Was that too long? Was her chin a shade too sharp? She swung her head sideways to see it in profile. The heavy curtain of hair swung forward and across her right eye so that she had to brush it back. Well, the chin was pointed, but at least it wasn't sharp. She faced the mirror again and picked up a brush and started on the long, heavy hair. Greta Garbo! She was all right, or so many men wouldn't tell her that she was–let alone the girls who were always coming to her for advice about their faces. But a film star–a famous one! She made a face at herself in the glass and went to eat her supper.

In fact Corporal Tatiana Romanova was a very beautiful girl indeed. Apart from her face, the tall, firm body moved particularly well. She had been a year in the ballet school in Leningrad and had abandoned dancing as a career only when she grew an inch over the prescribed limit of five feet six. The school had taught her to hold herself well and to walk well. And she looked wonderfully healthy, thanks to her passion for figure-skating, which she practised all through the year at the Dynamo ice-stadium and which had already earned her a place on the first Dynamo women's team. her arms and breasts were faultless. A purist would have disapproved of her behind. Its muscles were so hardened with exercise that it had lost the smooth downward feminine sweep, and now, round at the back and flat and hard at the sides, it jutted like a man's.

Corporal Romanova was admired far beyond the confines of the English translation section of the M.G.B. Central Index. Everyone agreed that it would not be long before one of the senior officers came across her and peremptorily hauled her out of her modest section to make her his mistress, or if absolutely necessary, his wife.

The girl poured the thick soup into a small china bowl, decorated with wolves chasing a galloping sleigh round the rim, broke some black bread into it and went and sat in her chair by the window and ate it slowly with a nice shiny spoon she had slipped into her bag not many weeks before after a gay evening at the Hotel Moskwa.

When she had finished, she washed up and went back to her chair and lit the first cigarette of the day (no respectable girl in Russia smokes in public, except in a restaurant, and it would have meant instant dismissal if she had smoked at her work) and listened impatiently to the whimpering discords of an orchestra from Turkmenistan. This dreadful oriental stuff they were always putting on to please the kulaks of one of those barbaric outlying states! Why couldn't they play something *kulturny*? Some of that modern jazz music, or something classical. This stuff was hideous. Worse, it was old fashioned.

The telephone rang harshly. She walked over and turned down the radio and picked up the receiver.

'Corporal Romanova?'

It was the voice of her dear Professor Denikin. But out of office hours he always called her Tatiana or even Tania. What did this mean?

The girl was wide-eyed and tense. 'Yes, Comrade Professor.'

The voice at the other end sounded strange and cold. 'In fifteen minutes, at 8.30, you are required for interview by Comrade Colonel Klebb, of Otdyel II. You will call on her in her apartment, No. 1875, on the eighth floor of your building. Is that clear?'

'But, Comrade, why? What is . . . What is . . . ?'

The odd, strained voice of her beloved Professor cut her short.

'That is all, Comrade Corporal.'

The girl held the receiver away from her face. She stared at it with frenzied eyes as if she could wring more words out of the circle of little holes in the black ear-piece. 'Hullo! Hullo!' The empty mouthpiece yawned at her. She realized that her hand and her forearm were aching with the strength of her grip. She bent slowly forward and put the receiver down on the cradle.

She stood for a moment, frozen, gazing blindly at the black machine. Should she call him back? No, that was out of the question. He had spoken as he had because he knew, and she knew, that every call, in and out of the building, was listened to or recorded. That was why he had not wasted a word. This was a State matter. With a message of this sort, you got rid of it as quickly as you could, in as few words as possible, and wiped your hands of it. You had got the dreadful card out of your hand. You had passed the Queen of Spaddes to someone else. Your hands were clean again.

The girl put her knuckles up to her open mouth and bit on them, staring at the telephone. What did they want her for? What had she done? Desperately she cast her mind back, scrabbling through the days, the months, the years. Had she made some terrible mistake in her work and they had just discovered it? Had she made some remark against the State, some joke that had been reported back? That was always possible. But which remark? When? If it had been a bad remark, she would have felt a twinge of guilt or fear at the time. Her conscience was clear. Or was it? Suddenly she remembered. What about the spoon she had stolen? Was it that? Government property! She would throw it out of the window, now, far to one side or the other. But no, it couldn't be that. That was too small. She shrugged her shoulders resignedly and her hand dropped to her side. She got up and moved towards the clothes cupboard to get out her best uniform, and her eyes were misty with the tears of fright and bewilderment of a child. It could be none of those things. SMERSH didn't send for one for that sort of thing. It must be something much, much worse.

The girl glanced through her wet eyes at the cheap watch on her wrist. Only seven minutes to go! A new panic seized her. She brushed her forearm across her eyes and grabbed down her parade uniform. On top of it all, whatever it was, to be late! She tore at the buttons of her white cotton blouse.

As she dressed and washed her face and brushed her hair, her mind went on probing at the evil mystery like an inquisitive child poking into a snake's hole with a stick. From whatever angle she explored the hole, there came an angry hiss.

Leaving out the nature of her guilt, contact with any tentacle of SMERSH was unspeakable. The very name of the organization was abhorred and avoided. SMERSH, 'Smiert Spionam', 'Death to Spies'. It was an obscene word, a word from the tomb, the very whisper of death, a word never mentioned even in secret office gossip among friends. Worst of all, within this horrible organization, Otdyel II, the Department of Torture and Death, was the central horror.

And the Head of Otdyel II, the woman, Rosa Klebb! Unbelievable things were whispered about this woman, things that came to Tatiana in her nightmares, things she forgot again during the day, but that she now paraded.

It was said that Rosa Klebb would let no torturing take place without her. There was a blood-spattered smock in her office, and a low camp-stool, and they said that when she was seen scurrying through the basement passages dressed in the smock and with the stool in her hand, the word would go round, and even the workers in SMERSH would hush their words and bend low over their papers–perhaps even cross their fingers in their pockets–until she was reported back in her room.

For, or so they whispered, she would take the camp-stool and draw it up close below the face of the man or woman that hung down over the edge of the interrogation table. Then she would squat down on the stool and look into the face and quietly say 'No. 1' or 'No. 10' or 'No. 25' and the inquisitors would know what she meant and they would begin. And she would watch the eyes in the face a few inches away from hers and breathe in the screams as if they were perfume. And, depending on the eyes, she would quietly change the torture, and say 'Now No. 36' or 'Now No. 64' and the inquisitors would do something else. As the courage and resistance seeped out of the eyes, and they began to weaken and beseech, she would start cooing softly. 'There, there my dove. Talk to me, my pretty one, and it will stop. It hurts. Ah me, it hurst so, my child. And one is so tired of the pain. One would like it to stop, and to be able to lie down in peace, and for it never to begin again. Your mother is here beside you, only waiting to stop the pain. She has a nice soft cosy bed all ready for you to sleep on and forget, forget, forget. Speak,' she would whisper lovingly. 'You have only to speak and you will have peace and no more pain.' If the eyes still resisted, the cooing would start again. 'But you are foolish, my pretty one. Oh so foolish. This pain is nothing. Nothing! You don't believe me, my little dove? Well then, your mother must try a little, but only a very little, of No. 87.' And the interrogators would hear and change their instruments and their aim, and she would squat there and watch the life slowly ebbing from the eyes until she had to speak loudly into the ear of the person or the words would not reach the brain.

But it was seldom, so they said, that the person had the will to travel far along SMERSH's road of pain, let alone to the end, and, when the soft voice promised peace, it nearly always won, for somehow Rosa Klebb knew from the eyes the moment when the adult had been broken down into a child crying for its mother. And she provided the image of the mother and melted the spirit where the harsh words of a man would have toughened it.

Then, after yet another suspect had been broken, Rosa Klebb would go back down the passage with her camp-stool and take off her newly soiled smock and get back to her work and the word would go round that all was over and normal activity would come back to the basement.

Tatiana, frozen by her thoughts, looked again at her watch. Four minutes to go. She ran her hands down her uniform and gazed once more at her white face in the glass. She turned and said farewell to the dear, familiar little room. Would she ever see it again?

She walked straight down the long corridor and rang for the lift.

When it came, she squared her shoulders and lifted her chin and walked into the lift as if it was the platform of the guillotine.

'Eighth,' she said to the girl operator. She stood facing the doors. Inside her, remembering a word she had not used since childhood, she repeated over and over 'My God–My God–My God.'

Chapter Nine

A Labour of Love

Outside the anonymous, cream painted door, Tatiana already smelled the inside of the room. When the voice told her curtly to come in, and she opened the door, it was the smell that filled her mind while she stood and stared into the eyes of the woman who sat behind the round table under the centre light.

It was the smell of the Metro on a hot evening–cheap scent concealing animal odours. People in Russia soak themselves in scent, whether they have had a bath or not, but mostly when they have not, and healthy, clean girls like Tatiana always walk home from the office, unless the rain or the snow is too bad, so as to avoid the stench in the trains and the Metro.

Now Tatiana was in a bath of the smell. Her nostrils twitched with disgust.

It was her disgust and her contempt for a person who could live in the middle of such a smell that helped her to look down into the yellowish eyes that stared at her through the square glass panes. Nothing could be read in them. They were receiving eyes, not giving eyes. They slowly moved all over her, like camera lenses, taking her in.

Colonel Klebb spoke:

'You are a fine-looking girl, Comrade Corporal. Walk across the room and back.'

What were these honeyed words? Taut with a new fear, fear of the notorious personal habits of the woman, Tatiana did as she was told.

'Take your jacket off. Put it down on the chair. Raise your hands above your head. Higher. Now bend and touch your toes. Upright. Good. Sit down.' The woman spoke like a doctor. She gestured to the chair across the table from her. Her staring, probing eyes hooded themselves as they bent over the file on the table.

It must be my *zapiska*, thought Tatiana. How interesting to see the actual instrument that ordered the whole of one's life. How thick it was–nearly two inches thick. What could be on all those pages? She looked across at the open folder with wide, fascinated eyes.

Colonel Klebb riffled through the last pages and shut down the cover. The cover was orange with a diagonal black stripe. What did those colours signify?

The woman looked up. Somehow Tatiana managed to look bravely back.

'Comrade Corporal Romanova.' It was the voice of authority, of the senior officer. 'I have good reports of your work. Your record is excellent, both in your duties and in sport. The State is pleased with you.'

Tatiana could not believe her ears. She felt faint with reaction. She blushed to the roots of her hair and then turned pale. She put out a hand to the table edge. She stammered in a weak voice, 'I am g-grateful, Comrade Colonel.'

'Because of your excellent services you have been singled out for a most important assignment. This is a great honour for you. Do you understand?'

Whatever it was, it was better than what might have been. 'Yes, indeed, Comrade Colonel.'

'This assignment carries much responsibility. It bears a higher rank. I congratulate you on your promotion, Comrade Corporal, on completion of the assignment, to the rank of Captain of State Security.'

This was unheard of for a girl of twenty-four! Tatiana sensed danger. She stiffened like an animal who sees the steel jaws beneath the meat. 'I am deeply honoured, Comrade Colonel.' She was unable to keep the wariness out of her voice.

Rosa Klebb grunted non-committally. She knew exactly what the girl must have thought when she got the summons. The effect of her kindly reception, her shock of relief at the good news, her reawakening fears, had been transparent. This was a beautiful, guileless, innocent girl. Just what the *konspiratsia* demanded. Now she must be loosened up. 'My dear,' she said smoothly. 'How remiss of me. This promotion should be celebrated in a glass of wine. You must not think we senior officers are inhuman. We will drink together. It will be a good excuse to open a bottle of French champagne.'

Rosa Klebb got up and went over to the sideboard where her batman had laid out what she had ordered.

'Try one of these chocolates while I wrestle with the cork. It is never easy getting out champagne corks. We girls really need a man to help us with that sort of work, don't we?'

The ghastly prattle went on as she put a spectacular box of chocolates in-front of Tatiana. She went back to the sideboard. 'They're from Switzerland. The very best. The soft centres are the round ones. The hard ones are square.'

Tatiana murmured her thanks. She reached out and chose a round one. It would be easier to swallow. Her mouth was dry with fear of the moment when she would finally see the trap and feel it snap round her neck. It must be something dreadful to need to be concealed under all this play-acting. The bite of chocolate stuck in her mouth like chewing-gum. Mercifully the glass of champagne was thrust into her hand.

Rosa Klebb stood over her. She lifted her glass merrily. '*Za vashe zdarovie*, Comrade Tatiana. And my warmest congratulations!'

Tatiana stitched a ghastly smile on her face. She picked up her glass and gave a little bow. '*Za vashe zdarovie*, Comrade Colonel.' She drained the glass, as is the custom in Russian drinking, and put it down in front of her.

Rosa Klebb immediately filled it again, slopping some over the table-top. 'And now to the health of your new department, Comrade.' She raised her glass. The sugary smile tightened as she watched the girl's reactions.

'To SMERSH!'

Numbly, Tatiana got to her feet. She picked up the full glass. 'To SMERSH.' The word scarcely came out. She choked on the champagne and had to take two gulps. She sat heavily down.

Rosa Klebb gave her no time for reflection. She sat down opposite and laid her hands flat on the table. 'And now to business, Comrade.' Authority was back in the voice. 'There is much work to be done.' She leant forward. 'Have you ever wished to live abroad, Comrade? In a foreign country?'

The champagne was having its effect on Tatiana. Probably worse was to come, but now let it come quickly.

'No, Comrade. I am happy in Moscow.'

'You have never thought what it might be like living in the West–all those beautiful clothes, the jazz, the modern things?'

'No, Comrade.' She was truthful. She had never thought about it.

'And if the State required you to live in the West?'

'I would obey.'

'Willingly?'

Tatiana shrugged her shoulders with a hint of impatience. 'One does what one is told.'

The woman paused. There was girlish conspiracy in the next question.

'Are you a virgin, Comrade?'

Oh, my God, thought Tatiana. 'No, Comrade Colonel.'

The wet lips glinted in the light.

'How many men?'

Tatiana coloured to the roots of her hair. Russian girls are reticent and prudish about sex. In Russia the sexual climate is mid-Victorian. These questions from the Klebb woman were all the more revolting for being asked in this cold inquisitorial tone by a State official she had never met before in her life. Tatiana screwed up her courage. She stared defensively into the yellow eyes. 'What is the purpose of these intimate questions please, Comrade Colonel?'

Rosa Klebb straightened. Her voice cut back like a whip. 'Remember yourself, Comrade. You are not here to ask questions. You forget to whom you are speaking. Answer me!'

Tatiana shrank back. 'Three men, Comrade Colonel.'

'When. How old were you?' The hard yellow eyes looked across the table into the hunted blue eyes of the girl and held them and commanded.

Tatiana was on the edge of tears. 'At school. When I was seventeen. Then at the Institute of Foreign Languages. I was twenty-two. Then last year. I was twenty-three. It was a friend I met skating.'

'Their names, please, Comrade.' Rosa Klebb picked up a pencil and pulled a scribbling pad towards her.

Tatiana covered her face with her hands and burst into tears. 'No,' she cried between her sobs. 'No, never, whatever you do to me. You have no right.'

'Stop that nonsense.' The voice was a hiss. 'In five minutes I could have those names from you, or anything else I wish to know. You are playing a dangerous game with me, Comrade. My patience will not last for ever.' Rosa Klebb paused. She was being too rough. 'For the moment we will pass on. Tomorrow you will give me the names. No harm will come to these men. They will be asked one or two questions about you–simple technical questions, that is all. Now sit up and dry your tears. We cannot have any more of this foolishness.'

Rosa Klebb got up and came round the table. She stood looking down at Tatiana. The voice became oily and smooth. 'Come, come, my dear. You must trust me. Your little secrets are safe with me. Here, drink some more champagne and forget this little unpleasantness. We must be friends. We have work to do together. You must learn, my dear Tania, to treat me as you would your mother. Here, drink this down.'

Tatiana pulled a handkerchief out of the waistband of her skirt and dabbed at her eyes. She reached out a trembling hand for the glass of champagne and sipped at it with bowed head.

'Drink it down, my dear.'

Rosa Klebb stood over the girl like some dreadful mother duck, clucking encouragement.

Obediently Tatiana emptied the glass. She felt drained of resistance, tired, willing to do anything to finish with this interview and get away somewhere and sleep. She thought, so this is what it is like on the interrogation table, and that is the voice the Klebb uses. Well, it was working. She was docile now. She would co-operate.

Rosa Klebb sat down. She observed the girl appraisingly from behind the motherly mask.

'And now, my dear, just one more intimate little question. As between girls. Do you enjoy making love? Does it give you pleasure? Much pleasure?'

Tatiana's hands came up again and covered her face. From behind them, in a muffled voice, she said, 'Well yes, Comrade Colonel. Naturally, when one is in love . . .' Her voice trailed away. What else could she say? What answer did this woman want?

'And supposing, my dear, you were not in love. Then would love-making with a man still give you pleasure?'

Tatiana shook her head indecisively. She took her hands down from her face and bowed her head. The hair fell down on either side in a heavy curtain. She was trying to think, to be helpful, but she couldn't imagine such a situation. She supposed . . . 'I suppose it would depend on the man, Comrade Colonel.'

'That is a sensible answer, my dear.' Rosa Klebb opened a drawer in the table. She took out a photograph and slipped it across to the girl. 'What about this man, for instance?'

Tatiana drew the photograph cautiously towards her as if it might catch fire. She looked down warily at the handsome, ruthless face. She tried to think, to imagine . . . 'I cannot tell, Comrade Colonel. He is good-looking. Perhaps if he was gentle . . .' She pushed the photograph anxiously away from her.

'No, keep it, my dear. Put it up beside your bed and think of this man. You will learn more about him later in your new work. And now,' the eyes glittered behind the square panes of glass, 'would you like to know what your new work is to be? The task for which you have been chosen from all the girls in Russia?'

'Yes, indeed, Comrade Colonel,' Tatiana looked obediently across at the intent face that was now pointing at her like a gun-dog.

The wet, rubbery lips parted enticingly. 'It is a simple, delightful duty you have been chosen for, Comrade Corporal–a real labour of love, as we say. It is a matter of falling in love. That is all. Nothing else. Just falling in love with this man.'

'But who is he? I don't even know him.'

Rosa Klebb's mouth revelled. This would give the silly chit of a girl something to think about.

'He is an English spy.'

'*Bozhi moi!*' Tatiana clapped a hand over her mouth as much to stifle the use of God's name as from terror. She sat, tense with the shock, and gazed at Rosa Klebb through wide, slightly drunk eyes.

'Yes,' said Rosa Klebb, pleased with the effect of her words. 'He is an English spy. Perhaps the most famous of them all. And from now on you are in love with him. So you had better get used to the idea. And no silliness, Comrade. We must be serious. This is an important State matter for which you have been chosen as the instrument. So no nonsense, please. Now for some practical details.' Rosa Klebb stopped. She said sharply, 'And take your hand away from your silly face. And stop looking like a frightened cow. Sit up in your chair and pay attention. Or it will be the worse for you. Understood?'

'Yes, Comrade Colonel.' Tatiana quickly straightened her back and sat up with her hands in her lap as if she was back at the Security Officers' School. Her mind was in a ferment, but this was no time for personal things. Her whole training told her that this was an operation for the State. She was now working for her country. Somehow she had come to be chosen for an important *konspiratsia*. As an officer in the M.G.B., she must do her duty and do it well. She listened carefully and with her whole professional attention.

'For the moment,' Rosa Klebb put on her official voice, 'I will be brief. You will hear more later. For the next few weeks you will be most carefully trained for this operation until you know exactly what to do in all contingencies. You will be taught certain foreign customs. You will be equipped with beautiful clothes. You will be instructed in all the arts of allurement. Then you will be sent to a foreign country, somewhere in Europe. There you will meet this man. You will seduce him. In this matter you will have no silly compunctions. Your body belongs to the State. Since your birth, the State has nourished it. Now your body must work for the State. Is that understood?'

'Yes, Comrade Colonel.' The logic was inescapable.

'You will accompany this man to England. There, you will no doubt be questioned. The questioning will be easy. The English do not use harsh methods. You will give such answers as you can without endangering the State. We will supply you with certain answers which we would like to be given. You will probably be sent to Canada. That is where the English send a certain category of foreign prisoner. You will be rescued and brought back to Moscow.' Rosa Klebb peered at the girl. She seemed to be accepting all this without question. 'You see, it is a comparatively simple matter. Have you any questions at this stage?'

'What will happen to the man, Comrade Colonel?'

'That is a matter of indifference to us. We shall simply use him as a means to introduce you into England. The object of the operation is to give false information to the British. We shall, of course, Comrade, be very glad to have your own impressions of life in England. The reports of a highly trained and intelligent girl such as yourself will be of great value to the State.'

'Really, Comrade Colonel!' Tatiana felt important. Suddenly it all sounded exciting. If only she could do it well. She would assuredly do her very best. But supposing she could not make the English spy love her. She looked again at the photograph. She put her head on one side. It was an attractive face. What were these 'arts of allurement' that the woman had talked about? What could they be? Perhaps they would help.

Satisfied, Rosa Klebb got up from the table. 'And now we can relax, my dear. Work is over for the night. I will go and tidy up and we will have a friendly chat together. I shan't be a moment. Eat up those chocolates or they will go to waste.' Rosa Klebb made a vague gesture of the hand and disappeared with a preoccupied look into the next room.

Tatiana sat back in her chair. So that was what it was all about! It really wasn't so bad after all. What a relief! And what an honour to have been chosen. How silly to have been so frightened! Naturally the great leaders of the State would not allow harm to come to an innocent citizen who worked hard and had no black marks on her *zapiska*. Suddenly she felt immensely grateful to the father-figure that was the State, and proud that she would now have a chance to repay some of her debt. Even the Klebb woman wasn't really so bad after all.

Tatiana was still cheerfully reviewing the situation when the bedroom door opened and 'the Klebb woman' appeared in the opening. 'What do you think of this my dear?' Colonel Klebb opened her dumpy arms and twirled on her toes like a mannequin. She struck a pose with one arm outstretched and the other arm crooked at her waist.

Tatiana's mouth had fallen open. She shut it quickly. She searched for something to say.

Colonel Krebb of SMERSH was wearing a semi-transparent nightgown in orange *crêpe de chine*. It had scallops of the same material round the low square neckline and scallops at the wrists of the broadly flounced sleeves. Underneath could be seen a brassière consisting of two large pink satin roses. Below, she wore old-fashioned knickers of pink satin with elastic above the knees. One dimpled knee, like a yellowish coconut, appeared thrust forward between the half open folds of the nightgown in the classic stance of the modeller. The feet were enclosed in pink satin slippers with pompoms of ostrich feathers. Rosa Klebb had taken off her spectacles and her naked face was now thick with mascara and rouge and lipstick.

She looked like the oldest and ugliest whore in the world.

Tatiana stammered, 'It is very pretty.'

'Isn't it,' twittered the woman. She went over to a broad couch in the corner of the room. It was covered with a garish piece of peasant tapestry. At the back, against the wall, were rather grimy satin cushions in pastel colours.

With a squeak of pleasure, Rosa Klebb threw herself down in the caricature of a Recamier pose. She reached up an arm and turned on a pink shaded table-lamp whose stem was a naked woman in sham Lalique glass. She patted the couch beside her.

'Turn out the top light, my dear. The switch is by the door. Then come and sit beside me. We must get to know each other better.'

Tatiana walked to the door. She switched off the top light. Her hand dropped decisively to the door knob. She turned it and opened the door and stepped coolly out into the corridor. Suddenly her nerve broke. She banged the door shut behind her and ran wildly off down the corridor with her hands over her ears against the pursuing scream that never came.

Chapter Ten

The Fuse Burns

It was the morning of the next day.

Colonel Klebb sat at her desk in the roomy office that was her headquarters in the underground basement of SMERSH. It was more an operations room than an office. One wall was completely papered with a map of the Western Hemisphere. The opposite wall was covered with the Eastern Hemisphere. Behind her desk and within reach of her left hand, a Telekrypton occasionally chattered out a signal *en clair*, duplicating another machine in the Cipher Department under the tall radio masts on the roof of the building. From time to time, when Colonel Klebb thought of it, she tore off the lengthening strip of tape and read through the signals. This was a formality. If anything important happened, her telephone would ring. Every agent of SMERSH throughout the world was controlled from this room, and it was a vigilant and iron control.

The heavy face looked sullen and dissipated. The chicken-skin under the eyes was pouched and the whites of the eyes were veined with red.

One of the three telephones at her side purred softly. She picked up the receiver. 'Send him in.'

She turned to Kronsteen who sat, picking his teeth thoughtfully with an opened paper clip, in an armchair up against the left-hand wall, under the toe of Africa.

'Granitsky.'

Kronsteen slowly turned his head and looked at the door.

Red Grant came in and closed the door softly behind him. He walked up to the desk and stood looking down, obediently, almost hungrily, into the eyes of his Commanding Officer. Kronsteen thought that he looked like a powerful mastiff, waiting to be fed.

Rosa Klebb surveyed him coldly. 'Are you fit and ready for work?'

'Yes, Comrade Colonel.'

'Let's have a look at you. Take off your clothes.'

Red Grant showed no surprise. He took off his coat and, after looking around for somewhere to put it, dropped it on the floor. Then, unselfconsciously, he took off the rest of his clothes and kicked off his shoes. The great red-brown body with its golden hair lit up the drab room. Grant stood relaxed, his hands held loosely at his sides and one knee bent slightly forward, as if he was posing for an art class.

Rosa Klebb got to her feet and came round the desk. She studied the body minutely, prodding here, feeling there, as if she was buying a horse. She went behind the man and continued her minute inspection. Before she came back in front of him, Kronsteen saw her slip something out of her jacket pocket and fit it into her hand. There was a glint of metal.

The woman came round and stood close up to the man's gleaming stomach, her right arm behind her back. She held his eyes in hers.

Suddenly, with terrific speed and the whole weight of her shoulder behind the blow, she whipped her right fist, loaded with a heavy brass knuckle-duster, round and exactly into the solar plexus of the man.

Whuck!

Grant let out a snort of surprise and pain. His knees gave slightly, and then straightened. For a flash the eyes closed tight with agony. Then they opened again and glared redly down into the cold yellow probing eyes behind the square glasses. Apart from an angry flush on the skin just below the breast bone, Grant showed no ill effects from a blow that would have sent any normal man writhing to the ground.

Rosa Klebb smiled grimly. She slipped the knuckle-duster back in her pocket and walked to her desk and sat down. She looked across at Kronsteen with a hint of pride. 'At least he is fit enough,' she said.

Kronsteen grunted.

The naked man grinned with sly satisfaction. He brought up one hand and rubbed his stomach.

Rosa Klebb sat back in her chair and watched him thoughtfully. Finally she said, 'Comrade Granitsky, there is work for you. An important task. More important than anything you have attempted. It is a task that will earn you a medal'–Grant's eyes gleamed–'for the target is a difficult and dangerous one. You will be in a foreign country, and alone. Is that clear?'

'Yes, Comrade Colonel.' Grant was excited. Here was a chance for that big step forward. What would the medal be? The Order of Lenin? He listened carefully.

'The target is an English spy. You would like to kill an English spy?'

'Very much indeed, Comrade Colonel.' Grant's enthusiasm was genuine. He asked nothing better than to kill an Englishman. He had accounts to settle with the bastards.

'You will need many weeks of training and preparation. On this assignment you will be operating in the guise of an English agent. Your manners and appearance are uncouth. You will have to learn at least some of the tricks,' the voice sneered, 'of a *chentleman*. You will be placed in the hands of a certain Englishman we have here. A former *chentleman* of the

Foreign Office in London. It will be his task to make you pass as some sort of an English spy. They employ many different kinds of men. It should not be difficult. And you will have to learn many other things. The operation will be at the end of August, but you will start your training at once. There is much to be done. Put on your clothes and report back to the A.D.C. Understood?'

'Yes, Comrade Colonel.' Grant knew not to ask any questions. He scrambled into his clothes, indifferent to the woman's eyes on him, and walked over to the door, buttoning his jacket. He turned. 'Thank you, Comrade Colonel.'

Rosa Klebb was writing up her note of the interview. She didn't answer or look up and Grant went out and closed the door softly behind him.

The woman threw down her pen and sat back.

'And now, Comrade Kronsteen. Are there any points to discuss before we put the full machinery in motion? I should mention that the Praesidium has approved the target and ratified the death warrant. I have reported the broad lines of your plan to Comrade General Grubozaboyschikov. He is in agreement. The detailed execution has been left entirely in my hands. The combined planning and operations staff has been selected and is waiting to begin work. Have you any last minute thoughts, Comrade?'

Kronsteen sat looking up at the ceiling, the tips of his fingers joined in front of him. He was indifferent to the condescension in the woman's voice. The pulse of concentration beat in his temples.

'This man Granitsky. He is reliable? You can trust him in a foreign country? He will not go private?'

'He has been tested for nearly ten years. He has had many opportunities to escape. He has been watched for signs of itching feet. There has never been a breath of suspicion. The man is in the position of a drug addict. He would no more abandon the Soviet Union than a drugger would abandon the source of his cocaine. He is my top executioner. There is no one better.'

'And this girl, Romanova. She was satisfactory?'

The woman said grudgingly, 'She is very beautiful. She will serve our purpose. She is not a virgin, but she is prudish and sexually unawakened. She will receive instruction. Her English is excellent. I have given her a certain version of her task and its object. She is co-operative. If she should show signs of faltering, I have the addresses of certain relatives, including children. I shall also have the names of her previous lovers. If necessary, it would be explained to her that these people will be hostages until her task is completed. She has an affectionate nature. Such a hint would be sufficient. But I do not anticipate any trouble from her.'

'Romanova. That is the name of a *buivshi*–of one of the former people. It seems odd to be using a Romanov for such a delicate task.'

'Her grandparents were distantly related to the Imperial Family. But she does not frequent *buivshi* circles. Anyway, all our grandparents were former people. There is nothing one can do about it.'

'Our grandparents were not called Romanov,' said Kronsteen dryly. 'However, so long as you are satisfied.' He reflected a moment. 'And this man Bond. Have we discovered his whereabouts?'

'Yes. The M.G.B. English network reports him in London. During the day, he goes to his headquarters. At night he sleeps in his flat in a district of London called Chelsea.'

'That is good. Let us hope he stays there for the next few weeks. That will mean that he is not engaged on some operation. He will be available to go after our bait when they get the scent. Meanwhile,' Kronsteen's dark, pensive eyes continued to examine a particular point on the ceiling, 'I have been studying the suitability of centres abroad. I have decided on Istanbul for the first contact. We have a good *apparat* there. The Secret Service has only a small station. The head of the station is reported to be a good man. He will be liquidated. The centre is conveniently placed for us, with short lines of communication with Bulgaria and the Black Sea. It is relatively far from London. I am working out details of the point of assassination and the means of getting this Bond there, after he has contacted the girl. It will be either in France or very near it. We have excellent leverage on the French press. They will make the most of this kind of story, with its sensational disclosures of sex and espionage. It also remains to be decided when Granitsky shall enter the picture. These are minor details. We must choose the cameramen and the other operatives and move them quietly into Istanbul. There must be no crowding of our *apparat* there, no congestion, no unusual activity. We will warn all departments that wireless traffic with Turkey is to be kept absolutely normal before and during the operation. We don't want the British interceptors smelling a rat. The Cipher Department has agreed that there is no Security objection to handing over the outer case of a Spektor machine. That will be attractive. The machine will go to the Special Devices section. They will handle its preparation.'

Kronsteen stopped talking. His gaze slowly came down from the ceiling. He rose thoughtfully to his feet. He looked across and into the watchful, intent eyes of the woman.

'I can think of nothing else at the moment, Comrade,' he said. 'Many details will come up and have to be settled from day to day. But I think the operation can safely begin.'

'I agree, Comrade. The matter can now go forward. I will issue the necessary directives.' The harsh, authoritative voice unbent. 'I am grateful for your co-operation.'

Kronsteen lowered his head one inch in acknowledgment. He turned and walked softly out of the room.

In the silence, the Telekrypton gave a warning ping and started up its mechanical chatter. Rosa Klebb stirred in her chair and reached for one of the telephones. She dialled a number.

'Operations Room,' said a man's voice.

Rosa Klebb's pale eyes, gazing out across the room, lit on the pink shape on the wall-map that was England. Her wet lips parted.

'Colonel Klebb speaking. The *konspiratsia* against the English spy Bond. The operation will commence forthwith.'

PART TWO

THE EXECUTION

Chapter Eleven

The Soft Life

The blubbery arms of the soft life had Bond round the neck and they were slowly strangling him. He was a man of war and when, for a long period, there was no war, his spirit went into a decline.

In his particular line of business, peace had reigned for nearly a year. And peace was killing him.

At 7.30 on the morning of Thursday, August 12th, Bond awoke in his comfortable flat in the plane-tree'd square off the King's Road and was disgusted to find that he was thoroughly bored with the prospect of the day ahead. Just as, in at least one religion, *accidie* is the first of the cardinal sins, so boredom, and particularly the incredible circumstance of waking up bored, was the only vice Bond utterly condemned.

Bond reached out and gave two rings on the bell to show May, his treasured Scottish housekeeper, that he was ready for breakfast. Then he abruptly flung the single sheet off his naked body and swung his feet to the floor.

There was only one way to deal with boredom–kick oneself out of it. Bond went down on his hands and did twenty slow press-ups, lingering over each one so that his muscles had no rest. When his arms could stand the pain no longer, he rolled over on his back and, with his hands at his sides, did the straight leg-lift until his stomach muscles screamed. He got to his feet and, after touching his toes twenty times, went over to arm and chest exercises combined with deep breathing until he was dizzy. Panting with the exertion, he went into the big white-tiled bathroom and stood in the glass shower cabinet under very hot and then cold hissing water for five minutes.

At last, after shaving and putting on a sleeveless dark blue Sea Island cotton shirt and navy blue tropical worsted trousers, he slipped his bare feet into black leather sandals and went through the bedroom into the long big-windowed sitting-room with the satisfaction of having sweated his boredom, at any rate for the time being, out of his body.

May, an elderly Scotswoman with iron grey hair and a handsome closed face, came in with the tray and put it on the table in the bay window together with *The Times*, the only paper Bond ever read.

Bond wished her good morning and sat down to breakfast.

'Good morning-s.' (To Bond, one of May's endearing qualities was that she would call no man 'sir' except–Bond had teased her about it years before–English kings and Winston Churchill. As a mark of exceptional regard, she accorded Bond an occasional hint of an 's' at the end of a word.)

She stood by the table while Bond folded his paper to the centre news page.

'Yon man was here again last night about the Televeesion.'

'What man was that?' Bond looked along the headlines.

'Yon man that's always coming. Six times he's been here pestering me since June. After what I said to him the first time about the sinful thing, you'd think he'd give up trying to sell us one. By hire purchase, too, if you please!'

'Persistent chaps these salesmen.' Bond put down his paper and reached for the coffee pot.

'I gave him a right piece of my mind last night. Disturbing folk at their supper. Asked him if he'd got any papers–anything to show who he was.'

'I expect that fixed him.' Bond filled his large coffee cup to the brim with black coffee.

'Not a bit of it. Flourished his union card. Said he had every right to earn his living. Electricians Union it was too. They're the Communist one, aren't they-s?'

'Yes, that's right,' said Bond vaguely. His mind sharpened. Was it possible *They* could be keeping an eye on him? He took a sip of the coffee and put the cup down. 'Exactly what did this man say, May?' he asked, keeping his voice indifferent, but looking up at her.

'He said he's selling Televeesion sets on commission in his spare time. And are we sure we don't want one. He says we're one of the only folk in the square that haven't got one. Sees there isn't one of those aerial things on the house, I dare say. He's always asking if you're at home so that he can have a word with you about it. Fancy his cheek! I'm surprised he hasn't thought to catch you coming in or going out. He's always asking if I'm expecting you home. Naturally I don't tell him anything about your movements. Respectable, quiet-spoken body, if he wasn't so persistent.'

Could be, thought Bond. There are many ways of checking up whether the owner's at home or away. A servant's appearance and reactions–a glance through the open door. 'Well, you're wasting your time because he's away,' would be the obvious reception if the flat was empty. Should he tell the Security Section? Bond shrugged his shoulders irritably. What the hell. There was probably nothing in it. Why should *They* be interested in him? And, if there was something in it, Security was quite capable of making him change his flat.

'I expect you've frightened him away this time.' Bond smiled up at May. 'I should think you've heard the last of him.'

'Yes-s,' said May doubtfully. At any rate she had carried out her orders to tell him if she saw anyone 'hanging about the place'. She bustled off with a whisper of the old-fashioned black uniform she persisted in wearing even in the heat of August.

Bond went back to his breakfast. Normally it was little straws in the wind like this that would start a persistent intuitive ticking in his mind, and, on other days, he would not have been happy until he had solved the problem of the man from the Communist Union who kept on coming to the house. Now, from months of idleness and disuse, the sword was rusty in the scabbard and Bond's mental guard was down.

Breakfast was Bond's favourite meal of the day. When he was stationed in

London it was always the same. It consisted of very strong coffee, from De Bry in New Oxford Street, brewed in an American *Chemex*, of which he drank two large cups, black and without sugar. The single egg, in the dark blue egg cup with a gold ring round the top, was boiled for three and a third minutes.

It was a very fresh, speckled brown egg from French *Marans* hens owned by some friend of May in the country. (Bond disliked white eggs and, faddish as he was in many small things, it amused him to maintain that there was such a thing as the perfect boiled egg.) Then there were two thick slices of wholewheat toast, a large pat of deep yellow Jersey butter and three squat glass jars containing Tiptree 'Little Scarlet' strawberry jam; Cooper's Vintage Oxford marmalade and Norwegian Heather Honey from Fortnum's. The coffee pot and the silver on the tray were Queen Anne, and the china was Minton, of the same dark blue and gold and white as the egg-cup.

That morning, while Bond finished his breakfast with honey, he pinpointed the immediate cause of his lethargy and of his low spirits. To begin with, Tiffany Case, his love for so many happy months, had left him and, after final painful weeks during which she had withdrawn to an hotel, had sailed for America at the end of July. He missed her badly and his mind still sheered away from the thought of her. And it was August, and London was hot and stale. He was due for leave, but he had not the energy or the desire to go off alone, or to try and find some temporary replacement for Tiffany to go with him. So he had stayed on in the half-empty headquarters of the Secret Service grinding away at the old routines, snapping at his secretary and rasping his colleagues.

Even M had finally got impatient with the surly caged tiger on the floor below, and, on Monday of this particular week, he had sent Bond a sharp note appointing him to a Committee of Inquiry under Paymaster Captain Troop. The note said that it was time Bond, as a senior officer in the Service, took a hand in major administrative problems. Anyway, there was no one else available. Headquarters were short-handed and the 00 Section was quiescent. Bond would pray report that afternoon, at 2.30, to Room 412.

It was Troop, reflected Bond, as he lit his first cigarette of the day, who was the most nagging and immediate cause of his discontent.

In every large business, there is one man who is the office tyrant and bugbear and who is cordially disliked by all the staff. This individual performs an unconsciously important role by acting as a kind of lightning conductor for the usual office hates and fears. In fact, he reduces their disruptive influence by providing them with a common target. The man is usually the general manager, or the Head of Admin. He is that indispensable man who is a watchdog over the small things–petty cash, heat and light, towels and soap in the lavatories, stationery supplies, the canteen, the holiday rota, the punctuality of the staff. He is the one man who has real impact on the office comforts and amenities and whose authority extends into the privacy and personal habits of the men and women of the organization. To want such a job, and to have the necessary qualifications for it, the man must have exactly those qualities which irritate and abrade. He must be a strong disciplinarian and indifferent to opinion. He must be a little dictator. In all well-run businesses there is such a man. In the Secret Service, it is Paymaster Captain Troop, R.N. Retired, Head of Admin., whose job it is, in his own words, 'to keep the place shipshape and Bristol fashion'.

It was inevitable that Captain Troop's duties would bring him into conflict with most of the organization, but it was particularly unfortunate that M could think of no one but Troop to spare as Chairman for this particular Committee.

For this was yet one more of those Committees of Inquiry dealing with the delicate intricacies of the Burgess and Maclean case, and with the lessons that could be learned from it. M had dreamed it up, five years after he had closed his own particular file on that case, purely as a sop to the Privy Council Inquiry into the Security Services which the Prime Minister had ordered in 1955.

At once Bond had got into a hopeless wrangle with Troop over the employment of 'intellectuals' in the Secret Service.

Perversely, and knowing it would annoy, Bond had put forward the proposition that, if M.I.5 and the Secret Service were to concern themselves seriously with the atom age 'intellectual spy', they must employ a certain number of intellectuals to counter them. 'Retired officers of the Indian Army,' Bond had pronounced, 'can't possibly understand the thought processes of a Burgess or a Maclean. They won't even know such people exist–let alone be in a position to frequent their cliques and get to know their friends and their secrets. Once Burgess and Maclean went to Russia, the only way to make contact with them again and, perhaps, when they got tired of Russia, turn them into double agents against the Russians, would have been to send their closest friends to Moscow and Prague and Budapest with orders to wait until one of these chaps crept out of the masonry and made contact. And one of them, probably Burgess, would have been driven to make contact by his loneliness and by his ache to tell his story to someone.* But they certainly wouldn't take the risk of revealing themselves to some with with a trench-coat and a cavalry moustache and a beta minus mind.'

'Oh really,' Troop had said with icy calm. 'So you suggest we should staff the organization with long-haired perverts. That's quite an original notion. I thought we were all agreed that homosexuals were about the worst security risk there is. I can't see the Americans handing over many atom secrets to a lot of pansies soaked in scent.'

'All intellectuals aren't homosexual. And many of them are bald. I'm just saying that . . .,' and so the argument had gone on intermittently through the hearings of the past three days, and the other committee had ranged themselves more or less with Troop. Now, today, they had to draw up their recommendations and Bond was wondering whether to take the unpopular step of entering a minority report.

How seriously did he feel about the whole question, Bond wondered as, at nine o'clock, he walked out of his flat and down the steps to his car? Was he just being petty and obstinate? Had he constituted himself into a one-man opposition only to give his teeth something to bite into? Was he so bored that he could find nothing better to do than make a nuisance of himself inside his own organization? Bond couldn't make up his mind. He felt restless and indecisive, and, behind it all, there was a nagging disquiet he couldn't put his finger on.

* Written in March 1956. I.F.

As he pressed the self-starter and the twin exhausts of the Bentley woke to their fluttering growl, a curious bastard quotation slipped from nowhere into Bond's mind.

'Those whom the Gods wish to destroy, they first make bored.'

Chapter Twelve

A Piece of Cake

As it turned out, Bond never had to make a decision on the Committee's final report.

He had complimented his secretary on a new summer frock, and was half way through the file of signals that had come in during the night, when the red telephone that could only mean M or his Chief-of-Staff gave its soft, peremptory burr.

Bond picked up the receiver. '007.'

'Can you come up?' It was the Chief-of-Staff.

'M?'

'Yes. And it looks like a long session. I've told Troop you won't be able to make the Committee.'

'Any idea what it's about?'

The Chief-of-Staff chuckled. 'Well, I have as a matter of fact. But you'd better hear about it from him. It'll make you sit up. There's quite a swerve on this one.'

As Bond put on his coat and went out into the corridor, banging the door behind him he had a feeling of certainty that the starter's gun had fired and that the dog days had come to an end. Even the ride up to the top floor in the lift and the walk down the long quiet corridor to the door of M's staff office seemed to be charged with the significance of all those other occasions when the bell of the red telephone had been the signal that had fired him, like a loaded projectile, across the world towards some distant target of M's choosing. And the eyes of Miss Moneypenny, M's private secretary, had that old look of excitement and secret knowledge as she smiled up at him and pressed the switch on the intercom.

'007's here, sir.'

'Send him in,' said the metallic voice, and the red light of privacy went on above the door.

Bond went through the door and closed it softly behind him. The room was cool, or perhaps it was the venetian blinds that gave an impression of coolness. They threw bars of light and shadow across the dark green carpet up to the edge of the big central desk. There the sunshine stopped so that the quiet figure behind the desk sat in a pool of suffused greenish shade. In the ceiling directly above the desk, a big twin-bladed tropical fan, a recent addition to M's room, slowly revolved, shifting the thundery August air that, even high up above the Regent's Park, was heavy and stale after a week of heat-wave.

M gestured to the chair opposite him across the red leather desk. Bond sat down and looked across into the tranquil, lined sailor's face that he loved, honoured and obeyed.

'Do you mind if I ask you a personal question, James?' M never asked his staff personal questions and Bond couldn't imagine what was coming.

'No, sir.'

M picked his pipe out of the big copper ash-tray and began to fill it, thoughtfully watching his fingers at work with the tobacco. He said harshly: 'You needn't answer, but it's to do with your, er, friend, Miss Case. As you know, I don't generally interest myself in these matters, but I did hear that you had been, er, seeing a lot of each other since that diamond business. Even some idea you might be going to get married.' M glanced up at Bond and then down again. He put the loaded pipe into his mouth and set a match to it. Out of the corner of his mouth, as he drew at the jigging flame, he said: 'Care to tell me anything about it?'

Now what? wondered Bond. Damn these office gossips. He said gruffly, 'Well, sir, we did get on well. And there was some idea we might get married. But then she met some chap in the American Embassy. On the Military Attaché's staff. Marine Corps major. And I gather she's going to marry him. They've both gone back to the States, as a matter of fact. Probably better that way. Mixed marriages aren't often a success. I gather he's a nice enough fellow. Probably suit her better than living in London. She couldn't really settle down here. Fine girl, but she's a bit neurotic. We had too many rows. Probably my fault. Anyway it's over now.'

M gave one of the brief smiles that lit up his eyes more than his mouth. 'I'm sorry if it went wrong, James,' he said. There was no sympathy in M's voice. He disapproved of Bond's 'womanizing', as he called it to himself, while recognizing that his prejudice was the relic of a Victorian upbringing. But, as Bond's chief, the last thing he wanted was for Bond to be permanently tied to one woman's skirts. 'Perhaps it's for the best. Doesn't do to get mixed up with neurotic women in this business. They hang on your gun-arm, if you know what I mean. Forgive me for asking about it. Had to know the answer before I told you what's come up. It's a pretty odd business. Be difficult to get you involved if you were on the edge of marrying or anything of that sort.'

Bond shook his head, waiting for the story.

'All right then,' said M. There was a note of relief in his voice. He leant back in his chair and gave several quick pulls on his pipe to get it going. 'This is what's happened. Yesterday there was a long signal in from Istanbul. Seems on Tuesday the Head of Station T got an anonymous typewritten message which told him to take a round ticket on the 8 p.m. ferry steamer from the Galata Bridge to the mouth of the Bosphorus and back. Nothing else. Head of T's an adventurous sort of chap, and of course he took the steamer. He stood up for'ard by the rail and waited. After about a quarter of an hour a girl came and stood beside him, a Russian girl, very good-looking, he says, and after they'd talked a bit about the view and so on, she suddenly switched and in the same sort of conversational voice she told him an extraordinary story.'

M paused to put another match to his pipe. Bond interjected, 'Who is Head of T, sir? I've never worked in Turkey.'

'Man called Kerim, Darko Kerim. Turkish father and English mother.

Remarkable fellow. Been Head of T since before the war. One of the best men we've got anywhere. Does a wonderful job. Loves it. Very intelligent and he knows all that part of the world like the back of his hand.' M dismissed Kerim with a sidways jerk of his pipe. 'Anyway, the girl's story was that she was a Corporal in the M.G.B. Had been in the show since she left school and had just got transferred to the Istanbul centre as a cipher officer. She'd engineered the transfer because she wanted to get out of Russia and come over.'

'That's good,' said Bond. 'Might be useful to have one of their cipher girls. But why does she want to come over?'

M looked across the table at Bond. 'Because she's in love.' He paused and added mildly, 'She says she's in love with you.'

'In love with *me*?'

'Yes, with you. That's what she says. Her name's Tatiana Romanova. Ever heard of her?'

'Good God, no! I mean, no, sir.' M smiled at the mixture of expressions on Bond's face. 'But what the hell does she mean? Has she ever met me? How does she know I exist?'

'Well,' said M. 'The whole thing sounds absolutely ridiculous. But it's so crazy that it just might be true. This girl is twenty-four. Ever since she joined the M.G.B. she's been working in their Central Index, the same as our Records. And she's been working in the English section of it. She's been there six years. One of the files she had to deal with was yours.'

'I'd like to see that one,' commented Bond.

'Her story is that she first took a fancy to the photographs they've got of you. Admired your looks and so on.' M's mouth turned downwards at the corners as if he had just sucked at a lemon. 'She read up all your cases. Decided that you were the hell of a fellow.'

Bond looked down his nose. M's face was non-committal.

'She said you particularly appealed to her because you reminded her of the hero of a book by some Russian fellow called Lermontov. Apparently it was her favourite book. This hero chap liked gambling and spent his whole time getting in and out of scraps. Anyway, you reminded her of him. She says she came to think of nothing else, and one day the idea came to her that if only she could transfer to one of their foreign centres she could get in touch with you and you would come and rescue her.'

'I've never heard such a crazy story, sir. Surely Head of T didn't swallow it.'

'Now wait a moment,' M's voice was testy. 'Just don't be in too much of a hurry simply because something's turned up you've never come across before. Suppose you happened to be a film star instead of being in this particular trade. You'd get daft letters from girls all over the world stuffed with Heaven knows what sort of rot about not being able to live without you and so on. Here's a silly girl doing a secretary's job in Moscow. Probably the whole department is staffed by women, like our Records. Not a man in the room to look at, and here she is, faced with your, er, dashing features on a file that's constantly coming up for review. And she gets what I believe they call a 'crush' on these pictures just as secretaries all over the world get crushes on these dreadful faces in the magazines.' M waved his pipe sideways to indicate his ignorance of these grisly female habits. 'The Lord knows I don't know much about these things, but you must admit that they happen.'

Bond smiled at the appeal for help. 'Well, as a matter of fact, sir, I'm beginning to see there is some sense in it. There's no reason why a Russian girl shouldn't be just as silly as an English one. But she must have got guts to do what she did. Does Head of T say if she realized the consequences if she was found out?'

'He said she was frightened out of her wits,' said M. 'Spent the whole time on the boat looking round to see if anybody was watching her. But it seems they were the usual peasants and commuters that take these boats, and as it was a late boat there weren't many passengers anyway. But wait a minute. You haven't heard half the story.' M took a long pull at his pipe and blew a cloud of smoke up towards the slowly turning fan above his head. Bond watched the smoke get caught up in the blades and whirled into nothingness. 'She told Kerim that this passion for you gradually developed into a phobia. She got to hate the sight of Russian men. In time this turned into a dislike of the régime and particularly of the work she was doing for them and, so to speak, against you. So she applied for a transfer abroad, and since her languages were very good–English and French–in due course she was offered Istanbul if she would join the Cipher Department, which meant a cut in pay. To cut a long story short, after six months' training, she got to Istanbul about three weeks ago. Then she sniffed about and soon got hold of the name of our man, Kerim. He's been there so long that everybody in Turkey knows what he does by now. He doesn't mind, and it takes people's eyes off the special men we send in from time to time. There's no harm in having a front man in some of these places. Quite a lot of customers would come to us if they knew where to go and who to talk to.'

Bond commented: 'The public agent often does better than the man who has to spend a lot of time and energy keeping under cover.'

'So she sent Kerim the note. Now she wants to know if he can help her.' M paused and sucked thoughtfully at his pipe. 'Of course Kerim's first reactions were exactly the same as yours, and he fished around looking for a trap. But he simply couldn't see what the Russians could gain from sending this girl over to us. All this time the steamer was getting further and further up the Bosphorus and soon it would be turning to come back to Istanbul. And the girl got more and more desperate as Kerim went on trying to break down her story. Then,' M's eyes glittered softly across at Bond, 'came the clincher.'

That glitter in M's eyes, thought Bond. How well he knew those moments when M's cold grey eyes betrayed their excitement and their greed.

'She had a last card to play. And she knew it was the ace of trumps. If she could come over to us, she would bring her cipher machine with her. It's a brand new Spektor machine. The thing we'd give our eyes to have.'

'God,' said Bond softly, his mind boggling at the immensity of the prize. The Spektor! The machine that would allow them to decipher the Top Secret traffic of all. To have that, even if its loss was immediately discovered and the settings changed, or the machine taken out of service in Russian embassies, and spy centres all over the world, would be a priceless victory. Bond didn't know much about cryptography, and, for security's sake, in case he was ever captured, wished to know as little as possible about its secrets, but at least he knew that, in the Russian secret service, loss of the Spektor would be counted a major disaster.

Bond was sold. At once he accepted all M's faith in the girl's story, however crazy it might be. For a Russian to bring them this gift, and take the appalling risk of bringing it, could only mean an act of desperation–of desperate infatuation if you liked. Whether the girl's story was true or not, the stakes were too high to turn down the gamble.

'You see, 007?' said M softly. It was not difficult to read Bond's mind from the excitement in his eyes. 'You see what I mean?'

Bond hedged. 'But did she say how she could do it?'

'Not exactly. But Kerim says she was absolutely definite. Some business about night duty. Apparently she's on duty alone certain nights of the week and sleeps on a camp bed in the office. She seemed to have no doubts about it, although she realized that she would be shot out of hand if anyone even dreamed of her plan. She was even worried about Kerim reporting all this back to me. Made him promise he would encode the signal himself and send it on a one-time-only pad and keep no copy. Naturally he did as she asked. Directly she mentioned the Spektor, Kerim knew he might be on to the most important coup that's come our way since the war.'

'What happened then, sir?'

'The steamer was coming up to a place called Ortakoy. She said she was going to get off there. Kerim promised to get a signal off that night. She refused to make any arrangements for staying in touch. Just said that she would keep her end of the bargain if we would keep ours. She said good night and mixed in the crowd going down the gang-plank and that was the last Kerim saw of her.'

M suddenly leant forward in his chair and looked hard at Bond. 'But of course he couldn't *guarantee* that we would make the bargain with her.'

Bond said nothing. He thought he could guess what was coming.

'This girl will only do these things on one condition.' M's eyes narrowed until they were fierce, significant slits. 'That you go out to Istanbul and bring her and the machine back to England.'

Bond shrugged his shoulders. That presented no difficulties. But . . . He looked candidly back at M. 'Should be a piece of cake, sir. As far as I can see there's only one snag. She's only seen photographs of me and read a lot of exciting stories. Suppose that when she sees me in the flesh, I don't come up to her expectations.'

'That's where the work comes in,' said M grimly. 'That's why I asked those questions about Miss Case. It's up to you to see that you *do* come up to her expectations.'

Chapter Thirteen

'B.E.A. Takes You There . . .'

The four small, square-ended propellers turned slowly, one by one, and became four whizzing pools. The low hum of the turbo-jets rose to a shrill smooth whine. The quality of the noise, and the complete absence of vibration, were different from the stuttering roar and straining horsepower of all other aircraft Bond had flown in. As the Viscount wheeled easily out to the shimmering east-west runway of London Airport, Bond felt as if he was sitting in an expensive mechanical toy.

There was a pause as the chief pilot gunned up the four turbo-jets into a banshee scream and then, with a jerk of released brakes, the 10.30 B.E.A. Flight 130 to Rome, Athens and Istanbul gathered speed and hurtled down the runway and up into a quick, easy climb.

In ten minutes they had reached 20,000 feet and were heading south along the wide air-channel that takes the Mediterranean traffic from England. The scream of the jets died to a low, drowsy whistle. Bond unfastened his seat-belt and lit a cigarette. He reached for the slim, expensive-looking attaché case on the floor beside him and took out *The Mask of Dimitrios* by Eric Ambler and put the case, which was very heavy in spite of its size, on the seat beside him. He thought how surprised the ticket clerk at London Airport would have been if she had weighed the case instead of letting it go unchecked as an 'overnight bag'. And if, in their turn, Customs had been intrigued by its weight, how interested they would have been when it was slipped under the Inspectoscope.

Q Branch had put together this smart-looking little bag, ripping out the careful handiwork of Swaine and Adeney to pack fifty rounds of ·25 ammunition, in two flat rows, between the leather and the lining of the spine. In each of the innocent sides there was a flat throwing knife, built by Wilkinsons, the sword makers, and the tops of their handles were concealed cleverly by the stitching at the corners. Despite Bond's efforts to laugh them out of it, Q's craftsmen had insisted on building a hidden compartment into the handle of the case, which, by pressure at a certain point, would deliver a cyanide death-pill into the palm of his hand. (Directly he had taken delivery of the case, Bond had washed this pill down the lavatory.) More important was the thick tube of Palmolive shaving cream in the otherwise guileless spongebag. The whole top of this unscrewed to reveal the silencer for the Beretta, packed in cotton wool. In case hard cash was needed, the lid of the attaché case contained fifty golden sovereigns. These could be poured out by slipping sideways one ridge of welting.

The complicated bag of tricks amused Bond, but he also had to admit that, despite its eight-pound weight, the bag was a convenient way of carrying the tools of his trade, which otherwise would have to be concealed about his body.

Only a dozen miscellaneous passengers were on the plane. Bond smiled at the thought of Leolia Ponsonby's horror if she knew that that made the load thirteen. The day before, when he had left M and had gone back to his office to arrange the details of his flight, his secretary had protested violently at the idea of his travelling on Friday the thirteenth.

'But it's always best to travel on the thirteenth,' Bond had explained patiently. 'There are practically no passengers and it's more comfortable and you get better service. I always choose the thirteenth when I can.'

'Well,' she had said resignedly, it's your funeral. But I shall spend the day worrying about you. And for heaven's sake don't go walking under ladders or anything silly this afternoon. You oughtn't to overplay your luck like this. I don't know what you're going to Turkey for, and I don't want to know. But I have a feeling in my bones.'

'Ah, those beautiful bones!' Bond had teased her. 'I'll take them out to dinner the night I get back.'

'You'll do nothing of the sort, she had said coldly. Later she had kissed him goodbye with a sudden warmth, and for the hundredth time Bond had wondered why he bothered with other women when the most darling of them all was his secretary.

The plane sang steadily on above the endless sea of whipped-cream clouds that looked solid enough to land on if the engines failed. The clouds broke up and a distant blue haze, far away to their left, was Paris. For an hour they flew high over the burned-up fields of France until, after Dijon, the land turned from a pale to a darker green as it sloped up into the Juras.

Lunch came. Bond put aside his book and the thoughts that kept coming between him and the printed page, and, while he ate, he gazed down at the cool mirror of the Lake of Geneva. As the pine forests began to climb towards the snow patches between the beautifully scoured teeth of the Alps, he remembered early skiing holidays. The plane skirted the great eye-tooth of Mont Blanc, a few hundred yards to port, and Bond looked down at the dirty grey elephant's skin of the glaciers and saw himself again, a young man in his teens, with the leading end of the rope round his waist, bracing himself against the top of a rock-chimney on the Aiguilles Rouges as his two companions from the University of Geneva inched up the smooth rock towards him.

And now? Bond smiled wryly at his reflection in the Perspex as the plane swung out of the mountains and over the grosgrained terazza of Lombardy. If that young James Bond came up to him in the street and talked to him, would he recognize the clean, eager youth that had been him at seventeen? And what would that youth think of him, the secret agent, the older James Bond? Would he recognize himself beneath the surface of this man who was tarnished with years of treachery and ruthlessness and fear–this man with the cold arrogant eyes and the scar down his cheek and the flat bulge beneath his left armpit? If the youth did recognize him what would his judgement be? What would he think of Bond's present assignment? What would he think of the dashing secret agent who was off across the world in a new and most romantic role–to pimp for England?

Bond put the thought of his dead youth out of his mind. Never job backwards. What-might-have-been was a waste of time. Follow your fate, and be satisfied with it, and be glad not to be a second-hand motor salesman, or a yellow-press journalist, pickled in gin and nicotine, or a cripple–or dead.

Gazing down on the sun-baked sprawl of Genoa and the gentle blue waters of the Mediterranean, Bond closed his mind to the past and focused it on the immediate future–on this business, as he sourly described it to himself, of 'pimping for England'.

For that, however else one might like to describe it, was what he was on his way to do–to seduce, and seduce very quickly, a girl whom he had never seen before, whose name he had heard yesterday for the first time. And all the while, however attractive she was–and Head of T had described her as 'very beautiful'–Bond's whole mind would have to be not on what she was, but on what she had–the dowry she was bringing with her. It would be like trying to marry a rich woman for her money. Would he be able to act the part? Perhaps he could make the right faces and say the right things, but would his body dissociate itself from his secret thoughts and effectively make the love he would declare? How did men behave credibly in bed when their whole minds were focused on the woman's bank balance? Perhaps there was an erotic stimulus in the notion that one was ravaging a sack of gold. But a cipher machine?

Elba passed below them and the plane slid into its fifty-mile glide towards Rome. Half an hour among the jabbering loudspeakers of Ciampini Airport, time to drink two excellent Americanos, and they were on their way again, flying steadily down towards the toe of Italy, and Bond's mind went back to sifting the minutest details of the rendezvous that was drawing closer at three hundred miles an hour.

Was it all a complicated M.G.B. plot of which he couldn't find the key? Was he walking into some trap that not even the tortuous mind of M could fathom? God knew M was worried about the possibility of such a trap. Every conceivable angle of the evidence, for and against, had been scrutinized–not only by M, but also by a full-dress operations meeting of Heads of Sections that had worked all through the afternoon and evening before. But, which ever way the case had been examined, no one had been able to suggest what the Russians might get out of it. They might want to kidnap Bond and interrogate him. But why Bond? He was an operating agent, unconcerned with the general working of the Service, carrying in his head nothing of use to the Russians except the details of his current duty and a certain amount of background information that could not possibly be vital. Or they might want to kill Bond, as an act of revenge. Yet he had not come up against them for two years. If they wanted to kill him, they had only to shoot him in the streets of London, or in his flat, or put a bomb in his car.

Bond's thoughts were interrupted by the stewardess. 'Fasten your seat-belts, please.' As she spoke the plane dropped sickeningly and soared up again with an ugly note of strain in the scream of the jets. The sky outside was suddenly black. Rain hammered on the windows. There came a blinding flash of blue and white light and a crash as if an anti-aircraft shell had hit them, and the plane heaved and bucketed in the belly of the electric storm that had ambushed them out of the mouth of the Adriatic.

Bond smelt the smell of danger. It is a real smell, something like the mixture of sweat and electricity you get in an amusement arcade. Again the lightning flung its hands across the windows. Crash! It felt as if they were the centre of the thunder clap. Suddenly the plane seemed incredibly small and frail. Thirteen passengers! Friday the Thirteenth! Bond thought of Loelia Ponsonby's words and his hands on the arms of his chair felt wet. How old is this plane, he wondered? How many flying hours has it done? Had the deathwatch beetle of metal fatigue got into the wings? How much of their strength had it eaten away? Perhaps he wouldn't get to Istanbul after all. Perhaps a plummeting crash into the Gulf of Corinth was going to be the destiny he had been scanning philosophically only an hour before.

In the centre of Bond was a hurricane-room, the kind of citadel found in old-fashioned houses in the tropics. These rooms are small, strongly built cells in the heart of the house, in the middle of the ground floor and sometimes dug down into its foundations. To this cell the owner and his family retire if the storm threatens to destroy the house, and they stay there until the danger is past. Bond went to his hurricane-room only when the situation was beyond his control and no other possible action could be taken. Now he retired to this citadel, closed his mind to the hell of noise and violent movement, and focused on a single stitch in the back of the seat in front of him, waiting with slackened nerves for whatever fate had decided for B.E.A. Flight No. 130.

Almost at once it got lighter in the cabin. The rain stopped crashing on the Perspex window and the noise of the jets settled back into their imperturbable whistle. Bond opened the door of his hurricane-room and stepped out. He slowly turned his head and looked curiously out of the window and watched the tiny shadow of the plane hastening far below across the quiet waters of the Gulf of Corinth. He heaved a deep sigh and reached into his hip-pocket for his gunmetal cigarette case. He was pleased to see his hands were dead steady as he took out his lighter and lit one of the Morland cigarettes with the three gold rings. Should he tell Lil that perhaps she had almost been right? He decided that if he could find a rude enough postcard in Istanbul he would.

The day outside faded through the colours of a dying dolphin and Mount Hymettus came at them, blue in the dusk. Down over the twinkling sprawl of Athens and then the Viscount was wheeling across the standard concrete air-strip with its drooping windsock and the notices in the strange dancing letters Bond had hardly seen since school.

Bond climbed out of the plane with the handful of pale, silent passengers and walked across to the transit lounge and up to the bar. He ordered a tumbler of Ouzo and drank it down and chased it with a mouthful of ice water. There was a strong bite under the sickly anisette taste and Bond felt the drink light a quick, small fire down his throat and in his stomach. He put down his glass and ordered another.

By the time the loudspeakers called him out again it was dusk and the half moon rode clear and high above the lights of the town. The air was soft with evening and the smell of flowers and there was the steady pulse-beat of the cicadas–zing-a-zing-a-zing–and the distant sound of a man singing. The voice was clear and sad and the song had a note of lament. Near the airport a dog barked excitedly at an unknown human smell. Bond suddenly realized that he had come into the East where the guard-dog howls all night. For some reason the realization sent a pang of pleasure and excitement into his heart.

They had only a ninety-minute flight to Istanbul, across the dark Aegean and the Sea of Marmara. An excellent dinner, with two dry Martinis and a half-bottle of Calvet claret, put Bond's reservations about flying on Friday the thirteenth, and his worries about his assignment, out of his mind and substituted a mood of pleased anticipation.

Then they were there and the plane's four propellers wheeled to a stop outside the fine modern airport of Yesilkoy, an hour's drive from Istanbul. Bond said goodbye and thank you for a good flight to the stewardess, carried the heavy little attaché case through the passport check into the customs, and waited for his suitcase to come off the plane.

So these dark, ugly, neat little officials were the modern Turks. He listened to their voices, full of broad vowels and quiet sibilants and modified u-sounds, and he watched the dark eyes that belied the soft, polite voices. They were bright, angry, cruel eyes that had only lately come down from the mountains. Bond thought he knew the history of those eyes. They were eyes that had been trained for centuries to watch over sheep and decipher small movements on far horizons. They were eyes that kept the knife-hand in sight without seeming to, that counted the grains of meal and the small fractions of coin and noted the flicker of the merchant's fingers. They were hard, untrusting, jealous eyes. Bond didn't take to them.

Outside the customs, a tall rangy man with drooping black moustaches stepped out of the shadows. He wore a smart dust-coat and a chauffeur's cap. He saluted and, without asking Bond his name, took his suitcase and led the way over to a gleaming aristocrat of a car–an old black basket-work Rolls Royce coupé-de-ville that Bond guessed must have been built for some millionaire of the '20s.

When the car was gliding out of the airport, the man turned and said politely over his shoulder, in excellent English, 'Kerim Bey thought you would prefer to rest tonight, sir. I am to call for you at nine tomorrow morning. What hotel are you staying at, sir?'

'The Kristal Palas.'

'Very good, sir.' The car sighed off down the wide modern road.

Behind them, in the dappled shadows of the airport parking place, Bond vaguely heard the crackle of a motor scooter starting up. The sound meant nothing to him and he settled back to enjoy the drive.

Chapter Fourteen

Darko Kerim

James Bond awoke early in his dingy room at the Kristal Palas on the heights of Pera and absent-mindedly reached down a hand to explore a sharp tickle on the outside of his right thigh. Something had bitten him during the night. Irritably he scratched the spot. He might have expected it.

When he had arrived the night before, to be greeted by a surly night-concierge in trousers and a collarless shirt, and had briefly inspected the entrance hall with the fly-blown palms in copper pots, and the floor and walls of discoloured Moorish tiles, he had known what he was in for. He had half thought of going to another hotel. Inertia, and a perverse liking for the sleazy romance that clings to old-fashioned Continental hotels, had decided him to stay, and he had signed in and followed the man up to the third floor in the old rope-and-gravity lift.

His room, with its few sticks of aged furniture and an iron bedstead, was what he had expected. He only looked to see if there were the blood spots of squashed bugs on the wall-paper behind the bedhead before dismissing the concierge.

He had been premature. When he went into the bathroom and turned on the hot tap it gave a deep sigh, then a deprecating cough, and finally ejected a small centipede into the basin. Bond morosely washed the centipede away with the thin stream of brownish water from the cold tap. So much, he had reflected wryly, for choosing an hotel because its name had amused him and because he had wanted to get away from the soft life of big hotels.

But he had slept well, and now, with the reservation that he must buy some insecticide, he decided to forget about his comforts and get on with the day.

Bond got out of bed, drew back the heavy red plush curtains and leant on the iron balustrade and looked out over one of the most famous views in the world–on his right the still waters of the Golden Horn, on his left the dancing waves of the unsheltered Bosphorus, and, in between, the tumbling roofs, soaring minarets and crouching mosques of Pera. After all, his choice had been good. The view made up for many bedbugs and much discomfort.

For ten minutes Bond stood and gazed out across the sparkling water barrier between Europe and Asia, then he turned back into the room, now bright with sunshine, and telephoned for his breakfast. His English was not understood, but his French at last got through. He turned on a cold bath and shaved patiently with cold water and hoped that the exotic breakfast he had ordered would not be a fiasco.

He was not disappointed. The yoghurt, in a blue china bowl, was deep yellow and with the consistency of thick cream. The green figs, ready peeled, were bursting with ripeness, and the Turkish coffee was jet black and with the burned taste that showed it had been freshly ground. Bond ate the delicious meal on a table drawn up beside the open window. He watched the steamers and the caïques criss-crossing the two seas spread out before him and wondered about Kerim and what fresh news there might be.

Punctually at nine, the elegant Rolls came for him and took him through Taksim square and down the crowded Istiklal and out of Asia. The thick black smoke of the waiting steamers, badged with the graceful crossed anchors of the Merchant Marine, streamed across the first span of the Galata Bridge and hid the other shore towards which the Rolls nosed forward through the bicycles and trams, the well-bred snort of the ancient bulb horn just keeping the pedestrians from under its wheels. Then the way was clear and the old European section of Istanbul glittered at the end of the broad half-mile of bridge with the slim minarets lancing up into the sky and the domes of the mosques, crouching at their feet, looking like big firm breasts. It should have been the Arabian Nights, but to Bond, seeing it first above the tops of trams and above the great scars of modern advertising along the river frontage, it seemed a once beautiful theatre-set that modern Turkey had thrown aside in favour of the steel and concrete flat-iron of the Istanbul-Hilton Hotel, blankly glittering behind him on the heights of Pera.

Across the bridge, the car nosed to the right down a narrow cobbled street parallel with the waterfront and stopped outside a high wooden porte-cochère.

A tough-looking watchman with a chunky, smiling face, dressed in frayed khaki, came out of a porter's lodge and saluted. He opened the car door and gestured for Bond to follow him. He led the way back into his lodge and through a door into a small courtyard with a neatly raked gravel parterre. In the centre was a gnarled eucalyptus tree at whose foot two white ring-doves were pecking about. The noise of the town was a distant rumble and it was quiet and peaceful.

They walked across the gravel and through another small door and Bond found himself at one end of a great vaulted godown with high circular windows through which dusty bars of sunshine slanted across a vista of bundles and bales of merchandise. There was a cool, musty scent of spices and coffee and, as Bond followed the watchman down the central passage-way, a sudden strong wave of mint.

At the end of the long warehouse was a raised platform enclosed by a balustrade. On it half a dozen young men and girls sat on high stools and wrote busily in fat, old-fashioned ledgers. It was like a Dickensian counting-house and Bond noticed that each high desk had a battered abacus beside the inkpot. Not one of the clerks looked up as Bond walked between them, but a tall, swarthy man with a lean face and unexpected blue eyes came forward from the furthest desk and took delivery of him from the watchman. He smiled warmly at Bond, showing a set of extremely white teeth, and led him to the back of the platform. He knocked on a fine mahogany door with a Yale lock and, without waiting for an answer, opened it and let Bond in and closed the door softly behind him.

'Ah, my friend. Come in. Come in.' A very large man in a beautifully cut cream tussore suit got up from a mahogany desk and came to meet him, holding out his hand.

A hint of authority behind the loud friendly voice reminded Bond that this was the Head of Station T, and that Bond was in another man's territory and juridically under his command. It was no more than a point of etiquette, but a point to remember.

Darko Kerim had a wonderfully warm dry handclasp. It was a strong Western handful of operative fingers–not the banana skin handshake of the East that makes you want to wipe your fingers on your coat-tails. And the big hand had a coiled power that said it could easily squeeze your hand tighter and tighter until finally it cracked your bones.

Bond was six feet tall, but this man was at least two inches taller and he gave the impression of being twice as broad and twice as thick as Bond. Bond looked up into two wide apart, smiling blue eyes in a large smooth brown face with a broken nose. The eyes were watery and veined with red, like the eyes of a hound who lies too often too close to the fire. Bond recognized them as the eyes of furious dissipation.

The face was vaguely gipsy-like in its fierce pride and in the heavy curling black hair and crooked nose, and the effect of a vagabond soldier of fortune was heightened by the small thin gold ring Kerim wore in the lobe of his right ear. It was a startlingly dramatic face, vital, cruel and debauched, but what one noticed more than its drama was that it radiated life. Bond thought he had never seen so much vitality and warmth in a human face. It was like being close to the sun, and Bond let go the strong dry hand and smiled back at Kerim with a friendliness he rarely felt for a stranger.

'Thanks for sending the car to meet me last night.'

'Ha!' Kerim was delighted. 'You must thank our friends too. You were met by both sides. They always follow my car when it goes to the airport.'

'Was it a Vespa or a Lambretta?'

'You noticed? A Lambretta. They have a whole fleet of them for their little men, the men I call "The Faceless Ones". They look so alike, we have never managed to sort them out. Little gangsters, mostly stinking Bulgars, who do their dirty work for them. But I expect this one kept well back. They don't get up close to the Rolls any more since the day my chauffeur stopped suddenly and then reversed back as hard as he could. Messed up the paintwork and bloodied the bottom of the chassis but it taught the rest of them manners.'

Kerim went to his chair and waved to an identical one across the desk. He pushed over a flat white box of cigarettes and Bond sat down and took a cigarette and lit it. It was the most wonderful cigarette he had ever tasted–the mildest and sweetest of Turkish tobacco in a slim long oval tube with an elegant gold crescent.

While Kerim was fitting one into a long nicotine-stained ivory holder, Bond took the opportunity to glance round the room, which smelled strongly of paint and varnish as if it had just been redecorated.

It was big and square and panelled in polished mahogany, except behind Kerim's chair where a length of Oriental tapestry hung down from the ceiling and gently moved in the breeze as if there was an open window behind it. But this seemed unlikely as light came from three circular windows high up in the walls. Perhaps, behind the tapestry, was a balcony looking out over the Golden Horn, whose waves Bond could hear lapping at the walls below. In the centre of the right-hand wall hung a gold-framed reproduction of Annigoni's portrait of the Queen. Opposite, also imposingly framed, was Cecil Beaton's war-time photograph of Winston Churchill looking up from his desk in the Cabinet Offices like a contemptuous bulldog. A broad bookcase stood against one wall and, opposite, a comfortably padded leather settee. In the centre of the room the big desk winked with polished brass handles. On the littered desk were three silver photograph frames, and Bond caught a sideways view of the copperplate script of two Mentions in Dispatches and the Military Division of the O.B.E.

Kerim lit his cigarette. He jerked his head back at the piece of tapestry. 'Our friends paid me a visit yesterday,' he said casually. 'Fixed a limpet bomb on the wall outside. Timed the fuse to catch me at my desk. By good luck, I had taken a few minutes off to relax on the couch over there with a young Rumanian girl who still believes that a man will tell secrets in exchange for love. The bomb went off at a vital moment. I refused to be disturbed, but I fear the experience was too much for the girl. When I released her, she had hysterics. I'm afraid she had decided that my love-making is altogether too violent.' He waved his cigarette holder apologetically. 'But it was a rush to get the room put to rights in time for your visit. New glass for the windows and my pictures, and the place stinks of paint. However.' Kerim sat back in his chair. There was a slight frown on his face. 'What I cannot understand is this sudden breach of the peace. We live together very amicably in Istanbul. We all have our work to do. It is unheard of that my *chers collègues* should suddenly declare war in this way. It is quite worrying. It can only lead to trouble for our Russian friends. I shall be forced to rebuke the man who did it when I have found out his name.' Kerim shook his head. 'It is most confusing. I am hoping it has nothing to do with this case of ours.'

'But was it necessary to make my arrival so public?' Bond asked mildly. 'The last thing I want is to get you involved in all this. Why send the Rolls to the airport? It only ties you in with me.'

Kerim's laugh was indulgent. 'My friend, I must explain something which you should know. We and the Russians and the Americans have a paid man in all the hotels. And we have all bribed an official of the Secret police at Headquarters and we receive a carbon copy of the list of all foreigners entering the country every day by air or train or sea. Given a few more days I could have smuggled you in through the Greek frontier. But for what purpose? Your existence here has to be known to the other side so that our friend can contact you. It is a condition she had laid down that she will make her own arrangements for the meeting. Perhaps she does not trust our security. Who knows? But she was definite about it and she said, as if I didn't know it, that her centre would immediately be advised of your arrival.' Kerim shrugged his broad shoulders. 'So why make things difficult for her? I am merely concerned with making things easy and comfortable for you so that you will at least enjoy your stay–even if it is fruitless.'

Bond laughed. 'I take it all back. I'd forgotten the Balkan formula. Anyway I'm under your orders here. You tell me what to do and I'll do it.'

Kerim waved the subject aside. 'And now, since we are talking of your comfort, how is your hotel? I was surprised you chose the Palas. It is little better than a disorderly house–what the French call a *baisodrome*. And it's quite a haunt of the Russians. Not that that matters.'

'It's not too bad. I just didn't want to stay at the Istanbul-Hilton or one of the other smart places.'

'Money?' Kerim reached into a drawer and took out a flat packet of new green notes. 'Here's a thousand Turkish pounds. Their real value, and their rate on the black market, is about twenty to the pound. The official rate is seven. Tell me when you've finished them and I'll give you as many more as you want. We can do our accounts after the game. It's muck, anyway. Ever since Croesus, the first millionaire, invented gold coins, money has depreciated. And the face of the coin has been debased as fast as its value. First the faces of gods were on the coins. Then the faces of kings. Then of presidents. Now there's no face at all. Look at this stuff!' Kerim tossed the money over to Bond. 'Today it's only paper, with a picture of a public building and the signature of a cashier. Muck! The miracle is that you can still buy things with it. However. What else? Cigarettes? Smoke only these. I will have a few hundred sent up to your hotel. They're the best. *Diplomates*. They're not easy to get. Most of them go to the Ministries and the Embassies. Anything else before we get down to business? Don't worry about your meals and your leisure. I will look after both. I shall enjoy it and, if you will forgive me, I wish to stay close to you while you are here.'

'Nothing else,' said Bond. 'Except that you must come over to London one day.'

'Never,' said Kerim definitely. 'The weather and the women are far too cold. And I am proud to have you here. It reminds me of the war. Now,' he rang a bell on his desk. 'Do you like your coffee plain or sweet? In Turkey we cannot talk seriously without coffee or raki and it is too early for raki.'

'Plain.'

The door behind Bond opened. Kerim barked an order. When the door was shut, Kerim unlocked a drawer and took out a file and put it in front of him. He smacked his hand down on it.

'My friend,' he said grimly, 'I do not know what to say about this case.' He leant back in his chair and linked his hands behind his neck. 'Has it ever occurred to you that our kind of work is rather like shooting a film? So often I have got everybody on location and I think I can start turning the handle. Then it's the weather, and then it's the actors, and then it's the accidents. And there is something else that also happens in the making of a film. Love appears in some shape or form, at the very worst, as it is now, between the two stars. To me that is the most confusing factor in this case, and the most inscrutable one. Does this girl really love her idea of you? Will she love you when she sees you? Will you be able to love her enough to make her come over?'

Bond made no comment. There was a knock on the door and the head clerk put a china eggshell, enclosed in gold filigree, in front of each of them and went out. Bond sipped his coffee and put it down. It was good, but thick with grains. Kerim swallowed his at a gulp and fitted a cigarette into his holder and lit it.

'But there is nothing we can do about this love matter,' Kerim continued, speaking half to himself. 'We can only wait and see. In the meantime there are other things.' He leant forward against the desk and looked across at Bond, his eyes suddenly very hard and shrewd.

'There is something going on in the enemy camp, my friend. It is not only this attempt to get rid of me. There are comings and goings. I have few facts,' he reached up a big index finger and laid it alongside his nose, 'but I have this.' He tapped the side of his nose as if he was patting a dog. 'But this is a good friend of mine and I trust him.' He brought his hand slowly and significantly down on to the desk and added softly, 'And if the stakes were not so big, I would say to you, "Go home my friend. Go home. There is something here to get away from".'

Kerim sat back. The tension went out of his voice. He barked out a harsh laugh. 'But we are not old women. And this is our work. So let us forget my nose and get on with the job. First of all, is there anything I can tell you that you do not know? The girl has made no sign of life since my signal and I have no other information. But perhaps you would like to ask me some questions about the meeting.'

'There's only one thing I want to know,' said Bond flatly. 'What do you think of this girl? Do you believe her story or not? Her story about me? Nothing else matters. If she hasn't got some sort of a hysterical crush on me, the whole business falls to the ground and it's some complicated M.G.B. plot we can't understand. Now. Did you believe the girl?' Bond's voice was urgent and his eyes searched the other man's face.

'Ah, my friend,' Kerim shook his head. He spread his arms wide. 'That is what I asked myself then, and it is what I ask myself the whole time since. But who can tell if a woman is lying about these things? Her eyes were bright–those beautiful innocent eyes. Her lips were moist and parted in that heavenly mouth. Her voice was urgent and frightened at what she was doing and saying. Her knuckles were white on the guard rail of the ship. But what was in her heart?' Kerim raised his hands, 'God alone knows.' He brought his hands down resignedly. He placed them flat on the desk and looked straight at Bond. 'There is only one way of telling if a woman really loves you, and even that way can only be read by an expert.'

'Yes,' said Bond dubiously. 'I know what you mean. In bed.'

Chapter Fifteen

Background to a Spy

Coffee came again, and then more coffee, and the big room grew thick with cigarette smoke as the two men took each shred of evidence, dissected it and put it aside. At the end of an hour they were back where they had started. It was up to Bond to solve the problem of this girl and, if he was satisfied with her story, get her and the machine out of the country.

Kerim undertook to look after the administrative problems. As a first step he picked up the telephone and spoke to his travel agent and reserved two seats on every outgoing plane for the next week–by B.E.A., Air France, S.A.S. and Turkair.

'And now you must have a passport,' he said. 'One will be sufficient. She can travel as your wife. One of my men will take your photograph and he will find a photograph of some girl who looks more or less like her. As a matter of fact, an early picture of Garbo would serve. There is a certain resemblance. He can get one from the newspaper files. I will speak to the Consul General. He's an excellent fellow who likes my little cloak-and-dagger plots. The passport will be ready by this evening. What name would you like to have?'

'Take one out of a hat.'

'Somerset. My mother came from there. David Somerset. Profession, Company Director. That means nothing. And the girl? Let us say Caroline. She looks like a Caroline. A couple of clean-limbed young English people with a taste for travel. Finance Control Form? Leave that to me. It will show eighty pounds in travellers' cheques, let's say, and a receipt from the bank to show you changed fifty while you were in Turkey. Customs? They never look at anything. Only too glad if somebody has bought something in the country. You will declare some Turkish Delight–presents for your friends in London. If you have to get out quickly, leave your hotel bill and luggage to me. They know me well enough at the Palas. Anything else?'

'I can't think of anything.'

Kerim looked at his watch. 'Twelve o'clock. Just time for the car to take you back to your hotel. There might be a message. And have a good look at your things to see if anyone has been inquisitive.'

He rang the bell and fired instructions at the head clerk who stood with his sharp eyes on Kerim's and his lean head straining forward like a whippet's.

Kerim led Bond to the door. There came again the warm powerful handclasp. 'The car will bring you to lunch,' he said. 'A little place in the Spice Bazaar.' His eyes looked happily into Bond's. 'And I am glad to be working with you. We will do well together.' He let go of Bond's hand. 'And now I have a lot of things to do very quickly. They may be the wrong things, but at any rate,' he grinned broadly, '*jouons mal, mais jouons vite*!'

The head clerk, who seemed to be some sort of chief-of-staff to Kerim, led Bond through another door in the wall of the raised platform. The heads were still bowed over the ledgers. There was a short passage with rooms on either side. The man led the way into one of these and Bond found himself in an extremely well-equipped dark-room and laboratory. In ten minutes he was out again on the street. The Rolls edged out of the narrow alley and back again on to the Galata Bridge.

A new concierge was on duty at the Kristal Palas, a small obsequious man with guilty eyes in a yellow face. He came out from behind the desk, his hands spread in apology. 'Effendi, I greatly regret. My colleague showed you to an inadequate room. It was not realized that you are a friend of Kerim Bey. Your things have been moved to No. 12. It is the best room in the hotel. In fact,' the concierge leered, 'it is the room reserved for honeymoon couples. Every comfort. My apologies, Effendi. The other room is not intended for visitors of distinction.' The man executed an oily bow, washing his hands.

If there was one thing Bond couldn't stand it was the sound of his boots being licked. He looked the concierge in the eyes and said, 'Oh.' The eyes slid away. 'Let me see this room. I may not like it. I was quite comfortable where I was.'

'Certainly, Effendi,' the man bowed Bond to the lift. 'But alas the plumbers are in your former room. The water supply . . .' the voice trailed away. The lift rose about ten feet and stopped at the first floor.

Well, the story of the plumbers makes sense, reflected Bond. And, after all, there was no harm in having the best room in the hotel.

The concierge unlocked a high door and stood back.

Bond had to approve. The sun streamed in through wide double windows that gave on to a small balcony. The motif was pink and grey and the style was mock French Empire, battered by the years, but still with all the elegance of the turn of the century. There were fine Bokhara rugs on the parquet floor. A glittering chandelier hung from the ornate ceiling. The bed against the right-hand wall was huge. A large mirror in a gold frame covered most of the wall behind it. (Bond was amused. The honeymoon room! Surely there should be a mirror on the ceiling as well.) The adjoining bathroom was tiled and fitted with everything, including a bidet and a shower. Bond's shaving things were neatly laid out.

The concierge followed Bond back into the bedroom, and when Bond said he would take the room, bowed himself gratefully out.

Why not? Bond again walked round the room. This time he carefully inspected the walls and the neighbourhood of the bed and the telephone. Why not take the room? Why would there be microphones or secret doors? What would be the point of them?

His suitcase was on a bench near the chest-of-drawers. He knelt down. No scratches round the lock. The bit of fluff he had trapped in the clasp was still there. He unlocked the suitcase and took out the little attaché case. Again no signs of interference. Bond locked the case and got to his feet.

He washed and went out of the room and down the stairs. No, there had been no messages for the Effendi. The concierge bowed as he opened the door of the Rolls. Was there a hint of conspiracy behind the permanent guilt in those eyes? Bond decided not to care if there was. The game, whatever it was, had to be played out. If the change of rooms had been the opening gambit, so much the better. The game had to begin somewhere.

As the car sped back down the hill, Bond's thoughts turned to Darko

Kerim. What a man for Head of Station T! His size alone, in this country of furtive, stunted little men, would give him authority, and his giant vitality and love of life would make everyone his friend. Where had this exuberant shrewd pirate come from? And how had he come to work for the Service? He was the rare type of man that Bond loved, and Bond already felt prepared to add Kerim to the half-dozen of those real friends whom Bond, who had no 'acquaintances', would be ready to take to his heart.

The car went back over the Galata Bridge and drew up outside the vaulted arcades of the Spice Bazaar. The chauffeur led the way up the shallow worn steps and into the fog of exotic scents, shouting curses at the beggars and sack-laden porters. Inside the entrance the chauffeur turned left out of the steam of shuffling, jabbering humanity and showed Bond a small arch in the thick wall. Turret-like stone steps curled upwards.

'Effendi, you will find Kerim Bey in the far room on the left. You have only to ask. He is known to all.'

Bond climbed the cool stairs to a small ante-room where a waiter, without asking his name, took charge and led him through a maze of small, colourfully tiled, vaulted rooms to where Kerim was sitting at a corner table over the entrance to the bazaar. Kerim greeted him boisterously, waving a glass of milky liquid in which ice tinkled.

'Here you are my friend! Now, at once, some raki. You must be exhausted after your sight-seeing.' He fired orders at the waiter.

Bond sat down in a comfortable-armed chair and took the small tumbler the waiter offered him. He lifted it towards Kerim and tasted it. It was identical with ouzo. He drank it down. At once the waiter refilled his glass.

'And now to order your lunch. They eat nothing but offal cooked in rancid olive oil in Turkey. At least the offal at the Misir Carsarsi is the best.'

The grinning waiter made suggestions.

'He says the Doner Kebab is very good today. I don't believe him, but it can be. It is very young lamb broiled over charcoal with savoury rice. Lots of onions in it. Or is there anything you prefer? A pilaff or some of those damned stuffed peppers they eat here? All right then. And you must start with a few sardines grilled *en papillotte*. They are just edible.' Kerim harangued the waiter. He sat back, smiling at Bond. 'That is the only way to treat these damned people. They love to be cursed and kicked. It is all they understand. It is in the blood. All this pretence of democracy is killing them. They wwant some sultans and wars and rape and fun. Poor brutes, in their striped suits and bowler hats. They are miserable. You've only got to look at them. However, to hell with them all. Any news?'

Bond shook his head. He told Kerim about the change of room and the untouched suitcase.

Kerim downed a glass of raki and wiped his mouth on the back of his hand. He echoed the thought Bond had had. 'Well, the game must begin sometime. I have made certain small moves. Now we can only wait and see. We will make a little foray into enemy territory after lunch. I think it will interest you. Oh, we shan't be seen. We shall move in the shadows, underground.' Kerim laughed delightedly at his cleverness. 'And now let us talk about other things. How do you like Turkey? No, I don't want to know. What else?'

They were interrupted by the arrival of their first course. Bond's sardines *en papillotte* tasted like any other fried sardines. Kerim set about a large plate of what appeared to be strips of raw fish. He saw Bond's look of interest. 'Raw fish,' he said. 'After this I shall have raw meat and lettuce and then I shall have a bowl of yoghourt. I am not a faddist, but I once trained to be a professional strong man. It is a good profession in Turkey. The public loves them. And my trainer insisted that I should eat only raw food. I got the habit. It is good for me, but,' he waved his fork, 'I do not pretend it is good for everyone. I don't care the hell what other people eat so long as they enjoy it. I can't stand sad eaters and sad drinkers.'

'Why did you decide not to be a strong man? How did you get into this racket?'

Kerim forked up a strip of fish and tore at it with his teeth. He drank down half a tumbler of raki. He lit a cigarette and sat back in his chair. 'Well,' he said with a sour grin, 'we might as well talk about me as about anything else. And you must be wondering "How did this big crazy man get into the Service?" I will tell you, but briefly, because it is a long story. You will stop me if you get bored. All right?'

'Fine.' Bond lit a *Diplomate*. He leant forward on his elbows.

'I come from Trebizond.' Kerim watched his cigarette smoke curl upwards. 'We were a huge family with many mothers. My father was the sort of man women can't resist. All women want to be swept off their feet. In their dreams they long to be slung over a man's shoulder and taken into a cave and raped. That was his way with them. My father was a great fisherman and his fame was spread all over the Black Sea. He went after the sword-fish. They are difficult to catch and hard to fight and he would always outdo all others after these fish. Women like their men to be heroes. He was a kind of hero in a corner of Turkey where it is a tradition for the men to be tough. He was a big, romantic sort of fellow. So he could have any woman he wanted. He wanted them all and sometimes killed other men to get them. Naturally he had many children. We all lived on top of each other in a great rambling old ruin of a house that our "aunts" made habitable. The aunts really amounted to a harem. One of them was an English governess from Istanbul my father had seen watching a circus. He took a fancy to her and she to him and that evening he put her on board his fishing boat and sailed up the Bosphorus and back to Trebizond. I don't think she ever regretted it. I think she forgot all the world except him. She died just after the war. She was sixty. The child before me had been by an Italian girl and the girl had called him Bianco. He was fair. I was dark. I got to be called Darko. There were fifteen of us children and we had a wonderful childhood. Our aunts fought often and so did we. It was like a gipsy encampment. It was held together by my father who thrashed us, women or children, when we were a nuisance. But he was good to us when we were peaceful and obedient. You cannot understand such a family?'

'The way you describe it I can.'

'Anyway so it was. I grew up to be nearly as big a man as my father, but better educated. My mother saw to that. My father only taught us to be clean and to go to the lavatory once a day and never to feel shame about anything in the world. My mother also taught me a regard for England, but that is by the way. By the time I was twenty, I had a boat of my own and I was making money. But I was wild. I left the big house and went to live in two small rooms on the waterfront. I wanted to have my women where my mother would not know. There was a stroke of bad luck. I had a little Bessarabian hell-cat. I had won her in a fight with some gipsies, here in the hills behind Istanbul. They came after me, but I got her on board the boat. I had to knock her unconscious first. She was still trying to kill me when we got back to Trebizond, so I got her to my place and took away all her clothes and kept her chained naked under the table. When I ate, I used to throw scraps to her under the table, like a dog. She had to learn who was master. Before that could happen, my mother did an unheard of thing. She visited my place without warning. She came to tell me that my father wanted to see me immediately. She found the girl. My mother was really angry with me for the first time in my life. Angry? She was beside herself. I was a cruel ne'er-do-well and she was ashamed to call me son. The girl must immediately be taken back to her people. My mother brought her some of her own clothes from the house. The girl put them on, but when the time came, she refused to leave me.' Darko Kerim laughed hugely. 'An interesting lesson in female psychology, my dear friend. However, the problem of the girl is another story. While my mother was fussing over her and getting nothing but gipsy curses for her pains, I was having an interview with my father, who had heard nothing of all this and who never did hear. My mother was like that. There was another man with my father, a tall, quiet Englishman with a black patch over one eye. They were talking about the Russians. The Englishman wanted to know what they were doing along their frontier, about what was going on at Batoum, their big oil and naval base only fifty miles away from Trebizond. He would pay good money for information. I knew English and I knew Russian. I had good eyes and ears. I had a boat. My father had decided that I would work for the Englishman. And that Englishman, my dear friend, was Major Dansey, my predecessor as Head of this Station. And the rest,' Kerim made a wide gesture with his cigarette holder, 'you can imagine.'

'But what about this training to be a professional strong man?'

'Ah,' said Kerim slyly, 'that was only a sideline. Our travelling circuses were almost the only Turks allowed through the frontier. The Russians cannot live without circuses. It is as simple as that. I was the man who broke chains and lifted weights by a rope between the teeth. I wrestled against the local strong men in the Russian villages. And some of those Georgians are giants. Fortunately they are stupid giants and I nearly always won. Afterwards, at the drinking, there was always much talk and gossip. I would look foolish and pretend not to understand. Every now and then I would ask an innocent question and they would laugh at my stupidity and tell me the answer.'

The second course came, and with it a bottle of Kavaklidere, a rich coarse burgundy like any other Balkan wine. The Kebab was good and tasted of smoked bacon fat and onions. Kerim ate a kind of Steak Tartare–a large flat hamburger of finely minced raw meat laced with peppers and chives and bound together with yolk of egg. He made Bond try a forkful. It was delicious. Bond said so.

'You ought to eat it every day,' said Kerim earnestly. 'It is good for those who wish to make much love. There are certain exercises you should do for the same purpose. These things are important to men. Or at least they are to me. Like my father, I consume a large quantity of women. But, unlike him, I also drink and smoke too much, and these things do not go well with making love. Nor does this work I do. Too many tensions and too much thinking. It takes the blood to the head instead of to where it should be for making love. But I am greedy for life. I do too much of everything all the time. Suddenly one day my heart will fail. The Iron Crab will get me as it got my father. But I am not afraid of The Crab. At least I shall have died from an honourable disease. Perhaps they will put on my tombstone. "This Man Died from Living Too Much".'

Bond laughed. 'Don't go too soon, Darko,' he said. 'M would be very displeased. He thinks the world of you.'

'He does?' Kerim searched Bond's face to see if he was telling the truth. He laughed delightedly. 'In that case I will not let The Crab have my body yet.' He looked at his watch. 'Come, James,' he said. 'It is good that you reminded me of my duty. We will have coffee in the office. There is not much time to waste. Every day at 2.30 the Russians have their council of war. Today you and I will do them the honour of being present at their deliberations.'

Chapter Sixteen

The Tunnel of Rats

Back in the cool office, while they waited for the inevitable coffee, Kerim opened a cupboard in the wall and pulled out sets of engineers' blue overalls. Kerim stripped to his shorts and dressed himself in one of the suits and pulled on a pair of rubber boots. Bond picked out a suit and a pair of boots that more or less fitted him and put them on.

With the coffee, the head clerk brought in two powerful flashlights which he put on the desk.

When the clerk had left the room Kerim said, 'He is one of my sons–the eldest one. The others in there are all my children. The chauffeur and the watchman are uncles of mine. Common blood is the best security. And this spice business is good cover for us all. M set me up in it. He spoke to friends of his in the City of London. I am now the leading spice merchant in Turkey. I have long ago repaid M the money that was lent me. My children are shareholders in the business. They have a good life. When there is secret work to be done and I need help, I choose the child who will be most suitable. They all have training in different secret things. They are clever and brave. Some have already killed for me. They would all die for me–and for M I have taught them he is just below God.' Kerim made a deprecating wave. 'But that is just to tell you that you are in good hands.'

'I hadn't imagined anything different.'

'Ha!' said Kerim non-committally. He picked up the torches and handed one to Bond. 'And now to work.'

Kerim walked over to the wide glass-fronted bookcase and put his hand behind it. There was a click and the bookcase rolled silently and easily along the wall to the left. Behind it was a small door, flush with the wall. Kerim pressed one side of the door and it swung inwards to reveal a dark tunnel with stone steps leading straight down. A dank smell, mixed with a faint zoo stench, came out into the room.

'You go first,' said Kerim. 'Go down the steps to the bottom and wait. I must fix the door.'

Bond switched on his torch and stepped through the opening and went carefully down the stairs. The light of the torch showed fresh masonry, and, twenty feet below, a glimmer of water. When Bond got to the bottom he found that the glimmer was a small stream running down a central gutter in the floor of an ancient stone-walled tunnel that sloped steeply up to the right. To the left, the tunnel went on downwards and would, he guessed, come out below the surface of the Golden Horn.

Out of range of Bond's light there was a steady, quiet, scuttling sound, and in the blackness hundreds of pinpoints of red light flickered and moved. It was the same uphill and downhill. Twenty yards away on either side, a thousand rats were looking at Bond. They were sniffing at his scent. Bond imagined the whiskers lifting slightly from their teeth. He had a quick moment of wondering what action they would take if his torch went out.

Kerim was suddenly beside him. 'It is a long climb. A quarter of an hour. I hope you love animals,' Kerim's laugh boomed hugely away up the tunnel. The rats scuffled and stirred. 'Unfortunately there is not much choice. Rats and bats. Squadrons of them, divisions–a whole air force and army. And we have to drive them in front of us. Towards the end of the climb it becomes quite congested. Let's get started. The air is good. It is dry underfoot on both sides of the stream. But in winter the floods come and then we have to use frogmen's suits. Keep your torch on my feet. If a bat gets in your hair, brush him off. It will not be often. Their radar is very good.'

They set off up the steep slope. The smell of the rats and of the droppings of bats was thick–a mixture of monkey house and chicken battery. It occurred to Bond that it would be days before he got rid of it.

Clusters of bats hung like bunches of withered grapes from the roof and when, from time to time, either Kerim's head or Bond's brushed against them, they exploded twittering into the darkness. Ahead of them as they climbed there was the forest of squeaking, scuffling red pin-points that grew denser on both sides of the central gutter. Occasionally Kerim flashed his torch forward and the light shone on a grey field sown with glittering teeth and glinting whiskers. When this happened, an extra frenzy seized the rats, and those nearest jumped on the backs of the others to get away. All the while, fighting tumbling grey bodies came sweeping down the central gutter and, as the pressure of the mass higher up the tunnel grew heavier, the frothing rear-rank came closer.

The two men kept their torches levelled like guns on the rear ranks until, after a good quarter of an hour's climb, they reached their destination.

It was a deep alcove of newly faced brick in the side of the tunnel. There were two benches on each side of a thick tarpaulin-wrapped object that came down from the ceiling of the alcove.

They stepped inside. Another few yards' climb, Bond thought, and mass hysteria must have seized the distant thousands of rats further up the tunnel. The horde would have turned. Out of sheer pressure for space, the rats would have braved the lights and hurled themselves down on to the two intruders, in spite of the two glaring eyes and the threatening scent.

'Watch,' said Kerim.

There was a moment of silence. Further up the tunnel the squeaking had stopped, as if at a word of command. Then suddenly the tunnel was a foot deep in a great wave of hurtling, scrambling grey bodies as, with a continuous high-pitched squeal, the rats turned and pelted back down the slope.

For minutes the sleek grey river foamed by outside the alcove until at last the numbers thinned and only a trickle of sick or wounded rats came limping and probing their way down the tunnel floor.

The scream of the horde slowly vanished down towards the river, until there was silence except for the occasional twitter of a fleeing bat.

Kerim gave a non-committal grunt. 'One of these days those rats will start dying. Then we shall have the plague in Istanbul again. Sometimes I feel guilty for not telling the authorities of this tunnel so that they can clean the place up. But I can't so long as the Russians are up here.' He jerked his head at the roof. He looked at his watch. 'Five minutes to go. They will be pulling up their chairs and fiddling with their papers. There will be the three permanent men–M.G.B., or one of them may be from army intelligence, G.R.U. And there will probably be three others. Two came in a fortnight ago, one through Greece and another through Persia. Another one arrived on Monday. God knows who they are, or what they are here for. And sometimes the girl, Tatiana, comes in with a signal and goes out again. Let us hope we will see her today. You will be impressed. She is something.'

Kerim reached up and untied the tarpaulin cover and pulled it downwards. Bond understood. The cover protected the shining butt of a submarine periscope, fully withdrawn. The moisture glistened on the thick grease of the exposed bottom joint. Bond chuckled. 'Where the hell did you get that from, Darko?'

'Turkish Navy. War surplus.' Kerim's voice did not invite further questions. 'Now Q Branch in London is trying to fix some way of wiring the damn thing for sound. It's not going to be easy. The lens at the top of this is no bigger than a cigarette-lighter, end on. When I raise it, it comes up to floor level in their room. In the corner of the room where it comes up, we cut a small mousehole. We did it well. Once when I came to have a look, the first thing I saw was a big mousetrap with a piece of cheese on it. At least it looked big through the lens.' Kerim laughed briefly. 'But there's not much room to fit a sensitive pick-up alongside the lens. And there's no hope of getting in again to do any more fiddling about with their architecture. The only way I managed to install this thing was to get my friends in the Public Works Ministry to turn the Russians out for a few days. The story was that the trams going up the hill were shaking the foundations of the houses. There had to be a survey. It cost me a few hundred pounds for the right pockets. The Public Works inspected half a dozen houses on either side of this one and declared the place safe. By that time, I and the family had finished our construction work. The Russians were suspicious as hell. I gather they went over the place with a toothcomb when they got back, looking for microphones and bombs and so on. But we can't work that trick twice. Unless Q Branch can think up something very clever, I shall have to be content with keeping an eye on them. One of these days they'll give away something useful. They'll be interrogating someone we're interested in or something of that sort.'

Alongside the matrix of the periscope in the roof of the alcove there was a pendulous blister of metal, twice the size of a football. 'What's that?' said Bond.

'Bottom half of a bomb–a big bomb. If anything happens to me, or if war breaks out with Russia, that bomb will be set off by radio-control from my office. It is sad [Kerim didn't look sad] but I fear that many innocent people will get killed besides the Russians. When the blood is on the boil, man is as unselective as nature.'

Kerim had been polishing away at the hooded eyepieces between the two handle-bars that stuck out on both sides of the base of the periscope. Now he glanced at his watch and bent down and gripped the two handles and slowly brought them up level with his chin. There was a hiss of hydraulics as the glistening stem of the periscope slid up into its steel sheath in the roof of the alcove. Kerim bent his head and gazed into the eyepieces and slowly inched up the handles until he could stand upright. He twisted gently. He centred the lens and beckoned to Bond. 'Just the six of them.'

Bond moved over and took the handles.

'Have a good look at them,' said Kerim. 'I know them, but you'd better get their faces in your mind. Head of the table is their Resident Director. On his left are his two staff. Opposite them are the three new ones. The latest, who looks quite an important chap, is on the Director's right. Tell me if they do anything except talk.'

Bond's first impulse was to tell Kerim not to make so much noise. It was as if he was in the room with the Russians, as if he was sitting in a chair in the corner, a secretary perhaps, taking shorthand of the conference.

The wide, all-round lens, designed for spotting aircraft as well as surface ships, gave him a curious picture–a mouse's eye view of a forest of legs below the fore-edge of the table, and various aspects of the heads belonging to the legs. The Director and his two colleagues were clear–serious dull Russian faces whose characteristics Bond filed away. There was the studious, professional face of the Director–thick spectacles, lantern jaw, big forehead and thin hair brushed back. On his left was a square wooden face with deep clefts on either side of the nose, fair hair *en brosse* and a nick out of the left ear. The third member of the permanent staff had a shifty Armenian face with clever bright almond eyes. He was talking now. His face wore a falsely humble look. Gold glinted in his mouth.

Bond could see less of the three visitors. Their backs were held towards him and only the profile of the nearest, and presumably most junior, showed clearly. This man's skin also was dark. He too would be from one of the southern republics. The jaw was badly shaved and the eye in profile was bovine and dull under a thick black brow. The nose was fleshy and porous. The upper lip was long over a sullen mouth and the beginning of a double chin. The tough black hair was cut very short so that most of the back of the neck looked blue to the level of the tips of the ears. It was a military haircut, done with mechanical clippers.

The only clues to the next man were an angry boil on the back of a fat bald neck, a shiny blue suit and rather bright brown shoes. The man was motionless during the whole period that Bond kept watch and apparently never spoke.

Now the senior visitor, on the right of the Resident Director, sat back and began talking. It was a strong, crag-like profile with big bones and a jutting chin under a heavy brown moustache of Stalin cut. Bond could see one cold grey eye under a bushy eyebrow and a low forehead topped by wiry grey-brown hair. This man was the only one who was smoking. He puffed busily at a tiny wooden pipe in the bowl of which stood half a cigarette. Every now and then he shook the pipe sideways so that the ash fell on the floor. His profile had more authority than any of the other faces and Bond guessed that he was a senior man sent down from Moscow.

Bond's eyes were getting tired. He twisted the handles gently and looked round the office as far as the blurring jagged edges of the mousehole would allow. He saw nothing of interest–two olive green filing cabinets, a hatstand by the door, on which he counted six more or less identical grey homburgs, and a sideboard with a heavy carafe of water and some glasses. Bond stood away from the eyepiece, rubbing his eyes.

'If only we could hear,' Kerim said, shaking his head sadly. It would be worth diamonds.'

'It would solve a lot of problems,' agreed Bond. Then, 'By the way Darko, how did you come on this tunnel? What was it built for?'

Kerim bent and gave a quick glance into the eyepieces and straightened up.

'It's a lost drain from the Hall of Pillars,' he said. 'The Hall of Pillars is now a thing for tourists. It's up above us on the heights of Istanbul, near St Sophia. A thousand years ago it was built as a reservoir in case of siege. It's a huge underground palace, a hundred yards long and about half as broad. It was made to hold millions of gallons of water. It was discovered again about four hundred years ago by a man called Gyllius. One day I was reading his account of finding it. He said it was filled in winter from "*a great pipe with a mighty noise*". It occurred to me that there might be another "*great pipe*" to empty it quickly if the city fell to the enemy. I went up to the Hall of Pillars and bribed the watchman and rowed about among the pillars all one night in a rubber dinghy with one of my boys. We went over the walls with a hammer and an echo-sounder. At one end, in the most likely spot, there was a hollow sound. I handed out more money to the Minister of Public Works and he closed the place for a week–"for cleaning". My little team got busy.' Kerim ducked down again for a look through the eyepieces and went on. 'We dug into the wall above waterlevel and came on the top of an arch. The arch was the beginning of a tunnel. We got into the tunnel and went down it. Quite exciting, not knowing where we were going to come out. And, of course, it went straight down the hill–under the Street of Books where the Russians have their place, and out into the Golden Horn, by the Galata Bridge, twenty yards away from my warehouse. So we filled in our hole in the Hall of Pillars and started digging from my end. That was two years ago. It took us a year and a lot of survey work to get directly under the Russians.' Kerim laughed. 'And now I suppose one of these days the Russians will decide to change their offices. By then I hope someone else will be Head of T.'

Kerim bent down to the rubber eyepieces. Bond saw him stiffen. Kerim said urgently. 'The door's opening. Quick. Take over. Here she comes.'

Chapter Seventeen

Killing Time

It was seven o'clock on the same evening and James Bond was back in his hotel. He had had a hot bath and a cold shower. He thought that he had at last scoured the zoo smell out of his skin.

He was sitting, naked except for his shorts, at one of the windows of his room, sipping a vodka and tonic and looking out into the heart of the great tragic sunset over the Golden Horn. But his eyes didn't see the torn cloth of gold and blood that hung behind the minaretted stage beneath which he had caught his first glimpse of Tatiana Romanova.

He was thinking of the tall beautiful girl with the dancer's long gait who had walked through the drab door with a piece of paper in her hand. She had stood beside her Chief and handed him the paper. All the men had looked up at her. She had blushed and looked down. What had that expression on the men's faces meant? It was more than just the way some men look at a beautiful girl. They had shown curiosity. That was reasonable. They wanted to know what was in the signal, why they were being disturbed. But what else? There had been slyness and contempt–the way people stare at prostitutes.

It had been an odd, enigmatic scene. This was part of a highly disciplined para-military organization. These were serving officers, each of whom would be wary of the others. And this girl was just one of the staff, with a Corporal's rank, who was now going through a normal routine. Why had they all unguardedly looked at her with this inquisitive contempt–almost as if she was a spy who had been caught and was going to be executed? Did they suspect her? Had she given herself away? But that seemed less likely as the scene played itself out. The Resident Director read the signal and the other men's eyes turned away from the girl and on to him. He said something, presumably repeating the text of the signal, and the men looked glumly back at him as if the matter did not interest them. Then the Resident Director looked up at the girl and the other eyes followed his. He said something with a friendly, inquiring expression. The girl shook her head and answered briefly. The other men now only looked interested. The Director said one word with a question mark on the end. The girl blushed deeply, and nodded, holding his eyes obediently. The other men smiled encouragement, slyly perhaps, but with approval. No suspicion there. No condemnation. The scene ended with a few sentences from the Director to which the girl seemed to say the equivalent of 'Yes, sir' and turned and walked out of the room. When she had gone, the Director said something with an expression of irony on his face and the men laughed heartily and the sly expression was back on their faces, as if what he had said had been obscene. Then they went back to their work.

Ever since, on their way back down the tunnel, and later in Kerim's office while they discussed what Bond had seen, Bond had racked his brains for a solution to this maddening bit of dumb crambo and now, looking without focus at the dying sun, he was still mystified.

Bond finished his drink and lit another cigarette. He put the problem away and turned his mind to the girl.

Tatiana Romanova. A Romanov. Well, she certainly looked like a Russian princess, or the traditional idea of one. The tall, fine-boned body that moved so gracefully and stood so well. The thick sweep of hair down to the shoulders and the quiet authority of the profile. The wonderful Garbo-esque face with its curiously shy serenity. The contrast between the level innocence of the big, deep blue eyes and the passionate promise of the wide mouth. And the way she had blushed and the way the long eyelashes had come down over the lowered eyes. Had that been the prudery of a virgin? Bond thought not. There was the confidence of having been loved in the proud breasts and the insolently lilting behind–the assertion of a body that knows what it can be for.

On what Bond had seen, could he believe that she was the sort of girl to fall in love with a photograph and a file? How could one tell? Such a girl would have a deeply romantic nature. There were dreams in the eyes and in the mouth. At that age, twenty-four, the Soviet machine would not yet have ground the sentiment out of her. The Romanov blood might well have given her a yearning for men other than the type of modern Russian officer she would meet–stern, cold, mechanical, basically hysterical and, because of their Party education, infernally dull.

It could be true. There was nothing to disprove her story in her looks. Bond wanted it to be true.

The telephone rang. It was Kerim. 'Nothing new?'

'No.'

'Then I will pick you up at eight.'

'I'll be ready.'

Bond laid down the receiver and slowly started to put on his clothes.

Kerim had been firm about the evening. Bond had wanted to stay in his hotel room and wait for the first contact to be made–a note, a telephone call, whatever it might be. But Kerim had said no. The girl had been adamant that she would choose her own time and place. It would be wrong for Bond to seem a slave to her convenience. 'That is bad psychology, my friend,' Kerim had insisted. 'No girl likes a man to run when she whistles. She would despise you if you made yourself too available. From your face and your dossier she would expect you to behave with indifference–even with insolence. She would want that. She wishes to court you, to buy a kiss,' –Kerim had winked–'from that cruel mouth. It is with an image she has fallen in love. Behave like the image. Act the part.'

Bond had shrugged his shoulders. 'All right, Darko. I daresay you're right. What do you suggest?'

'Live the life you would normally. Go home now and have a bath and a drink. The local vodka is all right if you drown it with tonic water. If nothing happens, I will pick you up at eight. We will have dinner at the place of a gipsy friend of mine. A man called Vavra. He is head of a tribe. I must anyway see him tonight. He is one of my best sources. He is finding out who tried to blow up my office. Some of his girls will dance for you. I will not suggest that they should entertain you more intimately. You must keep your sword sharp. There is a saying "Once a King, always a King. But once a Knight is enough!"'

Bond was smiling at the memory of Kerim's dictum when the telephone rang again. He picked up the receiver. It was only the car. As he went down the few stairs and out to Kerim in the waiting Rolls, Bond admitted to himself that he was disappointed.

They were climbing up the far hill through the poorer quarters above the Golden Horn when the chauffeur half turned his head and said something in a non-committal voice.

Kerim answered with a monosyllable. 'He says a Lambretta is on our tail. A Faceless One. It is of no importance. When I wish, I can make a secret of my movements. Often they have trailed this car for miles when there has been only a dummy in the back. A conspicuous car has its uses. They know this gipsy is a friend of mine, but I think they do not understand why. It will do no harm for them to know that we are having a night of relaxation. On a Saturday night, with a friend from England, anything else would be unusual.'

Bond looked back through the rear window and watched the crowded streets. From behind a stopped tram a motor scooter showed for a minute and then was hidden by a taxi. Bond turned away. He reflected briefly on the way the Russians ran their centres–with all the money and equipment in the world, while the Secret Service put against them a handful of adventurous, underpaid men, like this one, with his second-hand Rolls and his children to help him. Yet Kerim had the run of Turkey. Perhaps, after all, the right man was better than the right machine.

At half-past eight they stopped half way up a long hill on the outskirts of Istanbul at a dingy-looking open-air café with a few empty tables on the pavement. Behind it were the tops of trees over a high stone wall. They got out and the car drove off. They waited for the Lambretta, but its wasp-like buzz had stopped and at once it was on its way back down the hill. All they saw of the driver was a glimpse of a short squat man wearing goggles.

Kerim led the way through the tables and into the café. It seemed empty, but a man rose up quickly from behind the till. He kept one hand below the counter. When he saw who it was, he gave Kerim a nervous white smile. Something clanged to the floor. He stepped from behind the counter and led them out through the back and across a stretch of gravel to a door in the high wall and, after knocking once, unlocked it and waved them through.

There was an orchard with plank tables dotted about under the trees. In the centre was a circle of terrazza dancing floor. Round it were strung fairy lights, now dead, on poles planted in the ground. On the far side, at a long table, about twenty people of all ages had been sitting eating, but they had put down their knives and now looked towards the door. Some children had been playing in the grass behind the table. They also were now quiet and watching. The three-quarter moon showed everything up brightly and made pools of membraned shadow under the trees.

Kerim and Bond walked forward. The man at the head of the table said something to the others. He got up and came to meet them. The rest returned to their dinner and the children to their games.

The man greeted Kerim with reserve. He stood for a few moments making a long explanation to which Kerim listened attentively, occasionally asking a question.

The gipsy was an imposing, theatrical figure in Macedonian dress–white shirt with full sleeves, baggy trousers and laced soft leather top-boots. His hair was a tangle of black snakes. A large downward-drooping black moustache almost hid the full red lips. The eyes were fierce and cruel on either side of a syphilitic nose. The moon glinted on the sharp line of the jaw and the high cheekbones. His right hand, which had a gold ring on the thumb, rested on the hilt of a short curved dagger in a leather scabbard tipped with filigree silver.

The gipsy finished talking. Kerim said a few words, forceful and apparently complimentary, about Bond, at the same time stretching his hand out in Bond's direction as if he was a compère in a night-club commending a new turn. The gipsy stepped up to Bond and scrutinized him. He bowed abruptly. Bond followed suit. The gipsy said a few words through a sardonic smile. Kerim laughed and turned to Bond. 'He says if you are ever out of work you should come to him. He will give you a job–taming his women and killing for him. That is a great compliment to a *gajo*–a foreigner. You should say something in reply.'

'Tell him that I can't imagine he needs any help in these matters.'

Kerim translated. The gipsy politely bared his teeth. He said something walked back to the table, clapping his hands sharply. Two women got up and came towards him. He spoke to them curtly and they went back to the table and picked up a large earthenware dish and disappeared among the trees.

Kerim took Bond's arm and led him to one side.

'We have come on a bad night,' he said. 'The restaurant is closed. There are family troubles here which have to be solved–drastically, and in private. But I am an old friend and we are invited to share their supper. It will be disgusting but I have sent for raki. Then we may watch–but on condition that we do not interfere. I hope you understand, my friend.' Kerim gave Bond's arm an additional pressure. 'Whatever you see, you must not move or comment. A court has just been held and justice is to be done–their kind of justice. It is an affair of love and jealousy. Two girls of the tribe are in love with one of his sons. There is a lot of death in the air. They both threaten to kill the other to get him. If he chooses one, the unsuccessful one has sworn to kill him and the girl. It is an *impasse*. There is much argument in the tribe. So the son has been sent up into the hills and the two girls are to fight it out here tonight–to the death. The son has agreed to take the winner. The women are locked up in separate caravans. It will not be for the squeamish, but it will be a remarkable affair. It is a great privilege that we may be present. You understand? We are *gajos*. You will forget your sense of the proprieties? You will not interfere? They would kill you, and possibly me, if you did.'

'Darko,' said Bond. 'I have a French friend. A man called Mathis who is head of the Deuxième. He once said to me: "*J'aime les sensations fortes.*" I am like him. I shall not disgrace you. Men fighting women is one thing. Women fighting women is another. But what about the bomb? The bomb that blew up your office. What did he say about that?'

'It was the leader of the Faceless Ones. He put it there himself. They came down the Golden Horn in a boat and he climbed up a ladder and fixed it to the wall. It was bad luck he didn't get me. The operation was well thought out. The man is a gangster. A Bulgarian "refugee" called Krilencu. I shall have to have a reckoning with him. God knows why they suddenly want to kill me, but I cannot allow such annoyances. I may decide to take action later tonight. I know where he lives. In case Vavra knew the answer, I told my chauffeur to come back with the necessary equipment.'

A fiercely attractive young girl in a thick old-fashioned black frock, with strings of gold coins round her neck and about ten thin gold bracelets on each wrist, came over from the table and swept a low jingling curtsey in front of Kerim. She said something and Kerim replied.

'We are bidden to the table,' said Kerim. 'I hope you are good at eating with your fingers. I see they are all wearing their smartest clothes tonight. That girl would be worth marrying. She has a lot of gold on her. It is her dowry.'

They walked over to the table. Two places had been cleared on either side of the head gipsy. Kerim gave what sounded like a polite greeting to the table. There was a curt nod of acknowledgment. They sat down. In front of each of them was a large plate of some sort of ragout smelling strongly of garlic, a bottle of raki, a pitcher of water and a cheap tumbler. More bottles of raki, untouched, were on the table. When Kerim reached for his and poured himself half a tumblerful, everyone followed suit. Kerim added some water and raised his glass. Bond did the same. Kerim made a short and vehement speech and all raised their glasses and drank. The atmosphere became easier. An old woman next to Bond passed him a long loaf of bread and said something. Bond smiled and said 'thank you'. He broke off a piece and handed the loaf to Kerim who was picking among his ragout with thumb and forefinger. Kerim took the loaf with one hand and at the same time, with the other, he put a large piece of meat in his mouth and began to eat.

Bond was about to do the same when Kerim said sharply and quietly, 'With the right hand, James. The left hand is used for only one purpose among these people.'

Bond halted his left hand in mid-air and moved it on to grasp the nearest raki bottle. He poured himself another half tumblerful and started to eat with his right hand. The ragout was delicious but steaming hot. Bond winced each time he dipped his fingers into it. Everyone watched them eat and from time to time the old woman dipped her fingers into Bond's stew and chose a piece for him.

When they had scoured their plates, a silver bowl of water, in which rose leaves floated, and a clean linen cloth, were put between Bond and Kerim. Bond washed his fingers and his greasy chin and turned to his host and dutifully made a short speech of thanks which Kerim translated. The table murmured its appreciation. The head gipsy bowed towards Bond and said, according to Kerim, that he hated all *gajos* except Bond, whom he was proud to call his friend. Then he clapped his hands sharply and everybody got up from the table and began pulling the benches away and arranging them round the dance floor.

Kerim came round the table to Bond. They walked off together. 'How do you feel? They've gone to get the two girls.'

Bond nodded. He was enjoying the evening. The scene was beautiful and thrilling–the white moon blazing down on the ring of figures now settling on the benches, the glint of gold or jewellery as somebody shifted his position, the glaring pool of terrazza and, all around, the quiet, sentinel trees standing guard in their black skirts of shadow.

Kerim led Bond to a bench where the chief gipsy sat alone. They took places on his right.

A black cat with green eyes walked slowly across the terrazza and joined a group of children who were sitting quietly as if someone was about to come on to the dance floor and teach them a lesson. It sat down and began licking its chest.

Beyond the high wall, a horse neighed. Two of the gipsies looked over their shoulders towards the sound as if they were reading the cry of the horse. From the road came the silvery spray of a bicycle bell as someone sped down the hill.

The crouching silence was broken by the clang of a bolt being drawn. The door in the wall crashed back and two girls, spitting and fighting like angry cats, hurtled through and across the grass and into the ring.

Chapter Eighteen

Strong Sensations

The head gipsy's voice cracked out. The girls separated reluctantly and stood facing him. The gipsy began to speak in a tone of harsh denunciation.

Kerim put his hand up to his mouth and whispered behind it. 'Vevra is telling them that this is a great tribe of gipsies and they have brought dissension among it. He says there is no room for hatred among themselves, only against those outside. The hatred they have created must be purged so that the tribe can live peacefully again. They are to fight. If the loser is not killed she will be banished for ever. That will be the same as death. These people wither and die outside the tribe. They cannot live in our world. It is like wild beasts forced to live in a cage.'

While Kerim spoke, Bond examined the two beautiful, taut, sullen animals in the centre of the ring.

They were both gipsy-dark, with coarse black hair to their shoulders, and they were both dressed in the collection of rags you associate with shanty-town negroes–tattered brown shifts that were mostly darns and patches. One was bigger-boned than the other, and obviously stronger, but she looked sullen and slow-eyed and might not be quick on her feet. She was handsome in a rather leonine way, and there was a slow red glare in her heavy lidded eyes as she stood and listened impatiently to the head of the tribe. She ought to win, thought Bond. She is half an inch taller, and she is stronger.

Where this girl was a lioness, the other was a panther–lithe and quick and with cunning sharp eyes that were not on the speaker but sliding sideways, measuring inches, and the hands at her sides were curled into claws. The muscles of her fine legs looked hard as a man's. The breasts were small, and, unlike the big breasts of the other girl, hardly swelled the rags of her shift. She looks a dangerous little bitch of a girl, thought Bond. She will certainly get in the first blow. She will be too quick for the other.

At once he was proved wrong. As Vavra spoke his last word, the big girl, who, Kerim whispered, was called Zora, kicked hard sideways, without taking aim, and caught the other girl square in the stomach and, as the smaller girl staggered, followed up with a swinging blow of the fist to the side of the head that knocked her sprawling on to the stone floor.

'Oi, Vida,' lamented a woman in the crowd. She needn't have worried. Even Bond could see that Vida was shamming as she lay on the ground, apparently winded. He could see her eyes glinting under her bent arm as Zora's foot came flashing at her ribs.

Vida's hands flickered out together. They grasped the ankle and her head struck into the instep like a snake's. Zora gave a scream of pain and wrenched furiously at her trapped foot. It was too late. The other girl was up on one knee, and then standing erect, the foot still in her hands. She heaved upwards and Zora's other foot left the ground and she crashed full length.

The thud of the big girl's fall shook the ground. For a moment she lay still. With an animal snarl, Vida dived on top of her, clawing and tearing.

My God, what a hell-cat, thought Bond. Beside him, Kerim's breath hissed tensely through his teeth.

But the big girl protected herself with her elbows and knees and at last she managed to kick Vida off. She staggered to her feet and backed away, her lips bared from her teeth and the shift hanging in tatters from her splendid body. At once she went in to the attack again, her arms groping forward for a hold and, as the smaller girl leapt aside, Zora's hand caught the neck of her shift and split it down to the hem. But immediately Vida twisted in close under the reaching arms and her fists and knees thudded into the attacker's body.

This in-fighting was a mistake. The strong arms clamped shut round the smaller girl, trapping Vida's hands low down so that they could not reach up for Zora's eyes. And, slowly, Zora began to squeeze, while Vida's legs and knees thrashed ineffectually below.

Bond thought that now the big girl must win. All Zora had to do was to fall on the other girl. Vida's head would crack down on the stone and then Zora could do as she liked. But all of a sudden it was the big girl who began to scream. Bond saw that Vida's head was buried deep in the other's breasts. Her teeth were at work. Zora's arms let go as she reached for Vida's hair to pull the head back and away from her. But now Vida's hands were free and they were scrabbling at the big girl's body.

The girls tore apart and backed away like cats, their shining bodies glinting through the last rags of their shifts and blood showing on the exposed breasts of the big girl.

They circled warily, both glad to have escaped, and as they circled they tore off the last of their rags and threw them into the audience.

Bond held his breath at the sight of the two glistening, naked bodies, and he could feel Kerim's body tense beside him. The ring of gipsies seemed to have come closer to the two fighters. The moon shone on glittering eyes and there was the whisper of hot, panting breath.

Still the two girls circled slowly, their teeth bared and their breath coming harshly. The light glinted off their heaving breasts and stomachs and off their hard, boyish flanks. Their feet left dark sweat marks on the white stones.

Again it was the big girl, Zora, who made the first move with a sudden forward leap and arms held out like a wrestler's. But Vida stood her ground. Her right foot lashed out in a furious *coup de savate* that made a slap like a pistol shot. The big girl gave a wounded cry and clutched at herself. At once Vida's other foot kicked up to the stomach and she threw herself in after it.

There was a low growl from the crowd as Zora went down on her knees. Her hands went up to protect her face, but it was too late. The smaller girl was astride her, and her hands grasped Zora's wrists as she bore down on her with all her weight and bent her to the ground, her bared white teeth reaching towards the offered neck.

'BOOM!'

The explosion cracked the tension like a nut. A flash of flame lit the darkness behind the dance floor and a chunk of masonry sang past Bond's ear. Suddenly the orchard was full of running men and the head gipsy was slinking forward across the stone with his curved dagger held out in front of him. Kerim was going after him, a gun in his hand. As the gipsy passed the two girls, now standing wild-eyed and trembling, he shouted a word at them and they took to their heels and disappeared among the trees where the last of the women and children were already vanishing among the shadows.

Bond, the Beretta held uncertainly in his hand, followed slowly in the wake of Kerim towards the wide breach that had been blown out of the garden wall, and wondered what the hell was going on.

The stretch of grass between the hole in the wall and the dance floor was a turmoil of fighting, running figures. It was only as Bond came up with the fight that he distinguished the squat, conventionally dressed Bulgars from the swirling finery of the gipsies. There seemed to be more of the Faceless Ones than of the gipsies, almost two to one. As Bond peered into the struggling mass, a gipsy youth was ejected from it, clutching his stomach. He groped towards Bond, coughing terribly. Two small dark men came after him, their knives held low.

Instinctively Bond stepped to one side so that the crowd was not behind the two men. He aimed at their legs above the knees and the gun in his hand cracked twice. The two men fell, soundlessly, face downwards in the grass.

Two bullets gone. Only six left. Bond edged closer to the fight.

A knife hissed past his head and clanged on to the dance floor.

It had been aimed at Kerim, who came running out of the shadows with two men on his heels. The second man stopped and raised his knife to throw and Bond shot from the hip, blindly, and saw him fall. The other man turned and fled among the trees and Kerim dropped to one knee beside Bond, wrestling with his gun.

'Cover me,' he shouted. 'Jammed on the first shot. It's those bloody Bulgars. God knows what they think they're doing.'

A hand caught Bond round the mouth and yanked him backwards. On his way to the ground he smelled carbolic soap and nicotine. He felt a boot thud into the back of his neck. As he whirled over sideways in the grass he expected to feel the searing flame of a knife. But the men, and there were three of them, were after Kerim, and as Bond scrambled to one knee he saw the squat black figures pile down on the crouching man, who gave one lash upwards with his useless gun and then went down under them.

At the same moment as Bond leapt forward and brought his gun butt down on a round shaven head, something flashed past his eyes and the curved dagger of the head gipsy was growing out of a heaving back. Then Kerim was on his feet and the third man was running and a man was standing in the breach in the wall shouting one word, again and again, and one by one the attackers broke off their fights and doubled over to the man and past him and out on to the road.

'Shoot, James, shoot!' roared Kerim. 'That's Krilencu.' He started to run forward. Bond's gun spat once. But the man had dodged round the wall, and thirty yards is too far for night shooting with an automatic. As Bond lowered his hot gun, there came the staccato firing of a squadron of Lambrettas, and Bond stood and listened to the swarm of wasps flying down the hill.

There was silence except for the groans of the wounded. Bond listlessly watched Kerim and Vavra come back through the breach in the wall and walk among the bodies, occasionally turning one over with a foot. The other gipsies seeped back from the road and the older women came hurrying out of the shadows to tend their men.

Bond shook himself. What the hell had it all been about? Ten or a dozen men had been killed. What for? Whom had they been trying to get? Not him, Bond. When he was down and ready for the killing they had passed him by and made for Kerim. This was the second attempt on Kerim's life. Was it anything to do with the Romanova business? How could it possibly tie in?

Bond tensed. His gun spoke twice from the hip. The knife clattered harmlessly off Kerim's back. The figure that had risen from the dead twirled slowly round like a ballet dancer and toppled forward on his face. Bond ran forward. He had been just in time. The moon had caught the blade and he had had a clear field of fire. Kerim looked down at the twitching body. He turned to meet Bond.

Bond stopped in his tracks. 'You bloody fool,' he said angrily. 'Why the hell can't you take more care! You ought to have a nurse.' Most of Bond's anger came from knowing that it was he who had brought a cloud of death around Kerim.

Darko Kerim grinned shamefacedly. 'Now it is not good, James. You have saved my life too often. We might have been friends. Now the distance between us is too great. Forgive me, for I can never pay you back.' He held out his hand.

Bond brushed it aside. 'Don't be a damn fool, Darko,' he said roughly. 'My gun worked, that's all. Yours didn't. You'd better get one that does. For Christ's sake tell me what the hell this is all about. There's been too much blood splashing about tonight. I'm sick of it. I want a drink. Come and finish that raki.' He took the big man's arm.

As they reached the table, littered with the remains of the supper, a piercing, terrible scream came out of the depths of the orchard. Bond put his hand on his gun. Kerim shook his head. 'We shall soon know what the Faceless Ones were after,' he said gloomily. 'My friends are finding out. I can guess what they will discover. I think they will never forgive me for having been here tonight. Five of their men are dead.'

'There might have been a dead woman too,' said Bond unsympathetically. 'At least you've saved her life. Don't be stupid, Darko. These gipsies knew the risks when they started spying for you against the Bulgars. It was gang warfare.' He added a dash of water to two tumblers of raki.

They both emptied the glasses at one swallow. The head gipsy came up, wiping the tip of his curved dagger on a handful of grass. He sat down and accepted a glass of raki from Bond. He seemed quite cheerful. Bond had the impression that the fight had been too short for him. The gipsy said something, slyly.

Kerim chuckled. 'He said that his judgment was right. You killed well.

Now he wants you to take on those two women.'

'Tell him even one of them would be too much for me. But tell him I think they are fine women. I would be glad if he would do me a favour and call the fight a draw. Enough of his people have been killed tonight. He will need these two girls to bear children for the tribe.'

Kerim translated. The gipsy looked sourly at Bond and said a few bitter words.

'He says that you should not have asked him such a difficult favour. He says that your heart is too soft for a good fighter. But he says he will do what you ask.'

The gipsy ignored Bond's smile of thanks. He started talking fast to Kerim, who listened attentively, occasionally interrupting the flow with a question. Krilencu's name was often mentioned. Kerim talked back. There was deep contrition in his voice and he refused to allow himself to be stopped by protests from the other. There came a last reference to Krilencu. Kerim turned to Bond.

'My friend,' he said drily. 'It is a curious affair. It seems the Bulgars were ordered to kill Vavra and as many of his men as possible. That is a simple matter' They knew the gipsy had been working for me. Rather drastic, perhaps. But in killing, the Russians have not much finesse. They like mass death. Vavra was a main target. I was another. The declaration of war against me personally I can also understand. But it seems that you were not to be harmed. You were exactly described so that there should be no mistake. That is odd. Perhaps it was desired that there should be no diplomatic repercussions. Who can tell? The attack was well planned. They came to the top of the hill by a roundabout route and free-wheeled down so that we should hear nothing. This is a lonely place and there is not a policeman for miles. I blame myself for having treated these people too lightly.' Kerim looked puzzled and unhappy. He seemed to make up his mind. He said, 'But now it is midnight. The Rolls will be here. There remains a small piece of work to be done before we go home to bed. And it is time we left these people. They have much to do before it is light. There are many bodies to go into the Bosphorus and there is the wall to be repaired. By daylight there must be no trace of these troubles. Our friend wishes you very well. He says you must return, and that Zora and Vida are yours until their breasts fall. He refuses to blame me for what has happened. He says that I am to continue sending him Bulgars. Ten were killed tonight. He would like some more. And now we will shake him by the hand and go. That is all he asks of us. We are good friends, but we are also *gajos*. And I expect he does not want us to see his women weeping over their dead.'

Kerim stretched out his huge hand. Vavra took it and held it and looked into Kerim's eyes. For a moment his own fierce eyes seemed to go opaque. Then the gipsy let the hand drop and turned to Bond. The hand was dry and rough and padded like the paw of a big animal. Again the eyes went opaque. He let go of Bond's hand. He spoke rapidly and urgently to Kerim and turned his back on them and walked away towards the trees.

Nobody looked up from his work as Kerim and Bond climbed through the breach in the wall. The Rolls stood, glittering in the moonlight, a few yards down the road opposite the café entrance. A young man was sitting beside the chauffeur. Kerim gestured with his hand. 'That is my tenth son. He is called Boris. I thought I might need him. I shall.'

The youth turned and said, 'Good evening, sir.' Bond recognized him as one of the clerks in the warehouse. He was as dark and lean as the head clerk, and his eyes also were blue.

The car moved down the hill. Kerim spoke to the chauffeur in English. 'It is a small street off the Hippodrome Square. When we get there we will proceed softly. I will tell you when to stop. Have you got the uniforms and the equipment?'

'Yes, Kerim Bey.'

'All right. Make good speed. It is time we were all in bed.'

Kerim sank back in his seat. He took out a cigarette. They sat and smoked. Bond gazed out at the drab streets and reflected that sparse street-lighting is the sure sign of a poor town.

It was some time before Kerim spoke. Then he said, 'The gipsy said we both have the wings of death over us. He said that I am to beware of a son of the snows and you must beware of a man who is owned by the moon.' He laughed harshly. 'That is the sort of rigmarole they talk. But he says that Krilencu isn't either of these men. That is good.'

'Why?'

'Because I cannot sleep until I have killed that man. I do not know if what happened tonight has any connection with you and your assignment. I do not care. For some reason, war has been declared on me. If I do not kill Krilencu, at the third attempt he will certainly kill me. So we are now on our way to keep an appointment with him in Samarra.'

Chapter Nineteen

The Mouth of Marilyn Monroe

The car sped through the deserted streets, past shadowy mosques from which dazzling minarets lanced up towards the three-quarter moon, under the ruined Aqueduct and across the Ataturk Boulevard and north of the barred entrances to the Grand Bazaar. At the Column of Constantine the car turned right, through mean twisting streets that smelled of garbage, and finally debouched into a long ornamental square in which three stone columns fired themselves like a battery of space-rockets into the spangled sky.

'Slow,' said Kerim softly. They crept round the square under the shadow of the lime trees. Down a street on the east side, the lighthouse below the Seraglio Palace gave them a great yellow wink.

'Stop.'

The car pulled up in the darkness under the limes. Kerim reached for the door handle. 'We shan't be long, James. You sit up front in the driver's seat and if a policeman comes along just say "*Ben Bey Kerim'in ortagiyim*". Can you remember that? It means "I am Kerim Bey's partner". They'll leave you alone.'

Bond snorted. 'Thanks very much. But you'll be surprised to hear I'm coming with you. You're bound to get into trouble without me. Anyway I'm damned if I'm going to sit here trying to bluff policemen. The worst of learning one good phrase is that it sounds as if one knew the language. The policeman will come back with a barrage of Turkish and when I can't answer he'll smell a rat. Don't argue, Darko.'

'Well, don't blame me if you don't like this.' Kerim's voice was embarrassed. 'It's going to be a straight killing in cold blood. In my country you let sleeping dogs lie, but when they wake up and bite, you shoot them. You don't offer them a duel. All right?'

'Whatever you say,' said Bond. 'I've got one bullet left in case you miss.'

'Come on then,' said Kerim reluctantly. 'We've got quite a walk. The other two will be going another way.'

Kerim took a long walking-stick from the chauffeur, and a leather case. He slung them over his shoulder and they started off down the street into the yellow wink of the lighthouse. Their footsteps echoed hollowly back at them from the iron-shuttered shop frontages. There was not a soul in sight, not a cat, and Bond was glad he was not walking alone down this long street towards the distant baleful eye.

From the first, Istanbul had given him the impression of a town where, with the night, horror creeps out of the stones. It seemed to him a town the centuries had so drenched in blood and violence that, when daylight went out, the ghosts of its dead were its only population. His instinct told him, as it has told other travellers, that Istanbul was a town he would be glad to get out of alive.

They came to a narrow stinking alley that dived steeply down the hill to their right. Kerim turned into it and started gingerly down its cobbled surface. 'Watch your feet,' he said softly. 'Garbage is a polite word for what my charming people throw into their streets.'

The moon shone whitely down the moist river of cobbles. Bond kept his mouth shut and breathed through his nose. He put his feet down one after the other, flat-footedly, and with his knees bent, as if he was walking down a snow-slope. He thought of his bed in the hotel and of the comfortable cushions of the car under the sweetly smelling lime trees, and he wondered how many more kinds of dreadful stench he was going to run into during his present assignment.

They stopped at the bottom of the alley. Kerim turned to him with a broad white grin. He pointed upwards at a towering block of black shadow. 'Mosque of Sultan Ahmet. Famous Byzantine frescoes. Sorry I haven't got time to show you more of the beauties of my country.' Without waiting for Bond's reply, he cut off to the right and along a dusty boulevard, lined with cheap shops, that sloped down towards the distant glint that was the Sea of Marmara. For ten minutes they walked in silence. Then Kerim slowed and beckoned Bond into the shadows.

'This will be a simple operation,' he said softly. 'Krilencu lives down there, beside the railway line.' He gestured vaguely towards a cluster of red and green lights at the end of the boulevard. 'He hides out in a shack behind a bill-hoarding. There is a front door to the shack. Also a trapdoor to the street through the hoarding. He thinks no one knows of this. My two men will go in at the front door. He will slip out through the hoarding. Then I shoot him. All right?'

'If you say so.'

They walked on down the boulevard, keeping close to the wall. After ten minutes, they came in sight of the twenty-foot-high hoarding that formed a facing wall to the T intersection at the bottom of the street. The moon was behind the hoarding and its face was in shadow. Now Kerim walked even more carefully, putting each foot softly in front of him. About a hundred yards from the hoarding the shadows ended and the moon blazed whitely down on the intersection. Kerim stopped in the last dark doorway and stationed Bond in front of him, up against his chest. 'Now we must wait,' he whispered. Bond heard Kerim fiddling behind him. There came a soft plop as the lid of the leather case came off. A thin, heavy steel tube, about two feet long, with a bulge at each end, was pressed into Bond's hand. 'Sniperscope. German model,' whispered Kerim. 'Infra-red lens. Sees in the dark. Have a look at that big film advertisement over there. That face. Just below the nose. You'll see the outline of a trap-door. In direct line down from the signal box.'

Bond rested his forearm against the door jamb and raised the tube to his right eye. He focused it on the patch of black shadow opposite. Slowly the black dissolved into grey. The outline of a huge woman's face and some lettering appeared. Now Bond could read the lettering. It said: 'NIYAGARA. MARILYN MONROE VE JOSEPH COTTEN' and underneath, the cartoon feature, 'BONZO FUTBOLOU'. Bond inched the glass down the vast pile of Marilyn Monroe's hair, and the cliff of forehead, and down the two feet of nose to the cavernous nostrils. A faint square showed in the poster. It ran from below the nose into the great alluring curve of the lips. It was about three feet deep. From it, there would be a longish drop to the ground.

Behind Bond there sounded a series of soft clicks. Kerim held forward his walking-stick. As Bond had supposed, it was a gun, a rifle, with a skeleton butt which was also a twist breech. The squat bulge of a silencer had taken the place of the rubber tip.

'Barrel from the new 88 Winchester,' whispered Kerim proudly. 'Put together for me by a man in Ankara. Takes the ·308 cartridge. The short one. Three of them. Give me the glass. I want to get that trap-door lined up before my men go in at the front. Mind if I use your shoulder as a rest?'

'All right.' Bond handed Kerim the Sniperscope. Kerim clipped it to the top of the barrel and slid the gun along Bond's shoulder.

'Got it,' whispered Kerim. 'Where Vavra said. He's a good man that.' He lowered his gun just as two policemen appeared at the right-hand corner of the intersection. Bond stiffened.

'It's all right,' whispered Kerim. 'That's my boy and the chauffeur.' He put two fingers in his mouth. A very quick, very low-pitched whistle sounded for a fraction of a second. One of the policemen lifted his hand to the back of his neck. The two policemen turned and walked away, their boots ringing loudly on the paving stones.

'Few minutes more,' whispered Kerim. 'They've got to get round the back of that hoarding.' Bond felt the heavy barrel of the gun slip into place along his right shoulder.

The moonstruck silence was broken by a loud iron clang from the signal box behind the hoarding. One of the signal arms dropped. A green pinpoint of light showed among the cluster of reds. There was a soft slow rumble in the distance, away to the left by Seraglio Point. It came close and sorted itself into the heavy pant of an engine and the grinding clangour of a string of badly coupled goods trucks. A faint yellow glimmer shone along the embankment to the left. The engine came labouring into view above the hoarding.

The train slowly clanked by on its hundred-mile journey to the Greek frontier, a broken black silhouette against the silver sea, and the heavy cloud of smoke from its cheap fuel drifted towards them on the still air. As the red light on the brake van glimmered briefly and disappeared, there came the deeper rumble as the engine entered a cutting, and then two harsh, mournful whoops as it whistled its approach to the little station of Buyuk, a mile further down the line.

The rumble of the train died away. Bond felt the gun press deeper into his shoulder. He strained his eyes into the target of shadow. In the centre of it, a deeper square of blackness showed.

Bond cautiously lifted his left hand to shade his eyes from the moon. There came a hiss of breath from behind his right ear. 'He's coming.'

Out of the mouth of the huge, shadowed poster, between the great violet lips, half-open in ecstasy, the dark shape of a man emerged and hung down like a worm from the mouth of a corpse.

The man dropped. A ship going up towards the Bosphorus growled in the night like a sleepless animal in a zoo. Bond felt a prickle of sweat on his forehead. The barrel of the rifle depressed as the man stepped softly off the pavement towards them.

When he's at the edge of the shadow, he'll start to run, thought Bond. You damn fool, get the sights further down.

Now. The man bent for a quick sprint across the dazzling white street. He was coming out of the shadow. His right leg was bent forward and his shoulder was twisted to give him momentum.

At Bond's ear there was the clunk of an axe hitting into a tree-trunk. The man dived forward, his arms outstretched. There was a sharp 'tok' as his chin or his forehead hit the ground.

An empty cartridge tinkled down at Bond's feet. He heard the click of the next round going into the chamber.

The man's fingers scrabbled briefly at the cobbles. His shoes knocked on the road. Then he lay absolutely still.

Kerim grunted. The rifle came down off Bond's shoulder, Bond listened to the noises of Kerim folding up the gun and putting away the Sniperscope in its leather case.

Bond looked away from the sprawling figure in the road, the figure of the man who had been, but was no more. He had a moment of resentment against the life that made him witness these things. The resentment was not against Kerim. Kerim had twice been this man's target. In a way it had been a long duel, in which the man had fired twice to Kerim's once. But Kerim was the cleverer, cooler man, and the luckier, and that had been that. But Bond had never killed in cold blood, and he hadn't liked watching, and helping, someone else do it.

Kerim silently took his arm. They walked slowly away from the scene and back the way they had come.

Kerim seemed to sense Bond's thoughts. 'Life is full of death, my friend,' he said philosophically. 'And sometimes one is made the instrument of death. I do not regret killing that man. Nor would I regret killing any of those Russians we saw in that office today. They are hard people. With them, what you don't get from strength, you won't get from mercy. They are all the same, the Russians. I wish your government would realize it and be strong with them. Just an occasional little lesson in manners like I have taught them tonight.'

'In power politics, one doesn't often have the chance of being as quick and neat as you were tonight, Darko. And don't forget it's only one of their satellites you've punished, one of the men they always find to do their dirty work. Mark you,' said Bond, 'I quite agree about the Russians. They simply don't understand the carrot. Only the stick has any effect. Basically they're masochists. They love the knout. That's why they were so happy under Stalin. He gave it them. I'm not sure how they're going to react to the scraps of carrot they're being fed by Khrushchev and Co. As for England, the trouble today is that carrots for all are the fashion. At home and abroad. We don't show teeth any more–only gums.'

Kerim laughed harshly, but made no comment. They were climbing back up the stinking alley and there was no breath for talk. They rested at the top and then walked slowly towards the trees of the Hippodrome Square.

'So you forgive me for today?' It was odd to hear the longing for reassurance in the big man's usually boisterous voice.

'Forgive you? Forgive what? Don't be ridiculous.' There was affection in Bond's voice. 'You've got a job to do and you're doing it. I've been very impressed. You've got a wonderful set-up here. I'm the one who ought to apologize. I seem to have brought a great deal of trouble down on your head. And you've dealt with it. I've just tagged along behind. And I've got absolutely nowhere with my main job. M will be getting pretty impatient. Perhaps there'll be some sort of message at the hotel.'

But when Kerim took Bond back to the hotel and went with him to the desk there was nothing for Bond. Kerim clapped him on the back. 'Don't worry, my friend,' he said cheerfully. 'Hope makes a good breakfast. Eat plenty of it. I will send the car in the morning and if nothing has happened I will think of some more little adventures to pass the time. Clean your gun and sleep on it. You both deserve a rest.'

Bond climbed the few stairs and unlocked his door and locked and bolted it behind him. Moonlight filtered through the curtains. He walked across and turned on the pink-shaded lights on the dressing-table. He stripped off his clothes and went into the bathroom and stood for a few minutes under the shower. He thought how much more eventful Saturday the fourteenth had been than Friday the thirteenth. He cleaned his teeth and gargled with a sharp mouthwash to get rid of the taste of the day and turned off the bathroom light and went back into the bedroom.

Bond drew aside one curtain and opened wide the tall windows and stood, holding the curtains open and looking out across the great boomerang curve of water under the riding moon. The night breeze felt wonderfully cool on his naked body. He looked at his watch. It said two o'clock.

Bond gave a shuddering yawn. He let the curtains drop back into place. He bent to switch off the lights on the dressing-table. Suddenly he stiffened and his heart missed a beat.

There had been a nervous giggle from the shadows at the back of the room. A girl's voice said, 'Poor Mister Bond. You must be tired. Come to bed.'

Chapter Twenty

Black on Pink

Bond whirled round. He looked over to the bed, but his eyes were blind from gazing at the moon. He crossed the room and turned on the pink-shaded light by the bed. There was a long body under the single sheet. Brown hair was spread out on the pillow. The tips of fingers showed, holding the sheet up over the face. Lower down the breasts stood up like hills under snow.

Bond laughed shortly. He leaned forward and gave the hair a soft tug. There was a squeak of protest from under the sheet. Bond sat down on the edge of the bed. After a moment's silence a corner of the sheet was cautiously lowered and one large blue eye inspected him.

'You look very improper.' The voice was muffled by the sheet.

'What about you! And how did you get here?'

'I walked down two floors. I live here too.' The voice was deep and provocative. There was very little accent.

'Well, I'm going to get into bed.'

The sheet came quickly down to the chin and the girl pulled herself up on the pillows. She was blushing. 'Oh no. You mustn't.'

'But it's my bed. And anyway you told me to.' The face was incredibly beautiful. Bond examined it coolly. Thc blush deepened.

'That was only a phrase. To introduce myself.'

'Well I'm very glad to meet you. My name's James Bond.'

'Mine's Tatiana Romanova.' She sounded the second A of Tatiana and the first A of Romanova very long. 'My friends call me Tania.'

There was a pause while they looked at each other, the girl with curiosity, and with what might have been relief. Bond with cool surmise.

She was the first to break the silence. 'You look just like your photographs,' she blushed again. 'But you must put something on. It upsets me.'

'You upset me just as much. That's called sex. If I got into bed with you it wouldn't matter. Anyway, what have *you* got on?'

She pulled the sheet a fraction lower to show a quarter-inch black velvet ribbon round her neck. 'This.'

Bond looked down into the teasing blue eyes, now wide as if asking if the ribbon was inadequate. He felt his body getting out of control.

'Damn you, Tania. Where are the rest of your things? Or did you come down in the lift like that?'

'Oh no. That would not have been *kulturny*. They are under the bed.'

'Well, if you think you are going to get out of this room without . . .'

Bond left the sentence unfinished. He got up from the bed and went to put on one of the dark blue silk pyjama coats he wore instead of pyjamas.

'What you are suggesting is not *kulturny*.'

'Oh isn't it,' said Bond sarcastically. He came back to the bed and pulled up a chair beside it. He smiled down at her. 'Well I'll tell you something *kulturny*. You're one of the most beautiful women in the world.'

The girl blushed again. She looked at him seriously. 'Are you speaking the truth? I think my mouth is too big. Am I as beautiful as Western girls? I was once told I look like Greta Garbo. Is that so?'

'More beautiful,' said Bond. 'There is more light in your face. And your mouth isn't too big. It's just the right size. For me, anyway.'

'What is that–"light in the face"? What do you mean?'

Bond meant that she didn't look to him like a Russian spy. She seemed to show none of the reserve of a spy. None of the coldness, none of the calculation. She gave the impression of warmth of heart and gaiety. These things shone out through the eyes. He searched for a non-committal phrase. 'There is a lot of gaiety and fun in your eyes,' he said lamely.

Tatiana looked serious. 'That is curious,' she said. 'There is not much fun and gaiety in Russia. No one speaks of these things. I have never been told that before.'

Gaiety? She thought, after the last two months? How could she be looking gay? And yet, yes, there was a lightness in her heart. Was she a loose woman by nature? Or was it something to do with this man she had never seen before? Relief about him after the agony of thinking about what she had to do? It was certainly much easier than she had expected. He made it easy–made it fun, with a spice of danger. He was terribly handsome. And he looked very clean. Would he forgive her when they got to London and she told him? Told him that she had been sent to seduce him? Even the night on which she must do it and the number of the room? Surely he wouldn't mind very much. It was doing him no harm. It was only a way for her to get to England and make those reports. 'Gaiety and fun in her eyes.' Well, why not? It was possible. There was a wonderful sense of freedom being alone with a man like this and knowing that she would not be punished for it. It was really terribly exciting.

'You are very handsome,' she said. She searched for a comparison that would give him pleasure. 'You are like an American film star.'

She was startled by his reaction. 'For God's sake! That's the worst insult you can pay a man!'

She hurried to make good her mistake. How curious that the compliment didn't please him. Didn't everyone in the West want to look like a film star? 'I was lying,' she said. 'I wanted to give you pleasure. In fact you are like my favourite hero. He's in a book by a Russian called Lermontov. I will tell you about him one day.'

One day? Bond thought it was time to get down to business.

'Now listen, Tania.' He tried not to look at the beautiful face on the pillow. He fixed his eyes on the point of her chin. 'We've got to stop fooling and be serious. What *is* all this about? Are you really going to come back to England with me?' He raised his eyes to hers. It was fatal. She had opened them wide again in that damnable guilelessness.

'But of course!'

'Oh!' Bond was taken aback by the directness of her answer. He looked at her suspiciously. 'You're sure?'

'Yes.' Her eyes were truthful now. She had stopped flirting.

'You're not afraid?'

He saw a shadow cross her eyes. But it was not what he thought. She had remembered that she had a part to play. She was to be frightened of what she was doing. Terrified. It had sounded so easy, this acting, but now it was difficult. How odd! She decided to compromise.

'Yes. I am afraid. But not so much now. You will protect me. I thought you would.'

'Well, yes, of course I will.' Bond thought of her relatives in Russia. He quickly put the thought out of his mind. What was he doing? Trying to dissuade her from coming? He closed his mind to the consequences he imagined for her. 'There's nothing to worry about. I'll look after you.' And now for the question he had been shirking. He felt a ridiculous embarrassment. This girl wasn't in the least what he had expected. It was spoiling everything to ask the question. It had to be done.

'What about the machine?'

Yes. It was as if he had cuffed her across the face. Pain showed in her eyes, and the edge of tears.

She pulled the sheet over her mouth and spoke from behind it. Her eyes above the sheet were cold.

'So that's what you want.'

'Now listen.' Bond put nonchalance in his voice. 'This machine's got nothing to do with you and me. But my people in London want it.' He remembered security. He added blandly. 'It's not all that important. They know all about the machine and they think it's a wonderful Russian invention. They just want one to copy. Like your people copy foreign cameras and things.' God, how lame it sounded!

'Now you're lying,' a big tear rolled out of one wide blue eye and down the soft cheek and on to the pillow. She pulled the sheet up over her eyes.

Bond reached out and put his hand on her arm under the sheet. The arm flinched angrily away.

'Damn the bloody machine,' he said impatiently. 'But for God's sake, Tania, you must know that I've got a job to do. Just say one way or the other and we'll forget about it. There are lots more things to talk about. We've got to arrange our journey and so on. Of course my people want it or they wouldn't have sent me out to bring you home with it.'

Tatiana dabbed her eyes with the sheet. Brusquely she pulled the sheet down to her shoulders again. She knew that she had been forgetting her job. It had just been that . . . Oh well. If only he had said that the machine didn't matter to him so long as she would come. But that was too much to hope for. He was right. He had a job to do. So had she.

She looked up at him calmly. 'I will bring it. Have no fear. But do not let us mention it again. And now listen.' She sat up straighter on the pillows. 'We must go tonight.' She remembered her lesson. 'It is the only chance. This evening I am on night duty from six o'clock. I shall be alone in the office and I will take the Spektor.'

Bond's eyes narrowed. His mind raced as he thought of the problems that would have to be faced. Where to hide her. How to get her out to the first plane after the loss had been discovered. It was going to be a risky business. They would stop at nothing to get her and the Spektor back. Roadblock on the way to the airport. Bomb in the plane. Anything.

'That's wonderful, Tania.' Bond's voice was casual. 'We'll keep you hidden and then we'll take the first plane tomorrow morning.'

'Don't be foolish.' Tatiana had been warned that here would be some difficult lines in her part. 'We will take the train. This Orient Express. It leaves at nine tonight. Do you think I haven't been thinking this thing out? I won't stay a minute longer in Istanbul than I have to. We will be over the frontier at dawn. You must get the tickets and a passport. I will travel with you as your wife.' She looked happily up at him. 'I shall like that. In one of those coupés I have read about. They must be very comfortable. Like a tiny house on wheels. During the day we will talk and read and at night you will stand in the corridor outside our house and guard it.'

'Like hell I will,' said Bond. 'But look here, Tania. That's crazy. They're bound to catch up with us somewhere. It's four days and five nights to London on that train. We've got to think of something else.'

'I won't,' said the girl flatly. 'That's the only way I'll go. If you are clever, how can they find out?'

Oh God, she thought. Why had they insisted on this train? But they had been definite. It was a good place for love, they had said. She would have four days to get him to love her. Then, when they got to London, life would be easy for her. He would protect her. Otherwise, if they flew to London, she would be put straight into prison. The four days were essential. And, they had warned her, we will have men on the train to see you don't get off. So be careful and obey your orders. Oh God. Oh God. Yet now she longed for those four days with him in the little house on wheels. How curious! It had been her duty to force him. Now it was her passionate desire.

She watched Bond's thoughtful face. She longed to stretch out a hand to him and reassure him that it would be all right; that this was a harmless *konspiratsia* to get her to England: that no harm could come to either of them, because that was not the object of the plot.

'Well, I still think it's crazy,' said Bond, wondering what M's reaction would be. 'But I suppose it may work. I've got the passport. It will need a Yugoslav visa,' he looked at her sternly. 'Don't think I'm going to take you on the part of the train that goes through Bulgaria, or I shall think you want to kidnap me.'

'I do.' Tatiana giggled. 'That's exactly what I want to do.'

'Now shut up, Tania. We've got to work this out. I'll get the tickets and I'll have one of our men come along. Just in case. He's a good man. You'll like him. Your name's Caroline Somerset. Don't forget it. How are you going to get to the train!'

'Karolin Siomerset,' the girl turned the name over in her mind. 'It is a pretty name. And you are Mister Siomerset.' She laughed happily. 'That is fun. Do not worry about me. I will come to the train just before it leaves. It is the Sirkeci Station. I know where it is. So that is all. And we do not worry any more. Yes?'

'Suppose you lose your nerve? Suppose they catch you?' Suddenly Bond was worried at the girl's confidence. How could she be so certain? A sharp tingle of suspicion ran down his spine.

'Before I saw you, I was frightened. Now I am not.' Tatiana tried to tell herself that this was the truth. Somehow it nearly was. 'Now I shall not lose my nerve, as you call it. And they cannot catch me. I shall leave my things in the hotel and take my usual bag to the office. I cannot leave my fur coat behind. I love it too dearly. But today is Sunday and that will be an excuse to come to the office in it. Tonight at half-past eight I shall walk out and take a taxi to the station. And now you must stop looking so worried.' Impulsively, because she had to, she stretched out a hand towards him. 'Say that you are pleased.'

Bond moved to the edge of the bed. He took her hand and looked down into her eyes. God, he thought. I hope it's all right. I hope this crazy plan will work. Is this wonderful girl a cheat? Is she true? Is she real? The eyes told him nothing except that the girl was happy, and that she wanted him to love her, and that she was surprised at what was happening to her. Tatiana's other hand came up and round his neck and pulled him fiercely down to her. At first the mouth trembled under his and then, as passion took her, the mouth yielded into a kiss without end.

Bond lifted his legs on to the bed. While his mouth went on kissing her, his hand went to her left breast and held it, feeling the peak hard with desire under his fingers. His hand strayed on down across her flat stomach. Her legs shifted languidly. She moaned softly and her mouth slid away from his. Below the closed eyes the long lashes quivered like humming birds' wings.

Bond reached up and took the edge of the sheet and pulled it right down and threw it off the end of the huge bed. She was wearing nothing but the black ribbon round her neck and black silk stockings rolled above her knees. Her arms groped up for him.

Above them, and unknown to both of them, behind the gold-framed false mirror on the wall over the bed, the two photographers from SMERSH sat close together in the cramped *cabinet de voyeur*, as, before them, so many friends of the proprietor had sat on a honeymoon night in the stateroom of the Kristal Palas.

And the view-finders gazed coldly down on the passionate arabesques the two bodies formed and broke and formed again, and the clockwork mechanism of the cine-cameras whirred softly on and on as the breath rasped out of the open mouths of the two men and the sweat of excitement trickled down their bulging faces into their cheap collars.

Chapter Twenty-one

Orient Express

The great trains are going out all over Europe, one by one, but still, three times a week, the Orient Express thunders superbly over the 1,400 miles of glittering steel track between Istanbul and Paris.

Under the arc-lights, the long-chassied German locomotive panted quietly with the laboured breath of a dragon dying of asthma. Each heavy breath seemed certain to be the last. Then came another. Wisps of steam rose from the couplings between the carriages and died quickly in the warm August air. The Orient Express was the only live train in the ugly, cheaply architectured burrow that is Istanbul's main station. The trains on the other lines were engineless and unattended–waiting for tomorrow. Only Track No. 3, and its platform, throbbed with the tragic poetry of departure.

The heavy bronze cipher on the side of the dark blue coach said, 'COMPAGNIE INTERNATIONALE DES WAGON-LITS ET DES GRANDS EXPRESS EUROPÉENS'. Above the cipher, fitted into metal slots, was a flat iron sign that announced, in black capitals on white, ORIENT EXPRESS, and underneath, in three lines:

ISTANBUL THESSALONIKI BEOGRAD
VENEZIA MILAN
LAUSANNE PARIS

James Bond gazed vaguely at one of the most romantic signs in the world. For the tenth time he looked at his watch. 8.51. His eyes went back to the sign. All the towns were spelled in the language of the country except MILAN. Why not MILANO? Bond took out his handkerchief and wiped his face. Where the hell was the girl? Had she been caught? Had she had second thoughts? Had he been too rough with her last night, or rather this morning, in the great bed?

8.55 The quiet pant of the engine had stopped. There came an echoing whoosh as the automatic safety-valve let off the excess steam. A hundred yards away, through the milling crowd, Bond watched the station-master raise a hand to the engine driver and fireman and start walking slowly back down the train, banging the doors of the third-class carriages up front. Passengers, mostly peasants going back into Greece after a week-end with their relatives in Turkey, hung out of the windows and jabbered at the grinning crowd below.

Beyond, where the faded arc-lights stopped and the dark blue night and the stars showed through the crescent mouth of the station, Bond saw a red pinpoint turn to green.

The station-master came nearer. The brown uniformed wagon-lit attendant tapped Bond on the arm. '*En voiture, s'il vous plaît.*' The two rich-looking Turks kissed their mistresses–they were too pretty to be wives–and, with a barrage of laughing injunctions, stepped on to the little iron pedestal and up the two tall steps into the carriage. There were no other wagon-lit travellers on the platform. The conductor, with an impatient glance at the tall Englishman, picked up the iron pedestal and climbed with it into the train.

The station-master strode purposefully by. Two more compartments, the first- and second-class carriages, and then, when he reached the guard's van, he would lift the dirty green flag.

There was no hurrying figure coming up the platform from the *guichet*. High up above the *guichet*, near the ceiling of the station, the minute hand of the big illuminated clock jumped forward an inch and said 'Nine'.

A window banged down above Bond's head. Bond looked up. His immediate reaction was that the black veil was too wide-meshed. The intention to disguise the luxurious mouth and the excited blue eyes was amateurish.

'Quick.'

The train had begun to move. Bond reached for the passing hand-rail and swung up on to the step. The attendant was still holding open the door. Bond stepped unhurriedly through.

'Madam was late,' said the attendant. 'She came along the corridor. She must have entered by the last carriage.'

Bond went down the carpeted corridor to the centre coupé. A black 7 stood above a black 8 on the white metal lozenge. The door was ajar. Bond walked in and shut it behind him. The girl had taken off her veil and her black straw hat. She was sitting in the corner by the window. A long, sleek sable coat was thrown open to show a natural coloured shantung dress with a pleated skirt, honey-coloured nylons and a black crocodile belt and shoes. She looked composed.

'You have no faith, James.'

Bond sat down beside her. 'Tania,' he said, 'if there was a bit more room I'd put you across my knee and spank you. You nearly gave me heart failure. What happened?'

'Nothing,' said Tatiana innocently. 'What could happen? I said I would be here, and I am here. You have no faith. Since I am sure you are more interested in my dowry than in me, it is up there.'

Bond looked casually up. Two small cases were on the rack beside his suitcase. He took her hand. He said, 'Thank God you're safe.'

Something in his eyes, perhaps the flash of guilt, as he admitted to himself that he had been more interested in the girl than the machine, reassured her. She kept his hand in hers and sank contentedly back in her corner.

The train screeched slowly round Seraglio Point. The lighthouse lit up the roofs of the dreary shacks along the railway line. With his free hand Bond took out a cigarette and lit it. He reflected that they would soon be passing the back of the great bill-board where Krilencu had lived–until less than twenty-four hours ago. Bond saw again the scene in every detail. The white cross roads, the two men in the shadows, the doomed man slipping out through the purple lips.

The girl watched his face with tenderness. What was this man thinking? What was going on behind those cold level grey-blue eyes that sometimes turned soft and sometimes, as they had done last night before his passion had burned out in her arms, blazed like diamonds. Now they were veiled in thought. Was he worrying about them both? Worrying about their safety? If only she could tell him that there was nothing to fear, that he was only her passport to England–him and the heavy case the Resident Director had given her that evening in the office. The Director had said the same thing. 'Here is your passport to England, Corporal,' he had said cheerfully. 'Look.' He had unzipped the bag: 'A brand new Spektor. Be certain not to open the bag again or let it out of your compartment until you get to the other end. Or this Englishman will take it away from you and throw you on the dust-heap. It is this machine they want. Do not let them take it from you, or you will have failed in your duty. Understood?'

A signal box loomed up in the blue dusk outside the window. Tatiana watched Bond get up and pull down the window and crane out into the darkness. His body was close to her. She moved her knee so that it touched him. How extraordinary, this passionate tenderness that had filled her ever since she had seen him last night standing naked at the window, his arms up to hold the curtains back, his profile, under the tousled black hair, intent and pale in the moonlight. And then the extraordinary fusing of their eyes and their bodies. The flame that had suddenly lit between them–between the two secret agents, thrown together from enemy camps a whole world apart, each involved in his own plot against the country of the other, antagonists by profession, yet turned, and by the orders of their governments, into lovers.

Tatiana stretched out a hand and caught hold of the edge of the coat and tugged at it. Bond pulled up the window and turned. He smiled down at her. He read her eyes. He bent and put his hands on the fur over her breasts and kissed her hard on the lips. Tatiana leant back, dragging him with her.

There came a soft double knock on the door. Bond stood up. He pulled out his handkerchief and brusquely scrubbed the rouge off his lips. 'That'll be my friend Kerim,' he said. 'I must talk to him. I will tell the conductor to make up the beds. Stay here while he does it. I won't be long. I shall be outside the door.' He leant forward and touched her hand and looked at her wide eyes and at her rueful, half-open lips. 'We shall have all the night to ourselves. First I must see that you are safe.' He unlocked the door and slipped out.

Darko Kerim's huge bulk was blocking the corridor. He was leaning on the brass guard-rail, smoking and gazing moodily out towards the Sea of Marmara that receded as the long train snaked away from the coast and turned inland and northwards. Bond leaned on the rail beside him. Kerim looked into the reflection of Bond's face in the dark window. He said softly, 'The news is not good. There are three of them on the train.'

'Ah!' An electric tingle ran up Bond's spine.

'It's the three strangers we saw in that room. Obviously they're on to you and the girl.' Kerim glanced sharply sideways. 'That makes her a double. Or doesn't it?'

Bond's mind was cool. So the girl had been bait. And yet, and yet. No, damn it. She couldn't be acting. It wasn't possible. The cipher machine? Perhaps after all it wasn't in that bag. 'Wait a minute,' he said. He turned and knocked softly on the door. He heard her unlock it and slip the chain. He went in and shut the door. She looked surprised. She had thought it was the conductor come to make up the beds.

She smiled radiantly. 'You have finished?'

'Sit down, Tatiana. I've got to talk to you.'

Now she saw the coldness in his face and her smile went out. She sat down obediently with her hands in her lap.

Bond stood over her. Was there guilt in her face, or fear? No, only surprise and a coolness to match his own expression.

'Now listen, Tatiana,' Bond's voice was deadly. 'Something's come up. I must look into that bag and see if the machine is there.'

She said indifferently. 'Take it down and look.' She examined the hands in her lap. So now it was going to come. What the Director had said. They were going to take the machine and throw her aside, perhaps have her put off the train. Oh God! This man was going to do that to her.

Bond reached up and hauled down the heavy case and put it on the seat. He tore the zip sideways and looked in. Yes, a grey japanned metal case with three rows of squat keys, rather like a typewriter. He held the bag open towards her. 'Is that a Spektor?'

She glanced casually into the gaping bag. 'Yes.'

Bond zipped the bag shut and put it back on the rack. He sat down beside the girl. 'There are three M.G.B. men on the train. We know they are the ones who arrived at your centre on Monday. What are they doing here, Tatiana?' Bond's voice was soft. He watched her, searched her with all his senses.

She looked up. There were tears in her eyes. Were they the tears of a child found out? But there was no trace of guilt in her face. She only looked terrified of something.

She reached out a hand and then drew it back. 'You aren't going to throw me off the train now you've got the machine?'

'Of course not,' Bond said impatiently. 'Don't be idiotic. But we must know what these men are doing. What's it all about? Did you know they were going to be on the train?' He tried to read some clue in her expression. He could only see a great relief. And what else? A look of calculation? Or reserve? Yes, she was hiding something. But what?

Tatiana seemed to make up her mind. Brusquely she wiped the back of her hand across her eyes. She reached forward and put the hand on his knee. The streak of tears showed on the back of the hand. She looked into Bond's eyes, forcing him to believe her.

'James,' she said. 'I did not know these men were on the train. I was told they were leaving today. For Germany. I assumed they would fly. That is all I can tell you. Until we arrive in England, out of reach of my people, you must not ask me more. I have done what I said I would. I am here with the machine. Have faith in me. Do not be afraid for us. I am certain these men do not mean us harm. Absolutely certain. Have faith.' (Was she so certain, wondered Tatiana? Had the Klebb woman told her all the truth? But she also must have faith–faith in the orders she had been given. These men must be the guards to see that she didn't get off the train. They could mean no harm. Later, when they got to London, this man would hide her away out of reach of SMERSH and she would tell him everything he wanted to know. She had already decided this in the back of her mind. But God knew what would happen if she betrayed *Them* now. *They* would somehow get her, and him. She knew it. There were no secrets from these people. And *They* would have no mercy. So long as she played out her role, all would be well.) Tatiana watched Bond's face for a sign that he believed her.

Bond shrugged his shoulders. He stood up. 'I don't know what to think, Tatiana,' he said. 'You are keeping something from me, but I think it's something you don't know is important. And I believe you think we are safe. We may be. It may be a coincidence that these men are on the train. I must talk to Kerim and decide what to do. Don't worry. We will look after you. But now we must be very careful.'

Bond looked round the compartment. He tried the communicating door with the next coupé. It was locked. He decided to wedge it when the conductor had gone. He would do the same for the door into the passage. And he would have to stay awake. So much for the honeymoon on wheels! Bond smiled grimly to himself and rang for the conductor. Tatiana was looking anxiously up at him. 'Don't worry, Tania,' he said again. 'Don't worry about anything. Go to bed when the man has gone. Don't open the door unless you know it's me. I will sit up tonight and watch. Perhaps tomorrow it will be easier. I will make a plan with Kerim. He is a good man.'

The conductor knocked. Bond let him in and went out into the corridor. Kerim was still there gazing out. The train had picked up speed and was hurtling through the night, its harsh melancholy whistle echoing back at them from the walls of a deep cutting against the sides of which the lighted carriage windows flickered and danced. Kerim didn't move, but his eyes in the mirror of the window were watchful.

Bond told him of the conversation. It was not easy to explain to Kerim why he trusted the girl as he did. He watched the mouth in the window curl ironically as he tried to describe what he had read in her eyes and what his intuition told him.

Kerim sighed resignedly. 'James,' he said, 'you are now in charge. This is your part of the operation. We have already argued most of this out today–the danger of the train, the possibility of getting the machine home in the diplomatic bag, the integrity, or otherwise, of this girl. It certainly appears that she has surrendered unconditionally to you. At the same time you admit that you have surrendered to her. Perhaps only partially. But you have decided to trust her. In this morning's telephone talk with M he said that he would back your decision. He left it to you. So be it. But he didn't know we were to have an escort of three M.G.B. men. Nor did we. And I think that would have changed all our views. Yes?'

'Yes.'

'Then the only thing to do is eliminate these three men. Get them off the train. God knows what they're here for. I don't believe in coincidences any more than you. But one thing is certain. We are not going to share the train with these men. Right?'

'Of course.'

'Then leave it to me. At least for tonight. This is still may country and I have certain powers in it. And plenty of money. I cannot afford to kill them. The train would be delayed. You and the girl might get involved. But I shall arrange something. Two of them have sleeping berths. The senior man with the moustache and the little pipe is next door to you–here, in No. 6.' He gestured backwards with his head. 'He is travelling on a German passport under the name of "Melchior Benz, salesman". The dark one, the Armenian, is in No. 12. He, too, has a German passport–"Kurt Goldfarb, construction engineer". They have through tickets to Paris. I have seen their documents. I have a police card. The conductor made no trouble. He has all the tickets and passports in his cabin. The third man, the man with a boil on the back of his neck, turns out also to have boils on his face. A stupid, ugly looking brute. I have not seen his passport. He is travelling sitting up in the first-class, in the next compartment to me. He does not have to surrender his passport until the frontier. But he has surrendered his ticket.' Like a conjuror, Kerim flicked a yellow first-class ticket out of his coat pocket. He slipped it back. He grinned proudly at Bond.

'How the hell?'

Kerim chuckled. 'Before he settled down for the night, this dumb ox went to the lavatory. I was standing in the corridor and I suddenly remembered how we used to steal rides on the train when I was a boy. I gave him a minute. Then I walked up and rattled the lavatory door. I hung on to the handle very tight. "Ticket collector," I said in a loud voice. "Tickets please." I said it in French and again in German. There was a mumble from inside. I felt him try to open the door. I hung on tight so that he would think the door had stuck. "Do not derange yourself, *Monsieur*," I said politely. "Push the ticket under the door." There was more fiddling with the door handle and I could hear heavy breathing. Then there was a pause and a rustle under the door. There was the ticket. I said, "*Merci, Monsieur*" very politely. I picked up the ticket and stepped across the coupling into the next carriage.' Kerim airily waved a hand. 'The stupid oaf will be sleeping peacefully by now. He will think that his ticket will be given back to him at the frontier. He is mistaken. The ticket will be in ashes and the ashes will be on the four winds,' Kerim gestured towards the darkness outside. 'I will see that the man is put off the train, however much money he has got. He will be told that the circumstances must be investigated, his statements corroborated with the ticket agency. He will be allowed to proceed on a later train.'

Bond smiled at the picture of Kerim playing his private school trick. 'You're a card, Darko. What about the other two?'

Darko Kerim shrugged his massive shoulders. 'Something will occur to me,' he said confidently. 'The way to catch Russians is to make them look foolish. Embarrass them. Laugh at them. They can't stand it. We will somehow make these men sweat. Then we will leave it to the M.G.B. to punish them for failing in their duty. Doubtless they will be shot by their own people.'

While they were talking, the conductor had come out of No. 7. Kerim turned to Bond and put a hand on his shoulder. 'Have no fear, James,' he said cheerfully. 'We will defeat these people. Go to your girl. We will meet again in the morning. We shall not sleep much tonight, but that cannot be helped. Every day is different. Perhaps we shall sleep tomorrow.'

Bond watched the big man move off easily down the swaying corridor. He noticed that, despite the movement of the train, Kerim's shoulders never touched the walls of the corridor. Bond felt a wave of affection for the tough, cheerful professional spy.

Kerim disappeared into the conductor's cabin Bond turned and knocked softly on the door of No. 7.

Chapter Twenty-two

Out of Turkey

The train howled on through the night. Bond sat and watched the hurrying moonlit landscape and concentrated on keeping awake.

Everything conspired to make him sleep–the hasty metal gallop of the wheels, the hynoptic swoop of the silver telegraph wires, the occasional melancholy, reassuring moan of the steam whistle clearing their way, the drowsy metallic chatter of the couplings at each end of the corridor, the lullaby creak of the woodwork in the little room. Even the deep violet glimmer of the night-light above the door seemed to say, 'I will watch for you. Nothing can happen while I am burning. Close your eyes and sleep, sleep.'

The girl's head was warm and heavy on his lap. There was obviously just room for him to slip under the single sheet and fit close up against her, the front of his thighs against the backs of hers, his head in the spread curtain of her hair on the pillow.

Bond screwed up his eyes and opened them again. He cautiously lifted his wrist. Four o'clock. Only one more hour to the Turkish frontier. Perhaps he would be able to sleep during the day. He would give her the gun and wedge the doors again and she could watch.

He looked down at the beautiful sleeping profile. How innocent she looked, this girl from the Russian Secret Service–the lashes fringing the soft swell of the cheek, the lips parted and unaware, the long strand of hair that had strayed untidily across her forehead and that he wanted to brush back neatly to join the rest, the steady slow throb of the pulse in the offered neck. He felt a surge of tenderness and the impulse to gather her up in his arms and strain her tight against him. He wanted her to wake, from a dream perhaps, so that he could kiss her and tell her that everything was all right, and see her settle happily back to sleep.

The girl had insisted on sleeping like this. 'I won't go to sleep unless you hold me,' she had said. 'I must know you're there all the time. It would be terrible to wake up and not be touching you. Please James. Please *duschka*.'

Bond had taken off his coat and tie and had arranged himself in the corner with his feet up on his suitcase and the Beretta under the pillow within reach of his hand. She had made no comment about the gun. She had taken off all her clothes, except the black ribbon round her throat, and had pretended not to be provocative as she scrambled impudically into bed and wriggled herself into a comfortable position. She had held up her arms to him. Bond had pulled her head back by her hair and had kissed her once, long and cruelly. Then he had told her to go to sleep and had leant back and waited icily for his body to leave him alone. Grumbling sleepily, she had settled herself, with one arm flung across his thighs. At first she had held him tightly, but her arm had gradually relaxed and then she was asleep.

Brusquely Bond closed his mind to the thought of her and focused on the journey ahead.

Soon they would be out of Turkey. But would Greece be any easier? No love lost between Greece and England. And Yugoslavia? Whose side was Tito on? Probably both. Whatever the orders of the three M.G.B. men, either they already knew Bond and Tatiana were on the train or they would soon find out. He and the girl couldn't sit for four days in this coupé with the blinds drawn. Their presence would be reported back to Istanbul, telephoned from some station, and by the morning the loss of the Spektor would have been discovered. Then what? A hasty démarche through the Russian embassy in Athens or Belgrade? Have the girl taken off the train as a thief? Or was that all too simple? And if it was more complicated–if all this was part of some mysterious plot, some tortuous Russian conspiracy–should he dodge it? Should he and the girl leave the train at a wayside station, on the wrong side of the track, and hire a car and somehow get a plane to London?

Outside, the luminous dawn had begun to edge the racing trees and rocks with blue. Bond looked at his watch. Five o'clock. They would soon be at Uzunkopru. What was going on down the train behind him? What had Kerim achieved?

Bond sat back, relaxed. After all there was a simple, common-sense answer to his problem. If, between them, they could quickly get rid of the three M.G.B. agents, they would stick to the train and to their original plan. If not, Bond would get the girl and the machine off the train, somewhere in Greece, and take another route home. But, if the odds improved, Bond was for going on. He and Kerim were resourceful men. Kerim had an agent in

Belgrade who was going to meet the train. There was always the Embassy.

Bond's mind raced on adding up the pros, dismissing the cons. Behind his reasoning, Bond calmly admitted to himself that he had an insane desire to play the game out and see what it was all about. He wanted to take these people on and solve the mystery and, if it was some sort of a plot, defeat it. M had left him in charge. He had the girl and the machine under his hand. Why panic? What was there to panic about? It would be mad to run away and perhaps only escape one trap in order to fall into another one.

The train gave a long whistle and began to slacken speed.

Now for the first round. If Kerim failed. If the three men stayed on the train. . . .

Some goods-trucks, led by a straining engine, filed by. The silhouette of sheds showed briefly. With a jolt and a screech of couplings, the Orient Express took the points and swerved away from the through line. Four sets of rails with grass growing between them showed outside the window, and the empty length of the down platform. A cock crowed. The express slowed to walking speed and finally, with a sigh of vacuum brakes and a noisy whoosh of let-off steam, ground to a stop. The girl stirred in her sleep. Bond softly shifted her head on to the pillow and got up and slipped out of the door.

It was a typical Balkan wayside station–a façade of dour buildings in over-pointed stone, a dusty expanse of platform, not raised, but level with the ground so that there was a long step down from the train, some chickens pecking about and a few drab officials standing idly, unshaven, not even trying to look important. Up towards the cheap half of the train, a chattering horde of peasants with bundles and wicker baskets waited for the customs and passport control so that they could clamber aboard and join the swarm inside.

Across the platform from Bond was a closed door with a sign over it which said POLIS. Through the dirty window beside the door Bond thought he caught a glimpse of the head and shoulders of Kerim.

'*Passeports. Douanes!*'

A plain-clothes man and two policemen in dark green uniform with pistol holsters at their black belts entered the corridor. The wagon-lit conductor preceded them, knocking on the doors.

At the door of No. 12 the conductor made an indignant speech in Turkish, holding out the stack of tickets and passports and fanning them as if they were a pack of cards. When he had finished, the plain-clothes man, beckoning forward the two policemen, knocked smartly on the door and, when it was opened, stepped inside. The two policemen stood guard behind him.

Bond edged down the corridor. He could hear a jumble of bad German. One voice was cold, the other was frightened and hot. The passport and ticket of Herr Kurt Goldfarb were missing. Had Herr Goldfarb removed them from the conductor's cabin? Certainly not. Had Herr Goldfarb in truth ever surrendered his papers to the conductor? Naturally. Then the matter was unfortunate. An inquiry would have to be held. No doubt the German Legation in Istanbul would put the matter right (Bond smiled at this suggestion). Meanwhile, it was regretted that Herr Goldfarb could not continue his journey. No doubt he would be able to proceed tomorrow. Herr Goldfarb would get dressed. His luggage would be transported to the waiting-room.

The M.G.B. man who erupted into the corridor was the dark Caucasian type man, the junior of the 'visitors'. His sallow face was grey with fear. His hair was awry and he was dressed only in the bottom half of his pyjamas. But there was nothing comical about his desperate flurry down the corridor. He brushed past Bond. At the door of No. 6 he paused and pulled himself together. He knocked with tense control. The door opened on the chain and Bond glimpsed a thick nose and part of a moustache. The chain was slipped and Goldfarb went in. There was silence, during which the plain-clothes man dealt with the papers of two elderly French women in 9 and 10, and then with Bond's.

The officer barely glanced at Bond's passport. He snapped it shut and handed it to the conductor. 'You are travelling with Kerim Bey?' he asked in French. His eyes were remote.

'Yes.'

'*Merci, Monsieur. Bon voyage.*' The man saluted. He turned and rapped sharply on the door of No. 6. The door opened and he went in.

Five minutes later the door was flung back. The plain-clothes man, now erect with authority, beckoned forward the policemen. He spoke to them harshly in Turkish. He turned back to the coupé. 'Consider yourself under arrest, Mein Herr. Attempted bribery of officials is a grave crime in Turkey.' There was an angry clamour in Goldfarb's bad German. It was cut short by one hard sentence in Russian. A different Goldfarb, a Goldfarb with madman's eyes, emerged and walked blindly down the corridor and went into No. 12. A policeman stood outside the door and waited.

'And *your* papers, Mein Herr. Please step forward. I must verify this photograph.' The plain-clothes man held the green-backed German passport up to the light. 'Forward please.'

Reluctantly, his heavy face pale with anger, the M.G.B. man who called himself Benz stepped out into the corridor in a brilliant blue silk dressing-gown. The hard brown eyes looked straight into Bond's, ignoring him.

The plain-clothes man slapped the passport shut and handed it to the conductor. 'Your papers are in order, Mein Herr. And now, if you please, the baggage.' He went in, followed by the second policeman. The M.G.B. man turned his blue back on Bond and watched the search.

Bond noticed the bulge under the left arm of the dressing-gown, and the ridge of a belt round the waist. He wondered if he should tip off the plain-clothes man. He decided it would be better to keep quiet. He might be hauled in as a witness.

The search was over. The plain-clothes man saluted coldly and moved on down the corridor. The M.G.B. man went back into No. 6 and slammed the door behind him.

Pity, thought Bond. One had got away.

Bond turned back to the window. A bulky man, wearing a grey Homburg, and with an angry boil on the back of his neck, was being escorted through the door marked POLIS. Down the corridor a door slammed. Goldfarb, escorted by the policeman, stepped down off the train. With bent head, he walked across the dusty platform and disappeared through the same door.

The engine whistled, a new kind of whistle, the brave shrill blast of a Greek engine-driver. The door of the wagon-lit carriage clanged shut. The plain-clothes man and the second policeman appeared walking over to the station. The guard at the back of the train looked at his watch and held out his flag. There was a jerk and a diminishing crescendo of explosive puffs from the engine and the front section of the Orient Express began to move. The section that would be taking the northern route through the Iron Curtain–through Svilengrad on the Bulgarian frontier, only fifty miles away–was left beside the dusty platform, waiting.

Bond pulled down the window and took a last look back at the Turkish frontier, where two men would be sitting in a bare room under what amounted to sentence of death. Two birds down, he thought. Two out of three. The odds looked more respectable.

He watched the dead, dusty platform, with its chickens and the small black figure of the guard, until the long train took the points and jerked harshly on to the single main line. He looked away across the ugly, parched countryside towards the golden guinea sun climbing out of the Turkish plain. It was going to be a beautiful day.

Bond drew his head in out of the cool, sweet morning air. He pulled up the window with a bang.

He had made up his mind. He would stay on the train and see the thing through.

Chapter Twenty-three

Out of Greece

Hot coffee from the meagre little buffet at Pithion (there would be no restaurant car until midday), a painless visit from the Greek customs and passport control, and then the berths were folded away as the train hurried south towards the Gulf of Enez at the head of the Aegean. Outside, there was extra light and colour. The air was drier. The men at the little stations and in the fields were handsome. Sunflowers, maize, vines and racks of tobacco were ripening in the sun. It was, as Darko had said, another day.

Bond washed and shaved under the amused eyes of Tatiana. She approved of the fact that he put no oil on his hair. 'It is a dirty habit,' she said. 'I was told that many Europeans have it. We would not think of doing it in Russia. It dirties the pillows. But it is odd that you in the West do not use perfume. All our men do.'

'We wash,' said Bond dryly.

In the heat of her protests, there came a knock on the door. It was Kerim. Bond let him in. Kerim bowed towards the girl. What a charming domestic scene,' he commented cheerfully, lowering his bulk into the corner near the door. 'I have rarely seen a handsomer pair of spies.'

Tatiana glowered at him. 'I am not accustomed to Western jokes,' she said coldly.

Kerim's laugh was disarming. 'You'll learn, my dear. In England, they are great people for jokes. There it is considered proper to make a joke of everything. I also have learned to make jokes. They grease the wheels. I have been laughing a lot this morning. Those poor fellows at Uzunkopru. I wish I could be there when the police telephone the German Consulate in Istanbul. That is the worst of forged passports. They are not difficult to make, but it is almost impossible to forge also their birth certificate–the files of the country which is supposed to have issued them. I fear the careers of your two comrades have come to a sad end, Mrs Somerset.'

'How did you do it?' Bond knotted his tie.

'Money and influence. Five hundred dollars to the conductor. Some big talk to the police. It was lucky our friend tried a bribe. A pity that crafty Benz next door,' he gestured at the wall, 'didn't get involved. I couldn't do the passport trick twice. We will have to get him some other way. The man with the boils was easy. He knew no German and travelling without a ticket is a serious matter. Ah well, the day has started favourably. We have won the first round, but our friend next door will now be very careful. He knows what he has to reckon with. Perhaps that is for the best. It would have been a nuisance having to keep you both under cover all day. Now we can move about–even have lunch together, as long as you bring the family jewels with you. We must watch to see if he makes a telephone call at one of the stations. But I doubt if he could tackle the Greek telephone exchange. He will probably wait until we are in Yugoslavia. But there I have my machine. We can get reinforcements if we need them. It should be a most interesting journey. There is always excitement on the Orient Express,' Kerim got to his feet. He opened the door, 'and romance.' He smiled across the compartment. 'I will call for you at lunchtime! Greek food is worse than Turkish, but even my stomach is in the service of the Queen.'

Bond got up and locked the door. Tatiana snapped, 'Your friend is not *kulturny*! It is disloyal to refer to your Queen in that manner.'

Bond sat down beside her. 'Tania,' he said patiently, 'that is a wonderful man. He is also a good friend. As far as I am concerned he can say anything he likes. He is jealous of me. He would like to have a girl like you. So he teases you. It is a form of flirting. You should take it as a compliment.'

'You think so?' she turned her large blue eyes on his. 'But what he said about his stomach and the head of your State. That was being rude to your Queen. It would be considered very bad manners to say such a thing in Russia.'

They were still arguing when the train ground to a halt in the sunbaked, fly-swarming station of Alexandropolis. Bond opened the door into the corridor and the sun poured in across a pale mirrored sea that married, almost without horizon, into a sky the colour of the Greek flag.

They had lunch, with the heavy bag under the table between Bond's feet. Kerim quickly made friends with the girl. The M.G.B. man called Benz avoided the restaurant car. They saw him on the platform buying sandwiches and beer from a buffet on wheels. Kerim suggested they ask him to make a four at bridge. Bond suddenly felt very tired and his tiredness made him feel that they were turning this dangerous journey into a picnic. Tatiana noticed his silence. She got up and said that she must rest. As they went out of the wagon-restaurant they heard Kerim calling gaily for brandy and cigars.

Back in the compartment, Tatiana said firmly, 'Now it is you who will sleep.' She drew down the blind and shut out the hard afternoon light and the endless baked fields of maize and tobacco and wilting sunflowers. The compartment became a dark green underground cavern. Bond wedged the doors and gave her his gun and stretched out with his head in her lap and was immediately asleep.

The long train snaked along the north of Greece below the foothills of the Rhodope Mountains. Xanthi came, and Drama, and Serrai, and then they were in the Macedonian highlands and the line swerved due south towards Salonica.

It was dark when Bond awoke in the soft cradle of her lap. At once, as if she had been waiting for the moment, Tatiana took his face between her hands and looked down into his eyes and said urgently, '*Dushka*, how long shall we have this for?'

'For long.' Bond's thoughts were still luxurious with sleep.

'But for how long?'

Bond gazed up into the beautiful, worried eyes. He cleared the sleep out of his mind. It was impossible to see beyond the next three days on the train, beyond their arrival in London. One had to face the fact that this girl was an enemy agent. His feelings would be of no interest to the interrogators from his Service and from the Ministries. Other intelligence services would also want to know what this girl had to tell them about the machine she had worked for. Probably at Dover she would be taken away to 'The Cage', that well-sentried private house near Guildford, where she would be put in a comfortable, but oh so well-wired room. And the efficient men in plain clothes would come one by one and sit and talk with her, and the recorder would spin in the room below and the records would be transcribed and sifted for their grains of new fact–and, of course, for the contradictions they would trap her into. Perhaps they would introduce a stool-pigeon–a nice Russian girl who would commiserate with Tatiana over her treatment and suggest ways of escape, of turning double, of getting 'harmless' information back to her parents. This might go on for weeks or months. Meanwhile Bond would be tactfully kept away from her, unless the interrogators thought he could extract further secrets by using their feelings for each other. Then what? The changed name, the offer of a new life in Canada, the thousand pounds a year she would be given from the secret funds? And where would he be when she came out of it all? Perhaps the other side of the world. Or, if he was still in London, how much of her feeling for him would have survived the grinding of the interrogation machine? How much would she hate or despise the English after going through all this? And, for the matter of that, how much would have survived of his own hot flame?

'*Dushka*,' repeated Tatiana impatiently. 'How long?'

'As long as possible. It will depend on us. Many people will interfere. We shall be separated. It will not always be like this in a little room. In a few days we shall have to step out into the world. It will not be easy. It would be foolish to tell you anything else.'

Tatiana's face cleared. She smiled down at him. 'You are right. I will not ask any more foolish questions. But we must waste no more of these days.' She shifted his head and got up and lay down beside him.

An hour later, when Bond was standing in the corridor, Darko Kerim was suddenly beside him. He examined Bond's face. He said slyly, 'You should not sleep so long. You have been missing the historic landscape of northern Greece. And it is time for the *premier service*.'

'All you think about is food,' said Bond. He gestured back with his head. 'What about our friend?'

'He has not stirred. The conductor has been watching for me. That man will end up the richest conductor in the wagon-lit company. Five hundred dollars for Goldfarb's papers, and now a hundred dollars a day retainer until the end of the journey.' Kerim chuckled. 'I have told him he may even get a medal for his services to Turkey. He believes we are after a smuggling gang. They're always using this train for running Turkish opium to Paris. He is not surprised, only pleased that he is being paid so well. And now, have you found out anything more from this Russian princess you have in there? I still feel disquiet. Everything is too peaceful. Those two men we left behind may have been quite innocently bound for Berlin as the girl says. This Benz may be keeping to his room because he is frightened of us. All is going well with our journey. And yet, and yet . . .' Kerim shook his head. 'These Russians are great chess players. When they wish to execute a plot, they execute it brilliantly. The game is planned minutely, the gambits of the enemy are provided for. They are foreseen and countered. At the back of my mind,' Kerim's face in the window was gloomy, 'I have a feeling that you and I and this girl are pawns on a very big board–that we are being allowed our moves because they do not interfere with the Russian game.'

'But what is the object of the plot?' Bond looked out into the darkness. He spoke to his reflection in the window. 'What can they want to achieve? We always get back to that. Of course we have all smelt a conspiracy of some sort. And the girl may not even know that she's involved in it. I know she's hiding something, but I think it's only some small secret she thinks is unimportant. She says she'll tell me everything when we get to London. Everything? What does she mean? She only says that I must have faith–that there is no danger. You must admit, Darko,' Bond looked up for confirmation into the slow crafty eyes, 'that she's lived up to her story.'

There was no enthusiasm in Kerim's eyes. He said nothing.

Bond shrugged. 'I admit I've fallen for her. But I'm not a fool, Darko. I've been watching for any clue, anything that would help. You know one can tell a lot when certain barriers are down. Well they are down, and I know she's telling the truth. At any rate ninety per cent of it. And I know she thinks the rest doesn't matter. If she's cheating, she's also being cheated herself. On your chess analogy, that is possible. But you still get back to the question of what it's all in aid of.' Bond's voice hardened. 'And, if you want to know, all I ask is to go on with the game until we find out.'

Kerim smiled at the obstinate look on Bond's face. He laughed abruptly. 'If it was me, my friend, I would slip off the train at Salonica–with the machine, and, if you like, with the girl also, though that is not so important. I would take a hired car to Athens and get on the next plane for London. But I was not brought up "to be a sport".' Kerim put irony into the words. 'This is not a game to me. It is a business. For you it is different. You are a gambler. M also is a gambler. He obviously is, or he would not have given you a free hand. He also wants to know the answer to this riddle. So be it. But I like to play safe, to make certain, to leave as little as possible to chance. You think the odds look right, that they are in your favour?' Darko Kerim turned and faced Bond. His voice became insistent. 'Listen, my friend,' he put a huge hand on Bond's shoulder. 'This is a billiard table. An easy, flat, green billiard table. And you have hit your white ball and it is travelling easily and quietly towards the red. The pocket is alongside. Fatally, inevitably, you are going to hit the red and the red is going into that pocket. It is the law of the billiard table, the law of the billiard room. But, outside the orbit of these things, a jet pilot has fainted and his plane is diving straight at that billiard room, or a gas main is about to explode, or lightning is about to strike. And the building collapses on top of you and on top of the billiard table. Then what has happened to that white ball that could not miss the red ball, and to the red ball that could not miss the pocket? The white ball could not miss according to the laws of the billiard table. But the laws of the billiard table are not the only laws, and the laws governing the progress of this train, and of you to your destination, are also not the only laws in this particular game.'

Kerim paused. He dismissed his harangue with a shrug of the shoulders. 'You already know these things, my friend,' he said apologetically. 'And I have made myself thirsty talking platitudes. Hurry the girl up and we will go and eat. But watch for surprises, I beg of you.' He made a cross with his finger over the centre of his coat. 'I do not cross my heart. That is being too serious. But I cross my stomach, which is an important oath for me. There are surprises on the way for both of us. The gipsy said to watch out. Now I say the same. We can play the game on the billiard table, but we must both be on guard against the world outside the billiard room. My nose,' he tapped it, 'tells me so.'

Kerim's stomach made an indignant noise like a forgotten telephone receiver with an angry caller on the other end. 'There,' he said solicitously. 'What did I say? We must go and eat.'

They finished their dinner as the train pulled into the hideous modern junction of Thessaloniki. With Bond carrying the heavy little bag, they went back down the train and parted for the night. 'We shall soon be disturbed again,' warned Kerim. 'There is the frontier at one o'clock. The Greeks will be no trouble, but those Yugoslavs like waking up anyone who is travelling soft. If they annoy you, send for me. Even in their country there are some names I can mention. I am in the second compartment in the next carriage. I have it to myself. Tomorrow I will move into our friend Goldfarb's bed in No. 12. For the time being, the first-class is an adequate stable.'

Bond dozed wakefully as the train laboured up the moonlit valley of the Vardar towards the instep of Yugoslavia. Tatiana again slept with her head in his lap. He thought of what Darko had said. He wondered if he should not send the big man back to Istanbul when they had got safely through Belgrade. It was not fair to drag him across Europe on an adventure that was outside his territory and with which he had little sympathy. Darko obviously suspected that Bond had become infatuated with the girl and wasn't seeing the operation straight any more. Well, there was a grain of truth in that. It would certainly be safer to get off the train and take another route home. But, Bond admitted to himself, he couldn't bear the idea of running away from this plot, if it was a plot. If it wasn't, he equally couldn't bear the idea of sacrificing the three more days with Tatiana. And M had left the decision to him. As Darko had said, M also was curious to see the game through. Perversely, M too wanted to see what this whole rigmarole was about. Bond dismissed the problem. The journey was going well. Once again, why panic?

Ten minutes after they had arrived at the Greek frontier station of Idomeni there was a hasty knocking on the door. It woke the girl. Bond slipped from under her head. He put his ear to the door. 'Yes?'

'*Le conducteur, Monsieur*. There has been an accident. Your friend Kerim Bey.'

'Wait,' said Bond fiercely. He fitted the Beretta into its holster and put on his coat. He tore open the door.

'What is it?'

The conductor's face was yellow under the corridor light. 'Come.' He ran down the corridor towards the first-class.

Officials were clustered round the open door of the second compartment. They were standing, staring.

The conductor made a path for Bond. Bond reached the door and looked in.

The hair stirred softly on his head. Along the right-hand seat were two bodies. They were frozen in a ghastly death-struggle that might have been posed for a film.

Underneath was Kerim, his knees up in a last effort to rise. The taped hilt of a dagger protruded from his neck near the jugular vein. His head was thrust back and the empty bloodshot eyes stared up at the light. The mouth was contorted into a snarl. A thin trickle of blood ran down the chin.

Half on top of him sprawled the heavy body of the M.G.B. man called Benz, locked there by Kerim's left arm round his neck. Bond could see a corner of the Stalin moustache and the side of a blackened face. Kerim's right arm lay across the man's back, almost casually. The hand ended in a closed fist and the knob of a knife-hilt, and there was a wide stain on the coat under the hand.

Bond listened to his imagination. It was like watching a film. The sleeping Darko, the man slipping quietly through the door, the two steps forward and the swift stroke at the jugular. Then the last violent spasm of the dying man as he flung up an arm and clutched his murderer to him and plunged the knife down towards the fifth rib.

This wonderful man who had carried the sun with him. Now he was extinguished, totally dead.

Bond turned brusquely and walked out of sight of the man who had died for him.

He began, carefully, non-committally, to answer questions.

Chapter Twenty-four

Out of Danger?

The Orient Express steamed slowly into Belgrade at three o'clock in the afternoon, half an hour late. There would be an eight hours' delay while the other section of the train came in through the Iron Curtain from Bulgaria.

Bond looked out at the crowds and waited for the knock on the door that would be Kerim's man. Tatiana sat huddled in her sable coat beside the door, watching Bond, wondering if he would come back to her.

She had seen it all from the window–the long wicker baskets being brought out to the train, the flash of the police photographer's bulbs, the gesticulating *chef de train* trying to hurry up the formalities, and the tall figure of James Bond, straight and hard and cold as a butcher's knife, coming and going.

Bond had come back and had sat looking at her. He had asked sharp, brutal questions. She had fought desperately back, sticking coldly to her story, knowing that now, if she told him everything, told him for instance that SMERSH was involved, she would certainly lose him for ever.

Now she sat and was afraid, afraid of the web in which she was caught, afraid of what might have been behind the lies she had been told in Moscow–above all afraid that she might lose this man who had suddenly become the light in her life.

There was a knock on the door. Bond got up and opened it. A tough cheerful india-rubbery man, with Kerim's blue eyes and a mop of tangled fair hair above a brown face, exploded into the compartment.

'Stefan Trempo at your service,' the big smile embraced them both. 'They call me "Tempo". Where is the Chef?'

'Sit down,' said Bond. He thought to himself, I know it. This is another of Darko's sons.

The man looked sharply at them both. He sat down carefully between them. His face was extinguished. Now the bright eyes stared at Bond with a terrible intensity in which there was fear and suspicion. His right hand slipped casually into the pocket of his coat.

When Bond had finished, the man stood up. He didn't ask any questions. He said, 'Thank you, sir. Will you come, please. We will go to my apartment. There is much to be done.' He walked into the corridor and stood with his back to them, looking out across the rails. When the girl came out he walked down the corridor without looking back. Bond followed the girl, carrying the heavy bag and his little attaché case.

They walked down the platform and into the station square. It had started to drizzle. The scene, with its sprinkling of battered taxis and vista of dull modern buildings, was depressing. The man opened the rear door of a shabby Morris Oxford saloon. He got in front and took the wheel. They bumped their way over the cobbles and on to a slippery tarmac boulevard and drove for a quarter of an hour through wide, empty streets. They saw few pedestrians and not more than a handful of other cars.

They stopped half way down a cobbled side-street. Tempo led them through a wide apartment-house door and up two flights of stairs that had the smell of the Balkans–the smell of very old sweat and cigarette smoke and cabbage. He unlocked a door and showed them into a two-roomed flat with nondescript furniture and heavy red plush curtains drawn back to show the blank windows on the other side of the street. On a sideboard stood a tray with several unopened bottles, glasses and plates of fruit and biscuits–the welcome to Darko and to Darko's friends.

Tempo waved vaguely towards the drinks. 'Please, sir, make yourself and Madam at home. There is a bathroom. No doubt you would both like to have a bath. If you will excuse me, I must telephone!' The hard façade of the face was about to crumble. The man went quickly into the bedroom and shut the door behind him.

There followed two empty hours during which Bond sat and looked out of the window at the wall opposite. From time to time he got up and paced to and fro and then sat down again. For the first hour, Tatiana sat and pretended to look through a pile of magazines. Then she abruptly went into the bathroom and Bond vaguely heard water gushing into the bath.

At about 6 o'clock, Tempo came out of the bedroom. He told Bond that he was going out. 'There is food in the kitchen. I will return at nine and take you to the train. Please treat my flat as your own.' Without waiting for Bond's reply, he walked out and softly shut the door. Bond heard his foot on the stairs and the click of the front door and the self-starter of the Morris.

Bond went into the bedroom and sat on the bed and picked up the telephone and talked in German to the long-distance exchange.

Half an hour later there was the quiet voice of M.

Bond spoke as a travelling salesman would speak to the managing director of Universal Export. He said that his partner had gone very sick. Were there any fresh instructions?

'Very sick?'

'Yes, sir, very.'

'How about the other firm?'

'There were three with us, sir. One of them caught the same thing. The other two didn't feel well on the way out of Turkey. They left us at Uzunkopru–that's the frontier.'

'So the other firm's packed up?'

Bond could see M's face as he sifted the information. He wondered if the fan was slowly revolving in the ceiling, if M had a pipe in his hand, if the Chief of Staff was listening on the other wire.

'What are your ideas? Would you and your wife like to take another way home?'

'I'd rather you decided, sir. My wife's all right. The sample's in good condition. I don't see why it should deteriorate. I'm still keen to finish the trip. Otherwise it'll remain virgin territory. We shan't know what the possibilities are.'

'Would you like one of our other salesmen to give you a hand?'

'It shouldn't be necessary, sir. Just as you feel.'

'I'll think about it. So you really want to see this sales campaign through?'

Bond could see M's eyes glittering with the same perverse curiosity, the same rage to know, as he himself felt. 'Yes, sir. Now that I'm half way, it seems a pity not to cover the whole route.'

'All right then. I'll think about giving you another salesman to lend a hand.' There was a pause on the end of the line. 'Nothing else on your mind?'

'No, sir.'

'Goodbye, then.'

'Goodbye, sir.'

Bond put down the receiver. He sat and looked at it. He suddenly wished he had agreed with M's suggestion to give him reinforcements, just in case. He got up from the bed. At least they would soon be out of these damn Balkans and down into Italy. Then Switzerland, France–among friendly people, away from the furtive lands.

And the girl, what about her? Could he blame her for the death of Kerim? Bond went into the next room and stood again by the window, looking out, wondering, going back over everything, every expression and every gesture she had made since he had first heard her voice on that night in the Kristal Palas. No, he knew he couldn't put the blame on her. If she was an agent, she was an unconscious agent. There wasn't a girl of her age in the world who could have played this role, if it was a role she was playing, without betraying herself. And he liked her. And he had faith in his instincts. Besides, with the death of Kerim, had not the plot, whatever it was, played itself out? One day he would find out what the plot had been. For the moment he was certain. Tatiana was not a conscious part of it.

His mind made up, Bond walked over to the bathroom door and knocked.

She came out and he took her in his arms and held her to him and kissed her. She clung to him. They stood and felt the animal warmth come back between them, feeling it push back the cold memory of Kerim's death.

Tatiana broke away. She looked up at Bond's face. She reached up and brushed the black comma of hair away from his forehead.

Her face was alive. 'I am glad you have come back, James,' she said. And then, matter-of-factly, 'And now we must eat and drink and start our lives again.'

Later, after Slivovic and smoked ham and peaches, Tempo came and took them to the station and to the waiting express under the hard lights of the arcs. He said goodbye, quickly and coldly, and vanished down the platform and back into his dark existence.

Punctually at nine the new engine gave its new kind of noise and took the long train out on its all-night run down the valley of the Sava. Bond went along to the conductor's cabin to give him money and look through the passports of the new passengers.

Bond knew most of the signs to look for in forged passports, the blurred writing, the too exact imprints of the rubber stamps, the trace of old gum round the edges of the photograph, the slight transparencies on the pages where the fibres of the paper had been tampered with to alter a letter or a number, but the five new passports–three American and two Swiss–seemed innocent. The Swiss papers, favourites with the Russian forgers, belonged to a husband and wife, both over seventy, and Bond finally passed them and went back to the compartment and prepared for another night with Tatiana's head on his lap.

Vincovci came and then, against a flaming dawn, the ugly sprawl of Zagreb. The train came to a stop between lines of rusting locomotives captured from the Germans and still standing forlornly amongst the grass and weeds on the sidings. Bond read the plate on one of them–BERLINER MASCHINENBAU GMBH–as they slid out through the iron cemetery. Its long black barrel had been raked with machine gun bullets. Bond heard the scream of the dive-bomber and saw the upflung arms of the driver. For a moment he thought nostalgically and unreasonably of the excitement and turmoil of the hot war, compared with his own underground skirmishings since the war had turned cold.

They hammered into the mountains of Slovenia where the apple trees and the chalets were almost Austrian. The train laboured its way through Ljubliana. The girl awoke. They had breakfast of fried eggs and hard brown bread and coffee that was mostly chicory. The restaurant car was full of cheerful English and American tourists from the Adriatic coast, and Bond thought with a lift of the heart that by the afternoon they would be over the frontier into western Europe and that a third dangerous night was gone.

He slept until Sezana. The hard-faced Yugoslav plain-clothes men came on board. Then Yugoslavia was gone and Poggioreale came and the first smell of the soft life with the happy jabbering of Italian officals and the carefree upturned faces of the station crowd. The new diesel-electric engine gave a slap-happy whistle, the meadow of brown hands fluttered, and they were loping easily down into Venezia, towards the distant sparkle of Trieste and the gay blue of the Adriatic.

We've made it, thought Bond. I really think we've made it. He thrust the memory of the last three days away from him. Tatiana saw the tense lines in his face relax. She reached over and took his hand. He moved and sat close beside her. They looked out at the gay villas on the Corniche and at the sailing-boats and the people water-skiing.

The train clanged across some points and slid quietly into the gleaming station of Trieste. Bond got up and pulled down the window and they stood side by side, looking out. Suddenly Bond felt happy. He put an arm around the girl's waist and held her hard against him.

They gazed down at the holiday crowd. The sun shone through the tall clean windows of the station in golden shafts. The sparkling scene emphasized the dark and dirt of the countries the train had come from, and Bond watched with an almost sensuous pleasure the gaily dressed people pass through the patches of sunshine towards the entrance, and the sunburned people, the ones who had had their holidays, hasten up the platform to get their seats on the train.

A shaft of sun lit up the head of one man who seemed typical of this happy, playtime world. The light flashed briefly on golden hair under a cap, and on a young golden moustache. There was plenty of time to catch the train. The man walked unhurriedly. It crossed Bond's mind that he was an Englishman. Perhaps it was the familiar shape of the dark green Kangol cap, or the beige, rather well-used macintosh, that badge of the English tourist, or it may have been the grey-flannelled legs, or the scuffed brown shoes. But Bond's eyes were drawn to him, as if it was someone he knew, as the man approached up the platform.

The man was carrying a battered Revelation suitcase and, under the other arm, a thick book and some newspapers. He looks like an athlete, thought Bond. He has the wide shoulders and the healthy, good-looking bronzed face of a professional tennis player going home after a round of foreign tournaments.

The man came nearer. Now he was looking straight at Bond. With recognition? Bond searched his mind. Did he know this man? No. He would have remembered those eyes that stared out so coldly under the pale lashes. They were opaque, almost dead. The eyes of a drowned man. But they had some message for him. What was it? Recognition? Warning? Or just the defensive reaction to Bond's own stare?

The man came up with the wagon-lit. His eyes were now gazing levelly up the train. He walked past, the crêpe-soled shoes making no sound. Bond watched him reach for the rail and swing himself easily up the steps into the first-class carriage.

Suddenly Bond knew what the glance had meant, who the man was. Of course! This man was from the Service. After all M had decided to send along an extra hand. That was the message of those queer eyes. Bond would bet anything that the man would soon be along to make contact.

How like M to make absolutely sure!

Chapter Twenty-five

A Tie with a Windsor Knot

To make the contact easy, Bond went out and stood in the corridor. He ran over the details of the code of the day, the few harmless phrases, changed on the first of each month, that served as a simple recognition signal between English agents.

The train gave a jerk and moved slowly out into the sunshine. At the end of the corridor the communicating door slammed. There was no sound of steps, but suddenly the red and gold face was mirrored in the window.

'Excuse me. Could I borrow a match?'

'I use a lighter.' Bond produced his battered Ronson and handed it over.

'Better still.'

'Until they go wrong.'

Bond looked up into the man's face, expecting a smile at the completion of the childish 'Who goes there? Pass, Friend' ritual.

The thick lips writhed briefly. There was no light in the very pale blue eyes.

The man had taken off his macintosh. He was wearing an old reddish-brown tweed coat with his flannel trousers, a pale yellow Viyella summer shirt, and the dark blue and maroon zig-zagged tie of the Royal Artillery. It was tied with a Windsor knot. Bond mistrusted anyone who tied his tie with a Windsor knot. It showed too much vanity. It was often the mark of a cad. Bond decided to forget his prejudice. A gold signet ring, with an indecipherable crest, glinted on the little finger of the right hand that gripped the guard rail. The corner of a red bandana handkerchief flopped out of the breast pocket of the man's coat. On his left wrist there was a battered silver wrist watch with an old leather strap.

Bond knew the type–a minor public school and then caught up by the war. Field Security perhaps. No idea what to do afterwards so he stayed with the occupation troops. At first he would have been with the military police, then, as the senior men drifted home, there came promotion into one of the security services. Moved to Trieste where he did well enough. Wanted to stay on and avoid the rigours of England. Probably had a girl friend, or had married an Italian. The Secret Service had needed a man for the small post that Trieste had become after the withdrawal. This man was available. They took him on. He would be doing routine jobs–have some low-grade sources in the Italian and Yugoslav police, and in their intelligence networks. A thousand a year. A good life, without much being expected from him. Then, out of the blue, this had come along. Must have been a shock getting one of those Most Immediate signals. He'd probably be a bit shy of Bond. Odd face. The eyes looked rather mad. But so they did in most of these men doing secret work abroad. One had to be a bit mad to take it on. Powerful chap, probably on the stupid side, but useful for this kind of guard work. M had just taken the nearest man and told him to join the train.

All this went through Bond's mind as he photographed an impression of the man's clothes and general appearance. Now he said, 'Glad to see you. How did it happen?'

'Got a signal. Late last night. Personal from M. Shook me I can tell you, old man.'

Curious accent. What was it? A hint of brogue–cheap brogue. And something else Bond couldn't define. Probably came from living too long abroad and talking foreign languages all the time. And that dreadful 'old man' at the end. Shyness.

'Must have,' said Bond sympathetically. 'What did it say?

'Just told me to get on the Orient this morning and contact a man and a girl in the through carriage. More or less described what you look like. Then I was to stick by you and see you both through to Gay Paree. That's all, old man.'

Was there defensiveness in the voice? Bond glanced sideways. The pale eyes swivelled to meet his. There was a quick red glare in them. It was as if the safety door of a furnace had swung open. The blaze died. The door to the inside of the man was banged shut. Now the eyes were opaque again–the eyes of an introvert, of a man who rarely looks out into the world but is for ever surveying the scene inside him.

There's madness there all right, thought Bond, startled by the sight of it. Shell-shock perhaps, or schizophrenia. Poor chap, with that magnificent body. One day he would certainly crack. The madness would take control. Bond had better have a word to Personnel. Check up on his medical. By the way, what was his name?

'Well I'm very glad to have you along. Probably not much for you to do. We started off with three Redland men on our tail. They've been got rid of, but there may be others on the train. Or some more may get on. And I've got to get this girl to London without trouble. If you'd just hang about. Tonight we'd better stay together and share watches. It's the last night and I don't want to take any chances. By the way, my name's James Bond. Travelling as David Somerset. And that's Caroline Somerset in there.'

The man fished in his inside pocket and produced a battered note-case which seemed to contain plenty of money. He extracted a visiting card and handed it to Bond. It said 'Captain Norman Nash', and, in the left-hand bottom corner, 'Royal Automobile Club'.

As Bond put the card in his pocket he slipped his finger across it. It was engraved. 'Thanks,' he said. 'Well, Nash, come and meet Mrs Somerset. No reason why we shouldn't travel more or less together.' He smiled encouragingly.

Again the red glare quickly extinguished. The lips writhed under the young golden moustache. 'Delighted, old man.'

Bond turned to the door and knocked softly and spoke his name.

The door opened. Bond beckoned Nash in and shut the door behind him. The girl looked surprised.

'This is Captain Nash, Norman Nash. He's been told to keep an eye on us.'

'How do you do.' The hand came out hesitantly. The man touched it briefly. His stare was fixed. He said nothing. The girl gave an embarrassed little laugh, 'Won't you sit down?'

'Er, thank you.' Nash sat stiffly on the edge of the banquette. He seemed to remember something, something one did when one had nothing to say. He groped in the side pocket of his coat and produced a packet of Players. 'Will you have a, er, cigarette?' He prized open the top with a fairly clean thumbnail, stripped down the silver paper and pushed out the cigarettes. The girl took one. Nash's other hand flashed forward a lighter with the obsequious speed of a motor salesman.

Nash looked up. Bond was standing leaning against the door and wondering how to help this clumsy, embarrassed man. Nash held out the cigarettes and the lighter as if he was offering glass beads to a native chief. 'What about you, old man?'

'Thanks,' said Bond. He hated Virginia tobacco, but he was prepared to do anything to help put the man at ease. He took a cigarette and lit it. They certainly had to make do with some queer fish in the Service nowadays. How the devil did this man manage to get along in the semi-diplomatic society he would have to frequent in Trieste?

Bond said lamely. 'You look very fit, Nash. Tennis?'

'Swimming.'

'Been long in Trieste?'

There came the brief red glare. 'About three years.'

'Interesting work?'

'Sometimes. You know how it is, old man.'

Bond wondered how he could stop Nash calling him 'old man'. He couldn't think of a way. Silence fell.

Nash obviously felt it was his turn again. He fished in his pocket and produced a newspaper cutting. It was the front page of the *Corriere della Sera*. He handed it to Bond. 'Seen this, old man?' The eyes blazed and died.

It was the front page lead. The thick black lettering on the cheap newsprint was still wet. The headlines said:

TERRIBLE ESPLOSIONE IN ISTANBUL
UFFICIO SOVIETICO DISTRUTTO
TUTTI I PRESENTI UCCISI

Bond couldn't understand the rest. He folded the cutting and handed it back. How much did this man know? Better treat him as a strong-man arm and nothing else. 'Bad show,' he said. 'Gas main I suppose.' Bond saw again the obscene belly of the bomb hanging down from the roof of the alcove in the tunnel, the wires that started off down the damp wall on their way back to the plunger in the drawer of Kerim's desk. Who had pressed the plunger yesterday afternoon when Tempo had got through? The 'Head Clerk'? Or had they drawn lots and then stood round and watched as the hand went down and the deep roar had gone up in the Street of Books on the hill above. They would all have been there, in the cool room. With eyes that glittered with hate. The tears would be reserved for the night. Revenge would have come first. And the rats? How many thousand had been blasted down the tunnel? What time would it have been? About four o'clock. Had the daily meeting been on? Three dead in the room. How many more in the rest of the building? Friends of Tatiana, perhaps. He would have to keep the story from her. Had Darko been watching? From a window in Valhalla? Bond could hear the great laugh of triumph echoing round its walls. At any rate Kerim had taken plenty with him.

Nash was looking at him. 'Yes, I daresay it was a gas main,' he said without interest.

A hand-bell tinkled down the corridor, coming nearer. '*Deuxième Service. Deuxième Service. Prenez vos places, s'il vous plaît.*'

Bond looked across at Tatiana. Her face was pale. In her eyes there was an appeal to be saved from any more of this clumsy, non-*kulturny* man. Bond said, 'What about lunch?' She got up at once. 'What about you, Nash?'

Captain Nash was already on his feet. 'Had it, thanks old man. And I'd like to have a look up and down the train. Is the conductor–you know . . . ?' he made a gesture of fingering money.

'Oh yes, he'll co-operate all right,' said Bond. He reached up and pulled down the heavy little bag. He opened the door for Nash. 'See you later.'

Captain Nash stepped into the corridor. He said, 'Yes, I expect so, old man.' He turned left and strode off down the corridor, moving easily with the swaying of the train, his hands in his trouser pockets and the light blazing on the tight golden curls at the back of his head.

Bond followed Tatiana up the train. The carriages were crowded with holiday-makers going home. In the third-class corridors people sat on their bags chattering and munching at oranges and at hard-looking rolls with bits of Salami sticking out of them. The men carefully examined Tatiana as she squeezed by. The women looked appraisingly at Bond, wondering whether he made love to her well.

In the restaurant car, Bond ordered Americanos and a bottle of Chianti Broglio. The wonderful European hors d'œuvres came. Tatiana began to look more cheerful.

'Funny sort of man,' Bond watched her pick about among the little dishes. 'But I'm glad he's come along. I'll have a chance to get some sleep. I'm going to sleep for a week when we get home.'

'I do not like him,' the girl said indifferently. 'He is not *kulturny*. I do not trust his eyes.'

Bond laughed. 'Nobody's *kulturny* enough for you.'

'Did you know him before?'

'No. But he belongs to my firm.'

'What did you say his name is?'

'Nash. Norman Nash.'

She spelled it out. 'N.A.S.H.? Like that?'

'Yes.'

The girl's eyes were puzzled. 'I suppose you know what that means in Russian. *Nash* means "ours". In our Services, a man is *nash* when he is one of "our" men. He is *svoi* when he is one of "theirs"–when he belong to the enemy. And this man calls himself Nash. That is not pleasant.'

Bond laughed. 'Really, Tania. You do think of extraordinary reasons for not liking people. Nash is quite a common English name. He's perfectly harmless. At any rate he's tough enough for what we want him for.'

Tatiana made a face. She went on with her lunch.

Some *tagliatelli verdi* came, and the wine, and then a delicious escalope. 'Oh it is so good,' she said. 'Since I came out of Russia I am all stomach.' Her eyes widened. 'You won't let me get too fat, James. You won't let me get so fat that I am no use for making love? You will have to be careful, or I shall just eat all day long and sleep. You will beat me if I eat too much?'

'Certainly I will beat you.'

Tatiana wrinkled her nose. He felt the soft caress of her ankles. The wide eyes looked at him hard. The lashes came down demurely. 'Please pay,' she said. 'I feel sleepy.'

The train was pulling into Maestre. There was the beginning of the canals. A cargo gondola full of vegetables was moving slowly along a straight sheet of water into the town.

'But we shall be coming into Venice in a minute,' protested Bond. 'Don't you want to see it?'

'It will be just another station. And I can see Venice another day. Now I want you to love me. Please, James.' Tatiana leaned forward. She put a hand over his. 'Give me what I want. There is so little time.'

Then it was the little room again and the smell of the sea coming through the half-open window and the drawn blind fluttering with the wind of the train. Again there were the two piles of clothes on the floor, and the two whispering bodies on the banquette, and the slow searching hands. And the love-knot formed, and, as the train jolted over the points into the echoing station of Venice, there came the final lost despairing cry.

Outside the vacuum of the tiny room there sounded a confusion of echoing calls and metallic clanging and shuffling footsteps that slowly faded into sleep.

Padua came, and Vicenza, and a fabulous sunset over Verona flickered gold and red through the cracks of the blind. Again the little bell came tinkling down the corridor. They woke. Bond dressed and went into the corridor and leant against the guard rail. He looked out at the fading pink light over the Lombardy Plain and thought of Tatiana and of the future.

Nash's face slid up alongside his in the dark glass. Nash came very close so that his elbow touched Bond's. 'I think I've spotted one of the oppo, old man,' he said softly.

Bond was not surprised. He had assumed that, if it came, it would come tonight. Almost indifferently he said, 'Who is here?'

'Don't know what his real name is, but he's been through Trieste once or twice. Something to do with Albania. May be the Resident Director there. Now he's on an American passport. "Wilbur Frank." Calls himself a banker. In No. 9, right next to you. I don't think I could be wrong about him, old man.'

Bond glanced at the eyes in the big brown face. Again the furnace door was ajar. The red glare shone out and was extinguished.

'Good thing you spotted him. This may be a tough night. You'd better stick by us from now on. We mustn't leave the girl alone.'

'That's what I thought, old man.'

They had dinner. It was a silent meal. Nash sat beside the girl and kept his eyes on his plate. He held his knife like a fountain pen and frequently wiped it on his fork. He was clumsy in his movements. Half way through the meal, he reached for the salt and knocked over Tatiana's glass of Chianti. He apologized profusely. He made a great show of calling for another glass and filling it.

Coffee came. Now it was Tatiana who was clumsy. She knocked over her cup. She had gone very pale and her breath was coming quickly.

'Tatiana!' Bond half rose to his feet. But it was Captain Nash who jumped up and took charge.

'Lady's come over queer,' he said shortly. 'Allow me.' He reached down and put an arm round the girl and lifted her to her feet. 'I'll take her back to the compartment. You'd better look after the bag. And there's the bill. I can take care of her till you come.'

'Is all right,' protested Tatiana with the slack lips of deepening unconsciousness. 'Don' worry, James, I lie down.' Her head lolled against Nash's shoulder. Nash put one thick arm round her waist and manœuvred her quickly and efficiently down the crowded aisle and out of the restaurant car.

Bond impatiently snapped his fingers for the waiter. Poor darling. She must be dead beat. Why hadn't he thought of the strain she was going through? He cursed himself for his selfishness. Thank heavens for Nash. Efficient sort of chap, for all his uncouthness.

Bond paid the bill. He took up the heavy little bag and walked as quickly as he could down the crowded train.

He tapped softly on the door of No. 7. Nash opened the door. He came out with his finger on his lips. He closed the door behind him. 'Threw a bit of a faint,' he said. 'She's all right now. The beds were made up. She's gone to sleep in the top one. Been a bit much for the girl I expect, old man.'

Bond nodded briefly. He went into the compartment. A hand hung palely down from under the sable coat. Bond stood on the bottom bunk and gently tucked the hand under the corner of the coat. The hand felt very cold. The girl made no sound.

Bond stepped softly down. Better let her sleep. He went into the corridor.

Nash looked at him with empty eyes. 'Well, I suppose we'd better settle in for the night. I've got my book.' He held it up. '*War and Peace*. Been trying to plough through it for years. You take the first sleep, old man. You look pretty flaked out yourself. I'll wake you up when I can't keep my eyes open any longer.' He gestured with his head at the door of No. 9. 'Hasn't shown yet. Don't suppose he will if he's up to any monkey tricks.' He paused. 'By the way, you got a gun, old man?'

'Yes. Why, haven't you?'

Nash looked apologetic. ''Fraid not. Got a Luger at home, but it's too bulky for this sort of job.'

'Oh, well,' said Bond reluctantly. 'You'd better take mine. Come on in.'

They went in and Bond shut the door. He took out the Beretta and handed it over. 'Eight shots,' he said softly. 'Semi-automatic. It's on safe.'

Nash took the gun and weighed it professionally in his hand. He clicked the safe on and off.

Bond hated someone else touching his gun. He felt naked without it. He said gruffly, 'Bit on the light side, but it'll kill if you put the bullets in the right places.'

Nash nodded. He sat down near the window at the end of the bottom bunk. 'I'll take this end,' he whispered. 'Good field of fire.' He put his book down on his lap and settled himself.

Bond took off his coat and tie and laid them on the bunk beside him. He leant back against the pillows and propped his feet on the bag with the Spektor that stood on the floor beside his attaché case. He picked up his Ambler and found his place and tried to read. After a few pages he found that his concentration was going. He was too tired. He laid the book down on his lap and closed his eyes. Could he afford to sleep? Was there any other precaution they could take?

The wedges! Bond felt for them in the pocket of his coat. He slipped off the bunk and knelt and forced them hard under the two doors. Then he settled himself again and switched off the reading light behind his head.

The violet eye of the nightlight shone softly down.

'Thanks, old man,' said Captain Nash softly.

The train gave a moan and crashed into a tunnel.

Chapter Twenty-six

The Killing Bottle

The light nudge at his ankle woke Bond. He didn't move. His senses came to life like an animal's.

Nothing had changed. There were the noises of the train–the soft iron stride, pounding out the kilometres, the quiet creak of the woodwork, a tinkle from the cupboard over the washbasin where a toothglass was loose in its holder.

What had woken him? The spectral eye of the nightlight cast its deep velvet sheen over the little room. No sound came from the upper bunk. By the window, Captain Nash sat in his place, his book open on his lap, a flicker of moonlight from the edge of the blind showing white on the double page.

He was looking fixedly at Bond. Bond registered the intentness of the violet eyes. The black lips parted. There was a glint of teeth.

'Sorry to disturb you, old man. I feel in the mood for a talk!'

What was there new in the voice? Bond put his feet softly down to the floor. He sat up straighter. Danger, like a third man, was standing in the room.

'Fine,' said Bond easily. What had there been in those few words that had set his spine tingling? Was it the note of authority in Nash's voice? The idea came to Bond that Nash might have gone mad. Perhaps it was madness in the room, and not danger, that Bond could smell. His instincts about this man had been right. It would be a question of somehow getting rid of him at the next station. Where had they got to? When would the frontier come?

Bond lifted his wrist to look at the time. The violet light defeated the phosphorus numerals. Bond tilted the face towards the strip of moonlight from the window.

From the direction of Nash there came a sharp click. Bond felt a violent blow on his wrist. Splinters of glass hit him in the face. His arm was flung back against the door. He wondered if his wrist had been broken. He let his arm hang and flexed his fingers. They all moved.

The book was still open on Nash's lap, but now a thin wisp of smoke was coming out of the hole at the top of its spine and there was a faint smell of fireworks in the room.

The saliva dried in Bond's mouth as if he had swallowed alum.

So there had been a trap all along. And the trap had closed. Captain Nash had been sent to him by Moscow. Not by M. And the M.G.B. agent in No. 9, the man with an American passport, was a myth. And Bond had given Nash his gun. He had even put wedges under the doors so that Nash would feel more secure.

Bond shivered. Not with fear. With disgust.

Nash spoke. His voice was no longer a whisper, no longer oily. It was loud and confident.

'That will save us a great deal of argument, old man. Just a little demonstration. They think I'm pretty good with this little bag of tricks. There are ten bullets in it–·25 dum-dum, fired by an electric battery. You must admit the Russians are wonderful chaps for dreaming these things up. Too bad that book of yours is only for reading, old man.'

'For God's sake stop calling me "old man".' When there was so much to know, so much to think about, this was Bond's first reaction to utter catastrophe. It was the reaction of someone in a burning house who picks up the most trivial object to save from the flames.

'Sorry, old man. It's got to be a habit. Part of trying to be a bloody gentleman. Like these clothes. All from the wardrobe department. They said I'd get by like this. And I did, didn't I, old man? But let's get down to business. I expect you'd like to know what this is all about. Be glad to tell you. We've got about half an hour before you're due to go. It'll give me an extra kick telling the famous Mister Bond of the Secret Service what a bloody fool he is. You see, old man, you're not so good as you think. You're just a stuffed dummy and I've been given the job of letting the sawdust out of you.' The voice was even and flat, the sentences trailing away on a dead note. It was as if Nash was bored by the act of speaking.

'Yes,' said Bond. 'I'd like to know what it's all about. I can spare you half an hour.' Desperately he wondered: was there any way of putting this man off his stride? Upsetting his balance?

'Don't kid yourself, old man,' the voice was uninterested in Bond, or in the threat of Bond. Bond didn't exist except as a target. 'You're going to die in half an hour. No mistake about it. I've never made a mistake or I wouldn't have my job.'

'What is your job?'

'Chief Executioner of SMERSH.' There was a hint of life in the voice, a hint of pride. The voice went flat again. 'You know the name I believe, old man.'

SMERSH. So that was the answer–the worst answer of all. And this was their chief killer. Bond remembered the red glare that flickered in the opaque eyes. A killer. A psychopath–manic depressive, probably. A man who really enjoyed it. What a useful man for SMERSH to have found! Bond suddenly remembered what Vavra had said. He tried a long shot. 'Does the moon have any effect on you, Nash?'

The black lips writhed. 'Clever aren't you, Mister Secret Service. Think I'm barmy. Don't worry. I wouldn't be where I am if I was barmy.'

The angry sneer in the man's voice told Bond that he had touched a nerve. But what could he achieve by getting the man out of control? Better humour him and gain some time. Perhaps Tatiana. . . .

'Where does the girl come into all this?'

'Part of the bait,' the voice was bored again. 'Don't worry. She won't butt in on our talk. Fed her a pinch of chloral hydrate when I poured her that glass of wine. She'll be out for the night. And then for every other night. She's to go with you.'

'Oh really.' Bond slowly lifted his aching hand on to his lap, flexing the fingers to get the blood moving. 'Well, let's hear the story.'

'Careful, old man. No tricks. No Bulldog Drummond stuff'll get you out of this one. If I don't like even the smell of a move, it'll be just one bullet through the heart. Nothing more. That's what you'll be getting in the end. One through the centre of the heart. If you move it'll come a bit quicker. And don't forget who I am. Remember your wrist watch? I don't miss. Not ever.'

'Good show,' said Bond carelessly. 'But don't be frightened. You've got my gun. Remember? Get on with your story.'

'All right, old man, only don't scratch your ear while I'm talking. Or I'll shoot it off. See? Well, SMERSH decided to kill you–at least I gather it was decided even higher up, right at the top. Seems they want to take one good hard poke at the Secret Service–bring them down a peg or two. Follow me?'

'Why choose *me*?'

'Don't ask me, old man. But they say you've got quite a reputation in your outfit. The way you're going to be killed is going to bust up the whole show. It's been three months cooking, this plan, and it's a beaut. Got to be. SMERSH has made one or two mistakes lately. That Khoklov business for one. Remember the explosive cigarette case and all that? Gave the job to the wrong man. Should have given it to me. I wouldn't have gone over to the Yanks. However, to get back. You see, old man, we've got quite a planner in SMERSH. Man called Kronsteen. Great chess player. He said vanity would get you and greed and a bit of craziness in the plot. He said you'd all fall for the craziness in London. And you did, didn't you, old man?'

Had they? Bond remembered just how much the eccentric angles of the story had aroused their curiosity. And vanity? Yes, he had to admit that the idea of this Russian girl being in love with him had helped. And there had been the Spektor. That had decided the whole thing–plain greed for it. He said non-committally: 'We were interested.'

'Then came the operation. Our Head of Operations is quite a character. I'd say she's killed more people than anyone in the world–or arranged for them to be killed. Yes, it's a woman. Name of Klebb–Rosa Klebb. Real swine of a woman. But she certainly knows all the tricks.'

Rosa Klebb. So at the top of SMERSH there was a woman! If he could somehow survive this and get after her! The fingers of Bond's right hand curled softly.

The flat voice in the corner went on: 'Well, she found this Romanova girl. Trained her for the job. By the way, how was she in bed? Pretty good?'

No! Bond didn't believe it. That first night must have been staged. But afterwards? No. Afterwards had been real. He took the opportunity to shrug his shoulders. It was an exaggerated shrug. To get the man accustomed to movement.

'Oh, well. Not interested in that sort of thing myself. But they got some nice pictures of you two.' Nash tapped his coat pocket. 'Whole reel of 16 millimetre. That's going into her handbag. It'll look fine in the papers.' Nash laughed–a harsh, metallic laugh. 'They'll have to cut some of the juiciest bits, of course.'

The change of rooms at the hotel. The honeymoon suite. The big mirror behind the bed. How well it all fitted! Bond felt his hands wet with perspiration. He wiped them down his trousers.

'Steady, old man. You nearly got it then. I told you not to move, remember?'

Bond put his hands back on the book in his lap. How much could he develop these small movements? How far could he go? 'Get on with the story,' he said. 'Did the girl know these pictures were being taken? Did she know SMERSH was involved in all this?'

Nash snorted. 'Of course she didn't know about the pictures. Rosa didn't trust her a yard. Too emotional. But I don't know much about that side. We all worked in compartments. I'd never seen her until today. I only know what I picked up. Yes, of course the girl knew she was working for SMERSH. She was told she had to get to London and do a bit of spying there.'

The silly idiot, thought Bond. Why the hell hadn't she told him that SMERSH was involved? She must have been frightened even to speak the name. Thought he would have her locked up or something. She had always said he would tell him everything when she got to England. That he must have faith and not be afraid. Faith! When she hadn't the foggiest idea herself what was going on. Oh, well. Poor child. She had been as fooled as he had been. But any hint would have been enough–would have saved the life of Kerim, for instance. And what about hers and his own?

'Then this Turk of yours had to be got rid of. I gather that took a bit of doing. Tough nut. I suppose it was his gang that blew up our Centre in Istanbul yesterday afternoon. That's going to create a bit of a panic.'

'Too bad.'

'Doesn't worry me, old man. My end of the job's going to be easy.' Nash took a quick glance at his wrist watch. 'In about twenty minutes we go into the Simplon tunnel. That's where they want it done. More drama for the papers. One bullet for you. As we go into the tunnel. Just one in the heart. The noise of the tunnel will help in case you're a noisy dier–rattle and so forth. Then one in the back of the neck for her–with your gun–and out of the window she goes. Then one more for you with *your* gun. With your fingers wrapped round it, of course. Plenty of powder on your shirt. Suicide. That's what it'll look like at first. But there'll be two bullets in your heart. That'll come out later. More mystery! Search the Simplon again. Who was the man with the fair hair? They'll find the film in her bag, and in your pocket there'll be a long love letter from her to you–a bit threatening. It's a good one. SMERSH wrote it. It says that she'll give the film to the newspapers unless you marry her. That you promised to marry her if she stole the Spektor . . .' Nash paused and added in parenthesis, 'As a matter of fact, old man, the Spektor's bobby-trapped. When your cipher experts start fiddling with it, it's going to blow them all to glory. Not a bad dividend on the side.' Nash chuckled dully. 'And then the letter says that all she's got to offer you is the machine and her body–and all about her body and what you did with it. Hot stuff, that part! Right? So what's the story in the papers–the Left Wing ones that will be tipped off to meet the train? Old man, the story's got everything. Orient Express. Beautiful Russian spy murdered in Simplon tunnel. Filthy pictures. Secret cipher machine. Handsome British spy with career ruined murders her and commits suicide. Sex, spies, luxury train, Mr and Mrs Somerset . . .! Old man, it'll run for months! Talk of the Khoklov case! This'll knock spots off it. And what a poke in the eye for the famous Intelligence Service! Their best man, the famous James Bond. What a shambles. Then bang goes the cipher machine! What's your chief going to think of you? What's the public going to think? And the Goverment. And the Americans? Talk about security! No more atom secrets from the Yanks.' Nash paused to let it all sink in. With a touch of pride he said, 'Old man, this is going to be the story of the century!'

Yes, thought Bond. Yes. He was certainly right about that. The French papers would give it such a send-off there'd be no stopping it. They wouldn't mind how far they went with the pictures or anything else. There wasn't a press in the world that wouldn't pick it up. And the Spektor! Would M's people or the Deuxième have the sense to guess it was booby-trapped? How many of the best cryptographers in the West would go up with it? God, he must get out of this jam! But how?

The top of Nash's *War and Peace* yawned at him. Let's see. There would be the roar as the train went into the tunnel. Then at once the muffled click and the bullet. Bond's eyes stared into the violet gloom, measuring the depth of the shadow in his corner under the roof of the top bunk, remembering exactly where his attaché case stood on the floor, guessing what Nash would do after he had fired.

Bond said: 'You took a bit of a gamble on my letting you team up at Trieste. And how did you know the code of the month?'

Nash said patiently, 'You don't seem to get the picture, old man. SMERSH is good–really good. There's nothing better. We know your code of the month for every year. If anyone in your show noticed these things, noticed the pattern of them, like my show does, you'd realise that every January you lose one of your small chaps somewhere–maybe Tokyo, maybe Timbuctoo. SMERSH just picks one and takes him. Then they screw the code for the year out of him. Anything else he knows, of course. But it's the code they're after. Then it's passed round to the Centres. Simple as falling off a log, old man.'

Bond dug his nails into the palms of his hands.

'As for picking you up at Trieste, old man, I didn't. Rode down with you–in the front of the train. Got out as we stopped and walked back up the platform. You see, old man, we were waiting for you in Belgrade. Knew you'd call your Chief–or the Embassy or someone. Been listening in on that Yugoslav's telephone for weeks. Pity we didn't understand the codeword he shot through to Istanbul. Might have stopped the firework display, or anyway saved our chaps. But the main target was you, old man, and we certainly had you sewn up all right. You were in the killing bottle from the minute you got off that plane in Turkey. It was only a question of when to stuff the cork in.' Nash took another quick glance at his watch. He looked up. His grinning teeth glistened violet. 'Pretty soon now, old man. It's just cork-hours minus fifteen.'

Bond thought: we knew SMERSH was good, but we never knew they were as good as this. The knowledge was vital. Somehow he must get it back. He MUST. Bond's mind raced round the details of his pitifully thin, pitifully desperate plan.

He said: 'SMERSH seems to have thought things out pretty well. Must have taken a lot of trouble. There's only one thing . . .' Bond let his voice hang in the air.

'What's that, old man?' Nash, thinking of his report, was alert.

The train began to slow down. Domodossola. The Italian frontier. What about customs? But Bond remembered. There was no formalities for the through carriages until they got to France, to the frontier, Vallorbes. Even then not for the sleeping cars. These expresses cut straight across Switzerland. It was only people who got out at Brigue or Lausanne who had to go through customs in the stations.

'Well, come on, old man.' Nash sounded hooked.

'Not without a cigarette.'

'Okay. Go ahead. But if there's a move I don't like, you'll be dead.'

Bond slipped his right hand into his hip-pocket. He drew out his broad gunmetal cigarette case. Opened it. Took out a cigarette. Took his lighter out of his trouser pocket. Lit the cigarette and put the lighter back. He left the cigarette case on his lap beside the book. He put his left hand casually over the book and the cigarette case as if to prevent them slipping off his lap. He puffed away at his cigarette. If only it had been a trick one–magnesium flare, or anything he could throw in the man's face! If only his Service went in for those explosive toys! But at least he had achieved his objective and hadn't been shot in the process. That was a start.

'You see.' Bond described an airy circle with his cigarette to distract Nash's attention. His left hand slipped the flat cigarette case between the pages of his book. 'You see, it looks all right, but what about you? What are you going to do after we come out of the Simplon? The conductor knows you're mixed up with us. They'll be after you in a flash.'

'Oh that,' Nash's voice was bored again. 'You don't seem to have hoisted in that the Russians think these things out. I get off at Dijon and take a car to Paris. I get lost there. A bit of "Third Man" stuff won't do the story any harm. Anyway it'll come out later that they dig the second bullet out of you and can't find the second gun. They won't catch up with me. Matter of fact, I've got a date at noon tomorrow–Room 204 at the Ritz Hotel, making my report to Rosa. She wants to get the kudos for this job. Then I turn into her chauffeur and we drive to Berlin. Come to think of it, old man,' the flat voice showed emotion, became greedy, 'I think she may have the Order of Lenin for me in her bag. Lovely grub, as they say.'

The train began to move. Bond tensed. In a few minutes it would come. What a way to die, if he was going to die. Through his own stupidity–blind, lethal stupidity. And lethal for Tatiana. Christ! At any moment he could have done something to dodge this shambles. There had been no lack of opportunity. But conceit and curiosity and four days of love had sucked him along on the easy stream down which it had been planned that he should drift. That was the damnable part of the whole business–the triumph for SMERSH, the one enemy he had always sworn to defeat wherever he met it. We will do this, and he will do that. 'Comrades, it is easy with a vain fool like this Bond. Watch him take the bait. You will see. I tell you he's a fool. All Englishmen are fools.' And Tatiana, the lure–the darling lure. Bond thought of their first night. The black stockings and the velvet ribbon. And all the time SMERSH had been watching, watching him go through his conceited paces, as it had been planned that he would, so that the smear could be built up–the smear on him, the smear on M who had sent him to Istanbul, the smear on the Service that lived on the myth of its name. God, what a mess! If only . . . if only his tiny grain of a plan might work!

Ahead, the rumble of the train became a deep boom.

A few more seconds. A few more yards.

The oval mouth between the white pages seemed to gape wider. In a second the dark tunnel would switch out the moonlight on the pages and the blue tongue would lick out for him.

'Sweet dreams, you English bastard.'

The rumble became a great swift clanging roar.

The spine of the book bloomed flame.

The bullet, homing on Bond's heart, flashed over its two quiet yards.

Bond pitched forward on to the floor and lay sprawled under the funeral violet light.

Chapter Twenty-seven

Ten Pints of Blood

It had all depended on the man's accuracy. Nash had said that Bond would get one bullet through the heart. Bond had taken the gamble that Nash's aim was as good as he said it was. And it had been.

Bond lay like a dead man lies. Before the bullet, he had recalled the corpses he had seen–how their bodies had looked in death. Now he lay totally collapsed, like a broken doll, his arms and legs carefully outflung.

He explored his sensations. Where the bullet had crashed into the book, his ribs were on fire. The bullet must have gone through the cigarette case and then through the other half of the book. He could feel the hot lead over his heart. It felt as if it was burning insidc his ribs. It was only a sharp pain in his head where it had hit the woodwork, and the violet sheen on the scuffed toecaps against his nose, that said he wasn't dead.

Like an archaeologist, Bond explored the carefully planned ruin of his body. The position of the sprawled feet. The angle of the half-bent knee that would give purchase when it was needed. The right hand that seemed to be clawing at his pierced heart, was within inches, when he could release the book, of the little attaché case–within inches of the lateral stitching that held the flat-bladed throwing-knives, two edged and sharp as razors, that he had mocked when Q Branch had demonstrated the catch that held them. And his left hand, outflung in the surrender of death, rested on the floor and would provide upward leverage when the moment came.

Above him there sounded a long, cavernous yawn. The brown toecaps shifted. Bond watched the shoe-leather strain as Nash stood up. In a minute, with Bond's gun in his right hand, Nash would climb on to the bottom bunk and reach up and feel through the curtain of hair for the base of the girl's neck. Then the snout of the Beretta would nuzzle in after the probing fingers, Nash would press the trigger. The roar of the train would cover the muffled boom.

It would be a near thing. Bond desperately tried to remember simple anatomy. Where were the mortal places in the lower body of a man? Where did the main artery run? The Femoral. Down the inside of the thigh. And the External Iliac, or whatever it was called, that became the Femoral? Across the centre of the groin. If he missed both, it would be bad. Bond had no illusions about being able to beat this terrific man in unarmed combat.

The first violent stab of his knife had to be decisive.

The brown toecaps moved. They pointed towards the bunk. What was the man doing? There was no sound except the hollow iron clang as the great train tore through the Simplon–through the heart of the Wasenhorn and Monte Leone. The toothglass tinkled. The woodwork creaked comfortably. For a hundred yards on both sides of the little death cell rows of people were sleeping, or lying awake, thinking of their lives and loves, making little plans, wondering who would meet them at the Gare de Lyon. And, all the while, just along the corridor, death was riding with them down the same dark hole, behind the same great Diesel, on the same hot rails.

One brown shoe left the floor. It would have stepped half across Bond. The vulnerable arch would be open above Bond's head.

Bond's muscles coiled like a snake's. His right hand flickered a few centimetres to the hard stitching on the edge of the case. Pressed sideways. Felt the narrow shaft of the knife. Drew it softly half way out without moving his arm.

The brown heel lifted off the ground. The toe bent and took the weight.

Now the second foot had gone.

Softly move the weight here, take the purchase there, grasp the knife hard so that it wouldn't turn on a bone, and then. . . .

In one violent corkscrew of motion, Bond's body twisted up from the floor. The knife flashed.

The fist with the long steel finger, and all Bond's arm and shoulder behind it, lunged upwards. Bond's knuckles felt flannel. He held the knife in, forcing it further.

A ghastly wailing cry came down to him. The Beretta clattered to the floor. Then the knife was wrenched from Bond's hand as the man gave a convulsive twist and crashed down.

Bond had planned for the fall, but, as he sidestepped towards the window, a flailing hand caught him and sent him thudding on to the lower bunk. Before he could recover himself, up from the floor rose the terrible face, its eyes shining violet, the violet teeth bared. Slowly, agonizingly, the two huge hands groped for him.

Bond, half on his back, kicked out blindly. His shoe connected; but then his foot was held and twisted and he felt himself slipping downwards.

Bond's fingers scrabbled for a hold in the stuff of the bunk. Now the other hand had him by the thigh. Nails dug into him.

Bond's body was being twisted and pulled down. Soon the teeth would be at him. Bond hammered out with his free leg. It made no difference. He was going.

Suddenly Bond's scrabbling fingers felt something hard. The book! How did one work the thing? Which way up was it? Would it shoot him or Nash? Desperately Bond held it out towards the great sweating face. He pressed at the base of the cloth spine.

'Click!' Bond felt the recoil. 'Click-click-click-click.' Now Bond felt the heat under his fingers. The hands on his legs were going limp. The glistening face was drawing back. A noise came from the throat, a terrible gurgling noise. Then, with a slither and a crack, the body fell forward on to the floor and the head crashed back against the woodwork.

Bond lay and panted through clenched teeth. He stared up at the violet light above the door. He noticed that the loop of the filament waxed and waned. It crossed his mind that the dynamo under the carriage must be defective. He blinked his eyes to focus the light more closely. The sweat ran into them and stung. He lay still, doing nothing about it.

The galloping boom of the train began to change. It sounded hollower. With a final echoing roar, the Orient Express sped out into the moonlight and slackened speed.

Bond lazily reached up and pulled at the edge of the blind. He saw warehouses and sidings. Lights shone brightly, cleanly on the rails. Good, powerful lights. The lights of Switzerland.

The train slid quietly to a stop.

In a steady, singing silence, a small noise came from the floor. Bond cursed himself for not having made certain. He quickly bent down, listening. He held the book forward at the ready, just in case. No movement. Bond reached and felt for the jugular vein. No pulse. The man was quite dead. The corpse had been settling.

Bond sat back and waited impatiently for the train to move again. There was a lot to be done. Even before he could see to Tatiana, there would have to be the cleaning up.

With a jerk the long express started softly rolling. Soon the train would be slaloming fast down through the foothills of the Alps into the Canton Valais. Already there was a new sound in the wheels–a hurrying lilt, as if they were glad the tunnel was past.

Bond got to his feet and stepped over the sprawling legs of the dead man and turned on the top light.

What a shambles! The place looked like a butcher's shop. How much blood did the body contain? He remembered. Ten pints. Well, it would soon all be there. As long as it didn't spread into the passage! Bond stripped the bedclothes off the bottom bunk and set to work.

At last the job was done–the walls swabbed down around the covered bulk on the floor, the suitcases piled ready for the getaway at Dijon.

Bond drank down a whole carafe of water. Then he stepped up and gently shook the shoulder of fur.

There was no response. Had the man lied? Had he killed her with the poison?

Bond thrust his hand in against her neck. It was warm. Bond felt for the lobe of an ear and pinched it hard. The girl stirred sluggishly and moaned. Again Bond pinched the ear, and again. At last a muffled voice said, 'Don't.'

Bond smiled. He shook her. He went on shaking until Tatiana slowly turned over on her side. Two doped blue eyes gazed into his and closed again. 'What is it?' The voice was sleepily angry.

Bond talked to her and bullied her and cursed her. He shook her more roughly. At last she sat up. She gazed vacantly at him. Bond pulled her legs out so that they hung down over the edge. Somehow he manhandled her down on to the bottom bunk.

Tatiana looked terrible–the slack mouth, the upturned, sleep-drunk eyes, the tangle of damp hair. Bond got to work with a wet towel and her comb.

Lausanne came and, an hour later, the French frontier at Vallorbes. Bond left Tatiana and went out and stood in the corridor, just in case. But the customs and passport men brushed past him to the conductor's cabin, and, after five inscrutable minutes, went on down the train.

Bond stepped back into the compartment. Tatiana was asleep again. Bond looked at Nash's watch, which was now on his own wrist. 4.30. Another hour to Dijon. Bond set to work.

At last Tatiana's eyes opened wide. Her pupils were more or less centred. She said, 'Stop it now, James.' She closed her eyes again. Bond wiped the sweat off his face. He took the bags, one by one, to the end of the corridor and piled them against the exit. Then he went along to the conductor and told him that Madame was not well and that they would be leaving the train at Dijon.

Bond gave the conductor a final tip. 'Do not derange yourself,' he said. 'I have taken the luggage out so as not to disturb Madame. My friend, the one with fair hair, is a doctor. He has been sitting up with us all night. I have put him to sleep in my bunk. The man was exhausted. It would be kind not to waken him until ten minutes before Paris.'

'*Certainement, Monsieur*.' The conductor had not been showered with money like this since the good days of travelling millionaires. He handed over Bond's passport and tickets. The train began to slacken speed. '*Voilà que nous y sommes*.'

Bond went back to the compartment. He dragged Tatiana to her feet and out into the corridor and shut the door on the white pile of death beside the bunk.

At last they were down the steps and on to the hard, wonderful, motionless platform. A blue-smocked porter took their luggage.

The sun was beginning to rise. At that hour of the morning there were very few passengers awake. Only a handful in the third class, who had ridden 'hard' through the night, saw a young man help a young girl away from the dusty carriage with the romantic names on its side towards the drab door that said 'SORTIE'.

Chapter Twenty-eight

La Tricoteuse

The taxi drew up at the Rue Cambon entrance to the Ritz Hotel.

Bond looked at Nash's watch. 11.45. He must be dead punctual. He knew that if a Russian spy was even a few minutes early or late for a rendezvous the rendezvous was automatically cancelled. He paid off the taxi and went through the door on the left that leads into the Ritz bar.

Bond ordered a double vodka martini. He drank it half down. He felt wonderful. Suddenly the last four days, and particularly last night, were washed off the calendar. Now he was on his own, having his private adventure. All his duties had been taken care of. The girl was sleeping in a bedroom at the Embassy. The Spektor, still pregnant with explosive, had been taken away by the bomb-disposal squad of the Deauxième Bureau. He had spoken to his old friend René Mathis, now head of the Deauxième, and the concierge at the Cambon entrance to the Ritz had been told to give him a pass-key and to ask no questions.

René had been delighted to find himself again involved with Bond in *une affaire noire*. 'Have confidence, *cher* James,' he had said. 'I will execute your mysteries. You can tell me the story afterwards. Two laundry-men with a large laundry basket will come to Room 204 at 12.15. I shall accompany them dressed as the driver of their camion. We are to fill the laundry basket and take it to Orly and await an R.A.F. Canberra which will arrive at two o'clock. We hand over the basket. Some dirty washing which was in France will be in England. Yes?'

Head of Station F had spoken to M on the scrambler. He had passed over a short written report from Bond. He had asked for the Canberra. No, he had no idea what if was for. Bond had only shown up to deliver the girl and the Spektor. He had eaten a huge breakfast and had left the Embassy saying he would be back after lunch.

Bond looked again at the time. He finished his martini. He paid for it and walked out of the bar and up the steps to the concierge's lodge.

The concierge looked sharply at him and handed over a key. Bond walked over to the lift and got in and went up to the third floor.

The lift door clanged behind him. Bond walked softly down the corridor, looking at the numbers.

204. Bond put his right hand inside his coat and on to the taped butt of the Beretta. It was tucked into the waistband of his trousers. He could feel the metal of the silencer warm across his stomach.

He knocked once with his left hand.

'Come in.'

It was a quavering voice. An old woman's voice.

Bond tried the handle of the door. It was unlocked. He slipped the pass-key into his coat-pocket. He pushed the door open with one swift motion and stepped in and shut it behind him.

It was a typical Ritz sitting-room, extremely elegant, with good Empire furniture. The walls were white and the curtains and chair covers were of a small patterned chintz of red roses on white. The carpet was wine-red and close-fitted.

In a pool of sunshine, in a low armed chair beside a Directoire writing desk, a little old woman sat knitting.

The tinkle of the steel needles continued. The eyes behind light-blue tinted bi-focals examined Bond with polite curiosity.

'*Oui, Monsieur?*' The voice was deep and hoarse. The thickly powdered, rather puffy face under the white hair showed nothing but well-bred interest.

Bond's hand on the gun under his coat was taut as a steel spring. His half-closed eyes flickered round the room and back to the little old woman in the chair.

Had he made a mistake? Was this the wrong room? Should he apologize and get out? Could this woman possibly belong to SMERSH? She looked so exactly like the sort of respectable rich widow one would expect to find sitting by herself in the Ritz, whiling the time away with her knitting. The sort of woman who would have her own table, and her favourite waiter, in a corner of the restaurant downstairs–not, of course, the grill room. The sort of woman who would doze after lunch and then be fetched by an elegant black limousine with white side-walled tyres and be driven to the tea-room in the rue de Berri to meet some other rich crone. The old-fashioned black dress with the touch of lace at the throat and wrists, the thin gold chain that hung down over the shapeless bosom and ended in a folding lorgnette, the neat little feet in the sensible black-buttoned boots that barely touched the floor. It couldn't be Klebb! Bond had got the number of the room wrong. He could feel the perspiration under his arms. But now he would have to play the scene through.

'My name is Bond, James Bond.'

'And I, Monsieur, am the Comtesse Metterstein. What can I do for you?' The French was rather thick. She might be German Swiss. The needles tinkled busily.

'I am afraid Captain Nash has met with an accident. He won't be coming today. So I came instead.'

Did the eyes narrow a fraction behind the pale blue spectacles?

'I have not the pleasure of the Captain's acquaintance, Monsieur. Nor of yours. Please sit down and state your business.' The woman inclined her head an inch towards the high-backed chair beside the writing desk.

One couldn't fault her. The graciousness of it all was devastating. Bond walked across the room and sat down. Now he was about six feet away from her. The desk held nothing but a tall old-fashioned telephone with a receiver on a hook, and, within reach of her hand, an ivory-buttoned bellpush. The black mouth of the telephone yawned at Bond politely.

Bond stared rudely into the woman's face, examining it. It was an ugly face, toadlike, under the powder and under the tight cottage-loaf of white hair. The eyes were so light brown as to be almost yellow. The pale lips were wet and blubbery below the fringe of nicotine-stained moustache. Nicotine? Where were her cigarettes? There was no ashtray–no smell of smoke in the room.

Bond's hand tightened again on his gun. He glanced down at the bag of knitting, at the shapeless length of small-denier beige wool the woman was working on. The steel needles. What was there odd about them? The ends were discoloured as if they had been held in fire. Did knitting needles ever look like that?

'*Eh bien, Monsieur?*' Was there an edge to the voice? Had she read something in his face?

Bond smiled. His muscles were tense, waiting for any movement, any trick. 'It's no use,' he said cheerfully, gambling. You are Rosa Klebb. And you are Head of Otdyel II of SMERSH. You are a torturer and a murderer. You wanted to kill me and the Romanov girl. I am very glad to meet you at last.'

The eyes had not changed. The harsh voice was patient and polite. The woman reached out her left hand towards the bell-push. 'Monsieur, I am afraid you are deranged. I must ring for the *valet de chambre* and have you shown to the door.'

Bond never knew what saved his life. Perhaps it was the flash of realization that no wires led from the bellpush to the wall or into the carpet. Perhaps it was the sudden memory of the English 'Come in' when the expected knock came on the door. But, as her finger reached the ivory knob, he hurled himself sideways out of the chair.

As Bond hit the ground there was a sharp noise of tearing calico. Splinters from the back of his chair sprayed around him. The chair crashed to the floor.

Bond twisted over, tugging at his gun. Out of the corner of his eye he noticed a curl of blue smoke coming from the mouth of the 'telephone'. Then the woman was on him, the knitting needles glinting in her clenched fists.

She stabbed downwards at his legs. Bond lashed out with his feet and hurled her sideways. She had aimed at his legs! As he got to one knee. Bond knew what the coloured tips of the needles meant. It was poison. Probably one of those German nerve poisons. All she had to do was scratch him, even through his clothes.

Bond was on his feet. She was coming at him again. He tugged furiously at his gun. The silencer had caught. There was a flash of light. Bond dodged. One of the needles rattled against the wall behind him and the dreadful chunk of woman, the white bun of wig askew on her head, the slimy lips drawn back from her teeth, was on top of him.

Bond, not daring to use his naked fists against the needles, vaulted sideways over the desk.

Panting and talking to herself in Russian, Rosa Klebb scuttled round the desk, the remaining needle held forward like a rapier. Bond backed away, working at the stuck gun. The back of his legs came against a small chair. He let go the gun and reached behind him and snatched it up. Holding it by the back, with its legs pointing like horns, he went round the desk to meet her. But she was beside the bogus telephone. She swept it up and aimed it. Her hand went to the button. Bond leapt forward. He crashed the chair down. Bullets sprayed into the ceiling and plaster pattered down on his head.

Bond lunged again. The legs of the chair clutched the woman round the waist and over her shoulders. God she was strong! She gave way, but only to the wall. There she held her ground, spitting at Bond over the top of the chair, while the knitting needle quested towards him like a long scorpion's sting.

Bond stood back a little, holding the chair at arms' length. He took aim and high-kicked at the probing wrist. The needle sailed away into the room and pinged down behind him.

Bond came in closer. He examined the position. Yes, the woman was held firmly against the wall by the four legs of the chair. There was no way she could get out of the cage except by brute force. Her arms and legs and head were free, but the body was pinned to the wall.

The woman hissed something in Russian. She spat at him over the chair. Bond bent his head and wiped his face against his sleeve. He looked up and into the mottled face.

'That's all, Rosa,' he said. 'The Deuxième will be here in a minute. In an hour or so you'll be in London. You won't be seen leaving the hotel. You won't be seen going into England. In fact very few people will see you again. From now on you're just a number on a secret file. By the time we've finished with you you'll be ready for the lunatic asylum.'

The face, a few feet away, was changing. Now the blood had drained out of it, and it was yellow. But not, thought Bond, with fear. The pale eyes looked levelly into his. They were not defeated.

The wet, shapeless mouth lengthened in a grin.

'And where will you be when I am in the asylum, Mister Bond?'

'Oh, getting on with my life.'

'I think not, *Angliski spion*.'

Bond hardly noticed the words. He had heard the click of the door opening. A burst of laughter came from the room behind him.

'*Eh bien*,' it was the voice of delight that Bond remembered so well. 'The 70th position! Now, at last, I have seen everything. And invented by an Englishman! James, this really is an insult to my countrymen.'

'I don't recommend it,' said Bond over his shoulder. 'It's too strenuous. Anyway, you can take over now. I'll introduce you. Her name's Rosa. You'll like her. She's a big noise in SMERSH–she looks after the murdering, as a matter of fact.'

Mathis came up. There were two laundry-men with him. The three of them stood and looked respectfully into the dreadful face.

'Rosa,' said Mathis thoughtfully. 'But, this time, a Rosa Malheur. Well, well! But I am sure she is uncomfortable in that position. You two, bring along the *panier de fleurs*–she will be more comfortable lying down.

The two men walked to the door. Bond heard the creak of the laundry basket.

The woman's eyes were still locked in Bond's. She moved a little, shifting her weight. Out of Bond's sight, and not noticed by Mathis, who was still examining her face, the toe of one shiny buttoned boot pressed under the instep of the other. From the point of its toe there slid forward half an inch of thin knife blade. Like the knitting needles, the steel had a dirty bluish tinge.

The two men came up and put the big square basket down beside Mathis.

'Take her,' said Mathis. He bowed slightly to the woman. 'It has been an honour.'

'*Au revoir*, Rosa,' said Bond.

The yellow eyes blazed briefly.

'Farewell, Mister Bond.'

The boot, with its tiny steel tongue, flashed out.

Bond felt a sharp pain in his right calf. It was only the sort of pain you would get from a kick. He flinched and stepped back. The two men seized Rosa Klebb by the arms.

Mathis laughed. 'My poor James,' he said. 'Count on SMERSH to have the last word.'

The tongue of dirty steel had withdrawn into the leather. Now it was only a harmless bundle of old woman that was being lifted into the basket.

Mathis watched the lid being secured. He turned to Bond. 'It is a good day's work you have done, my friend,' he said. 'But you look tired. Go back to the Embassy and have a rest because this evening we must have dinner together. The best dinner in Paris. And I will find the loveliest girl to go with it.'

Numbness was creeping up Bond's body. He felt very cold. He lifted his hand to brush back the comma of hair over his right eyebrow. There was no feeling in his fingers. They seemed as big as cucumbers. His hand fell heavily to his side.

Breathing became difficult. Bond sighed to the depth of his lungs. He clenched his jaws and half closed his eyes, as people do when they want to hide their drunkenness.

Through his eyelashes he watched the basket being carried to the door. He prised his eyes open. Desperately he focused Mathis.

'I shan't need a girl, René,' he said thickly.

Now he had to gasp for breath. Again his hand moved up towards his cold face. He had an impression of Mathis starting towards him.

Bond felt his knees begin to buckle.

He said, or thought he said, 'I've already got the loveliest. . . .'

Bond pivoted slowly on his heel and crashed headlong to the wine-red floor.

DR NO

Chapter One

Hear You Loud and Clear

Punctually at six o'clock the sun set with a last yellow flash behind the Blue Mountains, a wave of violet shadow poured down Richmond Road, and the crickets and tree frogs in the fine gardens began to zing and tinkle.

Apart from the background noise of the insects, the wide empty street was quiet. The wealthy owners of the big, withdrawn houses–the bank managers, company directors and top civil servants–had been home since five o'clock and they would be discussing the day with their wives or taking a shower and changing their clothes. In half an hour the street would come to life again with the cocktail traffic, but now this very superior half-mile of 'Rich Road', as it was known to the tradesmen of Kingston, held nothing but the suspense of an empty stage and the heavy perfume of night-scented jasmine.

Richmond Road is the 'best' road in all Jamaica. It is Jamaica's Park Avenue, its Kensington Palace Gardens, its Avenue D'Iéna. The 'best' people live in its big old-fashioned houses, each in an acre or two of beautiful lawn set, too trimly, with the finest trees and flowers from the Botanical Gardens at Hope. The long, straight road is cool and quiet and withdrawn from the hot, vulgar sprawl of Kingston where its residents earn their money, and, on the other side of the T-intersection at its top, lie the grounds of King's House, where the Governor and Commander-in-Chief of Jamaica lives with his family. In Jamaica, no road could have a finer ending.

On the eastern corner of the top intersection stands No. 1 Richmond Road, a substantial two-storey house with broad white-painted verandas running round both floors. From the road a gravel path leads up to the pillared entrance through wide lawns marked out with tennis courts on which this evening, as on all evenings, the sprinklers are at work. This mansion is the social Mecca of Kingston. It is Queen's Club, which, for fifty years, has boasted the power and frequency of its blackballs.

Such stubborn retreats will not long survive in modern Jamaica. One day Queen's Club will have its windows smashed and perhaps be burned to the ground, but for the time being it is a useful place to find in a sub-tropical island–well run, well staffed and with the finest cuisine and cellar in the Caribbean.

At that time of day, on most evenings of the year, you would find the same four motor cars standing in the road outside the club. They were the cars belonging to the high bridge game that assembled punctually at five and played until around midnight. You could almost set your watch by these cars. They belonged, reading from the order in which they now stood against the kerb, to the Brigadier in command of the Caribbean Defence Force, to Kingston's leading criminal lawyer, and to the Mathematics Professor from Kingston University. At the tail of the line stood the black Sunbeam Alpine of Commander John Strangways, R.N. (Ret.), Regional Control Officer for the Caribbean–or, less discreetly, the local representative of the British Secret Service.

Just before six-fifteen, the silence of Richmond Road was softly broken. Three blind beggars came round the corner of the intersection and moved slowly down the pavement towards the four cars. They were Chigroes–Chinese negroes–bulky men, but bowed as they shuffled along, tapping at the kerb with their white sticks. They walked in file. The first man, who wore blue glasses and could presumably see better than the others, walked in front holding a tin cup against the crook of the stick in his left hand. The right hand of the second man rested on his shoulder and the right hand of the third on the shoulder of the second. The eyes of the second and third men were shut. The three men were dressed in rags and wore dirty jippa-jappa baseball caps with long peaks. They said nothing and no noise came from them except the soft tapping of their sticks as they came slowly down the shadowed pavement towards the group of cars.

The three blind men would not have been incongruous in Kingston, where there are many diseased people on the streets, but, in this quiet rich empty street, they made an unpleasant impression. And it was odd that they should all be Chinese negroes. This is not a common mixture of bloods.

In the cardroom, the sunburned hand reached out into the green pool of the centre table and gathered up the four cards. There was a quiet snap as the trick went to join the rest. 'Hundred honours,' said Strangways, 'and ninety below!' He looked at his watch and stood up. 'Back in twenty minutes. Your deal, Bill. Order some drinks. Usual for me. Don't bother to cook a hand for me while I'm gone. I always spot them.'

Bill Templar, the Brigadier, laughed shortly. He pinged the bell by his side and raked the cards in towards him. He said, 'Hurry up, blast you. You always let the cards go cold just as your partner's in the money.'

Strangways was already out of the door. The three men sat back resignedly in their chairs. The coloured steward came in and they ordered drinks for themselves and a whisky and water for Strangways.

There was this maddening interruption every evening at six-fifteen, about half way through their second rubber. At this time precisely, even if they were in the middle of a hand, Strangways had to go to his 'office' and 'make a call'. It was a damned nuisance. But Strangways was a vital part of their four and they put up with it. It was never explained what 'the call' was, and no one asked. Strangways's job was 'hush' and that was that. He was rarely away for more than twenty minutes and it was understood that he paid for his absence with a round of drinks.

The drinks came and the three men began to talk racing.

In fact, this was the most important moment in Strangways's day–the time of his duty radio contact with the powerful transmitter on the roof of the building in Regent's Park that is the headquarters of the Secret Service. Every day, at eighteen-thirty local time, unless he gave warning the day before that he would not be on the air–when he had business on one of the other islands in his territory, for instance, or was seriously ill–he would transmit his daily report and receive his orders. If he failed to come on the air precisely at six-thirty, there would be a second call, the 'Blue' call, at seven, and, finally, the 'Red' call at seven-thirty. After this, if his transmitter remained silent, it was 'Emergency', and Section III, his controlling authority in London, would urgently get on the job of finding out what had happened to him.

Even a 'Blue' call means a bad mark for an agent unless his 'Reasons in Writing' are unanswerable. London's radio schedules round the world are desperately tight and their minute disruption by even one extra call is a dangerous nuisance. Strangways had never suffered the ignominy of a 'Blue' call, let alone a 'Red', and was as certain as could be that he never would do so. Every evening, at precisely six-fifteen, he left Queen's Club, got into his car and drove for ten minutes up into the foothills of the Blue Mountains to his neat bungalow with the fabulous view over Kingston harbour. At six twenty-five he walked through the hall to the office at the back. He unlocked the door and locked it again behind him. Miss Trueblood, who passed as his secretary, but was in fact his No. 2 and a former Chief Officer W.R.N.S., would already be sitting in front of the dials inside the dummy filing cabinet. She would have the earphones on and would be making first contact, tapping out his call-sign, WXN, on 14 megacycles. There would be a shorthand pad on her elegant knees. Strangways would drop into the chair beside her and pick up the other pair of headphones and, at exactly six twenty-eight, he would take over from her and wait for the sudden hollowness in the ether that meant that WWW in London was coming in to acknowledge.

It was an iron routine. Strangways was a man of iron routine. Unfortunately, strict patterns of behaviour can be deadly if they are read by an enemy.

Strangways, a tall lean man with a black patch over the right eye and the sort of aquiline good looks you associate with the bridge of a destroyer, walked quickly across the mahogany panelled hallway of Queen's Club and pushed through the light mosquito-wired doors and ran down the three steps to the path.

There was nothing very much on his mind except the sensual pleasure of the clean fresh evening air and the memory of the finesse that had given him his three spades. There was this case, of course, the case he was working on, a curious and complicated affair that M had rather nonchalantly tossed over the air at him two weeks earlier. But it was going well. A chance lead into the Chinese community had paid off. Some odd angles had come to light–for the present the merest shadows of angles–but if they jelled, thought Strangways as he strode down the gravel path and into Richmond Road, he might find himself involved in something very odd indeed.

Strangways shrugged his shoulders. Of course it wouldn't turn out like that. The fantastic never materialized in his line of business. There would be some drab solution that had been embroidered by overheated imaginations and the usual hysteria of the Chinese.

Automatically, another part of Strangways's mind took in the three blind men. They were tapping slowly towards him down the sidewalk. They were about twenty yards away. He calculated that they would pass him a second or two before he reached his car. Out of shame for his own health and gratitude for it, Strangways felt for a coin. He ran his thumbnail down its edge to make sure it was a florin and not a penny. He took it out. He was parallel with the beggars. How odd, they were all Chigroes! How very odd! Strangways's hand went out. The coin clanged in the tin cup.

'Bless you, Master,' said the leading man. 'Bless you,' echoed the other two.

The car key was in Strangways's hand. Vaguely he registered the moment of silence as the tapping of the white sticks ceased. It was too late.

As Strangways had passed the last man, all three had swivelled. The back two had fanned out a step to have a clear field of fire. Three revolvers, ungainly with their sausage-shaped silencers, whipped out of holsters concealed among the rags. With disciplined precision the three men aimed at different points down Strangways's spine–one between the shoulders, one in the small of the back, one at the pelvis.

The three heavy coughs were almost one. Strangways's body was hurled forward as if it had been kicked. It lay absolutely still in the small puff of dust from the sidewalk.

It was six-seventeen. With a squeal of tyres, a dingy motor hearse with black plumes flying from the four corners of its roof took the T-intersection into Richmond Road and shot down towards the group on the pavement. The three men had just had time to pick up Strangways's body when the hearse slid to a stop abreast of them. The double doors at the back were open. So was the plain deal coffin inside. The three men manhandled the body through the doors and into the coffin. They climbed in. The lid was put on and the doors pulled shut. The three negroes sat down on three of the four little seats at the corners of the coffin and unhurriedly laid their white sticks beside them. Roomy black alpaca coats hung over the backs of the seats. They put the coats on over their rags. Then they took off their baseball caps and reached down to the floor and picked up black top hats and put them on their heads.

The driver, who also was a Chinese negro, looked nervously over his shoulder.

'Go, man. Go!' said the biggest of the killers. He glanced down at the luminous dial of his wrist watch. It said six-twenty. Just three minutes for the job. Dead on time.

The hearse made a decorous U-turn and moved at a sedate speed up to the intersection. There it turned right and at thirty miles an hour it cruised genteely up the tarmac highway towards the hills, its black plumes streaming the doleful signal of its burden and the three mourners sitting bolt upright with their arms crossed respectfully over their hearts.

'WXN calling WWW. . . . WXN calling WWW. . . . WXN . . . WXN . . . WXN . . .'

The centre finger of Mary Trueblood's right hand stabbed softly, elegantly, at the key. She lifted her left wrist. Six twenty-eight. He was a minute late. Mary Trueblood smiled at the thought of the little open Sunbeam tearing up the road towards her. Now, in a second, she would hear the quick step, then the key in the lock and he would be sitting beside her. There would be the apologetic smile as he reached for the earphones. 'Sorry Mary. Damned car wouldn't start.' Or, 'You'd think the blasted police knew my number by now. Stopped me at Halfway Tree.' Mary Trueblood took the second pair of earphones off their hook and put them on his chair to save him half a second.

'WXN calling WWW. . . . WXN calling WWW.' She tuned the dial a hair's breadth and tried again. Her watch said six twenty-nine. She began to worry. In a matter of seconds, London would be coming in. Suddenly she thought, God, what could she do if Strangways wasn't on time! It was useless for her to acknowledge London and pretend she was him–useless and dangerous. Radio Security would be monitoring the call, as they monitored every call from an agent. Those instruments which measured the minute peculiarities in an operator's 'fist' would at once detect it wasn't Strangways at the key. Mary Trueblood had been shown the forest of dials in the quiet room on the top floor at headquarters, had watched as the dancing hands registered the weight of each pulse, the speed of each cipher group, the stumble over a particular letter. The Controller had explained it all to her when she had joined the Caribbean station five years before–how a buzzer would sound and the contact be automatically broken if the wrong operator had come on the air. It was the basic protection against a Secret Service transmitter falling into enemy hands. And, if an agent had been captured and was being forced to contact London under torture, he had only to add a few hairbreadth peculiarities to his usual 'fist' and they would tell the story of his capture as clearly as if he had announced it *en clair*.

Now it had come! Now she was hearing the hollowness in the ether that meant London was coming in. Mary Trueblood glanced at her watch. Six-thirty. Panic! But now, at last, there were the footsteps in the hall. Thank God! In a second he would come in. She *must* protect him! Desperately she decided to take a chance and keep the circuit open.

'WWW calling WXN. . . . WWW calling WXN. . . . Can you hear me? . . . can you hear me?' London was coming over strong, searching for the Jamaica station.

The footsteps were at the door.

Coolly, confidently, she tapped back: 'Hear you loud and clear. . . . Hear you loud and clear. . . . Hear you . . .'

Behind her there was an explosion. Something hit her on the ankle. She looked down. It was the lock of the door.

Mary Trueblood swivelled sharply on her chair. A man stood in the doorway. It wasn't Strangways. It was a big negro with yellowish skin and slanting eyes. There was a gun in his hand. It ended in a thick black cylinder.

Mary Trueblood opened her mouth to scream.

The man smiled broadly. Slowly, lovingly, he lifted the gun and shot her three times in and around the left breast.

The girl slumped sideways off her chair. The earphones slipped off her golden hair on to the floor. For perhaps a second the tiny chirrup of London sounded out into the room. Then it stopped. The buzzer at the Controller's desk in Radio Security had signalled that something was wrong on WXN.

The killer walked out of the door. He came back carrying a box with a coloured label on it that said PRESTO FIRE, and a big sugar-sack marked TATE & LYLE. He put the box down on the floor and went to the body and roughly forced the sack over the head and down to the ankles. The feet stuck out. He bent them and crammed them in. He dragged the bulky sack out into the hall and came back. In the corner of the room the safe stood open, as he had been told it would, and the cipher books had been taken out and laid on the desk ready for work on the London signals. The man threw these and all the papers in the safe into the centre of the room. He tore down the curtains and added them to the pile. He topped it up with a couple of chairs. He opened the box of Presto firelighters and took out a handful and tucked them into the pile and lit them. Then he went out into the hall and lit similar bonfires in appropriate places. The tinder-dry furniture caught quickly and the flames began to lick up the panelling. The man went to the front door and opened it. Through the hibiscus hedge he could see the glint of the hearse. There was no noise except the zing of crickets and the soft tick-over of the car's engine. Up and down the road there was no other sign of life. The man went back into the smoke-filled hall and easily shouldered the sack and came out again, leaving the door open to make a draught. He walked swiftly down the path to the road. The back doors of the hearse were open. He handed in the sack and watched the two men force it into the coffin on top of Strangways's body. Then he climbed in and shut the doors and sat down and put on his top hat.

As the first flames showed in the upper windows of the bungalow, the hearse moved quietly from the sidewalk and went on its way up towards the Mona Reservoir. There the weighted coffin would slip down into its fifty-fathom grave and, in just forty-five minutes, the personnel and records of the Caribbean station of the Secret Service would have been utterly destroyed.

Chapter Two

Choice of Weapons

Three weeks later, in London, March came in like a rattlesnake.

From first light on March 1st, hail and icy sleet, with a Force 8 gale behind them, lashed at the city and went on lashing as the people streamed miserably to work, their legs whipped by the wet hems of their macintoshes and their faces blotching with the cold.

It was a filthy day and everybody said so–even M, who rarely admitted the existence of weather even in its extreme forms. When the old black Silver Wraith Rolls with the nondescript number-plate stopped outside the tall building in Regent's Park and he climbed stiffly out on to the pavement, hail hit him in the face like a whiff of small-shot. Instead of hurrying inside the building, he walked deliberately round the car to the window beside the chauffeur.

'Won't be needing the car again today, Smith. Take it away and go home. I'll use the tube this evening. No weather for driving a car. Worse than one of those PQ convoys.'

Ex-Leading Stoker Smith grinned gratefully. 'Aye-aye, sir. And thanks.' He watched the elderly erect figure walk round the bonnet of the Rolls and across the pavement and into the building. Just like the old boy. He'd always see the men right first. Smith clicked the gear lever into first and moved off, peering forward through the streaming windscreen. They didn't come like that any more.

M went up in the lift to the eighth floor and along the thick-carpeted corridor to his office. He shut the door behind him, took off his overcoat and scarf and hung them behind the door. He took out a large blue silk bandanna handkerchief and brusquely wiped it over his face. It was odd, but he wouldn't have done this in front of the porters or the liftman. He went over to his desk and sat down and bent towards the intercom. He pressed a switch. 'I'm in, Miss Moneypenny. The signals please, and anything else you've got. Then get me Sir James Molony. He'll be doing his rounds at St Mary's about now. Tell the Chief of Staff I'll see 007 in half an hour. And let me have the Strangways file.' M waited for the metallic 'Yes, sir' and released the switch.

He sat back and reached for his pipe and began filling it thoughtfully. He didn't look up when his secretary came in with the stack of papers and he even ignored the half dozen pink Most Immediates on top of the signal file. If they had been vital he would have been called during the night.

A yellow light winked on the intercom. M picked up the black telephone from the row of four. 'That you, Sir James? Have you got five minutes?'

'Six, for you.' At the other end of the line the famous neurologist chuckled. 'Want me to certify one of Her Majesty's Ministers?'

'Not today.' M frowned irritably. The old Navy had respected governments. 'It's about that man of mine you've been handling. We won't bother about the name. This is an open line. I gather you let him out yesterday. Is he fit for duty?'

There was a pause on the other end. Now the voice was professional, judicious. 'Physically he's as fit as a fiddle. Leg's healed up. Shouldn't be any after-effects. Yes, he's all right.' There was another pause. 'Just one thing, M. There's a lot of tension there, you know. You work these men of yours pretty hard. Can you give him something easy to start with? From what you've told me he's been having a tough time for some years now.'

M said gruffly, 'That's what he's paid for. It'll soon show if he's not up to the work. Won't be the first one that's cracked. From what you say, he sounds in perfectly good shape. It isn't as if he'd really been damaged like some of the patients I've sent you–men who've been properly put through the mangle.'

'Of course, if you put it like that. But pain's an odd thing. We know very little about it. You can't measure it–the difference in suffering between a woman having a baby and a man having a renal colic. And, thank God, the body seems to forget fairly quickly. But this man of yours has been in *real* pain, M. Don't think that just because nothing's been broken . . .'

'Quite, quite.' Bond had made a mistake and he had suffered for it. In any case M didn't like being lectured, even by one of the most famous doctors in the world, on how he should handle his agents. There had been a note of criticism in Sir James Molony's voice. M said abruptly, 'Ever hear of a man called Steincrohn–Dr Peter Steincrohn?'

'No, who's he?'

'American doctor. Written a book my Washington people sent over for our library. This man talks about how much punishment the human body can put up with. Gives a list of the bits of the body an average man can do without. Matter of fact, I copied it out for future reference. Care to hear the list?' M dug into his coat pocket and put some letters and scraps of paper on the desk in front of him. With his left hand he selected a piece of paper and unfolded it. He wasn't put out by the silence on the other end of the line. 'Hullo, Sir James! Well, here they are: "Gall bladder, spleen, tonsils, appendix, one of his two kidneys, one of his two lungs, two of his four or five quarts of blood, two-fifths of his liver, most of his stomach, four of his twenty-three feet of intestines and half of his brain."' M paused. When the silence continued at the other end, he said, 'Any comments, Sir James?'

There was a reluctant grunt at the other end of the telephone. 'I wonder he didn't add an arm and a leg, or all of them. I don't quite see what you're trying to prove.'

M gave a curt laugh. 'I'm not trying to prove anything, Sir James. It just struck me as an interesting list. All I'm trying to say is that my man seems to have got off pretty lightly compared with that sort of punishment. But,' M relented, 'don't let's argue about it.' He said in a milder voice, 'As a matter of fact I did have it in mind to let him have a bit of a breather. Something's come up in Jamaica.' M glanced at the streaming windows. 'It'll be more of a rest cure than anything. Two of my people, a man and a girl, have gone off together. Or that's what it looks like. Our friend can have a spell at being an inquiry agent–in the sunshine too. How's that?'

'Just the ticket. I wouldn't mind the job myself on a day like this.' But Sir James Molony was determined to get his message through. He persisted mildly, 'Don't think I wanted to interfere, M, but there are limits to a man's courage. I know you have to treat these men as if they were expendable, but presumably you don't want them to crack at the wrong moment. This one I've had here is tough. I'd say you'll get plenty more work out of him. But you know what Moran has to say about courage in that book of his.'

'Don't recall.'

'He says that courage is a capital sum reduced by expenditure. I agree with him. All I'm trying to say is that this particular man seems to have been spending pretty hard since before the war. I wouldn't say he's overdrawn–not yet, but there are limits.'

'Just so.' M decided that was quite enough of that. Nowadays, softness was everywhere. 'That's why I'm sending him abroad. Holiday in Jamaica. Don't worry, Sir James. I'll take care of him. By the way, did you ever discover what the stuff was that Russian woman put into him?'

'Got the answer yesterday.' Sir James Molony also was glad the subject had been changed. The old man was as raw as the weather. Was there any chance that he had got his message across into what he described to himself as M's thick skull? 'Taken us three months. It was a bright chap at the School of Tropical Medicine who came up with it. The drug was *fugu* poison. The Japanese use it for committing suicide. It comes from the sex organs of the Japanese globe-fish. Trust the Russians to use something no one's ever heard of. They might just as well have used curare. It has much the same effect–paralysis of the central nervous system. *Fugu*'s scientific name is Tetrodotoxin. It's terrible stuff and very quick. One shot of it like your man got and in a matter of seconds the motor and respiratory muscles are paralysed. At first the chap sees double and then he can't keep his eyes open. Next he can't swallow. His head falls and he can't raise it. Dies of respiratory paralysis.'

'Lucky he got away with it.'

'Miracle. Thanks entirely to that Frenchman who was with him. Got your man on the floor and gave him artificial respiration as if he was drowning. Somehow kept his lungs going until the doctor came. Luckily the doctor had worked in South America. Diagnosed curare and treated him accordingly. But it was a chance in a million. By the same token, what happened to the Russian woman?'

M said shortly, 'Oh, she died. Well, many thanks, Sir James. And don't worry about your patient. I'll see he has an easy time of it. Goodbye.'

M hung up. His face was cold and blank. He pulled over the signal file and went quickly through it. On some of the signals he scribbled a comment. Occasionally he made a brief telephone call to one of the Sections. When he had finished he tossed the pile into his *Out* basket and reached for his pipe and the tobacco jar made out of the base of a fourteen-pounder shell. Nothing remained in front of him except a buff folder marked with the Top Secret red star. Across the centre of the folder was written in block capitals: CARIBBEAN STATION, and underneath, in italics, *Strangways and Trueblood*.

A light winked on the intercom. M pressed down the switch. 'Yes?'

'007's here, sir.'

'Send him in. And tell the Armourer to come up in five minutes.'

M sat back. He put his pipe in his mouth and set a match to it. Through the smoke he watched the door to his secretary's office. His eyes were very bright and watchful.

James Bond came through the door and shut it behind him. He walked over to the chair across the desk from M and sat down.

'Morning, 007.'

'Good morning, sir.'

There was silence in the room except for the rasping of M's pipe. It seemed to be taking a lot of matches to get it going. In the background the fingernails of the sleet slashed against the two broad windows.

It was all just as Bond had remembered it through the months of being shunted from hospital to hospital, the weeks of dreary convalescence, the hard work of getting his body back into shape. To him this represented stepping back into life. Sitting here in this room opposite M was the symbol of normality he had longed for. He looked across through the smoke clouds into the shrewd grey eyes. They were watching him. What was coming? A post-mortem on the shambles which had been his last case? A curt relegation to one of the home sections for a spell of desk work? Or some splendid new assignment M had been keeping on ice while waiting for Bond to get back to duty?

M threw the box of matches down on the red leather desk. He leant back and clasped his hands behind his head.

'How do you feel? Glad to be back?'

'Very glad, sir. And I feel fine.'

'Any final thoughts about your last case? Haven't bothered you with it till you got well. You heard I ordered an inquiry. I believe the Chief of Staff took some evidence from you. Anything to add?'

M's voice was businesslike, cold. Bond didn't like it. Something unpleasant was coming. He said, 'No, sir. It was a mess. I blame myself for letting that woman get me. Shouldn't have happened.'

M took his hands from behind his neck and slowly leant forward and placed them flat on the desk in front of him. His eyes were hard. 'Just so.' The voice was velvet, dangerous. 'Your gun got stuck, if I recall. This Beretta of yours with the silencer. Something wrong there, 007. Can't afford that sort of mistake if you're to carry an 00 number. Would you prefer to drop it and go back to normal duties?'

Bond stiffened. His eyes looked resentfully into M's. The licence to kill for the Secret Service, the double-0 prefix, was a great honour. It had been earned hardly. It brought Bond the only assignments he enjoyed, the dangerous ones. 'No, I wouldn't, sir.'

'Then we'll have to change your equipment. That was one of the findings of the Court of Inquiry. I agree with it. D'you understand?'

Bond said obstinately, 'I'm used to that gun, sir. I like working with it. What happened could have happened to anyone. With any kind of gun.'

'I don't agree. Nor did the Court of Inquiry. So that's final. The only question is what you're to use instead.' M bent forward to the intercom. 'Is the Armourer there? Send him in.'

M sat back. 'You may not know it, 007, but Major Boothroyd's the greatest small-arms expert in the world. He wouldn't be here if he wasn't. We'll hear what he has to say.'

The door opened. A short slim man with sandy hair came in and walked over to the desk and stood beside Bond's chair. Bond looked up into his face. He hadn't often seen the man before, but he remembered the very wide apart clear grey eyes that never seemed to flicker. With a non-committal glance down at Bond, the man stood relaxed, looking across at M. He said 'Good morning, sir,' in a flat, unemotional voice.

'Morning, Armourer. Now I want to ask you some questions.' M's voice was casual. 'First of all, what do you think of the Beretta, the ·25?'

'Ladies' gun, sir.'

M raised ironic eyebrows at Bond. Bond smiled thinly.

'Really! And why do you say that?'

'No stopping power, sir. But it's easy to operate. A bit fancy-looking too, if you know what I mean, sir. Appeals to the ladies.'

'How would it be with a silencer?'

'Still less stopping power, sir. And I don't like silencers. They're heavy and get stuck in your clothing when you're in a hurry. I wouldn't recommend anyone to try a combination like that, sir. Not if they were meaning business.'

M said pleasantly to Bond, 'Any comment, 007?'

Bond shrugged his shoulders. 'I don't agree. I've used the ·25 Beretta for fifteen years. Never had a stoppage and I haven't missed with it yet. Not a bad record for a gun. It just happens that I'm used to it and I can point it straight. I've used bigger guns when I've had to–the ·45 Colt with the long barrel, for instance. But for close-up work and concealment I like the Beretta.' Bond paused. He felt he should give way somewhere. 'I'd agree about the silencer, sir. They're a nuisance. But sometimes you have to use them.'

'We've seen what happens when you do,' said M drily. 'And as for changing your gun, it's only a question of practice. You'll soon get the feel of a new one.' M allowed a trace of sympathy to enter his voice. 'Sorry, 007. But I've decided. Just stand up a moment. I want the Armourer to get a look at your build.'

Bond stood up and faced the other man. There was no warmth in the two pairs of eyes. Bond's showed irritation. Major Boothroyd's were indifferent, clinical. He walked round Bond. He said 'Excuse me' and felt Bond's biceps and forearms. He came back in front of him and said, 'Might I see your gun?'

Bond's hand went slowly into his coat. He handed over the taped Beretta with the sawn barrel. Boothroyd examined the gun and weighed it in his hand. He put it down on the desk. 'And your holster?'

Bond took off his coat and slipped off the chamois leather holster and harness. He put his coat on again.

With a glance at the lips of the holster, perhaps to see if they showed traces of snagging, Boothroyd tossed the holster down beside the gun with a motion that sneered. He looked across at M. 'I think we can do better than this, sir.' It was the sort of voice Bond's first expensive tailor had used.

Bond sat down. He just stopped himself gazing rudely at the ceiling. Instead he looked impassively across at M.

'Well, Armourer, what do you recommend?'

Major Boothroyd put on the expert's voice. 'As a matter of fact, sir,' he said modestly, 'I've just been testing most of the small automatics. Five thousand rounds each at twenty-five yards. Of all of them, I'd choose the Walther PPK 7·65 mm. It only came fourth after the Japanese M-14, the Russian Tokarev and the Sauer M-38. But I like its light trigger pull and the extension spur of the magazine gives a grip that should suit 007. It's a real stopping gun. Of course it's about a ·32 calibre as compared with the Beretta's ·25 but I wouldn't recommend anything lighter. And you can get ammunition for the Walther anywhere in the world. That gives it an edge on the Japanese and the Russian guns.'

M turned to Bond. 'Any comments?'

'It's a good gun, sir,' Bond admitted. 'Bit more bulky than the Beretta. How does the Armourer suggest I carry it?'

'Berns Martin Triple-draw holster,' said Major Boothroyd succinctly. 'Best worn inside the trouser band to the left. But it's all right below the shoulder. Stiff saddle leather. Holds the gun in with a spring. Should make for a quicker draw than that,' he gestured towards the desk. 'Three-fifths of a second to hit a man at twenty feet would be about right.'

'That's settled then.' M's voice was final. 'And what about something bigger?'

'There's only one gun for that, sir,' said Major Boothroyd stolidly. 'Smith & Wesson Centennial Airweight. Revolver. ·38 calibre. Hammerless, so it won't catch in clothing. Overall length of six and a half inches and it only weighs thirteen ounces. To keep down the weight, the cylinder holds only five cartridges. But by the time they're gone,' Major Boothroyd allowed himself a wintry smile, 'somebody's been killed. Fires the ·38 S & W Special. Very accurate cartridge indeed. With standard loading it has a muzzle velocity of eight hundred and sixty feet per second and muzzle energy of two hundred and sixty foot-pounds. There are various barrel lengths, three-and-a-half-inch, five-inch . . .'

'All right, all right.' M's voice was testy. 'Take it as read. If you say it's the best I'll believe you. So it's the Walther and the Smith & Wesson. Send up one of each to 007. With the harness. And arrange for him to fire them in. Starting today. He's got to be expert in a week. All right? Then thank you very much, Armourer. I won't detain you.'

'Thank you, sir,' said Major Boothroyd. He turned and marched stiffly out of the room.

There was a moment's silence. The sleet tore at the windows. M swivelled his chair and watched the streaming panes. Bond took the opportunity to glance at his watch. Ten o'clock. His eyes slid to the gun and holster on the desk. He thought of his fifteen years' marriage to the ugly bit of metal. He remembered the times its single word had saved his life–and the times when its threat alone had been enough. He thought of the days when he had literally dressed to kill–when he had dismantled the gun and oiled it and packed the bullets carefully into the springloaded magazine and tried the action once or twice, pumping the cartridges out on to the bedspread in some hotel bedroom somewhere around the world. Then the last wipe of a dry rag and the gun into the little holster and a pause in front of the mirror to see that nothing showed. And then out of the door and on his way to the rendezvous that was to end with either darkness or light. How many times had it saved his life? How many death sentences had it signed? Bond felt unreasonably sad. How could one have such ties with an inanimate object, an ugly one at that, and, he had to admit it, with a weapon that was not in the same class as the ones chosen by the Armourer? But he had the ties and M was going to cut them.

M swivelled back to face him. 'Sorry, James,' he said, and there was no sympathy in his voice. 'I know how you like that bit of iron. But I'm afraid it's got to go. Never give a weapon a second chance–any more than a man. I can't afford to gamble with the double-o section. They've got to be properly equipped. You understand that? A gun's more important than a hand or a foot in your job.'

Bond smiled thinly. 'I know, sir. I shan't argue. I'm just sorry to see it go.'

'All right then. We'll say no more about it. Now I've got some more news for you. There's a job come up. In Jamaica. Personnel problem. Or that's what it looks like. Routine investigation and report. The sunshine'll do you good and you can practise your new guns on the turtles or whatever they have down there. You can do with a bit of holiday. Like to take it on?'

Bond thought: He's got it in for me over the last job. Feels I let him down. Won't trust me with anything tough. Wants to see. Oh well! He said: 'Sounds rather like the soft life, sir. I've had almost too much of that lately. But if it's got to be done . . . If you say so, sir . . .'

'Yes,' said M. 'I say so.'

Chapter Three

Holiday Task

It was getting dark. Outside the weather was thickening. M reached over and switched on the green-shaded desklight. The centre of the room became a warm yellow pool in which the leather top of the desk glowed blood-red.

M pulled the thick file towards him. Bond noticed it for the first time. He read the reversed lettering without difficulty. What had Strangways been up to? Who was Trueblood?

M pressed a button on his desk. 'I'll get the Chief of Staff in on this,' he said. 'I know the bones of the case, but he can fill in the flesh. It's a drab little story, I'm afraid.'

The Chief of Staff came in. He was a colonel in the Sappers, a man of about Bond's age, but his hair was prematurely grey at the temples from the endless grind of work and responsibility. He was saved from a nervous breakdown by physical toughness and a sense of humour. He was Bond's best friend at headquarters. They smiled at each other.

'Bring up a chair, Chief of Staff. I've given 007 the Strangways case. Got to get the mess cleared up before we make a new appointment there. 007 can be acting Head of Station in the meantime. I want him to leave in a week. Would you fix that with the Colonial Office and the Governor? And now let's go over the case.' He turned to Bond. 'I think you knew Strangways, 007. See you worked with him on that treasure business about five years ago. What did you think of him?'

'Good man, sir. Bit highly strung. I'd have thought he'd have been relieved by now. Five years is a long time in the tropics.'

M ignored the comment. 'And his number two, this girl Trueblood, Mary Trueblood. Ever come across her?'

'No, sir.'

'I see she's got a good record. Chief Officer W.R.N.S. and then came to us. Nothing against her on her Confidential Record. Good-looker to judge from her photographs. That probably explains it. Would you say Strangways was a bit of a womanizer?'

'Could have been,' said Bond carefully, not wanting to say anything against Strangways, but remembering the dashing good looks. 'But what's happened to them, sir?'

'That's what we want to find out,' said M. 'They've gone, vanished into thin air. Both went on the same evening about three weeks ago. Left Strangways's bungalow burned to the ground–radio, codebooks, files. Nothing left but a few charred scraps. The girl left all her things intact. Must have taken only what she stood up in. Even her passport was in her room. But it would have been easy for Strangways to cook up two passports. He had plenty of blanks. He was Passport Control Officer for the island. Any number of planes they could have taken–to Florida or South America or one of the other islands in his area. Police are still checking the passenger lists. Nothing's come up yet, but they could always have gone to ground for a day or two and then done a bunk. Dyed the girl's hair and so forth. Airport security doesn't amount to much in that part of the world. Isn't that so, Chief of Staff?'

'Yes, sir.' The Chief of Staff sounded dubious. 'But I still can't understand that last radio contact.' He turned to Bond. 'You see, they began to make their routine contact at eighteen-thirty Jamaican time. Someone, Radio Security thinks it was the girl, acknowledged our WWW and then went off the air. We tried to regain contact but there was obviously something fishy and we broke off. No answer to the Blue Call, or to the Red. So that was that. Next day Section III sent 258 down from Washington. By that time the police had taken over and the Governor had already made up his mind and was trying to get the case hushed up. It all seemed pretty obvious to him. Strangways has had occasional girl trouble down there. Can't blame the chap myself. It's a quiet station. Not much to occupy his time. The Governor jumped to the obvious conclusions. So, of course, did the local police. Sex and machete fights are about all they understand. 258 spent a week down there and couldn't turn up a scrap of contrary evidence. He reported accordingly and we sent him back to Washington. Since then the police have been scraping around rather ineffectually and getting nowhere.' The Chief of Staff paused. He looked apologetically at M. 'I know you're inclined to agree with the Governor, sir, but that radio contact sticks in my throat. I just can't see where it fits into the runaway-couple picture. And Strangways's friends at his club say he was perfectly normal. Left in the middle of a rubber of bridge–always did, when it was getting close to his deadline. Said he'd be back in twenty minutes. Ordered drinks all round–again just as he always did–and left the club dead on six-fifteen, exactly to schedule. Then he vanished into thin air. Even left his car in front of the club. Now, why should he set the rest of his bridge four looking for him if he wanted to skip with the girl? Why not leave in the morning, or better still, late at night, after they'd made their radio call and tidied up their lives? It just doesn't make sense to me.'

M grunted non-committally. 'People in–er–love do stupid things,' he said gruffly. 'Act like lunatics sometimes. And anyway, what other explanation is there? Absolutely no trace of foul play–no reason for it that anyone can see. It's a quiet station down there. Same routines every month–an occasional communist trying to get into the island from Cuba, crooks from England thinking they can hide away just because Jamaica's so far from London. I don't suppose Strangways has had a big case since 007 was there.' He turned to Bond. 'On what you've heard, what do you think, 007? There's not much else to tell you.'

Bond was definite. 'I just can't see Strangways flying off the handle like that, sir. I daresay he was having an affair with the girl, though I wouldn't have thought he was a man to mix business with pleasure. But the Service was his whole life. He'd never have let it down. I can see him handing in his papers, and the girl doing the same, and then going off with her after you'd sent out reliefs. But I don't believe it was in him to leave us in the air like this. And from what you say of the girl, I'd say it would be much the same with her. Chief Officers W.R.N.S. don't go out of their senses.'

'Thank you, 007.' M's voice was controlled. 'These considerations had also crossed my mind. No one's been jumping to conclusions without weighing all the possibilities. Perhaps you can suggest another solution.'

M sat back and waited. He reached for his pipe and began filling it. The case bored him. He didn't like personnel problems, least of all messy ones like this. There were plenty of other worries waiting to be coped with round the world. It was only to give Bond the pretence of a job, mixed with a good rest, that he had decided to send him out to Jamaica to close the case. He put the pipe in his mouth and reached for the matches. 'Well?'

Bond wasn't going to be put off his stride. He had liked Strangways and he was impressed by the points the Chief of Staff had made. He said: 'Well, sir. For instance, what was the last case Strangways was working on? Had he reported anything, or was there anything Section III had asked him to look into. Anything at all in the last few months?'

'Nothing whatsoever.' M was definite. He took the pipe out of his mouth and cocked it at the Chief of Staff. 'Right?'

'Right, sir,' said the Chief of Staff. 'Only that damned business about the birds.'

'Oh that,' said M contemptuously. 'Some rot from the Zoo or somebody. Got wished on us by the Colonial Office. About six weeks ago, wasn't it?'

'That's right, sir. But it wasn't the Zoo. It was some people in America called the Audubon Society. They protect rare birds from extinction or something like that. Got on to our Ambassador in Washington, and the F.O. passed the buck to the Colonial Office. They shoved it on to us. Seems these bird people are pretty powerful in America. They even got an atom bombing range shifted on the West Coast because it interfered with some birds' nests.'

M snorted. 'Damned thing called a Whooping Crane. Read about it in the papers.'

Bond persisted. 'Could you tell me about it, sir? What did the Audubon people want us to do?'

M waved his pipe impatiently. He picked up the Strangways file and tossed it down in front of the Chief of Staff. 'You tell him, Chief of Staff,' he said wearily. 'It's all in there.'

The Chief of Staff took the file and riffled through the pages towards the back. He found what he wanted and bent the file in half. There was silence in the room while he ran his eye over three pages of typescript which Bond could see were headed with the blue and white cipher of the Colonial Office. Bond sat quietly, trying not to feel M's coiled impatience radiating across the desk.

The Chief of Staff slapped the file shut. He said, 'Well, this is the story as we passed it to Strangways on January 20th. He acknowledged receipt, but after that we heard nothing from him.' The Chief of Staff sat back in his chair. He looked at Bond. 'It seems there's a bird called a Roseate Spoonbill. There's a coloured photograph of it in here. Looks like a sort of pink stork with an ugly flat bill which it uses for digging for food in the mud. Not many years ago these birds were dying out. Just before the war there were only a few hundred left in the world, mostly in Florida and thereabouts. Then somebody reported a colony of them on an island called Crab Key between Jamaica and Cuba. It's British territory–a dependency of Jamaica. Used to be a guano island, but the quality of the guano was too low for the cost of digging it. When the birds were found there, it had been uninhabited for about fifty years. The Audubon people went there and ended up by leasing a corner as a sanctuary for these spoonbills. Put two wardens in charge and persuaded the airlines to stop flying over the island and disturbing the birds. The birds flourished and at the last count there were about five thousand of them on the island. Then came the war. The price of guano went up and some bright chap had the idea of buying the island and starting to work it again. He negotiated with the Jamaican Government and bought the place for ten thousand pounds with the condition that he didn't disturb the lease of the sanctuary. That was in 1943. Well, this man imported plenty of cheap labour and soon had the place working at a profit and it's gone on making a profit until recently. Then the price of guano took a dip and it's thought that he must be having a hard time making both ends meet.'

'Who is this man?'

'Chinaman, or rather half Chinese and half German. Got a daft name.

Calls himself Doctor No–Doctor Julius No.'

'No? Spelt like Yes?'

'That's right.'

'Any facts about him?'

'Nothing except that he keeps very much to himself. Hasn't been seen since he made his deal with the Jamaican Government. And there's no traffic with the island. It's his and he keeps it private. Says he doesn't want people disturbing the guanay birds who turn out his guano. Seems reasonable. Well, nothing happened until just before Christmas when one of the Audubon wardens, a Barbadian, good solid chap apparently, arrived on the north shore of Jamaica in a canoe. He was very sick. He was terribly burned–died in a few days. Before he died he told some crazy story about their camp having been attacked by a dragon with flames coming out of its mouth. This dragon had killed his pal and burned up the camp and gone roaring off into the bird sanctuary belching fire among the birds and scaring them off God knows where. He had been badly burned but he'd escaped to the coast and stolen a canoe and sailed all one night to Jamaica. Poor chap was obviously off his rocker. And that was that, except that a routine report had to be sent off to the Audubon Society. And they weren't satisfied. Sent down two of their big brass in a Beechcraft from Miami to investigate. There's an airstrip on the island. This Chinaman's got a Grumman Amphibian for bringing in supplies . . .'

M interjected sourly, 'All these people seem to have a hell of a lot of money to throw about on their damned birds.'

Bond and the Chief of Staff exchanged smiles. M had been trying for years to get the Treasury to give him an Auster for the Caribbean Station.

The Chief of Staff continued: 'And the Beechcraft crashed on landing and killed the two Audubon men. Well, that aroused these bird people to a fury. They got a corvette from the U.S. Training Squadron in the Caribbean to make a call on Doctor No. That's how powerful these people are. Seems they've got quite a lobby in Washington. The captain of the corvette reported that he was received very civilly by Doctor No but was kept well away from the guano workings. He was taken to the airstrip and examined the remains of the plane. Smashed to pieces, but nothing suspicious–came in to land too fast probably. The bodies of the two men and the pilot had been reverently embalmed and packed in handsome coffins which were handed over with quite a ceremony. The captain was very impressed by Doctor No's courtesy. He asked to see the wardens' camp and he was taken out there and shown the remains of it. Doctor No's theory was that the two men had gone mad because of the heat and the loneliness, or at any rate that one of them had gone mad and burned down the camp with the other inside it. This seemed possible to the captain when he'd seen what a godforsaken bit of marsh the men had been living in for ten years or more. There was nothing else to see and he was politely steered back to his ship and sailed away.' The Chief of Staff spread his hands. 'And that's the lot except that the captain reported that he saw only a handful of roseate spoonbills. When his report got back to the Audubon Society it was apparently the loss of their blasted birds that infuriated these people most of all, and ever since then they've been nagging at us to have an inquiry into the whole business. Of course nobody at the Colonial Office or in Jamaica's in the least interested. So in the end the whole fairy story was dumped in our lap.' The Chief of Staff shrugged his shoulders with finality. 'And that's how this pile of bumf,' he waved the file, 'or at any rate the guts of it, got landed on Strangways.'

M looked morosely at Bond. 'See what I mean, 007? Just the sort of mares' nest these old women's societies are always stirring up. People start preserving something–churches, old houses, decaying pictures, birds–and there's always a hullabaloo of some sort. The trouble is these sort of people get really worked up about their damned birds or whatever it is. They get the politicians involved. And somehow they all seem to have stacks of money. God knows where it comes from. Other old women, I suppose. And then there comes a point when someone has to do something to keep them quiet. Like this case. It gets shunted off on to me because the place is British territory. At the same time it's private land. Nobody wants to interfere officially. So I'm supposed to do what? Send a submarine to the island? For what? To find out what's happened to a covey of pink storks.' M snorted. 'Anyway, you asked about Strangways's last case and that's it.' M leant forward belligerently. 'Any questions? I've got a busy day ahead.'

Bond grinned. He couldn't help it. M's occasional outbursts of rage were so splendid. And nothing set him going so well as any attempt to waste the time and energies and slim funds of the Secret Service. Bond got to his feet. 'Perhaps if I could have the file, sir,' he said placatingly. 'It just strikes me that four people seem to have died more or less because of these birds. Perhaps two more did–Strangways and the Trueblood girl. I agree it sounds ridiculous, but we've got nothing else to go on.'

'Take it, take it,' said M impatiently. 'And hurry up and get your holiday over. You may not have noticed it, but the rest of the world happens to be in a bit of a mess.'

Bond reached across and picked up the file. He also made to pick up his Beretta and the holster. 'No,' said M sharply. 'Leave that. And mind you've got the hang of the other two guns by the time I see you again.'

Bond looked across into M's eyes. For the first time in his life he hated the man. He knew perfectly well why M was being tough and mean. It was deferred punishment for having nearly got killed on his last job. Plus getting away from this filthy weather into the sunshine. M couldn't bear his men to have an easy time. In a way Bond felt sure he was being sent on this cushy assignment to humiliate him. The old bastard.

With the anger balling up inside him like cat's fur, Bond said, 'I'll see to it, sir,' and turned and walked out of the room.

Chapter Four

Reception Committee

The sixty-eight tons deadweight of the Super Constellation hurtled high above the green and brown chequerboard of Cuba and, with only another hundred miles to go, started its slow declining flight towards Jamaica.

Bond watched the big green turtle-backed island grow on the horizon and the water below him turn from the dark blue of the Cuba Deep to the azure and milk of the inshore shoals. Then they were over the North Shore, over its rash of millionaire hotels, and crossing the high mountains of the interior. The scattered dice of smallholdings showed on the slopes and in clearings in the jungle, and the setting sun flashed gold on the bright worms of tumbling rivers and streams. 'Xaymaca' the Arawak Indians had called it–'The Land of Hills and Rivers'. Bond's heart lifted with the beauty of one of the most fertile islands in the world.

The other side of the mountains was in deep violet shadow. Lights were already twinkling in the foothills and spangling the streets of Kingston, but, beyond, the far arm of the harbour and the airport were still touched with the sun against which the Port Royal lighthouse blinked ineffectually. Now the Constellation was getting its nose down into a wide sweep beyond the harbour. There was a slight thump as the tricycle landing gear extended under the aircraft and locked into position, and a shrill hydraulic whine as the brake flaps slid out of the trailing edge of the wings. Slowly the great aircraft turned in again towards the land and for a moment the setting sun poured gold into the cabin. Then, the plane had dipped below the level of the Blue Mountains and was skimming down towards the single north–south runway. There was a glimpse of a road and telephone wires. Then the concrete, scarred with black skid-marks, was under the belly of the plane and there was the soft double thump of a perfect landing and the roar of reversing props as they taxied in towards the low white airport buildings.

The sticky fingers of the tropics brushed Bond's face as he left the aircraft and walked over to Health and Immigration. He knew that by the time he had got through Customs he would be sweating. He didn't mind. After the rasping cold of London, the stuffy, velvet heat was easily bearable.

Bond's passport described him as 'Import and Export Merchant'.

'What company, sir?'

'Universal Export.'

'Are you here on business or pleasure, sir?'

'Pleasure.'

'I hope you enjoy your stay, sir.' The negro immigration officer handed Bond his passport with indifference.

'Thank you.'

Bond walked out into the Customs hall. At once he saw the tall brown-skinned man against the barrier. He was wearing the same old faded blue shirt and probably the same khaki twill trousers he had been wearing when Bond first met him five years before.

'Quarrel!'

From behind the barrier the Cayman Islander gave a broad grin. He lifted his right forearm across his eyes in the old salute of the West Indians. 'How you, cap'n?' he called delightedly.

'I'm fine,' said Bond. 'Just wait till I get my bag through. Got the car?'

'Sure, cap'n.'

The Customs officer who, like most men from the waterfront, knew Quarrel, chalked Bond's bag without opening it and Bond picked it up and went out through the barrier. Quarrel took it from him and held out his right hand. Bond took the warm dry calloused paw and looked into the dark grey eyes that showed descent from a Cromwellian soldier or a pirate of Morgan's time. 'You haven't changed, Quarrel,' he said affectionately. 'How's the turtle fishing?'

'Not so bad, cap'n, an' not so good. Much de same as always.' He looked critically at Bond. 'Yo been sick, or somepun?'

Bond was surprised. 'As a matter of fact I have. But I've been fit for weeks. What made you say that?'

Quarrel was embarrassed. 'Sorry, cap'n,' he said, thinking he might have offended Bond. 'Dere some pain lines in yo face since de las' time.'

'Oh well,' said Bond. 'It was nothing much. But I could do with a spell of your training. I'm not as fit as I ought to be.'

'Sho ting, cap'n.'

They were moving towards the exit when there came the sharp crack and flash of a press camera. A pretty Chinese girl in Jamaican dress was lowering her Speed Graphic. She came up to them. She said with synthetic charm, 'Thank you, gentlemen. I am from the *Daily Gleaner*.' She glanced down at a list in her hand. 'Mister Bond, isn't it? And how long will you be with us, Mister Bond?'

Bond was offhand. This was a bad start. 'In transit,' he said shortly. 'I think you'll find there were more interesting people on the plane.'

'Oh no, I'm sure not, Mister Bond. You look very important. And what hotel will you be staying at?'

Damn, thought Bond. He said 'Myrtle Bank' and moved on.

'Thank you, Mister Bond,' said the tinkling voice. 'I hope you'll enjoy . . .'

They were outside. As they walked towards the parking place Bond said, 'Ever seen that girl at the airport before?'

Quarrel reflected. 'Reck'n not, cap'n. But de *Gleaner* have plenty camera gals.'

Bond was vaguely worried. There was no earthly reason why his picture should be wanted by the Press. It was five years since his last adventures on the island, and anyway his name had been kept out of the papers.

They got to the car. It was a black Sunbeam Alpine. Bond looked sharply at it and then at the number plate. Strangways's car. What the hell? 'Where did you get this, Quarrel?'

'A.D.C. tell me fe to take him, cap'n. Him say hit de only spare car dey have. Why, cap'n? Him no good?'

'Oh, it's all right, Quarrel,' said Bond resignedly. 'Come on, let's get going.'

Bond got into the passenger seat. It was entirely his fault. He might have guessed at the chance of getting this car. But it would certainly put the finger on him and on what he was doing in Jamaica if anyone happened to be interested.

They moved off down the long cactus-fringed road towards the distant lights of Kingston. Normally, Bond would have sat and enjoyed the beauty of it all–the steady zing of the crickets, the rush of warm, scented air, the ceiling of stars, the necklace of yellow lights shimmering across the harbour–but now he was cursing his carelessness and knowing what he shouldn't have done.

What he *had* done was to send one signal through the Colonial Office to the Governor. In it he had first asked that the A.D.C. should get Quarrel over from the Cayman Islands for an indefinite period on a salary of ten pounds a week. Quarrel had been with Bond on his last adventure in

Jamaica. He was an invaluable handyman with all the fine seaman's qualities of the Cayman Islander, and he was a passport into the lower strata of coloured life which would otherwise be closed to Bond. Everybody loved him and he was a splendid companion. Bond knew that Quarrel was vital if he was to get anywhere on the Strangways case–whether it was a case or just a scandal. Then Bond had asked for a single room and shower at the Blue Hills Hotel, for the loan of a car and for Quarrel to meet him with the car at the airport. Most of this had been wrong. In particular Bond should have taken a taxi to his hotel and made contact with Quarrel later. Then he would have seen the car and had a chance to change it.

As it was, reflected Bond, he might just as well have advertised his visit and its purpose in the *Gleaner*. He sighed. It was the mistakes one made at the beginning of a case that were the worst. They were the irretrievable ones, the ones that got you off on the wrong foot, that gave the enemy the first game. But was there an enemy? Wasn't he being over-cautious? On an impulse Bond turned in his seat. A hundred yards behind were two dim sidelights. Most Jamaicans drive with their headlights full on. Bond turned back. He said, 'Quarrel. At the end of the Palisadoes, where the left fork goes to Kingston and the right to Morant, I want you to turn quickly down the Morant road and stop at once and turn your lights off. Right? And now go like hell.'

'Okay, cap'n.' Quarrel's voice sounded pleased. He put his foot down to the floorboards. The little car gave a deep growl and tore off down the white road.

Now they were at the end of the straight. The car skidded round the curve where the corner of the harbour bit into the land. Another five hundred yards and they would be at the intersection. Bond looked back. There was no sign of the other car. Here was the signpost. Quarrel did a racing change and hurled the car round on a tight lock. He pulled in to the side and dowsed his lights. Bond turned and waited. At once he heard the roar of a big car at speed. Lights blazed on, looking for them. Then the car was past and tearing on towards Kingston. Bond had time to notice that it was a big American type taxicab and that there was no one in it but the driver. Then it was gone.

The dust settled slowly. They sat for ten minutes saying nothing. Then Bond told Quarrel to turn the car and take the Kingston road. He said, 'I think that car was interested in us, Quarrel. You don't drive an empty taxi back from the airport. It's an expensive run. Keep a watch out. He may find we've fooled him and be waiting for us.'

'Sho ting, cap'n,' said Quarrel happily. This was just the sort of life he had hoped for when he got Bond's message.

They came into the stream of Kingston traffic–buses, cars, horsedrawn carts, pannier-laden donkeys down from the hills, and the hand-drawn barrows selling violent coloured drinks. In the crush it was impossible to say if they were being followed. They turned off to the right and up towards the hills. There were many cars behind them. Any one of them could have been the American taxi. They drove for a quarter of an hour up to Halfway Tree and then on to the Junction Road, the main road across the island. Soon there was a neon sign of a green palm tree and underneath 'Blue Hills. THE hotel'. They drove in and up the drive lined with neatly rounded bushes of bougainvillaea.

A hundred yards higher up the road the black taxi waved the following drivers on and pulled in to the left. It made a U-turn in a break in the traffic and swept back down the hill towards Kingston.

The Blue Hills was a comfortable old-fashioned hotel with modern trimmings. Bond was welcomed with deference because his reservation had been made by King's House. He was shown to a fine corner room with a balcony looking out over the distant sweep of Kingston harbour. Thankfully he took off his London clothes, now moist with perspiration, and went into the glass-fronted shower and turned the cold water full on and stood under it for five minutes during which he washed his hair to remove the last dirt of big-city life. Then he pulled on a pair of Sea Island cotton shorts and, with sensual pleasure at the warm soft air on his nakedness, unpacked his things and rang for the waiter.

Bond ordered a double gin and tonic and one whole green lime. When the drink came he cut the lime in half, dropped the two squeezed halves into the long glass, almost filled the glass with ice cubes and then poured in the tonic. He took the drink out on to the balcony, and sat and looked out across the spectacular view. He thought how wonderful it was to be away from headquarters, and from London, and from hospitals, and to be here, at this moment, doing what he was doing and knowing, as all his senses told him, that he was on a good tough case again.

He sat for a while, luxuriously, letting the gin relax him. He ordered another and drank it down. It was seven-fifteen. He had arranged for Quarrel to pick him up at seven-thirty. They were going to have dinner together. Bond had asked Quarrel to suggest a place. After a moment of embarrassment, Quarrel had said that whenever he wanted to enjoy himself in Kingston he went to a waterfront nightspot called The Joy Boat. 'Hit no great shakes, cap'n,' he had said apologetically, 'but da food an' drinks an' music is good and I got a good fren' dere. Him owns de joint. Dey calls him "Pus-Feller" seein' how him once fought wit' a big hoctopus.'

Bond smiled to himself at the way Quarrel, like most West Indians, added an 'h' when it wasn't needed and took it off when it was. He went into his room and dressed in his old dark blue tropical worsted suit, a sleeveless white cotton shirt and a black knitted tie, looked in the glass to see that the Walther didn't show under his armpit and went down and out to where the car was waiting.

They swooped quietly down through the soft singing dusk into Kingston and turned to the left along the harbour side. They passed one or two smart restaurants and night clubs from which came the throb and twang of calypso music. There was a stretch of private houses that dwindled into a poor-class shopping centre and then into shacks. Then, where the road curved away from the sea, there was a blaze of golden neon in the shape of a Spanish galleon above green lettering that said 'The Joy Boat'. They pulled into a parking place and Bond followed Quarrel through the gate into a small garden of palm trees growing out of lawn. At the end was the beach and the sea. Tables were dotted about under the palms, and in the centre was a small deserted cement dance floor to one side of which a calypso trio in sequined scarlet shirts was softly improvising on 'Take her to Jamaica where the rum comes from'.

Only half the tables were filled, mostly by coloured people. There was a sprinkling of British and American sailors with their girls. An immensely fat negro in a smart white dinner jacket left one of the tables and came to meet them.

'Hi, Mister Q. Long time no see. Nice table for two?'

'That's right, Pus-Feller. Closer to da kitchen dan da music.'

The big man chuckled. He led them down towards the sea and placed them at a quiet table under a palm tree that grew out of the base of the restaurant building. 'Drinks gemmun?'

Bond ordered his gin and tonic with a lime, and Quarrel a Red Stripe beer. They scanned the menu and both decided on broiled lobster followed by a rare steak with native vegetables.

The drinks came. The glasses were dripping with condensation. The small fact reminded Bond of other times in hot climates. A few yards away the sea lisped on the flat sand. The three-piece began playing 'Kitch'. Above them the palm fronds clashed softly in the night breeze. A gecko chuckled somewhere in the garden. Bond thought of the London he had left the day before. He said, 'I like this place, Quarrel.'

Quarrel was pleased. 'Him a good fren of mine, da Pus-Feller. Him knows mostly what goes hon hin Kingston case you got hany questions, cap'n. Him come from da Caymans. Him an' me once share a boat. Then him go hoff one day catching boobies' heggs hat Crab Key. Went swimmin' to a rock for more heggs an' dis big hoctopus get him. Dey mosly small fellers roun' here but dey come bigger at da Crab seein' how its alongside de Cuba Deep, da deepest waters roun' dese parts. Pus-Feller have hisself a bad time wit dis hanimal. Bust one lung cuttin' hisself free. Dat scare him an him sell me his half of da boat an' come to Kingston. Dat were 'fore da war. Now him rich man whiles I go hon fishin'.' Quarrel chuckled at the quirk of fate.

'Crab Key,' said Bond. 'What sort of a place is that?'

Quarrel looked at him sharply. 'Dat a bad luck place now, cap'n,' he said shortly. 'Chinee gemmun buy him durin' da war and bring in men and dig bird-dirt. Don' let nobody land dere and don' let no one get hoff. We gives it a wide bert'.'

'Why's that?'

'Him have plenty watchmen. An' guns–machine guns. An' a radar. An' a spottin' plane. Frens o' mine have landed dere and him never been seen again. Dat Chinee keep him island plenty private. Tell da trut', cap'n,' Quarrel was apologetic, 'dat Crab Key scare me plenty.'

Bond said thoughtfully, 'Well, well.'

The food came. They ordered another round of drinks and ate. While they ate, Bond gave Quarrel an outline of the Strangways case. Quarrel listened carefully, occasionally asking questions. He was particularly interested in the birds on Crab Key, and what the watchman had said, and how the plane was supposed to have crashed. Finally he pushed his plate away. He wiped the back of his hand across his mouth. He took out a cigarette and lit it. He leant forward. 'Cap'n,' he said softly, 'I no mind if hit was birds or butterflies or bees. If dey was on Crab Key and da Commander was stickin' his nose into da business, yo kin bet yo bottom dollar him been mashed. Him and him girl. Da Chinee mash dem for sho.'

Bond looked carefully into the urgent grey eyes. 'What makes you so certain?'

Quarrel spread his hands. To him the answer was simple. 'Dat Chinee love him privacy. Him want be left alone. I know him kill ma frens order keep folk away from da Crab. Him a mos' powerful man. Him kill hanyone what hinterfere with him.'

'Why?'

'Don' rightly know, cap'n', said Quarrel indifferently. 'People dem want different tings in dis world. An what dem want sufficient dem gits.'

A glint of light caught in the corner of Bond's eye. He turned quickly. The Chinese girl from the airport was standing in the near-by shadows. Now she was dressed in a tight-fitting sheath of black satin slashed up one side almost to her hip. She had a Leica with a flash attachment in one hand. The other hand was in a leather case at her side. The hand came out holding a flashbulb. The girl slipped the base into her mouth to wet it and improve the contact and made to screw it into the reflector.

'Get that girl,' said Bond quickly.

In two strides Quarrel was up with her. He held out his hand. 'Evenin', missy,' he said softly.

The girl smiled. She let the Leica hang on the thin strap round her neck. She took Quarrel's hand. Quarrel swung her round like a ballet dancer. Now he had her hand behind her back and she was in the crook of his arm.

She looked up at him angrily. 'Don't. You're hurting.'

Quarrel smiled down into the flashing dark eyes in the pale, almond-shaped face. 'Cap'n like you take a drink wit' we,' he said soothingly. He came back to the table, moving the girl along with him. He hooked a chair out with his foot and sat her down beside him, keeping the grip on her wrist behind her back. They sat bolt upright, like quarrelling lovers.

Bond looked into the pretty, angry little face. 'Good evening. What are you doing here? Why do you want another picture of me?'

'I'm doing the nightspots,' the Cupid's bow of a mouth parted persuasively. 'The first picture of you didn't come out. Tell this man to leave me alone.'

'So you work for the *Gleaner*? What's your name?'

'I won't tell you.'

Bond cocked an eyebrow at Quarrel.

Quarrel's eyes narrowed. His hand behind the girl's back turned slowly. The girl struggled like an eel, her teeth clenched on her lower lip. Quarrel went on twisting. Suddenly she said 'Ow!' sharply and gasped, 'I'll tell!' Quarrel eased his grip. The girl looked furiously at Bond: 'Annabel Chung.'

Bond said to Quarrel, 'Call the Pus-Feller.'

Quarrel picked up a fork with his free hand and clanged it against a glass. The big negro hurried up.

Bond looked up at him. 'Ever seen this girl before?'

'Yes, boss. She come here sometimes. She bein' a nuisance? Want for me to send her away?'

'No. We like her,' said Bond amiably, 'but she wants to take a studio portrait of me and I don't know if she's worth the money. Would you call up the *Gleaner* and ask if they've got a photographer called Annabel Chung? If she really is one of their people she ought to be good enough.'

'Sure, boss.' The man hurried away.

Bond smiled at the girl. 'Why didn't you ask that man to rescue you?'

The girl glowered at him.

'I'm sorry to have to exert pressure,' said Bond, 'but my export manager in London said that Kingston was full of shady characters. I'm sure you're not one of them, but I really can't understand why you're so anxious to get my picture. Tell me why.'

'What I told you,' said the girl sulkily. 'It's my job.'

Bond tried other questions. She didn't answer them.

The Pus-Feller came up. 'That's right, boss. Annabel Chung. One of their freelance girls. They say she takes fine pictures. You'll be okay with her.' He looked bland. Studio portrait! Studio bed, more like.

'Thanks,' said Bond. The negro went away. Bond turned back to the girl. 'Freelance,' he said softly. 'That still doesn't explain who wanted my picture.' His face went cold. 'Now give!'

'No,' said the girl sullenly.

'All right, Quarrel. Go ahead.' Bond sat back. His instincts told him that this was the sixty-four thousand dollar question. If he could get the answer out of the girl he might be saved weeks of legwork.

Quarrel's right shoulder started to dip downwards. The girl squirmed towards him to ease the pressure, but he held her body away with his free hand. The girl's face strained towards Quarrel's. Suddenly she spat full in his eyes. Quarrel grinned and increased the twist. The girl's feet kicked wildly under the table. She hissed out words in Chinese. Sweat beaded on her forehead.

'Tell,' said Bond softly. 'Tell and it will stop and we'll be friends and have a drink.' He was getting worried. The girl's arm must be on the verge of breaking.

'——you.' Suddenly the girl's left hand flew up and into Quarrel's face. Bond was too slow to stop her. Something glinted and there was a sharp explosion. Bond snatched at her arm and dragged it back. Blood was streaming down Quarrel's cheek. Glass and metal tinkled on to the table. She had smashed the flashbulb on Quarrel's face. If she had been able to reach an eye it would have been blinded.

Quarrel's free hand went up and felt his cheek. He put it in front of his eyes and looked at the blood. 'Aha!' There was nothing but admiration and a feline pleasure in his voice. He said equably to Bond, 'We get nuthen out of dis gal, cap'n. She plenty tough. You want fe me to break she's arm?'

'Good God, no.' Bond let go the arm he was holding. 'Let her go.' He felt angry with himself for having hurt the girl and still failed. But he had learned something. Whoever was behind her held his people by a steel chain.

Quarrel brought the girl's right arm from be hind her back. He still held on to the wrist. Now he opened the girl's hand. He looked into her eyes. His own were cruel. 'You mark me, Missy. Now I mark you.' He brought up his other hand and took the Mount of Venus, the soft lozenge of flesh in the palm below her thumb, between his thumb and forefinger. He began to squeeze it. Bond could see his knuckles go white with the pressure. The girl gave a yelp. She hammered at Quarrel's hand and then at his face. Quarrel grinned and squeezed harder. Suddenly he let go. The girl shot to her feet and backed away from the table, her bruised hand at her mouth. She took her hand down and hissed furiously, 'He'll get you, you bastards!' Then, her Leica dangling, she ran off through the trees.

Quarrel laughed shortly. He took a napkin and wiped it down his cheek and threw it on the ground and took up another. He said to Bond, 'She's Love Moun' be sore long after ma face done get healed. Dat a fine piece of a woman, de Love Moun'. When him fat like wit' dat girl you kin tell her'll be good in bed. You know dat, cap'n?'

'No,' said Bond. 'That's new to me.'

'Sho ting. Dat piece of da han' most hindicative. Don' you worry 'bout she,' he added, noticing the dubious expression on Bond's face. 'Hers got nutting but a big bruise on she's Love Moun'. But boy, was dat a fat Love Moun'! I come back after dat gal sometime, see if ma teory is da troof.'

Appropriately the band started playing 'Don' touch me tomato'. Bond said, 'Quarrel, it's time you married and settled down. And you leave that girl alone or you'll get a knife between your ribs. Now come on. We'll get the check and go. It's three o'clock in the morning in London where I was yesterday. I need a night's sleep. You've got to start getting me into training. I think I'm going to need it. And it's about time you put some plaster on that cheek of yours. She's written her name and address on it.'

Quarrel grunted reminiscently. He said with quiet pleasure, 'Dat were some tough baby.' He picked up a fork and clanged it against his glass.

Chapter Five

Facts and Figures

'He'll get you. . . . He'll get you. . . . He'll get you, you bastards.'

The words were still ringing in Bond's brain the next day as he sat on his balcony and ate a delicious breakfast and gazed out across the riot of tropical gardens to Kingston, five miles below him.

Now he was sure that Strangways and the girl had been killed. Someone had needed to stop them looking any further into his business, so he had killed them and destroyed the records of what they were investigating. The same person knew or suspected that the Secret Service would follow up Strangways's disappearance. Somehow he had known that Bond had been given the job. He had wanted a picture of Bond and he had wanted to know where Bond was staying. He would be keeping an eye on Bond to see if Bond picked up any of the leads that had led to Strangways's death. If Bond did so, Bond also would have to be eliminated. There would be a car smash or a street fight or some other innocent death. And how, Bond wondered, would this person react to their treatment of the Chung girl? If he was as ruthless as Bond supposed, that would be enough. It showed that Bond was on to something. Perhaps Strangways had made a preliminary report to London before he was killed. Perhaps someone had leaked. The enemy would be foolish to take chances. If he had any sense, after the Chung incident, he would deal with Bond and perhaps also with Quarrel without delay.

Bond lit his first cigarette of the day–the first Royal Blend he had smoked for five years–and let the smoke come out between his teeth in a luxurious hiss. That was his 'Enemy Appreciation'. Now, who was this enemy?

Well, there was only one candidate, and a pretty insubstantial one at that, Doctor No, Doctor Julius No, the German Chinese who owned Crab Key and made his money out of guano. There had been nothing on this man in

Records and a signal to the F.B.I. had been negative. The affair of the roseate spoonbills and the trouble with the Audubon Society meant precisely nothing except, as M had said, that a lot of old women had got excited about some pink storks. All the same, four people had died because of these storks and, most significant of all to Bond, Quarrel was scared of Doctor No and his island. That was very odd indeed. Cayman Islanders, least of all Quarrel, did not scare easily. And why had Doctor No got this mania for privacy? Why did he go to such expense and trouble to keep people away from his guano island? Guano–bird dung. Who wanted the stuff? How valuable was it? Bond was due to call on the Governor at ten o'clock. After he had made his number he would get hold of the Colonial Secretary and try and find out all about the damned stuff and about Crab Key and, if possible, about Doctor No.

There was a double knock on the door. Bond got up and unlocked it. It was Quarrel, his left cheek decorated with a piratical cross of sticking-plaster. 'Mornin', cap'n. Yo said eight-tirty.'

'Yes, come on in, Quarrel. We've got a busy day. Had some breakfast?'

'Yes, tank you, cap'n. Salt fish an' ackee an' a tot of rum.'

'Good God,' said Bond. 'That's tough stuff to start the day on.'

'Mos' refreshin',' said Quarrel stolidly.

They sat down outside on the balcony. Bond offered Quarrel a cigarette and lit one himself. 'Now then,' he said. 'I'll be spending most of the day at King's House and perhaps at the Jamaica Institute. I shan't need you till tomorrow morning, but there are some things for you to do downtown. All right?'

'Okay, cap'n. Jes' yo say.'

'First of all, that car of ours is hot. We've got to get rid of if. Go down to Motta's or one of the other hire people and pick up the newest and best little self-drive car you can find, the one with the least mileage. Saloon. Take it for a month. Right? Then hunt around the waterfront and find two men who look as near as possible like us. One must be able to drive a car. Buy them both clothes, at least for their top halves, that look like ours. And the sort of hats we might wear. Say we want a car taken over to Montego tomorrow morning–by the Spanish Town, Ocho Rios road. To be left at Levy's garage there. Ring up Levy and tell him to expect it and to keep it for us. Right?'

Quarrel grinned. 'Yo want fox someone?'

'That's right. They'll get ten pounds each. Say I'm a rich American and I want my car to arrive in Montego Bay driven by a respectable couple of men. Make me out a bit mad. They must be here at six o'clock tomorrow morning. You'll be here with the other car. See they look the part and send them off in the Sunbeam with the roof down. Right?'

'Okay, cap'n.'

'What's happened to that house we had on the North Shore last time–Beau Desert at Morgan's Harbour? Do you know if it's let?'

'Couldn't say, cap'n. Hit's well away from de tourist places and dey askin' a big rent for it.'

'Well, go to Graham Associates and see if you can rent it for a month, or another bungalow near by. I don't mind what you pay. Say it's for a rich American, Mr James. Get the keys and pay the rent and say I'll write and confirm. I can telephone them if they want more details.' Bond reached into his hip pocket and brought out a thick wad of notes. He handed half of it to

Quarrel. 'Here's two hundred pounds. That should cover all this. Get in touch if you want some more. You know where I'll be.'

'Tanks, cap'n,' said Quarrel, awestruck by the big sum. He stowed it away inside his blue shirt and buttoned the shirt up to his neck. 'Anyting helse?'

'No, but take a lot of trouble about not being followed. Leave the car somewhere downtown and walk to these places. And watch out particularly for any Chinese near you.' Bond got up and they went to the door. 'See you tomorrow morning at six-fifteen and we'll get over to the North Coast. As far as I can see that's going to be our base for a while.'

Quarrel nodded. His face was enigmatic. He said 'Okay, cap'n' and went off down the corridor.

Half an hour later Bond went downstairs and took a taxi to King's House. He didn't sign the Governor's book in the cool hall. He was put in a waiting room for the quarter of an hour necessary to show him that he was unimportant. Then the A.D.C. came for him and took him up to the Governor's study on the first floor.

It was a large cool room smelling of cigar smoke. The Acting Governor, in a cream tussore suit and an inappropriate wing collar and spotted bow tie, was sitting at a broad mahogany desk on which there was nothing but the *Daily Gleaner*, the *Times Weekly* and a bowl of hibiscus blossoms. His hands lay flat on the desk in front of him. He was sixtyish with a red, rather petulant face and bright, bitter blue eyes. He didn't smile or get up. He said, 'Good morning, Mr–er–Bond. Please sit down.'

Bond took the chair across the desk from the Governor and sat down. He said, 'Good morning, sir,' and waited. A friend at the Colonial Office had told him his reception would be frigid. 'He's nearly at retiring age. Only an interim appointment. We had to find an Acting Governor to take over at short notice when Sir Hugh Foot was promoted. Foot was a great success. This man's not even trying to compete. He knows he's only got the job for a few months while we find someone to replace Foot. This man's been passed over for the Governor Generalship of Rhodesia. Now all he wants is to retire and get some directorships in the City. Last thing he wants is any trouble in Jamaica. He keeps on trying to close this Strangways case of yours. Won't like you ferreting about.'

The Governor cleared his throat. He recognized that Bond wasn't one of the servile ones. 'You wanted to see me?'

'Just to make my number, sir,' said Bond equably. 'I'm here on the Strangways case. I think you had a signal from the Secretary of State.' This was a reminder that the people behind Bond were powerful people. Bond didn't like attempts to squash him or his Service.

'I recall the signal. And what can I do for you? So far as we're concerned here the case is closed.'

'In what way "closed", sir?'

The Governor said roughly. 'Strangways obviously did a bunk with the girl. Unbalanced sort of fellow at the best of times. Some of your–er–colleagues, don't seem to be able to leave women alone.' The Governor clearly included Bond. 'Had to bail the chap out of various scandals before now. Doesn't do the Colony any good Mr–er–Bond. Hope your people will be sending us a rather better type of man to take his place. That is,' he added coldly, 'if a Regional Control man is really needed here. Personally I have every confidence in our police.'

Bond smiled sympathetically. 'I'll report your views, sir. I expect my Chief will like to discuss them with the Minister of Defence and the Secretary of State. Naturally, if you would like to take over these extra duties it will be a saving in manpower so far as my Service is concerned. I'm sure the Jamaican Constabulary is most efficient.'

The Governor looked at Bond suspiciously. Perhaps he had better handle this man a bit more carefully. 'This is an informal discussion, Mr Bond. When I have decided on my views I will communicate them myself to the Secretary of State. In the meantime, is there anyone you wish to see on my staff?'

'I'd like to have a word with the Colonial Secretary, sir.'

'Really? And why, pray?'

'There's been some trouble on Crab Key. Something about a bird sanctuary. The case was passed to us by the Colonial Office. My Chief asked me to look into it while I'm here.'

The Governor looked relieved. 'Certainly, certainly. I'll see that Mr Pleydell-Smith receives you straight away. So you feel we can leave the Strangways case to sort itself out? They'll turn up before long, never fear.' He reached over and rang a bell. The A.D.C. came in. 'This gentleman would like to see the Colonial Secretary, A.D.C. Take him along, would you? I'll call Mr Pleydell-Smith myself and ask him to make himself available.' He got up and came round the desk. He held out his hand. 'Goodbye then, Mr Bond. And I'm so glad we see eye to eye. Crab Key, eh? Never been there myself, but I'm sure it would repay a visit.'

Bond shook hands. 'That was what I was thinking. Goodbye, sir.'

'Goodbye, goodbye.' The Governor watched Bond's back retreating out of the door and himself returned well satisfied to his desk. 'Young whippersnapper,' he said to the empty room. He sat down and said a few peremptory words down the telephone to the Colonial Secretary. Then he picked up the *Times Weekly* and turned to the Stock Exchange prices.

The Colonial Secretary was a youngish shaggy-haired man with bright, boyish eyes. He was one of those nervous pipe smokers who are constantly patting their pockets for matches, shaking the box to see how many are left in it, or knocking the dottle out of their pipes. After he had gone through this routine two or three times in his first ten minutes with Bond, Bond wondered if he ever got any smoke into his lungs at all.

After pumping energetically at Bond's hand and waving vaguely at a chair, Pleydell-Smith walked up and down the room scratching his temple with the stem of his pipe. 'Bond. Bond. Bond! Rings a bell. Now let me see. Yes, by jove! You were the chap who was mixed up in that treasure business here. By jove, yes! Four, five years ago. Found the file lying around only the other day. Splendid show. What a lark! I say, wish you'd start another bonfire like that here. Stir the place up a bit. All they think of nowadays is Federation and their bloody self-importance. Self-determination indeed! They can't even run a bus service. And the colour problem! My dear chap, there's far more colour problem between the straight-haired and the crinkly-haired Jamaicans than there is between me and my black cook. However,' Pleydell-Smith came to rest beside his desk. He sat down opposite Bond and draped one leg over the arm of his chair. Reaching for a tobacco jar with the arms of King's College, Cambridge, on it, he dug into it and started filling his pipe. 'I mean to say I don't want to bore you with all that. You go ahead and bore me. What's your problem? Glad to help. I bet it's more interesting than this muck,' he waved at the pile of papers in his *In* tray.

Bond grinned at him. This was more like it. He had found an ally, and an intelligent one at that. 'Well,' he said seriously. 'I'm here on the Strangways case. But first of all I want to ask you a question that may sound odd. Exactly how did you come to be looking at that other case of mine? You say you found the file lying about. How was that? Had someone asked for it? I don't want to be indiscreet, so don't answer if you don't want to. I'm just inquisitive.'

Pleydell-Smith cocked an eye at him. 'I suppose that's your job.' He reflected, gazing at the ceiling. 'Well, now I come to think of it I saw it on my secretary's desk. She's a new girl. Said she was trying to get up to date with the files. Mark you,' the Colonial Secretary hastened to exonerate his girl, 'there were plenty of other files on her desk. It was just this one that caught my eye.'

'Oh, I see,' said Bond. 'It was like that.' He smiled apologetically. 'Sorry, but various people seem to be rather interested in me being here. What I really wanted to talk to you about was Crab Key. Anything you know about the place. And about this Chinaman, Doctor No, who bought it. And anything you can tell me about his guano business. Rather a tall order, I'm afraid, but any scraps will help.'

Pleydell-Smith laughed shortly through the stem of his pipe. He jerked the pipe out of his mouth and talked while he tamped down the burning tobacco with his matchbox. 'Bitten off a bit more than you can chew on guano. Talk to you for hours about it. Started in the Consular before I transferred to the Colonial Office. First job was in Peru. Had a lot to do with their people who administer the whole trade–*Compania Administradora del Guano*. Nice people.' The pipe was going now and Pleydell-Smith threw his matchbox down on the table. 'As for the rest, it's just a question of getting the file.' He rang a bell. In a minute the door opened behind Bond. 'Miss Taro, the file on Crab Key, please. The one on the sale of the place and the other one on that warden fellow who turned up before Christmas. Miss Longfellow will know where to find them.'

A soft voice said, 'Yes, sir.' Bond heard the door close.

'Now then, guano.' Pleydell-Smith tilted his chair back. Bond prepared to be bored. 'As you know, it's bird dung. Comes from the rear end of two birds, the masked booby and the guanay. So far as Crab Key is concerned, it's only the guanay, otherwise known as the green cormorant, same bird as you find in England. The guanay is a machine for converting fish into guano. They mostly eat anchovies. Just to show you how much fish they eat, they've found up to seventy anchovies inside one bird!' Pleydell-Smith took out his pipe and pointed it impressively at Bond. 'The whole population of Peru eats four thousand tons of fish a year. The sea birds of the country eat five hundred thousand tons!'

Bond pursed his lips to show he was impressed. 'Really.'

'Well, now,' continued the Colonial Secretary, 'every day each one of these hundreds of thousands of guanays eat a pound or so of fish and deposit an ounce of guano on the guanera–that's the guano island.'

Bond interrupted, 'Why don't they do it in the sea?'

'Don't know.' Pleydell-Smith took the question and turned it over in his mind. 'Never occurred to me. Anyway they don't. They do it on the land and they've been doing it since before Genesis. That makes the hell of a lot of bird dung–millions of tons of it on the Pescadores and the other guanera. Then, around 1850 someone discovered it was the greatest natural fertilizer in the world–stuffed with nitrates and phosphates and what have you. And the ships and the men came to the guaneras and simply ravaged them for twenty years or more. It's a time known as the "Saturnalia" in Peru. It was like the Klondyke. People fought over the muck, hi-jacked each other's ships, shot the workers, sold phoney maps of secret guano islands–anything you like. And people made fortunes out of the stuff.'

'Where does Crab Key come in?' Bond wanted to get down to cases.

'That was the only worthwhile guanera so far north. It was worked too, God knows who by. But the stuff had a low nitrate content. Water's not as rich round here as it is down along the Humboldt Current. So the fish aren't so rich in chemicals. So the guano isn't so rich either. Crab Key got worked on and off when the price was high enough, but the whole industry went bust, with Crab Key and the other poor-quality deposits in the van, when the Germans invented artificial chemical manure. By this time Peru had realized that she had squandered a fantastic capital asset and she set about organizing the remains of the industry and protecting the guanera. She nationalized the industry and protected the birds, and slowly, very slowly, the supplies built up again. Then people found that there were snags about the German stuff, it impoverishes the soil, which guano doesn't do, and gradually the price of guano improved and the industry staggered back to its feet. Now it's going fine, except that Peru keeps most of the guano to herself, for her own agriculture. And that was where Crab Key came in again.'

'Ah.'

'Yes,' said Pleydell-Smith, patting his pockets for the matches, finding them on the desk, shaking them against his ear, and starting his pipe-filling routine, 'at the beginning of the war, this Chinaman, who must be a wily devil, by the way, got the idea that he could make a good thing out of the old guanera on Crab Key. The price was about fifty dollars a ton on this side of the Atlantic and he bought the island from us, for about ten thousand pounds as I recall it, brought in labour and got to work. Been working it ever since. Must have made a fortune. He ships direct to Europe, to Antwerp. They send him a ship once a month. He's installed the latest crushers and separators. Sweats his labour, I daresay. To make a decent profit, he'd have to. Particularly now. Last year I heard he was only getting about thirty-eight to forty dollars a ton c.i.f. Antwerp. God knows what he must pay his labour to make a profit at that price. I've never been able to find out. He runs that place like a fortress–sort of forced labour camp. No one ever gets off it. I've heard some funny rumours, but no one's ever complained. It's his island, of course, and he can do what he likes on it.'

Bond hunted for clues. 'Would it really be so valuable to him, this place? What do you suppose it's worth?'

Pleydell-Smith said, 'The guanay is the most valuable bird in the world. Each pair produces about two dollars' worth of guano in a year without any expense to the owner. Each female lays an average of three eggs and raises two young. Two broods a year. Say they're worth fifteen dollars a pair, and say there are one hundred thousand birds on Crab Key, which is a reasonable guess on the old figures we have. That makes his birds worth a million and a half dollars. Pretty valuable property. Add the value of the installations, say another million, and you've got a small fortune on that hideous little place. Which reminds me,' Pleydell-Smith pressed the bell, 'what the hell has happened to those files? You'll find all the dope you want in them.'

The door opened behind Bond.

Pleydell-Smith said irritably, 'Really, Miss Taro. What about those files?'

'Very sorry, sir,' said the soft voice. 'But we can't find them anywhere.'

'What do you mean "can't find them"? Who had them last?'

'Commander Strangways, sir.'

'Well, I remember distinctly him bringing them back to this room. What happened to them then?'

'Can't say, sir,' the voice was unemotional. 'The covers are there but there's nothing inside them.'

Bond turned in his chair. He glanced at the girl and turned back. He smiled grimly to himself. He knew where the files had gone. He also knew why the old file on himself had been out on the Secretary's desk. He also guessed how the particular significance of 'James Bond, Import and Export Merchant' seemed to have leaked out of King's House, the only place where the significance was known.

Like Doctor No, like Miss Annabel Chung, the demure, efficient-looking little secretary in the hornrimmed glasses was a Chinese.

Chapter Six

The Finger on the Trigger

The Colonial Secretary gave Bond lunch at Queen's Club. They sat in a corner of the elegant mahogany-panelled dining room with its four big ceiling fans and gossiped about Jamaica. By the time coffee came, Pleydell-Smith was delving well below the surface of the prosperous, peaceful island the world knows.

'It's like this.' He began his antics with the pipe. 'The Jamaican is a kindly lazy man with the virtues and vices of a child. He lives on a very rich island but he doesn't get rich from it. He doesn't know how to and he's too lazy. The British come and go and take the easy pickings, but for about two hundred years no Englishman has made a fortune out here. He doesn't stay long enough. He takes a fat cut and leaves. It's the Portuguese Jews who make the most. They came here with the British and they've stayed. But they're snobs and they spend too much of their fortunes on building fine houses and giving dances. They're the names that fill the social column in the *Gleaner* when the tourists have gone. They're in rum and tobacco and they represent the big British firms over here–motor cars, insurance and so forth. Then come the Syrians, very rich too, but not such good businessmen. They have most of the stores and some of the best hotels. They're not a very good risk. Get overstocked and have to have an occasional fire to get liquid again. Then there are the Indians with their usual flashy trade in soft goods and the like. They're not much of a lot. Finally there are the Chinese, solid, compact, discreet–the most powerful clique in Jamaica. They've got the bakeries and the laundries and the best food stores. They keep to themselves and keep their strain pure.' Pleydell-Smith laughed, 'Not that they don't take the black girls when they want them. You can see the result all over Kingston–Chigroes–Chinese negroes and negresses. The Chigroes are a tough, forgotten race. They look down on the negroes and the Chinese look down on them. One day they may become a nuisance. They've got some of the intelligence of the Chinese and most of the vices of the black man. The police have a lot of trouble with them.'

Bond said, 'That secretary of yours. Would she be one of them?'

'That's right. Bright girl and very efficient. Had her for about six months. She was far the best of the ones that answered our advertisement.'

'She looks bright,' said Bond non-committally. 'Are they organized, these people? Is there some head of the Chinese negro community?'

'Not yet. But someone'll get hold of them one of these days. They'd be a useful little pressure group.' Pleydell-Smith glanced at his watch. 'That reminds me. Must be getting along. Got to go and read the riot act about those files. Can't think what happened to them. I distinctly remember . . .' He broke off. 'However, main point is that I haven't been able to give you much dope about Crab Key and this doctor fellow. But I can tell you there wasn't much you'd have found out from the files. He seems to have been a pleasant spoken chap. Very businesslike. Then there was that argument with the Audubon Society. I gather you know all about that. As for the place itself, there was nothing on the files but one or two pre-war reports and a copy of the last ordnance survey. Godforsaken bloody place it sounds. Nothing but miles of mangrove swamps and a huge mountain of bird dung at one end. But you said you were going down to the Institute. Why don't I take you there and introduce you to the fellow who runs the map section?'

An hour later Bond was ensconced in a corner of a sombre room with the ordnance survey map of Crab Key, dated 1910, spread out on a table in front of him. He had a sheet of the Institute's writing-paper and had made a rough sketch-map and was jotting down the salient points.

The overall area of the island was about fifty square miles. Three-quarters of this, to the east, was swamp and shallow lake. From the lake a flat river meandered down to the sea and came out halfway along the south coast into a small sandy bay. Bond guessed that somewhere at the headwaters of the river would be a likely spot for the Audubon wardens to have chosen for their camp. To the west, the island rose steeply to a hill stated to be five hundred feet high and ended abruptly with what appeared to be a sheer drop to the sea. A dotted line led from this hill to a box in the corner of the map which contained the words 'Guano deposits. Last workings 1880'.

There was no sign of a road, or even of a track on the island, and no sign of a house. The relief map showed that the island looked rather like a swimming water rat–a flat spine rising sharply to the head–heading west. It appeared to be about thirty miles due north of Galina Point on the north shore of Jamaica and about sixty miles south of Cuba.

Little else could be gleaned from the map. Crab Key was surrounded by shoal water except below the western cliff where the nearest marking was five hundred fathoms. After that came the plunge into the Cuba Deep. Bond folded the map and handed it in to the librarian.

Suddenly he felt exhausted. It was only four o'clock, but it was roasting in Kingston and his shirt was sticking to him. Bond walked out of the Institute and found a taxi and went back up into the cool hills to his hotel. He was well satisfied with his day, but nothing else could be done on this side of the island. He would spend a quiet evening at his hotel and be ready to get up early next morning and be away.

Bond went to the reception desk to see if there was a message from Quarrel. 'No messages, sir,' said the girl. 'But a basket of fruit came from King's House. Just after lunch. The messenger took it up to your room.'

'What sort of a messenger?'

'Coloured man, sir. Said he was from the A.D.C.'s office.'

'Thank you.' Bond took his key and went up the stairs to the first floor. It was ridiculously improbable. His hand on the gun under his coat, Bond softly approached his door. He turned the key and kicked the door open. The empty room yawned at him. Bond shut and locked the door. On his dressing table was a large, ornate basket of fruit–tangerines, grapefruit, pink bananas, soursop, star-apples and even a couple of hot-house nectarines. Attached to a broad ribbon on the handle was a white envelope. Bond removed it and held it up to the light. He opened it. On a plain sheet of expensive white writing paper was typed 'With the Compliments of His Excellency the Governor'.

Bond snorted. He stood looking at the fruit. He bent his ear to it and listened. He then took the basket by the handle and tipped its contents out on to the floor. The fruit bounced and rolled over the coconut matting. There was nothing but fruit in the basket. Bond grinned at his precautions. There was a last possibility. He picked up one of the nectarines, the most likely for a greedy man to choose first, and took it into the bathroom. He dropped it in the washbasin and went back to the bedroom and, after inspecting the lock, unlocked the wardrobe. Gingerly he lifted out his suitcase and stood it in the middle of the room. He knelt down and looked for the traces of talcum powder he had dusted round the two locks. They were smeared and there were minute scratches round the keyholes. Bond sourly examined the marks. These people were not as careful as some others he had had to deal with. He unlocked the case and stood it up on end. There were four innocent copper studs in the welting at the front right-hand corner of the lid. Bond prised at the top one of these studs with his nail and it eased out. He took hold of it and pulled out three feet of thick steel wire and put it on the floor beside him. This wire threaded through small wire loops inside the lid and sewed the case shut. Bond lifted the lid and verified that nothing had been disturbed. From his 'tool case' he took out a jeweller's glass and went back into the bathroom and switched on the light over the shaving mirror. He screwed the glass into his eye and gingerly picked the nectarine out of the washbasin and revolved it slowly between finger and thumb.

Bond stopped turning the nectarine. He had come to a minute pinhole, its edges faintly discoloured brown. It was in the crevice of the fruit, invisible except under a magnifying glass. Bond put the nectarine carefully down in the washbasin. He stood for a moment and looked thoughtfully into his eyes in the mirror.

So it *was* war! Well, well. How very interesting. Bond felt the slight tautening of the skin at the base of his stomach. He smiled thinly at his reflection in the mirror. So his instincts and his reasoning had been correct. Strangways and the girl had been murdered and their records destroyed because they had got too hot on the trail. Then Bond had come on the scene and, thanks to Miss Taro, they had been waiting for him. Miss Chung, and perhaps the taxi driver, had picked up the scent. He had been traced to the Blue Hills hotel. The first shot had been fired. There would be others. And whose finger was on the trigger? Who had got him so accurately in his sights? Bond's mind was made up. The evidence was nil. But he was certain of it. This was long range fire, from Crab Key. The man behind the gun was Doctor No.

Bond walked back into the bedroom. One by one he picked up the fruit and took each piece back to the bathroom and examined it through his glass. The pinprick was always there, concealed in the stalk-hole or a crevice. Bond rang down and asked for a cardboard box and paper and string. He packed the fruit carefully in the box and picked up the telephone and called King's House. He asked for the Colonial Secretary. 'That you, Pleydell-Smith? James Bond speaking. Sorry to bother you. Got a bit of a problem. Is there a public analyst in Kingston? I see. Well, I've got something I want analysed. If I sent the box down to you, would you be very kind and pass it on to this chap? I don't want my name to come into this. All right? I'll explain later. When you get his report would you send me a short telegram telling me the answer? I'll be at Beau Desert, over at Morgan's Harbour, for the next week or so. Be glad if you'd keep that to yourself too. Sorry to be so damned mysterious. I'll explain everything when I see you next. I expect you'll get a clue when you see what the analyst has to say. And by the way, tell him to handle the specimens carefully, would you. Warn him there's more in them than meets the eye. Very many thanks. Lucky I met you this morning. Goodbye.'

Bond addressed the parcel and went down and paid a taxi to deliver it at once to King's House. It was six o'clock. He went back to his room and had a shower and changed and ordered his first drink. He was about to take it out on the balcony when the telephone rang. It was Quarrel.

'Everyting fixed, cap'n.'

'Everything? That's wonderful. That house all right?'

'Everyting okay.' Quarrel repeated, his voice careful. 'See yo as yo done said, cap'n.'

'Fine,' said Bond. He was impressed with Quarrel's efficiency and a sense of security. He put down the telephone and went out on to the balcony.

The sun was just setting. The wave of violet shadow was creeping down towards the town and the harbour. When it hits the town, thought Bond, the lights will go on. It happened as he had expected. Above him there was the noise of a plane. It came into sight, a Super Constellation, the same flight that Bond had been on the night before. Bond watched it sweep out over the sea and then turn and come in to land at the Palisadoes airport. What a long way he had come since that moment, only twenty-four hours before, when the door of the plane had clanged open and the loudspeaker had said, 'This is Kingston, Jamaica. Will passengers please remain seated until the aircraft has been cleared by the Health Authorities.'

Should he tell M how the picture had changed? Should he make a report to the Governor? Bond thought of the Governor and dismissed that idea. But what about M? Bond had his own cipher. He could easily send M a signal through the Colonial Office. What would he say to M? That Doctor No had sent him some poisoned fruit? But he didn't even know that it was poisoned, or, for the matter of that, that it had come from Doctor No. Bond could see M's face as he read the signal. He saw him press down the lever on the intercom: 'Chief of Staff, 007's gone round the bend. Says someone's been trying to feed him a poisoned banana. Fellow's lost his nerve. Been in hospital too long. Better call him home.'

Bond smiled to himself. He got up and rang down for another drink. It wouldn't be quite like that, of course. But still . . . No, he'd wait until he had something more to show. Of course if something went badly wrong, and he hadn't sent a warning, he'd be in trouble. It was up to him to see that nothing did go wrong.

Bond drank his second drink and thought over the details of his plan. Then he went down and had dinner in the half-deserted dining-room and read the *Handbook of the West Indies*. By nine o'clock he was half asleep. He went back to his room and packed his bag ready for the morning. He telephoned down and arranged to be called at five-thirty. Then he bolted the door on the inside, and also shut and bolted the slatted jalousies across the windows. It would mean a hot, stuffy night. That couldn't be helped. Bond climbed naked under the single cotton sheet and turned over on his left side and slipped his right hand on to the butt of the Walther PPK under the pillow. In five minutes he was asleep.

The next thing Bond knew was that it was three o'clock in the morning. He knew it was three o'clock because the luminous dial of his watch was close to his face. He lay absolutely still. There was not a sound in the room. He strained his ears. Outside, too, it was deathly quiet. Far in the distance a dog started to bark. Other dogs joined in and there was a brief hysterical chorus which stopped as suddenly as it had begun. Then it was quite quiet again. The moon coming through the slats in the jalousies threw black and white bars across the corner of the room next to his bed. It was as if he was lying in a cage. What had woken him up? Bond moved softly, preparing to slip out of bed.

Bond stopped moving. He stopped as dead as a live man can.

Something had stirred on his right ankle. Now it was moving up the inside of his shin. Bond could feel the hairs on his leg being parted. It was an insect of some sort. A very big one. It was long, five or six inches–as long as his hand. He could feel dozens of tiny feet lightly touching his skin. What was it?

Then Bond heard something he had never heard before–the sound of the hair on his head rasping up on the pillow. Bond analysed the noise. It couldn't be! It simply couldn't! Yes, his hair was standing on end. Bond could even feel the cool air reaching his scalp between the hairs. How extraordinary! How very extraordinary! He had always thought it was a figure of speech. But why? Why was it happening to him?

The thing on his leg moved. Suddenly Bond realized that he was afraid, terrified. His instincts, even before they had communicated with his brain, had told his body that he had a centipede on him.

Bond lay frozen. He had once seen a tropical centipede in a bottle of spirit on the shelf in a museum. It had been pale brown and very flat and five or six inches long–about the length of this one. On either side of the blunt head there had been curved poison claws. The label on the bottle had said that its poison was mortal if it hit an artery. Bond had looked curiously at the corkscrew of dead cuticle and had moved on.

The centipede had reached his knee. It was starting up his thigh. Whatever happened he mustn't move, mustn't even tremble. Bond's whole consciousness had drained down to the two rows of softly creeping feet. Now they had reached his flank. God, it was turning down towards his groin! Bond set his teeth. Supposing it liked the warmth there! Supposing it tried to crawl into the crevices! Could he stand it? Supposing it chose that place to bite? Bond could feel it questing amongst the first hairs. It tickled. The skin on Bond's belly fluttered. There was nothing he could do to control it. But now the thing was turning up and along his stomach. Its feet were gripping tighter to prevent it falling. Now it was at his heart. If it bit there, surely it would kill him. The centipede trampled steadily on through the thin hairs on Bond's right breast up to his collar bone. It stopped. What was it doing? Bond could feel the blunt head questing blindly to and fro. What was it looking for? Was there room between his skin and the sheet for it to get through? Dare he lift the sheet an inch to help it. No. Never! The animal was at the base of his jugular. Perhaps it was intrigued by the heavy pulse there. Christ, if only he could control the pumping of his blood. Damn you! Bond tried to communicate with the centipede. It's nothing. It's not dangerous, that pulse. It means you no harm. Get on out into the fresh air!

As if the beast had heard, it moved on up the column of the neck and into the stubble on Bond's chin. Now it was at the corner of his mouth, tickling madly. On it went, up along the nose. Now he could feel its whole weight and length. Softly Bond closed his eyes. Two by two the pairs of feet, moving alternately, trampled across his right eyelid. When it got off his eye, should he take a chance and shake it off–rely on its feet slipping in his sweat? No, for God's sake! The grip of the feet was endless. He might shake one lot off, but not the rest.

With incredible deliberation the huge insect ambled across Bond's forehead. It stopped below the hair. What the hell was it doing now? Bond could feel it nuzzling at his skin. It was drinking! Drinking the beads of salt sweat. Bond was sure of it. For minutes it hardly moved. Bond felt weak with the tension. He could feel the sweat pouring off the rest of his body on to the sheet. In a second his limbs would start to tremble. He could feel it coming on. He would start to shake with an ague of fear. Could he control it, could he? Bond lay and waited, the breath coming softly through his open, snarling mouth.

The centipede started to move again. It walked into the forest of hair. Bond could feel the roots being pushed aside as it forced its way along. Would it like it there? Would it settle down? How did centipedes sleep? Curled up or at full length? The tiny millipedes he had known as a child, the ones that always seemed to find their way up the plughole into the empty bath, curled up when you touched them. Now it had come to where his head lay against the sheet. Would it walk out on to the pillow or would it stay on in the warm forest? The centipede stopped. Out! OUT! Bond's nerves screamed at it.

The centipede stirred. Slowly it walked out of his hair on to the pillow.

Bond waited a second. Now he could hear the rows of feet picking softly at the cotton. It was a tiny scraping noise, like soft fingernails.

With a crash that shook the room Bond's body jack-knifed out of bed and on to the floor.

At once Bond was on his feet and at the door. He turned on the light. He found he was shaking uncontrollably. He staggered to the bed. There it was, crawling out of sight over the edge of the pillow. Bond's first instinct was to twitch the pillow on to the floor. He controlled himself, waiting for his nerves to quieten. Then softly, deliberately, he picked up the pillow by one corner and walked into the middle of the room and dropped it. The centipede came out from under the pillow. It started to snake swiftly away across the matting. Now Bond was uninterested. He looked round for something to kill it with. Slowly he went and picked up a shoe and came back. The danger was past. His mind was now wondering how the centipede had got into his bed. He lifted the shoe and slowly, almost carelessly, smashed it down. He heard the crack of the hard carapace.

Bond lifted the shoe.

The centipede was whipping from side to side in its agony–five inches of grey-brown, shiny death. Bond hit it again. It burst open, yellowly.

Bond dropped the shoe and ran for the bathroom and was violently sick.

Chapter Seven

Night Passage

'By the way, Quarrel—' Bond dared a bus with 'Brown Bomber' painted above its windshield. The bus pulled over and roared on down the hill towards Kingston sounding a furious chord on its triple windhorn to restore the driver's ego,–'what do you know about centipedes?'

'Centipedes, cap'n?' Quarrel squinted sideways for a clue to the question. Bond's expression was casual. 'Well, we got some bad ones here in Jamaica. Tree, fo, five inches long. Dey kills folks. Dey mos'ly lives in de old houses in Kingston. Dey loves de rotten wood an' de mouldy places. Dey hoperates mos'ly at night. Why, cap'n? Yo seen one?'

Bond dodged the question. He had also not told Quarrel about the fruit. Quarrel was a tough man, but there was no reason to sow the seeds of fear. 'Would you expect to find one in a modern house, for instance? In your shoe, or in a drawer, or in your bed?'

'Nossir.' Quarrel's voice was definite. 'Not hunless dem put dere a purpose. Dese hinsecks love de holes and de crannies. Dey not love de clean places. Dey dirty-livin' hinsecks. Mebbe yo find dem in de bush, under logs an' stones. But never in de bright places.'

'I see.' Bond changed the subject. 'By the way, did those two men get off all right in the Sunbeam?'

'Sho ting, cap'n. Dey plenty happy wid de job. An' dey look plenty like yo an' me, cap'n.' Quarrel chuckled. He glanced at Bond and said hesitantly, 'I fears dey weren't very good citizens, cap'n. Had to find de two men wheres I could. Me, I'm a beggarman, cap'n. An' fo you, cap'n, I get a misrable no-good whiteman from Betsy's.'

'Who's Betsy?'

'She done run de lousiest brothel in town, cap'n,' Quarrel spat emphatically out of the window. 'Dis whiteman, he does de book-keepin'.'

Bond laughed. 'So long as he can drive a car. I only hope they get to Montego all right.'

'Don' yo worry,' Quarrel misunderstood Bond's concern. 'I say I tell de police dey stole de car if dey don'.'

They were at the saddleback at Stony Hill where the Junction Road dives down through fifty S-bends towards the North Coast. Bond put the little Austin A.30 into second gear and let it coast. The sun was coming up over the Blue Mountain peak and dusty shafts of gold lanced into the plunging valley. There were few people on the road–an occasional man going off to his precipitous smallholding on the flank of a hill, his three-foot steel cutlass dangling from his right hand, chewing at his breakfast, a foot of raw sugar cane held in his left, or a woman sauntering up the road with a covered basket of fruit or vegetables for Stony Hill market, her shoes on her head, to be donned when she got near the village. It was a savage, peaceful scene that had hardly changed, except for the surface of the road, for two hundred years or more. Bond almost smelled the dung of the mule train in which he would have been riding over from Port Royal to visit the garrison at Morgan's Harbour in 1750.

Quarrel interrupted his thoughts. 'Cap'n,' he said apologetically, 'beggin' yo pardon, but kin yo tell me what you have in mind for we? I'se bin puzzlin' an' Ah caint seem to figger hout yo game.'

'I've hardly figured it out myself, Quarrel.' Bond changed up into top and dawdled through the cool, beautiful glades of Castleton Gardens. 'I told you I'm here because Commander Strangways and his secretary have disappeared. Most people think they've gone off together. I think they've been murdered.'

'Dat so?' said Quarrel unemotionally. 'Who yo tink done hit?'

'I've come to agree with you. I think Doctor No, that Chinaman on Crab Key, had it done. Strangways was poking his nose into this man's affairs–something to do with the bird sanctuary. Doctor No has this mania for privacy. You were telling me so yourself. Seems he'll do anything to stop people climbing over his wall. Mark you, it's not more than a guess about Doctor No. But some funny things happened in the last twenty-four hours. That's why I sent the Sunbeam over to Montego, to lay a false scent. And that's why we're going to hide out at Beau Desert for a few days.'

'Den what, cap'n?'

'First of all I want you to get me absolutely fit–the way you trained me the last time I was here. Remember?'

'Sho, cap'n. Ah kin do dat ting.'

'And then I was thinking you and me might go and take a look at Crab Key.'

Quarrel whistled. The whistle ended on a downward note.

'Just sniff around. We needn't get too close to Doctor No's end. I want to take a look at this bird sanctuary. See for myself what happened to the wardens' camp. If we find anything wrong, we'll get away again and come back by the front door–with some soldiers to help. Have a full-dress inquiry. Can't do that until we've got something to go on. What do you think?'

Quarrel dug into his hip pocket for a cigarette. He made a fuss about lighting it. He blew a cloud of smoke through his nostrils and watched it whip out of the window. He said, 'Cap'n, Ah tink yo'se plumb crazy to trespass hon dat island.' Quarrel had wound himself up. He paused. There was no comment. He looked sideways at the quiet profile. He said more quietly, in an embarrassed voice, 'Jess one ting, cap'n. Ah have some folks back in da Caymans. Would yo consider takin' hout a life hinsurance hon me afore we sail?'

Bond glanced affectionately at the strong brown face. It had a deep cleft of worry between the eyes. 'Of course, Quarrel. I'll fix it at Port Maria tomorrow. We'll make it big, say five thousand pounds. Now then, how shall we go? Canoe?'

'Dat's right, cap'n.' Quarrel's voice was reluctant. 'We need a calm sea an' a light wind. Come hin on de Nor-easterly Trades. Mus' be a dark night. Dey startin' right now. By end of da week we git da secon' moon quarter. Where yo reckon to land, cap'n?'

'South shore near the mouth of the river. Then we'll go up the river to the lake. I'm sure that's where the wardens' camp was. So as to have fresh water and be able to get down to the sea to fish.'

Quarrel grunted without enthusiasm. 'How long we stayin', cap'n? Caint take a whole lot of food wit us. Bread, cheese, salt pork. No tobacco–caint risk da smoke an' light. Dat's mighty rough country, cap'n. Marsh an' mangrove.'

Bond said: 'Better plan for three days. Weather may break and stop us getting off for a night or two. Couple of good hunting knives. I'll take a gun. You never can tell.'

'No, sir,' said Quarrel emphatically. He relapsed into a brooding silence which lasted until they got to Port Maria.

They went through the little town and on round the headland to Morgan's Harbour. It was just as Bond remembered–the sugar-loaf of the Isle of Surprise rising out of the calm bay, the canoes drawn up beside the mounds of empty conch shells, the distant boom of the surf on the reef which had so nearly been his grave. Bond, his mind full of memories, took the car down the little side road and through the cane fields in the middle of which the gaunt ruin of the old Great House of Beau Desert Plantation stood up like a stranded galleon.

They came to the gate leading to the bungalow. Quarrel got out and opened the gate, and Bond drove through and pulled up in the yard behind the white single-storeyed house. It was very quiet. Bond walked round the house and across the lawn to the edge of the sea. Yes, there it was, the stretch of deep, silent water–the submarine path he had taken to the Isle of Surprise. It sometimes came back to him in nightmares. Bond stood looking at it and thinking of Solitaire, the girl he had brought back, torn and bleeding, from the sea. He had carried her across the lawn to the house. What had happened to her? Where was she? Brusquely Bond turned and walked back into the house, driving the phantoms away from him.

It was eight-thirty. Bond unpacked his few things and changed into sandals and shorts. Soon there was the delicious smell of coffee and frying bacon. They ate their breakfast while Bond fixed his training routine–up at seven, swim a quarter of a mile, breakfast, an hour's sunbathing, run a mile, swim again, lunch, sleep, sunbathe, swim a mile, hot bath and massage, dinner and asleep by nine.

After breakfast the routine began.

Nothing interrupted the grinding week except a brief story in the *Daily Gleaner* and a telegram from Pleydell-Smith. The *Gleaner* said that a Sunbeam Talbot, H. 2473, had been involved in a fatal accident on the Devil's Racecourse, a stretch of winding road between Spanish Town and Ocho Rios–on the Kingston–Montego route. A runaway lorry, whose driver was being traced, had crashed into the Sunbeam as it came round a bend. Both vehicles had left the road and hurtled into the ravine below. The two occupants of the Sunbeam, Ben Gibbons of Harbour Street, and Josiah Smith, no address, had been killed. A Mr Bond, an English visitor, who had been lent the car, was asked to contact the nearest police station.

Bond burned that copy of the *Gleaner*. He didn't want to upset Quarrel.

With only one day to go, the telegram came from Pleydell-Smith. It said:

> EACH OBJECT CONTAINED ENOUGH CYANIDE TO KILL A HORSE STOP SUGGEST YOU CHANGE YOUR GROCER STOP GOOD LUCK SMITH.

Bond also burned the telegram.

Quarrel hired a canoe and they spent three days sailing it. It was a clumsy shell cut out of a single giant cotton tree. It had two thin thwarts, two heavy paddles and a small sail of dirty canvas. It was a blunt instrument. Quarrel was pleased with it.

'Seven, eight hours, cap'n,' he said. 'Den we bring down de sail an' use de paddles. Less target for de radar to see.'

The weather held. The forecast from Kingston radio was good. The nights were black as sin. The two men got in their stores. Bond fitted himself out with cheap black canvas jeans and a dark blue shirt and rope-soled shoes.

The last evening came. Bond was glad he was on his way. He had only once been out of the training camp–to get the stores and arrange Quarrel's insurance–and he was chafing to get out of the stable and on to the track. He admitted to himself that this adventure excited him. It had the right ingredients–physical exertion, mystery, and a ruthless enemy. He had a good companion. His cause was just. There might also be the satisfaction of throwing the 'holiday in the sun' back in M's teeth. That had rankled. Bond didn't like being coddled.

The sun blazed beautifully into its grave.

Bond went into his bedroom and took out his two guns and looked at them. Neither was a part of him as the Beretta had been–an extension of his right hand–but he already knew them as better weapons. Which should he take? Bond picked up each in turn, hefting them in his hand. It had to be the heavier Smith & Wesson. There would be no close shooting, if there was any shooting, on Crab Key. Heavy, long-range stuff–if anything. The brutal, stumpy revolver had an extra twenty-five yards over the Walther. Bond fitted the holster into the waistband of his jeans and clipped in the gun. He put twenty spare rounds in his pocket. Was it over-insurance to take all this metal on what might only be a tropical picnic?

Bond went to the icebox and took a pint of Canadian Club Blended Rye and some ice and soda-water and went and sat in the garden and watched the last light flame and die.

The shadows crept from behind the house and marched across the lawn and enveloped him. The Undertaker's Wind that blows at night from the centre of the island, clattered softly in the tops of the palm trees. The frogs began to tinkle among the shrubs. The fireflies, the 'blink-a-blinks', as Quarrel called them, came out and began flashing their sexual morse. For a moment the melancholy of the tropical dusk caught at Bond's heart. He picked up the bottle and looked at it. He had drunk a quarter of it. He poured another big slug into his glass and added some ice. What was he drinking for? Because of the thirty miles of black sea he had to cross tonight? Because he was going into the unknown? Because of Doctor No?

Quarrel came up from the beach. 'Time, cap'n.'

Bond swallowed his drink and followed the Cayman Islander down to the canoe. It was rocking quietly in the water, its bows on the sand. Quarrel went aft and Bond climbed into the space between the forrard thwart and the bows. The sail, wrapped round the short mast, was at his back. Bond took up his paddle and pushed off, and they turned slowly and headed out for the break in the softly creaming waves that was the passage through the reef. They paddled easily, in unison, the paddles turning in their hands so that they did not leave the water on the forward stroke. The small waves slapped softly against the bows. Otherwise they made no noise. It was dark. Nobody saw them go. They just left the land and went off across the sea.

Bond's only duty was to keep paddling. Quarrel did the steering. At the opening through the reef there was a swirl and suck of conflicting currents and they were in amongst the jagged niggerheads and coral trees, bared like fangs by the swell. Bond could feel the strength of Quarrel's great sweeps with the paddle as the heavy craft wallowed and plunged. Again and again Bond's own paddle thudded against rock, and once he had to hold on as the canoe hit a buried mass of brain coral and slid off again. Then they were through, and far below thc boat there were indigo patches of sand and around them the solid oily feel of deep water.

'Okay, cap'n,' said Quarrel softly. Bond shipped his paddle and got down off one knee and sat with his back to the thwart. He heard the scratching of Quarrel's nails against canvas as he unwrapped the sail and then the sharp flap as it caught the breeze. The canoe straightened and began to move. It tilted slowly. There was a soft hiss under the bows. A handful of spray tossed up into Bond's face. The wind of their movement was cool and would soon get cold. Bond hunched up his knees and put his arms round them. The wood was already beginning to bite into his buttocks and his back. It crossed his mind that it was going to be the hell of a long and uncomfortable night.

In the darkness ahead Bond could just make out the rim of the world. Then came a layer of black haze above which the stars began, first sparsely and then merging into a dense bright carpet. The Milky Way soared overhead. How many stars? Bond tried counting a finger's length and was soon past the hundred. The stars lit the sea into a faint grey road and then arched away over the tip of the mast towards the black silhouette of Jamaica. Bond looked back. Behind the hunched figure of Quarrel there was a faraway cluster of lights which would be Port Maria. Already they were a couple of miles out. Soon they would be a tenth of the way, then a quarter, then half. That would be around midnight when Bond would take over. Bond sighed and put his head down to his knees and closed his eyes.

He must have slept because he was awakened by the clonk of a paddle against the boat. He lifted his arm to show that he had heard and glanced at the luminous blaze of his watch. Twelve-fifteen. Stiffly he unbent his legs and turned and scrambled over the thwart.

'Sorry, Quarrel,' he said, and it was odd to hear his voice. 'You ought to have shaken me up before.'

'Hit don signify, cap'n,' said Quarrel with a grey glint of teeth. 'Do yo good to sleep.'

Gingerly they slipped past each other and Bond settled in the stern and picked up the paddle. The sail was secured to a bent nail beside him. It was flapping. Bond brought the bows into the wind and edged them round so that the North Star was directly over Quarrel's bent head in the bows. For a time this would be fun. There was something to do.

There was no change in the night except that it seemed darker and emptier. The pulse of the sleeping sea seemed slower. The heavy swell was longer and the troughs deeper. They were running through a patch of phosphorus that winked at the bows and dripped jewels when Bond lifted the paddle out of the water. How safe it was, slipping through the night in this ridiculously vulnerable little boat. How kind and soft the sea could be. A covey of flying fish broke the surface in front of the bows and scattered like shrapnel. Some kept going for a time beside the canoe, flying as much as twenty yards before they dived into the wall of the swell. Was some bigger fish after them or did they think the canoe was a fish, or were they just playing? Bond thought of what was going on in the hundreds of fathoms below the boat, the big fish, the shark and barracuda and tarpon and sailfish quietly cruising, the shoals of kingfish and mackerel and bonito and, far below in the grey twilight of the great depths, the phosphorous jellied boneless things that were never seen, the fifty-foot squids, with eyes a foot wide, that streamed along like zeppelins, the last real monsters of the sea, whose size was only known from the fragments found inside whales. What would happen if a wave caught the canoe broadside and capsized them? How long would they last? Bond took an ounce more pains with his steering and put the thought aside.

One o'clock, two o'clock, three, four. Quarrel awoke and stretched. He called softly to Bond, 'Ah smells land, cap'n.' Soon there was a thickening of the darkness ahead. The low shadow slowly took on the shape of a huge swimming rat. A pale moon rose slowly behind them. Now the island showed distinctly, a couple of miles away, and there was the distant grumble of surf.

They changed places. Quarrel brought down the sail and they took up the paddles. For at least another mile, thought Bond, they would be invisible in the troughs of the waves. Not even radar would distinguish them from the crests. It was the last mile they would have to hurry over with the dawn not far off.

Now he too could smell the land. It had no particular scent. It was just something new in the nose after hours of clean sea. He could make out the white fringe of surf. The swell subsided and the waves became choppier. 'Now, cap'n,' called Quarrel, and Bond, the sweat already dropping off his chin, dug deeper and more often. God, it was hard work! The hulking log of wood which had sped along so well under the sail now seemed hardly to move. The wave at the bows was only a ripple. Bond's shoulders were aching like fire. The one knee he was resting on was beginning to bruise. His hands were cramped on the clumsy shaft of a paddle made of lead.

It was incredible, but they were coming up with the reef. Patches of sand showed deep under the boat. Now the surf was a roar. They followed along the edge of the reef, looking for an opening. A hundred yards inside the reef, breaking the sandline, was the shimmer of water running inland. The river! So the landfall had been all right. The wall of surf broke up. There was a patch of black oily current swelling over hidden coral heads. The nose of the canoe turned towards it and into it. There was a turmoil of water and a series of grating thuds, and then a sudden rush forward into peace and the canoe was moving slowly across a smooth mirror towards the shore.

Quarrel steered the boat towards the lee of a rocky promontory where the beach ended. Bond wondered why the beach didn't shine white under the thin moon. When they grounded and Bond climbed stiffly out he understood why. The beach was black. The sand was soft and wonderful to the feet but it must have been formed out of volcanic rock, pounded over the centuries, and Bond's naked feet on it looked like white crabs.

They made haste. Quarrel took three short lengths of thick bamboo out of the boat and laid them up the flat beach. They heaved the nose of the canoe on to the first and pushed the boat up the rollers. After each yard of progress, Bond picked up the back roller and brought it to the front. Slowly the canoe moved up the sand until at last it was over the back tideline and among the rocks and turtle grass and low sea-grape bushes. They pushed it another twenty yards inland into the beginning of the mangrove. There they covered it with dried seaweed and bits of driftwood from the tideline. Then Quarrel cut lengths of screwpalm and went back over their tracks, sweeping and tidying.

It was still dark, but the breath of grey in the east would soon be turning to pearl. It was five o'clock. They were dead tired. They exchanged a few words and Quarrel went off among the rocks on the promontory. Bond scooped out a depression in the fine dry sand under a thick bush of sea-grape. There were a few hermit crabs beside his bed. He picked up as many as he could find and hurled them into the mangrove. Then, not caring what other animals or insects might come to his smell and his warmth, he lay down full length in the sand and rested his head on his arm.

He was at once asleep.

Chapter Eight

The Elegant Venus

Bond awoke lazily. The feel of the sand reminded him where he was. He glanced at his watch. Ten o'clock. The sun through the round thick leaves of the sea-grape was already hot. A larger shadow moved across the dappled sand in front of his face. Quarrel? Bond shifted his head and peered through the fringe of leaves and grass that concealed him from the beach. He stiffened. His heart missed a beat and then began pounding so that he had to breathe deeply to quieten it. His eyes, as he stared through the blades of grass, were fierce slits.

It was a naked girl, with her back to him. She was not quite naked. She wore a broad leather belt round her waist with a hunting knife in a leather sheath at her right hip. The belt made her nakedness extraordinarily erotic. She stood not more than five yards away on the tideline looking down at something in her hand. She stood in the classical relaxed pose of the nude, all the weight on the right leg and the left knee bent and turning slightly inwards, the head to one side as she examined the things in her hand.

It was a beautiful back. The skin was a very light uniform *café au lait* with the sheen of dull satin. The gentle curve of the backbone was deeply indented, suggesting more powerful muscles than is usual in a woman, and the behind was almost as firm and rounded as a boy's. The legs were straight and beautiful and no pinkness showed under the slightly lifted left heel. She was not a coloured girl.

Her hair was ash blonde. It was cut to the shoulders and hung there and along the side of her bent cheek in thick wet strands. A green diving mask was pushed back above her forehead, and the green rubber thong bound her hair at the back.

The whole scene, the empty beach, the green and blue sea, the naked girl with the strands of fair hair, reminded Bond of something. He searched his mind. Yes, she was Botticelli's Venus, seen from behind.

How had she got there? What was she doing? Bond looked up and down the beach. It was not black, he now saw, but a deep chocolate brown. To the right he could see as far as the river mouth, perhaps five hundred yards away. The beach was empty and featureless except for a scattering of small pinkish objects. There were a lot of them, shells of some sort Bond supposed, and they looked decorative against the dark brown background. He looked to the left, to where, twenty yards away, the rocks of the small headland began. Yes, there was a yard or two of groove in the sand where a canoe had been drawn up into the shelter of the rocks. It must have been a light one or she couldn't have drawn it up alone. Perhaps the girl wasn't alone. But there was only one set of footprints leading down from the rocks to the sea and another set coming out of the sea and up the beach to where she now stood on the tideline. Did she live here, or had she too sailed over from Jamaica that night? Hell of a thing for a girl to do. Anyway, what in God's name *was* she doing here?

As if to answer him, the girl made a throwaway gesture of the right hand and scattered a dozen shells on the sand beside her. They were violet-pink and seemed to Bond to be the same as he had noticed on the beach. The girl looked down into her left hand and began to whistle softly to herself. There was a happy note of triumph in the whistle. She was whistling 'Marion', a plaintive little calypso that has now been cleaned up and made famous outside Jamaica. It had always been one of Bond's favourites. It went:

All day, all night, Marion,
Sittin' by the seaside siftin' sand . . .

The girl broke off to stretch her arms out in a deep yawn. Bond smiled to himself. He wet his lips and took up the refrain:

'The water from her eyes could sail a boat,
The hair on her head could tie a goat . . .'

The hands flew down and across her chest. The muscles of her behind bunched with tension. She was listening, her head, still hidden by the curtain of hair, cocked to one side.

Hesitantly she began again. The whistle trembled and died. At the first note of Bond's echo, the girl whirled round. She didn't cover her body with the two classical gestures. One hand flew downwards, but the other instead of hiding her breasts, went up to her face, covering it below the eyes, now wide with fear. 'Who's that?' The words came out in a terrified whisper.

Bond got to his feet and stepped out through the sea-grape. He stopped on the edge of the grass. He held his hands open at his sides to show they were empty. He smiled cheerfully at her. 'It's only me. I'm another trespasser. Don't be frightened.'

The girl dropped her hand down from her face. It went to the knife at her belt. Bond watched the fingers curl round the hilt. He looked up at her face. Now he realized why her hand had instinctively gone to it. It was a beautiful face, with wide-apart deep blue eyes under lashes paled by the sun. The mouth was wide and when she stopped pursing the lips with tension they would be full. It was a serious face and the jawline was determined–the face of a girl who fends for herself. And once, reflected Bond, she had failed to fend. For the nose was badly broken, smashed crooked like a boxer's. Bond stiffened with revolt at what had happened to this supremely beautiful girl. No wonder this was her shame and not the beautiful firm breasts that now jutted towards him without concealment.

The eyes examined him fiercely. 'Who are you? What are you doing here?' There was the slight lilt of a Jamaican accent. The voice was sharp and accustomed to being obeyed.

'I'm an Englishman. I'm interested in birds.'

'Oh,' the voice was doubtful. The hand still rested on the knife. 'How long have you been watching me? How did you get here?'

'Ten minutes, but no more answers until you tell me who *you* are.'

'I'm no one in particular. I come from Jamaica. I collect shells.'

'I came in a canoe. Did you?'

'Yes. Where is your canoe?'

'I've got a friend with me. We've hidden it in the mangroves.'

'There are no marks of a canoe landing.'

'We're careful. We covered them up. Not like you.' Bond gestured towards the rocks. 'You ought to take more trouble. Did you use a sail? Right up to the reef?'

'Of course. Why not? I always do.'

'Then they'll know you're here. They've got radar.'

'They've never caught me yet.' The girl took her hand away from her knife. She reached up and stripped off the diving mask and stood swinging it. She seemed to think she had the measure of Bond. She said, with some of the sharpness gone from her voice, 'What's your name?'

'Bond. James Bond. What's yours?'

She reflected. 'Rider.'

'What Rider?'

'Honeychile.'

Bond smiled.

'What's so funny about it?'

'Nothing. Honeychile Rider. It's a pretty name.'

She unbent. 'People call me "Honey".'

'Well, I'm glad to meet you.'

The prosaic phrase seemed to remind her of her nakedness. She blushed. She said uncertainly, 'I must get dressed.' She looked down at the scattered shells around her feet. She obviously wanted to pick them up. Perhaps she realized that the movement might be still more revealing than her present pose. She said sharply, 'You're not to touch those while I'm gone.'

Bond smiled at the childish challenge. 'Don't worry, I'll look after them.'

The girl looked at him doubtfully and then turned and walked stiff-legged over to the rocks and disappeared behind them.

Bond walked the few steps down the beach and bent and picked up one of the shells. It was alive and the two halves were shut tight. It appeared to be some kind of a cockle, rather deeply ribbed and coloured a mauve-pink. Along both edges of the hinge, thin horns stood out, about half a dozen to each side. It didn't seem to Bond a very distinguished shell. He replaced it carefully with the others.

He stood looking down at the shells and wondering. Was she really collecting them? It certainly looked like it. But what a risk to take to get them–the voyage over alone in the canoe and then back again. And she seemed to realize that this was a dangerous place. 'They've never caught me yet.' What an extraordinary girl. Bond's heart warmed and his senses stirred as he thought of her. Already, as he had found so often when people had deformities, he had almost forgotten her broken nose. It had somehow slipped away behind his memory of her eyes and her mouth and her amazingly beautiful body. Her imperious attitude and her quality of attack were exciting. The way she had reached for her knife to defend herself! She was like an animal whose cubs are threatened. Where did she live? Who were her parents? There was something uncared for about her–a dog that nobody wants to pet. Who was she?

Bond heard her footsteps riffling the sand. He turned to look at her. She was dressed almost in rags–a faded brown shirt with torn sleeves and a knee-length patched brown cotton skirt held in place by the leather belt with the knife. She had a canvas knapsack slung over one shoulder. She looked like a principal girl dressed as Man Friday.

She came up with him and at once went down on one knee and began picking up the live shells and stowing them in the knapsack.

Bond said, 'Are those rare?'

She sat back on her haunches and looked up at him. She surveyed his face. Apparently she was satisfied. 'You promise you won't tell anybody? Swear?'

'I promise,' said Bond.

'Well then, yes, they are rare. Very. You can get five dollars for a perfect specimen. In Miami. That's where I deal with. They're called *Venus elegans*–The Elegant Venus.' Her eyes sparkled up at him with excitement. 'This morning I found what I wanted. The bed where they live,' she waved towards the sea. 'You wouldn't find it though,' she added with sudden carefulness. 'It's very deep and hidden away. I doubt if you could dive that deep. And anyway,' she looked happy, 'I'm going to clear the whole bed today. You'd only get the imperfect ones if you came back here.'

Bond laughed. 'I promise I won't steal any. I really don't know anything about shells. Cross my heart.'

She stood up, her work completed. 'What about these birds of yours?

What sort are they? Are they valuable too? I won't tell either if you tell me. I only collect shells.'

'They're called roseate spoonbills,' said Bond. 'Sort of pink stork with a flat beak. Ever seen any?'

'Oh, *those*,' she said scornfully. 'There used to be thousands of them here. But you won't find many now. They scared them all away.' She sat down on the sand and put her arms round her knees, proud of her superior knowledge and now certain that she had nothing to fear from this man.

Bond sat down a yard away. He stretched out and turned towards her, resting on his elbow. He wanted to preserve the picnic atmosphere and try to find out more about this queer, beautiful girl. He said, easily, 'Oh, really. What happened? Who did it?'

She shrugged impatiently. 'The people here did it. I don't know who they are. There's a Chinaman. He doesn't like birds or something. He's got a dragon. He sent the dragon after the birds and scared them away. The dragon burned up their nesting places. There used to be two men who lived with the birds and looked after them. They got scared away too, or killed or something.'

It all seemed quite natural to her. She gave the facts indifferently, staring out to sea.

Bond said, 'This dragon. What kind is he? Have you ever seen him?'

'Yes, I've seen him.' She screwed up her eyes and made a wry face as if she was swallowing bitter medicine. She looked earnestly at Bond to make him share her feelings. 'I've been coming here for about a year, looking for shells and exploring. I only found these,' she waved at the beach, 'about a month ago. On my last trip. But I've found plenty of other good ones. Just before Christmas I thought I'd explore the river. I went up it to the top, where the birdmen had their camp. It was all broken up. It was getting late and I decided to spend the night there. In the middle of the night I woke up. The dragon was coming by only a few chains away from me. It had two great glaring eyes and a long snout. It had sort of short wings and a pointed tail. It was all black and gold.' She frowned at the expression on Bond's face. 'There was a full moon. I could see it quite clearly. It went by me. It was making a sort of roaring noise. It went over the marsh and came to some thick mangrove and it simply climbed over the bushes and went on. A whole flock of birds got up in front of it and suddenly a lot of fire came out of its mouth and it burned a lot of them up and all the trees they'd been roosting in. It was horrible. The most horrible thing I've ever seen.'

The girl leant sideways and peered at Bond's face. She sat up straight again and stared obstinately out to sea. 'I can see you don't believe me,' she said in a furious, tense voice. 'You're one of these city people. You don't believe anything. Ugh,' she shuddered with dislike of him.

Bond said reasonably, 'Honey, there just aren't such things as dragons in the world. You saw something that looked very like a dragon. I'm just wondering what it was.'

'How do you know there aren't such things as dragons?' Now he had made her really angry. 'Nobody lives on this end of the island. One could easily have survived here. Anyway, what do you think you know about animals and things? I've lived with snakes and things since I was a child. Alone. Have you ever seen a praying mantis eat her husband after they've made love? Have you ever seen the mongoose dance? Or an octopus dance? How long is a humming bird's tongue? Have you ever had a pet snake that wore a bell round its neck and rang it to wake you? Have you seen a scorpion get sunstroke and kill itself with its own sting? Have you seen the carpet of flowers under the sea at night? Do you know that a John Crow can smell a dead lizard a mile away . . . ?' The girl had fired these questions like scornful jabs with a rapier. Now she stopped, out of breath. She said hopelessly, 'Oh, you're just city folk like all the rest.'

Bond said, 'Honey, now look here. You know these things. I can't help it that I live in towns. I'd like to know about your things too. I just haven't had that sort of life. I know other things instead. Like . . .' Bond searched his mind. He couldn't think of anything as interesting as hers. He finished lamely, 'Like for instance that this Chinaman is going to be more interested in your visit this time. This time he's going to try and stop you getting away.' He paused and added, 'And me for the matter of that.'

She turned and looked at him with interest. 'Oh. Why? But then it doesn't really matter. One just hides during the day and gets away at night. He's sent dogs after me and even a plane. He hasn't got me yet.' She examined Bond with a new interest. 'Is it you he's after?'

'Well, yes,' admitted Bond. 'I'm afraid it is. You see we dropped the sail about two miles out so that their radar wouldn't pick us up. I think the Chinaman may have been expecting a visit from me. Your sail will have been reported and I'd bet anything he'll think your canoe was mine. I'd better go and wake my friend up and we'll talk it over. You'll like him. He's a Cayman Islander, name of Quarrel.'

The girl said, 'Well, I'm sorry if . . .' the sentence trailed away. Apologies wouldn't come easy to someone so much on the defensive. 'But after all I couldn't know, could I?' She searched his face.

Bond smiled into the questing blue eyes. He said reassuringly, 'Of course you couldn't. It's just bad luck–bad luck for you too. I don't suppose he minds too much about a solitary girl who collects shells. You can be sure they've had a good look at your footprints and found clues like that'–he waved at the scattered shells on the beach. 'But I'm afraid he'd take a different view of me. Now he'll try and hunt me down with everything he's got. I'm only afraid he may get you into the net in the process. Anyway,' Bond grinned reassuringly, 'we'll see what Quarrel has to say. You stay here.'

Bond got to his feet. He walked along the promontory and cast about him. Quarrel had hidden himself well. It took Bond five minutes to find him. He was lying in a grassy depression between two big rocks, half covered by a board of grey driftwood. He was still fast asleep, the brown head, stern in sleep, cradled on his forearm. Bond whistled softly and smiled as the eyes sprang wide open like an animal's. Quarrel saw Bond and scrambled to his feet, almost guiltily. He rubbed his big hands over his face as if he was washing it.

'Mornin', cap'n,' he said. 'Guess Ah been down deep. Dat China girl come to me.'

Bond smiled. 'I got something different,' he said. They sat down and Bond told him about Honeychile Rider and her shells and the fix they were in. 'And now it's eleven o'clock,' Bond added. 'And we've got to make a new plan.'

Quarrel scratched his head. He looked sideways at Bond. 'Yo don' plan we jess ditch dis girl?' he asked hopefully. 'Ain't nuttin to do wit we . . .' Suddenly he stopped. His head swivelled round and pointed like a dog's. He held up a hand for silence, listening intently.

Bond held his breath. In the distance, to the eastwards, there was a faint droning.

Quarrel jumped to his feet. 'Quick, cap'n,' he said urgently. 'Dey's a comin'.'

Chapter Nine

Close Shaves

Ten minutes later the bay was empty and immaculate. Small waves curled lazily in across the mirrored water inside the reef and flopped exhausted on the dark sand where the mauve shells glittered like shed toenails. The heap of discarded shells had gone and there was no longer any trace of footprints. Quarrel had cut branches of mangrove and had walked backwards sweeping carefully as he went. Where he had swept, the sand was of a different texture from the rest of the beach, but not too different as to be noticed from outside the reef. The girl's canoe had been pulled deeper among the rocks and covered with seaweed and driftwood.

Quarrel had gone back to the headland. Bond and the girl lay a few feet apart under the bush of sea-grape where Bond had slept, and gazed silently out across the water to the corner of the headland round which the boat would come.

The boat was perhaps a quarter of a mile away. From the slow pulse of the twin diesels Bond guessed that every cranny of the coastline was being searched for signs of them. It sounded a powerful boat. A big cabin cruiser, perhaps. What crew would it have? Who would be in command of the search? Doctor No? Unlikely. He would not trouble himself with this kind of police work.

From the west a wedge of cormorants appeared, flying low over the sea beyond the reef. Bond watched them. They were the first evidence he had seen of the guanay colony at the other end of the island. These, according to Pleydell-Smith's description, would be scouts looking for the silver flash of the anchovy near the surface. Sure enough, as he watched, they began to back-pedal in the air and then go into shallow dives, hitting the water like shrapnel. Almost at once a fresh file appeared from the west, then another and another that merged into a long stream and then into a solid black river of birds. For minutes they darkened the skyline and then they were down on the water, covering several acres of it, screeching and fighting and plunging their heads below the surface, cropping at the solid field of anchovy like piranha fish feasting on a drowned horse.

Bond felt a gentle nudge from the girl. She gestured with her head. 'The Chinaman's hens getting their corn.'

Bond examined the happy, beautiful face. She had seemed quite unconcerned by the arrival of the search party. To her it was only the game of hide-and-seek she had played before. Bond hoped she wasn't going to get a shock.

The iron thud of the diesels was getting louder. The boat must be just behind the headland. Bond took a last look round the peaceful bay and then fixed his eyes, through the leaves and grass, on the point of the headland inside the reef.

The knife of white bows appeared. It was followed by ten yards of empty polished deck, glass windshields, a low raked cabin with a siren and a blunt radio mast, the glimpse of a man inside at the wheel, then the long flat well of the stern and a drooping red ensign. Converted M.T.B., British Government surplus?

Bond's eyes went to the two men standing in the stern. They were pale-skinned negroes. They wore neat khaki ducks and shirts, broad belts, and deep visored baseball caps of yellow straw. They were standing side by side, bracing themselves against the slow swell. One of them was holding a long black loud-hailer with a wire attached. The other was manning a machine gun on a tripod. It looked to Bond like a Spandau.

The man with the loud-hailer let it fall so that it swung on a strap round his neck. He picked up a pair of binoculars and began inching them along the beach. The low murmur of his comments just reached Bond above the glutinous flutter of the diesels.

Bond watched the eyes of the binoculars begin with the headland and then sweep the sand. The twin eyes paused among the rocks and moved on. They came back. The murmur of comment rose to a jabber. The man handed the glasses to the machine gunner who took a quick glance through them and gave them back. The scanner shouted something to the helmsman. The cabin cruiser stopped and backed up. Now she lay outside the reef exactly opposite Bond and the girl. The scanner again levelled the binoculars at the rocks where the girl's canoe lay hidden. Again the excited jabber came across the water. Again the glasses were passed to the machine gunner who glanced through. This time he nodded decisively.

Bond thought: now we've had it. These men know their job.

Bond watched the machine gunner pull the bolt back to load. The double click came to him over the bubbling of the diesels.

The scanner lifted his loud-hailer and switched it on. The twanging echo of the amplifier moaned and screeched across the water. The man brought it up to his lips. The voice roared across the bay.

'Okay, folks! Come on out and you won't get hurt.'

It was an educated voice. There was a trace of American accent.

'Now then, folks,' the voice thundered, 'make it quick! We've seen where you came ashore. We've spotted the boat under the driftwood. We ain't fools an' we ain't fooling. Take it easy. Just walk out with your hands up. You'll be okay.'

Silence fell. The waves lapped softly on the beach. Bond could hear the girl breathing. The thin screeching of the cormorants came to them muted across the mile of sea. The diesels bubbled unevenly as the swell covered the exhaust pipe and then opened it again.

Softly Bond reached over to the girl and tugged at her sleeve. 'Come close,' he whispered. 'Smaller target.' He felt her warmth nearer to him. Her cheek brushed against his forearm. He whispered, 'Burrow into the sand.

Wriggle. Every inch'll help.' He began to worm his body carefully deeper into the depression they had scooped out for themselves. He felt her do the same. He peered out. Now his eyes were only just above the skyline of the top of the beach.

The man was lifting his loud-hailer. The voice roared. 'Okay, folks! Just so as you'll know this thing isn't for show.' He lifted his thumb. The machine gunner trained his gun into the tops of the mangroves behind the beach. There came the swift rattling roar Bond had last heard coming from the German lines in the Ardennes. The bullets made the same old sound of frightened pigeons whistling overhead. Then there was silence.

In the distance Bond watched the black cloud of cormorants take to the air and begin circling. His eyes went back to the boat. The machine gunner was feeling the barrel of his gun to see if it had warmed. The two men exchanged some words. The scanner picked up his loud-hailer.

''Kay, folks,' he said harshly. 'You've been warned. This is it.'

Bond watched the snout of the Spandau swing and depress. The man was going to start with the canoe among the rocks. Bond whispered to the girl, 'All right, Honey. Stick it. Keep right down. It won't last long.' He felt her hand squeeze his arm. He thought: poor little bitch, she's in this because of me. He leant to the right to cover her head and pushed his face deep into the sand.

This time the crash of noise was terrific. The bullets howled into the corner of the headland. Fragments of splintered rock whined over the beach like hornets. Ricochets twanged and buzzed off into the hinterland. Behind it all there was the steady road-drill hammer of the gun.

There was a pause. New magazine, thought Bond. Now it's us. He could feel the girl clutching at him. Her body was trembling along his flank. Bond reached out an arm and pressed her to him.

The roar of the gun began again. The bullets came zipping along the tideline towards them. There was a succession of quick close thuds. The bush above them was being torn to shreds. 'Zwip. Zwip. Zwip.' It was as if the thong of a steel whip was cutting the bush to pieces. Bits scattered around them, slowly covering them. Bond could smell the cooler air that meant they were now lying in the open. Were they hidden by the leaves and debris? The bullets marched away along the shoreline. In less than a minute the racket stopped.

The silence sang. The girl whimpered softly. Bond hushed her and held her tighter.

The loud-hailer boomed. 'Okay, folks. If you still got ears, we'll be along soon to pick up the bits. And we'll be bringing the dogs. 'Bye for now.'

The slow thud of the diesel quickened. The engine accelerated into a hasty roar and through the fallen leaves Bond watched the stern of the launch settle lower in the water as it made off to the west. Within minutes it was out of earshot.

Bond cautiously raised his head. The bay was serene, the beach unmarked. All was as before except for the stench of cordite and the sour smell of blasted rock. Bond pulled the girl to her feet. There were tear streaks down her face. She looked at him aghast. She said solemnly. 'That was horrible. What did they do it for? We might have been killed.'

Bond thought, this girl has always had to fend for herself, but only against nature. She knows the world of animals and insects and fishes and she's got the better of it. But it's been a small world, bounded by the sun and the moon and the seasons. She doesn't know the big world of the smoke-filled room, of the bullion broker's parlour, of the corridors and waiting rooms of government offices, of careful meetings on park seats–she doesn't know about the struggle for big power and big money by the big men. She doesn't know that she's been swept out of her rock pool into the dirty waters.

He said, 'It's all right, Honey. They're just a lot of bad men who are frightened of us. We can manage them.' Bond put his arm round her shoulders, 'And you were wonderful. As brave as anything. Come on now, we'll look for Quarrel and make some plans. Anyway, it's time we had something to eat. What do you eat on these expeditions?'

They turned and walked up the beach to the headland. After a minute she said in a controlled voice, 'Oh, there's stacks of food about. Sea urchins mostly. And there are wild bananas and things. I eat and sleep for two days before I come out here. I don't need anything.'

Bond held her more closely. He dropped his arms as Quarrel appeared on the skyline. Quarrel scrambled down among the rocks. He stopped, looking down. They came up with him. The girl's canoe was sawn almost in half by the bullets. The girl gave a cry. She looked desperately at Bond, 'My boat! How am I to get back?'

'Don' you worry, missy,' Quarrel appreciated the loss of a canoe better than Bond. He guessed it might be most of the girl's capital. 'Cap'n fix you up wit' anudder. An' yo come back wit' we. Us got a fine boat in de mangrove. Hit not get broke. Ah's bin to see him.' Quarrel looked at Bond. Now his face was worried. 'But cap'n, yo sees what I means about dese folk. Dey mighty tough men an' dey means business. Dese dogs dey speak of. Dose is police-houns–Pinschers dey's called. Big bastards. Mah frens tell me as der's a pack of twenty or moh. We better make plans quick–an' good.'

'All right, Quarrel. But first we must have something to eat. And I'm damned if I'm going to be scared off the island before I've had a good look. We'll take Honey with us.' He turned to the girl. 'Is that all right with you, Honey? You'll be all right with us. Then we'll sail home together.'

The girl looked doubtfully at him. 'I guess there's no alternative. I mean, I'd love to go with you if I won't be in the way. I really don't want anything to eat. But will you take me home as soon as you can? I don't want to see any more of those people. How long are you going to be looking at these birds?'

Bond said evasively, 'Not long. I've got to find out what happened to them and why. Then we'll be off.' He looked at his watch. 'It's twelve now. You wait here. Have a bathe or something. Don't walk about leaving footprints. Come on, Quarrel, we'd better get that boat hidden.'

It was one o'clock before they were ready. Bond and Quarrel filled the canoe with stones and sand until it sank in a pool among the mangroves. They smeared over their footprints. The bullets had left so much litter behind the shoreline that they could do most of their walking on broken leaves and twigs. They ate some of their rations–avidly, the girl reluctantly–and climbed across the rocks and into the shallow water off-shore. Then they trudged along the shallows towards the river mouth three hundred yards away down the beach.

It was very hot. A harsh, baking wind had sprung up from the north-east. Quarrel said this wind blew daily the year round. It was vital to the guanera. It dried the guano. The glare from the sea and from the shiny green leaves of the mangroves was dazzling. Bond was glad he had taken trouble to get his skin hardened to the sun.

There was a sandy bar at the river mouth and a long deep stagnant pool. They could either get wet or strip. Bond said to the girl, 'Honey, we can't be shy on this trip. We'll keep our shirts on because of the sun. Wear what's sensible and walk behind us.' Without waiting for her reply the two men took off their trousers. Quarrel rolled them and packed them in the knapsack with the provisions and Bond's gun. They waded into the ppool, Quarrel in front, then Bond, then the girl. The water came up to Bond's waist. A big silver fish leaped out of the pool and fell back with a splash. There were arrows on the surface where others fled out of their way. 'Tarpon,' commented Quarrel.

The pool converged into a narrow neck over which the mangroves touched. For a time they waded through a cool tunnel, and then the river broadened into a deep sluggish channel that meandered ahead among the giant spider-legs of the mangroves. The bottom was muddy and at each step their feet sank inches into slime. Small fish or shrimps wriggled and fled from under their feet, and every now and then they had to stoop to brush away leeches before they got hold. But otherwise it was easy going and quiet and cool among the bushes and, at least to Bond, it was a blessing to be out of the sun.

Soon, as they got away from the sea, it began to smell bad with the bad egg, sulphuretted hydrogen smell of marsh gas. The mosquitoes and sandflies began to find them. They liked Bond's fresh body. Quarrel told him to dip himself in the river water. 'Dem like dere meat wid salt on him,' he explained cheerfully. Bond took off his shirt and did as he was told. Then it was better and after a while Bond's nostrils even got used to the marsh gas, except when Quarrel's feet disturbed some aged pocket in the mud and a vintage bubble wobbled up from the bottom and burst stinking under his nose.

The mangroves became fewer and sparser and the river slowly opened out. The water grew shallower and the bottom firmer. Soon they came round a bend and into the open. Honey said, 'Better watch out now. We'll be easier to see. It goes on like this for about a mile. Then the river gets narrower until the lake. Then there's the sandspit the birdmen lived on.'

They stopped in the shadow of the mangrove tunnel and looked out. The river meandered sluggishly away from them towards the centre of the island. Its banks, fringed with low bamboo and sea-grape, would give only half shelter. From its western bank the ground rose slowly and then sharply up to the sugar-loaf about two miles away which was the guanera. Round the base of the mountain there was a scattering of Quonset huts. A zigzag of silver ran down the hillside to the huts – a Decauderville Track, Bond guessed, to bring the guano from the diggings down to the crusher and separator. The summit of the sugar-loaf was white, as if with snow. From the peak flew a smoky flag of guano dust. Bond could see the black dots of cormorants against the white background. They were landing and taking off like bees at a hive.

Bond stood and gazed at the distant glittering mountain of bird dung. So this was the kingdom of Doctor No! Bond thought he had never seen a more godforsaken landscape in his life.

He examined the ground between the river and the mountain. It seemed to be the usual grey dead coral broken, where there was a pocket of earth, by low scrub and screwpalm. No doubt a road or a track led down the mountainside to the central lake and the marshes. It looked bad stuff to cross unless there was. Bond noticed that all the vegetation was bent to the westwards. He imagined living the year round with that hot wind constantly scouring the island, the smell of the marsh gas and the guano. No penal colony could have a worse site than this.

Bond looked to the east. There the mangroves in the marshland seemed more hospitable. They marched away in a solid green carpet until they lost their outline in the dancing heat haze on the horizon. Over them a thick froth of birds tossed and settled and tossed again. Their steady scream carried over on the harsh wind.

Quarrel's voice broke in on Bond's thoughts. 'Dey's a comin', cap'n.'

Bond followed Quarrel's eyes. A big lorry was racing down from the huts, dust streaming from its wheels. Bond followed it for ten minutes until it disappeared amongst the mangroves at the head of the river. He listened. The baying of dogs came down on the wind.

Quarrel said, 'Dey'll come down de ribber, cap'n. Dem'll know we caint move 'cept up de ribber, assumin' we ain't dead. Dey'll surely come down de ribber to de beach and look for de pieces. Den mos' likely de boat come wit' a dinghy an' take de men and dogs off. Leastways, dat's what Ah'd do in dere place.'

Honey said, 'That's what they do when they look for me. It's quite all right. You cut a piece of bamboo and when they get near you go under the water and breathe through the bamboo till they've gone by.'

Bond smiled at Quarrel. He said, 'Supposing you get the bamboo while I find a good mangrove clump.'

Quarrel nodded dubiously. He started off upstream towards the bamboo thickets. Bond turned back into the mangrove tunnel.

Bond had avoided looking at the girl. She said impatiently, 'You needn't be so careful of looking at me. It's no good minding those things at a time like this. You said so yourself.'

Bond turned and looked at her. Her tattered shirt came down to the waterline. There was a glimpse of pale wavering limbs below. The beautiful face smiled at him. In the mangroves the broken nose seemed appropriate in its animalness.

Bond looked at her slowly. She understood. He turned and went on downstream and she followed him.

Bond found what he wanted, a crack in the wall of mangrove that seemed to go deeper. He said, 'Don't break a branch.' He bent his head and waded in. The channel went in ten yards. The mud under their feet became deeper and softer. Then there was a solid wall of roots and they could go no farther. The brown water flowed slowly through a wide, quiet pool. Bond stopped. The girl came close to him. 'This is real hide-and-seek,' she said tremulously.

'Yes, isn't it.' Bond was thinking of his gun. He was wondering how well it would shoot after a bath in the river–how many dogs and men he could get if they were found. He felt a wave of disquiet. It had been a bad break coming across this girl. In combat, like it or not, a girl is your extra heart. The enemy has two targets against your one.

Bond remembered his thirst. He scooped up some water. It was brackish and tasted of earth. It was all right. He drank some more. The girl put out her hand and stopped him. 'Don't drink too much. Wash your mouth out and spit. You could get fever.'

Bond looked at her quietly. He did as she told him.

Quarrel whistled from somewhere in the main stream. Bond answered and waded out towards him. They came back along the channel. Quarrel splashed the mangrove roots with water where their bodies might have brushed against them. 'Kill da smell of us,' he explained briefly. He produced his handful of bamboo lengths and began whittling and cutting them. Bond looked to his gun and the spare ammunition. They stood still in the pool so as not to stir up more mud.

The sunlight dappled down through the thick roof of leaves. The shrimps nibbled softly at their feet. Tension built up in the hot, crouching silence.

It was almost a relief to hear the baying of the dogs.

Chapter Ten

Dragon Spoor

The search party was coming fast down the river. The two men in bathing trunks and tall waders were having to run to keep up with the dogs. They were big Chinese negroes wearing shoulder holsters across their naked sweating chests. Occasionally they exchanged shouts that were mostly swear-words. Ahead of them the pack of big Dobermann Pinschers swam and floundered through the water, baying excitedly. They had a scent and they quested frenziedly, the diamond-shaped ears erect on the smooth, serpentine heads.

'May be a —ing crocodile,' yelled the leading man through the hubbub. He was carrying a short whip which he occasionally cracked like a whipper-in on the hunting field.

The other man converged towards him. He shouted excitedly, 'For my money it's the —ing limey! Bet ya he's lying up in the mangrove. Mind he doesn't give us a —ing ambush.' The man took the gun out of its holster and put it under his armpit and kept his hand on the butt.

They were coming out of the open river into the mangrove tunnel. The first man had a whistle. It stuck out of his broad face like a cigar butt. He blew a shrill blast. When the dogs swept on he laid about him with the whip. The dogs checked, whimpering as the slow current forced them to disobey orders. The two men took their guns and waded slowly downstream through the straggly legs of the mangroves.

The leading man came to the narrow break that Bond had found. He grasped a dog by the collar and swung it into the channel. The dog snorted eagerly and paddled forward. The man's eyes squinted at the mangrove roots on either side of the channel to see if they were scratched.

The dog and the man came into the small enclosed pool at the end of the channel. The man looked round disgustedly. He caught the dog by the collar and pulled him back. The dog was reluctant to leave the place. The man lashed down into the water with his whip.

The second man had been waiting at the entrance to the little channel.

The first man came out. He shook his head and they went on downstream, the dogs, now less excited, streaming ahead.

Slowly the noise of the hunt grew less and vanished.

For another five minutes nothing moved in the mangrove pool, then, in one corner among the roots, a thin periscope of bamboo rose slowly out of the water. Bond's face emerged, the forehead streaked with wet hair, like the face of a surfacing corpse. In his right hand under the water the gun was ready. He listened intently. There was dead silence, not a sound. Or was there? What was that soft swish out in the main stream? Was someone wading very quietly along in the wake of the hunt? Bond reached out on either side of him and softly touched the other two bodies that lay among the roots on the edge of the pool. As the two faces surfaced he put his finger to his lips. It was too late. Quarrel had coughed and spat. Bond made a grimace and nodded urgently towards the main stream. They all listened. There was dead silence. Then the soft swishing began again. Whoever it was was coming into the side-channel. The tubes of bamboo went back into the three mouths and the heads softly submerged again.

Underwater, Bond rested his head in the mud, pinched his nostrils with his left hand and pursed his lips round the tube. He knew the pool had been examined once already. He had felt the disturbance of the swimming dog. That time they had not been found. Would they get away with it again? This time there would have been less chance for the stirred mud to seep away out of the pool. If this searcher saw the darker brown stain, would he shoot into it or stab into it? What weapons would he have? Bond decided that he wouldn't take chances. At the first movement in the water near him he would get to his feet and shoot and hope for the best.

Bond lay and focused all his senses. What hell this controlled breathing was and how maddening the soft nibbling of the shrimps! It was lucky none of them had a sore on their bodies or the damned things would have eaten into it. But it had been a bright idea of the girl's. Without it the dogs would have got to them wherever they had hidden.

Suddenly Bond cringed. A rubber boot had stepped on his shin and slid off. Would the man think it was a branch? Bond couldn't chance it. With one surge of motion he hurled himself upwards, spitting out the length of bamboo.

Bond caught a quick impression of a huge body standing almost on top of him and of a swirling rifle butt. He lifted his left arm to protect his head and felt the jarring blow on his forearm. At the same time his right hand lunged forward and as the muzzle of his gun touched the glistening right breast below the hairless aureole he pulled the trigger.

The kick of the explosion, pent up against the man's body, almost broke Bond's wrist, but the man crashed back like a chopped tree into the water. Bond caught a glimpse of a huge rent in his side as he went under. The rubber waders thrashed once and the head, a Chinese negroid head, broke the surface, its eyes turned up and water pouring from its silently yelling mouth. Then the head went under again and there was nothing but muddy froth and a slowly widening red stain that began to seep away downstream.

Bond shook himself. He turned. Quarrel and the girl were standing behind him, water streaming from their bodies. Quarrel was grinning from ear to ear, but the girl's knuckles were at her mouth and her eyes were staring horror-struck at the reddened water.

Bond said curtly, 'I'm sorry, Honey. It had to be done. He was right on top of us. Come on, let's get going.' He took her roughly by the arm and thrust her away from the place and out into the main stream, only stopping when they had reached the open river at the beginning of the mangrove tunnel.

The landscape was empty again. Bond glanced at his watch. It had stopped at three o'clock. He looked at the westering sun. It might be four o'clock now. How much farther had they to go? Bond suddenly felt tired. Now he'd torn it. Even if the shot hadn't been heard–and it would have been well muffled by the man's body and by the mangroves–the man would be missed when the others rendezvoused, if Quarrel's guess was right, at the river mouth to be taken off to the launch. Would they come back up the river to look for the missing man? Probably not. It would be getting dark before they knew for certain that he was missing. They'd send out a search party in the morning. The dogs would soon get to the body. Then what?

The girl tugged at his sleeve. She said angrily, 'It's time you told me what all this is about? Why's everybody trying to kill each other? And who are you? I don't believe all this story about birds. You don't take a revolver after birds.'

Bond looked down into the angry, wide-apart eyes. 'I'm sorry, Honey. I'm afraid I've got you into a bit of a mess. I'll tell you all about it this evening when we get to the camp. It's just bad luck you being mixed up with me like this. I've got a bit of a war on with these people. They seem to want to kill me. Now I'm only interested in seeing us all off the island without anyone else getting hurt. I've got enough to go on now so that next time I can come back by the front door.'

'What do you mean? Are you some sort of a policeman? Are you trying to send this Chinaman to prison?'

'That's about it.' Bond smiled down at her. 'At least you're on the side of the angels. And now you tell me something. How much farther to the camp?'

'Oh, about an hour.'

'Is it a good place to hide? Could they find us there easily?'

'They'd have to come across the lake or up the river. It'll be all right so long as they don't send their dragon after us. He can go through the water. I've seen him do it.'

'Oh well,' said Bond diplomatically, 'let's hope he's got a sore tail or something.'

The girl snorted. 'All right, Mr Know-all,' she said angrily. 'Just you wait.'

Quarrel splashed out of the mangroves. He was carrying a rifle. He said apologetically. 'No harm 'n havin' anudder gun, cap'n. Looks like us may need hit.'

Bond took it. It was a U.S. Army Remington Carbine, ·300. These people certainly had the right equipment. He handed it back.

Quarrel echoed his thoughts. 'Dese is sly folks, cap'n. Dat man mus' of come sneakin' down soffly behind de udders to ketch us comin' out after de dawgs had passed. He sho is a sly mongoose, dat Doctor feller.'

Bond said thoughtfully, 'He must be quite a man.' He shrugged away his thoughts. 'Now let's get going. Honey say's there's another hour to the camp. Better keep to the left bank so as to get what cover we can from the hill.

For all we know they've got glasses trained on the river.' Bond handed his gun to Quarrel who stowed it in the sodden knapsack. They moved off again with Quarrel in the lead and Bond and the girl walking together.

They got some shade from the bamboo and bushes along the western bank, but now they had to face the full force of the scorching wind. They splashed water over their arms and faces to cool the burn. Bond's eyes were bloodshot with the glare and his arm ached intolerably where the gun butt had struck. And he was not looking forward to his dinner of soaking bread and cheese and salt pork. How long would they be able to sleep? He hadn't had much last night. It looked like the same ration again. And what about the girl? She had had none. He and Quarrel would have to keep watch and watch. And then tomorrow. Off into the mangrove again and work their way slowly back to the canoe across the eastern end of the island. It looked like that. And sail the following night. Bond thought of hacking a way for five miles through solid mangroves. What a prospect! Bond trudged on, thinking of M's 'holiday in the sunshine'. He'd certainly give something for M to be sharing it with him now.

The river grew narrower until it was only a stream between the bamboo clumps. Then it widened out into a flat marshy estuary beyond which the five square miles of shallow lake swept away to the other side of the island in a ruffled blue-grey mirror. Beyond, there was the shimmer of the airstrip and the glint of the sun on a single hangar. The girl told them to keep to the east and they worked their way slowly along inside the fringe of bushes.

Suddenly Quarrel stopped, his face pointing like a gun-dog's at the marshy ground in front of him. Two deep parallel grooves were cut into the mud, with a fainter groove in the centre. They were the tracks of something that had come down from the hill and gone across the marsh towards the lake.

The girl said indifferently, 'That's where the dragon's been.'

Quarrel turned the whites of his eyes towards her.

Bond walked slowly along the tracks. The outside ones were quite smooth with an indented curve. They could have been made by wheels, but they were vast–at least two feet across. The centre track was of the same shape but only three inches across, about the width of a motor tyre. The tracks were without a trace of tread, and they were fairly fresh. They marched along in a dead straight line and the bushes they crossed were squashed flat as if a tank had gone over them.

Bond couldn't imagine what kind of vehicle, if it was a vehicle, had made them. When the girl nudged him and whispered fiercely 'I told you so,' he could only say thoughtfully, 'Well, Honey, if it isn't a dragon, it's something else I've never seen before.'

Farther on, she tugged urgently at his sleeve. 'Look,' she whispered. She pointed forward to a big clump of bushes beside which the tracks ran. They were leafless and blackened. In the centre there showed the charred remains of birds' nests. 'He breathed on them,' she said excitedly.

Bond walked up to the bushes and examined them. 'He certainly did,' he admitted. Why had this particular clump been burned? It was all very odd.

The tracks swerved out towards the lake and disappeared into the water. Bond would have liked to follow them but there was no question of leaving cover. They trudged on, wrapped in their different thoughts.

Slowly the day began to die behind the sugar-loaf, and at last the girl pointed ahead through the bushes and Bond could see a long spit of sand running out into the lake. There were thick bushes of sea-grape along its spine and, halfway, perhaps a hundred yards from the shore, the remains of a thatched hut. It looked a reasonably attractive place to spend the night and it was well protected by the water on both sides. The wind had died and the water was soft and inviting. How heavenly it was going to be to take off their filthy shirts and wash in the lake, and, after the hours of squelching through the mud and stench of the river and the marsh, be able to lie down on the hard dry sand!

The sun blazed yellowly and sank behind the mountain. The day was still alive at the eastern tip of the island, but the black shadow of the sugar-loaf was slowly marching across the lake and would soon reach out and kill that too. The frogs started up, louder than in Jamaica, until the thick dusk was shrill with them. Across the lake a giant bull frog began to drum. The eerie sound was something between a tom-tom and an ape's roar. It sent out short messages that were suddenly throttled. Soon it fell silent. It had found what it had sent for.

They reached the neck of the sandspit and filed out along a narrow track. They came to the clearing with the smashed remains of the wattle hut. The big mysterious tracks led out of the water on both sides and through the clearing and over the near-by bushes as if the thing, whatever it was, had stampeded the place. Many of the bushes were burned or charred. There were the remains of a fireplace made of lumps of coral and a few scattered cooking pots and empty tins. They searched in the debris and Quarrel unearthed a couple of unopened tins of Heinz pork and beans. The girl found a crumpled sleeping-bag. Bond found a small leather purse containing five one-dollar notes, three Jamaica pounds and some silver. The two men had certainly left in a hurry.

They left the place and moved farther along to a small sandy clearing. Through the bushes they could see lights winking across the water from the mountain, perhaps two miles away. To the eastwards there was nothing but the soft black sheen of water under the darkening sky.

Bond said, 'As long as we don't show a light we should be fine here. The first thing is to have a good wash. Honey, you take the rest of the sandspit and we'll have the landward end. See you for dinner in about half an hour.'

The girl laughed. 'Will you be dressing?'

'Certainly,' said Bond. 'Trousers.'

Quarrel said, 'Cap'n, while dere's henough light I'll get dese tins open and get tings fixed for de night.' He rummaged in the knapsack. 'Here's yo trousers and yo gun. De bread don't feel so good but hit only wet. Hit eat okay an' mebbe hit dry hout come de mornin'. Guess we'd better eat de tins tonight an' keep de cheese an' pork. Dose tins is heavy an' we got plenty footin' tomorrow.'

Bond said, 'All right, Quarrel. I'll leave the menu to you.' He took the gun and the damp trousers and walked down into the shallow water and back the way they had come. He found a hard dry stretch of sand and took off his shirt and stepped back into the water and lay down. The water was soft but disgustingly warm. He dug up handfuls of sand and scrubbed himself with it, using it as soap. Then he lay and luxuriated in the silence and the loneliness.

The stars began to shine palely, the stars that had brought them to the island last night, a year ago, the stars that would take them away again tomorrow night, a year away. What a trip! But at least it had already paid off. Now he had enough evidence, and witnesses, to go back to the Governor and get a full-dress inquiry going into the activities of Doctor No. One didn't use machine guns on people, even on trespassers. And, by the same token, what was this thing of Doctor No's that had trespassed on the leasehold of the Audubon Society, the thing that had smashed their property and had possibly killed one of their wardens? That would have to be investigated too. And what would he find when he came back to the island through the front door, in a destroyer, perhaps, and with a detachment of marines? What would be the answer to the riddle of Doctor No? What was he hiding? What did he fear? Why was privacy so important to him that he would murder, again and again, for it? Who *was* Doctor No?

Bond heard splashing away to his right. He thought of the girl. And who, for the matter of that, was Honeychile Rider? That, he decided, as he climbed out on to dry land, was at least something that he ought to be able to find out before the night was over.

Bond pulled on his clammy trousers and sat down on the sand and dismantled his gun. He did it by touch, using his shirt to dry each part and each cartridge. Then he reassembled the gun and clicked the trigger round the empty cylinder. The sound was healthy. It would be days before it rusted. He loaded it and tucked it into the holster inside the waistband of his trousers and got up and walked back to the clearing.

The shadow of Honey reached up and pulled him down beside her. 'Come on,' she said, 'we're starving. I got one of the cooking pots and cleaned it out and we poured the beans into it. There's about two full handfuls each and a cricket ball of bread. And I'm not feeling guilty about eating your food because you made me work far harder than I would if I'd been alone. Here, hold out your hand.'

Bond smiled at the authority in her voice. He could just make out her silhouette in the dusk. Her head looked sleeker. He wondered what her hair looked like when it was combed and dry. What would she be like when she was wearing clean clothes over that beautiful golden body? He could see her coming into a room or across the lawn at Beau Desert. She would be a beautiful, ravishing, Ugly Duckling. Why had she never had the broken nose mended? It was an easy operation. Then she would be the most beautiful girl in Jamaica.

Her shoulder brushed against him. Bond reached out and put his hand down in her lap, open. She picked up his hand and Bond felt the cold mess of beans being poured into it.

Suddenly he smelled her warm animal smell. It was so sensually thrilling that his body swayed against her and for a moment his eyes closed.

She gave a short laugh in which there was shyness and satisfaction and tenderness. She said 'There,' maternally, and carried his laden hand away from her and back to him.

Chapter Eleven

Amidst the Alien Cane

It would be around eight o'clock, Bond thought. Apart from the background tinkle of the frogs it was very quiet. In the far corner of the clearing he could see the dark outline of Quarrel. There was the soft clink of metal as he dismantled and dried the Remington.

Through the bushes the distant yellow lights from the guanera made festive pathways across the dark surface of the lake. The ugly wind had gone and the hideous scenery lay drowned in darkness. It was cool. Bond's clothes had dried on him. The three big handfuls of food had warmed his stomach. He felt comfortable and drowsy and at peace. Tomorrow was a long way off and presented no problems except a great deal of physical exercise. Life suddenly felt easy and good.

The girl lay beside him in the sleeping-bag. She was lying on her back with her head cradled in her hands, looking up at the roof of stars. He could just make out the pale pool of her face. She said, 'James. You promised to tell me what this is all about. Come on. I shan't go to sleep until you do.'

Bond laughed. 'I'll tell if you'll tell. I want to know what you're all about.'

'I don't mind. I've got no secrets. But you first.'

'All right then.' Bond pulled his knees up to his chin and put his arms round them. 'It's like this. I'm a sort of policeman. They send me out from London when there's something odd going on somewhere in the world that isn't anybody else's business. Well, not long ago one of the Governor's staff in Kingston, a man called Strangways, friend of mine, disappeared. His secretary, who was a pretty girl, did too. Most people thought they'd run away together. I didn't. I . . .'

Bond told the story in simple terms, with good men and bad men, like an adventure story out of a book. He ended, 'So you see, Honey, it's just a question of getting back to Jamaica tomorrow night, all three of us in the canoe, and then the Governor will listen to us and send over a lot of soldiers to get this Chinaman to own up. I expect that'll mean he'll go to prison. He'll know that too and that's why he's trying to stop us. That's all. Now it's your turn.'

The girl said, 'You seem to live a very exciting life. Your wife can't like you being away so much. Doesn't she worry about you getting hurt?'

'I'm not married. The only people who worry about me getting hurt are my insurance company.'

She probed, 'But I suppose you have girls.'

'Not permanent ones.'

'Oh.'

There was a pause. Quarrel came over to them. 'Cap'n, Ah'll take de fust watch if dat suits. Be out on de point of de sandspit. Ah'll come call yo around midnight. Den mebbe yo take on till five and den we all git goin'. Need to get well away from dis place afore it's light.'

'Suits me,' said Bond. 'Wake me if you see anything. Gun all right?'

'Him's jess fine,' said Quarrel happily. He said, 'Sleep well, missy,' with a hint of meaning, and melted noiselessly away into the shadows.

'I like Quarrel,' said the girl. She paused, then, 'Do you really want to know about me? It's not as exciting as your story.'

'Of course I do. And don't leave anything out.'

'There's nothing to leave out. You could get my whole life on to the back of a postcard. To begin with I've never been out of Jamaica. I've lived all my life at a place called Beau Desert on the North Coast near Morgan's Harbour.'

Bond laughed. 'That's odd. So do I. At least for the moment. I didn't notice you about. Do you live up a tree?'

'Oh, I suppose you've taken the beach house. I never go near the place. I live in the Great House.'

'But there's nothing left of it. It's a ruin in the middle of the cane fields.'

'I live in the cellars. I've lived there since I was five. It was burned down then and my parents were killed. I can't remember anything about them so you needn't say you're sorry. At first I lived there with my black nanny. She died when I was fifteen. For the last five years I've lived there alone.'

'Good heavens.' Bond was appalled. 'But wasn't there anyone else to look after you? Didn't your parents leave any money?'

'Not a penny.' There was no bitterness in the girl's voice–pride if anything. 'You see the Riders were one of the old Jamaican families. The first one had been given the Beau Desert lands by Cromwell for having been one of the people who signed King Charles's death warrant. He built the Great House and my family lived in it on and off ever since. But then sugar collapsed and I suppose the place was badly run, and by the time my father inherited it there was nothing but debts–mortgages and things like that. So when my father and mother died the property was sold up. I didn't mind. I was too young. Nanny must have been wonderful. They wanted people to adopt me, the clergyman and the legal people did, but Nanny collected the sticks of furniture that hadn't been burned and we settled down in the ruins and after a bit no one came and interfered with us. She did a bit of sewing and laundry in the village and grew plantains and bananas and things and there was a big breadfruit tree up against the old house. We ate what the Jamaicans eat. And there was the sugar cane all round us and she made a fishpot which we used to go and take up every day. It was all right. We had enough to eat. Somehow she taught me to read and write. There was a pile of old books left from the fire. There was an encyclopedia. I started with A when I was about eight. I've got as far as the middle of T.' She said defensively, 'I bet I know more than you do about a lot of things.'

'I bet you do.' Bond was lost in the picture of the little flaxen-haired girl pattering about the ruins with the obstinate old negress watching over her and calling her in to do the lessons that must have been just as much a riddle to the old woman. 'Your nanny must have been a wonderful person.'

'She was a darling.' It was a flat statement. 'I thought I'd die when she did. It wasn't such fun after that. Before, I'd led a child's life; then I suddenly had to grow up and do everything for myself. And men tried to catch me and hurt me. They said they wanted to make love to me.' She paused. 'I used to be pretty then.'

Bond said seriously, 'You're one of the most beautiful girls I've ever seen.'

'With this nose? Don't be silly.'

'You don't understand.' Bond tried to find words that she would believe. 'Of course anyone can see your nose is broken. But since this morning I've hardly noticed it. When you look at a person you look into their eyes or at their mouth. That's where the expressions are. A broken nose isn't any more significant than a crooked ear. Noses and ears are bits of face-furniture. Some are prettier than others, but they're not nearly as important as the rest. They're part of the background of the face. If you had a beautiful nose as well as the rest of you you'd be the most beautiful girl in Jamaica.'

'Do you mean that?' her voice was urgent. 'Do you think I could be beautiful? I know some of me's all right, but when I look in the glass I hardly see anything except my broken nose. I'm sure it's like that with other people who are, who are–well–sort of deformed.'

Bond said impatiently, 'You're not deformed! Don't talk such nonsense. And anyway you can have it put right by a simple operation. You've only got to get over to America and it would be done in a week.'

She said angrily, 'How do you expect me to do that? I've got about fifteen pounds under a stone in my cellar. I've got three skirts and three shirts and a knife and a fishpot. I know all about these operations. The doctor at Port Maria found out for me. He's a nice man. He wrote to America. Do you know, to have it properly done it would cost me about five hundred pounds, what with the fare to New York and the hospital and everything?' Her voice became hopeless. 'How do you expect me to find that amount of money?'

Bond had already made up his mind what would have to be done about that. Now he merely said tenderly, 'Well, I expect there are ways. But anyway, go on with your story. It's very exciting–far more interesting than mine. You'd got to where your nanny died. What happened then?'

The girl began again reluctantly.

'Well, it's your fault for interrupting. And you mustn't talk about things you don't understand. I suppose people tell you you're good-looking. I expect you get all the girls you want. Well you wouldn't if you had a squint or a hare-lip or something. As a matter of fact,' he could hear the smile in her voice, 'I think I shall go to the obeahman when we get back and get him to put a spell on you and give you something like that.' She added lamely, 'Then we should be more alike.'

Bond reached out. His hand brushed against her. 'I've got other plans,' he said. 'But come on. I want to hear the rest of the story.'

'Oh well,' the girl sighed, 'I'll have to go back a bit. You see all the property is in cane and the old house stands in the middle of it. Well, about twice a year they cut the cane and send it off to the mill. And when they do that all the animals and insects and so on that live in the cane fields go into a panic and most of them have their houses destroyed and get killed. At cutting time some of them took to coming to the ruins of the house and hiding. My nanny was terrified of them to begin with, the mongooses and the snakes and the scorpions and so on, but I made a couple of the cellar rooms into sort of homes for them. I wasn't frightened of them and they never hurt me. They seemed to understand that I was looking after them. They must have told their friends or something because after a bit it was quite natural for them all to come trooping into their rooms and settling down there until the young cane had started to grow again. Then they all filed out and went back to living in the fields. I gave them what food we could spare when they were staying with us and they behaved very well except for making a bit of a smell and sometimes fighting amongst each other. But they all got quite tame with me, and their children did, too, and I could do anything with them. Of course the cane-cutters found out about this and saw me walking about with snakes round my neck and so forth, and they got frightened of me and thought I was obeah. So they left us absolutely alone.' She paused. 'That's where I found out so much about animals and insects. I used to spend a lot of time in the sea finding out about those people too. It was the same with birds. If you find out what all these people like to eat and what they're afraid of, and if you spend all your time with them you can make friends.' She looked up at him. 'You miss a lot not knowing about these things.'

'I'm afraid I do,' said Bond truthfully. 'I expect they're much nicer and more interesting than humans.'

'I don't know about that,' said the girl thoughtfully. 'I don't know many human people. Most of the ones I have met have been hateful. But I suppose they can be interesting too.' She paused. 'I hadn't ever really thought of liking them like I like the animals. Except for Nanny, of course. Until . . .' She broke off with a shy laugh. 'Well, anyway we all lived happily together until I was fifteen and Nanny died and then things got difficult. There was a man called Mander. A horrible man. He was the white overseer for the people who own the property. He kept coming to see me. He wanted me to move up to his house near Port Maria. I hated him and I used to hide when I heard his horse coming through the cane. One night he came on foot and I didn't hear him. He was drunk. He came into the cellar and fought with me because I wouldn't do what he wanted me to do. You know, the things people in love do.'

'Yes, I know.'

'I tried to kill him with my knife, but he was very strong and he hit me as hard as he could in the face and broke my nose. He knocked me unconscious and then I think he did things to me. I mean I know he did. Next day I wanted to kill myself when I saw my face and when I found what he had done. I thought I would have a baby. I would certainly have killed myself if I'd had a baby by that man. Anyway I didn't, so that was that. I went to the doctor and he did what he could for my nose and didn't charge me anything. I didn't tell him about the rest. I was too ashamed. The man didn't come back. I waited and did nothing until the next cane-cutting. I'd got my plan. I was waiting for the Black Widow spiders to come in for shelter. One day they came. I caught the biggest of the females and shut her in a box with nothing to eat. They're the bad ones, the females. Then I waited for a dark night without any moon. I took the box with the spider in it and walked and walked until I came to the man's house. It was very dark and I was frightened of the duppies I might meet on the road but I didn't see any. I waited in his garden in the bushes and watched him go up to bed. Then I climbed a tree and got on to his balcony. I waited there until I heard him snoring and then I crept through the window. He was lying naked on the bed under the mosquito net. I lifted the edge and opened the box and shook the spider out on to his stomach. Then I went away and came home.'

'God Almighty!' said Bond reverently. 'What happened to him?'

She said happily. 'He took a week to die. It must have hurt terribly. They do, you know. The obeahmen say there's nothing like it.' She paused. When Bond made no comment, she said anxiously, 'You don't think I did wrong, do you?'

'It's not a thing to make a habit of,' said Bond mildly. 'But I can't say I blame you the way it was. So what happened then?'

'Well then I just settled down again,' her voice was matter-of-fact. 'I had to concentrate on getting enough food, and of course all I wanted to do was to save up money to get my nose made good again.' She said persuasively, 'It really was quite a pretty nose before. Do you think the doctors can put it back to how it was?'

'They can make it any shape you like,' said Bond definitely. 'What did you make money at?'

'It was the encyclopedia. It told me that people collect seashells. That one could sell the rare ones. I talked to the local schoolmaster, without telling him my secret of course, and he found out that there's an American magazine called *Nautilus* for shell collectors. I had just enough money to subscribe to it and I began looking for the shells that people said they wanted in the advertisements. I wrote to a dealer in Miami and he started buying from me. It was thrilling. Of course I made some awful mistakes to begin with. I thought people would like the prettiest shells, but they don't. Very often they want the ugliest. And then when I found rare ones I cleaned them and polished them to make them look better. That's wrong too. They want shells just as they come out of the sea, with the animal in and all. So I got some formalin from the doctor and put it into the live shells to stop them smelling and sent them off to this man in Miami. I only got it right about a year ago and I've already made fifteen pounds. I'd worked out that now I knew how they wanted them, and if I was lucky, I ought to make at least fifty pounds a year. Then in ten years I would be able to go to America and have the operation. And then,' she giggled delightedly, 'I had a terrific stroke of luck. I went over to Crab Key. I'd been there before, but this was just before Christmas, and I found these purple shells. They didn't look very exciting, but I sent one or two to Miami and the man wrote back at once and said he could take as many as I could get at five dollars each for the whole ones. He said that I must keep the place where they live a dead secret as otherwise we'd what he called "spoil the market" and the price would get cheaper. It's just like having one's private gold mine. Now I may be able to save up the money in five years. That's why I was so suspicious of you when I found you on my beach. I thought you'd come to steal my shells.'

'You gave me a bit of a shock. I thought you must be Doctor No's girl friend.'

'Thanks very much.'

'But when you've had the operation, what are you going to do then? You can't go on living alone in a cellar all your life.'

'I thought I'd be a call girl.' She said it as she might have said 'nurse' or 'secretary'.

'Oh, what do you mean by that?' Perhaps she had picked up the expression without understanding it.

'One of those girls who has a beautiful flat and lovely clothes. You know what I mean,' she said impatiently. 'People ring them up and come and make love to them and pay them for it. They get a hundred dollars for each time in New York. That's where I thought I'd start. Of course,' she admitted, 'I might have to do it for less to begin with. Until I learned to do it really well. How much do you pay the untrained ones?'

Bond laughed. 'I really can't remember. It's quite a long time since I had one.'

She sighed. 'Yes, I suppose you can have as many women as you want for nothing. I suppose it's only the ugly men that pay. But that can't be helped. Any kind of job in the big towns must be dreadful. At least you can earn much more being a call girl. Then I can come back to Jamaica and buy Beau Desert. I'd be rich enough to find a nice husband and have some children. Now that I've found these Venus shells I've worked out that I might be back in Jamaica by the time I'm thirty. Won't that be lovely?'

'I like the last part of the plan. But I'm not so sure of the first. Anyway, where did you find out about these call girls? Were they under C in the encyclopedia?'

Of course not. Don't be silly. There was a big case about them in New York about two years ago. There was a rich playboy called Jelke. He had a whole string of girls. There was a lot about the case in the *Gleaner*. They gave all the prices and everything. And anyway, there are thousands of those sort of girls in Kingston, only of course not such good ones. They only get about five shillings and they have nowhere to go and do it except in the bush. My nanny told me about them. She said I mustn't grow up like them or I'd be very unhappy. I can see that for only five shillings. But for a hundred dollars . . .!'

Bond said, 'You wouldn't be able to keep all of that. You'd have to have a sort of manager to get the men, and then you'd have to bribe the police to leave you alone. And you could easily go to prison if something went wrong. I really don't think you'd like the work. I'll tell you what, with all you know about animals and insects and so on you could get a wonderful job looking after them in one of the American zoos. Or what about the Jamaica Institute? I'm sure you'd like that better. You'd be just as likely to meet a nice husband. Anyway you mustn't think of being a call girl any more. You've got a beautiful body. You must keep it for the men you love.'

'That's what people say in books,' she said doubtfully. 'The trouble is there aren't any men to love at Beau Desert.' She said shyly, 'You're the first Englishman I've ever talked to. I liked you from the beginning. I don't mind telling you these things at all. I suppose there are plenty of other people I should like if I could get away.'

'Of course there are. Hundreds. And you're a wonderful girl. I thought so directly I saw you.'

'Saw my behind you mean.' The voice was getting drowsy, but it was full of pleasure.

Bond laughed. 'Well, it was a wonderful behind. And the other side was wonderful too.' Bond's body began to stir with the memory of how she had been. He said gruffly, 'Now come on, Honey. It's time to go to sleep. There'll be plenty of time to talk when we get back to Jamaica.'

'Will there?' she said sleepily. 'Promise?'

'Promise.'

He heard her stir in the sleeping-bag. He looked down. He could just make out the pale profile turned towards him. She gave the deep sigh of a child before it falls asleep.

There was silence in the clearing. It was getting cold. Bond put his head down on his hunched knees. He knew it was no good trying to get to sleep. His mind was full of the day and of this extraordinary Girl Tarzan who had come into his life. It was as if some beautiful animal had attached itself to him. There would be no dropping the leash until he had solved her problems for her. He knew it. Of course there would be no difficulty about most of them. He could fix the operation–even, with the help of friends, find a proper job and a home for her. He had the money. He would buy her dresses, have her hair done, get her started in the big world. It would be fun. But what about the other side? What about the physical desire he felt for her? One could not make love to a child. But was she a child? There was nothing childish about her body or her personality. She was fully grown and highly intelligent in her fashion, and far more capable of taking care of herself than any girl of twenty Bond had ever met.

Bond's thoughts were interrupted by a tug at his sleeve. The small voice said, 'Why don't you go to sleep? Are you cold?'

'No, I'm fine.'

'It's nice and warm in the sleeping-bag. Would you like to come in? There's plenty of room.'

'No thank you, Honey. I'll be all right.'

There was a pause, then almost in a whisper, 'If you're thinking . . . I mean–you don't have to make love to me . . . We could go to sleep back to front, you know, like spoons.'

'Honey, darling, you go to sleep. It'd be lovely to be like that, but not tonight. Anyway I'll have to take over from Quarrel soon.'

'Yes, I see.' The voice was grudging. 'Perhaps when we get back to Jamaica.'

'Perhaps.'

'Promise. I won't go to sleep until you promise.'

Bond said desperately, 'Of course I promise. Now go to sleep, Honeychile.'

The voice whispered triumphantly, 'Now you owe me slave-time. You've promised. Good night, darling James.'

'Good night, darling Honey.'

Chapter Twelve

The Thing

The grip on Bond's shoulder was urgent. He was instantly on his feet.

Quarrel whispered fiercely, 'Somepn comin' across de water, cap'n! It de dragon fo sho!'

The girl woke up. She said anxiously, 'What's happened?'

Bond said, 'Stay there, Honey! Don't move. I'll be back.' He broke through the bushes on the side away from the mountain and ran along the sand with Quarrel at his elbow.

They came to the tip of the sandspit, twenty yards from the clearing. They stopped under cover of the final bushes. Bond parted them and looked through.

What was it? Half a mile away, coming across the lake, was a shapeless thing with two glaring orange eyes with black pupils. From between these, where the mouth might be, fluttered a yard of blue flame. The grey luminescence of the stars showed some kind of a domed head above two short batlike wings. The thing was making a low moaning roar that overlaid another noise, a deep rhythmic thud. It was coming towards them at about ten miles an hour, throwing up a creamy wake.

Quarrel whispered, 'Gawd, cap'n! What's dat fearful ting?'

Bond stood up. He said shortly, 'Don't know exactly. Some sort of a tractor affair dressed up to frighten. It's running on a diesel engine, so you can forget about dragons. Now let's see,' Bond spoke half to himself. 'No good running away. The thing's too fast for us and we know it can go over mangroves and swamp. Have to fight it here. What'll its weak spots be? The drivers. Of course they'll have protection. We don't know how much. Quarrel, you start firing at that dome on top when it gets to two hundred yards. Aim carefully and keep on firing. I'll go for its headlights when it gets to fifty yards. It's not running on tracks. Must have some kind of giant tyres, aeroplane tyres probably. I'll go for them too. Stay here. I'll go ten yards along. They may start firing back and we've got to keep the bullets away from the girl. Okay?' Bond reached out and squeezed the big shoulder. 'And don't worry too much. Forget about dragons. It's just some gadget of Doctor No's. We'll kill the drivers and capture the damn thing and ride it down to the coast. Save us shoe-leather. Right?'

Quarrel laughed shortly. 'Okay, cap'n. Since yo says so. But Ah sho hopes de Almighty knows he's no dragon too!'

Bond ran down the sand. He broke through the bushes until he had a field of fire. He called softly, 'Honey!'

'Yes, James.' There was relief in the near-by voice:

'Make a hole in the sand like we did on the beach. Behind the thickest roots. Get into it and lie down. There may be some shooting. Don't worry about dragons. This is just a painted up motor car with some of Doctor No's men in it. Don't be frightened. I'm quite close.'

'All right, James. Be careful.' The voice was high with fright.

Bond knelt on one knee in the leaves and sand and peered out.

Now the thing was only about three hundred yards away and its yellow headlights were lighting up the sandspit. Blue flames were still fluttering from the mouth. They were coming from a long snout mocked-up with gaping jaws and gold paint to look like a dragon's mouth. Flame-thrower! That would explain the burned bushes and the warden's story. The blue flames would be coming from some kind of an after-burner. The apparatus was now in neutral. What would its range be when the compression was unleashed?

Bond had to admit that the thing was an awesome sight as it moaned forward through the shallow lake. It was obviously designed to terrify. It would have frightened him but for the earthy thud of the diesel. Against native intruders it would be devastating. But how vulnerable would it be to people with guns who didn't panic?

He was answered at once. There came the crack of Quarrel's Remington.

A spark flew off the domed cabin and there was a dull clang. Quarrel fired another single shot and then a burst. The bullets hammered ineffectually against the cabin. There was not even a check in speed. The thing rolled on, swerving slightly to make for the source of gunfire. Bond cradled the Smith & Wesson on his forearm and took careful aim. The deep cough of his gun sounded above the rattle of the Remington. One of the headlamps shattered and went out. He fired four shots at the other and got it with the fifth and last round in the cylinder. The thing didn't care. It rolled straight on towards Quarrel's hiding place. Bond reloaded and began firing at the huge bulge of the tyres under the bogus black and gold wings. The range was now only thirty yards and he could have sworn that he hit the nearest wheel again and again. No effect. Solid rubber? The first breath of fear stirred Bond's skin.

He reloaded. Was the damn thing vulnerable from the rear? Should he dash out into the lake and try and board it? He took a step forward through the bushes. Then he froze, incapable of movement.

Suddenly, from the dribbling snout, a yellow-tipped bolt of blue flame had howled out towards Quarrel's hiding place. There was a single puff of orange and red flame from the bushes to Bond's right and one unearthly scream, immediately choked. Satisfied, the searing tongue of fire licked back into the snout. The thing turned on its axis and stopped dead. Now the blue hole of its mouth aimed straight at Bond.

Bond stood and waited for his unspeakable end. He looked into the blue jaws of death and saw the glowing red filament of the firer deep inside the big tube. He thought of Quarrel's body–there was no time to think of Quarrel–and imagined the blackened, smoking figure lying in the melted sand. Soon he, too, would flame like a torch. The single scream would be wrung from him and his limbs would jerk into the dancing pose of burned bodies. Then it would be Honey's turn. Christ, what had he led them into! Why had be been so insane as to take on this man with his devastating armoury. Why hadn't he been warned by the long finger that had pointed at him in Jamaica? Bond set his teeth. Hurry up, you bastards. Get it over.

There came the twang of a loud-hailer. A voice howled metallically, 'Come on out, Limey. And the doll. Quick, or you'll fry in hell like your pal.' To rub in the command the bolt of flame spat briefly towards him. Bond stepped back from the searing heat. He felt the girl's body against his back. She said hysterically, 'I had to come. I had to come.'

Bond said, 'It's all right, Honey. Keep behind me.'

He had made up his mind. There was no alternative. Even if death was to come later it couldn't be worse than this kind of death. Bond reached for the girl's hand and drew her after him out on to the sand.

The voice howled. 'Stop there. Good boy. And drop the pea-shooter. No tricks or the crabs'll be getting a cooked breakfast.'

Bond dropped his gun. So much for the Smith & Wesson. The Beretta would have been just as good against this thing. The girl whimpered. Bond squeezed her hand. 'Stick it, Honey,' he said. 'We'll get out of this somehow.' Bond sneered at himself for the lie.

There was the clang of an iron door being opened. From the back of the dome a man dropped into the water and walked towards them. There was a gun in his hand. He kept out of the line of fire of the flame-thrower. The fluttering blue flame lit up his sweating face. He was a Chinese negro, a big man, clad only in trousers. Something dangled from his left hand. When he came closer, Bond saw it was handcuffs.

The man stopped a few yards away. He said, 'Hold out your hands. Wrists together. Then walk towards me. You first, Limey. Slowly or you get an extra navel.'

Bond did as he was told. When he was within sweat-smell of the man, the man put his gun between his teeth and reached out and snapped the handcuffs on Bond's wrists. Bond looked into the face, gunmetal-coloured from the blue flames. It was a brutal, squinting face. It sneered at him. 'Dumb bastard,' said the man.

Bond turned his back on the man and started walking away. He was going to see Quarrel's body. He had to say goodbye to it. There was the roar of a gun. A bullet kicked up sand close to his feet. Bond stopped and turned slowly round. 'Don't be nervous,' he said. I'm going to take a look at the man you've just murdered. I'll be back.'

The man lowered his gun. He laughed harshly. 'Okay. Enjoy yourself. Sorry we ain't got a wreath. Come back quick or we give the doll a toastin'. Two minutes.'

Bond walked on towards the smoking clump of bushes. He got there and looked down. His eyes and mouth winced. Yes, it had been just as he had visualized. Worse. He said softly, 'I'm sorry Quarrel.' He kicked into the ground and scooped up a handful of cool sand between his manacled hands and poured it over the remains of the eyes. Then he walked slowly back and stood beside the girl.

The man waved them forward with his gun. They walked round the back of the machine. There was a small square door. A voice from inside said, 'Get in and sit on the floor. Don't touch anything or you get your fingers broke.'

They scrambled into the iron box. It stank of sweat and oil. There was just room for them to sit with their knees hunched up. The man with the gun followed them in and banged the door. He switched on a light and sat down on an iron tractor seat beside the driver. He said, 'Okay, Sam. Let's get goin'. You can put out the fire. It's light enough to steer by.'

There was a row of dials and switches on the instrument panel. The driver reached forward and pulled down a couple of the switches. He put the machine into gear and peered out through a narrow slit in the iron wall in front of him. Bond felt the machine turn. There came a faster beat from the engine and they moved off.

The girl's shoulder pressed against his. 'Where are they taking us?' The whisper trembled.

Bond turned his head and looked at her. It was the first time he had been able to see her hair when it was dry. Now it was disarrayed by sleep, but it was no longer a bunch of rats' tails. It hung heavily straight down to her shoulders, where it curled softly inwards. It was of the palest ash blonde and shone almost silver under the electric light. She looked up at him. The skin round her eyes and at the corners of her mouth was white with fear.

Bond shrugged with an indifference he didn't feel. He whispered, 'Oh, I expect we're going to see Doctor No. Don't worry too much, Honey. These men are just little gangsters. It'll be different with him. When we get to him don't you say anything. I'll talk for both of us.' He pressed her shoulder. 'I like the way you do your hair. I'm glad you don't cut it too short.'

Some of the tension went out of her face. 'How can you think of things like that?' She half smiled at him. 'But I'm glad you like it. I wash it in coconut oil once a week.' At the memory of her other life her eyes grew bright with tears. She bent her head down to her manacled hands to hide her tears. She whispered almost to herself, 'I'll try to be brave. It'll be all right as long as you're there.'

Bond shifted so that he was right up against her. He brought his handcuffed hands close up to his eyes and examined them. They were the American police model. He contracted his left hand, the thinner of the two, and tried to pull it through the squat ring of steel. Even the sweat on his skin was no help. It was hopeless.

The two men sat on their iron seats with their backs to them, indifferent. They knew they had total command. There wasn't room for Bond to give any trouble. Bond couldn't stand up or get enough momentum into his hands to do any damage to the backs of their heads with his handcuffs. If Bond somehow managed to open the hatch and drop into the water, where would that get him? They would at once feel the fresh air on their backs and stop the machine, and either burn him in the water or pick him up. It annoyed Bond that they didn't worry about him, that they knew he was utterly in their power. He also didn't like the idea that these men were intelligent enough to know that he presented no threat. Stupider men would have sat over him with a gun out, would have trussed him and the girl with inexpert thoroughness, might even have knocked them unconscious. These two knew their business. They were professionals, or had been trained to be professionals.

The two men didn't talk to each other. There was no nervous chatter about how clever they had been, about their destination, about how tired they were. They just drove the machine quietly, efficiently along, finishing their competent job.

Bond still had no idea what this contraption was. Under the black and gold paint and the rest of the fancy dress it was some sort of a tractor, but of a kind he had never seen or heard of. The wheels, with their vast smooth rubber tyres, were nearly twice as tall as himself. He had seen no trade name on the tyres, it had been too dark, but they were certainly either solid or filled with porous rubber. At the rear there had been a small trailing wheel for stability. An iron fin, painted black and gold, had been added to help the dragon effect. The high mudguards had been extended into short backswept wings. A long metal dragon's head had been added to the front of the radiator and the headlamps had been given black centres to makes 'eyes'. That was all there was to it, except that the cabin had been covered with an armoured dome and the flame-thrower added. It was, as Bond had thought, a tractor dressed up to frighten and burn–though why it had a flame-thrower instead of a machine gun he couldn't imagine. It was clearly the only sort of vehicle that could travel the island. Its huge wide wheels would ride over mangrove and swamp and across the shallow lake. It would negotiate the rough coral uplands and, since its threat would be at night, the heat in the iron cabin would remain at least tolerable.

Bond was impressed. He was always impressed by professionalism. Doctor No was obviously a man who took immense pains. Soon Bond would be meeting him. Soon he would be up against the secret of Doctor No. And then what? Bond smiled grimly to himself. He wouldn't be allowed to get away with his knowledge. He would certainly be killed unless he could escape or talk his way out. And what about the girl? Could Bond prove her innocence and have her spared? Conceivably, but she would never be let off the island. She would have to stay there for the rest of her life, as the mistress or wife of one of the men, or Doctor No himself if she appealed to him.

Bond's thoughts were interrupted by rougher going under the wheels. They had crossed the lake and were on the track that led up the mountain to the huts. The cabin tilted and the machine began to climb. In five minutes they would be there.

The co-driver glanced over his shoulder at Bond and the girl. Bond smiled cheerfully up at him. He said, 'You'll get a medal for this.'

The brown and yellow eyes looked impassively into his. The purple, blubbery lips parted in a sneer in which there was slow hate: 'Shut your —ing mouth.'.The man turned back.

The girl nudged him and whispered, 'Why are they so rude? Why do they hate us so much?'

Bond grinned down at her, 'I expect it's because we made them afraid. Perhaps they're still afraid. That's because we don't seem to be frightened of them. We must keep them that way.'

The girl pressed against him. 'I'll try.'

Now the climb was getting steeper. Grey light showed through the slots in the armour. Dawn was coming up. Outside, another day of brazen heat and ugly wind and the smell of marsh gas would be beginning. Bond thought of Quarrel, the brave giant who would not be seeing it, with whom they should now be setting off for the long trek through the mangrove swamps. He remembered the life insurance. Quarrel had smelled his death. Yet he had followed Bond unquestioningly. His faith in Bond had been stronger than his fear. And Bond had let him down. Would Bond also be the death of the girl?

The driver reached forward to the dashboard. From the front of the machine there sounded the brief howl of a police siren. It meandered into a dying moan. After a minute the machine stopped, idling in neutral. The man pressed a switch and took a microphone off a hook beside him. He spoke into it and Bond could hear the echoing voice of the loud-hailer outside. 'Okay. Got the Limey and the girl. Other man's dead. That's the lot. Open up.'

Bond heard a door being pulled sideways on iron rollers. The driver put in the clutch and they rolled slowly forward a few yards and stopped. The man switched off the engine. There was a clang as the iron hatch was opened from the outside. A gush of fresh air and a flood of brighter light came into the cabin. Hands took hold of Bond and dragged him roughly out backwards on to a cement floor. Bond stood up. He felt the prod of a gun in his side. A voice said, 'Stay where you are. No tricks.' Bond looked at the man. He was another Chinese negro, from the same stable as the others. The yellow eyes examined him curiously. Bond turned away indifferently. Another man was prodding the girl with his gun. Bond said sharply, 'Leave the girl alone.' He walked over and stood beside her. The two men seemed surprised. They stood, pointing their guns indecisively.

Bond looked around him. They were in one of the Quonset huts he had seen from the river. It was a garage and workshop. The 'dragon' had been halted over an examination pit in the concrete. A dismantled outboard motor lay on one of the benches. Strips of white sodium lighting ran along the ceiling. There was a smell of oil and exhaust smoke. The driver and his mate were examining the machine. Now they sauntered up.

One of the guards said, 'Passed the message along. The word is to send them through. Everything go okay?'

The co-driver, who seemed to be the senior man present, said, 'Sure. Bit of gunfire. Lights gone. May be some holes in the tyres. Get the boys crackin'–full overhaul. I'll put these two through and go get myself some shuteye.' He turned to Bond. 'Okay, git moving,' he gestured down the long hut.

Bond said, 'Get moving yourself. Mind your manners. And tell those apes to take their guns off us. They might let one off by mistake. They look dumb enough.'

The man came closer. The other three closed up behind him. Hate shone redly in their eyes. The leading man lifted a clenched fist as big as a small ham and held it under Bond's nose. He was controlling himself with an effort. He said tensely, 'Listen, mister. Sometimes us boys is allowed to join in the fun at the end. I'm just praying this'll be one of those times. Once we made it last a whole week. An, Jees, if I get you . . .' He broke off. His eyes were alight with cruelty. He looked past Bond at the girl. The eyes became mouths that licked their lips. He wiped his hands down the sides of his trousers. The tip of his tongue showed pinkly between the purple lips. He turned to the other three. 'What say, fellers?'

The three men were also looking at the girl. They nodded dumbly, like children in front of a Christmas tree.

Bond longed to run beserk among them, laying into their faces with his manacled wrists, accepting their bloody revenge. But for the girl he would have done it. Now all he had achieved with his brave words was to get her frightened. He said, 'All right, all right. You're four and we're two and we've got our hands tied. Come on. We won't hurt you. Just don't push us around too much. Doctor No might not be pleased.'

At the name, the men's faces changed. Three pairs of eyes looked whitely from Bond to the leader. For a minute the leader stared suspiciously at Bond, wondering, trying to fathom whether perhaps Bond had got some edge on their boss. His mouth opened to say something. He thought better of it. He said lamely, 'Okay, okay. We was just kiddin'.' He turned to the men for confirmation. 'Right?'

'Sure! Sure thing.' It was a ragged mumble. The men looked away.

The leader said gruffly, 'This way, mister.' He walked off down the long hut.

Bond took the girl's wrist and followed. He was impressed with the weight of Doctor No's name. That was something to remember if they had any more dealings with the staff.

The man came to a rough wooden door at the end of the hut. There was a bellpush beside it. He rang twice and waited. There came a click and the door opened to reveal ten yards of carpeted rock passage with another door, smarter and cream-painted, at the end.

The man stood aside. 'Straight ahead, mister. Knock on the door. The receptionist'll take over.' There was no irony in his voice and his eyes were impassive.

Bond led the girl into the passage. He heard the door shut behind them. He stopped and looked down at her. He said, 'Now what?'

She smiled tremulously. 'It's nice to feel carpet under one's feet.'

Bond squeezed her wrist. He walked forward to the cream-painted door and knocked.

The door opened. Bond went through with the girl at his heels. When he stopped dead in his tracks, he didn't feel the girl bump into him. He just stood and stared.

Chapter Thirteen

Mink-lined Prison

It was the sort of reception room the largest American corporations have on the President's floor in their New York skyscrapers. It was of pleasant proportions, about twenty feet square. The floor was close-carpeted in the thickest wine-red Wilton and the walls and ceiling were painted a soft dove grey. Colour lithograph reproductions of Degas ballet sketches were well hung in groups on the walls and the lighting was by tall modern standard lamps with dark green silk shades in a fashionable barrel design.

To Bond's right was a broad mahogany desk with a green leather top, handsome matching desk furniture and the most expensive type of intercom. Two tall antique chairs waited for visitors. On the other side of the room was a refectory-type table with shiny magazines and two more chairs. On both the desk and the table were tall vases of freshly cut hibiscus. The air was fresh and cool and held a slight, expensive fragrance.

There were two women in the room. Behind the desk, with pen poised over a printed form, sat an efficient-looking Chinese girl with hornrimmed spectacles below a bang of black hair cut short. Her eyes and mouth wore the standard receptionist's smile of welcome–bright, helpful, inquisitive.

Holding the door through which they had come, and waiting for them to move farther into the room so that she could close it, stood an older, rather matronly woman of about forty-five. She also had Chinese blood. Her appearance, wholesome, bosomy, eager, was almost excessively gracious. Her square cut pince-nez gleamed with the hostess's desire to make them feel at home.

Both women were dressed in spotless white, with white stockings and white suede brogues, like assistants in the most expensive American beauty-parlours. There was something soft and colourless about their skins as if they rarely went out of doors.

While Bond took in the scene, the woman at the door twittered conventional phrases of welcome as if they had been caught in a storm and had arrived late at a party.

'You poor dears. We simply didn't know when to expect you. We kept on being told you were on your way. First it was teatime yesterday, then dinner, and it was only half an hour ago we heard you would only be here in time for breakfast. You must be famished. Come along now and help Sister Rose fill in your forms and then I'll pack you both straight off to bed. You must be tired out.'

Clucking softly, she closed the door and ushered them forward to the desk. She got them seated in the chairs and rattled on, 'Now I'm Sister Lily and this is Sister Rose. She just wants to ask you a few questions. Now, let me see, a cigarette?' She picked up a tooled leather box. She opened it and put it on the desk in front of them. It had three compartments. She pointed with a little finger, 'Those are American, and those are Players, and those are Turkish.' She picked up an expensive desk-lighter and waited.

Bond reached out his manacled hands to take a Turkish cigarette.

Sister Lily gave a squeak of dismay. 'Oh, but really.' She sounded genuinely embarrassed. 'Sister Rose, the key, quickly. I've said again and again that patients are never to be brought in like that.' There was impatience and distaste in her voice. 'Really, that outside staff! It's time they had a talking to.'

Sister Rose was just as much put out. Hastily she scrabbled in a drawer and handed a key across to Sister Lily who, with much cooing and tut-tutting, unlocked the two pairs of handcuffs and walked behind the desk and dropped them as if they were dirty bandages into the wastepaper basket.

'Thank you.' Bond was unable to think of any way to handle the situation except to fall in with what was happening on the stage. He reached out and took a cigarette and lit it. He glanced at Honeychile Rider who sat looking dazed and nervously clutching the arms of her chair. Bond gave her a reassuring smile.

'Now, if you please.' Sister Rose bent over a long printed form on expensive paper. 'I promise to be as quick as I can. Your name please Mister—er . . .'

'Bryce, John Bryce.'

She wrote busily. 'Permanent address?'

'Care of the Royal Zoological Society, Regent's Park, London, England.'

'Profession.'

'Ornithologist.'

'Oh dear,' she dimpled at him, 'could you please spell that?'

Bond did so.

'Thank you so much. Now, let me see, Purpose of Visit?'

'Birds,' said Bond. 'I am also representative of the Audubon Society of New York. They have a lease of part of this island.'

'Oh, really.' Bond watched the pen writing down exactly what he had said. After the last word she put a neat query in brackets.

'And', Sister Rose smiled politely in the direction of Honeychile, 'your wife? Is she also interested in birds?'

'Yes, indeed.'

'And her first name?'

'Honeychile.'

Sister Rose was delighted, 'What a pretty name.' She wrote busily. 'And now just your next of kin and then we're finished.'

Bond gave M's real name as next of kin for both of them. He described him as 'uncle' and gave his address as 'Managing Director, Universal Export, Regent's Park, London'.

Sister Rose finished writing and said, 'There, that's done. Thank you so much, Mr Bryce, and I do hope you both enjoy your stay.'

'Thank you very much. I'm sure we will.' Bond got up. Honeychile Rider did the same, her face still expressionless.

Sister Lily said, 'Now come along with me, you poor dears.' She walked to a door in the far wall. She stopped with her hand on the cut-glass doorknob. 'Oh deary me, now I've gone and forgotten the number of their rooms! It's the Cream Suite, isn't it, Sister?'

'Yes, that's right. Fourteen and fifteen.'

'Thank you, my dear. And now,' she opened the door, 'if you'll just follow me. I'm afraid it's a terribly long walk.' She shut the door behind them and led the way. 'The Doctor's often talked of putting in one of those moving stairway things, but you know how it is with a busy man,' she laughed gaily. 'So many other things to think of.'

'Yes, I expect so,' said Bond politely.

Bond took the girl's hand and they followed the motherly bustling figure down a hundred yards of lofty corridor in the same style as the reception room but lit at frequent intervals by discreetly expensive wall-brackets.

Bond answered with polite monosyllables the occasional twittering comments Sister Lily threw over her shoulder. His whole mind was focused on the extraordinary circumstances of their reception. He was quite certain the two women had been genuine. Not a look or a word had been dropped that was out of place. It was obviously a front of some kind, but a solid one, meticulously supported by the decor and the cast. The lack of resonance in the room, and now in the corridor, suggested that they had stepped from the Quonset hut into the side of the mountain and that they were now walking through its base. At a guess they would be walking towards the west–towards the cliff-face with which the island ended. There was no moisture on the walls and the air was cool and pure with a strongish breeze coming towards them. A lot of money and good engineering had gone into the job. The pallor of the two women suggested that they spent all their time inside the mountain. From what Sister Lily had said it sounded as if they were part of an inside staff that had nothing to do with the strong-arm squad outside and perhaps didn't even understand what sort of men they were.

It was grotesque, concluded Bond as they came nearer to a door at the end of the corridor, dangerously grotesque, but it was no good wondering about it. He could only follow the lines of the gracious script. At least this was better than the backstage of the island outside.

At the door, Sister Lily rang. They had been expected. The door opened at once. An enchanting Chinese girl in a mauve and white flowered kimono stood smiling and bowing as Chinese girls are supposed to do. Again there was nothing but warmth and welcome in the pale, flowerlike face. Sister Lily cried, 'Here they are at last, May! Mr and Mrs John Bryce. And I know they must be exhausted so we must take them straight to their rooms for some breakfast and a sleep.' She turned to Bond. 'This is May. Such a dear girl. She will be looking after you both. Anything you want, just ring for May. She's a favourite with all our patients.'

Patients thought Bond. That's the second time she's used the word. He smiled politely at the girl. 'How do you do. Yes, we'd certainly both of us like to get to our rooms.'

May embraced them both with a warm smile. She said in a low, attractive voice, 'I do hope you'll both be comfortable, Mr Bryce. I took the liberty of ordering breakfast as soon as I heard you had come in. Shall we . . .?' Corridors branched off to left and right of double lift-doors set in the wall opposite. The girl led the way to the right. Bond and Honeychile followed with Sister Lily taking up the rear.

Numbered doors led off the corridor on either side. Now the decor was in the lightest pink with a dove grey carpet. The numbers on the doors were in the tens. The corridor came to an abrupt end with two doors side by side, 14 and 15. May opened the door of 14 and they followed her in.

It was a charming double bedroom in modern Miami style with dark green walls, dark polished mahogany floor with occasional thick white rugs, and well-designed bamboo furniture with a chintz of large red roses on a white background. There was a communicating door into a more masculine dressing-room and another that led into an extremely luxurious modern bathroom with a step-down bath and a bidet.

It was like being shown into the very latest Florida hotel suite–except for two details which Bond noticed. There were no windows and no inside handles to the doors.

May looked hopefully from one to the other.

Bond turned to Honeychile. He smiled at her. 'It looks very comfortable, don't you think, darling?'

The girl played with the edge of her skirt. She nodded, not looking at him.

There was a timid knock on the door and another girl, as pretty as May, tripped in with a loaded tray balanced on her upturned hand. She put it down on the centre table and pulled up two chairs. She whisked off the speckless linen cloth that covered the dishes and pattered out of the room. There was a delicious smell of bacon and coffee.

May and Sister Lily backed to the door. The older woman stopped on the threshold. 'And now we'll leave you two dear people in peace. If you want anything, just ring. The bells are by the bed. Oh, and by the way, you'll find plenty of fresh clothes in the cupboards. Chinese style, I'm afraid,' she twinkled apologetically, 'but I hope they're the right sizes. The wardrobe room only got the measurements yesterday evening. The Doctor has given strict orders that you're not to be disturbed. He'd be delighted if you'd join him for dinner this evening. He wants you to have the whole of the rest of the day to yourselves–to get settled down, you know.' She paused and looked from one to the other in smiling inquiry. 'Shall I say you . . .?'

'Yes, please,' said Bond. 'Tell the Doctor we shall be delighted to join him for dinner.'

'Oh, I know he'll be so pleased.' With a last twitter the two women softly withdrew and closed the door behind them.

Bond turned towards Honeychile. She looked embarrassed. She still avoided his eyes. It occurred to Bond that she could never have met such soft treatment or seen such luxury in her life. To her, all this must be far more strange and terrifying than what they had gone through outside. She stood and fiddled at the hem of her Man Friday skirt. There were streaks of dried sweat and salt and dust on her face. Her bare legs were filthy and Bond noticed that her toes were moving softly as they gripped nervously into the wonderful thick pile carpet.

Bond laughed. He laughed with real pleasure that her fear had been drowned in the basic predicament of clothes and how to behave, and he laughed at the picture they made–she in her rags and he in his dirty blue shirt and black jeans and muddy canvas shoes.

He went to her and took her hands. They were cold. He said, 'Honey, we're a couple of scarecrows. There's only one problem. Shall we have breakfast first while it's hot, or shall we get out of these rags and have a bath and eat the breakfast when it's cold? Don't worry about anything else. We're here in this wonderful little house and that's all that matters. Now then, what shall we do.'

She smiled uncertainly. The blue eyes searched his face for reassurance. 'You're not worried about what's going to happen to us?' She nodded at the room. 'Don't you think this is all a trap?'

'If it's a trap we're in it. There's nothing we can do now but eat the cheese. The only question is whether we eat it hot or cold.' He pressed her hands. 'Really, Honey. Leave the worrying to me. Just think where we were an hour ago. Isn't this better? Now come on and decide the really important things. Bath or breakfast?'

She said reluctantly, 'Well, if you think . . . I mean–I'd rather get clean first.' She added quickly, 'But you've got to help me.' She jerked her head towards the bathroom door. 'I don't know how to work one of those places. What do you do?'

Bond said seriously, 'It's quite easy. I'll fix it all ready for you. While you're having your bath, I'll have my breakfast. I'll keep yours warm.' Bond went to one of the built-in clothes cupboards and ran the door back. There were half a dozen kimonos, some silk and some linen. He took out a linen one at random. 'You take off your clothes and get into this and I'll get the bath ready. Later on you can choose the things you want to wear for bed and dinner.'

She said gratefully, 'Oh yes, James. If you'll just show me . . .' She started to unbutton her shirt.

Bond wanted to take her in his arms and kiss her. Instead he said abruptly, 'That's fine, Honey,' and went into the bathroom and turned on the taps.

There was everything in the bathroom–Floris Lime bath essence for men and Guerlain bathcubes for women. He crushed a cube into the water and at once the room smelled like an orchid house. The soap was Guerlain's Sapoceti, *Fleurs des Alpes*. In a medicine cupboard behind the mirror over the washbasin were toothbrushes and toothpaste, Steradent toothpicks, Rose mouthwash, dental floss, Aspirin and Milk of Magnesia. There was also an electric razor, Lentheric after-shave lotion, and two nylon hairbrushes and combs. Everything was brand new and untouched.

Bond looked at his filthy unshaven face in the mirror and smiled grimly into the grey, sunburned castaway's eyes. The coating on the pill was certainly of the very finest sugar. It would be wise to expect that the medicine inside would be of the bitterest.

He turned back to the bath and felt the water. It would be too hot for someone who presumably had never had a hot bath before. He let in some cold. As he bent over, two arms were thrown round his neck. He stood up. The golden body blazed in the white tiled bathroom. She kissed him hard and clumsily on the lips. He put his arms round her and crushed her to him, his heart pounding. She said breathlessly at his ear, 'The Chinese dress felt strange. Anyway, you told that woman we were married.'

Bond's hand was on her left breast. Its peak was hard with passion. Her stomach pressed against his. Why not? Why not? Don't be a fool! This is a crazy time for it. You're both in deadly danger. You must stay cold as ice to have any chance of getting out of this mess. Later! Later. Don't be weak.

Bond took his hand away from her breast and put it round her neck. He rubbed his face against hers and then brought his mouth round to hers and gave her one long kiss.

He stood away and held her at arm's length. For a moment they looked at each other, their eyes bright with desire. She was breathing fast, her lips parted so that he could see the glint of teeth. He said unsteadily, 'Honey, get into that bath before I spank you.'

She smiled. Without saying anything she stepped down into the bath and lay at full length. She looked up. The fair hair on her body glittered up through the water like golden sovereigns. She said provocatively, 'You've got to wash me. I don't know what to do. You've got to show me.'

Bond said desperately, 'Shut up, Honey. And stop flirting. Just take the soap and the sponge and start scrubbing. Damn you! This isn't the time for making love. I'm going to have breakfast.' He reached for the door handle and opened the door. She said softly, 'James!' He looked back. She was sticking her tongue out at him. He grinned savagely back at her and slammed the door.

Bond went into the dressing-room and stood in the middle of the floor and waited for his heart to stop pounding. He rubbed his hands over his face and shook his head to get rid of the thought of her.

To clear his mind he went carefully over both rooms looking for exits, possible weapons, microphones–anything that would add to his knowledge. There were none of these things. There was an electric clock on the wall which said eight-thirty and a row of bells beside the double bed. They said, Room Service, Coiffeur, Manicurist, Maid. There was no telephone. High up in a corner of both rooms was a small ventilator grille. Each was about two feet square. Useless. The doors appeared to be of some light metal, painted to match the walls. Bond threw the whole weight of his body against one of them. It didn't give a millimetre. Bond rubbed his shoulder. The place was a prison–an exquisite prison. It was no good arguing. The trap had shut tight on them. Now the only thing for the mice to do was to make the most of the cheese.

Bond sat down at the breakfast table. There was a large tumbler of pineapple juice in a silver-plated bowl of crushed ice. He swallowed it down and lifted the cover off his individual hot-plate. Scrambled eggs on toast, four rashers of bacon, a grilled kidney and what looked like an English pork sausage. There were also two kinds of hot toast, rolls inside a napkin, marmalade, honey and strawberry jam. The coffee was boiling hot in a large Thermos decanter. The cream smelled fresh.

From the bathroom came the sound of the girl crooning 'Marion'. Bond closed his ears to the sound and started on the eggs.

Ten minutes later, Bond heard the bathroom door open. He put down his toast and marmalade and covered his eyes with his hands. She laughed. She said, 'He's a coward. He's frightened of a simple girl.' Bond heard her rummaging in the cupboards. She went on talking, half to herself. 'I wonder why he's frightened. Of course if I wrestled with him I'd win easily. Perhaps he's frightened of that. Perhaps he's really not very strong. His arms and his chest look strong enough. I haven't seen the rest yet. Perhaps it's weak. Yes, that must be it. That's why he doesn't dare take his clothes off in front of me. H'm, now let's see, would he like me in this?' She raised her voice. 'Darling James, would you like me in white with pale blue birds flying all over me?'

'Yes, damn you,' said Bond through his hands. 'Now stop chattering to yourself and come and have breakfast. I'm getting sleepy.'

She gave a cry. 'Oh, if you mean it's time for us to go to bed, of course I'll hurry.'

There was a flurry of feet and Bond heard her sit down opposite. He took his hands down. She was smiling at him. She looked ravishing. Her hair was dressed and combed and brushed to kill, with one side falling down the side of the cheek and the other slicked back behind her ear. Her skin sparkled with freshness and the big blue eyes were alight with happiness. Now Bond loved the broken nose. It had become part of his thoughts of her and it suddenly occurred to him that he would be sad when she was just an immaculately beautiful girl like other beautiful girls. But he knew it would be no good trying to persuade her of that. She sat demurely, with her hands in her lap below the end of a cleavage which showed half her breasts and a deep vee of her stomach.

Bond said severely, 'Now listen, Honey. You look wonderful, but that isn't the way to wear a kimono. Pull it up right across your body and tie it tight and stop trying to look like a call girl. It just isn't good manners at breakfast.'

'Oh, you are a stuffy old beast.' She pulled her kimono an inch or two closer. 'Why don't you like playing? I want to play at being married.'

'Not at breakfast time,' said Bond firmly. 'Come on and eat up. It's delicious. And anyway, I'm filthy. I'm going to shave and have a bath.' He got up and walked round the table and kissed the top of her head. 'And as for playing, as you call it, I'd rather play with you than anyone in the world. But not now.' Without waiting for her answer he walked into the bathroom and shut the door.

Bond shaved and had a bath and a shower. He felt desperately sleepy. Sleep came to him in waves so that from time to time he had to stop what he was doing and bend his head down between his knees. When he came to brush his teeth he could hardly do it. Now he recognized the signs. He had been drugged. In the coffee or in the pineapple juice? It didn't matter. Nothing mattered. All he wanted to do was lie down on the tiled floor and shut his eyes. Bond weaved drunkenly to the door. He forgot that he was naked. That didn't matter either. Anyway the girl had finished her breakfast. She was in bed. He staggered over to her, holding on to the furniture. The kimono was lying in a pile on the floor. She was fast asleep, naked under a single sheet.

Bond gazed dreamily at the empty pillow beside her head. No! He found the switches and turned out the lights. Now he had to crawl across the floor and into his room. He got to his bed and pulled himself on to it. He reached out an arm of lead and jabbed at the switch on the bed-light. He missed it. The lamp crashed to the floor and the bulb burst. With a last effort Bond turned on his side and let the waves sweep over his head.

The luminous figures on the electric clock in the double room said nine-thirty.

At ten o'clock the door of the double room opened softly. A very tall thin figure was silhouetted against the lighted corridor. It was a man. He must have been six feet six tall. He stood on the threshold with his arms folded, listening. Satisfied, he moved slowly into the room and up to the bed. He knew the way exactly. He bent down and listened to the quiet breathing of the girl. After a moment he reached up to his chest and pressed a switch. A flashlight with a very broad diffused beam came on. The flashlight was attached to him by a belt that held it above the breast bone. He bent forward so that the soft light shone on the girl's face.

The intruder examined the girl's face for several minutes. One of his hands came up and took the sheet at her chin and softly drew the sheet down to the end of the bed. The hand that drew down the sheet was not a hand. It was a pair of articulated steel pincers at the end of a metal stalk that disappeared into a black silk sleeve. It was a mechanical hand.

The man gazed for a long time at the naked body, moving his chest to and fro so that every corner of the body came under the light. Then the claw came out again and delicately lifted a corner of the sheet from the bottom of the bed and drew it back over the girl. The man stood for another moment gazing down at the sleeping face, then he switched off the torch on his chest and moved quietly away across the room to the open door through which Bond was sleeping.

The man spent longer beside Bond's bed. He scrutinized every line, every shadow on the dark, rather cruel face that lay drowned, almost extinct, on the pillow. He watched the pulse in the neck and counted it and, when he had pulled down the sheet, he did the same with the area round the heart. He gauged the curve of the muscles on Bond's arms and thighs and looked thoughtfully at the hidden strength in the flat stomach. He even bent down close over the outflung open right hand and examined its life and fate lines.

Finally, with infinite care, the steel claw drew the sheet back up to Bond's neck. For another minute the tall figure stood over the sleeping man, then it swished softly away and out into the corridor and the door closed with a click.

Chapter Fourteen

Come Into My Parlour

The electric clock in the cool dark room in the heart of the mountain showed four-thirty.

Outside the mountain, Crab Key had sweltered and stunk its way through another day. At the eastern end of the island, the mass of birds, Louisiana herons, pelicans, avocets, sandpipers, egrets, flamingoes and the few roseate spoonbills, went on with building their nests or fished in the shallow waters of the lake. Most of the birds had been disturbed so often that year that they had given up any idea of building. In the past few months they had been raided at regular intervals by the monster that came at night and burned down their roosting places and the beginnings of their nests. This year many would not breed. There would be vague movements to migrate and many would die of the nervous hysteria that seizes bird colonies when they no longer have peace and privacy.

At the other end of the island, on the guanera that gave the mountain its snow-covered look, the fast swarm of cormorants had passed their usual day of gorging themselves with fish and paying back the ounce of previous manure to their owner and protector. Nothing had interfered with *their* nesting season. Now they were noisily fiddling with the untidy piles of sticks that would be their nests–each pile at exactly sixty centimetres from the next, for the guanay is a quarrelsome bird and this sixty-centimetre ring represents their sparring space. Soon the females would be laying the three eggs from which their master's flock would be increased by an average of two young cormorants.

Below the peak, where the diggings began, the hundred or so negro men and women who were the labour force were coming to the end of the day's shift. Another fifty cubic yards of guano had been dug out of the mountainside and another twenty yards of terrace had been added to the working level. Below, the mountainside looked like terraced vineyards in Upper Italy, except that here there were no vines, only deep barren shelves cut in the mountainside. And here, instead of the stink of marsh gas on the rest of the island, there was a strong ammoniac smell, and the ugly hot wind that kept the diggings dry blew the freshly turned whitish-brown dust into the eyes and ears and noses of the diggers. But the workers were used to the smell and the dust, and it was easy, healthy work. They had no complaints.

The last iron truck of the day started off on the Decauderville Track that snaked down the mountainside to the crusher and separator. A whistle blew and the workers shouldered their clumsy picks and moved lazily down towards the high-wired group of Quonset huts that was their compound. Tomorrow, on the other side of the mountain, the monthly ship would be coming in to the deep-water quay they had helped to build ten years before, but which, since then, they had never seen. That would mean fresh stores and fresh goods and cheap jewellery at the canteen. It would be a holiday. There would be rum and dancing and a few fights. Life was good.

Life was good, too, for the senior outside staff–all Chinese negroes like the men who had hunted Bond and Quarrel and the girl. They also stopped work in the garage and the machine shops and at the guard posts and filtered off the 'officers'' quarters. Apart from watch and loading duties, tomorrow would also be a holiday for most of them. They too would have their drinking and dancing, and there would be a new monthly batch of girls from 'inside'. Some 'marriages' from the last lot would continue for further months or weeks according to the taste of the 'husband', but for the others there would be a fresh choice. There would be some of the older girls who had had their babies in the creche and were coming back for a fresh spell of duty 'outside', and there would be a sprinkling of young ones who had come of age and would be 'coming out' for the first time. There would be fights over these and blood would be shed, but in the end the officers' quarters would settle down for another month of communal life, each officer with his woman to look after his needs.

Deep down in the cool heart of the mountain, far below this well-disciplined surface life, Bond awoke in his comfortable bed. Apart from a slight nembutal headache he felt fit and rested. Lights were on in the girl's room and he could hear her moving about. He swung his feet to the ground and, avoiding the fragments of glass from the broken lamp, walked softly over to the clothes cupboard and put on the first kimono that came to his hand. He went to the door. The girl had a pile of kimonos out on the bed and was trying them on in front of the wall mirror. She had on a very smart one in sky-blue silk. It looked wonderful against the gold of her skin. Bond said, 'That's the one.'

She whirled round, her hand at her mouth. She took it down. 'Oh, it's you!' She smiled at him. 'I thought you'd never wake up. I've been to look at you several times. I'd made up my mind to wake you at five. It's half past four and I'm hungry. Can you get us something to eat?'

'Why not.' Bond walked across to her bed. As he passed he put his arm round her waist and took her with him. He examined the bells. He pressed the one marked 'Room Service'. He said, 'What about the others? Let's have the full treatment.'

She giggled. 'But what's a manicurist?'

'Someone who does your nails. We must look our best for Doctor No.' At the back of Bond's mind was the urgent necessity to get his hands on some kind of weapon–a pair of scissors would be better than nothing. Anything would do.

He pressed two more bells. He let her go and looked round the room. Someone had come while they were asleep and taken away the breakfast things. There was a drink tray on a sideboard against the wall. Bond went over and examined it. It had everything. Propped among the bottles were two menus, huge double-folio pages covered with print. They might have been from the Savoy Grill, or the '21', or the Tour d'Argent. Bond ran his eye down one of them. It began with *Caviar double de Beluga* and ended with *Sorbet à la Champagne*. In between was every dish whose constituents would not be ruined by a deep freeze. Bond tossed it down. One certainly couldn't grumble about the quality of the cheese in the trap!

There was a knock on the door and the exquisite May came in. She was followed by two other twittering Chinese girls. Bond brushed aside their amiabilities, ordered tea and buttered toast for Honeychile and told them to look after her hair and nails. Then he went into the bathroom and had a couple of Aspirins and a cold shower. He put on his kimono again, reflected that he looked idiotic in it, and went back into the room. A beaming May asked if he would be good enough to select what he and Mrs Bryce could care to have for dinner. Without enthusiasm, Bond ordered caviar, grilled lamb cutlets and salad, and angels on horseback for himself. When Honeychile refused to make any suggestions, he chose melon, roast chicken à l'Anglaise and vanilla icecream with hot chocolate sauce for her.

May dimpled her enthusiasm and approval. 'The Doctor asks if seven forty-five for eight would be convenient.'

Bond said curtly that it would.

'Thank you so much, Mr Bryce. I will call for you at seven forty-four.'

Bond walked over to where Honeychile was being ministered to at the dressing-table. He watched the busy delicate fingers at work on her hair and her nails. She smiled at him excitedly in the mirror. He said gruffly, 'Don't let them make too much of a monkey out of you,' and went to the drink tray. He poured himself out a stiff Bourbon and soda and took it into his own room. So much for his idea of getting hold of a weapon. The scissors and files and probes were attached to the manicurist's waist by a chain. So were the scissors of the hairdresser. Bond sat down on his rumpled bed and lost himself in drink and gloomy reflections.

The women went. The girl looked in at him. When he didn't lift his head she went back into her room and left him alone. In due course Bond came into her room to get himself another drink. He said perfunctorily, 'Honey, you look wonderful.' He glanced at the clock on the wall and went back and drank his drink and put on another of the idiotic kimonos, a plain black one.

In due course there came the soft knock on the door and the two of them went silently out of the room and along the empty, gracious corridor. May stopped at the lift. Its doors were held open by another eager Chinese girl. They walked in and the doors shut. Bond noticed that the lift was made by Waygood Otis. Everything in the prison was de luxe. He gave an inward shudder of distaste. He noticed the reaction. He turned to the girl. 'I'm sorry, Honey. Got a bit of a headache.' He didn't want to tell her that all this luxury play-acting was getting him down, that he hadn't the smallest idea what it was all about, that he knew it was bad news, and that he hadn't an inkling of a plan of how to get them out of whatever situation they were in. That was the worst of it. There was nothing that depressed Bond's spirit so much as the knowledge that he hadn't one line of either attack or defence.

The girl moved closer to him. She said, 'I'm sorry, James. I hope it will go away. You're not angry with me about anything?'

Bond dredged up a smile. He said, 'No, darling. I'm only angry with myself.' He lowered his voice: 'Now, about this evening. Just leave the talking to me. Be natural and don't be worried by Doctor No. He may be a bit mad.'

She nodded solemnly. 'I'll do my best.'

The lift sighed to a stop. Bond had no idea how far down they had gone–a hundred feet, two hundred? The automatic doors hissed back and Bond and the girl stepped out into a large room.

It was empty. It was a high-ceilinged room about sixty feet long, lined on three sides with books to the ceiling. At first glance, the fourth wall seemed to be made of solid blue-black glass. The room appeared to be a combined study and library. There was a big paper-strewn desk in one corner and a central table with periodicals and newspapers. Comfortable club chairs, upholstered in red leather, were dotted about. The carpet was dark green, and the lighting, from standard lamps, was subdued. The only odd feature was that the drink tray and sideboard were up against the middle of the long glass wall, and chairs and occasional tables with ashtrays were arranged in a semi-circle round it so that the room was centred in front of the empty wall.

Bond's eye caught a swirl of movement in the dark glass. He walked across the room. A silvery spray of small fish with a bigger fish in pursuit fled across the dark blue. They disappeared, so to speak, off the edge of the screen. What was this? An aquarium? Bond looked upwards. A yard below the ceiling, small waves were lapping at the glass. Above the waves was a strip of greyer blue-black, dotted with sparks of light. The outlines of Orion were the clue. This was not an aquarium. This was the sea itself and the night sky. The whole of one side of the room was made of armoured glass. They were under the sea, looking straight into its heart, twenty feet down.

Bond and the girl stood transfixed. As they watched, there was the glimpse of two great goggling orbs. A golden sheen of head and deep flank showed for an instant and was gone. A big grouper? A silver swarm of anchovies stopped and hovered and sped away. The twenty-foot tendrils of a Portuguese man-o'-war drifted slowly across the window, glinting violet as they caught the light. Up above there was the dark mass of its underbelly and the outline of its inflated bladder, steering with the breeze.

Bond walked along the wall, fascinated by the idea of living with this slow, endlessly changing moving picture. A big tulip shell was progressing slowly up the window from the floor level, a frisk of demoiselles and angel fish and a ruby-red moonlight snapper were nudging and rubbing themselves against a corner of the glass and a sea centipede quested along, nibbling at the minute algae that must grow every day on the outside of the window. A long dark shadow paused in the centre of the window and then moved slowly away. If only one could see more!

Obediently, two great shafts of light, from off the 'screen', lanced out into the water. For an instant they searched independently. Then they converged on the departing shadow and the dull grey torpedo of a twelve-foot shark showed up in all its detail. Bond could even see the piglike pink eyes roll inquisitively in the light and the slow pulse of the slanting gill-rakers. For an instant the shark turned straight into the converged beam and the white half-moon mouth showed below the flat reptile's head. It stood poised for a second and then, with an elegant, disdainful swirl, the great swept-back tail came round and with a lightning quiver the shark had gone.

The searchlights went out. Bond turned slowly. He expected to see Doctor No, but still the room was empty. It looked static and lifeless compared with the pulsing mysteries outside the window. Bond looked back. What must this be like in the colours of day, when one could see everything perhaps for twenty yards or more? What must it be like in a storm when the waves crashed noiselessly against the glass, delving almost to the floor and then sweeping up and out of sight. What must it be like in the evening when the last golden shafts of the sun shone into the upper half of the room and the waters below were full of dancing motes and tiny water insects? What an amazing man this must be who had thought of this fantastically beautiful conception, and what an extraordinary engineering feat to have carried it out! How had he done it? There could only be one way. He must have built the glass wall deep inside the cliff and then delicately removed layer after layer of the outside rock until the divers could prise off the last skin of coral. But how thick was the glass? Who had rolled it for him? How had he got it to the island? How many divers had he used? How much, God in heaven, could it have cost?

'One million dollars.'

It was a cavernous, echoing voice, with a trace of American accent.

Bond turned slowly, almost reluctantly, away from the window.

Doctor No had come through a door behind his desk. He stood looking at them benignly, with a thin smile on his lips.

'I expect you were wondering about the cost. My guests usually think about the material side after about fifteen minutes. Were you?'

'I was.'

Still smiling (Bond was to get used to that thin smile), Doctor No came slowly out from behind the desk and moved towards them. He seemed to glide rather than take steps. His knees did not dent the matt, gunmetal sheen of his kimono and no shoes showed below the sweeping hem.

Bond's first impression was of thinness and erectness and height. Doctor No was at least six inches taller than Bond, but the straight immovable poise of his body made him seem still taller. The head also was elongated and tapered from a round, completely bald skull down to a sharp chin so that the impression was of a reversed raindrop–or rather oildrop, for the skin was of a deep almost translucent yellow.

It was impossible to tell Doctor No's age: as far as Bond could see, there were no lines on the face. It was odd to see a forehead as smooth as the top of the polished skull. Even the cavernous indrawn cheeks below the prominent cheekbones looked as smooth as fine ivory. There was something Dali-esque about the eyebrows, which were fine and black and sharply unswept as if they had been painted on as make-up for a conjurer. Below them, slanting jet black eyes stared out of the skull. They were without eyelashes. They looked like the mouths of two small revolvers, direct and unblinking and totally devoid of expression. The thin fine nose ended very close above a wide compressed wound of a mouth which, despite its almost permanent sketch of a smile, showed only cruelty and authority. The chin was indrawn towards the neck. Later Bond was to notice that it rarely moved more than slightly away from centre, giving the impression that the head and the vertebra were in one piece.

The bizarre, gliding figure looked like a giant venomous worm wrapped in grey tin-foil, and Bond would not have been surprised to see the rest of it trailing slimily along the carpet behind.

Doctor No came within three steps of them and stopped. The wound in the tall face opened. 'Forgive me for not shaking hands with you,' the deep voice was flat and even. 'I am unable to.' Slowly the sleeves parted and opened. 'I have no hands.'

The two pairs of steel pincers came out on their gleaming stalks and were held up for inspection like the hands of a praying mantis. Then the two sleeves joined again.

Bond felt the girl at his side give a start.

The black apertures turned towards her. They slid down to her nose. The voice said flatly, 'It is a misfortune.' The eyes came back to Bond. 'You were admiring my aquarium.' It was a statement, not a question. 'Man enjoys the beasts and the birds. I decided to enjoy also the fish. I find them far more varied and interesting. I am sure you both share my enthusiasm.'

Bond said, 'I congratulate you. I shall never forget this room.'

'No.' Again a statement, perhaps with a sardonic inflection, of fact. 'But we have much to talk about. And so little time. Please sit down. You will have a drink? Cigarettes are beside your chairs.'

Doctor No moved to a high leather chair and folded himself down on to the seat. Bond took the chair opposite. The girl sat between them and slightly back.

Bond felt a movement behind him. He looked over his shoulder. A short man, a Chinese negro, with the build of a wrestler, stood at the drink tray. He was dressed in black trousers and a smart white jacket. Black almond eyes in a wide moon face met his and slid incuriously away.

Doctor No said, 'This is my bodyguard. He is expert in many things. There is no mystery about his sudden appearance. I always carry what is known as a walkie-talkie here,' he inclined his chin towards the bosom on his kimono. 'Thus I can summon him when he is needed. What will the girl have?'

Not 'Your Wife'. Bond turned to Honeychile. Her eyes were wide and staring. She said quietly, 'A Coca-Cola, please.'

Bond felt a moment of relief. At least she was not being got down by the performance. Bond said, 'And I would like a medium Vodka dry Martini–with a slice of lemon peel. Shaken and not stirred, please. I would prefer Russian or Polish vodka.'

Doctor No gave his thin smile an extra crease. 'I see you are also a man who knows what he wants. On this occasion your desires will be satisfied. Do you not find that it is generally so? When one wants a thing one gets it? That is my experience.'

'The small things.'

'If you fail at the large things it means you have not large ambitions. Concentration, focus–that is all. The aptitudes come, the tools forge themselves. "Give me a fulcrum and I will move the world"–but only if the desire to move the world is there.' The thin lips bent minutely downwards in deprecation. 'But this is chatter. We are making conversation. Instead, let us talk. Both of us, I am sure, prefer talk to conversation. Is the Martini to your liking? You have cigarettes–enough and the right sort to cosset your cancer? So be it. Sam-sam, put the shaker beside the man and another bottle of Coca-Cola beside the girl. It should now be eight-ten. We will have dinner at nine o'clock precisely.'

Doctor No sat slightly more upright in his chair. He inclined himself forward, staring at Bond. There was a moment's silence in the room. Then Doctor No said, 'And now Mister James Bond of the Secret Service, let us tell each other our secrets. First, to show you that I hide nothing, I will tell you mine. Then you will tell me yours.' Doctor No's eyes blazed darkly. 'But let us tell each other the truth.' He drew one steel claw out of the wide sleeve and held it upwards. He paused, 'I shall do so. But you must do the same. If you do not, these,' he pointed the claw at his eyes, 'will know that you are lying.'

Doctor No brought the steel claw delicately in front of each eye and tapped the centre of each eyeball.

Each eyeball in turn emitted a dull ting. 'These', said Doctor No, 'see everything.'

Chapter Fifteen

Pandora's Box

James Bond picked up his glass and sipped at it thoughtfully. It seemed pointless to go on bluffing. His story of representing the Audubon Society was anyway a thin one which could be punctured by anyone who knew about birds. It was obvious that his own cover was in shreds. He must concentrate on protecting the girl. To begin with he must reassure her.

Bond smiled at Doctor No. He said, 'I know about your contact in King's House, Miss Taro. She is your agent. I have recorded the fact and it will be divulged in certain circumstances'–Doctor No's expression showed no interest–'as will other facts. But, if we are to have a talk, let us have it without any more stage effects. You are an interesting man. But it is not necessary to make yourself more interesting than you are. You have suffered the misfortune of losing your hands. You wear mechanical hands. Many men wounded in the war wear them. You wear contact lenses instead of spectacles. You use a walkie-talkie instead of a bell to summon your servant. No doubt you have other tricks. But, Doctor No, you are still a man who sleeps and eats and defecates like the rest of us. So no more conjuring tricks, please. I am not one of your guano diggers and I am not impressed by them.'

Doctor No inclined his head a fraction. 'Bravely spoken, Mister Bond. I accept the rebuke. I have no doubt developed annoying mannerisms from living too long in the company of apes. But do not mistake these mannerisms for bluff. I am a technician. I suit the tool to the material. I possess also a range of tools for working with refractory materials. However,' Doctor No raised his joined sleeves an inch and let them fall back in his lap, 'let us proceed with our talk. It is a rare pleasure to have an intelligent listener and I shall enjoy telling you the story of one of the most remarkable men in the world. You are the first person to hear it. I have not told it before. You are the only person I have ever met who will appreciate my story and also–' Doctor No paused for the significance of the last words to make itself felt–'keep it to himself.' He continued, 'The second of these considerations also applies to the girl.'

So that was it. There had been little doubt in Bond's mind ever since the Spandau had opened up on them, and since, even before then, in Jamaica, where the attempts on him had not been half-hearted. Bond had assumed from the first that this man was a killer, that it would be a duel to the death. He had had his usual blind faith that he would win the duel–all the way until the moment when the flame-thrower had pointed at him. Then he had begun to doubt. Now he knew. This man was too strong, too well equipped.

Bond said, 'There is no point in the girl hearing this. She has nothing to do with me. I found her yesterday on the beach. She is a Jamaican from Morgan's Harbour. She collects shells. Your men destroyed her canoe so I had to bring her with me. Send her away now and then back home. She won't talk. She will swear not to.'

The girl interrupted fiercely. 'I *will* talk! I shall tell everything. I'm not going to move. I'm going to stay with you.'

Bond looked at her. He said icily, 'I don't want you.'

Doctor No said softly, 'Do not waste your breath on these heroics. Nobody who comes to this island has ever left it. Do you understand? Nobody–not even the simplest fisherman. It is not my policy. Do not argue with me or attempt to bluff me. It is entirely useless.'

Bond examined the face. There was no anger in it, no obstinacy–nothing but a supreme indifference. He shrugged his shoulders. He looked at the girl and smiled. He said, 'All right, Honey. And I didn't mean it. I'd hate you to go away. We'll stay together and listen to what the maniac has to say.'

The girl nodded happily. It was as if her lover had threatened to send her out of the cinema and now had relented.

Doctor No said, in the same soft resonant voice, 'You are right, Mister Bond. That is just what I am, a maniac. All the greatest men are maniacs. They are possessed by a mania which drives them forward towards their goal. The great scientists, the artists, the philosophers, the religious leaders–all maniacs. What else but a blind singleness of purpose could have given focus to their genius, would have kept them in the groove of their purpose? Mania, my dear Mister Bond, is as priceless as genius. Dissipation of energy, fragmentation of vision, loss of momentum, the lack of follow-through–these are the vices of the herd.' Doctor No sat slightly back in his chair. 'I do not possess these vices. I am, as you correctly say, a maniac–a maniac, Mister Bond, with a mania for power. That'–the black holes glittered blankly at Bond through the contact lenses–'is the meaning of my life. That is why I am here. That is why you are here. That is why here exists.'

Bond picked up his glass and drained it. He filled it again from the shaker. He said, 'I'm not surprised. It's the old business of thinking you're the King of England, or the President of the United States, or God. The asylums are full of them. The only difference is that instead of being shut up, you've built your own asylum and shut yourself up in it. But why did you do it? Why does sitting shut up in this cell give you the illusion of power?'

Irritation flickered at the corner of the thin mouth. 'Mister Bond, power is sovereignty. Clausewitz's first principle was to have a secure base. From there one proceeds to freedom of action. Together, that is sovereignty. I have secured these things and much besides. No one else in the world possesses them to the same degree. They *cannot* have them. The world is too public. These things can only be secured in privacy. You talk of kings and presidents. How much power do they possess? As much as their people will allow them. Who in the world has the power of life or death over his people? Now that Stalin is dead, can you name any man except myself? And how do I possess that power, that sovereignty? Through privacy. Through the fact that nobody *knows*. Through the fact that I have to account to no one.'

Bond shrugged. 'That is only the illusion of power, Doctor No. Any man with a loaded revolver has the power of life and death over his neighbour. Other people beside you have murdered in secret and got away with it. In the end they generally get their deserts. A greater power than they possess is exerted upon them by the community. That will happen to you, Doctor No. I tell you, your search for power is an illusion because power itself is an illusion.'

Doctor No said equably, 'So is beauty, Mister Bond. So is art, so is money, so is death. And so, probably, is life. These concepts are relative. Your play upon words does not shake me. I know philosophy, I know ethics, and I know logic–better than you do, I daresay. But let us move away from this sterile debate. Let us return to where I began, with my mania for power, or, if you wish it, for the illusion of power. And please, Mister Bond,' again the extra crease in the fixed smile, 'please do not imagine that half an hour's conversation with you will alter the pattern of my life. Interest yourself rather in the history of my pursuit, let us put it, of an illusion.'

'Go ahead.' Bond glanced at the girl. She caught his eyes. She put her hand up to her mouth as if to conceal a yawn. Bond grinned at her. He wondered when it would amuse Doctor No to crack her pose of indifference.

Doctor No said benignly, 'I shall endeavour not to bore you. Facts are so much more interesting than theories, don't you agree?' Doctor No was not expecting a reply. He fixed his eye on the elegant tulip shell that had now wandered half way up the outside of the dark window. Some small silver fish squirted across the black void. A bluish prickle of phosphorescence meandered vaguely. Up by the ceiling, the stars shone more brightly through the glass.

The artificiality of the scene inside the room–the three people sitting in the comfortable chairs, the drinks on the sideboard, the rich carpet, the shaded lights, suddenly seemed ludicrous to Bond. Even the drama of it, the danger, were fragile things compared with the progress of the tulip shell up the glass outside. Supposing the glass burst. Supposing the stresses had been badly calculated, the workmanship faulty. Supposing the sea decided to lean a little more heavily against the window.

Doctor No said, 'I was the only son of a German Methodist missionary and a Chinese girl of good family. I was born in Pekin, but on what is known as "the wrong side of the blanket". I was an encumbrance. An aunt of my mother was paid to bring me up.' Doctor No paused. 'No love, you see, Mister Bond. Lack of parental care.' He went on, 'The seed was sown. I went to work in Shanghai. I became involved with the Tongs, with their illicit proceedings. I enjoyed the conspiracies, the burglaries, the murders, the arson of insured properties. They represented revolt against the father figure who had betrayed me. I loved the death and destruction of people and things. I became adept in the technique of criminality–if you wish to call it that. Then there was trouble. I had to be got out of the way. The Tongs considered me too valuable to kill. I was smuggled to the United States. I settled in New York. I had been given a letter of introduction, in code, to one of the two most powerful Tongs in America–the Hip Sings. I never knew what the letter said, but they took me on at once as a confidential clerk. In due course, at the age of thirty, I was made the equivalent of treasurer. The treasury contained over a million dollars. I coveted this money. Then began the great Tong Wars of the late 'twenties. The two great New York Tongs, my own, the Hip Sings, and our rival, the On Lee Ongs, joined in combat. Over the weeks, hundreds on both sides were killed and their houses and properties burned to the ground. It was a time of torture and murder and arson in which I joined with delight. Then the riot squads came. Almost the whole police force of New York was mobilized. The two underground armies were prised apart and the headquarters of the two Tongs were raided and the ringleaders sent to jail. I was tipped off about the raid on my own Tong, the Hip Sings. A few hours before it was due, I got to the safe and rifled the million dollars in gold and disappeared into Harlem and went to ground. I was foolish. I should have left America, gone to the farthest corner of the earth. Even from the condemned cells in Sing Sing the heads of my Tong reached out for me. They found me. The killers came in the night. They tortured me. I would not say where the gold was. They tortured me all through the night. Then, when they could not break me, they cut off my hands to show that the corpse was that of a thief, and they shot me through the heart and went away. But they did not know something about me. I am the one man in a million who has his heart on the right side of his body. Those are the odds against it, one in a million. I lived. By sheer will-power I survived the operation and the months in hospital. And all the time I planned and planned how to get away with the money–how to keep it, what to do with it.'

Doctor No paused. There was a slight flush at his temples. His body fidgeted inside his kimono. His memories had excited him. For a moment he closed his eyes, composing himself. Bond thought, now! Shall I leap at him and kill him? Break off my glass and do it with the jagged stem?

The eyes opened. 'I am not boring you? You are sure? For an instant I felt your attention wandering.'

'No.' The moment had passed. Would there be others? Bond measured the inches of the leap: noted that the jugular vein was in full view above the neck of the kimono.

The thin purple lips parted and the story went on. 'It was, Mister Bond, a time for clear, firm decisions. When they let me out of the hospital I went to Silberstein, the greatest stamp dealer in New York. I bought an envelope, just one envelope, full of the rarest postage stamps in the world. It took weeks to get them together. But I didn't mind what I paid–in New York, London, Paris, Zurich. I wanted my gold to be mobile. I invested it all in these stamps. I had foreseen the World War. I knew there would be inflation. I knew the best would appreciate, or at least hold its value. And meanwhile I was changing my appearance. I had all my hair taken out by the roots, my thick nose made thin, my mouth widened, my lips sliced. I could not get smaller, so I made myself taller. I wore built up shoes. I had weeks of traction on my spine. I held myself differently. I put away my mechanical hands and wore hands of wax inside gloves. I changed my name to Julius No–the Julius after my father and the No for my rejection of him and of all authority. I threw away my spectacles and wore contact lenses–one of the first pairs ever built. Then I went to Milwaukee, where there are no Chinamen, and enrolled myself in the faculty of medicine. I hid myself in the academic world, the world of libraries and laboratories and classrooms and campuses. And there, Mister Bond, I lost myself in the study of the human body and the human mind. Why? Because I wished to know what this clay is capable of. I had to learn what my tools were before I put them to use on my next goal–total security from physical weaknesses, from material dangers and from the hazards of living. Then, Mister Bond, from that secure base, armoured even against the casual slings and arrows of the world, I would proceed to the achievement of power–the power, Mister Bond, to do unto others what had been done unto me, the power of life and death, the power to decide, to judge, the power of absolute independence from outside authority. For that, Mister Bond, whether you like it or not, is the essence of temporal power.'

Bond reached for the shaker and poured himself a third drink. He looked at Honeychile. She seemed composed and indifferent–as if her mind was on other things. She smiled at him.

Doctor No said benignly, 'I expect you are both hungry. Pray be patient. I will be brief. So, if you recall, there I was, in Milwaukee. In due course, I completed my studies and I left America and went by easy stages round the world. I called myself "doctor" because doctors receive confidences and they can ask questions without arousing suspicion. I was looking for my headquarters. It had to be safe from the coming war, it had to be an island, it had to be entirely private, and it had to be capable of industrial development. In the end I purchased Crab Key. And here I have remained for fourteen years. They have been secure and fruitful years, without a cloud on the horizon. I was entertained by the idea of converting bird dung into gold, and I attacked the problem with passion. It seemed to me the ideal industry. There was a constant demand for the product. The birds require no care except to be left in peace. Each one is a simple factory for turning fish into dung. The digging of the guano is only a question of not spoiling the crop by digging too much. The sole problem is the cost of the labour. It was 1942.

The simple Cuban and Jamaican labourer was earning ten shillings a week cutting cane. I tempted a hundred of them over to the island by paying them twelve shillings a week. With guano at fifty dollars a ton I was well placed. But on one condition–that the wages remained constant. I ensured that by isolating my community from world inflation. Harsh methods have had to be used from time to time, but the result is that my men are content with their wages because they are the highest wages they have ever known. I brought in a dozen Chinese negroes with their families to act as overseers. They receive a pound a week per man. They are tough and reliable. On occasion I had to be ruthless with them, but they soon learned. Automatically my people increased in numbers. I added some engineers and some builders. We set to work on the mountain. Occasionally I brought in teams of specialists on high wages. They were kept apart from the others. They lived inside the mountain until their work was done and then left by ship. They put in the lighting and the ventilation and the lift. They built this room. Stores and furnishings came in from all over the world. These people built the sanatorium façade which will cover my operations in case one day there is a shipwreck or the Governor of Jamaica decides to pay me a call.' The lips glazed into a smile. 'You must admit that I am able, if I wish, to accord visitors a most fragrant reception–a wise precaution for the future! And gradually, methodically, my fortress was built while the birds defecated on top of it. It has been hard, Mister Bond.' The black eyes did not look for sympathy or praise. 'But by the end of last year the work was done. A secure, well-camouflaged base had been achieved. I was ready to proceed to the next step–an extension of my power to the outside world.'

Doctor No paused. He lifted his arms an inch and dropped them again resignedly in his lap. 'Mister Bond, I said that there was not a cloud in the sky during all these fourteen years. But one was there, all the time, below the horizon. And do you know what it was? It was a bird, a ridiculous bird called a roseate spoonbill! I will not weary you with the details, Mister Bond. You are already aware of some of the circumstances. The two wardens, miles away in the middle of the lake, were provisioned by launch from Cuba. They sent out their reports by the launch. Occasionally, ornithologists from America came by the launch and spent some days at the camp. I did not mind. The area is out of bounds to my men. The wardens were not allowed near my compounds. There was no contact. From the first I made it clear to the Audubon Society that I would not meet their representatives. And then what happens? One day, out of a clear sky, I get a letter by the monthly boat. The roseate spoonbills have become one of the bird wonders of the world. The Socicty gives me formal notification that they intend to build a hotel on their leasehold, near the river up which you came. Bird lovers from all over the world will come to observe the birds. Films will be taken. Crab Key, they told me in their flattering, persuasive letter, would become famous.'

'Mister Bond,' the arms were raised and dropped back. Irony gathered at the edges of the set smile. 'Can you believe it? This privacy I had achieved! The plans I had for the future! To be swept aside because of a lot of old women and their birds! I examined the lease. I wrote offering a huge sum to buy it. They refused. So I studied these birds. I found out about their habits. And suddenly the solution was there. And it was easy. Man had always been the worst predator on these birds. Spoonbills are extremely shy. They frighten easily. I sent to Florida for a marsh buggy–the vehicle that is used for oil prospecting, that will cover any kind of terrain. I adapted it to frighten and to burn–not only birds, but humans as well, for the wardens would have to go too. And, one night in December, my marsh buggy howled off across the lake. It smashed the camp, both wardens were reported killed–though one, it turned out, escaped to die in Jamaica–it burned the nesting places, it spread terror among the birds. Complete success! Hysteria spread among the spoonbills. They died in thousands. But then I get a demand for a plane to land on my airstrip. There was to be an investigation. I decide to agree. It seemed wiser. An accident is arranged. A lorry goes out of control down the airstrip as the plane is coming in. The plane is destroyed. All signs of the lorry are removed. The bodies are reverently placed in coffins and I report the tragedy. As I expected, there is further investigation. A destroyer arrives. I receive the captain courteously. He and his officers are brought round by sea and then led inland. They are shown the remains of the camp. My men suggest that the wardens went mad with loneliness and fought each other. The survivor set fire to the camp and escaped in his fishing canoe. The airstrip is examined. My men report that the plane was coming in too fast. The tyres must have burst on impact. The bodies are handed over. It is very sad. The officers are satisfied. The ship leaves. Peace reigns again.'

Doctor No coughed delicately. He looked from Bond to the girl and back again, 'And that, my friends, is my story–or rather the first chapter of what I am confident will be a long and interesting tale. Privacy has been re-established. There are now no roseate spoonbills, so there will be no wardens. No doubt the Audubon Society will decide to accept my offer for the rest of their lease. No matter. If they start their puny operations again, other misfortunes will befall them. This has been a warning to me. There will be no more interference.'

'Interesting,' said Bond. 'An interesting case history. So that was why Strangeways had to be removed. What did you do with him and his girl?'

'They are at the bottom of the Mona Reservoir. I sent three of my best men. I have a small but efficient machine in Jamaica. I need it. I have established a watch on the intelligence services in Jamaica and Cuba. It is necessary for my further operations. Your Mister Strangways became suspicious and started ferreting about. Fortunately, by this time, the routines of this man were known to me. His death and the girl's were a simple matter of timing. I had hoped to deal with you with similar expedition. You were fortunate. But I knew what type of a man you were from the files at King's House. I guessed that the fly would come to the spider. I was ready for you, and when the canoe showed up on the radar screen I knew you would not get away.'

Bond said, 'Your radar is not very efficient. There were two canoes. The one you saw was the girl's. I tell you she had nothing to do with me.'

'Then she is unfortunate. I happen to be needing a white woman for a small experiment. As we agreed earlier, Mister Bond, one generally gets what one wants.'

Bond looked thoughtfully at Doctor No. He wondered if it was worth while even trying to make a dent in this impregnable man. Was it worth wasting breath by threatening or bluffing? Bond had nothing but a miserable two of clubs up his sleeve. The thought of playing it almost bored him. Casually, indifferently he threw it down.

'Then you're out of luck, Doctor No. You are now a file in London. My thoughts on this case, the evidence of the poisoned fruit and the centipede and the crashed motor car, are on record. So are the names of Miss Chung and Miss Taro. Instructions were left with someone in Jamaica that my report should be opened and acted upon if I failed to return from Crab Key within three days.'

Bond paused. The face of Doctor No was impassive. Neither the eyes nor the mouth had flickered. The jugular vein throbbed evenly. Bond bent forward. He said softly, 'But because of the girl, and only because of her, Doctor No, I will strike a bargain. In exchange for our safe return to Jamaica, you may have a week's start. You may take your aeroplane and your packet of stamps and try to get away.'

Bond sat back. 'Any interest, Doctor No?'

Chapter Sixteen

Horizons of Agony

A voice behind Bond said quietly, 'Dinner is served.'

Bond swung round. It was the bodyguard. Beside him was another man who might have been his twin. They stood there, two stocky barrels of muscle, their hands buried in the sleeves of their kimonos, and looked over Bond's head at Doctor No.

'Ah, nine o'clock already.' Doctor No rose slowly to his feet. 'Come along. We can continue our conversation in more intimate surroundings. It is kind of you both to have listened to me with such exemplary patience. I hope the modesty of my cuisine and my cellar will not prove a further imposition.'

Double doors stood open in the wall behind the two white-jacketed men. Bond and the girl followed Doctor No through into a small octagonal mahogany-panelled room lit by a central chandelier in silver with storm glasses round the candles. Beneath it was a round mahogany table laid for three. Silver and glass twinkled warmly. The plain dark blue carpet was luxuriously deep. Doctor No took the centre high-backed chair and bowed the girl into the chair on his right. They sat down and unfolded napkins of white silk.

The hollow ceremony and the charming room maddened Bond. He longed to break it up with his own hands–to wind his silk napkin round Doctor No's throat and squeeze until the contact lenses popped out of the black, damnable eyes.

The two guards wore white cotton gloves. They served the food with a suave efficiency that was prompted by an occasional word in Chinese from Doctor No.

At first, Doctor No seemed preoccupied. He slowly ate through three bowls of different soup, feeding himself with a spoon with a short handle that fitted neatly between the pincers. Bond concentrated on hiding his fears from the girl. He sat relaxed and ate and drank with a forced good appetite. He talked cheerfully to the girl about Jamaica–about the birds and the animals and the flowers which were an easy topic for her. Occasionally his feet felt for hers under the table. She became almost gay. Bond thought they were putting on an excellent imitation of an engaged couple being given dinner by a detested uncle.

Bond had no idea if his thin bluff had worked. He didn't give much for their chances. Doctor No, and Doctor No's story, exuded impregnability. The incredible biography rang true. Not a word of it was impossible. Perhaps there were other people in the world with their private kingdoms–away from the beaten track, where there were no witnesses, where they could do what they liked. And what did Doctor No plan to do next, after he had squashed the flies that had come to annoy him? And if–when–he killed Bond and the girl, would London pick up the threads that Bond had picked up? Probably they would. There would be Pleydell-Smith. The evidence of the poisoned fruit. But where would Bond's replacement get with Doctor No? Not far. Doctor No would shrug his shoulders over the disappearance of Bond and Quarrel. Never heard of them. And there would be no link with the girl. In Morgan's Harbour they would think she had been drowned on one of her expeditions. It was hard to see what could interfere with Doctor No–with the second chapter of his life, whatever it was.

Underneath his chatter with the girl, Bond prepared for the worst. There were plenty of weapons beside his plate. When the cutlets came, perfectly cooked, Bond fiddled indecisively with the knives and chose the bread knife to eat them with. While he ate and talked, he edged the big steel meat knife towards him. An expansive gesture of his right hand knocked over his glass of champagne and in the split second of the crash his left hand flicked the knife into the deep sleeve of his kimono. In the midst of Bond's apologies and the confusion as he and the bodyguard mopped up the spilled champagne, Bond raised his left arm and felt the knife slip back to below his armpit and then fall inside the kimono against his ribs. When he had finished his cutlets he tightened the silk belt round his waist, shifting the knife across his stomach. The knife nestled comfortingly against his skin and gradually the steel grew warm.

Coffee came and the meal was ended. The two guards came and stood close behind Bond's chair and the girl's. They stood with their arms crossed on their chests, impassive, motionless, like executioners.

Doctor No put his cup softly down on its saucer. He laid his two steel claws down on the table in front of him. He sat a fraction more upright. He turned his body an inch in Bond's direction. Now there was no preoccupation in his face. The eyes were hard and direct. The thin mouth creased and opened. 'You have enjoyed your dinner, Mister Bond?'

Bond took a cigarette from the silver box in front of him and lit it. He played with the silver table-lighter. He smelled bad news coming. He must somehow pocket the lighter. Fire might perhaps be another weapon. He said easily, 'Yes. It was excellent.' He looked across at the girl. He leant forward in his chair and rested his forearms on the table. He crossed them, enveloping the lighter. He smiled at her. 'I hope I ordered what you like.'

'Oh yes, it was lovely.' For her the party was still going on.

Bond smoked busily, agitating his hands and forearms to create an atmosphere of movement. He turned to Doctor No. He stubbed out his cigarette and sat back in his chair. He folded his arms across his chest. The lighter was in his left armpit. He smiled cheerfully. 'And what happens now, Doctor No?'

'We can proceed to our after-dinner entertainment, Mister Bond.' The thin smile creased and vanished. 'I have examined your proposition from every angle. I do not accept it.'

Bond shrugged his shoulders. 'You are unwise.'

'No, Mister Bond. I suspect that your proposition is a gold brick. People in your trade do not behave as you suggest. They make routine reports to their headquarters. They keep their chief aware of the progress of their investigations. I know these things. Secret agents do not behave as you suggest you have done. You have been reading too many novels of suspense. Your little speech reeked of grease-paint and cardboard. No, Mister Bond, I do not accept your story. If it is true, I am prepared to face the consequences. I have too much at stake to be turned from my path. So the police come, the soldiers come. Where are a man and a girl? What man and what girl? I know nothing. Please go away. You are disturbing my guanera. Where is your evidence? Your search warrant? The English law is strict, gentlemen. Go home and leave me in peace with my beloved cormorants. You see, Mister Bond? And let us even say that the worst comes to the worst. That one of my agents talks, which is highly improbable (Bond remembered the fortitude of Miss Chung). What have I to lose? Two more deaths on the charge sheet. But, Mister Bond, a man can only be hanged once.' The tall pear-shaped head shook gently from side to side. 'Have you anything else to say? Any questions to ask? You both have a busy night ahead of you. Your time is getting short. And I must get my sleep. The monthly ship is putting in tomorrow and I have the loading to supervise. I shall have to spend the whole day down on the quay. Well, Mister Bond?'

Bond looked across at the girl. She had gone deathly pale. She was gazing at him, waiting for the miracle he would work. He looked down at his hands. He examined his nails carefully. He said, playing for time, 'And then what? After your busy day with the bird dung, what comes next on your programme? What is the next chapter you think you're going to write?'

Bond didn't look up. The deep quiet authoritative voice came to him as if it was coming down from the night sky.

'Ah, yes. You must have been wondering, Mister Bond. You have the habit of inquiry. It persists even to the last, even into the shadows. I admire such qualities in a man with only a few hours to live. So I will tell you. I will turn over the next page. It will console you. There is more to this place than bird dung. Your instincts did not betray you.' Doctor No paused for emphasis. 'This island, Mister Bond, is about to be developed into the most valuable technical intelligence centre in the world.'

'Really?' Bond kept his eyes bent on his hands.

'Doubtless you know that Turks Island, about three hundred miles from here through the Windward Passage, is the most important centre for testing the guided missiles of the United States?'

'It is an important centre, yes.'

'Perhaps you have read of the rockets that have been going astray recently? The multi-stage SNARK, for instance, that ended its flight in the forests of Brazil instead of the depths of the South Atlantic?'

'Yes.'

'You recall that it refused to obey the telemetred instructions to change its course, even to destroy itself. It developed a will of its own?'

'I remember.'

'There have been other failures, decisive failures, from the long list of prototypes–the ZUNI, MATADOR, PETREL, REGULUS, BOMARC–so many names, so many changes, I can't even remember them all. Well, Mister Bond,' Doctor No could not keep a note of pride out of his voice, 'it may interest you to know that the vast majority of those failures have been caused from Crab Key.'

'Is that so?'

'You do not believe me? No matter. Others do. Others who have seen the complete abandonment of one series, the MASTODON, because of its recurring navigational errors, its failure to obey the radio directions from Turks Island. Those others are the Russians. The Russians are my partners in this venture. They trained six of my men, Mister Bond. Two of those men are on watch at this moment, watching the radio frequencies, the beams on which these weapons travel. There is a million dollars' worth of equipment up above us in the rock galleries, Mister Bond, sending fingers up into the Heaviside Layer, waiting for the signals, jamming them, countering beams with other beams. And from time to time a rocket soars up on its way a hundred, five hundred miles into the Atlantic. And we track it, as accurately as they are tracking it in the Operations Room on Turks Island. Then, suddenly, our pulses go out to the rocket, its brain is confused, it goes mad, it plunges into the sea, it destroys itself, it roars off at a tangent. Another test has failed. The operators are blamed, the designers, the manufacturers. There is panic in the Pentagon. Something else must be tried, different frequencies, different metals, a different radio brain. Of course,' Doctor No was fair, 'we too have our difficulties. We track many practice shoots without being able to get through to the brain of the new rocket. But then we communicate urgently with Moscow. Yes, they have even given us a cipher machine with our own frequencies and routines. And the Russians get thinking. They make suggestions. We try them out. And then, one day, Mister Bond, it is like catching the attention of a man in a crowd. Up in the stratosphere the rocket acknowledges our signal. We are recognized and we can speak to it and change its mind.' Doctor No paused. 'Do you not find that interesting, Mister Bond, this little sideline to my business in guano? It is, I assure you, most profitable. It might be still more so. Perhaps Communist China will pay more. Who knows? I already have my feelers out.'

Bond lifted his eyes. He looked thoughtfully at Doctor No. So he *had* been right. There *had* been more, much more, in all this than met the eye. This was a big game, a game that explained everything, a game that was certainly, in the international espionage market, well worth the candle. Well, well! Now the pieces in the puzzle fell firmly into place. For this it was certainly worth scaring away a few birds and wiping out a few people. Privacy? Of course Doctor No would have to kill him and the girl. Power? This was it. Doctor No had really got himself into business.

Bond looked into the two black holes with a new respect. He said, 'You'll have to kill a lot more people to keep this thing in your hands, Doctor No. It's worth a lot of money. You've got a good property here–a better one than I thought. People are going to want to cut themselves a piece of this cake. I wonder who will get to you first and kill you. Those men up there', he gestured towards the ceiling, 'who were trained in Moscow? They're the technicians. I wonder what Moscow is telling them to do? You wouldn't know that, would you?'

Doctor No said, 'You persist in underestimating me, Mister Bond. You are an obstinate man, and stupider than I had expected. I am aware of these possibilities. I have taken one of these men and made him into a private monitor. He has duplicates of the ciphers and of the cipher machine. He lives in another part of the mountain. The others think that he died. He watches on all the routine times. He gives me a second copy of all the traffic that passes. So far, the signals from Moscow have been innocent of any sign of conspiracy. I am thinking of these things constantly, Mister Bond. I take precautions and I shall take further precautions. As I said, you underestimate me.'

'I don't underestimate you, Doctor No. You're a very careful man, but you've got too many files open on you. In my line of business, the same thing applies to me. I know the feeling. But you've got some really bad ones. The Chinese one, for instance. I wouldn't like to have that one. The F.B.I. should be the least painful–robbery and false identity. But do you know the Russians as well as I do? You're a "best friend" at the moment. But the Russians don't have partners. They'll want to take you over–buy you out with a bullet. Then there's the file you've started with my Service. You really want me to make that one fatter? I shouldn't do it if I were you, Doctor No. They're a tenacious lot of people in my Service. If anything happens to me and the girl, you'll find Crab Key's a very small and naked little island.'

'You cannot play for high stakes without taking risks, Mister Bond. I accept the dangers and, so far as I can, I have equipped myself against them. You see, Mister Bond,' the deep voice held a hint of greed, 'I am on the edge of still greater things. The Chapter Two to which I referred holds the promise of prizes which no one but a fool would throw away because he was afraid. I have told you that I can bend the beams on which these rockets fly, Mister Bond. I can make them change course and ignore their radio control. What would you say, Mister Bond, if I could go further? If I could bring them down into the sea near this island and salvage the secrets of their construction. At present American destroyers, far out in the South Atlantic, salvage these missiles when they come to the end of their fuel and parachute down into the sea. Sometimes the parachutes fail to open. Sometimes the self-destruction devices fail to operate. No one on Turks Island would be surprised if every now and then the prototype of a new series broke off its flight and came down near Crab Key. To begin with, at least, it would be put down to mechanical failure. Later, perhaps, they would discover that other radio signals besides theirs were guiding their rockets. A jamming war would start. They would try and locate the origin of the false signals. Directly I found they were looking for me, I would have one last fling. Their rockets would go mad. They would land on Havana, on Kingston. They would turn round and home on Miami. Even without warheads, Mister Bond, five tons of metal arriving at a thousand miles an hour can cause plenty of damage in a crowded town. And then what? There would be panic, a public outcry. The experiments would have to cease. The Turks Island base would have to close down. And how much would Russia pay for that to happen, Mister Bond? And how much for each of the prototypes I captured for them? Shall we say ten million dollars for the whole operation? Twenty million? It would be a priceless victory in the armaments race. I could name my figure. Don't you agree, Mister Bond? And don't you agree that these considerations make your arguments and threats seem rather puny?'

Bond said nothing. There was nothing to say. Suddenly he was back in the quiet room high up above Regent's Park. He could hear the rain slashing softly against the window and M's voice, impatient, sarcastic, saying, 'Oh, some damned business about birds . . . holiday in the sun'll do you good . . . routine inquiry.' And he, Bond, had taken a canoe and a fisherman and a picnic lunch and had gone off–how many days, how many weeks ago?–'to have a look'. Well, he had had his look into Pandora's Box. He had found out the answers, been told the secrets–and now? Now he was going to be politely shown the way to his grave, taking the secrets with him and the waif he had picked up and dragged along with him on his lunatic adventure. The bitterness inside Bond came up into his mouth so that for a moment he thought he was going to retch. He reached for his champagne and emptied the glass. He said harshly, 'All right, Doctor No. Now let's get on with the cabaret. What's the programme–knife, bullet, poison, rope? But make it quick, I've seen enough of you.'

Doctor No's lips compressed into a thin purple line. The eyes were hard as onyx under the billiard ball forehead and skull. The polite mask had gone. The Grand Inquisitor sat in the high-backed chair. The hour had struck for the *peine forte et dure*.

Doctor No spoke a word and the two guards took a step forward and held the two victims above the elbows, forcing their arms back against the sides of their chairs. There was no resistance. Bond concentrated on holding the lighter in his armpit. The white-gloved hands on his biceps felt like steel bands. He smiled across at the girl. 'I'm sorry about this, Honey. I'm afraid we're not going to be able to play together after all.'

The girl's eyes in the pale face were blue-black with fear. Her lips trembled. She said, 'Will it hurt?'

'Silence!' Doctor No's voice was the crack of a whip. 'Enough of this foolery. Of course it will hurt. I am interested in pain. I am also interested in finding out how much the human body can endure. From time to time I make experiments on those of my people who have to be punished. And on trespassers like yourselves. You have both put me to a great deal of trouble. In exchange I intend to put you to a great deal of pain. I shall record the length of your endurance. The facts will be noted. One day my findings will be given to the world. Your deaths will have served the purposes of science. I never waste human material. The German experiments on live humans during the war were of great benefit to science. It is a year since I put a girl to death in the fashion I have chosen for you, woman. She was a negress. She lasted three hours. She died of terror. I have wanted a white girl for comparison. I was not surprised when your arrival was reported. I get what I want.' Doctor No sat back in his chair. His eyes were now fixed on the girl, watching her reactions. She stared back at him, half hypnotized, like a bush mouse in front of a rattlesnake.

Bond set his teeth.

'You are a Jamaican, so you will know what I am talking about. This island is called Crab Key. It is called by that name because it is infested with crabs, land crabs–what they call in Jamaica "black crabs". You know them. They weigh about a pound each and they are as big as saucers. At this time of year they come up in thousands from their holes near the shore and climb up towards the mountain. There, in the coral uplands, they go to ground again in holes in the rock and spawn their broods. They march up in armies of hundreds at a time. They march through everything and over everything. In Jamaica they go through houses that are in their path. They are like the lemmings of Norway. It is a compulsive migration.' Doctor No paused. He said softly, 'But there is a difference. The crabs devour what they find in their path. And at present, woman, they are "running". They are coming up the mountainside in their tens of thousands, great red and orange and black waves of them, scuttling and hurrying and scraping against the rock above us at this moment. And tonight, in the middle of their path, they are going to find the naked body of a woman pegged out–a banquet spread for them–and they will feel the warm body with their feeding pincers, and one will make the first incision with his fighting claws and then . . . and then . . .'

There was a moan from the girl. Her head fell forward slackly on to her chest. She had fainted. Bond's body heaved in his chair. A string of obscenities hissed out between his clenched teeth. The huge hands of the guard were like fire round his arms. He couldn't even move the chair-legs on the floor. After a moment he desisted. He waited for his voice to steady, then he said, with all the venom he could put into the words, 'You bastard. You'll fry in hell for this.'

Doctor No smiled thinly. 'Mister Bond, I do not admit the existence of hell. Console yourself. Perhaps they will start at the throat or the heart. The movement of the pulse will attract them. Then it will not be long.' He spoke a sentence in Chinese. The guard behind the girl's chair leant forward and plucked her bodily out of the chair as if she had been a child and slung the inert body over his shoulder. Between the dangling arms the hair fell down in a golden shower. The guard went to the door and opened it and went out, closing it noiselessly behind him.

For a moment there was silence in the room. Bond thought only of the knife against his skin and of the lighter under his armpit. How much damage could he do with the two pieces of metal? Could he somehow get within range of Doctor No?

Doctor No said quietly, 'You said that power was an illusion, Mister Bond. Do you change your mind? My power to select this particular death for the girl is surely not an illusion. However, let us proceed to the method of your departure. That also has its novel aspects. You see, Mister Bond, I am interested in the anatomy of courage–in the power of the human body to endure. But how to measure human endurance? How to plot a graph of the will to survive, the tolerance of pain, the conquest of fear? I have given much thought to the problem, and I believe I have solved it. It is, of course, only a rough and ready method, and I shall learn by experience as more and more subjects are put to the test. I have prepared you for the experiment as best I could. I gave you a sedative so that your body should be rested and I have fed you well so that you may be at full strength. Future–what shall I call them–patients, will have the same advantages. All will start equal in that respect. After that it will be a question of the individual's courage and powers of endurance.' Doctor No paused, watching Bond's face. 'You see, Mister Bond, I have just finished constructing an obstacle race, an assault course against death. I will say no more about it because the element of surprise is one of the constituents of fear. It is the unknown dangers that are the worst, that bear most heavily on the reserves of courage. And I flatter myself that the gauntlet you will run contains a rich assortment of the unexpected. It will be particularly interesting, Mister Bond, that a man of your physical qualities is to be my first competitor. It will be most interesting to observe how far you get down the course I have devised. You should put up a worthy target figure for future runners. I have high expectations of you. You should go far, but when, as is inevitable, you have finally failed at an obstacle, your body will be recovered and I shall most meticulously examine the physical state of your remains. The data will be recorded. You will be the first dot on a graph. Something of an honour, is it not, Mister Bond?'

Bond said nothing. What the hell did all this mean? What could this test consist of? Would it be possible to survive it? Could he conceivably escape from it and get to the girl before it was too late, even if it was only to kill her and save her from her torture? Silently Bond gathered his reserves of courage, steeling his mind against the fear of the unknown that already had him by the throat, focusing his whole will on survival. Somehow, above all else, he must cling to his weapons.

Doctor No rose and stepped away from his chair. He walked slowly to the door and turned. The menacing black holes looked back at Bond from just below the lintel of the door. The head was inclined a fraction. The purple lips creased back. 'Run a good race for me, Mister Bond. My thoughts, as they say, will be with you.'

Doctor No turned away and the door closed softly behind the long thin gunmetal back.

Chapter Seventeen

The Long Scream

There was a man on the lift. The doors were open, waiting. James Bond, his arms still locked to his sides, was marched in. Now the dining-room would be empty. How soon would the guards go back, start clearing away the dinner, notice the missing things? The doors hissed shut. The liftman stood in front of the buttons so that Bond could not see which he had pressed. They were going up. Bond tried to estimate the distance. The lift sighed to a stop. The time seemed rather less than when he had come down with the girl. The doors opened on to an uncarpeted corridor with rough grey paint on the stone walls. It ran about twenty yards straight ahead.

'Hold it, Joe,' said Bond's guard to the liftman. 'Be right with you.'

Bond was marched down the corridor past doors numbered with letters of the alphabet. There was a faint hum of machinery in the air and behind one door Bond thought he could catch the crackle of radio static. It sounded as if they might be in the engine-room of the mountain. They came to the end door. It was marked with a black Q. It was ajar and the guard pushed Bond into the door so that it swung open. Through the door was a grey painted stone cell about fifteen feet square. There was nothing in it except a wooden chair on which lay, laundered and, neatly folded, Bond's black canvas jeans and his blue shirt.

The guard let go of Bond's arms. Bond turned and looked into the broad yellow face below the crinkly hair. There was a hint of curiosity and pleasure in the liquid brown eyes. The man stood holding the door handle. He said, 'Well, this is it, bud. You're at the starting gate. You can either sit here and rot or find your way out on to the course. Happy landings.'

Bond thought it was just worth trying. He glanced past the guard to where the liftman was standing beside his open doors, watching them. He said softly, 'How would you like to earn ten thousand dollars, guaranteed, and a ticket to anywhere in the world?' He watched the man's face. The mouth spread in a wide grin to show brownish teeth worn to uneven points by years of chewing sugar-cane.

'Thanks, Mister. I'd rather stay alive.' The man made to close the door. Bond whispered urgently, 'We could get out of here together.'

The thick lips sneered. The man said, 'Shove it!' The door shut with a solid click.

Bond shrugged his shoulders. He gave the door a cursory glance. It was made of metal and there was no handle on the inside. Bond didn't waste his shoulder on it. He went to the chair and sat down on the neat pile of his clothes and looked round the cell. The walls were entirely naked except for a ventilation grille of thick wire in one corner just below the ceiling. It was wider than his shoulders. It was obviously the way out into the assault course. The only other break in the walls was a thick glass porthole, no bigger than Bond's head, just above the door. Light from the corridor filtered through it into the cell. There was nothing else. It was no good wasting any more time. It would now be about ten-thirty. Outside, somewhere on the slope of the mountain, the girl would already be lying, waiting for the rattle of claws on the grey coral. Bond clenched his teeth at the thought of the pale body spreadeagled out there under the stars. Abruptly he stood up. What the hell was he doing sitting still. Whatever lay on the other side of the wire grille, it was time to go.

Bond took out his knife and the lighter and threw off the kimono. He dressed in the trousers and shirt and stowed the lighter in his hip pocket. He tried the edge of the knife with his thumb. It was very sharp. It would be better still if he could get a point on it. He knelt on the floor and began whittling the rounded end on the stone. After a precious quarter of an hour he was satisfied. It was no stiletto, but it would serve to stab as well as cut. Bond put the knife between his teeth and set the chair below the grille and climbed on to it. The grille! Assuming he could tear it off its hinges, the frame of quarter-inch wire might straighten into a spear. That would make a third weapon. Bond reached up with crooked fingers.

The next thing he knew was a searing pain up his arm and the crack of his head hitting the stone floor. He lay, stunned, with only the memory of a blue flash and the hiss and crackle of electricity to tell him what had hit him.

Bond got to his knees and stayed there. He bent his head down and shook it slowly from side to side like a wounded animal. He noticed a smell of burning flesh. He lifted his right hand up to his eyes. There was the red smear of an open burn across the inside of his fingers. Seeing it brought the pain. Bond spat out a four-letter word. Slowly he got to his feet. He squinted up at the wire grille as if it might strike at him again, like a snake. Grimly he set the chair upright against the wall. He picked up his knife and cut a strip off the discarded kimono and tied it firmly across his fingers. Then he climbed up again on to the chair and looked at the grille. He was meant to get through it. The shock had been to soften him up–a taste of pain to come. Surely he had fused the blasted thing. Surely they would have switched off the current. He looked at it only for an instant, then the fingers of his left hand crooked and went straight up to the impersonal wire mesh. His fingers went through the wire rim and gripped.

Nothing! Nothing at all–just wire. Bond grunted. He felt his nerves slacken. He tugged at the wire. It gave an inch. He tugged again and it came away in his hand and dangled down from two strands of copper flex that disappeared into the wall. Bond pulled the grille loose from the flex and got down from the chair. Yes, there was join in the frame. He set to work unravelling the mesh. Then using the chair as a hammer, he straightened the heavy wire.

After ten minutes, Bond had a crooked spear about four feet long. One end, where it had originally been cut by the pliers, was jagged. It would not pierce a man's clothes, but it would be good enough for the face and neck. By using all his strength and the crack at the bottom of the metal door, Bond turned the blunt end into a clumsy crook. He measured the wire against his leg. It was too long. He bent it double and slipped the spear down a trouser leg. Now it hung from his waistband to just above the knee. He went back to the chair and climbed up again and reached, nervously, for the edge of the ventilator shaft. There was no shock. Bond heaved up and through the opening and lay on his stomach looking along the shaft.

The shaft was about four inches wider than Bond's shoulders. It was circular and of polished metal. Bond reached for his lighter, blessing the inspiration that had made him take it, and flicked it on. Yes, zinc sheeting that looked new. The shaft stretched straight ahead, featureless except for the ridges where the sections of pipe joined. Bond put the lighter back in his pocket and snaked forward.

It was easy going. Cool air from the ventilating system blew strongly in Bond's face. The air held no smell of the sea–it was the canned stuff that comes from an air-conditioning plant. Doctor No must have adapted one of the shafts to his purpose. What hazards had he built into it to test out his victims? They would be ingenious and painful–designed to reduce the resistance of the victim. At the winning post, so to speak, there would be the *coup de grâce*–if the victim ever got that far. It would be something conclusive, something from which there would be no escape, for there would be no prizes in this race except oblivion–an oblivion, thought Bond, he might be glad to win. Unless of course Doctor No had been just a bit too clever. Unless he had underestimated the will to survive. That, thought Bond, was his only hope–to try to survive the intervening hazards, to get through at least to the last ditch.

There was a faint luminosity ahead. Bond approached it carefully, his senses questing in front of him like antennae. It grew brighter. It was the glint of light against the end of the lateral shaft. He went on until his head touched the metal. He twisted over on his back. Straight above him, at the top of fifty yards or so of vertical shaft, was a steady glimmer. It was like looking up a long gun barrel. Bond inched round the square bend and stood upright. So he was supposed to climb straight up this shining tube of metal without a foothold! Was it possible? Bond expanded his shoulders. Yes, they gripped the sides. His feet could also get a temporary purchase, though they would slip except where the ridges at the joints gave him an ounce of upward leverage. Bond shrugged his shoulders and kicked off his shoes. It was no good arguing. He would just have to try.

Six inches at a time, Bond's body began to worm up the shaft–expand shoulders to grip the sides, lift feet, lock knees, force the feet outwards against the metal and, as the feet slipped downwards with his weight, contract shoulders and raise them a few inches higher. Do it again, and again and again and again. Stop at each tiny bulge where the sections joined and use the millimetre of extra support to get some breath and measure the next lap. Otherwise don't look up, think only of the inches of metal that have to be conquered one by one. Don't worry about the glimmer of light that never grows brighter or nearer. Don't worry about losing your grip and falling to smash your ankles at the bottom of the shaft. Don't worry about cramp. Don't worry about your screaming muscles or the swelling bruises on your shoulders and the sides of your feet. Just take the silver inches as they come, one by one, and conquer them.

But then the feet began to sweat and slip. Twice Bond lost a yard before his shoulders, scalding with the friction, could put on the brake. Finally he had to stop altogether to let his sweat dry in the downward draught of air. He waited for a full ten minutes, staring at his faint reflection in the polished metal, the face split in half by the knife between the teeth. Still he refused to look up to see how much more there was. It might be too much to bear. Carefully Bond wiped each foot against a trouser-leg and began again.

Now half Bond's mind was dreaming while the other half fought the battle. He wasn't even conscious of the strengthening breeze or the slowly brightening light. He saw himself as a wounded caterpillar crawling up a waste pipe towards the plug-hole of a bath. What would he see when he got through the plug-hole? A naked girl drying herself? A man shaving? Sunlight streaming through an open window into an empty bathroom?

Bond's head bumped against something. The plug was in the plug-hole! The shock of disappointment made him slip a yard before his shoulders got a fresh grip. Then he realized. He was at the top! Now he noticed the bright light and the strong wind. Feverishly, but with a more desperate care, he heaved up again until his head touched. The wind was coming into his left ear. Cautiously he turned his head. It was another lateral shaft. Above him light was shining through a thick porthole. All he had to do was inch himself round and grip the edge of the new shaft and somehow gather enough strength to heave himself in. Then he would be able to lie down.

With an extra delicacy, born of panic that something might now go wrong, that he might make a mistake and plummet back down the shaft to land in a crackle of bone, Bond, his breath steaming against the metal, carried out the manœuvre and, with his last ounce of strength, jack-knifed into the opening and crumpled full length on his face.

Later–how much later?–Bond's eyes opened and his body stirred. The cold had woken him from the fringe of total unconsciousness into which his body had plunged. Painfully he rolled over on his back, his feet and shoulders screaming at him, and lay gathering his wits and summoning more strength. He had no idea what time it was or whereabouts he was inside the mountain. He lifted his head and looked back at the porthole above the yawning tube out of which he had come. The light was yellowish and the glass looked thick. He remembered the porthole in Room Q. There had been nothing breakable about that one, nor, he guessed, would there be here.

Suddenly, behind the glass, he saw movement. As he watched, a pair of eyes materialized from behind the electric light bulb. They stopped and looked at him, the bulb making a yellow glass nose between them. They gazed incuriously at him and then they were gone. Bond's lips snarled back from his teeth. So his progress was going to be observed, reported back to Doctor No!

Bond said out loud, viciously, '——them all,' and turned sullenly back on his stomach. He raised his head and looked forward. The tunnel shimmered away into blackness. Come on! No good hanging about. He picked up his knife and put it back between his teeth and winced his way forward.

Soon there was no more light. Bond stopped from time to time and used the lighter, but there was nothing but blackness ahead. The air began to get warmer in the shaft, and, perhaps fifty yards further, definitely hot. There was the smell of heat in the air, metallic heat. Bond began to sweat. Soon his body was soaked and he had to pause every few minutes to wipe his eyes. There came a right-hand turn in the shaft. Round it the metal of the big tube was hot against his skin. The smell of heat was very strong. There came another right-angled turn. As soon as Bond's head got round he quickly pulled out his lighter and lit it and then snaked back and lay panting. Bitterly he examined the new hazard, probing it, cursing it. His light had flickered on discoloured, oyster-hued zinc. The next hazard was to be heat!

Bond groaned aloud. How could his bruised flesh stand up to that? How could he protect his skin from the metal? But there wasn't anything he could do about it. He could either go back, or stay where he was, or go on. There was no other decision to make, no other shift or excuse. There was one, and only one, grain of consolation. This would not be heat that would kill, only maim. This would not be the final killing ground–only one more test of how much he could take.

Bond thought of the girl and of what she was going through. Oh well. Get on with it. Now, let's see. . . .

Bond took his knife and cut off the whole front of his shirt and sliced it into strips. The only hope was to put some wrapping round the parts of his body that would have to bear the brunt–his hands and his feet. His knees and elbows would have to get along with their single covering of cotton fabric. Wearily he set to work, cursing softly.

Now he was ready. One, two, three . . .

Bond turned the corner and forged forward into the heat stench.

Keep your naked stomach off the ground! Contract your shoulders! Hands, knees, toes; hands, knees, toes. Faster, faster! Keep going fast so that each touch on the ground is quickly taken over by the next.

The knees were getting it worst, taking the bulk of Bond's weight. Now the padded hands were beginning to smoulder. There was a spark, and another one, and then a worm of red as the sparks began to run. The smoke from the stuff smarted in Bond's sweating eyes. God, he couldn't do any more! There was no air. His lungs were bursting. Now his two hands shed sparks as he thrust them forward. The stuff must be nearly gone. Then the flesh would burn. Bond lurched and his bruised shoulder hit the metal. He screamed. He went on screaming, regularly, with each contact of hand or knee or toes. Now he was finished. Now it was the end. Now he would fall flat and slowly fry to death. No! He must drive on, screaming, until his flesh was burned to the bone. The skin must have already gone from the knees. In a moment the balls of his hands would meet the metal. Only the sweat running down his arms could be keeping the pads of stuff damp. Scream, scream, scream! It helps the pain. It tells you you're alive. Go on! Go on! It can't be much longer. This isn't where you're supposed to die. You are still alive. Don't give up! You can't!

Bond's right hand hit something that gave before it. There was a stream of ice-cold air. His other hand hit, then his head. There was a tinny noise. Bond felt the lower edge of an asbestos baffle scrape down his back. He was through. He heard the baffle bang shut. His hands came up against solid wall. They quested to left and right. It was a right-angled bend. His body followed blindly round the corner. The cool air felt like daggers in his lungs. Gingerly he laid his fingers down on the metal. It was cold! With a groan Bond fell on his face and lay still.

Sometime later the pain revived him. Bond turned sluggishly over on his back. Vaguely he noticed the lighted porthole above him. Vaguely he took in the eyes gazing down on him. Then he let the black waves take him away again.

Slowly, in the darkness, the blisters formed across the skin and the bruised feet and shoulders stiffened. The sweat dried on the body and then on the rags of clothing, and the cool air soaked down into the overheated lungs and began its insidious work. But the heart beat on, strongly and regularly inside the tortured envelope, and the healing sorceries of oxygen and rest pumped life back into the arteries and veins and recharged the nerves.

Years later, Bond awoke. He stirred. As his eyes opened and met the other pair, inches away behind the glass, pain took him and shook him like a rat. He waited for the shock to die. He tried again, and then again, until he had measured the strength of his adversary. Then Bond, to hide himself away from the witness, turned over on his stomach and took the full blast of it. Again he waited, exploring his body for its reactions, testing the strength of the resolve that was left in the batteries. How much more could he take now? Bond's lips drew back from his teeth and he snarled into the darkness. It was an animal sound. He had come to the end of his human reactions to pain and adversity. Doctor No had got him cornered. But there were animal reserves of desperation left and, in a strong animal, those reserves are deep.

Slowly, agonizingly, Bond snaked a few yards away from the eyes and then reached for his lighter and lit it. Ahead there was only the black full moon, the yawning circular mouth that led into the stomach of death. Bond put back the lighter. He took a deep breath and got to his hands and knees. The pain was no greater, only different. Slowly, stiffly, he winced forward.

The cotton fabric at Bond's knees and elbows had burned away. Numbly his mind registered the moisture as his blisters burst against the cool metal. As he moved, he flexed his fingers and toes, testing the pain. Slowly he got the measure of what he could do, what hurt most. This pain is supportable, he argued to himself. If I had been in an aeroplane crash, they would only diagnose superficial contusions and burns. I would be out of hospital in a few days. There's nothing wrong with me. I'm a survivor from the crash. It hurts, but it's nothing. Think of the bits and pieces of the other passengers. Be thankful. Put it out of your mind. But, nagging behind these reflections, was the knowledge that he had not yet had the crash–that he was still on his way towards it, his resistance, his effectiveness reduced. When would it come? What shape would it take? How much more was he to be softened up before he reached the killing ground?

Ahead in the darkness the tiny red pin-points might have been an hallucination, specks before the eyes as a result of exhaustion. Bond stopped and screwed up his eyes. He shook his head. No, they were still there. Slowly he snaked closer. Now they were moving. Bond stopped again. He listened. Above the quiet thumping of his heart there was a soft, delicate rustling. The pin-points had increased in number. Now there were twenty or thirty, shifting to and fro, some quickly, some slowly, all over the circle of blackness ahead. Bond reached for his lighter. He held his breath as he lit the little yellow flame. The red pin-points went out. Instead, a yard ahead of him, very narrow mesh wire, almost as fine as muslin, blocked the shaft.

Bond inched forward, the lighter held before him. It was some sort of a cage with small things living in it. He could hear them scuttling back, away from the light. A foot away from the mesh he dowsed the light and waited for his eyes to get used to the dark. As he waited, listening, he could hear the tiny scuttling back towards him, and gradually the forest of red-points gathered again, peering at him through the mesh.

What was it? Bond listened to the pounding of his heart. Snakes? Scorpions? Centipedes?

Carefully he brought his eyes close up to the little glowing forest. He inched the lighter up beside his face and suddenly pressed the lever. He caught a glimpse of tiny claws hooked through the mesh and of dozens of thick furry feet and of furry sacklike stomachs topped by big insect heads that seemed to be covered with eyes. The things plopped hurriedly off the wire on to the tin and scurried back and huddled in a grey-brown furry mass at the end of the cage.

Bond squinted through the mesh, moving the light back and forward. Then he dowsed the light, to save fuel, and let the breath come through his teeth in a quiet sigh.

They were spiders, giant tarantulas, three or four inches long. There were twenty of them in the cage. And somehow he had to get past them.

Bond lay and rested and thought while the red eyes gathered again in front of his face.

How deadly were these things? How much of the tales about them were myth? They could certainly kill animals, but how mortal to men were these giant spiders with the long soft friendly fur of a borzoi? Bond shuddered. He remembered the centipede. The touch of the tarantulas would be much softer. They would be like tiny teddy bears' paws against one's skin–until they bit and emptied their poison sacs into you.

But again, would this be Doctor No's killing ground? A bite or two perhaps–to send one into a delirium of pain. The horror of having to burst through the mesh in the darkness–Doctor No would not have reckoned with Bond's lighter–and squash through the forest of eyes, crushing some soft bodies, but feeling the jaws of the others lance home. And then more bites from the ones that had caught in the clothing. And then the creeping agony of the poison. That would have been the way Doctor No's mind would have worked–to send one screaming on one's way. To what? To the final fence?

But Bond had the lighter and the knife and the wire spear. All he neeeded was the nerve, and infinite, infinite precision.

Bond softly opened the jaws of the lighter and pulled the wick out an inch with his thumb and fingernail to give a bigger flame. He lit it and, as the spiders scuttled back, he pierced the thin wire mesh with his knife. He made a hole near the frame and cut down sideways and round. Then he seized the flap of wire and wrenched it out of the frame. It tore like stiff calico and came away in one piece. He put the knife back between his teeth and snaked through the opening. The spiders cowered before the flame of the lighter and crowded back on top of each other. Bond slid the wire spear out of his trousers and jabbed the blunt, doubled wire into the middle of them. He jabbed again and again, fiercely pulping the bodies. When some of the spiders tried to escape towards him he waved the light at them and smashed the fugitives one by one. Now the living spiders were attacking the dead and wounded and all Bond had to do was bash and bash into the writhing, sickening mess of blood and fur.

Slowly all movement slackened and then ceased. Were they all dead? Were some shamming? The flame of the lighter was beginning to die. He would have to chance it. Bond reached forward and shovelled the dead mess to one side. Then he took his knife from between his teeth and reached out and slashed open the second curtain of wire, bending the flap down over the heap of pulped bodies. The light flickered and became a red glow. Bond gathered himself and shot his body over the bloody pile of corpses and through the jagged frame.

He had no idea what bits of metal he touched or whether he had put his knee or his foot among the spiders. All he knew was that he had got through. He heaved himself yards on along the shaft and stopped to gather his breath and his nerve.

Above him a dim light came on. Bond squinted sideways and upwards, knowing what he would see. The slanting yellow eyes behind the thick glass looked keenly down at him. Slowly, behind the bulb, the head moved from side to side. The eyelids dropped in mock pity. A closed fist, the thumb pointing downwards in farewell and dismissal, inserted itself between the bulb and the glass. Then it was withdrawn. The light went out. Bond turned his face back to the floor of the shaft and rested his forehead on the cool metal. The gesture said that he was coming into the last lap, that the observers had finished with him until they came for his remains. It took an extra ounce of heart out of Bond that there had been no gesture of praise, however small, that he had managed to survive so far. These Chigroes hated him. They only wanted him to die, and as miserably as possible.

Bond's teeth ground softly together. He thought of the girl and the thought gave him strength. He wasn't dead yet. Damn it, he wouldn't die! Not until the heart was torn from his body.

Bond tensed his muscles. It was time to go. With extra care he put his weapons back in their places and painfully began to drag himself on into the blackness.

The shaft was beginning to slope gently downwards. It made the going easier. Soon the slope grew steeper so that Bond could almost slide along under the momentum of his weight. It was a blessed relief not to have to make the effort with his muscles. There was a glimmer of grey light ahead, nothing more than a lessening of the darkness, but it was a change. The quality of the air seemed to be different. There was a new, fresh smell to it. What was it? The sea?

Suddenly Bond realized that he was slipping down the shaft. He opened his shoulders and spread his feet to slow himself. It hurt and the braking effect was small. Now the shaft was widening. He could no longer get a grip! He was going faster and faster. A bend was just ahead. And it was a bend downwards!

Bond's body crashed into the bend and round it. Christ, he was diving head downwards! Desperately Bond spread his feet and hands. The metal flayed his skin. He was out of control, diving, diving down a gun barrel. Far below there was a circle of grey light. The open air? The sea? The light was tearing up at him. He fought for breath. Stay alive, you fool! Stay alive!

Head first, Bond's body shot out of the shaft and fell through the air, slowly, slowly, down towards the gun-metal sea that waited for him a hundred feet below.

Chapter Eighteen

Killing Ground

Bond's body shattered the mirror of the dawn sea like a bomb.

As he had hurtled down the silver shaft towards the widening disc of light, instinct had told him to get his knife from between his teeth, to get his hands forward to break his fall, and to keep his head down and his body rigid. And, at the last fraction of a second when he glimpsed the up-rushing sea, he had managed to take a gulp of breath. So Bond hit the water in the semblance of a dive, his outstretched clenched fists cleaving a hole for his skull and shoulders, and though, by the time he had shot twenty feet below the surface, he had lost consciousness, the forty-mile-an-hour impact with the water failed to smash him.

Slowly the body rose to the surface and lay, head down, softly rocking in the ripples of the dive. The water-choked lungs somehow contrived to send a last message to the brain. The legs and arms thrashed clumsily. The head turned up, water pouring from its open mouth. It sank. Again the legs jerked, instinctively trying to get the body upright in the water. This time, coughing horribly, the head jerked above the surface and stayed there. The arms and legs began to move feebly, paddling like a dog, and, through the red and black curtain, the bloodshot eyes saw the lifeline and told the sluggish brain to make for it.

The killing ground was a narrow deep water inlet at the base of the towering cliff. The lifeline towards which Bond struggled, hampered by the clumsy spear in his trouser-leg, was a strong wire fence, stretched from the rock walls of the inlet and caging it off from the open sea. The two-feet squares of thick wire were suspended from a cable six feet above the surface and disappeared, algae encrusted, into the depths.

Bond got to the wire and hung, crucified. For fifteen minutes he stayed like that, his body occasionally racked with vomiting, until he felt strong enough to turn his head and see where he was. Blearily his eyes took in the towering cliffs above him and the narrow vee of softly breathing water. The place was in deep grey shadow, cut off from the dawn by the mountain, but out at sea there was the pearly iridescence of first light that meant that for the rest of the world the day was dawning. Here it was dark and gloomy and brooding.

Sluggishly Bond's mind puzzled over the wire fence. What was its purpose, closing off this dark cleft of sea? Was it to keep things out, or keep them in? Bond gazed vaguely down into the black depths around him. The wire strands vanished into nothingness below his clinging feet. There were small fish round his legs below the waist. What were they doing? They seemed to be feeding, darting in towards him and then backing away, catching at black strands. Strands of what? Of cotton from his rags? Bond shook his head to clear it. He looked again. No, they were feeding off his blood.

Bond shivered. Yes, blood was seeping off his body, off the torn shoulders, the knees, the feet, into the water. Now for the first time he felt the pain of the sea water on his sores and burns. The pain revived him, quickened his mind. If these small fish liked it, what about barracuda and shark? Was that what the wire fence was for, to keep man-eating fish from escaping to sea. Then why hadn't they been after him already? To hell with it! The first thing was to crawl up the wire and get over to the other side. To put the fence between him and whatever lived in this black aquarium.

Weakly, foothold by foothold, Bond climbed up the wire and over the top and down again to where he could rest well above the water. He hooked the thick cable under his arms and hung, a bit of washing on a line, and gazed vaguely down at the fish that still fed from the blood that dripped off his feet.

Now there was nothing much left of Bond, not many reserves. The last dive down the tube, the crash of impact and the half-death from drowning had squeezed him like a sponge. He was on the verge of surrender, on the verge of giving one small sigh and then slipping back into the soft arms of the water. How beautiful it would be to give in at last and rest–to feel the sea softly take him to its bed and turn out the light.

It was the explosive flight of the fish from their feeding ground that shook Bond out of his death-dreaming. Something had moved far below the surface. There was a distant shimmer. Something was coming slowly up on the landward side of the fence.

Bond's body tautened. His hanging jaw slowly shut and the slackness cleared from his eyes. With the electric shock of danger, life flooded back into him, driving out the lethargy, pumping back the will to survive.

Bond uncramped the fingers that, a long time ago, his brain had ordered not to lose his knife. He flexed his fingers and took a fresh grip of the silver-plated handle. He reached down and touched the crook of the wire spear that still hung inside his trouser-leg. He shook his head sharply and focused his eyes. Now what?

Below him the water quivered. Something was stirring in the depths, something huge. A great length of luminescent greyness showed, poised far down in the darkness. Something snaked up from it, a whiplash as thick as Bond's arm. The tip of the thong was swollen to a narrow oval, with regular budlike markings. It swirled through the water where the fish had been and was withdrawn. Now there was nothing but the huge grey shadow. What was it doing? Was it . . .? Was it tasting the blood?

As if in answer, two eyes as big as footballs slowly swam up and into Bond's vision. They stopped, twenty feet below his own, and stared up through the quiet water at his face.

Bond's skin crawled on his back. Softly, wearily, his mouth uttered one bitter four-lettered word. So this was the last surprise of Doctor No, the end of the race!

Bond stared down, half hypnotized, into the wavering pools of eye far below. So this was the giant squid, the mythical kraken that could pull ships beneath the waves, the fifty-foot-long monster that battled with whales, that weighed a ton or more. What else did he know about them? That they had two long seizing tentacles and ten holding ones. That they had a huge blunt beak beneath eyes that were the only fishes' eyes that worked on the camera principle, like a man's. That their brains were efficient, that they could shoot backwards through the water at thirty knots, by jet-propulsion. That explosive harpoons burst in their jellied mantle without damaging them. That . . . but the bulging black and white targets of the eyes were rising up towards him. The surface of the water shivered. Now Bond could see the forest of tentacles that flowered out of the face of the thing. They were weaving in front of the eyes like a bunch of thick snakes. Bond could see the dots of the suckers on their undersides. Behind the head, the great flap of the mantle softly opened and closed, and behind that the jellied sheen of the body disappeared into the depths. God, the thing was as big as a railway engine!

Softly, discreetly. Bond snaked his feet and then his arms through the squares in the wire, lacing himself into them, according himself so that the tentacles would have either to tear him to bits or wrench down the wire barrier with him. He squinted to right and left. Either way it was twenty yards along the wire to the land. And movement, even if he was capable of it, would be fatal. He must stay dead quiet and pray that the thing would lose interest. If it didn't . . . Softly Bond's fingers clenched on the puny knife.

The eyes watched him, coldly, patiently. Delicately, like the questing trunk of an elephant, one of the long seizing tentacles broke the surface and palped its way up the wire towards his leg. It reached his foot. Bond felt the hard kiss of the suckers. He didn't move. He dared not reach down and lose the grip of his arms through the wire. Softly the suckers tugged, testing the amount of yield. It was not enough. Like a huge slimy caterpillar, the tentacle walked slowly on up the leg. It got to the bloody, blistered kneecap and stopped there, interested. Bond's teeth gritted with the pain. He could imagine the message going back down the thick tentacle to the brain: Yes, it's good to eat! And the brain signalling back: then get it! Bring it to me!

The suckers walked on up the thigh. The tip of the tentacle was pointed, then it splayed out so that it almost covered the width of Bond's thigh and then tapered off to a wrist. That was Bond's target. He would just have to take the pain and the horror and wait for the wrist to come within range.

A breeze, the first soft breeze of early morning, whispered across the metal surface of the inlet. It raised small waves that slapped gently against the sheer walls of the cliff. A wedge of cormorants took off from the guanera, five hundred feet above the inlet, and, cackling softly, made out to sea. As they swept over, the noise that had disturbed them reached Bond–the triple blast of a ship's siren that means it is ready to take on cargo. It came from Bond's left. The jetty must be round the corner from the northern arm of the inlet. The tanker from Antwerp had come in. Antwerp! Part of the world outside–the world that was a million miles away, out of Bond's reach–surely out of his reach for ever. Just round that corner, men would be in the galley, having breakfast. The radio would be playing. There would be the sizzle of bacon and eggs, the smell of coffee . . . breakfast cooking. . . .

The suckers were at his hip. Bond could see into the horny cups. A stagnant sea smell reached him as the hand slowly undulated upwards. How tough was the mottled grey-brown jelly behind the hand? Should he stab? No, it must be a quick hard slash, straight across, like cutting a rope. Never mind about cutting into his own skin.

Now! Bond took a quick glance into the two football eyes, so patient, so incurious. As he did so the other seizing arm broke the surface and shot straight up at his face. Bond jerked back and the hand curled into a fist round the wire in front of his eyes. In a second it would shift to an arm or shoulder and he would be finished. Now!

The first hand was on his ribs. Almost without taking aim, Bond's knife-hand slashed down and across. He felt the blade bite into the puddingy flesh and then the knife was almost torn from his grip as the wounded tentacle whipped back into the water. For a moment the sea boiled around him, Now the other hand let go the wire and slapped across his stomach. The pointed hand stuck like a leech, all the power of the suckers furiously applied. Bond screamed as the suckers bit into his flesh. He slashed madly, again and again. God, his stomach was being torn out! The wire shook with the struggle. Below him the water boiled and foamed. He would have to give in. One more stab, this time into the back of the hand. It worked! The hand jerked free and snaked down and away leaving twenty red circles, edged with blood, across his skin.

Bond had no time to worry about them. Now the head of the squid had broken the surface and the sea was being thrashed into foam by the great heaving mantle round it. The eyes were glaring up at him, redly, venomously, and the forest of feeding arms was at his feet and legs, tearing the cotton fabric away and flailing back. Bond was being pulled down, inch by inch. The wire was biting into his armpits. He could even feel his spine being stretched. If he held on he would be torn in half. Now the eyes and the great triangular beak were right out of the water and the beak was reaching up for his feet. There was one hope, only one!

Bond thrust his knife between his teeth and his hand dived for the crook of the wire spear. He tore it out, got it between his two hands and wrenched the doubled wire almost straight. He would have to let go with one arm to stoop and get within range. If he missed, he would be torn to shreds on the fence.

Now, before he died of the pain! Now, now!

Bond let his whole body slip down the ladder of wire and lunged through and down with all his force.

He caught a glimpse of the tip of his spear lancing into the centre of a black eyeball and then the whole sea erupted up at him in a fountain of blackness and he fell and hung upside down by the knees, his head an inch from the surface of the water.

What had happened? Had he gone blind? He could see nothing. His eyes were stinging and there was a horrible fish taste in his mouth. But he could feel the wire cutting into the tendons behind his knees. So he must be alive! Dazedly Bond let go the spear from his trailing hand and reached up and felt for the nearest strand of wire. He got a hold and reached up his other hand and slowly, agonizingly, pulled himself up so that he was sitting in the fence. Streaks of light came into his eyes. He wiped a hand across his face. Now he could see. He gazed at his hand. It was black and sticky. He looked down at his body. It was covered with black slime, and blackness stained the sea for twenty yards around. Then Bond realized. The wounded squid had emptied its ink sac at him.

But where was the squid? Would it come back? Bond searched the sea. Nothing, nothing but the spreading stain of black. Not a movement. Not a ripple. Then don't wait! Get away from here! Get away quick! Wildly Bond looked to right and left. Left was towards the ship, but also towards Doctor No. But right was towards nothing. To build the wire fence the men must have come from the left, from the direction of the jetty. There would be some sort of a path. Bond reached for the top cable and frantically began to edge along the swaying fence towards the rocky headland twenty yards away.

The stinking, bleeding, black scarecrow moved its arms and legs quite automatically. The thinking, feeling apparatus of Bond was no longer part of his body. It moved alongside his body, or floated above it, keeping enough contact to pull the strings that made the puppet work. Bond was like a cut worm, the two halves of which continue to jerk forward although life has gone and been replaced by the mock life of nervous impulses. Only, with Bond, the two halves were not yet dead. Life was only in abeyance in them. All he needed was an ounce of hope, an ounce of reassurance that it was still worth while trying to stay alive.

Bond got to the rock face. Slowly he let himself down to the bottom rung of wire. He gazed vaguely at the softly heaving sheen of water. It was black, impenetrable, as deep as the rest. Should he chance it? He must! He could do nothing until he had washed off the caking slime and blood, the horrible stale fish-smell. Moodily, fatalistically, he took off the rags of his shirt and trousers and hung them on the wire. He looked down at his brown and white body, striped and pock-marked with red. On an instinct he felt his pulse. It was slow but regular. The steady thump of life revived his spirits. What the hell was he worrying about? He was alive. The wounds and bruises on his body were nothing–absolutely nothing. They looked ugly, but nothing was broken. Inside the torn envelope, the machine was quietly, solidly ticking over. Superficial cuts and abrasions, bloody memories, deathly exhaustion–these were hurts that an accident ward would sneer at. Get on, you bastard! Get moving! Clean yourself and wake up. Count your blessings. Think of the girl. Hang on to life like you've hung on to the knife between your teeth. Stop being sorry for yourself. To hell with what happened just now. Get down into the water and wash!

Ten minutes later, Bond, his wet rags clinging to his scrubbed, stinging body and his hair slicked back out of his eyes, climbed over the top of the headland.

Yes, it was as he had guessed. A narrow rocky track, made by the feet of the workers, led down the other side and round the bulge of the cliff.

From close by came various sounds and echoes. A crane was working. He could hear the changing beat of its engine. There were iron ship-noises and the sound of water splashing into the sea from a bilge pump.

Bond looked up at the sky. It was pale blue. Clouds tinged with golden pink were trailing away towards the horizon. Far above him the cormorants were wheeling round the guanera. Soon they would be going off to feed. Perhaps even now they were watching the scout groups far out at sea locating the fish. It would be about six o'clock, the dawn of a beautiful day.

Bond, leaving drops of blood behind him, picked his way carefully down the track and along the bottom of the shadowed cliff. Round the bend, the track filtered through a maze of giant, tumbled boulders. The noises grew louder. Bond crept softly forward, watching his footholds for loose stones. A voice called out, startlingly close, 'Okay to go?' There was a distant answer: 'Okay.' The crane engine accelerated. A few more yards. One more boulder. And another. Now!

Bond flattened himself against the rock and warily inched his head round the corner.

Chapter Nineteen

A Shower of Death

Bond took one long comprehensive look and pulled back.

He leant against the cool face of rock and waited for his breathing to get back to normal. He lifted his knife close up to his eyes and carefully examined the blade. Satisfied, he slipped it behind him and down the waistband of his trousers up against his spine. There it would be handy but protected from hitting against anything. He wondered about the lighter. He took it out of his hip pocket. As a hunk of metal it might be useful, but it wouldn't light any more and it might scrape against the rock. He put it down on the ground away from his feet.

Then Bond sat down and meticulously went over the photograph that was in his brain.

Round the corner, not more than ten yards away, was the crane. There was no back to the cabin. Inside it a man sat at the controls. It was the Chinese negro boss, the driver of the marsh buggy. In front of him the jetty ran twenty yards out into the sea and ended in a T. An aged tanker of around ten thousand tons deadweight was secured alongside the top of the T. It stood well out of water, its decks perhaps twelve feet above the quay. The tanker was called *Blanche*, and the *Ant* of Antwerp showed at her stern. There was no sign of life on board except one figure lolling at the wheel in the enclosed bridge. The rest of the crew would be below, battened away from the guano dust. From just to the right of the crane, an overhead conveyor-belt in a corrugated-iron housing ran out from the cliff-face. It was carried on high stanchions above the jetty and stopped just short of the hold of the tanker. Its mouth ended in a huge canvas sock, perhaps six feet in diameter. The purpose of the crane was to lift the wire-framed mouth of the sock so that it hung directly over the hold of the tanker and to move it to right or left to give even distribution. From out of the mouth of the sock, in a solid downward jet, the scrambled-egg-coloured guano dust was pouring into the hold of the tanker at a rate of tons a minute.

Below, on the jetty, to the left and to leeward of the drifting smoke of the guano dust, stood the tall, watchful figure of Doctor No.

That was all. The morning breeze feathered the deepwater anchorage, still half in shadow beneath the towering cliffs, the conveyor-belt thudded quietly on its rollers, the crane's engine chuffed rhythmically. There was no other sound, no other movement, no other life apart from the watch at the ship's wheel, the trusty working at the crane, and Doctor No, seeing that all went well. On the other side of the mountain men would be working, feeding the guano to the conveyor-belt that rumbled away through the bowels of the rock, but on this side no one was allowed and no one was necessary. Apart from aiming the canvas mouth of the conveyor, there was nothing else for anyone to do.

Bond sat and thought, measuring distances, guessing at angles, remembering exactly where the crane driver's hands and feet were on the levers and the pedals. Slowly, a thin, hard smile broke across the haggard, sunburned face. Yes! It was on! It could be done. But softly, gently, slowly! The prize was almost intolerably sweet.

Bond examined the soles of his feet and his hands. They would serve. They would have to serve. He reached back and felt the handle of the knife. Shifted it an inch. He stood up and took several slow deep breaths, ran his hands through his salt- and sweat-matted hair, rubbed them harshly up and down his face and then down the tattered sides of his black jeans. He gave a final flex to his fingers. He was ready.

Bond stepped up to the rock and inched an eye round. Nothing had changed. His guess at the distances had been right. The crane driver was watchful, absorbed. The neck above the open khaki shirt was naked, offered, waiting. Twenty yards away, Doctor No, also with his back to Bond, stood sentry over the thick rich cataract of whity-yellow dust. On the bridge, the watch was lighting a cigarette.

Bond looked along the ten yards of path that led past the back of the crane. He picked out the places he would put each foot. Then he came out from behind the rock and ran.

Bond ran to the right of the crane, to a point he had chosen where the lateral side of the cabin would hide him from the driver and the jetty. He got there and stopped, crouching, listening. The engine hurried on, the conveyor-belt rumbled steadily out of the mountain above and behind him. There was no change.

The two iron footholds at the back of the cabin, inches away from Bond's face, looked solid. Anyway the noise of the engine would drown small sounds. But he would have to be quick to yank the man's body out of the seat and get his own hands and feet on the controls. The single stroke of the knife would have to be mortal. Bond felt along his own collarbone, felt the soft triangle of skin beneath which the jugular pumped, remembered the angle of approach behind the man's back, reminded himself to force the blade and hold it in.

For a final second he listened, then he reached behind his back for the knife and went up the iron steps and into the cabin with the stealth and speed of a panther.

At the last moment there was no need to hurry. Bond stood behind the man's back, smelling him. He had time to raise his knife hand almost to the roof of the cabin, time to summon every ounce of strength, before he swept the blade down and into the square inch of smooth, brownish-yellow skin.

The man's hands and legs splayed away from the controls. His face strained back towards Bond. It seemed to Bond that there was a flash of recognition in the bulging eyes before the whites rolled upwards. Then a strangled noise came from the open mouth and the big body rolled sideways off its iron seat and crashed to the floor.

Bond's eyes didn't even follow it as far as the ground. He was already in the seat and reaching for the pedals and levers. Everything was out of control. The engine was running in neutral, the wire hawser was tearing off the drum, the tip of the crane was bending slowly forwards like a giraffe's neck, the canvas mouth of the conveyor-belt had wilted and was now pouring its column of dust between the jetty and the ship. Doctor No was staring upwards. His mouth was open. Perhaps he was shouting something.

Coolly, Bond reined the machine in, slowly easing the levers and pedals back to the angles at which the driver had been holding them. The engine accelerated, the gears bit and began to work again. The hawser slowed on the spinning drum and reversed, bringing the canvas mouth up and over the ship. The tip of the crane lifted and stopped. The scene was as before. Now!

Bond reached forward for the iron wheel which the driver had been handling when Bond had caught his first glimpse of him. Which way to turn it? Bond tried to the left. The tip of the crane veered slightly to the right. So be it. Bond spun the wheel to the right. Yes, by God, it was answering, moving across the sky, carrying the mouth of the conveyor with it.

Bond's eyes flashed to the jetty. Doctor No had moved. He had moved a few paces to a stanchion that Bond had missed. He had a telephone in his hand. He was getting through to the other side of the mountain. Bond could see his hand frantically jiggling the receiver arm, trying to attract attention.

Bond whirled the director wheel. Christ, wouldn't it turn any faster? In seconds Doctor No would get through and it would be too late. Slowly the tip of the crane arced across the sky. Now the mouth of the conveyor was spewing the dust column down over the side of the ship. Now the yellow mound was marching silently across the jetty. Five yards, four, three, two! Don't look round, you bastard! Arrh, got you! Stop the wheel! Now, *you* take it, Doctor No!

At the first brush of the stinking dust column, Doctor No had turned. Bond saw the long arms fling wide as if to embrace the thudding mass. One knee rose to run. The mouth opened and a thin scream came up to Bond above the noise of the engine. Then there was a brief glimpse of a kind of dancing snowman. And then only a mound of yellow bird dung that grew higher and higher.

'God!' Bond's voice gave back an iron echo from the walls of the cabin. He thought of the screaming lungs stuffing with the filthy dust, the body bending and then falling under the weight, the last impotent kick of the heels, the last flash of thought–rage, horror, defeat?–and then the silence of the stinking tomb.

Now the yellow mountain was twenty feet high. The stuff was spilling off the sides of the jetty into the sea. Bond glanced at the ship. As he did so, there came three blasts on its siren. The noise crashed round the cliffs. There came a fourth blast which didn't stop. Bond could see the watch holding on to the lanyard as he craned out of the bridge window, looking down. Bond took his hands off the controls and let them rip. It was time to go.

He slipped off the iron seat and bent over the dead body. He took the revolver out of the holster and looked at it. He smiled grimly–Smith & Wesson ·38, the regular model. He slipped it down inside his waistband. It was fine to feel the heavy cold metal against his skin. He went to the door of the cabin and dropped down to the ground.

An iron ladder ran up the cliff behind the crane to where the conveyor-housing jutted out. There was a small door in the corrugated iron wall of the housing. Bond scrambled up the ladder. The door opened easily, letting out a puff of guano dust, and he clambered through.

Inside, the clanking of the conveyor-belt over its rollers was deafening, but there were dim inspection lights in the stone ceiling of the tunnel and a narrow catwalk that stretched away into the mountain alongside the hurrying river of dust. Bond moved quickly along it, breathing shallowly against the fishy ammoniac smell. At all costs he must get to the end before the significance of the ship's siren and of the unanswered telephone overcame the fear of the guards.

Bond half ran and half stumbled through the echoing, stinking tunnel. How far would it be? Two hundred yards? And then what? Nothing for it but to break out of the tunnel mouth and start shooting–cause a panic and hope for the best. He would get hold of one of the men and wring out of him where the girl was. Then what? When he got to the place on the mountainside, what would he find? What would be left of her?

Bond ran on faster, his head down, watching the narrow breadth of planking, wondering what would happen if he missed his footing and slipped into the rushing river of guano dust. Would he be able to get off the belt again or would he be whirled away and down until he was finally spewed out on to the burial mound of Doctor No?

When Bond's head hit into the soft stomach and he felt the hands at his throat, it was too late to think of his revolver. His only reaction was to throw himself down and forward at the legs. The legs gave against his shoulder and there was a shrill scream as the body crashed down on his back.

Bond had started the heave that would hurl his attacker sideways and on to the conveyor-belt when the quality of the scream and something light and soft about the impact of the body froze his muscles.

It couldn't be!

As if in answer, sharp teeth bit deeply into the calf of his right leg and an elbow jabbed viciously, knowledgeably, backwards into his groin.

Bond yelled with the pain. He tried to squirm sideways to protect himself, but even as he shouted 'Honey!' the elbow thudded into him again.

The breath whistled through Bond's teeth with the agony. There was only one way to stop her without throwing her on to the conveyor-belt. He took a firm grip of one ankle and heaved himself to his knees. He stood upright, holding her slung over his shoulder by one leg. The other foot banged against his head, but half-heartedly, as if she too realized that something was wrong.

'Stop it, Honey! It's me!'

Through the din of the conveyor-belt, Bond's shout got through to her. He heard her cry 'James!' from somewhere near the floor. He felt her hands clutch at his legs. 'James, James!'

Bond slowly let her down. He turned and knelt and reached for her. He put his arms round her and held her tightly to him. 'Oh Honey, Honey. Are you all right?' Desperately unbelieving, he strained her to him.

'Yes, James! Oh, yes!' He felt her hands at his back and his hair. 'Oh, James, my darling!' she fell against him, sobbing.

'It's all right, Honey.' Bond smoothed her hair. 'And Doctor No's dead. But now we've got to run for it. We've got to get out of here. Come on! How can we get out of the tunnel? How did you get here? We've got to hurry!'

As if in comment, the conveyor-belt stopped with a jerk.

Bond pulled the girl to her feet. She was wearing a dirty suit of workmen's blue dungarees. The sleeves and legs were rolled up. The suit was far too big for her. She looked like a girl in a man's pyjamas. She was powdered white with guano dust except where the tears had marked her cheeks. She said breathlessly, 'Just up there! There's a side tunnel that leads to the machine shops and the garage. Will they come after us?'

There was no time to talk. Bond said urgently, 'Follow me!' and started running. Behind him her feet padded softly in the hollow silence. They came to the fork where the side tunnel led off into the rock. Which way would the men come? Down the side tunnel or along the catwalk in the main tunnel? The sound of voices booming far up the side tunnel answered him. Bond drew the girl a few feet up the main tunnel. He brought her close to him and whispered, 'I'm sorry, Honey. I'm afraid I'm going to have to kill them.'

'Of course.' The answering whisper was matter of fact. She pressed his hand and stood back to give him room. She put her hands up to her ears.

Bond eased the gun out of his waistband. Softly he broke the cylinder sideways and verified with his thumb that all six chambers were loaded. Bond knew he wasn't going to like this, killing again in cold blood, but these men would be the Chinese negro gangsters, the strong-arm guards who did the dirty work. They would certainly be murderers many times over. Perhaps they were the ones who had killed Strangways and the girl. But there was no point in trying to ease his conscience. It was kill or be killed. He must just do it efficiently.

The voices were coming closer. There were three men. They were talking loudly, nervously. Perhaps it was many years since they had even thought of going through the tunnel. Bond wondered if they would look round as they came out into the main tunnel. Or would he have to shoot them in the back?

Now they were very close. He could hear their shoes scuffing the ground.

'That makes ten bucks you owe me, Sam.'

'Not after tonight it won't be. Roll them bones, boy. Roll them bones.'

'No dice for me tonight, feller. I'm going' to cut maself a slice of de white girl.'

'Haw, haw, haw.'

The first man came out, then the second, then the third. They were carrying their revolvers loosely in their right hands.

Bond said sharply, 'No, you won't.'

The three men whirled round. White teeth glinted in open mouths. Bond shot the rear man in the head and the second man in the stomach. The front man's gun was up. A bullet whistled past Bond and away up the main tunnel. Bond's gun crashed. The man clutched at his neck and spun slowly round and fell across the conveyor-belt. The echoes thundered slowly up and down the tunnel. A puff of fine dust rose in the air and settled. Two of the bodies lay still. The man with the stomach shot writhed and jerked.

Bond tucked his hot gun into the waistband of his trousers. He said roughly to the girl, 'Come on.' He reached for her hand and pulled her after him into the mouth of the side tunnel. He said, 'Sorry about that, Honey,' and started running, pulling her after him by the hand. She said, 'Don't be stupid.' Then there was no sound but the thud of their naked feet on the stone floor.

The air was clean in the side tunnel and it was easier going but, after the tension of the shooting, pain began to crowd in again and take possession of Bond's body. He ran automatically. He hardly thought of the girl. His whole mind was focused on taking the pain and on the problems that waited at the end of the tunnel.

He couldn't tell if the shots had been heard and he had no idea what opposition was left. His only plan was to shoot anyone who got in his way and somehow get to the garage and the marsh buggy. That was their only hope of getting away from the mountain and down to the coast.

The dim yellow bulbs in the ceiling flicked by overhead. Still the tunnel stretched on. Behind him, Honey stumbled. Bond stopped, cursing himself for not having thought of her. She reached for him and for a moment she leaned against him panting. 'I'm sorry, James. It's just that . . .'

Bond held her to him. He said anxiously, 'Are you hurt, Honey?'

'No, I'm all right. It's just that I'm so terribly tired. And my feet got rather cut on the mountain. I fell a lot in the dark. If we could walk a bit. We're nearly there. And there's a door into the garage before we get to the machine shop. Couldn't we go in there?'

Bond hugged her to him. He said, 'That's just what I'm looking for, Honey. That's our only hope of getting away. If you can stick it till we get there, we've got a real chance.'

Bond put his arm round her waist and took her weight. He didn't trust himself to look at her feet. He knew they must be bad. It was no good being sorry for each other. There wasn't time for it if they were to stay alive.

They started moving again, Bond's face grim with the extra effort, the girl's feet leaving bloody footsteps on the ground, and almost immediately she whispered urgently and there was a wooden door in the wall of the tunnel and it was ajar and no sound came from the other side.

Bond took out his gun and gently eased the door open. The long garage was empty. Under the neon lights the black and gold painted dragon on wheels looked like a float waiting for the Lord Mayor's Show. It was pointing towards the sliding doors and the hatch of the armoured cabin stood open. Bond prayed that the tank was full and that the mechanic had carried out his orders to get the damage fixed.

Suddenly, from somewhere outside, there was the sound of voices. They came nearer, several of them, jabbering urgently.

Bond took the girl by the hand and ran forward. There was only one place to hide–in the marsh buggy. The girl scrambled in. Bond followed, softly pulling the door shut behind him. They crouched, waiting. Bond thought: only three rounds left in the gun. Too late he remembered the rack of weapons on the wall of the garage. Now the voices were outside. There came the clang of the door being slid back on its runners and a confusion of talk.

'How d'ya know they were shootin'?'

'Couldn't been nuthen else. I should know.'

'Better take rifles. Here, Joe! Take that one, Lemmy! An' some pineapples. Box under da table.'

There was the metallic noise of bolts being slid home and safety catches clicked.

'Some feller must a gone nuts. Couldn't ha been da Limey. You ever seen da big pus-feller in da creek? Cheessus! An' da rest of da tricks da Doc fixed up in da tube? An' dat white gal. She cain't have been in much shape dis mornin'. Any of you men bin to have a look?'

'Nossir.'

'No.'

'No.'

'Haw, haw. I'se sho surprised at you fellers. Dat's a fine piece of ass out dere on de crab walk.'

More rattling and shuffling of feet, then, 'Okay let's go! Two abreast till we gets to da main tunnel. Shoot at da legs. Whoever's makin' trouble, da Doc'll sure want him to play wit.'

'Tee-hee.'

Feet echoed hollowly on the concrete. Bond held his breath as they filed by. Would they notice the shut door of the buggy? But they went on down the garage and into the tunnel and the noise of them slowly faded away.

Bond touched the girl's arm and put his finger to his lips. Softly he eased open the door and listened again. Nothing. He dropped to the ground and walked round the buggy and went to the half-open entrance. Cautiously he edged his head round. There was no one in sight. There was a smell of frying food in the air that brought the saliva to Bond's mouth. Dishes and pans clattered in the nearest building, about twenty yards away, and from one of the further Quonsets came the sound of a guitar and man's voice singing a calypso. Dogs started to bark half-heartedly and then were silent. The Dobermann Pinschers.

Bond turned and ran back to the end of the garage. No sound came from the tunnel. Softly Bond closed the tunnel door and locked and bolted it. He went to the arms-rack on the wall and chose another Smith & Wesson and a Remington carbine. He verified that they were loaded and went to the door of the marsh buggy and handed them in to the girl. Now the entrance door. Bond put his shoulder to it and softly eased it wide open. The corrugated iron rumbled hollowly. Bond ran back and scrambled through the open hatch and into the driver's seat. 'Shut it, Honey,' he whispered urgently and bent and turned the ignition key.

The needle on the gauge swung to Full. Pray God the damned thing would start up quickly. Some diesels were slow. Bond stamped his foot down on the starter.

The grinding rattle was deafening. It must be audible all over the compound! Bond stopped and tried again. The engine fluttered and died. And again, and this time the blessed thing fired and the strong iron pulse hammered as Bond revved it up. Now, gently into gear. Which one? Try this. Yes, it bit. Brake off, you bloody fool! Christ, it had nearly stalled. But now they were out and on the track and Bond rammed his foot down to the floor.

'Anyone after us?' Bond had to shout above the noise of the diesel.

'No. Wait! Yes, there's a man come out of the huts! And another! They're waving and shouting at us. Now some more are coming out. One of them's run off to the right. Another's gone back into the hut. He's come out with a rifle. He's lying down. He's firing!'

'Close the slot! Lie down on the floor!' Bond glanced at the speedometer. Twenty. And they were on a slope. There was nothing more to get out of the machine. Bond concentrated on keeping the huge bucking wheels on the track. The cabin bounced and swayed on the springs. It was a job to keep his hands and feet on the controls. An iron fist clanged against the cabin. And another. What was the range? Four hundred? Good shooting! But that would be the lot. He shouted, 'Take a look, Honey! Open the slot an inch.'

'The man's got up. He's stopped firing. They're all looking after us–a whole crowd of them. Wait, there's something else. The dogs are coming! There's no one with them. They're just tearing down the track after us. Will they catch us?'

'Doesn't matter if they do. Come and sit by me, Honey. Hold tight. Mind your head against the roof.' Bond eased up on the throttle. She was beside him. He grinned sideways at her. 'Hell, Honey. We've made it. When we get down to the lake I'll stop and shoot up the dogs. If I know those brutes I've only got to kill one and the whole pack'll stop to eat him.'

Bond felt her hand at his neck. She kept it there as they swayed and thundered down the track. At the lake, Bond went on fifty yards into the water and turned the machine round and put it in neutral. Through the oblong slot he could see the pack streaming round the last bend. He reached down for the rifle and pushed it through the aperture. Now the dogs were in the water and swimming. Bond kept his finger on the trigger and sprayed bullets into the middle of them. One floundered, kicking. Then another and another. He could hear their snarling screams above the clatter of the engine. There was blood in the water. A fight had started. He saw one dog leap on one of the wounded ones and sink its teeth into the back of its neck. Now they all seemed to have gone berserk. They were milling around in the frothing bloody water. Bond emptied his magazine among them and dropped the gun on the floor. He said, 'That's that, Honey,' and put the machine into gear and swung it round and began rolling at an easy speed across the shallow lake towards the distant gap in the mangroves that was the mouth of the river.

For five minutes they moved along in silence. Then Bond put a hand on the girl's knee and said, 'We should be all right now, Honey. When they find the boss is dead there'll be panic. I guess some of the brighter ones will try and get away to Cuba in the plane or the launch. They'll worry about their skins, not about us. All the same, we'll not take the canoe out until it's dark. I guess it's about ten by now. We should be at the coast in an hour. Then we'll rest up and try and get in shape for the trip. Weather looks all right and there'll be a bit more moon tonight. Think you can make it?'

Her hand squeezed his neck. 'Of course I can, James. But what about you? Your poor body! It's nothing but burns and bruises. And what are those red marks across your stomach?'

'Tell you later. I'll be okay. But you tell me what happened to you last night. How in hell did you manage to get away from the crabs? What went wrong with that bastard's plan? All night long I could only think of you out there being slowly eaten to death. God, what a thing to have dreamed up! What happened?'

The girl was actually laughing. Bond looked sideways. The golden hair was tousled and the blue eyes were heavy with lack of sleep, but otherwise she might just be coming home from a midnight barbecue.

'That man thought he knew everything. Silly old fool.' She might have been talking about a stupid schoolteacher. 'He's much more impressed by the black crabs than I am. To begin with, I don't mind any animal touching me, and anyway those crabs wouldn't think of even nipping someone if they stay quite still and haven't got an open sore or anything. The whole point is that they don't really like meat. They live mostly on plants and things. If he was right and he did kill a black girl that way, either she had an open wound or she must have died of fright. He must have wanted to see if I'd stand it. Filthy old man. I only fainted down there at dinner because I knew he'd have something much worse for you.'

'Well, I'm damned. I wish to heaven I'd known that. I thought of you being picked to pieces.'

The girl snorted. 'Of course it wasn't very nice having my clothes taken off and being tied down to pegs in the ground. But those black men didn't dare touch me. They just made jokes and then went away. It wasn't very comfortable out there on the rock, but I was thinking of you and of how I could get at Doctor No and kill him. Then I heard the crabs beginning to run–that's what we call it in Jamaica–and soon they came scurrying and rattling along–hundreds of them. I just lay still and thought of you. They walked round me and over me. I might have been a rock for all they cared. They tickled a bit. One annoyed me by trying to pull out a bit of my hair. But they don't smell or anything, and I just waited for the early morning when they crawl into holes and go to sleep. I got quite fond of them. They were company. Then they got fewer and fewer and finally stopped coming and I could move. I pulled at all the pegs in turn and then concentrated on my right hand one. In the end I got it out of the crack in the rock and the rest was easy. I got back to the buildings and began scouting about. I got into the machine shop near the garage and found this filthy old suit. Then the conveyor thing started up not far away and I thought about it and I guessed it must be taking the guano through the mountain. I knew you must be dead by then,' the quiet voice was matter of fact, 'so I thought I'd get to the conveyor somehow and get through the mountain and kill Doctor No. I took a screwdriver to do it with.' She giggled. 'When we ran into each other, I'd have stuck it into you only it was in my pocket and I couldn't get to it. I found the door in the back of the machine shop and walked through and into the main tunnel. That's all.' She caressed the back of his neck. 'I ran along watching my step and the next thing I knew was your head hitting me in the stomach.' She giggled again. 'Darling. I hope I didn't hurt you too much when we were fighting. My nanny told me always to hit men there.'

Bond laughed. 'She did, did she?' He reached out and caught her by the hair and pulled her face to him. Her mouth felt its way round his cheek and locked itself against his.

The machine gave a sideways lurch. The kiss ended. They had hit the first mangrove roots at the entrance to the river.

Chapter Twenty

Slave-time

'You're quite sure of all this?'

The Acting Governor's eyes were hunted, resentful. How could these things have been going on under his nose, in one of Jamaica's dependencies? What would the Colonial Office have to say about it? He already saw the long, pale blue envelope marked 'personal. For Addressee Only', and the foolscap page with those very wide margins: 'The Secretary of State for the Colonies has instructed me to express to you his surprise . . .'

'Yes, sir. Quite sure.' Bond had no sympathy for the man. He hadn't liked the reception he had had on his last visit to King's House, nor the mean comments on Strangways and the girl. He liked the memory of them even less now that he knew his friend and the girl were at the bottom of the Mona Reservoir.

'Er–well we mustn't let any of this get out to the Press. You understand that? I'll send my report in to the Secretary of State by the next bag. I'm sure I can rely on your . . .'

'Excuse me, sir.' The Brigadier in command of the Caribbean Defence Force was a modern young soldier of thirty-five. His military record was good enough for him to be unimpressed by relics from the Edwardian era of Colonial Governors, whom he collectively referred to as 'feather-hatted fuddy-duddies'. 'I think we can assume that Commander Bond is unlikely to communicate with anyone except his Department. And if I may say so, sir, I submit that we should take steps to clear up Crab Key without waiting for approval from London. I can provide a platoon ready to embark by this evening. H.M.S. *Narvik* came in yesterday. If the programme of receptions and cocktail parties for her could possibly be deferred for forty-eight hours or so . . .' The Brigadier let his sarcasm hang in the air.

'I agree with the Brigadier, sir.' The voice of the Police Superintendent was edgy. Quick action might save him from a reprimand, but it would have to be quick. 'And in any case I shall have to proceed immediately against the various Jamaicans who appear to be implicated. I'll have to get the divers working at Mona. If this case is to be cleaned up we can't afford to wait for London. As Mister–er–Commander Bond says, most of these negro gangsters will probably be in Cuba by now. Have to get in touch with my opposite number in Havana and catch up with them before they take to the hills or go underground. I think we ought to move at once, sir.

There was silence in the cool shadowy room where the meeting was being held. On the ceiling above the massive mahogany conference table there was an unexpected dapple of sunlight. Bond guessed that it shone up through the slats of the jalousies from a fountain or a lily pond in the garden outside the tall windows. Far away there was the sound of tennis balls being knocked about. Distantly a young girl's voice called, 'Smooth. Your serve, Gladys.'

The Governor's children? Secretaries? From one end of the room King George VI, from the other end the Queen, looked down the table with grace and good humour.

'What do you think, Colonial Secretary?' The Governor's voice was hustled.

Bond listened to the first few words. He gathered that Pleydell-Smith agreed with the other two. He stopped listening. His mind drifted into a world of tennis courts and lily ponds and kings and queens, of London, of people being photographed with pigeons on their heads in Trafalgar Square, of the forsythia that would soon be blazing on the bypass roundabouts, of May, the treasured housekeeper in his flat off the King's Road sitting down to her tea (here it was eleven in the morning, it would be four in the afternoon in London), of the early rush-hour tube trains of the evening shaking the foundations of the Regency house of which he owned the ground floor. Of the douce weather of England: the soft airs, the 'heat' waves, the cold spells–'The only country where you can take a walk every day of the year'–Chesterfield's Letters? And then Bond thought of Crab Key, of the hot ugly wind beginning to blow, of the stink of the marsh gas from the mangrove swamps, the jagged grey, dead coral in whose holes the black crabs were now squatting, the black and red eyes moving swiftly on their stalks as a shadow–a cloud, a bird–broke their small horizons. Down in the bird colony the brown and white and pink birds would be stalking in the shallows, or fighting or nesting, while up on the guanera the cormorants would be streaming back from their breakfast to deposit their milligramme of rent to the landlord who would no longer be collecting. And where would the landlord be? The men from the S.S. *Blanche* would have dug him out. The body would have been examined for signs of life and then put somewhere. Would they have washed the yellow dust off him and dressed him in his kimono while the Captain radioed Antwerp for instructions? And where had Doctor No's soul gone to? Had it been a bad soul or just a mad one? Bond thought of the burned twist down in the swamp that had been Quarrel. He remembered the soft ways of the big body, the innocence in the grey, horizon-seeking eyes, the simple lusts and desires, the reverence for superstitions and instincts, the childish faults, the loyalty and even love that Quarrel had given him–the warmth, there was only one word for it, of the man. Surely he hadn't gone to the same place as Doctor No. Whatever happened to dead people, there was surely one place for the warm and another for the cold. And which, when the time came, would he, Bond, go to?

The Colonial Secretary was mentioning Bond's name. Bond pulled himself together.

'. . . survived is quite extraordinary. I do think, sir, that we should show our gratitude to Commander Bond and to his Service by accepting his recommendations. It does seem, sir, that he has done at least three-quarters of the job. Surely the least we can do is look after the other quarter.'

The Governor grunted. He squinted down the table at Bond. The chap didn't seem to be paying much attention. But one couldn't be sure with these Secret Service fellows. Dangerous chaps to have around, sniffing and snooping. And their damned Chief carried a lot of guns in Whitehall. Didn't do to get on the wrong side of him. Of course there was something to be said for sending the *Narvik*. News would leak, of course. All the Press of the world would be coming down on his head. But then suddenly the Governor saw the headlines: 'GOVERNOR TAKES SWIFT ACTION . . . ISLAND'S STRONG MAN INTERVENES . . . THE NAVY'S THERE!' Perhaps after all it would be better to do it that way. Even go down and see the troops off himself. Yes, that was it, by jove. Cargill, of the *Gleaner*, was coming to lunch. He'd drop a hint or two to the chap and make sure the story got proper coverage. Yes, that was it. That was the way to play the hand.

The Governor raised his hands and let them fall flat on the table in a gesture of submission. He embraced the conference with a wry smile of surrender.

'So I am overruled, gentlemen. Well, then,' the voice was avuncular, telling the children that just this once . . . 'I accept your verdict. Colonial Secretary, will you please call upon the commanding officer of H.M.S. *Narvik* and explain the position. In strict confidence, of course. Brigadier, I leave the military arrangements in your hands. Superintendent, you will know what to do.' The Governor rose. He inclined his head regally in the direction of Bond. 'And it only remains to express my appreciation to Commander–er–Bond, for his part in this affair. I shall not fail to mention your assistance, Commander, to the Secretary of State.'

Outside the sun blazed down on the gravel sweep. The interior of the Hillman Minx was a Turkish bath. Bond's bruised hands cringed as they took the wheel.

Pleydell-Smith leant through the window. He said, 'Ever heard the Jamaican expression "rarse"?'

'No.'

'"Rarse, man" is a vulgar expression meaning–er–"stuff it up". If I may say so, it would have been appropriate for you to have used the expression just now. However,' Pleydell-Smith gave a wave of his hand which apologized for his Chief and dismissed him, 'is there anything else I can do for you? You really think you ought to go back to Beau Desert? They were quite definite at the hospital that they want to have you for a week.'

'Thanks,' said Bond shortly, 'but I've got to get back. See the girl's all right. Would you tell the hospital I'll be back tomorrow? You got off that signal to my Chief?'

'Urgent rates.'

'Well, then,' Bond pressed the self-starter, 'I guess that's the lot. You'll see the Jamaica Institute people about the girl, won't you? She really knows the hell of a lot about the natural history side of the island. Not from books either. If they've got the right sort of job . . . Like to see her settled. I'll take her up to New York myself and see her through the operation. She'd be ready to start in a couple of weeks after that. Incidentally,' Bond looked embarrassed, 'she's really the hell of a fine girl. When she comes back . . . if you and your wife . . . You know. Just so there's someone to keep an eye on her.'

Pleydell-Smith smiled. He thought he had the picture. He said, 'Don't worry about that. I'll see to it. Betty's rather a hand at that sort of thing. She'll like taking the girl under her wing. Nothing else? See you later in the week, anyway. That hospital's the hell of a place in this heat. You might care to spend a night or two with us before you go ho–I mean to New York. Glad to have you–er–both.'

'Thanks. And thanks for everything else.' Bond put the car into gear and went off down the avenue of flaming tropical shrubbery. He went fast, scattering the gravel on the bends. He wanted to get the hell away from King's House, and the tennis, and the kings and queens. He even wanted to get the hell away from the kindly Pleydell-Smith. Bond liked the man, but all he wanted now was to get back across the Junction Road to Beau Desert and away from the smooth world. He swung out past the sentry at the gates and on to the main road. He put his foot down.

The night voyage under the stars had been without incident. No one had come after them. The girl had done most of the sailing. Bond had not argued with her. He had lain in the bottom of the boat, totally collapsed, like a dead man. He had woken once or twice and listened to the slap of the sea against the hull and watched her quiet profile under the stars. Then the cradle of the soft swell had sent him back to sleep and to the nightmares that reached out after him from Crab Key. He didn't mind them. He didn't think he would ever mind a nightmare now. After what had happened the night before, it would have to be strong stuff that would ever frighten him again.

The crunch of a nigger-head against the hull had woken him. They were coming through the reef into Morgan's Harbour. The first quarter moon was up, and inside the reef the sea was a silver mirror. The girl had brought the canoe through under sail. They slid across the bay to the little fringe of sand and the bows under Bond's head sighed softly into it. She had had to help him out of the boat and across the velvet lawn and into the house. He had clung to her and cursed her softly as she had cut his clothes off him and taken him into the shower. She had said nothing when she had seen his battered body under the lights. She had turned the water full on and taken soap and washed him down as if he had been a horse. Then she led him out from under the water and dabbed him softly dry with towels that were soon streaked with blood. He had seen her reach for the bottle of Milton. He had groaned and taken hold of the washbasin and waited for it. Before she had begun to put it on him, she had come round and kissed him on the lips. She had said softly, 'Hold tight, my darling. And cry. It's going to hurt,' and as she splashed the murderous stuff over his body the tears of pain had run out of his eyes and down his cheeks without shame.

Then there had been a wonderful breakfast as the dawn flared up across the bay, and the ghastly drive over to Kingston to the white table of the surgery in the emergency ward. Pleydell-Smith had been summoned. No questions had been asked. Merthiolate had been put on the wounds and tannic ointment on the burns. The efficient negro doctor had written busily in the duty report. What? Probably just 'Multiple burns and contusions.' Then, with promises to come into the private ward on the next day, Bond had gone off with Pleydell-Smith to King's House and to the first of the meetings that had ended with the full-dress conference. Bond had enciphered a short signal to M via the Colonial Office which he had coolly concluded with: 'REGRET MUST AGAIN REQUEST SICK LEAVE STOP SURGEONS REPORT FOLLOWS STOP KINDLY INFORM ARMOURER SMITH AND WESSON INEFFECTIVE AGAINST FLAME-THROWER ENDIT.'

Now, as Bond swung the little car down the endless S-bends towards the

North Shore, he regretted the gibe. M wouldn't like it. It was cheap. It wasted cipher groups. Oh, well! Bond swerved to avoid a thundering red bus with 'Brownskin Gal' on the destination plate. He had just wanted M to know that it hadn't quite been a holiday in the sun. He would apologize when he sent in his written report.

Bond's bedroom was cool and dark. There was a plate of sandwiches and a Thermos full of coffee beside the turned-down bed. On the pillow was a sheet of paper with big childish writing. It said, 'You are staying with me tonight. I can't leave my animals. They were fussing. And I can't leave you. And you owe me slave-time. I will come at seven. Your H.'

In the dusk she came across the lawn to where Bond was sitting finishing his third glass of Bourbon-on-the-rocks. She was wearing a black and white striped cotton skirt and a tight sugar-pink blouse. The golden hair smelled of cheap shampoo. She looked incredibly fresh and beautiful. She reached out her hand and Bond took it and followed her up the drive and along a narrow well-trodden path through the sugar-cane. It wound along for quite a way through the tall whispering sweet-scented jungle. Then there was a patch of tidy lawn up against thick broken stone walls and steps that led down to a heavy door whose edges glinted with light.

She looked up at him from the door. 'Don't be frightened. The cane's high and they're most of them out.'

Bond didn't know what he had expected. He had vaguely thought of a flat earthen floor and rather damp walls. There would be a few sticks of furniture, a broken bedstead covered with rags, and a strong zoo smell. He had been prepared to be careful about hurting her feelings.

Instead it was rather like being inside a very large tidy cigar-box. The floor and ceiling were of highly polished cedar that gave out a cigar-box smell and the walls were panelled with wide split bamboo. The light came from a dozen candles in a fine silver chandelier that hung from the centre of the ceiling. High up in the walls there were three square windows through which Bond could see the dark blue sky and the stars. There were several pieces of good nineteenth-century furniture. Under the chandelier a table was laid for two with expensive-looking old-fashioned silver and glass.

Bond said, 'Honey, what a lovely room. From what you said I thought you lived in a sort of zoo.'

She laughed delightedly. 'I got out the old silver and things. It's all I've got. I had to spend the day polishing it. I've never had it out before. It does look rather nice, doesn't it? You see, generally there are a lot of little cages up against the wall. I like having them with me. It's company. But now that you're here . . .' She paused. 'My bedroom's in there,' she gestured at the other door. 'It's very small, but there's room for both of us. Now come on. I'm afraid it's cold dinner–just lobsters and fruit.'

Bond walked over to her. He took her in his arms and kissed her hard on the lips. He held her and looked down into the shining blue eyes. 'Honey, you're a wonderful girl. You're one of the most wonderful girls I've ever known. I hope the world's not going to change you too much. D'you really want to have that operation? I love your face–just as it is. It's part of you. Part of all this.'

She frowned and freed herself. 'You're not to be serious tonight. Don't talk about these things. I don't want to talk about them. This is my night with you. Please talk about love. I don't want to hear about anything else. Promise? Now come on. You sit there.'

Bond sat down. He smiled up at her. He said, 'I promise.'

She said, 'Here's the mayonnaise. It's not out of a bottle. I made it myself. And take some bread and butter.' She sat down opposite him and began to eat, watching him. When she saw that he seemed satisfied she said, 'Now you can start telling me about love. Everything about it. Everything you know.'

Bond looked across into the flushed, golden face. The eyes were bright and soft in the candlelight, but with the same imperious glint they had held when he had first seen her on the beach and she had thought he had come to steal her shells. The full red lips were open with excitement and impatience. With him she had no inhibitions. They were two loving animals. It was natural. She had no shame. She could ask him anything and would expect him to answer. It was as if they were already in bed together, lovers. Through the tight cotton bodice the points of her breasts showed, hard and roused.

Bond said, 'Are you a virgin?'

'Not quite. I told you. That man.'

'Well . . .' Bond found he couldn't eat any more. His mouth was dry at the thought of her. He said, 'Honey, I can either eat or talk love to you. I can't do both.'

'You're going over to Kingston tomorrow. You'll get plenty to eat there. Talk love.'

Bond's eyes were fierce blue slits. He got up and went down on one knee beside her. He picked up her hand and looked into it. At the base of the thumb the Mount of Venus swelled luxuriously. Bond bent his head down into the warm soft hand and bit softly into the swelling. He felt her other hand in his hair. He bit harder. The hand he was holding curled round his mouth. She was panting. He bit still harder. She gave a little scream and wrenched his head away by the hair.

'What are you doing?' Her eyes were wide and dark. She had gone pale. She dropped her eyes and looked at his mouth. Slowly she pulled his head towards her.

Bond put out a hand to her left breast and held it hard. He lifted her captive, wounded hand and put it round his neck. Their mouths met and clung, exploring.

Above them the candles began to dance. A big hawk-moth had come in through one of the windows. It whirred round the chandelier. The girl's closed eyes opened, looked at the moth. Her mouth drew away. She smoothed the handful of his hair back and got up, and without saying anything took down the candles one by one and blew them out. The moth whirred away through one of the windows.

The girl stood away from the table. She undid her blouse and threw it on the floor. Then her skirt. Under the glint of moonlight she was a pale figure with a central shadow. She came to Bond and took him by the hand and lifted him up. She undid his shirt and slowly, carefully took it off. Her body, close to him, smelled of new-mown hay and sweet pepper. She led him away from the table and through a door. The filtering moonlight shone down on a single bed. On the bed was a sleeping-bag, its mouth laid open.

The girl let go his hand and climbed into the sleeping-bag. She looked up at him. She said, practically, 'I bought this today. It's a double one. It cost a lot of money. Take those off and come in. You promised. You owe me slave-time.'

'But . . .'

'Do as you're told.'

GOLDFINGER

GOLDFINGER

Goldfinger said, 'Mr Bond they have a saying in Chicago: "Once is happenstance, twice is coincidence, and third time it's enemy action."'

To
my gentle reader
William Plomer

PART ONE

HAPPENSTANCE

Chapter One

Reflections in a Double Bourbon

James Bond, with two double bourbons inside him, sat in the final departure lounge of Miami Airport and thought about life and death.

It was part of his profession to kill people. He had never liked doing it and when he had to kill he did it as well as he knew how and forgot about it. As a secret agent who held the rare double-O prefix–the licence to kill in the Secret Service–it was his duty to be as cool about death as a surgeon. If it happened, it happened. Regret was unprofessional–worse, it was death-watch beetle in the soul.

And yet there had been something curiously impressive about the death of the Mexican. It wasn't that he hadn't deserved to die. He was an evil man, a man they call in Mexico a *capungo*. A capungo is a bandit who will kill for as little as forty pesos, which is about twenty-five shillings–though probably he had been paid more to attempt the killing of Bond–and, from the look of him, he had been an instrument of pain and misery all his life. Yes, it had certainly been time for him to die; but when Bond had killed him, less than twenty-four hours before, life had gone out of the body so quickly, so utterly, that Bond had almost seen it come out of his mouth as it does, in the shape of a bird, in Haitian primitives.

What an extraordinary difference there was between a body full of person and a body that was empty! Now there is someone, now there is no one. This had been a Mexican with a name and an address, an employment card and perhaps a driving licence. Then something had gone out of him, out of the envelope of flesh and cheap clothes, and had left him an empty paper bag waiting for the dustcart. And the difference, the thing that had gone out of the stinking Mexican bandit, was greater than all Mexico.

Bond looked down at the weapon that had done it. The cutting edge of his right hand was red and swollen. It would soon show a bruise. Bond flexed the hand, kneading it with his left. He had been doing the same thing at intervals through the quick plane trip that had got him away. It was a painful process, but if he kept the circulation moving the hand would heal more quickly. One couldn't tell how soon the weapon would be needed again. Cynicism gathered at the corners of Bond's mouth.

'National Airlines, "Airline of the Stars", announces the departure of their flight NA 106 to La Guardia Field, New York. Will all passengers please proceed to gate number seven. All aboard, please.'

The Tannoy switched off with an echoing click. Bond glanced at his watch. At least another ten minutes before Transamerica would be called. He signalled to a waitress and ordered another double bourbon on the rocks.

When the wide, chunky glass came, he swirled the liquor round for the ice to blunt it down and swallowed half of it. He stubbed out the butt of his cigarette and sat, his chin resting on his left hand, and gazed moodily across the twinkling tarmac to where the last half of the sun was slipping gloriously into the Gulf.

The death of the Mexican had been the finishing touch to a bad assignment, one of the worst–squalid, dangerous and without any redeeming feature except that it had got him away from headquarters.

A big man in Mexico had some poppy fields. The flowers were not for decoration. They were broken down for opium which was sold quickly and comparatively cheaply by the waiters at a small café in Mexico City called the 'Madre de Cacao'. The Madre de Cacao had plenty of protection. If you needed opium you walked in and ordered what you wanted with your drink. You paid for your drink at the caisse and the man at the caisse told you how many noughts to add to your bill. It was an orderly commerce of no concern to anyone outside Mexico. Then, far away in England, the Government, urged on by the United Nations' drive against drug smuggling, announced that heroin would be banned in Britain. There was alarm in Soho and also among respectable doctors who wanted to save their patients agony. Prohibition is the trigger of crime. Very soon the routine smuggling channels from China, Turkey and Italy were run almost dry by the illicit stock-piling in England. In Mexico City, a pleasant-spoken Import and Export merchant called Blackwell had a sister in England who was a heroin addict. He loved her and was sorry for her and, when she wrote that she would die if someone didn't help, he believed that she wrote the truth and set about investigating the illicit dope traffic in Mexico. In due course, through friends and friends of friends, he got to the Madre de Cacao and on from there to the big Mexican grower. In the process, he came to know about the economics of the trade, and he decided that if he could make a fortune and at the same time help suffering humanity he had found the Secret of Life. Blackwell's business was in fertilizers. He had a warehouse and a small plant and a staff of three for soil testing and plant research. It was easy to persuade the big Mexican that, behind this respectable front, Blackwell's team could busy itself extracting heroin from opium. Carriage to England was swiftly arranged by the Mexican. For the equivalent of a thousand pounds a trip, every month one of the diplomatic couriers of the Ministry of Foreign Affairs carried an extra suitcase to London. The price was reasonable. The contents of the suitcase, after the Mexican had deposited it at the Victoria Station left-luggage office and had mailed the ticket to a man called Schwab, c/o Boox-an-Pix, Ltd, W.C.1, were worth twenty thousand pounds.

Unfortunately Schwab was a bad man, unconcerned with suffering humanity. He had the idea that if American juvenile delinquents could consume millions of dollars' worth of heroin every year, so could their Teddy boy and girl cousins. In two rooms in Pimlico, his staff watered the heroin with stomach powder and sent it on its way to the dance halls and amusement arcades.

Schwab had already made a fortune when the C.I.D. Ghost Squad got on to him. Scotland Yard decided to let him make a little more money while they investigated the source of his supply. They put a close tail on Schwab and in due course were led to Victoria Station and thence to the Mexican courier. At that stage, since a foreign country was concerned, the Secret

Service had had to be called in and Bond was ordered to find out where the courier got his supplies and to destroy the channel at source.

Bond did as he was told. He flew to Mexico City and quickly got to the Madre de Cacao. Thence, posing as a buyer for the London traffic, he got back to the big Mexican. The Mexican received him amiably and referred him to Blackwell. Bond had rather taken to Blackwell. He knew nothing about Blackwell's sister, but the man was obviously an amateur and his bitterness about the heroin ban in England rang true. Bond broke into his warehouse one night and left a thermite bomb. He then went and sat in a café a mile away and watched the flames leap above the horizon of roof-tops and listened to the silver cascade of the fire-brigade bells. The next morning he telephoned Blackwell. He stretched a handkerchief across the mouthpiece and spoke through it.

'Sorry you lost your business last night. I'm afraid your insurance won't cover those stocks of soil you were researching.'

'Who's that? Who's speaking?'

'I'm from England. That stuff of yours has killed quite a lot of young people over there. Damaged a lot of others. Santos won't be coming to England any more with his diplomatic bag. Schwab will be in jail by tonight. That fellow Bond you've been seeing, he won't get out of the net either. The police are after him now.'

Frightened words came back down the line.

'All right, but just don't do it again. Stick to fertilizers.'

Bond hung up.

Blackwell wouldn't have had the wits. It was obviously the big Mexican who had seen through the false trail. Bond had taken the precaution to move his hotel, but that night, as he walked home after a last drink at the Copacabana, a man suddenly stood in his way. The man wore a dirty white linen suit and a chauffeur's white cap that was too big for his head. There were deep blue shadows under Aztec cheek-bones. In one corner of the slash of a mouth there was a toothpick and in the other a cigarette. The eyes were bright pinpricks of marihuana.

'You like woman? Make jigajig?'

'No.'

'Coloured girl? Fine jungle tail?'

'No.'

'Mebbe pictures?'

The gesture of the hand slipping into the coat was so well known to Bond, so full of old dangers, that, when the hand flashed out and the long silver finger went for his throat, Bond was on balance and ready for it.

Almost automatically, Bond went into the 'Parry Defence against Underhand Thrust' out of the book. His right arm cut across, his body swivelling with it. The two forearms met mid-way between the two bodies, banging the Mexican's knife arm off target and opening his guard for a crashing short-arm chin jab with Bond's left. Bond's stiff, locked wrist had not travelled far, perhaps two feet, but the heel of his palm, with fingers spread for rigidity, had come up and under the man's chin with terrific force. The blow almost lifted the man off the sidewalk. Perhaps it had been that blow that had killed the Mexican, broken his neck, but as he staggered back on his way to the ground, Bond had drawn back his right hand and slashed sideways at the taut, offered throat. It was the deadly hand-edge blow to the

Adam's apple, delivered with the fingers locked into a blade, that had been the stand-by of the Commandos. If the Mexican was still alive, he was certainly dead before he hit the ground.

Bond stood for a moment, his chest heaving, and looked at the crumpled pile of cheap clothes flung down in the dust. He glanced up and down the street. There was no one. Some cars passed. Others had perhaps passed during the fight, but it had been in the shadows. Bond knelt down beside the body. There was no pulse. Already the eyes that had been so bright with marihuana were glazing. The house in which the Mexican had lived was empty. The tenant had left.

Bond picked up the body and laid it against a wall in deeper shadow. He brushed his hands down his clothes, felt to see if his tie was straight and went on to his hotel.

At dawn Bond had got up and shaved and driven to the airport where he took the first plane out of Mexico. It happened to be going to Caracas. Bond flew to Caracas and hung about in the transit lounge until there was a plane for Miami, a Transamerica Constellation that would take him on that same evening to New York.

Again the Tannoy buzzed and echoed. 'Transamerica regrets to announce a delay on their flight TR 618 to New York due to a mechanical defect. The new departure time will be at eight a.m. Will all passengers please report to the Transamerica ticket counter where arrangements for their overnight accommodation will be made. Thank you.'

So! That too! Should he transfer to another flight or spend the night in Miami? Bond had forgotten his drink. He picked it up and, tilting his head back, swallowed the bourbon to the last drop. The ice tinkled cheerfully against his teeth. That was it. That was an idea. He would spend the night in Miami and get drunk, stinking drunk so that he would have to be carried to bed by whatever tart he had picked up. He hadn't been drunk for years. It was high time. This extra night, thrown at him out of the blue, was a spare night, a gone night. He would put it to good purpose. It was time he let himself go. He was too tense, too introspective. What the hell was he doing, glooming about this Mexican, this capungo who had been sent to kill him? It had been kill or get killed. Anyway, people were killing other people all the time, all over the world. People were using their motor cars to kill with. They were carrying infectious diseases around, blowing microbes in other people's faces, leaving gas-jets turned on in kitchens, pumping out carbon monoxide in closed garages. How many people, for instance, were involved in manufacturing H-bombs, from the miners who mined the uranium to the shareholders who owned the mining shares? Was there any person in the world who wasn't somehow, perhaps only statistically, involved in killing his neighbour?

The last light of the day had gone. Below the indigo sky the flare paths twinkled green and yellow and threw tiny reflections off the oily skin of the tarmac. With a shattering roar a DC7 hurtled down the main green lane. The windows in the transit lounge rattled softly. People got up to watch. Bond tried to read their expressions. Did they hope the plane would crash–give them something to watch, something to talk about, something to fill their empty lives? Or did they wish it well? Which way were they willing the sixty passengers? To live or to die?

Bond's lips turned down. Cut it out. Stop being so damned morbid. All this is just reaction from a dirty assignment. You're stale, tired of having to be tough. You want a change. You've seen too much death. You want a slice of life–easy, soft, high.

Bond was conscious of steps approaching. They stopped at his side. Bond looked up. It was a clean, rich-looking, middle-aged man. His expression was embarrassed, deprecating.

'Pardon me, but surely it's Mr Bond . . . Mr–er–James Bond?'

Chapter Two

Living It Up

Bond liked anonymity. His 'Yes, it is' was discouraging.

'Well, that's a mighty rare coincidence.' The man held out his hand. Bond rose slowly, took the hand and released it. The hand was pulpy and unarticulated–like a hand-shaped mud pack, or an inflated rubber glove. 'My name is Du Pont. Junius Du Pont. I guess you won't remember me, but we've met before. Mind if I sit down?'

The face, the name? Yes, there *was* something familiar. Long ago. Not in America. Bond searched the files while he summed the man up. Mr Du Pont was about fifty–pink, clean-shaven and dressed in the conventional disguise with which Brooks Brothers cover the shame of American millionaires. He wore a single-breasted dark tan tropical suit and a white silk shirt with a shallow collar. The rolled ends of the collar were joined by a gold safety pin beneath the knot of a narrow dark red and blue striped tie that fractionally wasn't the Brigade of Guards'. The cuffs of the shirt protruded half an inch below the cuffs of the coat and showed cabochon crystal links containing miniature trout flies. The socks were charcoal-grey silk and the shoes were old and polished mahogany and hinted Peal. The man carried a dark, narrow-brimmed straw Homburg with a wide claret ribbon.

Mr Du Pont sat down opposite Bond and produced cigarettes and a plain gold Zippo lighter. Bond noticed that he was sweating slightly. He decided that Mr Du Pont was what he appeared to be, a very rich American, mildly embarrassed. He knew he had seen him before, but he had no idea where or when.

'Smoke?'

'Thank you.' It was a Parliament. Bond affected not to notice the offered lighter. He disliked held-out lighters. He picked up his own and lit the cigarette.

'France, '51, Royale les Eaux.' Mr Du Pont looked eagerly at Bond. 'That Casino. Ethel, that's Mrs Du Pont, and me were next to you at the table the night you had the big game with the Frenchman.'

Bond's memory raced back. Yes, of course. The Du Ponts had been Nos. 4 and 5 at the baccarat table. Bond had been 6. They had seemed harmless people. He had been glad to have such a solid bulwark on his left on that fantastic night when he had broken Le Chiffre. Now Bond saw it all again–the bright pool of light on the green baize, the pink crab hands across the table scuttling out for the cards. He smelled the smoke and the harsh tang of his own sweat. That had been a night! Bond looked across at Mr Du Pont and smiled at the memory. 'Yes, of course I remember. Sorry I was slow. But that was quite a night. I wasn't thinking of much except my cards.'

Mr Du Pont grinned back, happy and relieved. 'Why, gosh, Mr Bond. Of course I understand. And I do hope you'll pardon me for butting in. You see . . .' He snapped his fingers for a waitress. 'But we must have a drink to celebrate. What'll you have?'

'Thanks, Bourbon on the rocks.'

'And dimple Haig and water.' The waitress went away.

Mr Du Pont leant forward, beaming. A whiff of soap or after-shave lotion came across the table. Lentheric? 'I knew it was you. As soon as I saw you sitting there. But I thought to myself, Junius, you don't often make an error over a face, but let's just go make sure. Well, I was flying Transamerican tonight and, when they announced the delay, I watched your expression and, if you'll pardon me, Mr Bond, it was pretty clear from the look on your face that you had been flying Transamerican too.' He waited for Bond to nod. He hurried on. 'So I ran down to the ticket counter and had me a look at the passenger list. Sure enough, there it was, "J. Bond".'

Mr Du Pont sat back, pleased with his cleverness. The drinks came. He raised his glass. 'Your very good health, sir. This sure is my lucky day.'

Bond smiled non-committally and drank.

Mr Du Pont leant forward again. He looked round. There was nobody at the near-by tables. Nevertheless he lowered his voice. 'I guess you'll be saying to yourself, well, it's nice to see Junius Du Pont again, but what's the score? Why's he so particularly happy at seeing me on just this night?' Mr Du Pont raised his eyebrows as if acting Bond's part for him. Bond put on a face of polite inquiry. Mr Du Pont leant still farther across the table. 'Now, I hope you'll forgive me, Mr Bond. It's not like me to pry into other people's secre . . . er–affairs. But, after that game at Royale. I did hear that you were not only a grand card player, but also that you were–er–how shall I put it?–that you were a sort of–er–investigator. You know, kind of intelligence operative.' Mr Du Pont's indiscretion had made him go very red in the face. He sat back and took out a handkerchief and wiped his forehead. He looked anxiously at Bond.

Bond shrugged his shoulders. The grey-blue eyes that looked into Mr Du Pont's eyes, which had turned hard and watchful despite his embarrassment, held a mixture of candour, irony and self-deprecation. 'I used to dabble in that kind of thing. Hangover from the war. One still thought it was fun playing Red Indians. But there's no future in it in peacetime.'

'Quite, quite.' Mr Du Pont made a throwaway gesture with the hand that held the cigarette. His eyes evaded Bond's as he put the next question, waited for the next lie. (Bond thought, there's a wolf in this Brooks Brothers clothing. This is a shrewd man.) 'And now you've settled down?' Mr Du Pont smiled paternally. 'What did you choose, if you'll pardon the question?'

'Import and Export. I'm with Universal. Perhaps you've come across them.'

Mr Du Pont continued to play the game. 'Hm. Universal. Let me see.

Why, yes, sure I've heard of them. Can't say I've ever done business with them, but I guess it's never too late.' He chuckled fatly. 'I've got quite a heap of interests all over the place. Only stuff I can honestly say I'm not interested in is chemicals. Maybe it's my misfortune, Mr Bond, but I'm not one of the chemical Du Ponts.'

Bond decided that the man was quite satisfied with the particular brand of Du Pont he happened to be. He made no comment. He glanced at his watch to hurry Mr Du Pont's play of the hand. He made a note to handle his own cards carefully. Mr Du Pont had a nice pink kindly baby-face with a puckered, rather feminine turn-down mouth. He looked as harmless as any of the middle-aged Americans with cameras who stand outside Buckingham Palace. But Bond sensed many tough, sharp qualities behind the fuddyduddy façade.

Mr Du Pont's sensitive eye caught Bond's glance at his watch. He consulted his own. 'My, oh my! Seven o'clock and here I've been talking away without coming to the point. Now, see here, Mr Bond. I've got me a problem on which I'd greatly appreciate your guidance. If you can spare me the time and if you were counting on stopping over in Miami tonight I'd reckon it a real favour if you'd allow me to be your host.' Mr Du Pont held up his hand. 'Now, I think I can promise to make you comfortable. So happens I own a piece of the Floridiana. Maybe you heard we opened around Christmas time? Doing a great business I'm happy to say. Really pushing that little old Fountain Blue,' Mr Du Pont laughed indulgently. 'That's what we call the Fontainebleau down here. Now, what do you say, Mr Bond? You shall have the best suite–even if it means putting some good paying customers out on the sidewalk. And you'd be doing me a real favour.' Mr Du Pont looked imploring.

Bond had already decided to accept–blind. Whatever Mr Du Pont's problem–blackmail, gangsters, women–it would be some typical form of rich man's worry. Here was a slice of the easy life he had been asking for. Take it. Bond started to say something politely deprecating. Mr Du Pont interrupted. 'Please, please, Mr Bond. And believe me, I'm grateful, very grateful indeed.' He snapped his fingers for the waitress. When she came, he turned away from Bond and settled the bill out of Bond's sight. Like many very rich men he considered that showing his money, letting someone see how much he tipped, amounted to indecent exposure. He thrust his roll back into his trousers pocket (the hip pocket is not the place among the rich) and took Bond by the arm. He sensed Bond's resistance to the contact and removed his hand. They went down the stairs to the main hall.

'Now, let's just straighten out your reservation.' Mr Du Pont headed for the Transamerica ticket counter. In a few curt phrases Mr Du Pont showed his power and efficiency in his own, his American, realm.

'Yes, Mr Du Pont. Surely, Mr Du Pont. I'll take care of that, Mr Du Pont.'

Outside, a gleaming Chrysler Imperial sighed up to the kerb. A tough-looking chauffeur in a biscuit-coloured uniform hurried to open the door. Bond stepped in and settled down in the soft upholstery. The interior of the car was deliciously cool, almost cold. The Transamerican representative bustled out with Bond's suitcase, handed it to the chauffeur and, with a half-bow, went back into the Terminal. 'Bill's on the Beach,' said Mr Du Pont to the chauffeur and the big car slid away through the crowded parking lots and out on to the parkway.

Mr Du Pont settled back. 'Hope you like stone crabs, Mr Bond. Ever tried them?'

Bond said he had, that he liked them very much.

Mr Du Pont talked about Bill's on the Beach and about the relative merits of stone and Alaska crab meat while the Chrysler Imperial sped through downtown Miami, along Biscayne Boulevard and across Biscayne Bay by the Douglas MacArthur Causeway. Bond made appropriate comments, letting himself be carried along on the gracious stream of speed and comfort and rich small-talk.

They drew up at a white-painted, mock-Regency frontage in clapboard and stucco. A scrawl of pink neon said: BILL'S ON THE BEACH. While Bond got out, Mr Du Pont gave his instructions to the chauffeur. Bond heard the words. 'The Aloha Suite,' and 'If there's any trouble, tell Mr Fairlie to call me here. Right?'

They went up the steps. Inside, the big room was decorated in white with pink muslin swags over the windows. There were pink lights on the tables. The restaurant was crowded with sunburned people in expensive tropical get-ups–brilliant garish shirts, jangling gold bangles, dark glasses with jewelled rims, cute native straw hats. There was a confusion of scents. The wry smell of bodies that had been all day in the sun came through.

Bill, a pansified Italian, hurried towards them. 'Why, Mr Du Pont. Is a pleasure, sir. Little crowded tonight. Soon fix you up. Please this way please.' Holding a large leather-bound menu above his head the man weaved his way between the diners to the best table in the room, a corner table for six. He pulled out two chairs, snapped his fingers for the maître d'hôtel and the wine waiter, spread two menus in front of them, exchanged compliments with Mr Du Pont and left them.

Mr Du Pont slapped his menu shut. He said to Bond, 'Now, why don't you just leave this to me? If there's anything you don't like, send it back.' And to the head waiter, 'Stone crabs. Not frozen. Fresh. Melted butter. Thick toast. Right?'

'Very good, Mr Du Pont.' The wine waiter, washing his hands, took the waiter's place.

'Two pints of pink champagne. The Pommery '50. Silver tankards. Right?'

'Vairry good, Mr Du Pont. A cocktail to start?'

Mr Du Pont turned to Bond. He smiled and raised his eyebrows.

Bond said, 'Vodka martini, please. With a slice of lemon peel.'

'Make it two,' said Mr Du Pont. 'Doubles.' The wine waiter hurried off. Mr Du Pont sat back and produced his cigarettes and lighter. He looked round the room, answered one or two waves with a smile and a lift of the hand and glanced at the neighbouring tables. He edged his chair nearer to Bond's. 'Can't help the noise, I'm afraid,' he said apologetically. 'Only come here for the crabs. They're out of this world. Hope you're not allergic to them. Once brought a girl here and fed her crabs and her lips swelled up like cycle tyres.'

Bond was amused at the change in Mr Du Pont–this racy talk, the authority of manner once Mr Du Pont thought he had got Bond on the hook, on his payroll. He was a different man from the shy embarrassed suitor who had solicited Bond at the airport. What did Mr Du Pont want from Bond? It would be coming any minute now, the proposition. Bond said, 'I haven't got any allergies.'

'Good, good.'

There was a pause. Mr Du Pont snapped the lid of his lighter up and down several times. He realized he was making an irritating noise and pushed it away from him. He made up his mind. He said, speaking at his hands on the table in front of him, 'You ever play Canasta, Mr Bond?'

'Yes, it's a good game. I like it.'

'Two-handed Canasta?'

'I have done. It's not so much fun. If you don't make a fool of yourself–if neither of you do–it tends to even out. Law of averages in the cards. No chance of making much difference in the play.'

Mr Du Pont nodded emphatically. 'Just so. That's what I've said to myself. Over a hundred games or so, two equal players will end up equal. Not such a good game as Gin or Oklahoma, but in a way that's just what I like about it. You pass the time, you handle plenty of cards, you have your ups and downs, no one gets hurt. Right?'

Bond nodded. The martinis came. Mr Du Pont said to the wine waiter, 'Bring two more in ten minutes.' They drank. Mr Du Pont turned and faced Bond. His face was petulant, crumpled. He said, 'What would you say, Mr Bond, if I told you I'd lost twenty-five thousand dollars in a week playing two-handed Canasta?' Bond was about to reply. Mr Du Pont held up his hand. 'And mark you, I'm a good card player. Member of the Regency Club. Play a lot with people like Charlie Goren, Johnny Crawford–at bridge that is. But what I mean, I know my way around at the card table.' Mr Du Pont probed Bond's eyes.

'If you've been playing with the same man all the time, you've been cheated.'

'Ex-actly.' Mr Du Pont slapped the table-cloth. He sat back. 'Ex-actly. That's what I said to myself after I'd lost–lost for four whole days. So I said to myself, this bastard is cheating me and by golly I'll find out how he does it and have him hounded out of Miami. So I doubled the stakes and then doubled them again. He was quite happy about it. And I watched every card he played, every movement. Nothing! Not a hint or a sign. Cards not marked. New pack whenever I wanted one. My own cards. Never looked at my hand–couldn't, as I always sat dead opposite him. No kibitzer to tip him off. And he just went on winning and winning. Won again this morning. And again this afternoon. Finally I got so mad at the game–I didn't show it, mind you–' Bond might think he had not been a sport–'I paid up politely. But, without telling this guy, I just packed my bag and got me to the airport and booked on the first plane to New York. Think of that!' Mr Du Pont threw up his hands. 'Running away. But twenty-five grand is twenty-five grand. I could see it getting to fifty, a hundred. And I just couldn't stand another of these damned games and I couldn't stand not being able to catch this guy out. So I took off. What do you think of that? Me, Junius Du Pont, throwing in the towel because I couldn't take the licking any more!'

Bond grunted sympathetically. The second round of drinks came. Bond was mildly interested, he was always interested in anything to do with cards. He could see the scene, the two men playing and playing and the one man quietly shuffling and dealing away and marking up his score while the other was always throwing his cards into the middle of the table with a gesture of controlled disgust. Mr Du Pont was obviously being cheated. How? Bond said, 'Twenty-five thousand's a lot of money. What stakes were you playing?'

Mr Du Pont looked sheepish. 'Quarter a point, then fifty cents, then a dollar. Pretty high I guess with the games averaging around two thousand points. Even at a quarter, that makes five hundred dollars a game. At a dollar a point, if you go on losing, it's murder.'

'You must have won sometimes.'

'Oh sure, but somehow, just as I'd got the s.o.b. all set for a killing, he'd put down as many of his cards as he could meld. Got out of the bag. Sure, I won some small change, but only when he needed a hundred and twenty to go down and I'd got all the wild cards. But you know how it is with Canasta, you have to discard right. You lay traps to make the other guy hand you the pack. Well, darn it, he seemed to be psychic! Whenever I laid a trap, he'd dodge it, and almost every time he laid one for me I'd fall into it. As for giving me the pack–why, he'd choose the damndest cards when he was pushed–discard singletons, aces, God knows what, and always get away with it. It was just as if he knew every card in my hand.'

'Any mirrors in the room?'

'Heck, no! We always played outdoors. He said he wanted to get himself a sunburn. Certainly did that. Red as lobster. He'd only play in the mornings and afternoons. Said if he played in the evening he couldn't get to sleep.'

'Who is this man, anyway? What's his name?'

'Goldfinger.'

'First name?'

'Auric. That means golden, doesn't it? He certainly is that. Got flaming red hair.'

'Nationality?'

'You won't believe it, but he's a Britisher. Domiciled in Nassau. You'd think he'd be a Jew from the name, but he doesn't look it. We're restricted at the Floridiana. Wouldn't have got in if he had been. Nassavian passport. Age forty-two. Unmarried. Profession, broker. Got all this from his passport. Had me a peek via the house detective when I started to play with him.'

'What sort of broker?'

Du Pont smiled grimly. 'I asked him. He said, "Oh, anything that comes along." Evasive sort of fellow. Clams up if you ask him a direct question. Talks away quite pleasantly about nothing at all.'

'What's he worth?'

'Ha!' said Mr Du Pont explosively. 'That's the damnedest thing. He's loaded. But loaded! I got my bank to check with Nassau. He's lousy with it. Millionaires are a dime a dozen in Nassau, but he's rated either first or second among them. Seems he keeps his money in gold bars. Shifts them around the world a lot to get the benefit of changes in the gold price. Acts like a damn federal bank. Doesn't trust currencies. Can't say he's wrong in that, and seeing how he's one of the richest men in the world there must be something to his system. But the point is, if he's as rich as that, what the hell does he want to take a lousy twenty-five grand off me for?'

A bustle of waiters round their table saved Bond having to think up a reply. With ceremony, a wide silver dish of crabs, big ones, their shells and claws broken, was placed in the middle of the table. A silver sauceboat brimming with melted butter and a long rack of toast was put beside each of their plates. The tankards of champagne frothed pink. Finally, with an oily smirk, the head waiter came behind their chairs and, in turn, tied round their necks long white silken bibs that reached down to the lap.

Bond was reminded of Charles Laughton playing Henry VIII, but neither Mr Du Pont nor the neighbouring diners seemed surprised at the hoggish display. Mr Du Pont, with a gleeful 'Every man for himself', raked several hunks of crab on to his plate, doused them liberally in melted butter and dug in. Bond followed suit and proceeded to eat, or rather devour, the most delicious meal he had had in his life.

The meat of the stone crabs was the tenderest, sweetest shellfish he had ever tasted. It was perfectly set off by the dry toast and slightly burned taste of the melted butter. The champagne seemed to have the faintest scent of strawberries. It was ice cold. After each helping of crab, the champagne cleaned the palate for the next. They ate steadily and with absorption and hardly exchanged a word until the dish was cleared.

With a slight belch, Mr Du Pont for the last time wiped butter off his chin with his silken bib and sat back. His face was flushed. He looked proudly at Bond. He said reverently, 'Mr Bond, I doubt if anywhere in the world a man has eaten as good a dinner as that tonight. What do you say?'

Bond thought, I asked for the easy life, the rich life. How do I like it? How do I like eating like a pig and hearing remarks like that? Suddenly the idea of ever having another meal like this, or indeed any other meal with Mr Du Pont, revolted him. He felt momentarily ashamed of his disgust. He had asked and it had been given. It was the puritan in him that couldn't take it. He had made his wish and the wish had not only been granted, it had been stuffed down his throat. Bond said, 'I don't know about that, but it was certainly very good.'

Mr Du Pont was satisfied. He called for coffee. Bond refused the offer of cigars or liqueurs. He lit a cigarette and waited with interest for the catch to be presented. He knew there would be one. It was obvious that all this was part of the come-on. Well, let it come.

Mr Du Pont cleared his throat. 'And now, Mr Bond, I have a proposition to put to you.' He stared at Bond, trying to gauge his reaction in advance.

'Yes?'

'It surely was providential to meet you like that at the airport.' Mr Du Pont's voice was grave, sincere. 'I've never forgotten our first meeting at Royale. I recall every detail of it–your coolness, your daring, your handling of the cards.' Bond looked down at the table-cloth. But Mr Du Pont had got tired of his peroration. He said hurriedly, 'Mr Bond, I will pay you ten thousand dollars to stay here as my guest until you have discovered how this man Goldfinger beats me at cards.'

Bond looked Mr Du Pont in the eye. He said, 'That's a handsome offer, Mr Du Pont. But I have to get back to London. I must be in New York to catch my plane within forty-eight hours. If you will play your usual sessions tomorrow morning and afternoon I should have plenty of time to find out the answer. But I must leave tomorrow night, whether I can help you or not. Done?'

'Done,' said Mr Du Pont.

Chapter Three

The Man with Agoraphobia

The flapping of the curtains wakened Bond. He threw off the single sheet and walked across the thick pile carpet to the picture window that filled the whole of one wall. He drew back the curtains and went out on to the sun-filled balcony.

The black and white chequer-board tiles were warm, almost hot to the feet although it could not yet be eight o'clock. A brisk inshore breeze was blowing off the sea, straining the flags of all nations that flew along the pier of the private yacht basin. The breeze was humid and smelt strongly of the sea. Bond guessed it was the breeze that the visitors like, but the residents hate. It would rust the metal fittings in their homes, fox the pages of their books, rot their wallpaper and pictures, breed damp-rot in their clothes.

Twelve storeys down the formal gardens, dotted with palm trees and beds of bright croton and traced with neat gravel walks between avenues of bougainvillaea, were rich and dull. Gardeners were working, raking the paths and picking up leaves with the lethargic slow motion of coloured help. Two mowers were at work on the lawns and, where they had already been, sprinklers were gracefully flinging handfuls of spray.

Directly below Bond, the elegant curve of the Cabana Club swept down to the beach–two storeys of changing-rooms below a flat roof dotted with chairs and tables and an occasional red and white striped umbrella. Within the curve was the brilliant green oblong of the Olympic-length swimming-pool fringed on all sides by row upon row of mattressed steamer chairs on which the customers would soon be getting their fifty-dollar-a-day sunburn. White-jacketed men were working among them, straightening the lines of chairs, turning the mattresses and sweeping up yesterday's cigarette butts. Beyond was the long, golden beach and the sea, and more men–raking the tideline, putting up the umbrellas, laying out mattresses. No wonder the neat card inside Bond's wardrobe had said that the cost of the Aloha Suite was two hundred dollars a day. Bond made a rough calculation. If he was paying the bill, it would take him just three weeks to spend his whole salary for the year. Bond smiled cheerfully to himself. He went back into the bedroom, picked up the telephone and ordered himself a delicious, wasteful breakfast, a carton of king-size Chesterfields and the newspapers.

By the time he had shaved and had an ice-cold shower and dressed it was eight o'clock. He walked through into the elegant sitting-room and found a waiter in a uniform of plum and gold laying out his breakfast beside the window. Bond glanced at the *Miami Herald*. The front page was devoted to yesterday's failure of an American ICBM at the near-by Cape Canaveral and a bad upset in a big race at Hialeah.

Bond dropped the paper on the floor and sat down and slowly ate his breakfast and thought about Mr Du Pont and Mr Goldfinger.

His thoughts were inconclusive. Mr Du Pont was either a much worse player than he thought, which seemed unlikely on Bond's reading of his tough, shrewd character, or else Goldfinger was a cheat. If Goldfinger cheated at cards, although he didn't need the money, it was certain that he had also made himself rich by cheating or sharp practice on a much bigger scale. Bond was interested in big crooks. He looked forward to his first sight of Goldfinger. He also looked forward to penetrating Goldfinger's highly successful and, on the face of it, highly mysterious method of fleecing Mr Du Pont. It was going to be a most entertaining day. Idly Bond waited for it to get under way.

The plan was that he would meet Mr Du Pont in the garden at ten o'clock. The story would be that Bond that flown down from New York to try and sell Mr Du Pont a block of shares from an English holding in a Canadian Natural Gas property. The matter was clearly confidential and Goldfinger would not think of questioning Bond about details. Shares, Natural Gas, Canada. That was all Bond needed to remember. They would go along together to the roof of the Cabana Club where the game was played and Bond would read his paper and watch. After luncheon, during which Bond and Mr Du Pont would discuss their 'business', there would be the same routine. Mr Du Pont had inquired if there was anything else he could arrange. Bond had asked for the number of Mr Goldfinger's suite and a pass-key. He had explained that if Goldfinger was any kind of a professional card-sharp, or even an expert amateur, he would travel with the usual tools of the trade–marked and shaved cards, the apparatus for the Short Arm Delivery, and so forth. Mr Du Pont had said he would give Bond the key when they met in the garden. He would have no difficulty getting one from the manager.

After breakfast, Bond relaxed and gazed into the middle distance of the sea. He was not keyed up by the job on hand, only interested and amused. It was just the kind of job he had needed to clear his palate after Mexico.

At half past nine Bond left his suite and wandered along the corridors of his floor, getting lost on his way to the elevator in order to reconnoitre the lay-out of the hotel. Then, having met the same maid twice, he asked his way and went down in the elevator and moved among the scattering of early risers through the Pineapple Shopping Arcade. He glanced into the Bamboo Coffee Shoppe, the Rendezvous Bar, the La Tropicala dining-room, the Kittekat Klub for children and the Boom-Boom Nighterie. He then went purposefully out into the garden. Mr Du Pont, now dressed 'for the beach' by Abercrombie & Fitch, gave him the pass-key to Goldfinger's suite. They sauntered over to the Cabana Club and climbed the two short flights of stairs to the top deck.

Bond's first view of Mr Goldfinger was startling. At the far corner of the roof, just below the cliff of the hotel, a man was lying back with his legs up on a steamer chair. He was wearing nothing but a yellow satin bikini slip, dark glasses and a pair of wide tin wings under his chin. The wings, which appeared to fit round his neck, stretched out across his shoulders and beyond them and then curved up slightly to rounded tips.

Bond said, 'What the hell's he wearing round his neck?'

'You never seen one of those?' Mr Du Pont was surprised. 'That's a gadget to help your tan. Polished tin. Reflects the sun up under your chin and behind the ears–the bits that wouldn't normally catch the sun.'

'Well, well,' said Bond.

When they were a few yards from the reclining figure Mr Du Pont called out cheerfully, in what seemed to Bond an overloud voice, 'Hi there!'

Mr Goldfinger did not stir.

Mr Du Pont said in his normal voice. 'He's very deaf.' They were now at Mr Goldfinger's feet. Mr Du Pont repeated his hail.

Mr Goldfinger sat up sharply. He removed his dark glasses. 'Why, hullo there.' He unhitched the wings from round his neck, put them carefully on the ground beside him and got heavily to his feet. He looked at Bond with slow, inquiring eyes.

'Like you to meet Mr Bond, James Bond. Friend of mine from New York. Countryman of yours. Come down to try and talk me into a bit of business.'

Mr Goldfinger held out a hand. 'Pleased to meet you, Mr Bomb.'

Bond took the hand. It was hard and dry. There was the briefest pressure and it was withdrawn. For an instant Mr Goldfinger's pale, china-blue eyes opened wide and stared hard at Bond. They stared right through his face to the back of his skull. Then the lids drooped the shutter closed over the X-ray, and Mr Goldfinger took the exposed plate and slipped it away in his filing system.

'So no game today.' The voice was flat, colourless. The words were more of a statement than a question.

'Whaddya mean, no game?' shouted Mr Du Pont boisterously. 'You weren't thinking I'd let you hang on to my money? Got to get it back or I shan't be able to leave this darned hotel,' Mr Du Pont chuckled richly. 'I'll tell Sam to fix the table. James here says he doesn't know much about cards and he'd like to learn the game. That right, James?' He turned to Bond. 'Sure you'll be all right with your paper and the sunshine?'

'I'd be glad of the rest,' said Bond. 'Been travelling too much.'

Again the eyes bored into Bond and then drooped. 'I'll get some clothes on. I had intended to have a golf lesson this afternoon from Mr Armour at the Boca Raton. But cards have priority among my hobbies. My tendency to un-cock the wrists too early with the mid-irons will have to wait.' The eyes rested incuriously on Bond. 'You play golf, Mr Bomb?'

Bond raised his voice. 'Occasionally, when I'm in England.'

'And where do you play?'

'Huntercombe.'

'Ah–a pleasant little course. I have recently joined the Royal St Marks. Sandwich is close to one of my business interests. You know it?'

'I have played there.'

'What is your handicap?'

'Nine.'

'That is a coincidence. So is mine. We must have a game one day.' Mr Goldfinger bent down and picked up his tin wings. He said to Mr Du Pont, 'I will be with you in five minutes.' He walked slowly off towards the stairs.

Bond was amused. This social sniffing at him had been done with just the right casual touch of the tycoon who didn't really care if Bond was alive or dead but, since he was there and alive, might as well place him in an approximate category.

Mr Du Pont gave instructions to a steward in a white coat. Two others were already setting up a card table. Bond walked to the rail that surrounded the roof and looked down into the garden, reflecting on Mr Goldfinger.

He was impressed. Mr Goldfinger was one of the most relaxed men Bond had ever met. It showed in the economy of his movement, of his speech, of his expressions. Mr Goldfinger wasted no effort, yet there was something coiled, compressed, in the immobility of the man.

When Goldfinger had stood up, the first thing that had struck Bond was that everything was out of proportion. Goldfinger was short, not more than five feet tall, and on top of the thick body and blunt, peasant legs was set, almost directly into the shoulders, a huge and it seemed exactly round head. It was as if Goldfinger had been put together with bits of other people's bodies. Nothing seemed to belong. Perhaps, Bond thought, it was to conceal his ugliness that Goldfinger made such a fetish of sunburn. Without the red-brown camouflage the pale body would be grotesque. The face, under the cliff of crew-cut carroty hair, was as startling, without being as ugly, as the body. It was moon-shaped without being moonlike. The forehead was fine and high and the thin sandy brows were level above the large light blue eyes fringed with pale lashes. The nose was fleshily aquiline between high cheekbones and cheeks that were more muscular than fat. The mouth was thin and dead straight, but beautifully drawn. The chin and jaws were firm and glinted with health. To sum up, thought Bond, it was the face of a thinker, perhaps a scientist, who was ruthless, sensual, stoical and tough. An odd combination.

What else could he guess? Bond always mistrusted short men. They grew up from childhood with an inferiority complex. All their lives they would strive to be big–bigger than the others who had teased them as a child. Napoleon had been short, and Hitler. It was the short men that caused all the trouble in the world. And what about a misshapen short man with red hair and a bizarre face? That might add up to a really formidable misfit. One could certainly feel the repressions. There was a powerhouse of vitality humming in the man that suggested that if one stuck an electric bulb into Goldfinger's mouth it would light up. Bond smiled at the thought. Into what channels did Goldfinger release his vital force? Into getting rich? Into sex? Into power? Probably into all three. What could his history be? Today he might be an Englishman. What had he been born? Not a Jew–though there might be Jewish blood in him. Not a Latin or anything farther south. Not a Slav. Perhaps a German–no, a Balt! That's where he would have come from. One of the old Baltic provinces. Probably got away to escape the Russians. Goldfinger would have been warned–or his parents had smelled trouble and they had got him out in time. And what had happened then? How had he worked his way up to being one of the richest men in the world? One day it might be interesting to find out. For the time being it would be enough to find out how he won at cards.

'All set?' Mr Du Pont called to Goldfinger who was coming across the roof towards the card table. With his clothes on–a comfortably fitting dark blue suit, a white shirt open at the neck–Goldfinger cut an almost passable figure. But there was no disguise for the great brown and red football of a head and the flesh-coloured hearing aid plugged into the left ear was not an improvement.

Mr Du Pont sat with his back to the hotel. Goldfinger took the seat opposite and cut the cards. Du Pont won the cut, pushed the other pack over to Goldfinger, tapped them to show they were already shuffled and he couldn't bother to cut, and Goldfinger began the deal.

Bond sauntered over and took a chair at Mr Du Pont's elbow. He sat back, relaxed. He made a show of folding his paper to the sports page and watched the deal.

Somehow Bond had expected it, but this was no card-sharp. Goldfinger dealt quickly and efficiently, but with no hint of the Mechanic's Grip, those vital three fingers curled round the long edge of the cards and the index finger at the outside short upper edge–the grip that means you are armed for dealing Bottoms or Seconds. And he wore no signet ring for pricking the cards, no surgical tape round a finger for marking them.

Mr Du Pont turned to Bond. 'Deal of fifteen cards,' he commented. 'You draw two and discard one. Otherwise straight Regency rules. No monkey business with the red treys counting one, three, five, eight, or any of that European stuff.'

Mr Du Pont picked up his cards. Bond noticed that he sorted them expertly, not grading them according to value from left to right, or holding his wild cards, of which he had two, at the left–a pattern that might help a watchful opponent. Mr Du Pont concentrated his good cards in the centre of his hand with the singletons and broken melds on either side.

The game began. Mr Du Pont drew first, a miraculous pair of wild cards. His face betrayed nothing. He discarded casually. He only needed two more good draws to go out unseen. But he would have to be lucky. Drawing two cards doubles the chance of picking up what you want, but it also doubles the chance of picking up useless cards that will only clutter up your hand.

Goldfinger played a more deliberate game, almost irritatingly slow. After drawing, he shuffled through his cards again and again before deciding on his discard.

On the third draw, Du Pont had improved his hand to the extent that he now needed only one of five cards to go down and out and catch his opponent with a handful of cards which would all count against him. As if Goldfinger knew the danger he was in, he went down for fifty and proceeded to make a canasta with three wild cards and four fives. He also got rid of some more melds and ended with only four cards in his hand. In any other circumstances it would have been ridiculously bad play. As it was, he had made some four hundred points instead of losing over a hundred, for, on the next draw Mr Du Pont filled his hand and, with most of the edge taken off his triumph by Goldfinger's escape, went down unseen with the necessary two canastas.

'By golly, I nearly screwed you that time.' Mr Du Pont's voice had an edge of exasperation. 'What in hell told you to cut an' run?'

Goldfinger said indifferently, 'I smelled trouble.' He added up his points, announced them and jotted them down, waiting for Mr Du Pont to do the same. Then he cut the cards and sat back and regarded Bond with polite interest.

'Will you be staying long, Mr Bomb?'

Bond smiled. 'It's Bond, B-O-N-D. No, I have to go back to New York tonight.'

'How sad.' Goldfinger's mouth pursed in polite regret. He turned back to the cards and the game went on. Bond picked up his paper and gazed, unseeing, at the baseball scores, while he listened to the quiet routine of the game. Goldfinger won that hand and the next and the next. He won the game. There was a difference of one thousand five hundred points–one thousand five hundred dollars to Goldfinger.

'There it goes again!' It was the plaintive voice of Mr Du Pont.

Bond put down his paper. 'Does he usually win?'

'Usually!' The word was a snort. 'He always wins.'

They cut again and Goldfinger began to deal.

Bond said, 'Don't you cut for seats? I often find a change of seat helps the luck. Hostage to fortune and so on.'

Goldfinger paused in his deal. He bent his gaze gravely on Bond. 'Unfortunately, Mr Bond, that is not possible or I could not play. As I explained to Mr Du Pont at our first game, I suffer from an obscure complaint–agoraphobia—the fear of open spaces. I cannot bear the open horizon. I must sit and face the hotel.' The deal continued.

'Oh, I'm so sorry.' Bond's voice was grave, interested. 'That's a very rare disability. I've always been able to understand claustrophobia, but not the other way round. How did it come about?'

Goldfinger picked up his cards and began to arrange his hand. 'I have no idea,' he said equably.

Bond got up. 'Well, I think I'll stretch my legs for a bit. See what's going on in the pool.'

'You do just that,' said Mr Du Pont jovially. 'Just take it easy, James. Plenty of time to discuss business over lunch. I'll see if I can't dish it out to my friend Goldfinger this time instead of taking it. Be seeing you.'

Goldfinger didn't look up from his cards. Bond strolled down the roof, past the occasional splayed-out body, to the rail at the far end that overlooked the pool. For a time he stood and contemplated the ranks of pink and brown and white flesh laid out below him on the steamer chairs. The heavy scent of suntan oil came up to him. There were a few children and young people in the pool. A man, obviously a professional diver, perhaps the swimming instructor, stood on the high-dive. He balanced on the balls of his feet, a muscled Greek god with golden hair. He bounced once, casually, and flew off and down, his arms held out like wings. Lazily they arrowed out to cleave the water for the body to pass through. The impact left only a brief turbulence. The diver jack-knifed up again, shaking his head boyishly. There was a smattering of applause. The man trudged slowly down the pool, his head submerged, his shoulders moving with casual power. Bond thought, good luck to you! You won't be able to keep this up for more than another five or six years. High-divers couldn't take it for long–the repeated shock to the skull. With ski-jumping, which had the same shattering effect on the frame, high-diving was the shortest-lived sport. Bond radioed to the diver, 'Cash in quick! Get into films while the hair's still gold.'

Bond turned and looked back down the roof towards the two Canasta players beneath the cliff of the hotel. So Goldfinger liked to face the hotel. Or was it that he liked Mr Du Pont to have his back to it? And why? Now, what was the number of Goldfinger's suite? No. 200, the Hawaii Suite. Bond's on the top floor was 1200. So, all things being equal, Goldfinger's would be directly below Bond's, on the second floor, twenty yards or so above the roof of the Cabana Club–twenty yards from the card table. Bond counted down. He closely examined the frontage that should be Goldfinger's. Nothing. An empty sun balcony. An open door into the dark interior of the suite. Bond measured distances, angles. Yes, that's how it might be. That's how it must be! Clever Mr Goldfinger!

Chapter Four

Over the Barrel

After luncheon–the traditional shrimp cocktail, 'native' snapper with a minute paper cup of tartare sauce, roast prime ribs of beef *au jus*, and pineapple *surprise*–it was time for the siesta before meeting Goldfinger at three o'clock for the afternoon session.

Mr Du Pont, who had lost a further ten thousand dollars or more, confirmed that Goldfinger had a secretary. 'Never seen her. Sticks to the suite. Probably just some chorine he's brought down for the ride.' He smiled wetly. 'I mean the daily ride. Why? You on to something?'

Bond was non-committal. 'Can't tell yet. I probably won't be coming down this afternoon. Say I got bored watching–gone into the town.' He paused. 'But if my idea's right, don't be surprised at what may happen. If Goldfinger starts to behave oddly, just sit quiet and watch. I'm not promising anything. I think I've got him, but I may be wrong.'

Mr Du Pont was enthusiastic. 'Good for you, boyo!' he said effusively. 'I just can't wait to see that bastard over the barrel. Damn his eyes!'

Bond took the elevator up to his suite. He went to his suitcase and extracted an M3 Leica, an MC exposure meter, a K2 filter and a flash-holder. He put a bulb in the holder and checked the camera. He went to his balcony, glanced at the sun to estimate where it would be at about three-thirty and went back into the sitting-room, leaving the door to the balcony open. He stood at the balcony door and aimed the exposure meter. The exposure was one-hundredth of a second. He set this on the Leica, put the shutter at f 11, and the distance at twelve feet. He clipped on a lens hood and took one picture to see that all was working. Then he wound on the film, slipped in the flash-holder and put the camera aside.

Bond went to his suitcase again and took out a thick book–*The Bible Designed to be Read as Literature*–opened it and extracted his Walther PPK in the Berns Martin holster. He slipped the holster inside his trouser band to the left. He tried one or two quick draws. They were satisfactory. He closely examined the geography of his suite, on the assumption that it would be exactly similar to the Hawaii. He visualized the scene that would almost certainly greet him when he came through the door of the suite downstairs. He tried his pass-key in the various locks and practised opening the doors noiselessly. Then he pulled a comfortable chair in front of the open balcony door and sat and smoked a cigarette while he gazed out across the sea and thought of how he would put things to Goldfinger when the time came.

At three-fifteen, Bond got up and went out on to the balcony and cautiously looked down at the two tiny figures across the square of green baize. He went back into the room and checked the exposure meter on the Leica. The light was the same. He slipped on the coat of his dark blue tropical worsted suit, straightened his tie and slung the strap of the Leica round his neck so that the camera hung at his chest. Then, with a last look round, he went out and along to the elevator. He rode down to the ground floor and examined the shop windows in the foyer. When the elevator had gone up again, he walked to the staircase and slowly climbed up two floors. The geography of the second floor was identical with the twelfth. Room 200 was where he had expected it to be. There was no one in sight. He took out his pass-key and silently opened the door and closed it behind him. In the small lobby, a raincoat, a light camel-hair coat and a pale grey Homburg hung on hooks. Bond took his Leica firmly in his right hand, held it up close to his face and gently tried the door to the sitting-room. It was not locked. Bond eased it open.

Even before he could see what he expected to see he could hear the voice. It was a low, attractive, girl's voice, an English voice. It was saying, 'Drew five and four. Completed canasta in fives with two twos. Discarding four. Has singletons in kings, knaves, nines, sevens.'

Bond slid into the room.

The girl was sitting on two cushions on top of a table which had been pulled up a yard inside the open balcony door. She had needed the cushions to give her height. It was at the top of the afternoon heat and she was naked except for a black brassière and black silk briefs. She was swinging her legs in a bored fashion. She had just finished painting the nails on her left hand. Now she stretched the hand out in front of her to examine the effect. She brought the hand back close to her lips and blew on the nails. Her right hand reached sideways and put the brush back in the Revlon bottle on the table beside her. A few inches from her eyes were the eyepieces of a powerful-looking pair of binoculars supported on a tripod whose feet reached down between her sunburned legs to the floor. Jutting out from below the binoculars was a microphone from which wires led to a box about the size of a portable record player under the table. Other wires ran from the box to a gleaming indoor aerial on the sideboard against the wall.

The briefs tightened as she leant forward again and put her eyes to the binoculars. 'Drew a queen and a king. Meld of queens. Can meld kings with a joker. Discarding seven.' She switched off the microphone.

While she was concentrating, Bond stepped swiftly across the floor until he was almost behind her. There was a chair. He stood on it, praying it wouldn't squeak. Now he had the height to get the whole scene in focus. He put his eye to the view-finder. Yes, there it was, all in line, the girl's head, the edge of the binoculars, the microphone and, twenty yards below, the two men at the table with Mr Du Pont's hand of cards held in front of him. Bond could distinguish the reds and the blacks. He pressed the button.

The sharp explosion of the bulb and the blinding flash of light forced a quick scream out of the girl. She swivelled round.

Bond stepped down off the chair. 'Good afternoon.'

'Whoryou? Whatyouwant?' The girl's hand was up to her mouth. Her eyes screamed at him.

'I've got what I want. Don't worry. It's all over now. And my name's Bond, James Bond.'

Bond put his camera carefully down on the chair and came and stood in the radius of her scent. She was very beautiful. She had the palest blonde hair. It fell heavily to her shoulders, unfashionably long. Her eyes were deep blue against a lightly sunburned skin and her mouth was bold and generous and would have a lovely smile.

She stood up and took her hand away from her mouth. She was tall, perhaps five feet ten, and her arms and legs looked firm as if she might be a swimmer. Her breasts thrust against the black silk of the brassière.

Some of the fear had gone out of her eyes. She said in a low voice, 'What are you going to do?'

'Nothing to you. I may tease Goldfinger a bit. Move over like a good girl and let me have a look.'

Bond took the girl's place and looked through the glasses. The game was going on normally. Goldfinger showed no sign that his communications had broken down.

'Doesn't he mind not getting the signals? Will he stop playing?'

She said hesitatingly, 'It's happened before when a plug pulled or something. He just waits for me to come through again.'

Bond smiled at her. 'Well, let's let him stew for a bit. Have a cigarette and relax,' he held out a packet of Chesterfields. She took one. 'Anyway it's time you did the nails on your right hand.'

A smile flickered across her mouth. 'How long were you there? You gave me a frightful shock.'

'Not long, and I'm sorry about the shock. Goldfinger's been giving poor old Mr Du Pont shocks for a whole week.'

'Yes,' she said doubtfully. 'I suppose it's really rather mean. But he's very rich, isn't he?'

'Oh yes. I shouldn't lose any sleep over Mr Du Pont. But Goldfinger might choose someone who can't afford it. Anyway, he's a zillionaire himself. Why does he do it? He s crawling with money.'

Animation flooded back into her face. 'I know. I simply can't understand him. It's a sort of mania with him, making money. He can't leave it alone. I've asked him why and all he says is that one's a fool not to make money when the odds are right. He's always going on about the same thing, getting the odds right. When he talked me into doing this,' she waved her cigarette at the binoculars, 'and I asked him why on earth he bothered, took these stupid risks, all he said was, "That's the second lesson. When the odds aren't right, make them right."'

Bond said, 'Well, it's lucky for him I'm not Pinkertons or the Miami Police Department.'

The girl shrugged her shoulders. 'Oh, that wouldn't worry him. He'd just buy you off. He can buy anyone off. No one can resist gold.'

'What do you mean?'

She said indifferently, 'He always carries a million dollars' worth of gold about with him except when he's going through the Customs. Then he just carries a belt full of gold coins round his stomach. Otherwise it's in thin sheets in the bottom and sides of his suitcases. They're really gold suitcases covered with leather.'

'They must weigh a ton.'

'He always travels by car, one with special springs. And his chauffeur is a huge man. He carries them. No one else touches them.'

'Why does he carry around all that gold?'

'Just in case he needs it. He knows that gold will buy him anything he wants. It's all twenty-four carat. And anyway he loves gold, really loves it like people love jewels or stamps or–well,' she smiled, 'women.'

Bond smiled back. 'Does he love you?'

She blushed and said indignantly, 'Certainly not.' Then, more reasonably, 'Of course you can think anything you like. But really he doesn't. I mean, I think he likes people to *think* that we–that I'm–that it's a question of love and all that. You know. He's not very prepossessing and I suppose it's a question of–well–of vanity or something.'

'Yes, I see. So you're just a kind of secretary?'

'Companion,' she corrected him. 'I don't have to type or anything.' She suddenly put her hand up to her mouth. 'Oh, but I shouldn't be telling you all this! You won't tell him, will you? He'd fire me.' Fright came into her eyes. 'Or something. I don't know what he'd do. He's the sort of man who might do anything.'

'Of course I won't tell. But this can't be much of a life for you. Why do you do it?'

She said tartly, 'A hundred pounds a week and all this,' she waved at the room, 'doesn't grow on trees. I save up. When I've saved enough I shall go.'

Bond wondered if Goldfinger would let her. Wouldn't she know too much? He looked at the beautiful face, the splendid, unselfconscious body. She might not suspect it, but, for his money, she was in very bad trouble with this man.

The girl was fidgeting. Now she said with an embarrassed laugh, 'I don't think I'm very properly dressed. Can't I go and put something on over these?'

Bond wasn't sure he could trust her. It wasn't he who was paying the hundred pounds a week. He said airily, 'You look fine. Just as respectable as those hundreds of people round the pool. Anyway,' he stretched, 'it's about time to light a fire under Mr Goldfinger.'

Bond had been glancing down at the game from time to time. It seemed to be proceeding normally. Bond bent again to the binoculars. Already Mr Du Pont seemed to be a new man, his gestures were expansive, the half-profile of his pink face was full of animation. While Bond watched, he took a fistful of cards out of his hand and spread them down–a pure canasta in kings. Bond tilted the binoculars up an inch. The big red-brown moon face was impassive, uninterested. Mr Goldfinger was waiting patiently for the odds to adjust themselves back in his favour. While Bond watched, he put up a hand to the hearing aid, pushing the amplifier more firmly into his ear, ready for the signals to come through again.

Bond stepped back. 'Neat little machine,' he commented. 'What are you transmitting on?'

'He told me, but I can't remember.' She screwed up her eyes. 'A hundred and seventy somethings. Would it be mega-somethings?'

'Megacycles. Might be, but I'd be surprised if he doesn't get a lot of taxicabs and police messages mixed up with your talk. Must have fiendish concentration.' Bond grinned. 'Now then. All set? It's time to pull the rug away.'

Suddenly she reached out and put a hand on his sleeve. There was a Claddagh ring on the middle finger–two gold hands clasped round a gold heart. There were tears in her voice. 'Must you? Can't you leave him alone? I don't know what he'll do to me. Please.' She hesitated. She was blushing furiously. 'And I like you. It's a long time since I've seen someone like you. Couldn't you just stay here for a little more?' She looked down at the ground.

'If only you'd leave him alone I'd do–' the words came out in a rush–'I'd do *anything*.'

Bond smiled. He took the girl's hand off his arm and squeezed it. 'Sorry. I'm being paid to do this job and I must do it. Anyway–' his voice went flat–'I want to do it. It's time someone cut Mr Goldfinger down to size. Ready?'

Without waiting for an answer he bent to the binoculars. They were still focused on Goldfinger. Bond cleared his throat. He watched the big face carefully. His hand felt for the microphone switch and pressed it down.

There must have been a whisper of static in the deaf aid. Goldfinger's expression didn't alter, but he slowly raised his face to heaven and then down again, as if in benediction.

Bond spoke softly, menacingly into the microphone. 'Now hear me, Goldfinger.' He paused. Not a flicker of expression, but Goldfinger bent his head a fraction as if listening. He studied his cards intently, his hands quite still.

'This is James Bond speaking. Remember me? The game's finished and it's time to pay. I have a photograph of the whole set-up, blonde, binoculars, microphone and you and your hearing aid. This photograph will not go to the F.B.I. and Scotland Yard so long as you obey me exactly. Nod your head if you understand.'

The face was still expressionless. Slowly the big round head bent forward and then straightened itself.

'Put your cards down face upwards on the table.'

The hands went down. They opened and the cards slid off the fingers on to the table.

'Take out your cheque book and write a cheque to cash for fifty thousand dollars. That is made up as follows, thirty-five you have taken from Mr Du Pont. Ten for my fee. The extra five for wasting so much of Mr Du Pont's valuable time.'

Bond watched to see that his order was being obeyed. He took a glance at Mr Du Pont. Mr Du Pont was leaning forward, gaping.

Mr Goldfinger slowly detached the cheque and counter-signed it on the back.

'Right. Now jot this down on the back of your cheque book and see you get it right. Book me a compartment on the Silver Meteor to New York tonight. Have a bottle of vintage champagne on ice in the compartment and plenty of caviar sandwiches. The best caviar. And keep away from me. And no monkey business. The photograph will be in the mails with a full report to be opened and acted upon if I don't show up in good health in New York tomorrow. Nod if you understand.'

Again the big head came slowly down and up again. Now there were traces of sweat on the high, unlined forehead.

'Right, now hand the cheque across to Mr Du Pont and say, "I apologize humbly. I have been cheating you." Then you can go.'

Bond watched the hand go across and drop the cheque in front of Mr Du Pont. The mouth opened and spoke. The eyes were placid, slow. Goldfinger had relaxed. It was only money. He had paid his way out.

'Just a moment, Goldfinger, you're not through yet.' Bond glanced up at the girl. She was looking at him strangely. There was misery and fear but also a look of submissiveness, of longing.

'What's your name?'

'Jill Masterton.'

Goldfinger had stood up, was turning away. Bond said sharply, 'Stop.'

Goldfinger stopped in mid-stride. Now his eyes looked up at the balcony. They had opened wide, as when Bond had first met him. Their hard, level, X-ray gaze seemed to find the lenses of the binoculars, travel down them and through Bond's eyes to the back of his skull. They seemed to say, 'I shall remember this, Mr Bond.'

Bond said softly, 'I'd forgotten. One last thing. I shall be taking a hostage for the ride to New York. Miss Masterton. See that she's at the train. Oh, and make that compartment a drawing-room. That's all.'

Chapter Five

Night Duty

It was a week later. Bond stood at the open window of the seventh-floor office of the tall building in Regent's Park that is the headquarters of the Secret Service. London lay asleep under a full moon that rode swiftly over the town through a shoal of herring-bone clouds. Big Ben sounded three. One of the telephones rang in the dark room. Bond turned and moved quickly to the central desk and the pool of light cast by the green shaded reading-lamp. He picked up the black telephone from the rank of four.

He said, 'Duty officer.'

'Station H, sir.'

'Put them on.'

There was the echoing buzz and twang of the usual bad radio connection with Hongkong. Why were there always sunspots over China? A sing-song voice asked, 'Universal Export?'

'Yes.'

A deep, close voice–London–said, 'You're through to Hongkong. Speak up, please.'

Bond said impatiently, 'Clear the line, please.'

The sing-song voice said, 'You're through now. Speak up, please.'

'Hullo! Hullo! Universal Export?'

'Yes.'

'Dickson speaking. Can you hear me?'

'Yes.'

'That cable I sent you about the shipment of mangoes. Fruit. You know?'

'Yes. Got it here.' Bond pulled the file towards him. He knew what it was about. Station H wanted some limpet mines to put paid to three Communist spy junks that were using Macao to intercept British freighters and search them for refugees from China.

'Must have payment by the tenth.'

That would mean that the junks were leaving, or else that the guards on the junks would be doubled after that date, or some other emergency.

Bond said briefly, 'Wilco.'

'Thanks. 'Bye.'

''Bye.' Bond put down the receiver. He picked up the green receiver and dialled Q Branch and talked to the section duty officer. It would be all right. There was a B.O.A.C. Britannia leaving in the morning. Q Branch would see that the crate caught the plane.

Bond sat back. He reached for a cigarette and lit it. He thought of the badly air-conditioned little office on the waterfront in Hongkong, saw the sweat marks on the white shirt of 279, whom he knew well and who had just called himself Dickson. Now 279 would probably be talking to his number two: 'It's okay. London says can do. Let's just go over this ops. schedule again.' Bond smiled wryly. Better they than he. He'd never liked being up against the Chinese. There were too many of them. Station H might be stirring up a hornets' nest, but M had decided it was time to show the opposition that the Service in Hongkong hadn't quite gone out of business.

When, three days before, M had first told him his name was down for night duty, Bond hadn't taken to the idea. He had argued that he didn't know enough about the routine work of the stations, that it was too responsible a job to give a man who had been in the double-O section for six years and who had forgotten all he had ever known about station work.

'You'll soon pick it up,' M had said unsympathetically. 'If you get in trouble there are the duty section officers or the Chief of Staff–or me, for the matter of that.' (Bond had smiled at the thought of waking M up in the middle of the night because some man in Cairo or Tokyo was in a flap.) 'Anyway, I've decided. I want all senior officers to do their spell of routine.' M had looked frostily across at Bond. 'Matter of fact, 007, I had the Treasury on to me the other day. Their liaison man thinks the double-O section is redundant. Says that kind of thing is out of date. I couldn't bother to argue'–M's voice was mild. 'Just told him he was mistaken.' (Bond could visualize the scene.) 'However, won't do any harm for you to have some extra duties now you're back in London. Keep you from getting stale.'

And Bond wasn't minding it. He was half way through his first week and so far it had just been a question of common sense or passing routine problems on down to the sections. He rather liked the peaceful room and knowing everybody's secrets and being occasionally fed coffee and sandwiches by one of the pretty girls from the canteen.

On the first night the girl had brought him tea. Bond had looked at her severely. 'I don't drink tea. I hate it. It's mud. Moreover it's one of the main reasons for the downfall of the British Empire. Be a good girl and make me some coffee.' The girl had giggled and scurried off to spread Bond's dictum in the canteen. From then on he had got his coffee. The expression 'a cup of mud' was seeping through the building.

A second reason why Bond enjoyed the long vacuum of night duty was that it gave him time to get on with a project he had been toying with for more than a year–a handbook of all secret methods of unarmed combat. It was to be called *Stay Alive!* It would contain the best of all that had been written on the subject by the Secret Services of the world. Bond had told no one of the project, but he hoped that, if he could finish it, M would allow it to be added to the short list of Service manuals which contained the tricks and techniques of Secret Intelligence.

Bond had borrowed the original textbooks, or where necessary, translations, from Records. Most of the books had been captured from enemy agents or organizations. Some had been presented to M by sister Services such as O.S.S., C.I.A. and the Deuxième. Now Bond drew towards him a particular prize, a translation of the manual, entitled simply *Defence*, issued to operatives of SMERSH, the Soviet organization of vengeance and death.

That night he was half way through Chapter Two, whose title, freely translated, was 'Come-along and Restraint Holds'. Now he went back to the book and read for half an hour through the sections dealing with the conventional 'Wrist Come-along', 'Arm Lock Come-along', 'Forearm Lock', 'Head Hold' and 'Use of Neck Pressure Points'.

After half an hour, Bond thrust the typescript away from him. He got up and went across to the window and stood looking out. There was a nauseating toughness in the blunt prose the Russians used. It had brought on another of the attacks of revulsion to which Bond had succumbed ten days before at Miami Airport. What was wrong with him? Couldn't he take it any more? Was he going soft, or was he only stale? Bond stood for a while watching the moon riding, careering, through the clouds. Then he shrugged his shoulders and went back to his desk. He decided that he was as fed up with the variations of violent physical behaviour as a psychoanalyst must become with the mental aberrations of his patients.

Bond read again the passage that had revolted him: 'A drunken woman can also usually be handled by using the thumb and forefinger to grab the lower lip. By pinching hard and twisting, as the pull is made, the woman will come along.'

Bond grunted. The obscene delicacy of that 'thumb and forefinger'! Bond lit a cigarette and stared into the filament of the desk light, switching his mind to other things, wishing that a signal would come in or the telephone ring. Another five hours to go before the nine o'clock report to the Chief of Staff or to M, if M happened to come in early. There was something nagging at his mind, something he had wanted to check on when he had the time. What was it? What had triggered off the reminder? Yes, that was it, 'forefinger'–Goldfinger. He would see if Records had anything on the man.

Bond picked up the green telephone and dialled Records.

'Doesn't ring a bell, sir. I'll check and call you back.'

Bond put down the receiver.

It had been a wonderful trip up in the train. They had eaten the sandwiches and drunk the champagne and then, to the rhythm of the giant diesels pounding out the miles, they had made long, slow love in the narrow berth. It had been as if the girl was starved of physical love. She had woken him twice more in the night with soft demanding caresses, saying nothing, just reaching for his hard, lean body. The next day she had twice pulled down the roller blinds to shut out the hard light and had taken him by the hand and said, 'Love me, James' as if she was a child asking for a sweet.

Even now Bond could hear the quick silver poem of the level-crossing bells, the wail of the big windhorn out front and the quiet outside clamour at the stations when they lay and waited for the sensual gallop of the wheels to begin again.

Jill Masterton had said that Goldfinger had been relaxed, indifferent over his defeat. He had told the girl to tell Bond that he would be over in England in a week's time and would like to have that game of golf at Sandwich.

Nothing else–no threats, no curses. He had said he would expect the girl back by the next train. Jill had told Bond she would go. Bond had argued with her. But she was not frightened of Goldfinger. What could he do to her? And it was a good job.

Bond had decided to give her the ten thousand dollars Mr Du Pont had shuffled into his hand with a stammer of thanks and congratulations. Bond made her take the money. 'I don't want it,' Bond had said. 'Wouldn't know what to do with it. Anyway, keep it as mad money in case you want to get away in a hurry. It ought to be a million. I shall never forget last night and today.'

Bond had taken her to the station and had kissed her once hard on the lips and had gone away. It hadn't been love, but a quotation had come into Bond's mind as his cab moved out of Pennsylvania station: 'Some love is fire, some love is rust. But the finest, cleanest love is lust.' Neither had had regrets. Had they committed a sin? If so, which one? A sin against chastity? Bond smiled to himself. There was a quotation for that too, and from a saint–Saint Augustine: 'Oh Lord, give me Chastity. But don't give it yet!'

The green telephone rang. 'Three Goldfingers, sir, but two of them are dead. The third's a Russian post office in Geneva. Got a hairdressing business. Slips the messages into the right-hand coat pocket when he brushes the customers down. He lost a leg at Stalingrad. Any good, sir? There's plenty more on him.'

'No thanks. That couldn't be my man.'

'We could put a trace through C.I.D. Records in the morning. Got a picture, sir?'

Bond remembered the Leica film. He hadn't even bothered to have it developed. It would be quicker to mock up the man's face on the Identicast. He said, 'Is the Identicast room free?'

'Yes, sir. And I can operate it for you if you like.'

'Thanks. I'll come down.'

Bond told the switchboard to let heads of sections know where he would be and went out and took the lift down to Records on the first floor.

The big building was extraordinarily quiet at night. Beneath the silence, there was a soft whisper of machinery and hidden life–the muffled clack of a typewriter as Bond passed a door, a quickly suppressed stammer of radio static as he passed another, the soft background whine of the ventilation system. It gave you the impression of being in a battleship in harbour.

The Records duty officer was already at the controls of the Identicast in the projection room. He said to Bond, 'Could you give me the main lines of the face, sir? That'll help me leave out the slides that are obviously no good.'

Bond did so and sat back and watched the lighted screen.

The Identicast is a machine for building up an approximate picture of a suspect–or of someone who has perhaps only been glimpsed in a street or a train or in a passing car. It works on the magic lantern principle. The operator flashes on the screen various head-shapes and sizes. When one is recognized it stays on the screen. Then various haircuts are shown, and then all the other features follow and are chosen one by one–different shapes of eyes, noses, chins, mouths, eyebrows, cheeks, ears. In the end there is the whole picture of a face, as near as the scanner can remember it, and it is photographed and put on record.

It took some time to put together Goldfinger's extraordinary face, but the final result was an approximate likeness in monochrome. Bond dictated one or two notes about the sunburn, the colour of the hair and the expression of the eyes, and the job was done.

'Wouldn't like to meet that on a dark night,' commented the man from Records. 'I'll put it through to C.I.D. when they come on duty. You should get the answer by lunch time.'

Bond went back to the seventh floor. On the other side of the world it was around midnight. Eastern stations were closing down. There was a flurry of signals that had to be dealt with, the night's log to be written up, and then it was eight o'clock. Bond telephoned the canteen for his breakfast. He had just finished it when there came the harsh purr of the red telephone. M! Why the hell had he got in half an hour early?

'Yes, sir.'

'Come up to my office, 007. I want to have a word before you go off duty.'

'Sir.' Bond put the telephone back. He slipped on his coat and ran a hand through his hair, told the switchboard where he would be, took the night log and went up in the lift to the eighth and top floor. Neither the desirable Miss Moneypenny nor the Chief of Staff was on duty. Bond knocked on M's door and went in.

'Sit down, 007.' M was going through the pipe-lighting routine. He looked pink and well scrubbed. The lined sailor's face above the stiff white collar and loosely tied spotted bow-tie was damnably brisk and cheerful. Bond was conscious of the black stubble on his own chin and of the all-night look of his skin and clothes. He sharpened his mind.

'Quiet night?' M had got his pipe going. His hard, healthy eyes regarded Bond attentively.

'Pretty quiet, sir. Station H—'

M raised his left hand an inch or two. 'Never mind. I'll read all about it in the log. Here, I'll take it.'

Bond handed over the Top Secret folder. M put it to one side. He smiled one of his rare, rather sardonic, bitten-off smiles. 'Things change, 007. I'm taking you off night duty for the present.'

Bond's answering smile was taut. He felt the quickening of the pulse he had so often experienced in this room. M had got something for him. He said, 'I was just getting into it, sir.'

'Quite. Have plenty of opportunity later on. Something's come up. Odd business. Not really your line of country, except for one particular angle which'–M jerked his pipe sideways in a throwaway gesture–'may not be an angle at all.'

Bond sat back. He said nothing, waiting.

'Had dinner with the Governor of the Bank last night. One's always hearing something new. At least, all this was new to me. Gold–the seamy side of the stuff. Smuggling, counterfeiting, all that. Hadn't occurred to me that the Bank of England knew so much about crooks. Suppose it's part of the Bank's job to protect our currency.' M jerked his eyebrows up. 'Know anything about gold?'

'No, sir.'

'Well, you will by this afternoon. You've got an appointment with a man called Colonel Smithers at the Bank at four o'clock. That give you enough time to get some sleep?'

'Yes, sir.'

'Good. Seems that this man Smithers is head of the Bank's research department. From what the Governor told me, that's nothing more or less than a spy system. First time I knew they had one. Just shows what watertight compartments we all work in. Anyway, Smithers and his chaps keep an eye out for anything fishy in the banking world–particularly any monkeying about with our currency and bullion reserves and what not. There was that business the other day of the Italians who were counterfeiting sovereigns. Making them out of real gold. Right carats and all that. But apparently a sovereign or a French napoleon is worth much more than its melted-down value in gold. Don't ask me why. Smithers can tell you that if you're interested. Anyway, the Bank went after these people with a whole battery of lawyers–it wasn't technically a criminal offence–and, after losing in the Italian courts, they finally nailed them in Switzerland. You probably read about it. Then there was that business of dollar balances in Beirut. Made quite a stir in the papers. Couldn't understand it myself. Some crack in the fence we put round our currency. The wide City boys had found it. Well, it's Smithers's job to smell out that kind of racket. The reason the Governor told me all this is because for years, almost since the war apparently, Smithers has had a bee in his bonnet about some big gold leak out of England. Mostly deduction, plus some kind of instinct. Smithers admits he's got damned little to go on, but he's impressed the Governor enough for him to get permission from the P.M. to call us in.' M broke off. He looked quizzically at Bond. 'Ever wondered who are the richest men in England?'

'No, sir.'

'Well, have a guess. Or rather, put it like this: Who are the richest Englishmen?'

Bond searched his mind. There were a lot of men who sounded rich or who were made to sound rich by the newspapers. But who really *had* it, liquid, in the bank? He had to say something. He said hesitatingly, 'Well, sir, there's Sassoon. Then that shipping man who keeps to himself–er–Ellerman. They say Lord Cowdray is very rich. There are the bankers–Rothschilds, Barings, Hambros. There was Williamson, the diamond man. Oppenheimer in South Africa. Some of the dukes may still have a lot of money.' Bond's voice trailed away.

'Not bad. Not bad at all. But you've missed out the joker in the pack. Man I'd never thought of until the Governor brought up his name. He's the richest of the lot. Man called Goldfinger, Auric Goldfinger.'

Bond couldn't help himself. He laughed sharply.

'What's the matter?' M's voice was testy. 'What the hell is there to laugh about?'

'I'm sorry, sir.' Bond got hold of himself. 'The truth is, only last night I was building his face up on the Identicast.' He glanced at his watch. In a strangled voice he said, 'Be on its way to C.I.D. Records. Asked for a Trace on him.'

M was getting angry. 'What the hell's all this about? Stop behaving like a bloody schoolboy.'

Bond said soberly, 'Well, sir, it's like this . . .' Bond told the story, leaving nothing out.

M's face cleared. He listened with all his attention, leaning forward across the desk. When Bond had finished, M sat back in his chair. He said 'Well,

well . . . well' on a diminishing scale. He put his hands behind his head and gazed for minutes at the ceiling.

Bond could feel the laughter coming on again. How would the C.I.D. word the resounding snub he would get in the course of the day? He was brought sharply back to earth by M's next words. 'By the way, what happened to that ten thousand dollars?'

'Gave it to the girl, sir.'

'Really! Why not to the White Cross?'

The White Cross Fund was for the families of Secret Service men and women who were killed on duty.

'Sorry, sir.' Bond was not prepared to argue that one.

'Humpf.' M had never approved of Bond's womanizing. It was anathema to his Victorian soul. He decided to let it pass. He said, 'Well, that's all for now, 007. You'll be hearing all about it this afternoon. Funny about Goldfinger. Odd chap. Seen him once or twice at Blades. He plays bridge there when he's in England. He's the chap the Bank of England's after.' M paused. He looked mildly across the table at Bond. As from this moment, so are you.'

Chapter Six

Talk of Gold

Bond walked up the steps and through the fine bronze portals and into the spacious, softly echoing entrance hall of the Bank of England and looked around him. Under his feet glittered the brilliant golden patterns of the Boris Anrep mosaics; beyond, through twenty-foot-high arched windows, green grass and geraniums blazed in the central courtyard. To right and left were spacious vistas of polished Hopton Wood stone. Over all hung the neutral smell of air-conditioned air and the heavy, grave atmosphere of immense riches.

One of the athletic-looking, pink frock-coated commissionaires came up to him. 'Yes, sir?'

'Colonel Smithers?'

'Commander Bond, sir? This way please.' The commissionaire moved off to the right between the pillars. The bronze doors of a discreetly hidden lift stood open. The lift rose a few feet to the first floor. Now there was a long panelled corridor ending in a tall Adams window. The floor was close-carpeted in beige Wilton. The commissionaire knocked at the last of several finely carved oak doors that were just so much taller and more elegant than ordinary doors. A grey-haired woman was sitting at a desk. She looked as if she had once taken a double first. The walls of the room were lined with grey metal filing cabinets. The woman had been writing on a quarto pad of yellow memorandum paper. She smiled with a hint of conspiracy, picked up a telephone and dialled a number. 'Commander Bond is here.' She put the telephone back and stood up. 'Will you come this way?' She crossed the room to a door covered with green baize and held it open for Bond to go through.

Colonel Smithers had risen from his desk. He said gravely, 'Nice of you to have come. Won't you sit down?' Bond took the chair. 'Smoke?' Colonel Smithers pushed forward a silver box of Senior Service and himself sat down and began to fill a pipe. Bond took a cigarette and lit it.

Colonel Smithers looked exactly like someone who would be called Colonel Smithers. He had obviously been a colonel, probably on the staff, and he had the smooth, polished, basically serious mien that fitted his name. But for his horn-rimmed glasses, he might have been an efficient, not very well-fed courtier in a royal household.

Bond felt boredom gathering in the corners of the room. He said encouragingly, 'It seems that you are to tell me all about gold.'

'So I understand. I had a note from the Governor. I gather I need keep nothing from you. Of course you understand'–Colonel Smithers looked over Bond's right shoulder–'that most of what I shall have to say will be confidential.' The eyes swept quickly across Bond's face.

Bond's face was stony.

Colonel Smithers felt the silence that Bond had intended he should feel. He looked up, saw that he had put his foot in it, and tried to make amends. 'Obviously I needn't have mentioned the point. A man with your training . . .'

Bond said, 'We all think our own secrets are the only ones that matter. You're probably right to remind me. Other people's secrets are never quite as important as one's own. But you needn't worry. I shall discuss things with my chief but with no one else.'

'Quite, quite. Nice of you to take it that way. In the Bank one gets into the habit of being over-discreet. Now then,' Colonel Smithers scurried for cover into his subject. 'This business of gold. I take it it's not a matter you've thought about a great deal?'

'I know it when I see it.'

'Aha, yes–well now, the great thing to remember about gold is that it's the most valuable and most easily marketable commodity in the world. You can go to any town in the world, almost to any village, and hand over a piece of gold and get goods or services in exchange. Right?' Colonel Smither's voice had taken on a new briskness. His eyes were alight. He had his lecture pat. Bond sat back. He was prepared to listen to anyone who was master of his subject, any subject. 'And the next thing to remember,' Colonel Smithers held up his pipe in warning, 'is that gold is virtually untraceable. Sovereigns have no serial numbers. If gold bars have Mint marks stamped on them the marks can be shaved off or the bar can be melted down and made into a new bar. That makes it almost impossible to check on the whereabouts of gold, or its origins, or its movements round the world. In England, for instance, we at the Bank can only count the gold in our own vaults, in the vaults of other banks and at the Mint, and make a rough guess at the amounts held by the jewellery trade and the pawnbroking fraternity.'

'Why are you so anxious to know how much gold there is in England?'

'Because gold and currencies backed by gold are the foundation of our international credit. We can only tell what the true strength of the pound is, and other countries can only tell it, by knowing the amount of valuta we have behind our currency. And my main job, Mr Bond'–Colonel Smithers's bland eyes had become unexpectedly sharp–'is to watch for any leakage of gold out of England–out of anywhere in the sterling area. And when I spot a leakage, an escape of gold towards some country where it can be exchanged more profitably than at our official buying price, it is my job to put the C.I.D. Gold Squad on to the fugitive gold and try to get it back into our vaults, plug the leak and arrest the people responsible. And the trouble is, Mr Bond'–Colonel Smithers gave a forlorn shrug of the shoulders–'that gold attracts the biggest, the most ingenious criminals. They are very hard, very hard indeed, to catch.'

'Isn't all this only a temporary phase? Why should this shortage of gold go on? They seem to be digging it out of Africa fast enough. Isn't there enough to go round? Isn't it just like any other black market that disappears when the supplies are stepped up, like the penicillin traffic after the war?'

'I'm afraid not, Mr Bond. It isn't quite as easy as that. The population of the world is increasing at the rate of five thousand four hundred every hour of the day. A small percentage of those people become gold hoarders, people who are frightened of currencies, who like to bury some sovereigns in the garden or under the bed. Another percentage needs gold fillings for their teeth. Others need gold-rimmed spectacles, jewellery, engagement rings. All these new people will be taking tons of gold off the market every year. New industries need gold wire, gold plating, amalgams of gold. Gold has extraordinary properties which are being put to new uses every day. It is brilliant, malleable, ductile, almost unalterable and more dense than any of the common metals except platinum. There's no end to its uses. But it has two defects. It isn't hard enough. It wears out quickly, leaves itself on the linings of our pockets and in the sweat of our skins. Every year, the world's stock is invisibly reduced by friction. I said that gold has two defects.' Colonel Smithers looked sad. 'The other and by far the major defect is that it is the talisman of fear. Fear, Mr Bond, takes gold out of circulation and hoards it against the evil day. In a period of history when every tomorrow may be the evil day, it is fair enough to say that a fat proportion of the gold that is dug out of one corner of the earth is at once buried again in another corner.'

Bond smiled at Colonel Smithers's eloquence. This man lived gold, thought gold, dreamed gold. Well, it was an interesting subject. He might just as well wallow in the stuff. In the days when Bond had been after the diamond smugglers he had had first to educate himself in the fascination, the myth of the stones. He said, 'What else ought I to know before we get down to your immediate problem?'

'You're not bored? Well, you were suggesting that gold production was so vast nowadays that it ought to take care of all these various consumers. Unfortunately that is not so. In fact the gold content of the world is being worked out. You may think that large areas of the world have still to be explored for gold. You would be mistaken. Broadly speaking, there only remains the land under the sea and the sea itself, which has a notable gold content. People have been scratching the surface of the world for gold for thousands of years. There were the great gold treasures of Egypt and Mycenae, Montezuma and the Incas. Crœsus and Midas emptied the Middle Eastern territories of gold. Europe was worked for it–the valleys of the Rhine and the Po, Malaga and the plains of Granada. Cyprus was emptied, and the Balkans. India got the fever. Ants coming up from under the earth carrying grains of gold led the Indians to their alluvial fields. The Romans worked Wales and Devon and Cornwall. In the Middle Ages there were the finds in Mexico and Peru. These were followed by the opening up of the Gold Coast, then called Negro-land, and after that came the Americas. The famous gold rushes of the Yukon and Eldorado, and the rich strikes at Eureka sounded off the first modern Gold Age. Meanwhile, in Australia, Bendigo and Ballarat had come into production, and the Russian deposits at Lena and in the Urals were making Russia the largest gold producer in the world in the middle of the nineteenth century. Then came the second modern Gold Age–the discoveries on the Witwatersrand. These were helped by the new method of cyaniding instead of separation of the gold from the rock by mercury. Today we are in the third Gold Age with the opening up of the Orange Free State deposits.' Colonel Smithers threw up his hands. 'Now, gold is pouring out of the earth. Why, the whole production of the Klondike and the Homestake and Eldorado, which were once the wonder of the world, would only add up to two or three years of today's production from Africa! Just to show you, from 1500 to 1900, when approximate figures were kept, the whole world produced about eighteen thousand tons of gold. From 1900 to today we have dug up forty-one thousand tons! At this rate, Mr Bond,' Colonel Smithers leaned forward earnestly, '–and please don't quote me–but I wouldn't be surprised if in fifty years' time we have not totally exhausted the gold content of the earth!'

Bond, smothered by this cataract of gold history, found no difficulty in looking as grave as Colonel Smithers. He said, 'You certainly make a fascinating story of it. Perhaps the position isn't as bad as you think. They're already mining oil under the sea. Perhaps they'll find a way of mining gold. Now, about this smuggling.'

The telephone rang. Colonel Smithers impatiently snatched up the receiver. 'Smithers speaking.' He listened, irritation growing on his face. 'I'm sure I sent you a note about the summer fixtures, Miss Philby. The next match is on Saturday against the Discount Houses.' He listened again. 'Well, if Mrs Flake won't play goals, I'm afraid she'll have to stand down. It's the only position on the field we've got for her. Everybody can't play centre forward. Yes, please do. Say I'll be greatly obliged if just this once. I'm sure she'll be very good–right figure and all that. Thank you, Miss Philby.'

Colonel Smithers took out a handkerchief and mopped his forehead. 'Sorry about that. Sports and welfare are becoming almost too much of a fetish at the Bank. I've just had the women's hockey team thrown into my lap. As if I hadn't got enough to do with the annual gymkhana coming on. However–' Colonel Smithers waved these minor irritations aside–'as you say, time to get on to the smuggling. Well, to begin with, and taking only England and the sterling area, it's a very big business indeed. We employ three thousand staff at the Bank, Mr Bond, and of those no less than one thousand work in the exchange control department. Of those at least five hundred, including my little outfit, are engaged in controlling the illicit movements of valuta, the attempts to smuggle or to evade the Exchange Control Regulations.'

'That's a lot.' Bond measured it against the Secret Service which had a total force of two thousand. 'Can you give me an example of smuggling? In gold. I can't understand these dollar swindles.'

'All right.' Colonel Smithers now talked in the soft, tired voice of an overworked man in the service of his Government. It was the voice of the specialist in a particular line of law enforcement. It said that he knew most things connected with that line and that he could make a good guess at all the rest. Bond knew the voice well, the voice of the first-class Civil Servant. Despite his prosiness, Bond was beginning to take to Colonel Smithers. 'All right. Supposing you have a bar of gold in your pocket about the size of a couple of packets of Players. Weight about five and a quarter pounds. Never mind for the moment where you got it from–stole it or inherited it or something. That'll be twenty-four carat–what we call a thousand fine. Now, the law says you have to sell that to the Bank of England at the controlled price of twelve pounds ten per ounce. That would make it worth around a thousand pounds. But you're greedy. You've got a friend going to India or perhaps you're on good terms with an airline pilot or a steward on the Far East run. All you have to do is cut your bar into thin sheets or plates–you'd soon find someone to do this for you–and sew the plates–they'd be smaller than playing cards–into a cotton belt, and pay your friend a commission to wear it. You could easily afford a hundred pounds for the job. Your friend flies off to Bombay and goes to the first bullion dealer in the bazaar. He will be given one thousand seven hundred pounds for your five-pound bar and you're a richer man than you might have been. Mark you,' Colonel Smithers waved his pipe airily, 'that's only seventy per cent profit. Just after the war you could have got three hundred per cent. If you'd done only half a dozen little operations like that every year you'd be able to retire by now.'

'Why the high price in India?' Bond didn't really want to know. He thought M might ask him.

'It's a long story. Briefly, India is shorter of gold, particularly for her jewellery trade, than any other country.'

'What's the size of this traffic?'

'Huge. To give you an idea, the Indian Intelligence Bureau and their Customs *captured* forty-three thousand ounces in 1955. I doubt if that's one per cent of the traffic. Gold's been coming into India from all points of the compass. Latest dodge is to fly it in from Macao and drop it by parachute to a reception committee–a ton at a time–like we used to drop supplies to the Resistance during the war.'

'I see. Is there anywhere else I can get a good premium for my gold bar?'

'You could get a small premium in most countries–Switzerland, for instance–but it wouldn't be worth your while. India's still the place.'

'All right,' said Bond. 'I think I've got the picture. Now what's your particular problem?' He sat back and lit a cigarette. He was greatly looking forward to hearing about Mr Auric Goldfinger.

Colonel Smithers's eyes took on their hard, foxy look. He said, 'There's a man who came over to England in 1937. He was a refugee from Riga. Name of Auric Goldfinger. He was only twenty when he arrived, but he must have been a bright lad because he smelled that the Russians would be swallowing his country pretty soon. He was a jeweller and goldsmith by trade, like his father and grandfather who had refined gold for Fabergé. He had a little money and probably one of those belts of gold I was telling you about. Stole it from his father, I daresay. Well, soon after he'd been naturalized–he was a harmless sort of chap and in a useful trade and he had no difficulty in getting his papers–he started buying up small pawnbrokers all over the country. He put in his own men, paid them well and changed the name of the shops to "Goldfinger". Then he turned the shops over to selling cheap jewellery and buying old gold–you know the sort of place: "Best Prices for Old Gold. Nothing too Large, Nothing too Small", and he had his own particular slogan: "Buy Her Engagement Ring With Grannie's Locket." Goldfinger did very well. Always chose good sites, just on the dividing line between the well-to-do streets and the lower-middle. Never touched stolen goods and got a good name everywhere with the police. He lived in London and toured his shops once a month and collected all the old gold. He wasn't interested in the jewellery side. He let his managers run that as they liked.' Colonel Smithers looked quizzically at Bond. 'You may think these lockets and gold crosses and things are pretty small beer. So they are, but they mount up if you've got twenty little shops, each one buying perhaps half a dozen bits and pieces every week. Well, the war came and Goldfinger, like all other jewellers, had to declare his stock of gold. I looked up his figure in our old records. It was fifty ounces for the whole chain!–just enough of a working stock to keep his shops supplied with ring settings and so forth, what they call jeweller's findings in the trade. Of course, he was allowed to keep it. He tucked himself away in a machine-tool firm in Wales during the war–well out of the firing line–but kept as many of his shops operating as he could. Must have done well out of the G.I.s who generally travel with a Gold Eagle or a Mexican fifty-dollar piece as a last reserve. Then, when peace broke out, Goldfinger got moving. He bought himself a house, pretentious sort of place, at Reculver, at the mouth of the Thames. He also invested in a well-found Brixham trawler and an old Silver Ghost Rolls Royce–armoured car, built for some South American president who was killed before he could take delivery. He set up a little factory called "Thanet Alloy Research" in the grounds of his house and staffed it with a German metallurgist, a prisoner of war who didn't want to go back to Germany, and half a dozen Korean stevedores he picked up in Liverpool. They didn't know a word of any civilized language so they weren't any security risk. Then, for ten years, all we know is that he made one trip a year to India in his trawler and a few trips in his car every year to Switzerland. Set up a subsidiary of his alloy company near Geneva. He kept his shops going. Gave up collecting the old gold himself–used one of his Koreans whom he had taught to drive a car. All right, perhaps Mr Goldfinger is not a very honest man, but he behaves himself and keeps in well with the police, and with much more blatant fiddling going on all over the country nobody paid him any attention.'

Colonel Smithers broke off. He looked apologetically at Bond. 'I'm not boring you? I do want you to get the picture of the sort of man this is–quiet, careful, law-abiding and with the sort of drive and single-mindedness we all admire. We didn't even hear of him until he suffered a slight misfortune. In the summer of 1954, his trawler, homeward bound from India, went ashore on the Goodwins and he sold the wreck for a song to the Dover Salvage Company. When this company started breaking the ship up and got as far as the hold they found the timbers impregnated with a sort of brown powder which they couldn't put a name to. They sent a specimen to a local chemist. They were surprised when he said the stuff was gold. I won't bother you with the formula, but you see gold can be made to dissolve in a mixture of hydrochloric and nitric acids, and reducing agents–sulphur dioxide or oxalic acid–precipitate the metal as a brown powder. This powder can be reconstituted into gold ingots by melting at around a thousand degrees Centigrade. Have to watch the chlorine gas, but otherwise it's a simple process.

'The usual nosey parker in the salvage firm gossiped to one of the Dover Customs men and in due course a report filtered up through the police and the C.I.D. to me, together with a copy of the cargo clearance papers for each of Goldfinger's trips to India. These gave all the cargoes as mineral dust base for crop fertilizers–all perfectly credible because these modern fertilizers do use traces of various minerals in their make-up. The whole picture was clear as crystal. Goldfinger had been refining down his old gold, precipitating it into this brown powder and shipping it to India as fertilizer. But could we pin it on him? We could not. Had a quiet look at his bank balance and tax returns. Twenty thousand pounds at Barclays in Ramsgate. Income tax and super tax paid promptly each year. Figures showed the natural progress of a well-run jewellery business. We dressed a couple of the Gold Squad up and sent them down to knock on the door of Mr Goldfinger's factory at Reculver. "Sorry, sir, routine inspection for the Small Engineering Section of the Ministry of Labour. We have to make sure the Factory Acts are being observed for safety and health." "Come in. Come in." Mr Goldfinger positively welcomed them. Mark you, he may have been tipped off by his bank manager or someone, but that factory was entirely devoted to designing a cheap alloy for jewellers' findings–trying out unusual metals like aluminium and tin instead of the usual copper and nickel and palladium that are used in gold alloys. There were traces of gold about, of course, and furnaces to heat up to two thousand degrees and so forth, but after all Goldfinger was a jeweller and smelter in a small way, and all this was perfectly above-board. The Gold Squad retired discomfited, our legal department decided thc brown dust in the trawler's timbers was not enough to prosecute on without supporting evidence, and that was more or less that, except'–Colonel Smithers slowly wagged the stem of his pipe–'that I kept the file open and started sniffing around the banks of the world.'

Colonel Smithers paused. The rumble of the City came through the half-open window high up in the wall behind his chair. Bond glanced surreptitiously at his watch. Five o'clock. Colonel Smithers got up from his chair. He placed both hands palm downwards on the desk and leant forward. 'It took me five years, Mr Bond, to find out that Mr Goldfinger, in ready money, is the richest man in England. In Zürich, in Nassau, in Panama, in New York, he has twenty million pounds' worth of gold bars on safe deposit. And those bars, Mr Bond, are not Mint bars. They don't carry any official marks of origin whatsoever. They're bars that Mr Goldfinger has melted himself. I flew to Nassau and had a look at the five million pounds' worth or so he holds there in the vaults of the Royal Bank of Canada. Oddly enough, like all artists, he couldn't refrain from signing his handiwork. It needs a microscope to see it, but somewhere, on each Goldfinger bar, a minute letter Z has been scratched in the metal. And that gold, or most of it, belongs to England. The Bank can do nothing about it, so we are asking you to bring Mr Goldfinger to book, Mr Bond, and get that gold back. You know about the currency crisis and the high bank rate? Of course. Well, England needs that gold, badly–and the quicker the better.'

Chapter Seven

Thoughts in a D.B.III

Bond followed Colonel Smithers to the lift. While they waited for it, Bond glanced out of the tall window at the end of the passage. He was looking down into the deep well of the back courtyard of the Bank. A trim chocolate-brown lorry with no owner's name had come into the courtyard through the triple steel gates. Square cardboard boxes were being unloaded from it and put on to a short conveyor belt that disappeared into the bowels of the Bank.

Colonel Smithers came over. 'Fivers,' he commented. 'Just come up from our printing works at Loughton.'

The lift came and they got in. Bond said, 'I'm not very impressed by the new ones. They look like any other country's money. The old ones were the most beautiful money in the world.'

They walked across the entrance hall, now dimly lit and deserted. Colonel Smithers said, 'As a matter of fact I agree with you. Trouble was that those Reichsbank forgeries during the war were a darn sight too good. When the Russians captured Berlin, amongst the loot they got hold of the plates. We asked the Narodni Bank for them, but they refused to give them up. We and the Treasury decided it was too dangerous. At any moment, if Moscow had been inclined, they could have started a major raid on our currency. We had to withdraw the old fivers. The new ones aren't much to look at, but at least they'd be hell to forge.'

The night guard let them out on to the steps. Threadneedle Street was almost deserted. The long City night was beginning. Bond said goodbye to Colonel Smithers and walked along to the Tube. He had never thought very much about the Bank of England, but now that he had been inside the place he decided that the Old Lady of Threadneedle Street might be old but she still had some teeth left in her head.

Bond had been told to report back to M at six. He did so. M's face was no longer pink and shining. The long day had knocked it about, stressed it, shrunken it. When Bond went in and took the chair across the desk, he noticed the conscious effort M made to clear his mind, cope with the new problem the day was to fling at him. M straightened himself in his chair and reached for his pipe. 'Well?'

Bond knew the false belligerance of that particular bark. He told the gist of the story in less than five minutes.

When he had finished, M said thoughtfully, 'Suppose we've got to take it on. Don't understand a thing about the pound and bank rate and all that but everyone seems to be taking it damned seriously. Personally I should have thought the strength of the pound depended on how hard we all worked rather than how much gold we'd got. Germans didn't have much gold after the war. Look where they've got in ten years. However, that's probably too easy an answer for the politicians–or more likely too difficult. Got any ideas how to tackle this chap Goldfinger? Any way of getting closer to him, offering to do some dirty work for him or something like that?'

Bond said thoughtfully, 'I wouldn't get anywhere sucking up to him, asking him for a job or something of that sort, sir. I should say he's the sort of man who only respects people who are tougher or smarter than he is. I've given him one beating and the only message I got from him was that he'd like me to play golf with him. Perhaps I'd better do just that.'

'Fine way for one of my top men to spend his time.' The sarcasm in M's voice was weary, resigned. 'All right. Go ahead. But if what you say is right, you'd better see that you beat him. What's your cover story?'

Bond shrugged. 'I hadn't thought, sir. Perhaps I'd better be thinking of leaving Universal Export. No future in it. Having a holiday while I look round. Thinking of emigrating to Canada. Fed up here. Something like that. But perhaps I'd better play it the way the cards fall. I wouldn't think he's an easy man to fool.'

'All right. Report progress. And don't think I'm not interested in this case.' M's voice had changed. So had his expression. His eyes had become urgent, commanding. 'Now I'll give you one piece of information the Bank didn't give you. It just happens that I also know what Mr Goldfinger's bars look like. As a matter of fact I was handling one today–scratched Z and all. It had come in with that haul we made last week when the Redland Resident Director's office "caught fire" in Tangier. You'll have seen the signals. Well, that's the twentieth of these particular gold bars that have come our way since the war.'

Bond interrupted, 'But that Tangier bar was out of the SMERSH safe.'

'Exactly. I've checked. All the other nineteen bars with the scratched Z have been taken from SMERSH operatives.' M paused. He said mildly, 'D'you know, 007, I wouldn't be at all surprised if Goldfinger doesn't turn out to be the foreign banker, the treasurer so to speak, of SMERSH.'

James Bond flung the D.B.III though the last mile of straight and did a racing change down into third and then into second for the short hill before the inevitable traffic crawl through Rochester. Leashed in by the velvet claw of the front discs, the engine muttered its protest with a mild back-popple from the twin exhausts. Bond went up into third again, beat the lights at the bottom of the hill and slid resignedly up to the back of the queue that would crawl on for a quarter of an hour–if he was lucky–through the sprawl of Rochester and Chatham.

Bond settled back into second and let the car idle. He reached for the wide gunmetal case of Morland cigarettes on the neighbouring bucket seat, fumbled for one and lit it from the dashboard.

He had chosen the A2 for preference to the A20 to Sandwich because he wanted to take a quick look at Goldfinger-land–Reculver and those melancholy forsaken reaches of the Thames which Goldfinger had chosen for his parish. He would then cross the Isle of Thanet to Ramsgate and leave his bag at the Channel Packet, have an early lunch and be off to Sandwich.

The car was from the pool. Bond had been offered the Aston Martin or a Jaguar 3·4. He had taken the D.B.III. Either of the cars would have suited his cover–a well-to-do, rather adventurous young man with a taste for the good, the fast things of life. But the D.B.III had the advantage of an up-to-date triptyque, an inconspicuous colour–battleship grey–and certain extras which might or might not come in handy. These included switches to alter the type and colour of Bond's front and rear lights if he was following or being followed at night, reinforced steel bumpers, fore and aft, in case he needed to ram, a long-barrelled Colt ·45 in a trick compartment under the driver's seat, a radio pick-up tuned to receive an apparatus called the Homer, and plenty of concealed space that would fox most Customs men.

Bond saw a chance and picked up fifty yards, sliding into a ten-yard gap left by a family saloon of slow reactions. The man at the wheel, who wore that infallible badge of the bad driver, a hat clamped firmly on the exact centre of his head, hooted angrily. Bond reached out of the window and raised an enigmatically clenched fist. The hooting stopped.

And now what about this theory of M's? It made sense. The Russians were notoriously incompetent payers of their men. Their centres were always running out of funds–their men complaining to Moscow that they couldn't afford a square meal. Perhaps SMERSH couldn't get the valuta out of the Ministry of Home Security. Or perhaps the Ministry of Home Security couldn't get the money out of the Ministry of Finance. But it had always been the same–endless money troubles that resulted in missed chances, broken promises and waste of dangerous radio time. It would make sense to have a clever financial brain somewhere outside Russia who could not only transmit funds to the centres but also, in this case, make profits large enough to run the SMERSH centres abroad without any financial assistance from Moscow. Not only that. On the side, Goldfinger was appreciably damaging the currency base of an enemy country. If all this was correct, it was typical of SMERSH–a brilliant scheme, faultlessly operated by an outstanding man. And that, reflected Bond as he roared up the hill into Chatham, putting half a dozen cars behind him, would partly explain Goldfinger's greed for more and still more money. Devotion to the cause, to SMERSH, and perhaps the dangled prize of an Order of Lenin, would be the spur to pick up even ten or twenty thousand dollars when the odds were right or could be favourably adjusted. The funds for Red Revolution, for the discipline by fear that was the particular speciality of SMERSH, could never be big enough. Goldfinger was not making the money for himself. He was making it for the conquest of the world. The minor risk of being found out, as he had been by Bond, was nothing. Why? What could the Bank of England get him if every single one of his past operations could be exposed? Two years? Three?

The traffic was thinning through the outskirts of Gillingham. Bond started motoring again, but easily now, not hurrying, following his thoughts as the hands and feet went through their automatic responses.

So, in 'thirty-seven, SMERSH must have sent Goldfinger out with the belt of gold round his young waist. He had shown his special aptitudes, his acquisitive bent, during his training in the spy school in Leningrad. He would have been told there would be a war, that he must dig himself in and start quietly accumulating. Goldfinger must never dirty his hands, never meet an agent, never receive or pass a message. Some routine would have been arranged. 'Second-hand '39 Vauxhall. First offer of £1000 secures', 'Immaculate Rover, £2000', 'Bentley, £5000'. Always an advertisement that would not attract attention or correspondence. The prices would be just too high, the description inadequate. In the Agony column of *The Times*, perhaps. And, obediently, Goldfinger would have the two thousand pounds or the five thousand pounds gold bar at one of a long, a very long series of post-boxes that had been arranged in Moscow before he left. A particular bridge, a hollow tree, under a rock in a stream somewhere, anywhere in England. And he would never, on any account, visit that post-box again. It was up to Moscow to see that the agent got to the hidden treasure. Later, after the war, when Goldfinger was blossoming out, when he had become a big man, the post-boxes would no longer be bridges and trees. Now he would be given dates and safety deposit box numbers, left-luggage lockers at stations. But still there would be the rule that Goldfinger must never revisit the scene, never endanger himself. Perhaps he would only get his instructions once a year, at a casual meeting in some park, in a letter slipped into his pocket on a train journey. But always it would be bars of gold, anonymous, untraceable if captured–except for the tiny Z that his vanity had scratched on his handiwork and that a dull dog at the Bank of England called Colonel Smithers had happened upon in the course of his duties.

Now Bond was running through the endless orchards of the Faversham growers. The sun had come out from behind the smog of London. There was the distant gleam of the Thames on his left. There was traffic on the river–long, glistening tankers, stubby merchantmen, antediluvian Dutch Schuyts. Bond left the Canterbury road and switched on to the incongruously rich highway that runs through the cheap bungaloid world of the holiday lands–Whitstable, Herne Bay, Birchington, Margate. He still idled along at fifty, holding the racing wheel on a light rein, listening to the relaxed purr of the exhausts, fitting the bits of his thoughts into the jigsaw as he had done two nights before with Goldfinger's face on the Identicast.

And, Bond reflected, while Goldfinger was pumping a million, two million pounds a year into the bloody maw of SMERSH, he was pyramiding his reserves, working on them, making them work for him whenever the odds were right, piling up the surplus for the day when the trumpets would sound in the Kremlin and every golden sinew would be mobilized. And no one outside Moscow had been watching the process, no one suspected that Goldfinger–the jeweller, the metallurgist, the resident of Reculver and Nassua, the respected member of Blades, of the Royal St Marks at Sandwich–was one of the greatest conspirators of all time, that he had financed the murder of hundreds, perhaps thousands of victims of SMERSH all over the world. SMERSH, 'Smiert Spionam', Death to Spies–the murder Apparat of the High Praesidium! And only M suspected it, only Bond knew it. And here was Bond, launched against this man by a series of flukes, a train of coincidence that had been started by a plane breaking down on the other side of the world. Bond smiled grimly to himself. How often in his profession had it been the same–the tiny acorn of coincidence that soared into the mighty oak whose branches darkened the sky. And now, once again, he was setting out to bring the dreadful growth down. With what? A bag of golf clubs?

A repainted sky-blue Ford Popular with large yellow ears was scurrying along the crown of the road ahead. Mechanically Bond gave the horn ring a couple of short, polite jabs. There was no reaction. The Ford Popular was doing its forty. Why should anyone want to go more than that respectable speed? The Ford obstinately hunched its shoulders and kept on its course. Bond gave it a sharp blast, expecting it to swerve. He had to touch his brakes when it didn't. Damn the man! Of course! The usual tense figure, hands held too high up on the wheel, and the inevitable hat, this time a particularly hideous black bowler, square on a large bullet head. Oh well, thought Bond, they weren't *his* stomach ulcers. He changed down and contemptuously slammed the D.B.III past on the inside. Silly bastard!

Another five miles and Bond was through the dainty teleworld of Herne Bay. The howl of Manston sounded away on his right. A flight of three Super Sabres came in to land. They skimmed below his right-hand horizon as if they were diving into the earth. With half his mind, Bond heard the roar of their jets catch up with them as they landed and taxied in to the hangars. He came up with a crossroads. To the left the signpost said RECULVER. Underneath was the ancient monument sign for Reculver church. Bond slowed, but didn't stop. No hanging about. He motored slowly on, keeping his eyes open. The shoreline was too exposed for a trawler to do anything but beach or anchor. Probably Goldfinger had used Ramsgate. Quiet little port. Customs and police who were probably only on the look-out for brandy coming over from France. There was a thick clump of trees between the road and the shore, a glimpse of roofs and of a medium-sized factory chimney with a thin plume of light smoke or steam. That would be it. Soon there was the gate of a long drive. A discreetly authoritative sign said THANET ALLOYS, and underneath: NO ADMITTANCE EXCEPT ON BUSINESS. All very respectable. Bond drove slowly on. There was nothing more to be seen. He took the next right-hand turn across the Manston plateau to Ramsgate.

It was twelve o'clock. Bond inspected his room, a double with bathroom, on the top floor of the Channel Packet, unpacked his few belongings and went down to the snack bar where he had one vodka and tonic and two rounds of excellent ham sandwiches with plenty of mustard. Then he got back into his car and drove slowly over to the Royal St Marks at Sandwich.

Bond carried his clubs to the professional's shop and through to the workroom. Alfred Blacking was winding a new grip on to a driver.

'Hullo, Alfred.'

The professional looked up sharply. His sunburned, leathery face broke into a wide smile. 'Why, if it isn't Mr James!' They shook hands. 'Must be fifteen, twenty years. What brings you down here, sir? Someone was telling me only the other day that you're in the diplomatic or something. Always abroad. Well, I never! Still the same flat swing, sir?' Alfred Blacking joined his hands and gave a low, flat sweep.

'Afraid so, Alfred. Never had time to get myself out of it. How's Mrs Blacking and Cecil?'

'Can't complain, sir. Cecil was runner-up in the Kent Championship last year. Should win it this year if he can only get out of the shop and on to the course a bit more.'

Bond propped his clubs up against the wall. It was good to be back. Everything was just the same. There had been a time in his teens when he had played two rounds a day every day of the week at St Marks. Blacking had always wanted to take him in hand. 'A bit of practice, Mr James, and you'd be scratch. No fooling. You really would. What do you want to hang around at six for? It's all there except for that flat swing and wanting to hit the ball out of sight when there's no point in it. And you've got the temperament. A couple of years, perhaps only one, and I'd have you in the Amateur.' But something had told Bond that there wasn't going to be a great deal of golf in his life and if he liked the game he'd better forget about lessons and just play as much of it as he could. Yes, it would be about twenty years since he had played his last round on St Marks. He'd never been back–even when there had been that bloody affair of the Moonraker at Kingsdown, ten miles down the coast. Perhaps it had been sentimentality. Since St Marks, Bond had got in a good deal of weekend golf when he was at headquarters. But always on the courses round London–Huntercombe, Swinley, Sunningdale, the Berkshire. Bond's handicap had gone up to nine. But he was a real nine–had to be with the games he chose to play, the ten-pound Nassaus with the tough cheery men who were always so anxious to stand you a couple of double kümmels after lunch.

'Any chance of a game, Alfred?'

The professional glanced through his back window at the parking space round the tall flag-pole. He shook his head. 'Doesn't look too good, sir. Don't get many players in the middle of the week at this time of year.'

'What about you?'

'Sorry, sir. I'm booked. Playing with a member. It's a regular thing. Every day at two o'clock. And the trouble is that Cecil's gone over to Princes to get in some practice for the championship. What a dashed nuisance!' (Alfred never used a stronger oath.) 'It *would* happen like that. How long are you staying, sir?'

'Not long. Never mind. I'll knock a ball round with a caddie. Who's this chap you're playing with?'

'A Mr Goldfinger, sir.' Alfred looked discouraging.

'Oh, Goldfinger. I know the chap. Met him the other day in America.'

'You did, sir?' Alfred obviously found it difficult to believe that anyone knew Mr Goldfinger. He watched Bond's face carefully for any further reaction.

'Any good?'

'So-so, sir. Pretty useful off nine.'

'Must take his game damned seriously if he plays with you every day.'

'Well, yes, sir.' The professional's face had the expression Bond remembered so well. It meant that Blacking had an unfavourable view of a particular member but that he was too good a servant of the club to pass it on.

Bond smiled. He said, 'You haven't changed, Alfred. What you mean is that no one else will play with him. Remember Farquharson? Slowest player in England. I remember you going round and round with him twenty years ago. Come on. What's the matter with Goldfinger?'

The professional laughed. He said, 'It's you that hasn't changed, Mr James. You always were dashed inquisitive.' He came a step closer and lowered his voice. 'The truth is, sir, some members think Mr Goldfinger is just a little bit hot. You know, sir. Improves his lie and so forth.' The professional took the driver he was holding, took up a stance, gazed towards an imaginary hole and banged the head of the club up and down on the floor as if addressing an imaginary ball. 'Let me see now, is this a brassie lie? What d'you think, caddie?' Alfred Blacking chuckled. 'Well, of course, by the time he's finished hammering the ground behind the ball, the ball's been raised an inch and it *is* a brassie lie.' Alfred Blacking's face closed up again. He said non-committally, 'But that's only gossip, sir. I've never seen anything. Quiet-spoken gentleman. He's got a place at Reculver. Used to come here a lot. But for the last few years he's only been coming to England for a few weeks at a time. Rings up and asks if anyone's wanting a game and when there isn't anyone he books Cecil or me. Rang up this morning and asked if there was anyone about. There's sometimes a stranger drops in.' Alfred Blacking looked quizzically at Bond. 'I suppose you wouldn't care to take him on this afternoon? It'll look odd you being here and short of a game. And you knowing him and all. He might think I'd been trying to keep him to myself or something. That wouldn't do.'

'Nonsense, Alfred. And you've got your living to make. Why don't we play a three-ball?'

'He won't play them, sir. Says they're too slow. And I agree with him. And don't you worry about my fee. There's a lot of work to do in the shop and I'll be glad to an afternoon to get down to it.' Alfred Blacking glanced at his watch. 'He'll be along any minute now. I've got a caddie for you. Remember Hawker?' Alfred Blacking laughed indulgently. 'Still the same old Hawker. He'll be another that'll be glad to see you down here again.'

Bond said, 'Well thanks, Alfred. I'd be interested to see how this chap plays. But why not leave it like this? Say I've dropped in to get a club made up. Old member. Used to play here before the war. And I need a new number four wood anyway. Your old one has started to give at the seams a bit. Just be casual. Don't say you've told me he's about. I'll stay in the shop so it'll give him a chance to take his choice without offending me. Perhaps he won't like my face or something. Right?'

'Very good, Mr James. Leave it to me. That's his car coming now, sir.' Blacking pointed through the window. Half a mile away, a bright yellow car was turning off the road and coming up the private drive. 'Funny looking contraption. Sort of motor car we used to see here when I was a boy.'

Bond watched the old Silver Ghost sweep majestically up the drive towards the club. She was a beauty! The sun glittered off the silver radiator and off the engine-turned aluminium shield below the high perpendicular glass cliff of the windscreen. The luggage rail on the roof of the heavy coach-built limousine body–so ugly twenty years ago, so strangely beautiful today–was polished brass, as were the two Lucas 'King of the Road' headlamps that stared so haughtily down the road ahead, and the wide mouth of the old boa-constrictor bulb horn. The whole car, except for a black roof and black carrosserie lines and curved panels below the windows, was primrose yellow. It crossed Bond's mind that the South American president might have had it copied from the famous yellow fleet in which Lord Lonsdale had driven to the Derby and Ascot.

And now? In the driver's seat sat a figure in a café-au-lait dust coat and cap, his big round face obscured by black-rimmed driving goggles. Beside him was a squat figure in black with a bowler hat placed firmly on the middle of his head. The two figures stared straight in front of them with a curious immobility. It was almost as if they were driving a hearse.

The car was coming closer. The six pairs of eyes–the eyes of the two men and the great twin orbs of the car–seemed to be looking straight through the little window and into Bond's eyes.

Instinctively, Bond took a few paces back into the dark recesses of the workroom. He noticed the movement and smiled to himself. He picked up somebody's putter and bent down and thoughtfully addressed a knot in the wooden floor.

PART TWO

COINCIDENCE

Chapter Eight

All to Play For

'Good afternoon, Blacking. All set?' The voice was casual, authoritative. 'I see there's a car outside. Not somebody looking for a game, I suppose?'

'I'm not sure, sir. It's an old member come back to have a club made up. Would you like me to ask him, sir?'

'Who is it? What's his name?'

Bond smiled grimly. He pricked his ears. He wanted to catch every inflection.

'A Mr Bond, sir.'

There was a pause. 'Bond?' The voice had not changed. It was politely interested. 'Met a fellow called Bond the other day. What's his first name?'

'James, sir.'

'Oh yes.' Now the pause was longer. 'Does he know I'm here?' Bond could sense Goldfinger's antennae probing the situation.

'He's in the workshop, sir. May have seen your car drive up.' Bond thought: Alfred's never told a lie in his life. He's not going to start now.

'Might be an idea.' Now Goldfinger's voice unbent. He wanted something from Alfred Blacking, some information. 'What sort of a game does this chap play? What's his handicap?'

'Used to be quite useful when he was a boy, sir. Haven't seen his game since then.'

'Hm.'

Bond could feel the man weighing it all up. Bond smelled that the bait was going to be taken. He reached into his bag and pulled out his driver and started rubbing down the grip with a block of shellac. Might as well look busy. A board in the shop creaked. Bond honed away industriously, his back to the open door.

'I think we've met before.' The voice from the doorway was low, neutral.

Bond looked quickly over his shoulder. 'My God, you made me jump. Why–' recognition dawned–'it's Gold, Goldman . . . er–Goldfinger.' He hoped he wasn't overplaying it. He said with a hint of dislike, or mistrust, 'Where have you sprung from?'

'I told you I played down here. Remember?' Goldfinger was looking at him shrewdly. Now the eyes opened wide. The X-ray gaze pierced through to the back of Bond's skull.

'No.'

'Did not Miss Masterton give you my message?'

'No. What was it?'

'I said I would be over here and that I would like a game of golf with you.'

'Oh, well,' Bond's voice was coldly polite, 'we must do that some day.'

'I was playing with the professional. I will play with you instead.' Goldfinger was stating a fact.

There was no doubt that Goldfinger was hooked. Now Bond must play hard to get.

'Why not some other time? I've come to order a club. Anyway I'm not in practice. There probably isn't a caddie.' Bond was being as rude as he could. Obviously the last thing he wanted to do was play with Goldfinger.

'I also haven't played for some time.' (Bloody liar, thought Bond.) 'Ordering a club will not take a moment.' Goldfinger turned back into the shop, 'Blacking, have you got a caddie for Mr Bond?'

'Yes, sir.'

'Then that is arranged.'

Bond wearily thrust his driver back into his bag. 'Well, all right then.' He thought of a final way of putting Goldfinger off. He said roughly, 'But I warn you I like playing for money. I can't be bothered to knock a ball round just for the fun of it.' Bond felt pleased with the character he was building up for himself.

Was there a glint of triumph, quickly concealed, in Goldfinger's pale eyes? He said indifferently, 'That suits me. Anything you like. Off handicap, of course. I think you said you're nine.'

'Yes.'

Goldfinger said carefully, 'Where, may I ask?'

'Huntercombe.' Bond was also nine at Sunningdale. Huntercombe was an easier course. Nine at Huntercombe wouldn't frighten Goldfinger.

'And I also am nine. Here. Up on the board. So it's a level game. Right?'

Bond shrugged. 'You'll be too good for me.'

'I doubt it. However,' Goldfinger was offhand, 'tell you what I'll do. That bit of money you removed from me in Miami. Remember? The big figure was ten. I like a gamble. It will be good for me to have to try. I will play you double or quits for that.'

Bond said indifferently, 'That's too much.' Then, as if he thought better of it, thought he might win, he said–with just the right amount of craft mixed with reluctance–'Of course you can say that was "found money". I won't miss it if it goes again. Oh, well, all right. Easy come easy go. Level match. Ten thousand dollars it is.'

Goldfinger turned away. He said, and there was a sudden sweetness in the flat voice. 'That's all arranged then, Mr Blacking. Many thanks. Put your fee down on my account. Very sorry we shall be missing our game. Now, let me pay the caddie fees.'

Alfred Blacking came into the workroom and picked up Bond's clubs. He looked very directly at Bond. He said, 'Remember what I told you, sir.' One eye closed and opened again. 'I mean about that flat swing of yours. It needs watching–all the time.'

Bond smiled at him. Alfred had long ears. He might not have caught the figure, but he knew that somehow this was to be a key game. 'Thanks, Alfred. I won't forget. Four Penfolds–with hearts on them. And a dozen tees. I won't be a minute.'

Bond walked through the shop and out to his car. The bowler-hatted man was polishing the metal work of the Rolls with a cloth. Bond felt rather than saw him stop and watch Bond take out his zip bag and go into the club house. The man had a square flat yellow face. One of the Koreans?

Bond paid his green-fee to Hampton, the steward, and went into the changing-room. It was just the same–the same tacky smell of old shoes and socks and last summer's sweat. Why was it a tradition of the most famous golf clubs that their standard of hygiene should be that of a Victorian private school? Bond changed his socks and put on the battered old pair of nailed Saxones. He took off the coat of his yellowing black and white hound's-tooth suit and pulled on a faded black wind-cheater. Cigarettes? Lighter? He was ready to go.

Bond walked slowly out, preparing his mind for the game. On purpose he had needled this man into a high, tough match so that Goldfinger's respect for him should be increased and Goldfinger's views of Bond–that he was the type of ruthless, hard adventurer who might be very useful to Goldfinger–would be confirmed. Bond had thought that perhaps a hundred-dollars! There had probably never been such a high singles game in history–except in the finals of American Championships or in the big amateur Calcutta Sweeps where it was the backers rather than the players who had the money on. Goldfinger's private accounting must have taken a nasty dent. He wouldn't have liked that. He would be aching to get some of his money back. When Bond had talked about playing high, Goldfinger had seen his chance. So be it. But one thing was certain, for a hundred reasons Bond could not afford to lose.

He turned into the shop and picked up the balls and tees from Alfred Blacking.

'Hawker's got the clubs, sir.'

Bond strolled out across the five hundred yards of shaven seaside turf that led to the first tee. Goldfinger was practising on the putting green. His caddie stood near by, rolling balls to him. Goldfinger putted in the new fashion–between his legs with a mallet putter. Bond felt encouraged. He didn't believe in the system. He knew it was no good practising himself. His old hickory Calamity Jane had its good days and its bad. There was nothing to do about it. He knew also that the St Marks practice green bore no resemblance, in speed or texture, to the greens on the course.

Bond caught up with the limping, insouciant figure of his caddie who was sauntering along chipping at an imaginary ball with Bond's blaster. 'Afternoon, Hawker.'

'Afternoon, sir.' Hawker handed Bond the blaster and threw down three used balls. His keen sardonic poacher's face split in a wry grin of welcome. 'How've you been keepin', sir? Played any golf in the last twenty years? Can you still put them on the roof of the starter's hut?' This referred to the day when Bond, trying to do just that before a match, had put two balls through the starter's window.

'Let's see.' Bond took the blaster and hefted it in his hand, gauging the distance. The tap of the balls on the practice green had ceased. Bond addressed the ball, swung quickly, lifted his head and shanked the ball almost at right angles. He tried again. This time it was a dunch. A foot of turf flew up. The ball went ten yards. Bond turned to Hawker, who was looking his most sardonic. 'It's all right, Hawker. Those were for show. Now then, one for you.' He stepped up to the third ball, took his club back slowly and whipped the club head through. The ball soared a hundred feet, paused elegantly, dropped eighty feet on to the thatched roof of the starter's hut and bounced down.

Bond handed back the club. Hawker's eyes were thoughtful, amused. He said nothing. He pulled out the driver and handed it to Bond. They walked together to the first tee, talking about Hawker's family.

Goldfinger joined them, relaxed, impassive. Bond greeted Goldfinger's caddie, an obsequious, talkative man called Foulks whom Bond had never liked. Bond glanced at Goldfinger's clubs. They were a brand new set of American Ben Hogans with smart St Marks leather covers for the woods. The bag was one of the stitched black leather holdalls favoured by American pros. The clubs were in individual cardboard tubes for easy extraction. It was a pretentious outfit, but the best.

'Toss for honour?' Goldfinger flicked a coin.

'Tails.'

It was heads. Goldfinger took out his driver and unpeeled a new ball. He said, 'Dunlop 65. Number One. Always use the same ball. What's yours?'

'Penfold. Hearts.'

Goldfinger looked keenly at Bond. 'Strict Rules of Golf?'

'Naturally.'

'Right.' Goldfinger walked on to the tee and teed up. He took one or two careful, concentrated practice swings. It was a type of swing Bond knew well–the grooved, mechanical, repeating swing of someone who had studied the game with great care, read all the books and spent five thousand pounds on the finest pro teachers. It would be a good, scoring swing which might not collapse under pressure. Bond envied it.

Goldfinger took up his stance, waggled gracefully, took his club head back in a wide slow arc and, with his eyes glued to the ball, broke his wrists correctly. He brought the club head mechanically, effortlessly, down and through the ball and into a rather artificial, copybook finish. The ball went straight and true about two hundred yards down the fairway.

It was an excellent, uninspiring shot. Bond knew that Goldfinger would be capable of repeating the same swing with different clubs again and again round the eighteen holes.

Bond took his place, gave himself a lowish tee, addressed the ball with careful enmity and, with a flat, racket-player's swing in which there was just too much wrist for safety, lashed the ball away. It was a fine, attacking drive that landed past Goldfinger's ball and rolled on fifty yards. But it had had a shade of draw and ended on the edge of the left-hand rough.

They were two good drives. As Bond handed his club to Hawker and strolled off in the wake of the more impatient Goldfinger, he smelled the sweet smell of the beginning of a knock-down-and-drag-out game of golf on a beautiful day in May with the larks singing over the greatest seaside course in the world.

The first hole of the Royal St Marks is four hundred and fifty yards long–four hundred and fifty yards of undulating fairway with one central bunker to trap a mis-hit second shot and a chain of bunkers guarding three-quarters of the green to trap a well-hit one. You can slip through the unguarded quarter, but the fairway slopes to the right there and you are more likely to end up with a nasty first-chip-of-the-day out of the rough. Goldfinger was well placed to try for this opening. Bond watched him take what was probably a spoon, make his two practice swings and address the ball.

Many unlikely people play golf, including people who are blind, who have only one arm, or even no legs, and people often wear bizarre clothes to the game. Other golfers don't think them odd, for there are no rules of appearance or dress at golf. That is one of its minor pleasures. But Goldfinger had made an attempt to look smart at golf and that is the only way of dressing that is incongruous on a links. Everything matched in a blaze of rust-coloured tweed from the buttoned 'golfer's cap' centred on the huge, flaming red hair, to the brilliantly polished, almost orange shoes. The plus-four suit was too well cut and the plus-fours themselves had been pressed down the sides. The stockings were of a matching heather mixture and had green garter tabs. It was as if Goldfinger had gone to his tailor and said, 'Dress me for golf–you know, like they wear in Scotland.' Social errors made no impression on Bond, and for the matter of that he rarely noticed them. With Goldfinger it was different. Everything about the man had grated on Bond's teeth from the first moment he had seen him. The assertive blatancy of his clothes was just part of the malevolent animal magnetism that had affected Bond from the beginning.

Goldfinger executed his mechanical, faultless swing. The ball flew true but just failed to make the slope and curled off to the right to finish pin high off the green in the short rough. Easy five. A good chip could turn it into a four, but it would have to be a good one.

Bond walked over to his ball. It was lying cocked up, just off the fairway. Bond took his number four wood. Now for the 'all air route'–a soaring shot that would carry the cross-bunkers and give him two putts for a four. Bond remembered the dictum of the pros: 'It's never too early to start winning.' He took it easy, determined not to press for the long but comfortable carry.

As soon as Bond had hit the shot he knew it wouldn't do. The difference between a good golf shot and a bad one is the same as the difference between a beautiful and a plain woman–a matter of millimetres. In this case, the club face had gone through just that one millimetre too low under the ball. The arc of flight was high and soft–no legs. Why the hell hadn't he taken a spoon or a two iron off that lie? The ball hit the lip of the far bunker and fell back. Now it was the blaster, and fighting for a half.

Bond never worried too long about his bad or stupid shots. He put them behind him and thought of the next. He came up with the bunker, took his blaster and measured the distance to the pin. Twenty yards. The ball was lying well back. Should he splash it out with a wide stance and an outside-in swing, or should be blast it and take plenty of sand? For safety's sake he would blast it out. Bond went down into the bunker. Head down and follow well through. The easiest shot in golf. Try and put it dead. The wish, half way down his back swing, hurried the hands in front of the club head. The loft was killed and there was the ball rolling back off the face. Get it out, you bloody fool, and hole a long putt! Now Bond took too much sand. He was out, but barely on the green. Goldfinger bent to his chip and kept his head down until the ball was half way to the hole. The ball stopped three inches from the pin. Without waiting to be given the putt, Goldfinger turned his back on Bond and walked off towards the second tee. Bond picked up his ball and took his driver from Hawker.

'What does he say his handicap is, sir?'

'Nine. It's a level match. Have to do better than that though. Ought to have taken my spoon for the second.'

Hawker said encouragingly, 'It's early days yet, sir.'

Bond knew it wasn't. It was always too early to start losing.

Chapter Nine

The Cup and the Lip

Goldfinger had already teed up. Bond walked slowly behind him, followed by Hawker. Bond stood and leant on his driver. He said, 'I thought you said we would be playing the strict rules of golf. But I'll give you that putt. That makes you one up.'

Goldfinger nodded curtly. He went through his practice routine and hit his usual excellent, safe drive.

The second hole is a three hundred and seventy yard dog-leg to the left with deep cross-bunkers daring you to take the tiger's line. But there was a light helping breeze. For Goldfinger it would now be a five iron for his second. Bond decided to try and make it easier for himself and only have a wedge for the green. He laid his ears back and hit the ball hard and straight for the bunkers. The breeze got under the slight draw and winged the ball on and over. The ball pitched and disappeared down into the gully just short of the green. A four. Chance of a three.

Goldfinger strode off without comment. Bond lengthened his stride and caught up. 'How's the agoraphobia? Doesn't all this wide open space bother it?'

'No.'

Goldfinger deviated to the right. He glanced at the distant, half-hidden flag, planning his second shot. He took his five iron and hit a good, careful shot which took a bad kick short of the green and ran down into the thick grass to the left. Bond knew that territory. Goldfinger would be lucky to get down in two.

Bond walked up to his ball, took the wedge and flicked the ball on to the green with plenty of stop. The ball pulled up and lay a yard past the hole. Goldfinger executed a creditable pitch but missed the twelve-foot putt. Bond had two for the hole from a yard. He didn't wait to be given the hole but walked up and putted. The ball stopped an inch short. Goldfinger walked off the green. Bond knocked the ball in. All square.

The third is a blind two hundred and forty yards, all carry, a difficult three. Bond chose his brassie and hit a good one. It would be on or near the green. Goldfinger's routine drive was well hit but would probably not have enough steam to carry the last of the rough and trickle down into the saucer of the green. Sure enough, Goldfinger's ball was on top of the protecting mound of rough. He had a nasty, cuppy lie, with a tuft just behind the ball. Goldfinger stood and looked at the lie. He seemed to make up his mind. He stepped past his ball to take a club from the caddie. His left foot came down just behind the ball, flattening the tuft. Goldfinger could now take his putter. He did so and trickled the ball down the bank towards the hole. It stopped three feet short.

Bond frowned. The only remedy against a cheat at golf is not to play with him again. But that was no good in this match. Bond had no intention of playing with the man again. And it was no good starting a you-did-I-didn't argument unless he caught Goldfinger doing something even more outrageous. Bond would just have to try and beat him, cheating and all.

Now Bond's twenty-foot putt was no joke. There was no question of going for the hole. He would have to concentrate on laying dead. As usual, when one plays to go dead, the ball stopped short–a good yard short. Bond took a lot of trouble about the putt and holed it, sweating. He knocked Goldfinger's ball away. He would go on giving Goldfinger missable putts until suddenly Bond would ask him to hole one. Then that one might look just a bit more difficult.

Still all square. The fourth is four hundred and sixty yards. You drive over one of the tallest and deepest bunkers in the United Kingdom and then have a long second shot across an undulating hilly fairway to a plateau green guarded by a final steep slope which makes it easier to take three putts than two.

Bond picked up his usual fifty yards on the drive and Goldfinger hit two of his respectable shots to the gully below the green. Bond, determined to get up, took a brassie instead of a spoon and went over the green and almost up against the boundary fence. From there he was glad to get down in three for a half.

The fifth was again a long carry, followed by Bond's favourite second shot on the course–over bunkers and through a valley between high sand-dunes to a distant, taunting flag. It is a testing hole for which the first essential is a well-placed drive. Bond stood on the tee, perched high up in the sand-hills, and paused before the shot while he gazed at the glittering distant sea and at the faraway crescent of white cliffs beyond Pegwell Bay. Then he took up his stance and visualized the tennis court of turf that was his target. He took the club back as slowly as he knew how and started down for the last terrific acceleration before the club head met the ball. There was a dull clang on his right. It was too late to stop. Desperately Bond focused the ball and tried to keep his swing all in one piece. There came the ugly clonk of a mis-hit ball. Bond's head shot up. It was a lofted hook. Would it have the legs? Get on! Get on! The ball hit the top of a mountain of rough and bounced over. Would it reach the beginning of the fairway?

Bond turned towards Goldfinger and the caddies, his eye fierce. Goldfinger was straightening up. He met Bond's eyes indifferently. 'Sorry. Dropped my driver.'

'Don't do it again,' said Bond curtly. He stood down off the tee and handed his driver to Hawker. Hawker shook his head sympathetically. Bond took out a cigarette and lit it. Goldfinger hit his drive the dead straight regulation two hundred yards.

They walked down the hill in a silence which Goldfinger unexpectedly broke. 'What is the firm you work for?'

'Universal Export.'

'And where do they hang out?'

'London. Regent's Park.'

'What do they export?'

Bond woke up from his angry ruminations. Here, pay attention! This is work, not a game. All right, he put you off your drive, but you've got your cover to think about. Don't let him needle you into making mistakes about it. Build up your story. Bond said casually, 'Oh everything from sewing-machines to tanks.'

'What's your speciality?'

Bond could feel Goldfinger's eyes on him. He said, 'I look after the small arms side. Spend most of my time selling miscellaneous ironmongery to sheiks and rajahs–anyone the Foreign Office decides doesn't want the stuff to shoot at us with.'

'Interesting work.' Goldfinger's voice was flat, bored.

'Not very. I'm thinking of quitting. Came down here for a week's holiday to think it out. Not much future in England. Rather like the idea of Canada.'

'Indeed?'

They were past the rough and Bond was relieved to find that his ball had got a forward kick off the hill on to the fairway. The fairway curved slightly to the left and Bond had even managed to pick up a few feet on Goldfinger. It was Goldfinger to play. Goldfinger took out his spoon. He wasn't going for the green but only to get over the bunkers and through the valley.

Bond waited for the usual safe shot. He looked at his own lie. Yes, he could take his brassie. There came the wooden thud of a mis-hit. Goldfinger's ball, hit off the heel, sped along the ground and into the stony wastes of Hell Bunker–the widest bunker and the only unkempt one, because of the pebbles, on the course.

For once Homer had nodded–or rather, lifted his head. Perhaps his mind had been half on what Bond had told him. Good show! But Goldfinger might still get down in three more. Bond took out his brassie. He couldn't afford to play safe. He addressed the ball, seeing in his mind's eye its eighty-eight-millimetre trajectory through the valley and then the two or three bounces that would take it on to the green. He laid off a bit to the right to allow for his draw. Now!

There came a soft clinking away to his right. Bond stood away from his ball. Goldfinger had his back to Bond. He was gazing out to sea, rapt in its contemplation, while his right hand played 'unconsciously' with the money in his pocket.

Bond smiled grimly. He said, 'Could you stop shifting bullion till after my shot?'

Goldfinger didn't turn round or answer. The noise stopped.

Bond turned back to his shot, desperately trying to clear his mind again. Now the brassie was too much of a risk. It needed too good a shot. He handed it to Hawker and took his spoon and banged the ball safely through the valley. It ran on well and stopped on the apron. A five, perhaps a four.

Goldfinger got well out of the bunker and put his chip dead. Bond putted too hard and missed the one back. Still all square.

The sixth, appropriately called 'The Virgin', is a famous short hole in the world of golf. A narrow green, almost ringed with bunkers, it can need anything from an eight to a two iron according to the wind. Today, for Bond, it was a seven. He played a soaring shot, laid off to the right for the wind to bring it in. It ended twenty feet beyond the pin with a difficult putt over and down a shoulder. Should be a three. Goldfinger took his five and played it straight. The breeze took it and it rolled into the deep bunker on the left. Good news! That would be the hell of a difficult three.

They walked in silence to the green. Bond glanced into the bunker. Goldfinger's ball was in a deep heel-mark. Bond walked over to his ball and listened to the larks. This was going to put him one up. He looked for Hawker to take his putter, but Hawker was on the other side of the green, watching with intent concentration Goldfinger play his shot. Goldfinger got down into the bunker with his blaster. He jumped up to get a view of the hole and then settled himself for the shot. As his club went up Bond's heart lifted. He was going to try and flick it out–a hopeless technique from that buried lie. The only hope would have been to explode it. Down came the club, smoothly, without hurry. With hardly a handful of sand the ball curved up out of the deep bunker, bounced once and lay dead!

Bond swallowed. Blast his eyes! How the hell had Goldfinger managed that? Now, out of sour grapes, Bond must try for his two. He went for it, missed the hole by an inch and rolled a good yard past. Hell and damnation! Bond walked slowly up to the putt, knocking Goldfinger's ball away. Come on, you bloody fool! But the spectre of the big swing–from an almost certain one up to a possible one down–made Bond wish the ball into the hole instead of tapping it in. The coaxed ball, lacking decision, slid past the lip. One down!

Now Bond was angry with himself. He, and he alone, had lost that hole. He had taken three putts from twenty feet. He really must pull himself together and get going.

At the seventh, five hundred yards, they both hit good drives and Goldfinger's immaculate second lay fifty yards short of the green. Bond took his brassie. Now for the equalizer! But he hit from the top, his club head came down too far ahead of the hands and the smothered ball shot into one of the right-hand bunkers. Not a good lie, but he must put it on the green. Bond took a dangerous seven and failed to get it out. Goldfinger got his five. Two down. They halved the short eighth in three. At the ninth, Bond, determined to turn only one down, again tried to do too much off a poor lie. Goldfinger got his four to Bond's five. Three down at the turn! Not too good. Bond asked Hawker for a new ball. Hawker unwrapped it slowly, waiting for Goldfinger to walk over the hillock to the next tee. Hawker said softly, 'You saw what he did at The Virgin, sir?'

'Yes, damn him. It was an amazing shot.'

Hawker was surprised. 'Oh, you didn't see what he did in the bunker, sir?'

'No, what? I was too far away.'

The other two were out of sight over the rise. Hawker silently walked down into one of the bunkers guarding the ninth green, kicked a hole with his toe and dropped the ball in the hole. He then stood just behind the half-buried ball with his feet close together. He looked up at Bond. 'Remember he jumped up to look at the line to the hole, sir?'

'Yes.'

'Just watch this, sir.' Hawker looked towards the ninth pin and jumped, just as Goldfinger had done, as if to get the line. Then he looked up at Bond again and pointed to the ball at his feet. The heavy impact of the two feet just behind the ball had levelled the hole in which it had lain and had squeezed the ball out so that it was now perfectly teed for an easy shot–for just the easy cut-up shot which had seemed utterly impossible from Goldfinger's lie at The Virgin.

Bond looked at his caddie for a moment in silence. Then he said, 'Thanks, Hawker. Give me the bat and the ball. Somebody's going to be second in this match, and I'm damned if it's going to be me.'

'Yes, sir,' said Hawker stolidly. He limped off on the short cut that would take him half way down the tenth fairway.

Bond sauntered slowly over the rise and down to the tenth tee. He hardly looked at Goldfinger who was standing on the tee swishing his driver impatiently. Bond was clearing his mind of everything but cold, offensive resolve. For the first time since the first tee, he felt supremely confident. All he needed was a sign from heaven and his game would catch fire.

The tenth at the Royal St Marks is the most dangerous hole on the course. The second shot, to the skiddy plateau green with cavernous bunkers to right and left and a steep hill beyond, has broken many hearts. Bond remembered that Philip Scrutton, out in four under fours in the Gold Bowl, had taken a fourteen at this hole, seven of them ping-pong shots from one bunker to another, to and fro across the green. Bond knew that Goldfinger would play his second to the apron, or short of it, and be glad to get a five. Bond must go for it and get his four.

Two good drives and, sure enough, Goldfinger well up on the apron with his second. A possible four. Bond took his seven, laid off plenty for the breeze and fired the ball off into the sky. At first he thought he had laid off too much, but then the ball began to float to the left. It pitched and stopped dead in the soft sand blown on to the green from the right-hand bunker. A nasty fifteen-foot putt. Bond would now be glad to get a half. Sure enough, Goldfinger putted up to within a yard. That, thought Bond as he squared up to his putt, he will have to hole. He hit his own putt fairly smartly to get it through the powdering of sand and was horrified to see it going like lightning across the skiddy green. God, he was going to have not a yard, but a two-yard putt back! But suddenly, as if drawn by a magnet, the ball swerved straight for the hole, hit the back of the tin, bounced up and fell into the cup with an audible rattle. The sign from heaven! Bond went up to Hawker, winked at him and took his driver.

They left the caddies and walked down the slope and back to the next tee. Goldfinger said coldly. 'That putt ought to have run off the green.'

Bond said off-handedly, 'Always give the hole a chance!' He teed up his ball and hit his best drive of the day down the breeze. Wedge and one putt? Goldfinger hit his regulation shot and they walked off again. Bond said, 'By the way, what happened to that nice Miss Masterton?'

Goldfinger looked straight in front of him. 'She left my employ.'

Bond thought, good for her! He said, 'Oh, I must get in touch with her again. Where did she go to?'

'I couldn't say.' Goldfinger walked away from Bond towards his ball. Bond's drive was out of sight, over the ridge that bisected the fairway. It wouldn't be more than fifty yards from the pin. Bond thought he knew what would be in Goldfinger's mind, what is in most golfers' minds when they smell the first scent of a good lead melting away. Bond wouldn't be surprised to see that grooved swing quicken a trifle. It did. Goldfinger hooked into a bunker on the left of the green.

Now was the moment when it would be the end of the game if Bond made a mistake, let his man off the hook. He had a slightly downhill lie, otherwise an easy chip–but to the trickiest green on the course. Bond played it like a man. The ball ended six feet from the pin. Goldfinger played well out of his bunker, but missed the longish putt. Now Bond was only one down.

They halved the dog-leg twelfth in inglorious fives and the longish thirteenth also in fives, Goldfinger having to hole a good putt to do so.

Now a tiny cleft of concentration had appeared on Goldfinger's massive, unlined forehead. He took a drink of water from the tap beside the fourteenth tee. Bond waited for him. He didn't want a sharp clang from that tin cup when it was out-of-bounds over the fence to the right and the drive into the breeze favouring a slice! Bond brought his left hand over to increase his draw and slowed down his swing. The drive, well to the left, was only just adequate, but at least it had stayed in bounds. Goldfinger, apparently unmoved by the out-of-bounds hazard, hit his standard shot. They both negotiated the transverse canal without damage and it was another half in five. Still one down and now only four to play.

The four hundred and sixty yards fifteenth is perhaps the only hole where the long hitter may hope to gain one clear shot. Two smashing woods will just get you over the line of bunkers that lie right up against the green. Goldfinger had to play short of them with his second. He could hardly improve on a five and it was up to Bond to hit a really godlike second shot from a barely adequate drive.

The sun was on its way down and the shadows of the four men were beginning to lengthen. Bond had taken up his stance. It was a good lie. He had kept his driver. There was dead silence as he gave his two incisive waggles. This was going to be a vital stroke. Remember to pause at the top of the swing, come down slow and whip the club head through at the last second. Bond began to take the club back. Something moved at the corner of his right eye. From nowhere the shadow of Goldfinger's huge head approached the ball on the ground, engulfed it and moved on. Bond let his swing take itself to pieces in sections. Then he stood away from his ball and looked up. Goldfinger's feet were still moving. He was looking carefully up at the sky.

'Shades please, Goldfinger.' Bond's voice was furiously controlled.

Goldfinger stopped and looked slowly at Bond. The eyebrows were raised a fraction in inquiry. He moved back and stood still, saying nothing.

Bond went back to his ball. Now then, relax! To hell with Goldfinger. Slam that ball on to the green. Just stand still and hit it. There was a moment when the world stood still, then . . . then somehow Bond did hit it–on a low trajectory that mounted gracefully to carry the distant surf of the bunkers. The ball hit the bank below the green, bounced high with the impact and rolled out of sight into the saucer round the pin.

Hawker came up and took the driver out of Bond's hand. They walked on together. Hawker said seriously, 'That's one of the finest shots I've seen in thirty years.' He lowered his voice. 'I thought he'd fixed you then, sir.'

'He damned nearly did, Hawker. It was Alfred Blacking that hit that ball, not me.' Bond took out his cigarettes, gave one to Hawker and lit his own. He said quietly, 'All square and three to play. We've got to watch those next three holes. Know what I mean?'

'Don't you worry, sir. I'll keep my eye on him.'

They came up with the green. Goldfinger had pitched on and had a long putt for a four, but Bond's ball was only two inches away from the hole. Goldfinger picked up his ball and walked off the green. They halved the short sixteenth in good threes. Now there were the two long holes home. Fours would win them. Bond hit a fine drive down the centre. Goldfinger pushed his far out to the right into deep rough. Bond walked along trying not to be too jubilant, trying not to count his chickens. A win for him at this hole and he would only need a half at the eighteenth for the match. He prayed that Goldfinger's ball would be unplayable or, better still, lost.

Hawker had gone on ahead. He had already laid down his bag and was busily–far too busily to Bond's way of thinking–searching for Goldfinger's ball when they came up.

It was bad stuff–jungle country, deep thick luxuriant grass whose roots still held last night's dew. Unless they were very lucky, they couldn't hope to find the ball. After a few minutes' search Goldfinger and his caddie drifted away still wider to where the rough thinned out into isolated tufts. That's good, thought Bond. That wasn't anything like the line. Suddenly he trod on something. Hell and damnation. Should he stamp it in. He shrugged his shoulders, bent down and gently uncovered the ball so as not to improve the lie. Yes it was a Dunlop 65. 'Here you are,' he called grudgingly. 'Oh no, sorry. You play with a Number One, don't you?'

'Yes,' came back Goldfinger's voice impatiently.

'Well, this is a Number Seven.' Bond picked it up and walked over to Goldfinger.

Goldfinger gave the ball a cursory glance. He said, 'Not mine,' and went on poking among the tufts with the head of his driver.

It was a good ball, unmarked and almost new. Bond put it in his pocket and went back to his search. He glanced at his watch. The statutory five minutes was almost up. Another half-minute and by God he was going to claim the hole. Strict rules of golf, Goldfinger had stipulated. All right my friend, you shall have them!

Goldfinger was casting back towards Bond, diligently prodding and shuffling through the grass.

Bond said, 'Nearly time, I'm afraid.'

Goldfinger grunted. He started to say something when there came a cry from his caddie, 'Here you are, sir. Number One Dunlop.'

Bond followed Goldfinger over to where the caddie stood on a small plateau of higher ground. He was pointing down. Bond bent and inspected the ball. Yes, an almost new Dunlop One and in an astonishingly good lie. It was miraculous–more than miraculous. Bond stared hard from Goldfinger to his caddie. 'Must have had the hell of a lucky kick,' he said mildly.

The caddie shrugged his shoulders. Goldfinger's eyes were calm, untroubled. 'So it would seem.' He turned to his caddie. 'I think we can get a spoon to that one, Foulks.'

Bond walked thoughtfully away and then turned to watch the shot. It was one of Goldfinger's best. It soared over a far shoulder of rough towards the green. Might just have caught the bunker on the right.

Bond walked on to where Hawker, a long blade of grass dangling from his wry lips, was standing on the fairway watching the shot finish. Bond smiled bitterly at him. He said in a controlled voice. 'Is my good friend in the bunker, or is the bastard on the green?'

'Green, sir,' said Hawker unemotionally.

Bond went up to his ball. Now things had got tough again. Once more he was fighting for a half after having a certain win in his pocket. He glanced towards the pin, gauging the distance. This was a tricky one. He said, 'Five or six?'

'The six should do it, sir. Nice form shot.' Hawker handed him the club.

Now then, clear your mind. Keep it slow and deliberate. It's an easy shot. Just punch it so that it's got plenty of zip to get up the bank and on to the green. Stand still and head down. Click! The ball, hit with a slightly closed face, went off on just the medium trajectory Bond had wanted. It pitched below the bank. It was perfect! No, damn it. It had hit the bank with its second bounce, stopped dead, hesitated and then rolled back and down again. Hell's bells! Was it Hagen who had said, 'You drive for show, but you putt for dough'? Getting dead from below that bank was one of the most difficult putts on the course. Bond reached for his cigarettes and lit one, already preparing his mind for the next crucial shot to save the hole–so long as that bastard Goldfinger didn't hole his from thirty feet!

Hawker walked along by his side. Bond said, 'Miracle finding that ball.'

'It wasn't his ball, sir.' Hawker was stating a fact.

'What do you mean?' Bond's voice was tense.

'Money passed, sir. White, probably a fiver. Foulks must have dropped that ball down his trouser leg.'

'Hawker!' Bond stopped in his tracks. He looked round. Goldfinger and his caddie were fifty yards away, walking slowly towards the green. Bond said fiercely, 'Do you swear to that? How can you be sure?'

Hawker gave a half-ashamed, lop-sided grin. But there was a crafty belligerence in his eye. 'Because his ball was lying under my bag of clubs, sir.' When he saw Bond's open-mouthed expression he added apologetically, 'Sorry, sir. Had to do it after what he's been doing to you. Wouldn't have mentioned it, but I had to let you know he's fixed you again.'

Bond had to laugh. He said admiringly, 'Well, you *are* a card, Hawker. So you were going to win the match for me all on your own!' He added bitterly, 'But, by God, that man's the flaming limit. I've got to get him. I've simply got to. Now let's think!' They walked slowly on.

Bond's left hand was in his trouser pocket, absent-mindedly fingering the ball he had picked up in the rough. Suddenly the message went to his brain. Got it! He came close to Hawker. He glanced across at the others. Goldfinger had stopped. His back was to Bond and he was taking the putter out of his bag. Bond nudged Hawker. 'Here, take this.' He slipped the ball into the gnarled hand. Bond said softly, urgently, 'Be certain you take the flag. When you pick up the balls from the green, whichever way the hole has gone, give Goldfinger this one. Right?'

Hawker walked stolidly forward. His face was expressionless. 'Got it, sir,' he said in his normal voice. 'Will you take the putter for this one?'

'Yes.' Bond walked up to his ball. 'Give me a line, would you?'

Hawker walked up on to the green. He stood sideways to the line of the putt and then stalked round to behind the flag and crouched. He got up. 'Inch outside the right lip, sir. Firm putt. Flag, sir?'

'No. Leave it in, would you.'

Hawker stood away. Goldfinger was standing by his ball on the right of the green. His caddie had stopped at the bottom of the slope. Bond bent to the putt. Come on, Calamity Jane! This one has got to go dead or I'll put you across my knee. Stand still. Club head straight back on the line and follow through towards the hole. Give it a chance. Now! The ball, hit firmly in the middle of the club, had run up the bank and was on its way to the hole. But too hard, damn it! Hit the stick! Obediently the ball curved in, rapped the stick hard and bounced back three inches–dead as a doornail!

Bond let out a deep sigh and picked up his discarded cigarette. He looked over at Goldfinger. Now then, you bastard. Sweat that one out. And by God if you hole it! But Goldfinger couldn't afford to try. He stopped two feet short. 'All right, all right,' said Bond generously. 'All square and one to go.' It was vital that Hawker should pick up the balls. If he had made Goldfinger hole the short putt it would have been Goldfinger who would have picked the ball out of the hole. Anyway, Bond didn't want Goldfinger to miss that putt. That wasn't part of the plan.

Hawker bent down and picked up the balls. He rolled one towards Bond and handed the other to Goldfinger. They walked off the green, Goldfinger leading as usual. Bond noticed Hawker's hand go to his pocket. Now, so long as Goldfinger didn't notice anything on the tee!

But, with all square and one to go, you don't scrutinize your ball. Your motions are more or less automatic. You are thinking of how to place your drive, of whether to go for the green with the second or play to the apron, of the strength of the wind–of the vital figure four that must somehow be achieved to win or at least to halve.

Considering that Bond could hardly wait for Goldfinger to follow him and hit, just once, that treacherous Dunlop Number Seven that looked so very like a Number One, Bond's own drive down the four hundred and fifty yard eighteenth was praiseworthy. If he wanted to, he could now reach the green–if he wanted to!

Now Goldfinger was on the tee. Now he had bent down. The ball was on the peg, its lying face turned up at him. But Goldfinger had straightened, had stood back, was taking his two deliberate practice swings. He stepped up to the ball, cautiously, deliberately. Stood over it, waggled, focusing the ball minutely. Surely he would see! Surely he would stop and bend down at the last minute to inspect the ball! Would the waggle never end? But now the club head was going back, coming down, the left knee bent correctly in towards the ball, the left arm straight as a ramrod. Crack! The ball sailed off, a beautiful drive, as good as Goldfinger had hit, straight down the fairway.

Bond's heart sang. Got you, you bastard! Got you! Blithely Bond stepped down from the tee and strolled off down the fairway planning the next steps which could now be as eccentric, as fiendish as he wished. Goldfinger was beaten already–hoist with his own petard! Now to roast him, slowly, exquisitely.

Bond had no compunction. Goldfinger had cheated him twice and got away with it. But for his cheats at the Virgin and the seventeenth, not to mention his improved lie at the third and various times he had tried to put Bond off, Goldfinger would have been beaten by now. If it needed one cheat by Bond to rectify the score-sheet that was only poetic justice. And besides, there was more to this than a game of golf. It was Bond's duty to win. By his reading of Goldfinger he *had* to win. If he was beaten, the score between the two men would have been equalized. If he won the match, as he now had, he would be two up on Goldfinger–an intolerable state of affairs, Bond guessed, to a man who saw himself as all powerful. This man Bond,

Goldfinger would say to himself, *has* something. He has qualities I can use. He is a tough adventurer with plenty of tricks up his sleeve. This is the sort of man I need for–for what? Bond didn't know. Perhaps there would be nothing for him. Perhaps his reading of Goldfinger was wrong, but there was certainly no other way of creeping up on the man.

Goldfinger cautiously took out his spoon for the longish second over cross-bunkers to the narrow entrance to the green. He made one more practice swing than usual and then hit exactly the right, controlled shot up to the apron. A certain five, probably a four. Much good would it do him!

Bond, after a great show of taking pains, brought his hands down well ahead of the club and smothered his number three iron so that the topped ball barely scrambled over the cross-bunkers. He then wedged the ball on to the green twenty feet past the pin. He was where he wanted to be–enough of a threat to make Goldfinger savour the sweet smell of victory, enough to make Goldfinger really sweat to get his four.

And now Goldfinger really was sweating. There was a savage grin of concentration and greed as he bent to the long putt up the bank and down to the hole. Not too hard, not too soft. Bond could read every anxious thought that would be running through the man's mind. Goldfinger straightened up again, walked deliberately across the green to behind the flag to verify his line. He walked slowly back beside his line, brushing away–carefully, with the back of his hand–a wisp or two of grass, a speck of top-dressing. He bent again and made one or two practice swings and then stood to the putt, the veins standing out on his temples, the cleft of concentration deep between his eyes.

Goldfinger hit the putt and followed through on the line. It was a beautiful putt that stopped six inches past the pin. Now Goldfinger would be sure that unless Bond sank his difficult twenty-footer, the match was his!

Bond went through a long rigmarole of sizing up his putt. He took his time, letting the suspense gather like a thunder cloud round the long shadows on the livid, fateful green.

'Flag out, please. I'm going to sink this one.' Bond charged the words with a deadly certitude, while debating whether to miss the hole to the right or the left or leave it short. He bent to the putt and missed the hole well on the right.

'Missed it, by God!' Bond put bitterness and rage into his voice. He walked over to the hole and picked up the two balls, keeping them in full view.

Goldfinger came up. His face was glistening with triumph. 'Well, thanks for the game. Seems I was just too good for you after all.'

'You're a good nine handicap,' said Bond with just sufficient sourness. He glanced at the balls in his hand to pick out Goldfinger's and hand it to him. He gave a start of surprise. 'Hullo!' He looked sharply at Goldfinger. 'You play a Number One Dunlop, don't you?'

'Yes, of course.' A sixth sense of disaster wiped the triumph off Goldfinger's face. 'What is it? What's the matter?'

'Well,' said Bond apologetically. ''Fraid you've been playing with the wrong ball. Here's my Penfold Hearts and this is a Number Seven Dunlop.' He handed both balls to Goldfinger. Goldfinger tore them off his palm and examined them feverishly.

Slowly the colour flooded over Goldfinger's face. He stood, his mouth working, looking from the balls to Bond and back to the balls.

Bond said softly, 'Too bad we were playing to the rules. Afraid that means you lose the hole. And, of course, the match.' Bond's eyes observed Goldfinger impassively.

'But, but . . .'

This was what Bond had been looking forward to–the cup dashed from the lips. He stood and waited, saying nothing.

Rage suddenly burst Goldfinger's usually relaxed face like a bomb. 'It was a Dunlop Seven you found in the rough. It was your caddie that gave me this ball. On the seventeenth green. He gave me the wrong ball on purpose, the damned che—'

'Here, steady on,' said Bond mildly. 'You'll get a slander action on your hands if you aren't careful. Hawker, did you give Mr Goldfinger the wrong ball by mistake or anything?'

'No, sir.' Hawker's face was stolid. He said indifferently, 'If you want my opinion, sir, the mistake may have been made at the seventeenth when the gentleman found his ball pretty far off the line we'd all marked it on. A Seven looks very much like a One. I'd say that's what happened, sir. It would have been a miracle for the gentleman's ball to have ended up as wide as where it was found.'

'Tommy rot!' Goldfinger gave a snort of disgust. He turned angrily on Bond. 'You saw that was a Number One my caddie found.'

Bond shook his head doubtfully. 'I didn't really look closely, I'm afraid. However,' Bond's voice became brisk, businesslike, 'It's really the job of the player to make certain he's using the right ball, isn't it? I can't see that anyone else can be blamed if you tee the wrong ball up and play three shots with it. Anyway,' he started walking off the green, 'many thanks for the match. We must have it again one day.'

Goldfinger, lit with glory by the setting sun, but with a long black shadow tied to his heels, followed Bond slowly, his eyes fixed thoughtfully on Bond's back.

Chapter Ten

Up at The Grange

There are some rich men who use their riches like a club. Bond, luxuriating in his bath, thought that Goldfinger was one of them. He was the kind of man who thought he could flatten the world with his money, bludgeoning aside annoyances and opposition with his heavy wad. He had thought to break Bond's nerve by playing him for ten thousand dollars–a flea-bite to him but obviously a small fortune to Bond. In most circumstances he might have succeeded. It needs an iron nerve to 'wait for it' on your swing, to keep your head down on the short putts, when big money hangs on every shot, over eighteen holes. The pros, playing for their own bread and butter and for their families', know the cold breath of the poor-house on the back of their necks as they come to the eighteenth tee all square. That is why they lead careful lives, not smoking or drinking, and why the one that wins is usually the one with the least imagination.

But, in Bond's case, Goldfinger could not have known that high tension was Bond's natural way of life and that pressure and danger relaxed him. And he could not have known that Bond wanted to play Goldfinger for the highest possible stakes and that he would have the funds of the Secret Service behind him if he lost. Goldfinger, so used to manipulating others, had been blind to the manipulation for once being practised upon himself.

Or had he been? Thoughtfully Bond got out of the bath and dried himself. That powerful dynamo inside the big round head would be humming at this very moment, wondering about Bond, knowing he had been out-cheated, asking itself how it came about that twice Bond had appeared out of the blue and twice queered his pitch. Had Bond played his cards right? Had he made himself appear an interesting challenge, or would Goldfinger's sensitive nose smell a threat? In the latter case there would be no follow-up by Goldfinger and Bond would have to bow out of the case and leave it to M to devise a new approach. How soon would he know if the big fish was hooked? This one would take plenty of time sniffing the bait. It would be good to have just one small bite to tell him he had chosen the right lure.

There was a knock on the door of his bedroom. Bond wrapped the towel round him and walked through. He opened the door. It was the hall porter. 'Yes?'

'Telephone message from a Mr Goldfinger, sir. His compliments and would you care to come to his house for dinner tonight. It's The Grange over at Reculver, sir. Six-thirty for drinks beforehand and not to bother to dress.'

'Please thank Mr Goldfinger and say I shall be delighted.' Bond shut the door and walked across to the open window and stood looking out across the quiet evening sea. 'Well, well! Talk of the devil!' Bond smiled to himself, 'And then go and sup with him! What was that about a long spoon?'

At six o'clock Bond went down to the bar and had a large vodka and tonic with a slice of lemon peel. The bar was empty save for a group of American Air Force officers from Manston. They were drinking whisky and water and talking baseball. Bond wondered if they had spent the day toting a hydrogen bomb round the skies over Kent, over the four little dots in the dunes that had been his match with Goldfinger. He thought wryly, Not too much of that whisky, cousins, paid for his drink, and left.

He motored slowly over to Reculver, savouring the evening and the drink inside him and the quiet bubble of the twin exhausts. This was going to be an interesting dinner-party. Now was the moment to sell himself to Goldfinger. If he put a foot wrong he was out, and the pitch would have been badly queered for his successor. He was unarmed–it would be fatal for Goldfinger to smell that kind of rat. He felt a moment's qualm. But that was going too fast. No state of war had been declared–the opposite if anything. When they had parted at the golf club, Goldfinger had been cordial in a rather forced, oily fashion. He had inquired where he should send Bond's winnings and Bond had given him the address of Universal Export. He had asked where Bond was staying and Bond had told him and added that he would only be at Ramsgate a few days while he made up his mind about his future. Goldfinger hoped that they would one day have a return match but, alas, he was leaving for France tomorrow and wasn't certain when he would be back. Flying?

Yes, taking the Air Ferry from Lydd. Well, thanks for the match. And thank you, Mr Bond. The eyes had given Bond one last X-ray treatment, as if fixing him for a last time in Goldfinger's filing system, and then the big yellow car had sighed away.

Bond had had a good look at the chauffeur. He was a chunky flat-faced Japanese, or more probably Korean, with a wild, almost mad glare in dramatically slanting eyes that belonged in a Japanese film rather than in a Rolls Royce on a sunny afternoon in Kent. He had the snout-like upper lip that sometimes goes with a cleft palate, but he said nothing and Bond had no opportunity of knowing whether his guess was right. In his tight, almost bursting black suit and farcical bowler hat he looked rather like a Japanese wrestler on his day off. But he was not a figure to make one smile. If one had been inclined to smile, a touch of the sinister, the unexplained, in the tight shining patent-leather black shoes that were almost dancing pumps, and in the heavy black leather driving gloves, would have changed one's mind. There was something vaguely familiar to Bond in the man's silhouette. It was when the car drove away and Bond had a glimpse of the head from the rear that he remembered. Those were the head and shoulders and bowler hat of the driver of the sky-blue Ford Popular that had so obstinately hugged the crown of the Herne Bay road at about twelve o'clock that morning. Where had he been coming from? What errand had he been on? Bond remembered something Colonel Smithers had said. Could this have been the Korean who now travelled the country collecting the old gold from the chain of Goldfinger jewellery shops? Had the boot of the innocent, scurrying little saloon been stuffed with the week's takings of presentation watches, signet rings, lockets, gold crosses? As he watched the high, primrose-yellow silhouette of the Silver Ghost disappearing towards Sandwich, Bond thought the answer was yes.

Bond turned off the main road into the drive and followed it down between high Victorian evergreens to the gravel sweep in front of just the sort of house that would be called The Grange–a heavy, ugly, turn-of-the-century mansion with a glass-enclosed portico and sun parlour whose smell of trapped sunshine, rubber plants and dead flies came to Bond in his imagination before he had switched off the engine. Bond got slowly out of the car and stood looking at the house. Its blank, well-washed eyes stared back at him. The house had a background noise, a heavy rhythmic pant like a huge animal with a rather quick pulse. Bond assumed it came from the factory whose plumed chimney reared up like a giant cautionary finger from the high conifers to the right where the stabling and garages would normally be. The quiet watchful façade of the house seemed to be waiting for Bond to do something, make some offensive move to which there would be a quick reply. Bond shrugged his shoulders to lighten his thoughts and went up the steps to the opaque glass-panelled door and pressed the bell. There was no noise of it ringing, but the door slowly opened. The Korean chauffeur still had his bowler hat on. He looked without interest at Bond. He stood motionless, his left hand on the inside doorknob and his outstretched right pointing like a signpost into the dark hall of the house.

Bond walked past him, vanquishing a desire either to stamp on his neat black feet or hit him very hard indeed in the centre of his tightly buttoned black stomach. This Korean matched up with what he had always heard about Koreans, and anyway Bond wanted to do something violent to the heavy, electric atmosphere of the house.

The gloomy hall was also the main living-room. A meagre fire flickered behind the fire-irons in the wide hearth and two club chairs and a Knole sofa stood impassively watching the flames. Between them on a low settee was a well-stocked drink tray. The wide spaces surrounding this spark of life were crowded with massive Rothschildian pieces of furniture of the Second Empire, and ormolu, tortoiseshell, brass and mother-of-pearl winked back richly at the small fire. Behind this orderly museum, dark panelling ran up to a first-floor gallery which was reached by a heavy curved stairway to the left of the hall. The ceiling was laced with the sombre wood-carving of the period.

Bond was standing taking all this in when the Korean came silently up. He flung out his signpost of an arm towards the drink tray and the chairs. Bond nodded and stayed where he was. The Korean walked past him and disappeared through a door into what Bond assumed were the servants' quarters. The silence, helped by the slow iron tick of a massively decorated grandfather clock, gathered and crept nearer.

Bond walked over and stood with his back to the poor fire. He stared offensively back at the room. What a dump! What a bloody awful deathly place to live in. How did one, could one, live in this rich heavy morgue amongst the conifers and evergreens when a hundred yards away there was light and air and wide horizons? Bond took out a cigarette and lit it. What did Goldfinger do for enjoyment, for fun, for sex? Perhaps he didn't need these things. Perhaps the pursuit of gold slaked all his thirsts.

Somewhere in the distance a telephone rang. The bell shrilled twice and stopped. There was the murmur of a voice, then steps echoed down a passage and a door under the stairway opened. Goldfinger came through and quietly closed the door behind him. He was wearing a plum-coloured velvet dinner jacket. He came slowly across the polished wood floor. He didn't hold out his hand. He said, smiling with his mouth, 'It was kind of you to come at such short notice, Mr Bond. You were alone and so was I and it occurred to me that we might discuss the price of corn.'

It was the sort of remark that rich men make to each other. Bond was amused at being made a temporary member of the club. He said, 'I was delighted to get the invitation. I was already bored with worrying over my problems. Ramsgate hasn't much to offer.'

'No. And now I have an apology to make. I have had a telephone call. One of my staff–I employ Koreans, by the way–has had some minor trouble with the Margate police and I must go over and straighten it out. Some incident at the fun fair, I understand. These people get easily over-excited. My chauffeur will drive me and we should not be more than half an hour. Meanwhile I fear I must leave you to your own devices. Please help yourself to drinks. There are magazines to read. Will you forgive me? Not more than half an hour I assure you.'

'That's quite all right,' Bond felt there was something fishy in this. He couldn't put his finger on what it was.

'Well then, au revoir.' Goldfinger went to the front door. 'But I must give you some light. It's really very dark in here.' Goldfinger brushed his hand down a wall-plate of switches and suddenly lights blazed all over the hall–from standard lamps, wall brackets, and four clusters in the ceiling. Now the room was as bright as a film studio. It was an extraordinary transformation. Bond, half dazzled, watched Goldfinger open the front door and stride out. In a minute he heard the sound of a car, but not the Rolls, rev up noisily, change gear and go off fast down the drive.

On an instinct, Bond walked over to the front door and opened it. The drive was empty. In the distance he saw the lights of the car turn left-handed on the main road and make off in the direction of Margate. He turned back into the house and closed the door. He stood still, listening. The silence, except for the heavy clock-tick, was complete. He walked across to the service door and opened it. A long dark passage disappeared towards the back of the house. Bond bent forward, all his senses alert. Silence, dead silence. Bond shut the door and looked thoughtfully round the brilliantly lit hall. He had been left alone in Goldfinger's house, alone with its secrets. Why?

Bond walked over to the drink tray and poured himself a strong gin and tonic. There certainly had been a telephone call, but it could easily have been an arranged call from the factory. The story of the servant was plausible and it was reasonable that Goldfinger should go himself to bail the man out and take his chauffeur with him. Goldfinger had twice mentioned that Bond would be alone for half an hour during which he 'would be left to his own devices'. This could be innocent, or it could be an invitation for Bond to show his hand, commit some indiscretion. Was somebody watching him? How many of these Koreans were there and what were they doing? Bond glanced at his watch. Five minutes had gone. He made up his mind. Trap or no trap, this was too good a chance to miss. He would have a quick look round–but an innocent one, with some sort of a cover story to explain why he had left the hall. Where should he begin? A look at the factory. His story? That his car had given trouble on the way over–choked petrol feed probably–and that he had gone to see if there was a mechanic who could give him a hand. Flimsy, but it would do. Bond downed his drink and went purposefully to the service door and walked through.

There was a light switch. He turned on the light and walked swiftly down a long passage. It ended with a blank wall and two doors to right and left. He listened for an instant at the left-hand one and heard muffled kitchen noises. He opened the right-hand door and found himself in the paved garage yard he might have expected. The only odd thing about it was that it was brilliantly lit by arc lights. The long wall of the factory occupied the far side and now the rhythmic engine thump was very loud. There was a plain wooden door low down in the wall opposite. Bond walked across the yard to it, looking around him with casual interest. The door was unlocked. He opened it with discretion and walked through, leaving the door ajar. He found himself in a small empty office lit by one naked bulb hanging from the ceiling. There was a desk with papers on it, a time-clock, a couple of filing cabinets and a telephone. Another door led from the office into the main factory space and there was a window beside the door for keeping an eye on the workmen. It would be the foreman's office. Bond walked to the window and looked through.

Bond didn't know what he had expected, but there seemed to be the usual accoutrements of a small metal-working business. Facing him were the open mouths of two blast furnaces, their fires now drawn. Beside these stood a row of kilns for the molten metal, of which sheets of different sizes and colours stood against the wall near by. There was the polished steel table of a circular saw, a diamond saw presumably, for cutting the sheets, and to the left in the shadows a big oil engine connected to a generator pounded away making power. To the right, under arc lights, a group of five men in overalls, four of them Koreans, were at work on–of all things–Goldfinger's Rolls Royce. It stood there gleaming under the lights, immaculate save for the right-hand door which had been taken off its hinges and now lay across two near-by benches minus its door panel. As Bond watched, two men picked up the new door panel, a heavy, discoloured sheet of aluminium-coloured metal, and placed it on the door frame. There were two hand riveters on the floor and soon, Bond thought, the men would rivet the panel into place and paint it to match the rest of the car. All perfectly innocent and above-board. Goldfinger had dented the panel that afternoon and had had a quick repair job done in preparation for his trip tomorrow. Bond gave a quick, sour look round, withdrew from the window and went out by the factory door and closed it softly behind him. Nothing there, damn it. And now what was his story? That he had not wanted to disturb the men at their work–perhaps after dinner, if one of them had a moment.

Bond walked unhurriedly back the way he had come and regained the hall without misadventure.

Bond looked at his watch. Ten minutes to go. Now for the first floor. The secrets of a house are in the bedrooms and bathrooms. Those are the private places where the medicine cabinets, the dressing-table, the bedside drawers, reveal the intimate things, the frailties. Bond had a bad headache. He had gone to look for an aspirin. He acted the part for an invisible audience, massaged his temples, glanced up at the gallery, walked decisively across the floor and climbed the stairs. The gallery gave on to a brightly lit passage. Bond walked down it opening the doors and glancing in. But they were spare bedrooms, the beds not made up. They held a smell of must and shut windows. A large ginger cat appeared from nowhere and followed him, mewing and rubbing itself against his trouser legs. The end room was the one. Bond went in and closed the door to a crack.

All the lights were on. Perhaps one of the servants was in the bathroom. Bond walked boldly across to the communicating door and opened it. More lights, but no one. It was a big bathroom, probably a spare room converted into a bathroom and, in addition to the bath and lavatory, it held various fitness machines–a rowing machine, a fixed bicycle wheel, Indian clubs and a Ralli Health Belt. The medicine cabinet contained nothing except a great variety of purges–senna pods, cascara, Calsalettes, Enos and various apparatus for the same purpose. There were no other drugs and no aspirin. Bond went back into the bedroom and again drew a blank. It was a typical man's room, comfortable, lived in, with plenty of fitted cupboards. It even smelled neutral. There was a small bookcase beside the bed in which all the books were history or biography, all in English. The drawer of the bedside table yielded a solitary indiscretion, a yellow-backed copy of *The Hidden Sight of Love*, Palladium Publications, Paris.

Bond glanced at his watch. Five more minutes. It was time to go. He took a last look round the room and moved to the door. Suddenly he stopped. What was it he had noticed almost subconsciously ever since he had come into the room? He sharpened his senses. There was an incongruity somewhere. What was it? A colour? An object? A smell? A sound? That was it! From where he stood he could hear the faintest, mosquito-shrill whine. It was almost extra-sensory in its pitch. Where did it come from? What was making it? Now there was something else in the room, something that Bond knew all too well, the smell of danger.

Tensely Bond stepped closer to the fitted cupboard beside the door, softly opened it. Yes, it came from inside the cupboard, from behind a range of sports coats that reached down to the top of three banks of drawers. Sharply Bond swept the coats aside. His jaws clenched at what was behind them.

From three slots near the top of the cupboard, sixteen-millimetre film was inching down in three separate strips into a deep bin behind the false front of the drawers. The bin was almost half full of the slimy snakes of the stuff. Bond's eyes narrowed tensely as he watched the damning evidence coil slowly down on to the pile. So that was it–ciné-cameras, three of them, their lenses concealed God knows where–in the hall, in the garage courtyard, in this room–had been watching his every move from the moment Goldfinger had left the house, switching on the cameras, and, of course, the dazzling lights, as he went out of the door. Why hadn't Bond seen the significance of those lights? Why hadn't he had the elementary imagination to see the trap as well as smell it? Cover stories, indeed! What use were they now when he had spent half an hour snooping round and finding nothing for his pains? That too! He had discovered nothing–unearthed no secret. It had all been an idiotic waste of time. And now Goldfinger had him. He was finished, hopelessly blown. Was there any way of saving something from the wreckage? Bond stood riveted, staring at the slow cataracts of film.

Let's see now! Bond's mind raced, thinking of ways out, excuses, discarding them all. Well, at least by opening the cupboard door he had exposed some of the film. Then why not expose it all? Why not, but how? How could the open cupboard door be explained except by his doing? There came a miaow from the open slit of the bedroom door. The cat! Why shouldn't the cat have done it? Pretty thin, but at least it was the shadow of an alibi. Bond opened the door. He picked the cat up in his arms. He went back with it to the cupboard, stroking it brusquely. It purred. Bond leant over the bin of film, picking it up in handfuls so that it would all get the light. Then, when he was satisfied that it must be ruined, he tossed it back and dropped the cat in on top of it. The cat would not be able to get out easily. With any luck it would settle down and go to sleep. Bond left the cupboard door three inches ajar to spoil the continuing film and the bedroom door the same amount and ran down the passage. At the top of the stairs he slowed and sauntered down. The empty hall yawned at his play-acting. He walked across to the fireplace, dashed more drink into his glass and picked up *The Field.* He turned to the golf commentary by Bernard Darwin, ran his eye down it to see what it was about, and then settled into one of the club chairs and lit a cigarette.

What had he found out? What was there on the plus side? Precious little except that Goldfinger suffered from constipation and a dirty mind and that he had wanted to put Bond through an elementary test. He had certainly done it expertly. This was no amateur. The technique was fully up to SMERSH standards, and it was surely the technique of somebody with a very great deal to hide. And now what would happen? For the cat alibi to stand up, Goldfinger would have to have left two doors, one of them vital, ajar, and the cat had got into the room and been intrigued by the whine of the cameras. Most unlikely, almost incredible. Goldfinger would be ninety per cent certain it was Bond–but only ninety. There would still be that ten per cent of uncertainty. Would Goldfinger have learnt much more than he knew before–that Bond was a tricky, resourceful customer and that Bond had been inquisitive, might be a thief? He would guess Bond had been to the bedroom, but Bond's other movements, for whatever they were worth, would remain a secret on the exposed film.

Bond got up and took a handful of other magazines and threw them down beside his chair. The only thing for him to do was brazen it out and make a note for the future, if there was to be a future, that he had better wake his ideas up and not make any more mistakes. There wouldn't be enough ginger cats in the world to help him out of one more tight spot like the one he was in.

There had been no noise of a car coming down the drive, not a sound from the door, but Bond felt the evening breeze on his neck and he knew that Goldfinger had come back into the room.

Chapter Eleven

The Odd-Job Man

Bond threw down *The Field* and stood up. The front door closed noisily. Bond turned. 'Hullo.' His face registered polite surprise. 'Didn't hear you arrive. How did it go?'

Goldfinger's expression was equally bland. They might have been old friends, neighbours in the country who were accustomed to drop in on each other for a drink. 'Oh, it sorted itself out. My chap had had a row in a pub with some American Air Force men who had called him a bloody Jap. I explained to the police that Koreans don't like being called Japs. They let him off with a caution. Terribly sorry to have been so long. Hope you weren't bored. Do have another drink.'

'Thanks. But it's hardly seemed five minutes since you left. Been reading what Darwin had to say about the fourteen club rule. Interesting point of view . . .' Bond launched into a detailed review of the article, adding his own comments on the rule.

Goldfinger stood patiently until it was over. He said, 'Yes, it's a complicated business. Of course you play rather a different game from me, more workmanlike. With my kind of swing, I find I need all the clubs I'm allowed. Well, I'll just go up and wash and then we'll have dinner. Shan't be a moment.'

Bond busied himself noisily with pouring another drink, sat down and picked up *Country Life*. He watched Goldfinger climb the stairs and disappear down the corridor. He could visualize every step. He found he was reading the periodical upside down. He turned it round and stared blindly at a fine photograph of Blenheim Palace.

There was dead silence upstairs. Then a distant lavatory chain was pulled and a door clicked shut. Bond reached for his drink, took a deep swallow and put the glass down beside his chair. Goldfinger was coming down the stairs.

Bond turned the pages of *Country Life* and flicked ash off his cigarette into the grate.

Now Goldfinger was crossing the floor towards him. Bond lowered his paper and looked up. Goldfinger was carrying the ginger cat tucked carelessly under one arm. He reached the fireplace, bent forward and pressed the bell.

He turned towards Bond. 'Do you like cats?' His gaze was flat, incurious.

'Sufficiently.'

The service door opened. The chauffeur stood in the frame. He still wore his bowler hat and his shiny black gloves. He gazed impassively at Goldfinger. Goldfinger crooked a finger. The chauffeur approached and stood within the circle by the fire.

Goldfinger turned to Bond. He said conversationally, 'This is my handy man.' He smiled thinly. 'That is something of a joke. Oddjob, show Mr Bond your hands.' He smiled again at Bond. 'I call him Oddjob because that describes his functions on my staff.'

The Korean slowly pulled off his gloves and came and stood at arm's length from Bond and held out his hands palm upwards. Bond got up and looked at them. They were big and fat with muscle. The fingers all seemed to be the same length. They were very blunt at the tips and the tips glinted as if they were made of yellow bone.

'Turn them over and show Mr Bond the sides.'

There were no finger-nails. Instead there was this same, yellowish carapace. The man turned the hands sideways. Down each edge of the hands was a hard ridge of the same bony substance.

Bond raised his eyebrows at Goldfinger.

Goldfinger said, 'We will have a demonstration.' He pointed at the thick oak banisters that ran up the stairs. The rail was a massive six inches by four thick. The Korean obediently walked over to the stairs and climbed a few steps. He stood with his hands at his sides, gazing across at Goldfinger like a good retriever. Goldfinger gave a quick nod. Impassively the Korean lifted his right hand high and straight above his head and brought the side of it down like an axe across the heavy polished rail. There was a splintering crash and the rail sagged, broken through the centre. Again the hand went up and flashed down. This time it swept right through the rail leaving a jagged gap. Splinters clattered down on to the floor of the hall. The Korean straightened himself and stood to attention, waiting for further orders. There was no flush of effort in his face and no hint of pride in his achievement.

Goldfinger beckoned. The man came back across the floor. Goldfinger said, 'His feet are the same, the outside edges of them. Oddjob, the mantelpiece.' Goldfinger pointed at the heavy shelf of carved wood above the fireplace. It was about seven feet off the ground–six inches higher than the top of the Korean's bowler hat.

'Garch a har?'

'Yes, take off your coat and hat.' Goldfinger turned to Bond. 'Poor chap's got a cleft palate. I shouldn't think there are many people who understand him beside me.'

Bond reflected how useful that would be, a slave who could only communicate with the world through his interpreter–better even than the deaf mutes of the harems, more tightly bound to his master, more secure.

Oddjob had taken off his coat and hat and placed them neatly on the floor. Now he rolled his trouser legs up to the knee and stood back in the wide well-planted stance of the judo expert. He looked as if a charging elephant wouldn't put him off balance.

'Better stand back, Mr Bond.' The teeth glittered in the wide mouth. 'This blow snaps a man's neck like a daffodil.' Goldfinger drew aside the low settee with the drink tray. Now the Korean had a clear run. But he was only three long steps away. How could he possibly reach the high mantelpiece?

Bond watched, fascinated. Now the slanting eyes in the flat yellow mask were glinting with a fierce intentness. Faced by such a man, thought Bond, one could only go down on one's knees and wait for death.

Goldfinger lifted his hand. The bunched toes in the polished soft leather shoes seemed to grip the ground. The Korean took one long crouching stride with knees well bent and then whirled off the ground. In mid-air his feet slapped together like a ballet dancer's, but higher than a ballet dancer's have ever reached, and then the body bent sideways and downwards and the right foot shot out like a piston. There came a crashing thud. Gracefully the body settled back down on the hands, now splayed on the floor, the elbows bent to take the weight and then straightened sharply to throw the man up and back on his feet.

Oddjob stood to attention. This time there was a gleam of triumph in his flat eyes as he looked at the three-inch jagged bite the edge of his foot had taken out of the mantelpiece.

Bond looked at the man in deep awe. And only two nights ago he, Bond, had been working on his manual of unarmed combat! There was nothing, absolutely nothing, in all his reading, all his experience, to approach what he had just witnessed. This was not a man of flesh and blood. This was a living club, perhaps the most dangerous animal on the face of the earth. Bond had to do it, had to give homage to this uniquely dreadful person. He held out his hand.

'Softly, Oddjob.' Goldfinger's voice was the crack of a whip.

The Korean bowed his head and took Bond's hand in his. He kept his fingers straight and merely bent his thumb in a light clasp. It was like holding a piece of board. He released Bond's hand and went to his neat pile of clothes.

'Forgive me, Mr Bond, and I appreciate your gesture.' Goldfinger's face showed his approval. 'But Oddjob doesn't know his own strength–particularly when he is keyed up. And those hands are like machine-tools. He could have crushed your hand to pulp without meaning to. Now then,' Oddjob had dressed and was standing respectfully at attention, 'you did well, Oddjob. I'm glad to see you are in training. Here–' Goldfinger took the cat from under his arm and tossed it to the Korean who caught it eagerly–'I am tired of seeing this animal around. You may have it for dinner.' The Korean's eyes gleamed. 'And tell them in the kitchen that we will have our own dinner at once.'

The Korean inclined his head sharply and turned away.

Bond hid his disgust. He realized that all this exhibition was simply a message to him, a warning, a light rap on the knuckles. It said, 'You see my power, Mr Bond. I could easily have killed you or maimed you. Oddjob was giving an exhibition and you got in the way. I would certainly be innocent, and Oddjob would get off with a light sentence. Instead, the cat will be punished in your place. Bad luck on the cat, of course.'

Bond said casually, 'Why does the man always wear that bowler hat?'

'Oddjob!' The Korean had reached the service door. 'The hat.' Goldfinger pointed at a panel in the woodwork near the fireplace.

Still holding the cat under his left arm, Oddjob turned and walked stolidly back towards them. When he was half way across the floor, and without pausing or taking aim, he reached up to his hat, took it by the rim and flung it sideways with all his force. There was a loud clang. For an instant the rim of the bowler hat stuck an inch deep in the panel Goldfinger had indicated, then it fell and clattered on the floor.

Goldfinger smiled politely at Bond. 'A light but very strong alloy, Mr Bond. I fear that will have damaged the felt covering, but Oddjob will put on another. He's surprisingly quick with a needle and thread. As you can imagine, that blow would have smashed a man's skull or half severed his neck. A homely and a most ingeniously concealed weapon, I'm sure you'll agree.'

'Yes, indeed.' Bond smiled with equal politeness. 'Useful chap to have around.'

Oddjob had picked up his hat and disappeared. There came the boom of a gong. 'Ah, dinner! Shall we go in?' Goldfinger led the way to a door concealed in the panelling to the right of the fireplace. He pressed a hidden latch and they walked through.

The small dining-room matched the heavy wealth of the hall. It was brilliantly lit from a central chandelier and by candles on a round table that glittered with silver and glass. They sat down opposite each other. Two yellow-faced servants in white mess-jackets brought dishes from a loaded serving-table. The first course was some curried mess with rice. Goldfinger noticed Bond's hesitation. He gave a dry chuckle. 'It's all right, Mr Bond. Shrimp, not the cat.'

'Ah.' Bond's expression was non-committal.

'Please try the Moselle. I hope it will be to your taste. It is a Piesporter Goldtröpfchen '53. Help yourself. These people are as likely to pour it into your plate as your glass.'

There was a slim bottle in an ice bucket in front of Bond. He poured some of the wine and tasted it. It was nectar and ice cold. Bond congratulated his host. Goldfinger gave a curt nod.

'I don't myself drink or smoke, Mr Bond. Smoking I find the most ridiculous of all the varieties of human behaviour and practically the only one that is entirely against nature. Can you imagine a cow or any animal taking a mouthful of smouldering straw then breathing in the smoke and blowing it out through its nostrils? Pah!' Goldfinger showed a rare trace of emotion. 'It is a vile practice. As for drinking, I am something of a chemist and I have yet to find a liquor that is free from traces of a number of poisons, some of them deadly, such as fusel oil, acetic acid, ethylacetate, acetaldehyde and furfurol. A quantity of some of these poisons taken neat would kill you. In the small amounts you find in a bottle of liquor they produce various ill effects most of which are lightly written off as "a hangover".' Goldfinger paused with a forkful of curried shrimp half way to his mouth. 'Since you are a drinker, Mr Bond, I will give you one word of good advice. Never drink so-called Napoleon brandy, particularly when it is described as "aged in the wood". That particular potion contains more of the poisons I have mentioned than any other liquor I have analysed. Old bourbon comes next.' Goldfinger closed his animadversions with a mouthful of shrimp.

'Thank you. I'll remember. Perhaps for those reasons I have recently taken to vodka. They tell me its filtration through activated charcoal is a help.' Bond, dredging this piece of expertise out of dim recollections of something he had read, was rather proud of having been able to return Goldfinger's powerful serve.

Goldfinger glanced at him sharply. 'You seem to understand something of these matters. Have you studied chemistry?'

'Only dabbled in it.' It was time to move on. 'I was very impressed by that chauffeur of yours. Where did he learn that fantastic combat stuff? Where did it come from? Is that what the Koreans use?'

Goldfinger patted his mouth with his napkin. He snapped his fingers. The two men cleared away the plates and brought roast duckling and a bottle of Mouton Rothschild 1947 for Bond. When they had withdrawn into immobility at each end of the serving-table, Goldfinger said, 'Have you ever heard of Karate? No? Well that man is one of the three in the world who have achieved the Black Belt in Karate. Karate is a branch of judo, but it is to judo what a Spandau is to a catapult.'

'I could see that.'

'The demonstration was an elementary one. Mr Bond–' Goldfinger held up the drumstick he had been gnawing–'I can tell you that if Oddjob had used the appropriate single blow on any one of seven spots on your body, you would now be dead.' Goldfinger bit at the side of the drumstick with relish.

Bond said seriously, 'That's interesting. I only know five ways of killing Oddjob with one blow.'

Goldfinger seemed not to hear the comment. He put down his drumstick and took a deep draught of water. He sat back and spoke while Bond went on eating the excellent food. 'Karate, Mr Bond, is based on the theory that the human body possesses five striking surfaces and thirty-seven vulnerable spots–vulnerable, that is, to an expert in Karate whose finger-tips, the side of the hands and the feet are hardened into layers of corn, which is far stronger and more flexible than bone. Every day of his life, Mr Bond, Oddjob spends one hour hitting either sacks of unpolished rice or a strong post whose top is wound many times round with thick rope. He then spends another hour at physical training which is more that of a ballet school than of a gymnasium.'

'When does he practise tossing the bowler hat? Bond had no intention of succumbing to this psychological warfare.

Goldfinger frowned at the interruption. 'I have never inquired,' he said without humour. 'But I think you can take it that Oddjob keeps his eye in at all his skills. However, you were asking where Karate originated. It originated in China where wandering Buddhist priests became an easy prey for footpads and bandits. Their religion did not allow them to carry weapons, so they developed their own form of unarmed combat. The inhabitants of Okinawa refined the art to its present form when the Japanese forbade them to carry weapons. They developed the five striking surfaces of the human body–the fist, the edge of the hand, the finger-tips, the ball of the foot and the elbows–and toughened them until they were enveloped in layers of corn. There is a no follow-through in a Karate blow. The entire body is stiffened at the moment of impact, with the emphasis on the hips, and then instantly relaxed so that balance is never lost. It is astonishing what Oddjob can do. I have seen him hit a brick wall with his entire force and not hurt his hand. He can split three half-inch boards, piled one upon the other, with one blow of his hand. You have seen what he can do with his foot.'

Bond took a deep draught of the delicious claret. 'All this must be rather hard on your furniture.'

Goldfinger shrugged. 'I have no more use for this house. I thought a demonstration would amuse you. I hope you agree that Oddjob earned his cat.' The X-ray eyes blazed briefly across the table.

'Does he train on cats?'

'He regards them as a great delicacy. He acquired the taste during a famine in his country when he was young.'

Bond thought it was time to delve rather more deeply. 'Why do you need such a man? He can't be very good company.'

'Mr Bond–' Goldfinger snapped his fingers for the two servants–'it happens that I am a rich man, a very rich man, and the richer the man the more he needs protection. The ordinary bodyguard or detective is usually a retired policeman. Such men are valueless. Their reactions are slow, their methods old-fashioned, and they are open to bribery. Moreover, they have a respect for human life. That is no good if I wish to stay alive. The Koreans have no such feelings. That is why the Japanese employed them as guards for their prison camps during the war. They are the cruellest, most ruthless people in the world. My own staff are hand picked for these qualities. They have served me well. I have no complaints. Nor have they. They are well paid and well fed and housed. When they want women, street women are brought down from London, well remunerated for their services and sent back. The women are not much to look at, but they are white and that is all the Koreans ask–to submit the white race to the grossest indignities. There are sometimes accidents but–' the pale eyes gazed blankly down the table–'money is an effective winding-sheet.'

Bond smiled.

'You like the aphorism? It is my own.'

An excellent cheese soufflé came and was followed by coffee. They ate in silence, both apparently comfortable and relaxed by these confidences. Bond certainly was. Goldfinger, obviously by design, was letting his hair down–not far, not farther than his shoulders, but he was showing Bond one of his private faces, presumably the one to which he thought Bond would respond–the ruthlessly efficient, cold-blooded tycoon. Perhaps, after all, Bond's spying in the house, which Goldfinger must at least presume, had revealed something about Bond that Goldfinger was pleased to know–that Bond had a crooked side to him, that he wasn't 'a gentleman' in more than appearance. Now there should be more probing and then, with luck, the proposition would follow.

Bond sat back and lit a cigarette. He said, 'That's a beautiful car you've got. Must be about the last of the series. About 1925, wasn't it–two blocks of three cylinders with two plugs for each cylinder, one set fired from the mag. and the other from the coil?'

'You are correct. But in other respects I have had to introduce some modifications. I have added five leaves to the springs and fitted disc brakes to the rear wheels to increase the braking power. The Servo-operated front-wheel brakes were not sufficient.'

'Oh. Why not? The top speed wouldn't be more than fifty. The body can't be all that heavy.'

Goldfinger raised his eyebrows. 'You think not? One ton of armour plating and armour-plated glass make a big difference.'

Bond smiled. 'Ah! I see. You certainly do take good care of yourself. But how does that work flying the Channel? Doesn't the car go through the floor of the plane?'

'I take a plane to myself. The Silver City company knows the car. It is a regular routine, twice a year.'

'Just touring round Europe?'

'A golfing holiday.'

'Great fun. Always wanted to do it myself.'

Goldfinger didn't take the bait. 'You can afford to now.'

Bond smiled. 'Oh, that extra ten thousand dollars. But I may need that if I decide to move to Canada.'

'You think you could make money there? Do you want to make a lot of money?'

Bond's voice was eager. 'Very much. There's no other point in working.'

'Unfortunately most ways of making big money take a long time. By the time one has made the money one is too old to enjoy it.'

'That's the trouble. I'm always on the look-out for short-cuts. You won't find them here. Taxation's too heavy.'

'Quite. And the laws are strict.'

'Yes. I found that out.'

'Indeed?'

'Got on the fringe of the heroin racket. Only just got out without burning my fingers. Of course this'll go no further?'

Goldfinger shrugged his shoulders. 'Mr Bond, someone said that "law is the crystallized prejudices of the community". I agree with that definition. It happens to apply most strongly to the traffic in drugs. Even if it didn't, I am not concerned with assisting the police.'

'Well, it was like this . . .' Bond launched into the story of the Mexican traffic, swapping roles with Blackwell. He ended up, 'I was lucky to get away with it, but it didn't make me particularly popular with Universal Export.'

'I daresay not. An interesting story. You seem to have shown resource. You are not tempted to continue in the same line of business?'

Bond shrugged his shoulders. 'A bit too tricky. To judge by this Mexican, the big men in the business aren't quite big enough when it comes to the pinch. When things got tough he didn't fight back–except with his mouth.'

'Well, Mr Bond,' Goldfinger got up from the table and Bond followed suit. 'It's been an interesting evening. I don't know that I would go back into heroin. There are safer ways of making big money. You want to be certain that the odds are right and then you should hazard everything. Doubling one's money isn't easy and the chances don't occur frequently. You would like to hear another of my aphorisms?'

'Yes.'

'Well, Mr Bond,' Goldfinger gave the rich man's thin smile. 'The safest way to double your money is fold it twice and put it in your pocket.'

Bond, the bank clerk harkening to the bank manager, smiled dutifully but made no comment. This just wasn't good enough. He was getting nowhere. But instinct told him not to put his foot down on the accelerator.

They went back into the hall. Bond held out his hand. 'Well, many thanks for the excellent dinner. Time I went and got some sleep. Perhaps we shall run into each other again some day.'

Goldfinger pressed Bond's hand briefly and pushed it away from him. It was another mannerism of the millionaire subconsciously afraid of 'the touch'. He looked hard at Bond. He said enigmatically, 'I shouldn't be at all surprised, Mr Bond.'

On his way across the Isle of Thanet in the moonlight, Bond turned the phrase over and over in his mind. He undressed and got into bed thinking of it, unable to guess its significance. It would mean that Goldfinger intended to get in touch with Bond, or it could mean that Bond must try and keep in touch with Goldfinger. Heads the former, tails the latter. Bond got out of bed and took a coin from the dressing-table and tossed it. It came down tails. So it was up to him to keep close to Goldfinger!

So be it. But his cover would have to be pretty darn good the next time they 'ran into' each other. Bond got back into bed and was instantly asleep.

Chapter Twelve

Long Tail on a Ghost

Punctually at nine the next morning Bond got on to the Chief of Staff: 'James here. I've had a look at the property. Been all over it. Had dinner last night with the owner. I can say pretty well for certain that the managing director's view is right. Something definitely wrong about the property. Not enough facts to send you a surveyor's report. Owner's going abroad tomorrow, flying from Ferryfield. Wish I knew his departure time. Like to have another sight of his Rolls. Thought I'd make him a present of a portable wireless set. I'll be going over a bit later in the day. Could you get Miss Ponsonby to book me? Destination unknown for the present. I'll be keeping in touch. Anything your end?'

'How did the game of golf go?'

'I won.'

There was a chuckle at the other end. 'Thought you had. Pretty big stakes, weren't they?'

'How did you know?'

'Had Mr Scotland on last night. Said he'd had a tip on the telephone that someone of your name was in possession of a large amount of undeclared dollars. Had we got such a person and was it true? Chap wasn't very senior and didn't know about Universal. Told him to have a word with the Commissioner and we got an apology this morning about the same time as your secretary found an envelope containing ten thousand dollars in your mail! Pretty sly of your man, wasn't it?'

Bond smiled. Typical of Goldfinger to have thought of a way of getting him into trouble over the dollars. Probably made the call to Scotland Yard directly after the game. He had wanted to show Bond that if you gave

Goldfinger a knock you'd get at least a thorn in your hand. But the Universal Export cover seemed to have stuck. Bond said, 'That's pretty hot! The twister! You might tell the managing director that this time it goes to the White Cross. Can you fix the other things?'

'Of course. Call you back in a few minutes. But watch your step abroad and call us at once if you get bored and need company. So long.'

''Bye.' Bond put down the receiver. He got up and set about packing his bag. He could see the scene in the Chief of Staff's office as the conversation was played back off the tape while the Chief of Staff translated the call to Miss Moneypenny. 'Says he agrees that Goldfinger is up to something big but he can't make out what. G is flying this morning with his Rolls from Ferryfield. 007 wants to follow. (Let's say two hours later to let G get well away on the other side. Fix the reservation, would you?) He wants us to have a word with Customs so that he can take a good look at the Rolls and plant a Homer in the boot. (Fix that too, please.) He'll keep in touch through stations in case he needs help . . .'

And so forth. It was an efficient machine. Bond finished packing and, when the London call came giving him his various clearances, he went downstairs, paid his bill and got quickly out of Ramsgate on to the Canterbury road.

London had said that Goldfinger was booked on a special flight leaving at twelve. Bond got to Ferryfield by eleven, made himself known to the Chief Passport Control and the Customs officers who were expecting him, had his car taken out of sight into an empty hangar and sat and smoked and talked minor shop with the passport men. They thought he was from Scotland Yard. He let them go on thinking it. No, he said. Goldfinger was all right. It was possible that one of his servants was trying to smuggle something out of the country. Rather confidential. If Bond could just be left alone with the car for ten minutes? He wanted to have a look at the tool kit. Would the Customs give the rest of the Rolls their Grade A going over for hidden compartments? They'd be glad to do so.

At eleven-forty-five one of the Customs men put his head round the door. He winked at Bond. 'Coming in now. Chauffeur on board. Going to ask both to board the plane before the car. Tell them it's something to do with the weight distribution. Not so phoney as it sounds. We know this old crate. She's armour-plated. Weighs about three tons. Call you when we're ready.'

'Thanks.' The room emptied. Bond took the fragile little parcel out of his pocket. It contained a dry-cell battery wired to a small vacuum tube. He ran his eye over the wiring and put the apparatus back in his coat pocket and waited.

At eleven-fifty-five the door opened. The officer beckoned. 'No trouble. They're on the plane.'

The huge gleaming Silver Ghost stood in the Customs bay out of sight of the plane. The only other car was a dove-grey Triumph TR3 convertible with its hood down. Bond went to the back of the Rolls. The Customs men had unscrewed the plate of the spare tool compartment. Bond pulled out the tray of tools and made a show of minutely examining them and the tray. He knelt down. Under cover of rummaging at the sides of the compartment, he slipped the battery and tube into the back of it. He replaced the tool tray. It fitted all right. He stood up and brushed his hands together. 'Negative,' he said to the Customs officer.

The officer fitted the plate on and screwed it down with the square key. He stood up. 'Nothing funny about the chassis or the bodywork. Plenty of room in the frame and upholstery but we couldn't get at them without doing a major job. All right to go?'

'Yes, and thanks.' Bond walked back into the office. He heard the quick solid whine of the old self-starter. A minute later, the car came out of the bay and idled superbly over to the loading ramp. Bond stood at the back of the office and watched it being eased up the ramp. The big jaws of the Bristol Freighter clanged shut. The chocks were jerked away and the dispatcher raised a thumb. The two engines coughed heavily and fired and the great silver dragonfly trundled off towards the runway.

When the plane was on the runway, Bond walked round to his car and climbed into the driver's seat. He pressed a switch under the dash. There was a moment's silence, then a loud harsh howl came from the hidden loud-speaker. Bond turned a knob. The howl diminished to a deep drone. Bond waited until he heard the Bristol take off. As the plane rose and made for the coast the drone diminished. In five minutes it had gone. Bond tuned the set and picked it up again. He followed it for five minutes as the plane made off across the Channel and then switched the set off. He motored round to the Customs bay, told the A.A. that he would be back at one-thirty for the two o'clock flight, and drove slowly off towards a pub he knew in Rye. From now on, so long as he kept within about a hundred miles of the Rolls, the Homer, the rough radio transmitter he had slipped into its tool compartment, would keep contact with Bond's receiver. All he had to do was watch the decibels and not allow the noise to fade. It was a simple form of direction finding which allowed one car to put a 'long tail' on another and keep in touch without any danger of being spotted. On the other side of the Channel, Bond would have to discover the road Goldfinger had taken out of Le Touquet, get well within range and close up near big towns or wherever there was a major fork or crossroads. Sometimes Bond would make a wrong decision and have to do some fast motoring to catch up again. The D.B.III would look after that. It was going to be fun playing hare and hounds across Europe. The sun was shining out of a clear sky. Bond felt a moment's sharp thrill down his spine. He smiled to himself, a hard, cold, cruel smile. Goldfinger, he thought, for the first time in your life you're in trouble–bad trouble.

There is always an *agent cycliste* at the dangerous crossroads where Le Touquet's quiet N38 meets the oily turbulence of the major N1. Yes, certainly he had seen the Rolls. One could not fail to remark it. A real aristocrat of a car. To the right, monsieur, towards Abbeville. He will be an hour ahead, but with that *bolide* of yours . . . !

As soon as Bond had cleared his papers at the airport, the Homer had picked up the drone of the Rolls. But it was impossible to tell if Goldfinger was heading north–for the Low Countries or Austria or Germany–or if he was off to the south. For that sort of fix you needed two radio cars to get a bearing. Bond raised a hand to the agent and gave his engine the gun. He would have to close up fast. Goldfinger would be through Abbeville and would already have taken the major fork on to N1 for Paris or N28 for Rouen. A lot of time and distance would be wasted if Bond made the wrong guess.

Bond swept along the badly cambered road. He took no chances but covered the forty-three kilometres to Abbeville in a quarter of an hour. The drone of the Homer was loud. Goldfinger couldn't be more than twenty miles ahead. But which way at the fork? On a guess Bond took the Paris road. He beat the car along. For a time there was little change in the voice of the Homer. Bond could be right or wrong. Then, imperceptibly, the drone began to fade. Blast! Turn back or press on fast and take one of the secondary roads across to Rouen and catch up with him there? Bond hated turning back. Ten kilometres short of Beauvais he turned right. For a time it was bad going but then he was on to the fast N30 and could afford to drift into Rouen, led on by the beckoning voice of his pick-up. He stopped on the outskirts of the town and listened with one ear while consulting his Michelin. By the waxing drone he could tell that he had got ahead of Goldfinger. But now there was another vital fork, not quite so easy to retrieve if Bond guessed wrong again. Either Goldfinger would take the Alençon–Le Mans–Tours route to the south, or he meant to move south-east, missing Paris, by way of Evreux, Chartres and Orleans. Bond couldn't afford to get closer to the centre of Rouen and perhaps catch a glimpse of the Rolls and of the way it would take. He would have to wait until the Homer went on the wane and then make his own guess.

It was a quarter of an hour later before Bond could be sure that the Rolls was well past. This time he again took the left leg of the fork. He thrust the pedal into the floor and hurried. Yes. This time the drone was merging into a howl. Bond was on the track. He slowed to forty, tuned down his receiver to a whisper and idled along, wondering where Goldfinger was heading for.

Five o'clock, six, seven. The sun set in Bond's driving mirror and still the Rolls sped on. They were through Dreux and Chartres and on to the long straight fifty-mile stretch into Orleans. If that was to be the night stop the Rolls wouldn't have done badly at all–over two hundred and fifty miles in something over six hours. Goldfinger was certainly no slouch when it came to motoring. He must be keeping the old Silver Ghost at maximum outside the towns. Bond began to close up.

There were rear-lights ahead–dim ones. Bond had his fog lights on. He switched on the Marchals. It was some little sports car. Bond closed up. M.G.? Triumph? Austin Healey? It was a pale grey Triumph two-seater with the hood up. Bond blinked his lights and swept past. Now there was the glare of another car ahead. Bond dowsed his headlamps and drove on the fogs. The other car was a mile down the road. Bond crept up on it. At a quarter of a mile, he flashed the Marchals on and off for a quick look. Yes, it was the Rolls. Bond dropped back to a mile and stayed there, vaguely noticing the dim lights of the TR3 in his mirror. On the outskirts of Orleans, Bond pulled into the side of the road. The Triumph growled casually past.

Bond had never cared for Orleans. It was a priest and myth ridden town without charm or gaiety. It was content to live off Joan of Arc and give the visitor a hard, holy glare while it took his money. Bond consulted his Michelin. Goldfinger would stop at five-star hotels and eat fillets of sole and roast chicken. It would be the Arcades for him–perhaps the Moderne. Bond would have liked to stay outside the town and sleep on the banks of the Loire in the excellent Auberge de la Montespan, his belly full of *quenelles de brochet*. He would have to stick closer to his fox. He decided on the Hôtel de la Gare and dinner at the station buffet.

When in doubt, Bond always chose the station hotels. They were adequate, there was plenty of room to park the car and it was better than even chances that the Buffet de la Gare would be excellent. And at the station one could hear the heart-beat of the town. The night-sounds of the trains were full of its tragedy and romance.

The drone on the receiver had stayed constant for ten minutes. Bond noted his way to the three hotels and cautiously crept into the town. He went down to the river and along the lighted *quais*. He had been right. The Rolls was outside the Arcades. Bond turned back into the town and made for the station.

The Hôtel de la Gare was all he had expected–cheap, old-fashioned, solidly comfortable. Bond had a hot bath, went back to his car to make sure the Rolls hadn't moved, and walked into the station restaurant and ate one of his favourite meals–two *œufs cocotte à la crème*, a large *sole meunière* (Orleans was close enough to the sea. The fish of the Loire are inclined to be muddy) and an adequate Camembert. He drank a well-iced pint of Rosé d'Anjou and had a Hennessy's Three Star with his coffee. At ten-thirty he left the restaurant, checked on the Rolls and walked the virtuous streets for an hour. One more check on the Rolls and bed.

At six o'clock the next morning the Rolls hadn't moved. Bond paid his bill, had a *café complet*–with a double ration of coffee–at the station, motored down to the *quais* and backed his car up a side street. This time he could not afford to make a mistake. Goldfinger would either cross the river and head south to join N7 for the Riviera, or he would follow the north bank of the Loire, also perhaps for the Riviera, but also on the route for Switzerland and Italy. Bond got out of the car and lounged against the parapet of the river wall, watching between the trunks of the plane trees. At eight-thirty, two small figures came out of the Arcades. The Rolls moved off. Bond watched it follow the *quais* until it was out of sight, then he got behind the wheel of the Aston Martin and set off in pursuit.

Bond motored comfortably along the Loire in the early summer sunshine. This was one of his favourite corners of the world. In May, with the fruit trees burning white and the soft wide river still big with the winter rains, the valley was green and young and dressed for love. He was thinking this when, before Châteauneuf, there was a shrill scream from twin Bosch horns and the little Triumph tore past. The hood was down. There was the blur of a pretty face hidden by white motoring goggles with dark blue lenses. Although Bond only saw the edge of a profile–a slash of red mouth and the fluttering edge of black hair under a pink handkerchief with white spots, he knew she was pretty from the way she held her head. There was the authority of someone who is used to being admired, combined with the self-consciousness of a girl driving alone and passing a man in a smart car.

Bond thought: That *would* happen today! The Loire is dressed for just that–chasing that girl until you run her to ground at lunch-time, the contact at the empty restaurant by the river, out in the garden under the vine trellis. The *friture* and the ice-cold Vouvray, the cautious sniffing at each other and then the two cars motoring on in convoy until that evening, well down to the south, there would be the place they had agreed on at lunch–olive trees, crickets singing in the indigo dusk, the discovery that they liked each other and that their destinations could wait. Then, next day ('No, not tonight. I don't know you well enough, and besides I'm tired') they would leave her car in the hotel garage and go off in his at a tangent, slowly, knowing there was no hurry for anything, driving to the west, away from the big roads. What was that place he had always wanted to go to, simply because of the name? Yes, Entre Deux Seins, a village near Les Baux. Perhaps there wasn't even an inn there. Well, then they would go on to Les Baux itself, at the Bouches du Rhône on the edge of the Camargue. There they would take adjoining rooms (not a double room, it would be too early for that) in the fabulous Baumanière, the only hotel-restaurant in France with Michelin's supreme accolade. They would eat the *gratin de langouste* and perhaps, because it was traditional on such a night, drink champagne. And then . . .

Bond smiled at his story and at the dots that ended it. Not today. Today you're working. Today is for Goldfinger, not for love. Today the only scent you may smell is Goldfinger's expensive after-shave lotion, not . . . what would she use? English girls made mistakes about scent. He hoped it would be something slight and clean. Balmain's Vent Vert perhaps, or Caron's Muguet. Bond tuned up his receiver for reassurance, then hushed it and motored on, relaxed, playing with his thoughts of the girl, filling in the details. Of course he might meet up with her again. They seemed to be keeping pretty close company. She must have spent the night in Orleans. Where? What a waste. But wait a minute! Suddenly Bond woke up from his day-dreaming. The open hood reminded him. He'd seen that Triumph before. It had been at Ferryfield, must have taken the flight after Goldfinger. It was true he hadn't seen the girl or noted the registration number, but surely it was the same. If so, for her to be still on Goldfinger's tail after three hundred miles was more than coincidence. And she had been driving with dimmed lights the night before! Here, what's going on?

Bond stepped on the accelerator. He was approaching Nevers. He'd anyway have to close up for the next big turning. He would kill two birds with one stone and also see what the girl was up to. If she was keeping station somewhere between him and Goldfinger there would have to be some furious thinking. And it would be a blasted nuisance. It was hard enough keeping up with Goldfinger. With another tail sandwiched between them, it would become hellish difficult.

She was still there, perhaps two miles behind the Rolls, keeping well back. As soon as he caught sight of her little glittering rump (as he described it to himself) Bond slowed. Well, well! Who *was* she? What the hell was all this about? Bond motored on, his face morose and thoughtful.

The little convoy kept on, still following the wide black sheen of N7 that runs like a thick, dangerous nerve down through the heart of France. But at Moulins Bond nearly lost the scent. He had to double back quickly and get on to N73. Goldfinger had turned at right angles and was now making for Lyons and Italy, or for Mâcon and Geneva. Bond had to do some fast motoring and then was only just in time to avoid running into trouble. He had not worried much about the pitch of the Homer. He had counted on a sight of the Triumph to slow him down. Suddenly he realized that the drone was becoming a howl. If he hadn't braked hard down from the ninety he was doing, he would have been on top of the Rolls. As it was, he was barely creeping along when he came over a rise and saw the big yellow car stopped by the wayside a mile ahead. There was a blessed cart-track. Bond swerved into it and stopped under cover of a low hedge. He took a small pair of binoculars out of the glove compartment, got out of the car and walked back.

Yes, damn it! Goldfinger was sitting below a small bridge on the bank of a stream. He was wearing a white dust coat and white linen driving helmet in the style of German tourists. He was eating, having a picnic. The sight made Bond hungry. What about his own lunch? He examined the Rolls. Through the rear window he could see part of the Korean's black shape in the front seat. There was no sign of the Triumph. If the girl had still been on Goldfinger's tail she would have had no warning. She would have just kept her head down and stepped on the gas. Now she would be somewhere ahead, waiting in ambush for the Rolls to come by. Or would she? Perhaps Bond's imagination had run away with him. She was probably on her way to the Italian lakes to join an aunt, some friends, a lover.

Now Goldfinger was on his feet. Tidy man. That's right, pick up the scraps of paper and tuck them away carefully under the bridge. Why not throw them in the stream? Suddenly Bond's jaws tightened. What did those actions of Goldfinger remind him of? Was Bond romancing again, or was the bridge a post box? Had Goldfinger been instructed to leave something, one of his bars of gold, under this particular bridge? France, Switzerland, Italy. It was convenient for all of them–the Communist cell in Lyons for instance, one of the strongest in France. And this was a good place to use with a clear field of view up and down the road.

Goldfinger scrambled up the bank. Bond drew back under cover. He heard the distant grind of the old self-starter. He cautiously watched the Rolls until it had disappeared.

It was a pretty bridge over a pretty stream. It had a survey number set in the arch–79/6–the sixth bridge from some town on N79. Easy to find. Bond got quickly out of the car and slid down the shallow bank. It was dark and cool under the arch. There were the shadows of fish in the slow, clear, pebbled water. Bond searched the edge of the masonry near the grass verge. Exactly in the centre, below the road, there was a patch of thick grass against the wall. Bond parted the grass. There was a sprinkling of freshly turned earth. Bond dug with his fingers.

There was only one. It was smooth to the touch and brick-shaped. It needed some strength to lift it. Bond brushed the earth off the dull yellow metal and wrapped the heavy bar in his handkerchief. He held the bar under his coat and climbed back up the bank on to the empty road.

Chapter Thirteen

'If You Touch Me There . . .'

Bond felt pleased with himself. A whole lot of people were going to get very angry with Goldfinger. You can do a lot of dirty work with twenty thousand pounds. Now plans would have to be altered, conspiracies postponed, perhaps even lives saved. And, if it ever got to an inquiry by SMERSH, which was unlikely as they were the sort of realistic people who cut their losses, it could only be assumed that some sheltering tramp had found the gold bar.

Bond lifted the secret flap under the passenger seat and slipped the bar inside. Dangerous stuff. He would have to contact the next station of the Service and hand it over to them. They would get it back to London in the Embassy bag. Bond would have to report this quickly. It confirmed a lot. M might even want to warn the Deuxième and have the bridge watched to see who came. But Bond hoped that would not happen. He didn't want a scare started just when he was getting closer to Goldfinger. He wanted the skies over Goldfinger to be blue and clear.

Bond got moving. Now there were other things to think about. He must catch up with the Rolls before Mâcon and get the next fork, to Geneva or Lyons, right. He must solve the problem of the girl and if possible get her off the road. Pretty or not, she was confusing the issue. And he must stop and buy himself something to eat and drink. It was one o'clock and the sight of Goldfinger eating had made him hungry. And it was time to fill up and check the water and oil.

The drone of the Homer grew louder. He was in the outskirts of Mâcon. He must close up and take the risk of being spotted. The busy traffic would hide his low-slung car. It was vital to know if the Rolls crossed the Saône for the Bourg road or if it turned right at the bridge and joined the N6 for Lyons. Far down the Rue Rambuteau there was a glimpse of yellow. Over the railway bridge and through the little square. The high yellow box kept on towards the river. Bond watched the passers-by turn their heads to follow the gleaming Rolls. The river. Would Goldfinger turn right or keep on across the bridge? The Rolls kept straight on. So it was Switzerland! Bond followed over into the suburb of St Laurent. Now for a butcher and a baker and a wine shop. A hundred yards ahead the golden head of a calf hung over the pavement. Bond glanced in his driving mirror. Well, well! The little Triumph was only feet away from his tail. How long had she been there? Bond had been so intent on following the Rolls that he hadn't glanced back since entering the town. She must have been hiding up a side street. So! Now coincidence was certainly out. Something must be done. Sorry, sweetheart. I've got to mess you up. I'll be as gentle as I can. Hold tight. Bond stopped abruptly in front of the butcher's shop. He banged the gears into reverse. There was a sickening scrunch and tinkle. Bond switched off his engine and got out.

He walked round to the back of the car. The girl, her face tense with anger, had one beautiful silken leg on the road. There was an indiscreet glimpse of white thigh. The girl stripped off her goggles and stood, legs braced and arms akimbo. The beautiful mouth was taut with anger.

The Aston Martin's rear bumper was locked into the wreckage of the Triumph's lamps and radiator grille. Bond said amiably, 'If you touch me there again you'll have to marry me.'

The words were hardly out of his mouth before the open palm cracked across his face. Bond put up a hand and rubbed his cheek. Now there was quite a crowd. There was a murmur of approval and ribaldry. 'Allez y la gosse! Maintenant le knock-out!'

The girl's rage had not dissipated with the blow. 'You bloody fool! What the hell do you think you're doing?'

Bond thought: if only pretty girls were always angry they would be beautiful. He said, 'Your brakes can't be up to much.'

'*My* brakes! What the hell do you mean? You reversed into me.'

'Gears slipped. I didn't know you were so close.' It was time to calm her down. 'I'm most frightfully sorry. I'll pay for all the repairs and everything. It really is bad luck. Let's see what the damage is. Try and back away. Doesn't look as if our bumpers have over-ridden.' Bond put a foot on the Triumph's bumpers and rocked.

'Don't you dare touch my car! Leave it alone.' Angrily the girl climbed back into the driver's seat. She pressed the self-starter. The engine fired. Metal clanged under the bonnet. She switched off and leant out. 'There you are, you idiot! You've smashed the fan.'

Bond had hoped he had. He got into his own car and eased it away from the Triumph. Bits of Triumph, released by Bond's bumper, tinkled on to the road. He got out again. The crowd had thinned. There was a man in a mechanic's overalls. He volunteered to call a breakdown van and went off to do so. Bond walked over to the Triumph. The girl had got out and was waiting for him. Her expression had changed. Now she was more composed. Bond noticed that her eyes, which were dark blue, watched his face carefully.

Bond said, 'It really won't be too bad. Probably knocked the fan out of alignment. They'll put temporary headlamps in the sockets and straighten up the chrome. You'll be off again by tomorrow morning. Now,' Bond reached into his pocket for his notecase, 'this is maddening for you and I'll certainly take all the blame. Here's a hundred thousand francs to cover the damage and your expenses for the night and telephoning your friends and so on. Please take it and call it quits. I'd love to stay here and see you get on the road all right tomorrow morning. But I've got an appointment this evening and I've simply got to make it.'

'No.' The one word was cool, definite. The girl put her hands behind her back and waited.

'But . . .' What was it she wanted, the police? Have him charged with dangerous driving?

'I've got an appointment this evening too. I've got to make it. I've got to get to Geneva. Will you please take me there? It's not far. Only about a hundred miles. We could do it in two hours in that.' She gestured at the D.B.III. 'Will you? Please?'

There was a desperate urgency in the voice. No cajolery, no threats, only a blazing need.

For the first time Bond examined her as more than a pretty girl who perhaps–they were the only explanations Bond had found to fit the facts–wanted to be picked up by Goldfinger or had a blackmail on him. But she didn't look capable of either of these things. There was too much character in the face, too much candour. And she wasn't wearing the uniform of a seductress. She wore a white, rather masculine cut, heavy silk shirt. It was open at the neck, but it would button up to a narrow military collar. The shirt had long wide sleeves gathered at the wrists. The girl's nails were unpainted and her only piece of jewellery was a gold ring on her engagement finger (true or false?). She wore a very wide black stitched leather belt with double brass buckles. It rose at the back to give some of the support of a racing driver's corset belt. Her short skirt was charcoal-grey and pleated. Her shoes were expensive-looking black sandals which would be comfortable and cool for driving. The only touch of colour was the pink handkerchief which she had taken off her head and now held by her side with the white goggles. It all looked very attractive. But the get-up reminded Bond more of an equipment than a young girl's dress. There was something faintly mannish and open-air about the whole of her behaviour and appearance. She might, thought Bond, be a member of the English women's ski team, or spend a lot of her time in England hunting or show-jumping.

Although she was a very beautiful girl she was the kind who leaves her beauty alone. She had made no attempt to pat her hair into place. As a result, it looked as a girl's hair should look–untidy, with bits that strayed and a rather crooked parting. It provided the contrast of an uneven, jagged dark frame for the pale symmetry of the face, the main features of which were blue eyes under dark brows, a desirable mouth, and an air of determination and independence that came from the high cheek-bones and the fine line of the jaw. There was the same air of self-reliance in her figure. She held her body proudly–her fine breasts out-thrown and unashamed under the taut silk. Her stance, with feet slightly parted and hands behind her back, was a mixture of provocation and challenge.

The whole picture seemed to say, 'Now then, you handsome bastard, don't think you can "little woman" me. You've got me into this mess and, by God, you're going to get me out! You may be attractive, but I've got my life to run, and I know where I'm going.'

Bond weighed her request. How much of a nuisance would she be? How soon could he get rid of her and get on with his business? Was there any security risk? Against the disadvantages, there was his curiosity about her and what she was up to, the memory of the fable he had spun round her and which had now taken its first step towards realization, and, finally, the damsel-in-distress business–any woman's appeal for help.

Bond said curtly, 'I'll be glad to take you to Geneva. Now then,' he opened up the back of the Aston Martin, 'let's get your things in. While I fix up about the garage here's some money. Please buy us lunch–anything you like for yourself. For me, six inches of Lyon sausage, a loaf of bread, butter, and half a litre of Mâcon with the cork pulled.'

Their eyes met and exchanged a flurry of masculine/feminine master/slave signals. The girl took the money. 'Thank you. I'll get the same things for myself.' She went to the boot of the Triumph and unlocked it. 'No, don't bother. I can manage these.' She hauled out a bag of golf clubs with the cover zipped shut and a small, expensive looking suitcase. She brought them over to the Aston Martin and, rejecting Bond's offer of help, fitted them in alongside Bond's suitcase. She watched him lock the back of the car and went back to the Triumph. She took out a wide, black-stitched leather shoulder bag.

Bond said, 'What name and address shall I give?'

'What?'

Bond repeated his question, wondering if she would lie about the name or the address, or both.

She said, 'I shall be moving about. Better say the Bergues at Geneva. The name's Soames. Miss Tilly Soames.' There was no hesitation. She went into the butcher's shop.

A quarter of an hour later they were on their way.

The girl sat upright and kept her eyes on the road. The drone on the Homer was faint. The Rolls must have gained fifty miles. Bond hurried. They flashed through Bourg and over the river at Pont d'Ain. Now they were in the foothills of the Jura and there were the S-bends of N84. Bond went at them as if he was competing in the Alpine Trials. After the girl had swayed against him twice she kept her hand on the handle on the dash and rode with the car as if she were his spare driver. Once, after a particularly sharp dry skid that almost took them over the side, Bond glanced at her profile. Her lips were parted and her nostrils slightly flared. The eyes were alight. She was enjoying herself.

They came to the top of the pass and there was the run down towards the Swiss frontier. Now the Homer was sending out a steady howl. Bond thought, I must take it easy or we shall be running into them at the Customs. He put his hand under the dash and tuned the noise down. He pulled in to the side of the road. They sat in the car and ate a polite but almost silent picnic, neither making any attempt at conversation, both, it seemed, with other things on their minds. After ten minutes, Bond got going again. He sat relaxed, motoring easily down the curving road through the young whispering pines.

The girl said, 'What's the noise?'

'Magneto whine. Gets worse when I hurry. Started at Orleans. Have to get it fixed tonight.'

She seemed satisfied with this mumbo-jumbo. She said diffidently, 'Where are you heading for? I hope I haven't taken you very far out of your way.'

Bond said in a friendly voice, 'Not at all. As a matter of fact, I'm going to Geneva too. But I may not stop there tonight. May have to get on. Depends on my meeting. How long will you be there?'

'I don't know. I'm playing golf. There's the Swiss Women's Open Championship at Divonne. I'm not really that class, but I thought it would be good for me to try. Then I was going to play on some of the other courses.'

Fair enough. No reason why it shouldn't be true. But Bond was certain it wasn't the whole truth. He said, 'Do you play a lot of golf? What's your home course?'

'Quite a lot. Temple.'

It had been an obvious question. Was the answer true, or just the first golf course she had thought of? 'Do you live near there?'

'I've got an aunt who lives at Henley. What are you doing in Switzerland. Holiday?'

'Business. Import and Export.'

'Oh.'

Bond smiled to himself. It was a stage conversation. The voices were polite stage voices. He could see the scene, beloved of the English theatre–the drawing-room, sunshine on hollyhocks outside french windows, the couple sitting on the sofa, on the edge of it, she pouring out the tea. 'Do you take sugar?'

They came out into the foothills. There was a long straight stretch of road and in the distance the small group of buildings of the French Customs.

The girl gave him no chance to get a glimpse of her passport. As soon as the car stopped she said something about tidying up and disappeared into the 'Dames'. Bond had gone through the Controle and was dealing with the triptyque when she reappeared, her passport stamped. At the Swiss Customs she chose the excuse of getting something out of her suitcase. Bond hadn't got time to hang about and call her bluff.

Bond hurried on into Geneva and pulled up at the imposing entrance of the Bergues. The *baggagiste* took her suitcase and golf clubs. They stood together on the steps. She held out her hand. 'Goodbye.' There was no melting of the candid blue eyes. 'And thank you. You drive beautifully.' Her mouth smiled. 'I'm surprised you got into the wrong gear at Mâcon.'

Bond shrugged. 'It doesn't often happen. I'm glad I did. If I can get my business finished, perhaps we could meet again.'

'That would be nice.' The tone of voice said it wouldn't be. The girl turned and went in through the swing-doors.

Bond ran down to his car. To hell with her! Now to pick up Goldfinger. Then to the little office on the Quai Wilson. He tuned the Homer and waited a couple of minutes. Goldfinger was close, but moving away. He could either be following the right or the left bank of the lake. From the pitch of the Homer, he was at least a mile outside the town. Which way? To the left towards Lausanne? To the right towards Evian? The D.B.III was already on the left-hand road. Bond decided to follow its nose. He got moving.

Bond caught up with the high yellow silhouette just before Coppet, the tiny lakeside hamlet made famous by Madame de Staël. He hid behind a lorry. At his next reconnaissance the Rolls had disappeared. Bond motored on, watching to the left. At the entrance to the village, big solid iron gates were closing in a high wall. Dust hung in the air. Above the wall was a modest placard. It said, in faded yellow on blue, ENTREPRISES AURIC A.G. The fox had gone to earth!

Bond went on until he found a turning to the left. He followed this until there was a lane which led back through the vineyards to the woods behind Coppet and to the château of Madame de Staël. Bond stopped among the trees. Now he should be directly above the Entreprises Auric. He took his binoculars, got out and followed a foot-path down towards the village. Soon, on his right, was a spiked iron railing. There was rolled barbed wire along its top. A hundred yards lower down the hill the railing merged into a high stone wall. Bond walked slowly back up the path looking for the secret entrance the children of Coppet would have made to get at the chestnut trees. He found it–two bars of the railing widened to allow a small body through. Bond stood on the lower railing with all his weight, widened the gap by another couple of inches and wormed his way through.

Bond walked warily through the trees, watching each step for dead branches. The trees thinned. There were glimpses of a huddle of low buildings behind a small *manoir*. Bond picked the thick trunk of a fir tree and got behind it. Now he was looking down on the buildings. The nearest was about a hundred yards away. There was an open courtyard. In the middle of the courtyard stood the dusty Silver Ghost.

Bond took out the binoculars and examined everything minutely.

The house was a well-proportioned square block of old red brick with a slate roof. It consisted of two storeys and an attic floor. It would probably contain four bedrooms and two principal rooms. The walls were partly covered by a very old wistaria in full bloom. It was an attractive house. In his mind's eye Bond could see the white-painted panelling inside. He smelled the sweet musty sunshiny smell of the rooms. The back door gave on to the wide paved courtyard in which stood the Rolls. The courtyard was open on Bond's side but closed on the other two sides by single-storey corrugated iron workshops. A tall zinc chimney rose from the angle of the two workshops. The chimney was topped by a zinc cowl. On top of the zinc cowl was the revolving square mouth of what looked to Bond like the Decca radar scanner you see on the bridges of most ships. The apparatus whirled steadily round. Bond couldn't imagine what purpose it served on the roof of this little factory among the trees.

Suddenly the silence and immobility of the peaceful scene were broken. It was as if Bond had put a penny in the slot of a diorama on Brighton pier. Somewhere a tinny clock struck five. At the signal, the back door of the house opened and Goldfinger came out, still dressed in his white linen motoring coat, but without the helmet. He was followed by a nondescript, obsequious little man with a tooth-brush moustache and horn-rimmed spectacles. Goldfinger looked pleased. He went up to the Rolls and patted its bonnet. The other man laughed politely. He took a whistle out of his waistcoat pocket and blew it. A door in the right-hand workshop opened and four workmen in blue overalls filed out and walked over to the car. From the open door they had left there came a whirring noise and a heavy engine started up and settled into the rhythmic pant Bond remembered from Reculver.

The four men disposed themselves round the car. At a word from the little man, who was presumably the foreman, they began to take the car to pieces. By the time they had lifted the four doors off their hinges, removed the bonnet cover from the engine and had set about the rivets on one of the mudguards, it was clear that they were methodically stripping the car of its armour plating.

Almost as soon as Bond had come to this conclusion, the black, bowler-hatted figure of Oddjob appeared at the back door of the house and made some sort of a noise at Goldfinger. With a word to the foreman, Goldfinger went indoors and left the workmen to it.

It was time for Bond to get going. He took a last careful look round to fix the geography in his mind and edged back among the trees.

'I am from Universal Export.'

'Oh yes?' Behind the desk there was a reproduction of the Annigoni portrait of the Queen. On the other walls were advertisements for Ferguson tractors and other agricultural machinery. From outside the wide window came the hum of traffic along the Quai Wilson. A steamer hooted. Bond glanced out of the window and watched it ride across the middle distance. It left an enchanted wake across the flawless evening mirror of the lake. Bond looked back into the politely inquiring eyes in the bland, neutral, businessman's face.

'We were hoping to do business with you.'

'What sort of business?'

'Important business.'

The man's face broke into a smile. He said cheerfully, 'It's 007, isn't it? Thought I recognized you. Well now, what can I do for you?' The voice became cautious. 'Only one thing, better make it quick and get along. There's been the hell of a heat on since the Dumont business. They've got me taped–the locals and Redland. All very peaceful of course, but you won't want them sniffing round you.'

'I thought it might be like that. It's only routine. Here,' Bond unbuttoned his shirt and took out the heavy chunk of gold. 'Get that back, would you?

And transmit this when you have a chance.' The man pulled a pad towards him and wrote in shorthand to Bond's dictation.

When the man had finished he put the pad in his pocket. 'Well, well! Pretty hot stuff. Wilco. My routine's at midnight. This'–he indicated the gold–'can go to Berne for the bag. Anything else?'

'Ever heard of the 'Entreprises Auric'' at Coppet? Know what they do?'

'I know what every engineering business in the area does. Have to. Tried to sell them some hand riveters last year. They make metal furniture. Pretty good stuff. The Swiss railways take some of it, and the airlines.'

'Know which airlines?'

The man shrugged. 'I heard they did all the work for Mecca, the big charter line to India. Their terminus is Geneva. They're quite a big competitor with All-India. Mecca's privately owned. Matter of fact, I did hear that Auric & Co. had some money in it. No wonder they've got the contract for the seating.

A slow, grim smile spread across Bond's face. He got up and held out his hand. 'You don't know it, but you've just done a whole jigsaw puzzle in under a minute. Many thanks. Best of luck with the tractor business. Hope we'll meet again one day.'

Out in the street, Bond got quickly into his car and drove along the *quai* to the Bergues. So that was the picture! For two days he'd been trailing a Silver Ghost across Europe. It was an armour-plated Silver Ghost. He'd watched the last bit of plating being riveted on in Kent, and the whole lot being stripped off at Coppet. Those sheets would already be in the furnaces at Coppet, ready to be modelled into seventy chairs for a Mecca Constellation. In a few days' time those chairs would be stripped off the plane in India and replaced with aluminium ones. And Goldfinger would have made what? Half a million pounds? A million?

For the Silver Ghost wasn't silver at all. It was a Golden Ghost–all the two tons of its bodywork. Solid, eighteen-carat, white gold.

Chapter Fourteen

Things that go Thump in the Night

James Bond booked in at the Hôtel des Bergues, took a bath and shower and changed his clothes. He weighed the Walther PPK in his hand and wondered whether he should take it or leave it behind. He decided to leave it. He had no intention of being seen when he went back to the Entreprises Auric. If, by dreadful luck, he was seen, it would spoil everything to get into a fight. He had his story, a poor one, but at least one that would not break his cover. He would have to rely on that. But Bond did choose a particular pair of shoes that were rather heavier than one could expect from their casual build.

At the desk he asked if Miss Soames was in. He was not surprised when the receptionist said they had no Miss Soames staying in the hotel. The only question was whether she had left the hotel when Bond was out of sight or had registered under another name.

Bond motored across the beautiful Pont du Mont Blanc and along the brightly lit *quai* to the Bavaria, a modest Alsatian brasserie that had been the rendezvous of the great in the days of the League of Nations. He sat by the window and drank Enzian washed down with pale Löwenbrau. He thought first about Goldfinger. There was now no doubt what he was up to. He financed a spy network, probably SMERSH, and he made fortunes smuggling gold to India, the country where he could get the biggest premium. After the loss of his Brixham trawler, he had thought out this new way. He first made it known that he had an armoured car. That would only be considered eccentric. Many English bodybuilders exported them. They used to go to Indian rajahs; now they went to oil sheiks and South American presidents. Goldfinger had chosen a Silver Ghost because, with his modifications, the chassis was strong enough, the riveting was already a feature of the bodywork, and there was the largest possible area of metal sheeting. Perhaps Goldfinger had run it abroad once or twice to get Ferryfield used to it. Then, on the next trip, he took off the armour plating in his works at Reculver. He substituted eighteen-carat white gold. Its alloy of nickel and silver would be strong enough. The colour of the metal would not betray him if he got in a smash or if the bodywork were scratched. Then off to Switzerland and to the little factory. The workmen would have been as carefully picked as the ones at Reculver. They would take off the plates and mould them into aircraft seats which would then be upholstered and installed in Mecca Airlines–run presumably by some stooge of Goldfinger's who got a cut on each 'gold run'. On these runs–once, twice, three times a year?–the plane would accept only light freight and a few passengers. At Bombay or Calcutta the plane would need an overhaul, be re-equipped. It would go to the Mecca hangar and have new seats fitted. The old ones, the gold ones, would go to the bullion brokers. Goldfinger would get his sterling credit in Nassau or wherever he chose. He would have made his hundred, or two hundred, per cent profit and could start the cycle all over again, from the 'We Buy Old Gold' shops in Britain to Reculver–Geneva–Bombay.

Yes, thought Bond, gazing out across the glistening, starlit lake, that's how it would be–a top-notch smuggling circuit with a minimum risk and maximum profit. How Goldfinger must smile as he pressed the bulb of the old boa-constrictor horn and swept past the admiring policemen of three countries! He certainly seemed to have the answer–the philosopher's stone, the finger of gold! If he hadn't been such an unpleasant man, if he wasn't doing all this to sustain the trigger finger of SMERSH, Bond would have felt admiration for this monumental trickster whose operations were so big that they worried even the Bank of England. As it was, Bond only wanted to destroy Goldfinger, seize his gold, get him behind bars. Goldfinger's gold-lust was too strong, too ruthless, too dangerous to be allowed the run of the world.

It was eight o'clock. The Enzian, the firewater distilled from gentian that is responsible for Switzerland's chronic alcoholism, was beginning to warm Bond's stomach and melt his tensions. He ordered another double and with it a choucroute and a carafe of Fondant.

And what about the girl, this pretty, authoritarian joker that had suddenly been faced in the deal? What in hell was she about? What about this golf story? Bond got up and went to the telephone booth at the back of the room. He got on to the *Journal de Genève* and through to the sports editor. The man was helpful, but surprised at Bond's question. No. The various championships were of course played in the summer when the other national programmes were finished and it was possible to lure a good foreign entry to Switzerland. It was the same with all other European countries. They liked to bring in as many British and American players as possible. It increased the gates. 'Pas de quoi, monsieur.'

Bond went back to his table and ate his dinner. So much for that. Whoever she was, she was an amateur. No professional would use a cover that could be broken down by one telephone call. It had been in the back of Bond's mind–reluctantly, because he liked the girl and was excited by her–that she could, she just could have been an agent of SMERSH sent to keep an eye on Goldfinger, or Bond or both. She had some of the qualities of a secret agent, the independence, the strength of character, the ability to walk alone. But that idea was out. She hadn't got the training.

Bond ordered a slice of gruyère, pumpernickel and coffee. No, she was an enigma. Bond only prayed that she hadn't got some private plot involving either him or Goldfinger that was going to mess up his own operation.

And his own job was so nearly finished! All he needed was the evidence of his own eyes that the story he had woven round Goldfinger and the Rolls was the truth. One look into the works at Coppet–one grain of white gold dust–and he could be off to Berne that very night and be on to the duty officer over the Embassy scrambler. Then, quietly, discreetly, the Bank of England would freeze Goldfinger's accounts all over the world and perhaps, already tomorrow, the Special Branch of the Swiss police would be knocking on the door of Enterprises Auric. Extradition would follow, Goldfinger would go to Brixton, there would be a quiet, rather complicated case in one of the smuggling courts like Maidstone or Lewes. Goldfinger would get a few years, his naturalization would be revoked and his gold hoard, illegally exported, would trickle back into the vaults below the Bank of England. And SMERSH would gnash its blood-stained teeth and add another page to Bond's bulging zapiska.

Time to go for the last lap. Bond paid his bill and went out and got into his car. He crossed the Rhône and motored slowly along the glittering *quai* through the evening traffic. It was an average night for his purpose. There was a blazing three-quarter moon to see by, but not a breath of wind to hide his approach through the woods to the factory. Well, there was no hurry. They would probably be working through the night. He would have to take it very easily and carefully. The geography of the place and the route he had plotted for himself ran before Bond's eyes like a film while the automatic pilot that is in all good drivers took the car along the wide white highway beside the sleeping lake.

Bond followed his route of the afternoon. When he had turned off the main road he drove on his sidelights. He nosed the car off the lane into a clearing in the woods and switched off the engine. He sat and listened. In the heavy silence there was only a soft ticking from the hot metal under the bonnet and the hasty trip of the dashboard clock. Bond got out, eased the door shut and walked softly down the little path through the trees.

Now he could hear the soft heavy pant of the generator engine . . . thumpah . . . thumpah . . . thumpah. It seemed a watchful, rather threatening noise. Bond reached the gap in the iron bars, slipped through and stood, straining his senses forward through the moon-dappled trees.

THUMPAH . . . THUMPAH . . . THUMPAH. The great iron puffs were on top of him, inside his brain. Bond felt the skin-crawling tickle at the groin that dates from one's first game of hide and seek in the dark. He smiled to himself at the animal danger signal. What primeval chord had been struck by this innocent engine noise coming out of the tall zinc chimney? The breath of a dinosaur in its cave? Bond tightened his muscles and crept forward foot by foot, moving small branches carefully out of his way, placing each step as cautiously as if he was going through a minefield.

The trees were thinning. Soon he would be up with the big sheltering trunk he had used before. He looked for it and then stood frozen, his pulse racing. Below the trunk of his tree, spreadeagled on the ground, was a body.

Bond opened his mouth wide and breathed slowly in and out to release the tension. Softly he wiped his sweating palms down his trousers. He dropped slowly to his hands and knees and stared forward, his eyes widened like camera lenses.

The body under the tree moved, shifted cautiously to a new position. A breath of wind whispered in the tops of the trees. The moonbeams danced quickly across the body and then were still. There was a glimpse of thick black hair, black sweater, narrow black slacks. And something else–a straight gleam of metal along the ground. It began beneath the clump of black hair and ran past the trunk of the trees into the grass.

Bond slowly, wearily bent his head and looked at the ground between his spread hands. It was the girl, Tilly. She was watching the buildings below. She had a rifle–a rifle that must have been among the innocent golf clubs–ready to fire on them. Damn and blast the silly bitch!

Bond slowly relaxed. It didn't matter who she was or what she was up to. He measured the distance, planned each stride–the trajectory of the final spring, left hand to her neck, right to the gun. Now!

Bond's chest skidded over the hump of the buttocks and thudded into the small of the girl's back. The impact emptied the breath out of her with a soft grunt. The fingers of Bond's left hand flew to the throat and found the carotid artery. His right hand was on the waist of the rifle's stock. He prised the fingers away, felt that the safety catch was on and reached the rifle far to one side.

Bond eased the weight of his chest off the girl's back and moved his fingers away from her neck. He closed them softly over her mouth. Beneath him, he felt the body heave, the lungs labouring for breath. She was still out. Carefully Bond gathered the two hands behind the girl's back and held them with his right. Beneath him the buttocks began to squirm. The legs jerked. Bond pinned the legs to the ground with his stomach and thighs, noting the strong muscles bunched under him. Now the breath was rasping through his fingers. Teeth gnawed at his hand. Bond inched carefully forwards along the girl. He got his mouth through her hair to her ear. He whispered urgently, 'Tilly, for Christ's sake. Stay still! This is me, Bond. I'm a friend. This is vital. Something you don't know about. Will you stay still and listen?'

The teeth stopped reaching for his fingers. The body relaxed and lay soft under his. After a time, the head nodded once.

Bond slid off her. He lay beside her, still holding her hands prisoned behind her back. He whispered, 'Get your breath. But tell me, were you after Goldfinger?'

The pale face glanced sideways and away. The girl whispered fiercely into the ground, 'I was going to kill him.'

Some girl Goldfinger had put in the family way. Bond let go her hands. She brought them up and rested her head on them. Her whole body shuddered with exhaustion and released nerves. The shoulders began to shake softly. Bond reached out a hand and smoothed her hair, quietly, rhythmically. His eyes carefully went over the peaceful, unchanged scene below. Unchanged? There was something. The radar thing on the cowl of the chimney. It wasn't going round any more. It had stopped with its oblong mouth pointing in their direction. The fact had no significance for Bond. Now the girl wasn't crying any more. Bond nuzzled his mouth close to her ear. Her hair smelled of jasmine. He whispered, 'Don't worry. I'm after him too. And I'm going to damage him far worse than you could have done. I've been sent after him by London. They want him. What did he do to you?'

She whispered, almost to herself, 'He killed my sister. You knew her–Jill Masterton.'

Bond said fiercely, 'What happened?'

'He has a woman once a month. Jill told me this when she first took the job. He hypnotizes them. Then he–he paints them gold.'

'Christ! Why?'

'I don't know. Jill told me he's mad about gold. I suppose he sort of thinks he's–that sort of possessing gold. You know–marrying it. He gets some Korean servant to paint them. The man has to leave their backbones unpainted. Jill couldn't explain that. I found out it's so they wouldn't die. If their bodies were completely covered with gold paint, the pores of the skin wouldn't bc able to breathe. Then they'd die. Afterwards, they're washed down by the Korean with resin or something. Goldfinger gives them a thousand dollars and sends them away.'

Bond saw the dreadful Oddjob with his pot of gold paint, Goldfinger's eyes gloating over the glistening statue, the fierce possession. 'What happened to Jill?'

'She cabled me to come. She was in an emergency ward in a hospital in Miami. Goldfinger had thrown her out. She was dying. The doctors didn't know what was the matter. She told me what had happened to her–what he had done to her. She died the same night.' The girl's voice was dry–matter of fact. 'When I got back to England I went to Train, the skin specialist. He told me this business about the pores of the skin. It had happened to some cabaret girl who had to pose as a silver statue. He showed me details of the case and the autopsy. Then I knew what had happened to Jill. Goldfinger had had her painted all over. He had murdered her. It must have been out of revenge for–for going with you.' There was a pause. The girl said dully, 'She told me about you. She–she liked you. She told me if ever I met you I was to give you this ring.'

Bond closed his eyes tight, fighting with a wave of mental nausea. More death! More blood on his hands. This time, as the result of a careless gesture, a piece of bravado that had led to twenty-four hours of ecstasy with a beautiful girl who had taken his fancy and, in the end, rather more than his fancy. And this petty sideswipe at Goldfinger's ego had been returned by Goldfinger a thousand, a millionfold. 'She left my employ'–the flat words in the sunshine at Sandwich two days before. How Goldfinger must have enjoyed saying that! Bond's fingernails dug into the palms of his hands. By God, he'd pin this murder on Goldfinger if it was the last act of his life. As for himself . . . ? Bond knew the answer. This death he would not be able to excuse as being part of his job. This death he would have to live with.

The girl was pulling at her finger–at the Claddagh ring, the entwined hands round the gold heart. She put her knucle to her mouth. The ring came off. She held it up for Bond to take. The tiny gold circle, silhouetted against the trunk of the tree, glittered in the moonlight.

The noise in Bond's ear was something between a hiss and a shrill whistle. There was a dry, twanging thud. The aluminium feathers of the steel arrow trembled like a humming bird's wings in front of Bond's eyes. The shaft of the arrow straightened. The gold ring tinkled down the shaft until it reached the bark of the tree.

Slowly, almost incuriously, Bond turned his head.

Ten yards away–half in moonlight, half in shadow–the black melon-headed figure crouched, its legs widely straddled in the judo stance. The left arm, thrust forward against the glinting semicircle of the bow, was straight as a duellist's. The right hand, holding the feathers of the second arrow, was rigid against the right cheek. Behind the head, the taut right elbow lanced back in frozen suspense. The silver tip of the second arrow pointed exactly between the two pale raised profiles.

Bond breathed the words, 'Don't move an inch.' Aloud he said, 'Hullo, Oddjob. Damned good shot.'

Oddjob jerked the tip of the arrow upwards.

Bond got to his feet, shielding the girl. He said softly out of the corner of his mouth, 'He must's see the rifle.' He said to Oddjob, speaking casually, peaceably, 'Nice place Mr Goldfinger has here. Want to have a word with him sometime. Perhaps it's a bit late tonight. You might tell him I'll be along tomorrow.' Bond said to the girl, 'Come on, darling. We've had our walk in the woods. Time to get back to the hotel.' He took a step away from Oddjob towards the fence.

Oddjob stamped his forward foot. The point of the second arrow swung to the centre of Bond's stomach.

'Oargn.' Oddjob jerked his head sideways and downwards towards the house.

'Oh, you think he'd like to see us now? All right. You don't think we'll be disturbing him? Come on, darling.' Bond led the way to the left of the tree, away from the rifle that lay in the shadowed grass.

As they went slowly down the hill, Bond talked softly to the girl, briefing her. 'You're my girl friend. I brought you out from England. Seem surprised and interested by our little adventure. We're in a tough spot. Don't try any tricks.' Bond jerked back his head. 'This man's a killer.'

The girl said angrily, 'If only you hadn't interfered.'

'Same to you,' said Bond shortly. He took it back, 'I'm sorry, Tilly. Didn't mean that. But I don't think you could have got away with it.'

'I had my plans. I'd have been over the frontier by midnight.'

Bond didn't answer. Something had caught his eye. On top of the tall chimney, the oblong mouth of the radar-thing was revolving again. It was that that had spotted them–heard them. It must be some kind of sonic detector. What a bag of tricks this man was! Bond hadn't meant to underestimate Goldfinger. Had he managed to do so–decisively? Perhaps, if he had had his gun . . . ? No. Bond knew that even his split-second draw wouldn't have beaten the Korean–wouldn't do so now. There was a total deadliness about this man. Whether Bond had been armed or unarmed, it would have been a man fighting a tank.

They reached the courtyard. As they did so, the back door of the house opened. Two more Koreans, who might have been the servants from Reculver, ran out towards them through the warm splash of electric light. They carried ugly-looking polished sticks. 'Stop!' Both men wore the savage, empty grin that men from Station J, who had been in Japanese prison camps, had described to Bond. 'We search. No trouble or . . .' The man who had spoken, cut the air with a whistling lash of his stick. 'Hands up!'

Bond put his hands slowly up. He said to the girl, 'Don't react . . . whatever they do.'

Oddjob came forward and stood, menacingly, watching the search. The search was expert. Bond coldly watched the hands on the girl, the grinning faces.

'Okay. Come!'

They were herded through the open door and along a stone-flagged passage to the narrow entrance hall at the front of the house. The house smelled as Bond had imagined it would–musty and fragrant and summery. There were white-panelled doors. Oddjob knocked on one of them.

'Yes?'

Oddjob opened the door. They were prodded through.

Goldfinger sat at a big desk. It was neatly encumbered with important-looking papers. The desk was flanked by grey metal filing cabinets. Beside the desk, within reach of Goldfinger's hand, stood a short-wave wireless set on a low table. There was an operator's keyboard and a machine that ticked busily and looked like a barograph. Bond guessed that this had something to do with the detector that had intercepted them.

Goldfinger wore his purple velvet smoking-jacket over an open-necked white silk shirt. The open neck showed a tuft of orange chest-hair. He sat very erect in a high-backed chair. He hardly glanced at the girl. The big china-blue eyes were fixed on Bond. They showed no surprise. They held no expression except a piercing hardness.

Bond blustered, 'Look here, Goldfinger. What the hell's all this about? You put the police on to me over that ten thousand dollars and I got on your tracks with my girl friend here, Miss Soames. I've come to find out what the hell you mean by it. We climbed the fence–I know it's trespassing, but I wanted to catch you before you moved on somewhere else. Then this ape of yours came along and damned near killed one of us with his bow and arrow. Two more of your bloody Koreans held us up and searched us. What the hell's going on? If you can't give me a civil answer and full apologies I'll put the police on you.'

Goldfinger's flat, hard stare didn't flicker. He might not have heard Bond's angry-gentleman's outburst. The finely chiselled lips parted. He said, 'Mr Bond, they have a saying in Chicago: "Once is happenstance. Twice is coincidence. The third time it's enemy action." Miami, Sandwich and now Geneva. I propose to wring the truth out of you.' Goldfinger's eyes slid slowly past Bond's head. 'Oddjob. The Pressure Room.'

PART THREE
ENEMY ACTION

Chapter Fifteen

The Pressure Room

Bond's reaction was automatic. There was no reason behind it. He took one quick step forward and hurled himself across the desk at Goldfinger. His body, launched in a shallow dive, hit the top of the desk and ploughed through the litter of papers. There was a heavy thud as the top of his head crashed into Goldfinger's breastbone. The momentum of the blow rocked Goldfinger in his chair. Bond kicked back at the edge of the desk, got a purchase and rammed forward again. As the chair toppled backwards and the two bodies went down in the splintering woodwork, Bond's fingers got to the throat and his thumbs went into its base and downwards with every ounce of his force.

Then the whole house fell on Bond, a baulk of timber hit him at the base of the neck and he rolled sluggishly off Goldfinger on to the floor and lay still.

The vortex of light through which Bond was whirling slowly flattened into a disc, a yellow moon, and then into a burning Cyclops eye. Something was written round the fiery eyeball. It was a message, an important message for him. He must read it. Carefully, one by one, Bond spelled out the tiny letters. The message said: SOCIÉTÉ ANONYME MAZDA. What was its significance? A hard bolt of water hit Bond in the face. The water stung his eyes and filled his mouth. He retched desperately and tried to move. He couldn't. His eyes cleared, and his brain. There was a throbbing pain at the back of his neck. He was staring up into a big enamelled light bowl with one powerful bulb. He was on some sort of a table and his wrists and ankles were bound to its edges. He felt with his fingers. He felt polished metal.

A voice, Goldfinger's voice, flat, uninterested, said, 'Now we can begin.'

Bond turned his head towards the voice. His eyes were dazzled by the light. He squeezed them hard and opened them. Goldfinger was sitting in a canvas chair. He had taken off his jacket and was in his shirt sleeves. There were red marks round the base of his throat. On a folding table beside him were various tools and metal instruments and a control panel. On the other side of the table Tilly Masterton sat in another chair. She was strapped to it by her wrists and ankles. She sat bolt upright as if she was in school. She looked incredibly beautiful, but shocked, remote. Her eyes gazed vacantly at Bond. She was either drugged or hypnotized.

Bond turned his head to the right. A few feet away stood the Korean. He still wore his bowler hat but now he was stripped to the waist. The yellow skin of his huge torso glinted with sweat. There was no hair on it. The flat pectoral muscles were as broad as dinner plates and the stomach was concave below the great arch of the ribs. The biceps and forearms, also hairless, were as thick as thighs. The ten-minutes-to-two oil slicks of the eyes looked pleased, greedy. The mouthful of blackish teeth formed an oblong grin of anticipation.

Bond raised his head. The quick look round hurt. They were in one of the factory workrooms. White light blazed round the iron doors of two electric furnaces. There were bluish sheets of metal stacked in wooden frames. From somewhere came the whir of a generator. There was a distant, muffled sound of hammering, and, behind the sound, the faraway iron pant of the power plant.

Bond glanced down the table on which he lay spreadeagled. He let his head fall back with a sigh. There was a narrow slit down the centre of the polished steel table. At the far end of the slit, like a foresight framed in the vee of his parted feet, were the glinting teeth of a circular saw.

Bond lay and stared up at the little message on the lamp bulb. Goldfinger began to speak in a relaxed conversational voice. Bond pulled the curtains tight across the ghastly peep-show of his imagination and listened.

'Mr Bond, the word "pain" comes from the Latin *poena* meaning "penalty"–that which must be paid. You must now pay for the inquisitiveness which your attack upon me proves, as I suspected, to be inimical. Curiosity, as they say, killed the cat. This time it will have to kill two cats, for I fear I must also count this girl an enemy. She tells me she is staying at the Bergues. One telephone call proved that to be false. Oddjob was sent to where you were both hidden and recovered her rifle and also a ring which it happens that I recognize. Under hypnotism the rest came out. This girl came here to kill me. Perhaps you did too. You have both failed. Now must come the *poena*. Mr Bond–' the voice was weary, bored–'I have had many enemies in my time. I am very successful and immensely rich, and riches, if I may inflict another of my aphorisms upon you, may not make you friends but they greatly increase the class and variety of your enemies.'

'That's very neatly put.'

Goldfinger ignored the interruption. 'If you were a free man, with your talent for inquiry, you would be able to find round the world the relics of those who have wished me ill, or who have tried to thwart me. There have, as I said, been many of these people and you would find, Mr Bond, that their remains resemble those of hedgehogs squashed upon the roads in summertime.'

'Very poetic simile.'

'By chance, Mr Bond. I am a poet in deeds–not often in words. I am concerned to arrange my actions in appropriate and effective patterns. But that is by the way. I wish to convey to you that it was a most evil day for you when you first crossed my path and, admittedly in a very minor fashion, thwarted a minuscule project upon which I was engaged. On that occasion it was someone else who suffered the *poena* that should have been meted out to you. An eye was taken for the eye, but it was not yours. You were lucky and, if you had then found an oracle to consult, the oracle would have said to you, "Mr Bond, you have been fortunate. Keep away from Mr Auric Goldfinger. He is a most powerful man. If Mr Goldfinger wanted to crush you, he would only have to turn over in his sleep to do so."'

'You express yourself most vividly.' Bond turned his head. The great brown and orange football of a head was bent slightly forward. The round moon-face was bland, indifferent. Casually, one hand reached out to the control panel and pressed down a switch. There came a slow metallic growl from the end of the table on which Bond lay. It curved quickly up to a harsh whine and then to a shrill high whistle that was barely audible. Bond turned his head wearily away. How soon could he manage to die? Was there any way he could hasten death? A friend of his had survived the Gestapo. He had described to Bond how he had tried to commit suicide by holding his breath. By superhuman will-power, after a few minutes without breathing, unconsciousness had come. But, with the blackout of the senses, will and intention had also left the body. At once reason was forgotten. The body's instinct to live manned the pumps and got breath back into the body again. But Bond could try it. There was nothing else to help him through the pain barrier before the blessing of death. For death was the only exit. He knew he could never squeal to Goldfinger and live with himself again–even in the unlikely event that Goldfinger could be bought off with the truth. No, he must stick to his thin story and hope that the others who would now follow him on Goldfinger's trail would have better luck. Who would M choose? Probably 008, the second killer in the small section of three. He was a good man, more careful than Bond. M would know that Goldfinger had killed Bond and he would give 008 licence to kill in return. 258 in Geneva would put him on to the scent that would end with Bond's inquiry about the Entreprises Auric. Yes, fate would catch up with Goldfinger if Bond could only keep his mouth shut. If he gave the least clue away, Goldfinger would escape. That was unthinkable.

'Now then, Mr Bond.' Goldfinger's voice was brisk. 'Enough of these amiabilities. Sing, as my Chicago friends put it, and you will die quickly and painlessly. The girl also. Sing not, and your death will be one long scream. The girl I shall then give to Oddjob, as I did that cat, for supper. Which is it to be?'

Bond said, 'Don't be a fool, Goldfinger. I told my friends at Universal where I was going and why. The girl's parents know that she went with me. I made inquiries about this factory of yours before we came here. We shall be traced here very easily. Universal is powerful. You will have the police after you within days of our disappearance. I will make a deal with you. Let us go and nothing more will be heard of the matter. I will vouch for the girl. You are making a stupid mistake. We are two perfectly innocent people.'

Goldfinger said in a bored voice, 'I'm afraid you don't understand, Mr Bond. Whatever you have managed to find out about me, which I suspect is very little, can only be a grain of the truth. I am engaged upon gigantic enterprises. To take the gamble of letting either of you leave here alive would be quite ludicrous. It is out of the question. As for my being bothered by the police, I shall be delighted to receive them if they come. Those of my Koreans who can speak won't do so–nor will the mouths of my electric furnaces which will have vaporized you both and all your belongings at two thousand degrees Centigrade. No, Mr Bond, make your choice. Perhaps I can encourage you'–there came the noise of a lever moving across iron teeth. 'The saw is now approaching your body at about one inch every minute. Meanwhile,' he glanced at Oddjob and held up one finger, 'a little massage from Oddjob. To begin with, only grade one. Grades two and three are still more persuasive.'

Bond closed his eyes. The sickly zoo-smell of Oddjob enveloped him. Big, rasping fingers set to work on him carefully, delicately. A pressure here, combined with a pressure there, a sudden squeeze, a pause, and then a quick, sharp blow. Always the hard hands were surgically accurate. Bond ground his teeth until he thought they would break. The sweat of pain began to form pools in the sockets of his closed eyes. The shrill whine of the saw was getting louder. It reminded Bond of the sawdust-scented sounds of long ago summer evenings at home in England. Home? This was his home, this cocoon of danger he had chosen to live in. And here he would be buried 'in some corner of a foreign blast furnace that is for ever two thousand degrees Centigrade'. God rest ye merry gentlemen of the Secret Service! What should he give himself as an epitaph? What should be his 'famous last words'? That you have no choice about your birth, but you can choose the way you die? Yes, it would look well on a tombstone–not *Savoir vivre* but *Savoir mourir*.

'Mr Bond.' Goldfinger's voice held an ounce of urgency. 'Is this really necessary? Just tell me the truth. Who are you? Who sent you here? What do you know? Then it will be so easy. You shall both have a pill. There will be no pain. It will be like taking a sleeping draught. Otherwise it will be so messy–so messy and distressing. And are you being fair to the girl? Is this the behaviour of an English gentleman?'

Oddjob's torment had stopped. Bond turned his head slowly towards the voice and opened his eyes. He said, 'Goldfinger, there is nothing more to tell because there is nothing. If you will not accept my first bargain I will make you another. The girl and I will work for you. How about that? We are capable people. You could put us to good use.'

'And get a knife, two knives in my back? Thank you no, Mr Bond.'

Bond decided it was time to stop talking. It was time to start winding up the mainspring of will-power that must not run down again until he was dead. Bond said politely, 'Then you can go and——yourself.' He expelled all the breath from his lungs and closed his eyes.

'Even I am not capable of that, Mr Bond,' said Goldfinger with good humour. 'And now, since you have chosen the stony path instead of the smooth, I must extract what interest I can from your predicament by making the path as stony as possible. Oddjob, grade two.'

The lever on the table moved across iron teeth. Now Bond could feel the wind of the saw between his knees. The hands came back.

Bond counted the slowly pounding pulse that utterly possessed his body. It was like the huge panting power plant in the other part of the factory but, in his case, it was slowly decelerating. If only it would slow down quicker. What was this ridiculous will to live that refused to listen to the brain? Who was making the engine run on although the tank was dry of fuel? But he must empty his mind of thought, as well as his body of oxygen. He must become a vacuum, a deep hole of unconsciousness.

Still the light burned red through his eyelids. Still he could feel the bursting pressure in his temples. Still the slow drum of life beat in his ears.

A scream tried to force is way through the clamped teeth.

Die damn you die die damn you die damn you die damn you die damn you die . . .

Chapter Sixteen

The Last and the Biggest

The wings of a dove, the heavenly choir, Hark the Herald Angels Sing–what else ought he to remember about Paradise? It was all so exactly like what he had been told in the nursery–this sensation of flying, the darkness, the drone of a million harps. He really must try and remember the dope about the place. Let's see now, one got to the Pearly Gates . . .

A deep fatherly voice said, almost in his ear, 'This is your captain speaking.' (Well, well. Who was this. Saint Peter?) We are coming in to land now. Will you please fasten your seat belts and extinguish your cigarettes. Thank you.'

There must be a whole lot of them, going up together. Would Tilly be on the same trip? Bond squirmed with embarrassment. How would he introduce her to the others, to Vesper for instance? And when it came to the point, which would he like the best? But perhaps it would be a big place with countries and towns. There was probably no more reason why he should run into one of his former girl friends here than there had been on earth. But still there were a lot of people he'd better avoid until he got settled in and found out the form. Perhaps, with so much love about, these things wouldn't matter. Perhaps one just loved all the girls one met. Hm. Tricky business!

With these unworthy thoughts in his mind, Bond relapsed into unconsciousness.

The next thing he knew was a gentle sensation of swaying. He opened his eyes. The sun blinded them. He closed them again. A voice above and behind his head said, 'Watch it, bud. That ramp's steeper than it looks.' Almost immediately there was a heavy jolt. A surly voice in front said, 'Cheesus, you're telling me. Why in hell can't they put down rubber.'

Bond thought angrily, that's a fine way to talk up here. Just because I'm new and they think no one's listening.

There was the bang of a swing door. Something hit Bond sharply on a protruding elbow. He shouted 'Hey!' and tried to reach his elbow and rub it, but his hands wouldn't move.

'Whaddya know. Hey, Sam, better call the doc. This one's come round.'

'Sure! Here, put him alongside the other.' Bond felt himself being lowered. It was cooler now. He opened his eyes. A big round Brooklyn face was bent over his. The eyes met his and smiled. The metal supports of the stretcher touched the ground. The man said, 'How ya feelin', mister?'

'Where am I?' Now there was panic in Bond's voice. He tried to rise but couldn't. He felt the sweat break out on his body. God! Was this still part of the old life? At the thought of it, a wave of grief poured through his body. Tears burned his eyes and trickled down his cheeks.

'Hey, hey! Take it easy, mister. You're okay. This is Idlewild, New York. You're in America now. No more troubles, see.' The man straightened up.

He thought Bond was a refugee from somewhere. 'Sam, get movin'. This guy's in shock.'

'Okay, okay.' The two voices receded, mumbling anxiously.

Bond found he could move his head. He looked round. He was in a white-painted ward–presumably something to do with the health department of the airport. There was a row of tidy beds. Sun poured down from high windows, but it was cool, air-conditioned. He was on a stretcher on the floor. There was another one next to it. He strained his head sideways. It was Tilly. She was unconscious. Her pale face, framed in the black hair, pointed at the ceiling.

The door at the end of the ward sighed open. A doctor in a white coat stood and held it. Goldfinger, looking brisk, cheerful, walked swiftly down between the beds. He was followed by Oddjob. Bond wearily closed his eyes. Christ! So that was the score.

Feet gathered round his stretcher. Goldfinger said breezily, 'Well, they certainly look in good shape, eh, Doctor? That's one of the blessings of having enough money. When one's friends or one's staff are ill one can get them the very best medical attention. Nervous breakdowns, both of them. And in the same week! Would you believe it? But I blame myself for working them both too hard. Now it's my duty to get them back on their feet again. Dr Foch–he's the best man in Geneva, by the way–was quite definite. He said, "They need rest, Mr Goldfinger. Rest, rest and again rest." He gave them sedatives and now they're on their way to the Harkness Pavilion at the Presbyterian.' Goldfinger chuckled fatly. 'Sow and you shall reap, eh, Doctor? When I gave the Harkness a million dollars' worth of X-ray equipment, I certainly never expected anything back. But now? I only had to put through a call and they've got two fine rooms waiting for them. Now then—' there was a rustle of notes–'thank you for all your help with Immigration. Fortunately they both had valid visas and I think Immigration was satisfied that Mr Auric Goldfinger was a sufficient guarantee that neither of them wants to overthrow the United States Government by force, what?'

'Yes indeed, and thank you Mr Goldfinger. Anything I can do . . . I understand you have a private ambulance waiting outside.'

Bond opened his eyes and looked at where the doctor's voice came from. He saw a pleasant, serious young man with rimless glasses and a crew-cut. Bond said quietly and with desperate sincerity, 'Doctor, there is absolutely nothing wrong with me or this girl. We have been drugged and brought here against our will. Neither of us works or has ever worked for Goldfinger. I am warning you that we have been kidnapped. I demand to see the Chief of Immigration. I have friends in Washington and New York. They will vouch for me, I beg of you to believe me.' Bond held the man's eyes in his, willing him to believe.

The doctor looked worried. He turned to Goldfinger. Goldfinger shook his head–discreetly so that Bond would not be insulted. A surreptitious hand went up and tapped the side of his head away from Bond. Goldfinger raised helpless eyebrows. 'You see what I mean, Doctor? It's been like this for days. Total nervous prostration combined with persecution mania. Dr Foch said they often go together. It may need weeks at the Harkness. But I'm going to pull him round if it's the last thing I do. It's the shock of these unfamiliar surroundings. Perhaps a shot of intraval sodium . . .'

The doctor bent to his black bag. 'I guess you're right, Mr Goldfinger. So long as Harkness is looking after the case.' There came the tinkle of instruments.

Goldfinger said, 'It's terribly sad to see a man break down so utterly, a man who has been one of my best assistants.' He bent a sweet, fatherly smile on Bond. There was a catch in his voice. 'You'll be all right, James. Just relax and have a nice sleep. I was afraid the flight might be too much for you. Just relax and leave everything to me.'

Bond felt the swab on his arm. He heaved. Against his will, a shower of curses poured from his lips. Then he felt the needle and opened his mouth and screamed and screamed while the doctor knelt beside him and delicately, patiently, wiped away the sweat from his forehead.

Now it was a grey painted box of a room. There were no windows. Light came from a single bowl lamp inset in the centre of the ceiling. Round the lamp were concentric slits in the plaster and there was the neutral smell and faint hum of air-conditioning. Bond found he could sit up. He did so. He felt drowsy but well. He suddenly realized that he was ravenously hungry and thirsty. When had he last had a meal? Two, three days ago? He put his feet down on the floor. He was naked. He examined his body. Oddjob had been careful. There was no sign of damage save for the group of needle-marks on his right forearm. He got up, conquering dizziness, and took a few steps in the room. He had been lying on a ship's type bunk with drawers under it. The only other furniture in the room was a plain deal table and an upright wooden chair. Everything was clean, functional, Spartan. Bond knelt to the drawers under the bunk and opened them. They contained all the contents of his suitcase except his watch and the gun. Even the rather heavy shoes he had been wearing on his expedition to Entreprises Auric were there. He twisted one of the heels and pulled. The broad double-sided knife slid smoothly out of its scabbard in the sole. With the fingers wrapped round the locked heel it made a workmanlike stabbing dagger. Bond verified that the other shoe held its knife and clicked the heels back into position. He pulled out some clothes and put them on. He found his cigarette case and lighter and lit a cigarette. There were two doors of which one had a handle. He opened this one. It led into a small, well-appointed bathroom and lavatory. His washing and shaving things were neatly laid out. There were a girl's things beside them. Bond softly opened the other door into the bathroom. It was a similar room to his own. Tilly Masterton's black hair showed on the pillow of the bunk. Bond tiptoed over and looked down. She was sleeping peacefully, a half-smile on the beautiful mouth. Bond went back into the bathroom, softly closed the door and went to the mirror over the basin and looked at himself. The black stubble looked more like three days than two. He set to work to clean himself up.

Half an hour later, Bond was sitting on the edge of his bunk thinking, when the door without a handle opened abruptly. Oddjob stood in the entrance. He looked incuriously at Bond. His eyes flickered carefully round the room. Bond said sharply, 'Oddjob, I want a lot of food, quickly. And a bottle of bourbon, soda and ice. Also a carton of Chesterfields, king-size, and either my own watch or another one as good as mine. Quick march! Chop-chop! And tell Goldfinger I want to see him, but not until I've had something to eat. Come on! Jump to it! Don't stand there looking inscrutable. I'm hungry.'

Oddjob looked redly at Bond as if wondering which piece to break. He opened his mouth, uttered a noise between an angry bark and a belch, spat drily on the floor at his feet and stepped back, whirling the door shut. When the slam should have come, the door decelerated abruptly and closed with a soft, decisive, double click.

The encounter put Bond in good humour. For some reason Goldfinger had decided against killing them. He wanted them alive. Soon Bond would know why he wanted them alive but, so long as he did, Bond intended to stay alive on his own terms. Those terms included putting Oddjob and any other Korean firmly in his place, which, in Bond's estimation, was rather lower than apes in the mammalian hierarchy.

By the time an excellent meal together with everything else, including his watch, Bond had asked for, had been brought by one of the Korean servants, Bond had learned nothing more about his circumstances except that his room was close to water and not far from a railway bridge. Assuming his room was in New York, it was either on the Hudson or the East River. The railway was electric and sounded like a subway, but Bond's New York geography was not good enough to place it. His watch had stopped. When he asked the time he got no answer.

Bond had eaten all the food on the tray and was smoking and sipping a solid bourbon and soda when the door opened. Goldfinger came in alone. He was wearing a regulation businessman's clothes and looked relaxed and cheerful. He closed the door behind him and stood with his back to it. He looked searchingly at Bond. Bond smoked and looked politely back.

Goldfinger said, 'Good morning, Mr Bond. I see you are yourself again. I hope you prefer being here to being dead. So as to save you the trouble of asking a lot of conventional questions, I will tell you where you are and what has happened to you. I will then put to you a proposition to which I require an unequivocal reply. You are a more reasonable man than most, so I need only give you one brief warning. Do not attempt any dramatics. Do not attack me with a knife or a fork or that bottle. If you do, I shall shoot you with this.' A small-calibre pistol grew like a black thumb out of Goldfinger's right fist. He put the hand with the gun back in his pocket. 'I very seldom use these things. When I have had to, I have never needed more than one ·25-calibre bullet to kill. I shoot at the right eye, Mr Bond. And I never miss.'

Bond said, 'Don't worry, I'm not as accurate as that with a bourbon bottle.' He hitched up the knee of his trousers and put one leg across the other. He sat relaxed. 'Go ahead.'

'Mr Bond,' Goldfinger's voice was amiable. 'I am an expert in many other materials beside metals and I have a keen appreciation of everything that is one thousand fine, as we say of the purest gold. In comparison with that degree of purity, of value, human material is of a very low grade indeed. But occasionally one comes across a piece of this stuff that can at least be put to the lower forms of use. Oddjob is an example of what I mean–simple, unrefined clay, capable of limited exploitation. At the last moment my hand hesitated to destroy a utensil with the durability I observed in yourself. I may have made a mistake in staying my hand. In any case I shall take the fullest steps to protect myself from the consequences of my impulse. It was something you said that saved your life. You suggested that you and Miss Masterton would work for me. Normally I would have no use for either of you, but it just happens that I am on the brink of a certain enterprise in which the services of both of you could be of a certain minimal assistance. So I took the gamble. I gave you both the necessary sedatives. Your bills were paid and your things fetched from the Bergues where Miss Masterton turned out to be registered under her real name. I sent a cable in your name to Universal Export. You had been offered employment in Canada. You were flying over to explore the prospects. You were taking Miss Masterton as your secretary. You would write further details. A clumsy cable, but it will serve for the short period I require your services. (It won't, thought Bond, unless you included in the text one of the innocent phrases that would tell M that the cable was authentic. By now, the Service would know he was working under enemy control. Wheels would be turning very fast indeed.) And in case you think, Mr Bond, that my precautions were inadequate, that you will be traced, let me tell you that I am no longer in the least interested about your true identity nor the strength and resources of your employers. You and Miss Masterton have utterly disappeared, Mr Bond. So have I, so have all my staff. The airport will refer inquiries to the Harkness Pavilion at the Presbyterian Hospital. The hospital will never have heard of Mr Goldfinger nor of his patients. The F.B.I. and the C.I.A. have no record of me, for I have no criminal history. No doubt the immigration authorities will have details of my comings and goings over the years, but these will not be helpful. As for my present whereabouts, and yours, Mr Bond, we are now in the warehouse of the Hi-speed Trucking Corporation, a formerly respectable concern which I own through nominees and which has been equipped, most thoroughly, as the secret headquarters for the enterprise of which I spoke. You and Miss Masterton will be confined to these quarters. Here you will live and work and possibly, though personally I have doubts about Miss Masterton's inclinations in that respect, make love.'

'And what will our work consist of?'

'Mr Bond—' For the first time since Bond had known Goldfinger, the big, bland face, always empty of expression, showed a trace of life. A look almost of rapture illuminated the eyes. The finely chiselled lips pursed into a thin, beatic curve. 'Mr Bond, all my life I have been in love. I have been in love with gold. I love its colour, its brilliance, its divine heaviness. I love the texture of gold, that soft sliminess that I have learnt to gauge so accurately by touch that I can estimate the fineness of a bar to within one carat. And I love the warm tang it exudes when I melt it down into a true golden syrup. But, above all, Mr Bond, I love the power that gold alone gives to its owner–the magic of controlling energy, exacting labour, fulfilling one's every wish and whim and, when need be, purchasing bodies, minds, even souls. Yes, Mr Bond, I have worked all my life for gold and, in return, gold has worked for me and for those enterprises that I have espoused. I ask you,' Goldfinger gazed earnestly at Bond, 'is there any other substance on earth that so rewards its owner?'

'Many people have become rich and powerful without possessing an ounce of the stuff. But I see your point. How much have you managed to collect and what do you do with it?'

'I own about twenty million pounds' worth, about as much as a small country. It is now all in New York. I keep it where I need it. My treasure of gold is like a compost heap. I move it here and there over the face of the earth and, wherever I choose to spread it, that corner blossoms and blooms. I reap the harvest and move on. At this moment I am proposing to encourage, to force, a certain American enterprise with my golden compost. Therefore the gold bars are in New York.'

'How do you choose these enterprises? What attracts you to them?'

'I espouse any enterprise that will increase my stock of gold. I invest, I smuggle, I steal.' Goldfinger made a small gesture of the hands, opening the palms persuasively. 'If you will follow the simile, regard history as a train speeding along through time. Birds and animals are disturbed by the noise and tumult of the train's passage, they fly away from it or run fearfully or cower, thinking they hide. I am like the hawk that follows the train–you have no doubt seen them doing this, in Greece for instance–ready to pounce on anything that may be flushed by the train's passage, by the passage of history. To give you a simple example: the progress of history produces a man who invents penicillin. At the same time, history creates a world war. Many people are dying or afraid of dying. Penicillin will save them. Through bribery at certain military establishments on the Continent, I obtain stocks of penicillin. I water these down with some harmless powder or liquid and sell them at immense profit to those who crave the stuff. You see what I mean, Mr Bond? You have to wait for the prey, watch it carefully and then pounce. But, as I say, I do not search out such enterprises. I allow the train of history to flush them towards me.'

'What's the latest one? What have Miss Masterton and I got to do with it?'

'The latest one, Mr Bond, is the last one. It is also the biggest.' Goldfinger's eyes were now blank, focused inwards. His voice became low, almost reverential at what he saw. 'Man has climbed Everest and he has scraped the depths of the ocean. He has fired rockets into outer space and split the atom. He has invented, devised, created in every realm of human endeavour, and everywhere he has triumphed, broken records, achieved miracles. I said in every realm, but there is one that has been neglected, Mr Bond. That one is the human activity loosely known as crime. The so-called criminal exploits committed by individual humans–I do not of course refer to their idiotic wars, their clumsy destruction of each other–are of miserable dimensions: little bank robberies, tiny swindles, picayune forgeries. And yet, ready to hand, a few hundred miles from here, opportunity for the greatest crime in history stands waiting. The stage is set, the gigantic prize is offered. Only the actors are missing. But the producer is at last here, Mr Bond'–Goldfinger raised a finger and tapped his chest–'and he has chosen his cast. This very afternoon the script will be read to the leading actors. Then rehearsals will begin and, in one week, the curtain will go up for the single, the unique performance. And then will come the applause, the applause for the greatest extra-legal coup of all time. And, Mr Bond, the world will rock with that applause for centuries.'

Now a dull fire burned in Goldfinger's big pale eyes and there was a touch of extra colour in his red-brown cheeks. But he was still calm, relaxed, profoundly convinced. There's no trace here, reflected Bond, of the madman, the visionary. Goldfinger had some fantastic exploit in mind, but he had gauged the odds and knew they were right. Bond said, 'Well, come on. What is it, and what do we have to do about it?'

'It is a robbery, Mr Bond. A robbery against no opposition, but one that will need detailed execution. There will be much paper-work, many administrative details to supervise. I was going to do this myself until you offered your services. Now you will do it, with Miss Masterton as your secretary. You have already been partly remunerated for this work with your life. When the operation is successfully completed you will receive one million pounds in gold. Miss Masterton will receive half a million.'

Bond said enthusiastically, 'Now you're talking. What are we going to do? Rob the end of the rainbow?'

'Yes,' Goldfinger nodded. 'That is exactly what we are going to do. We are going to burgle fifteen billion dollars' worth of gold bullion, approximately half the supply of mined gold in the world. We are going, Mr Bond, to take Fort Knox.'

Chapter Seventeen

Hoods' Congress

'Fort Knox.' Bond shook his head seriously. 'Isn't that rather a tall order for two men and a girl?'

Goldfinger shrugged impatiently. 'Please put away your sense of humour for one week, Mr Bond. Then laugh as much as you please. I shall have under my command approximately one hundred men and women. These people will be hand picked from the six most powerful gangster groups in the United States. This force will amount to the toughest and most compact fighting unit that has ever been assembled in peace time.'

'All right. How many men guard the vault at Fort Knox?'

Goldfinger slowly shook his head. He knocked once on the door behind him. The door flicked open. Oddjob stood on the threshold, crouching, alert. When he saw that the meeting was still peaceful he straightened himself and waited. Goldfinger said, 'You will have many questions to ask, Mr Bond. They will all be answered this afternoon. Beginning at two-thirty. It is now exactly twelve o'clock.' Bond glanced at his watch and adjusted it. 'You and Miss Masterton will attend the meeting at which the proposition will be put to the heads of the six organisations I have mentioned. No doubt these people will ask the same questions as occur to you. Everything will be explained. Afterwards you will settle down to detailed work with Miss Masterton. Ask for what you want. Oddjob will see to your welfare and also be on permanent guard. Do not be obstreperous or you will instantly be killed. And do not waste time trying to escape or to contact the outside world. I have hired your services and I shall require every ounce of them. Is that a bargain?'

Bond said drily, 'I've always wanted to be a millionaire.'

Goldfinger didn't look at him. He looked at his fingernails. Then he gave Bond one last hard glance and went out and shut the door behind him.

Bond sat and gazed at the closed door. He brusquely ran both hands through his hair and down over his face. He said 'Well, well' aloud to the empty room, got up and walked through the bathroom to the girl's bedroom. He knocked on the door.

'Who is it?'

'Me. Are you visible?'

'Yes.' The voice was unenthusiastic. 'Come in.'

She was sitting on the edge of the bed, pulling on a shoe. She was wearing the things Bond had first seen her in. She looked cool and collected and unsurprised by her surroundings. She looked up at Bond. Her eyes were aloof, disdainful. She said coldly, precisely, 'You've got us into this. Get us out.'

Bond said amiably, 'I may be able to. I got us out of our graves.'

'After getting us into them.'

Bond looked thoughtfully at the girl. He decided it would be ungallant to spank her, so to speak, on an empty stomach. He said, 'This won't get us anywhere. We're in this together, whether we like it or not. What do you want for breakfast or lunch? It's a quarter past twelve. I've eaten. I'll order yours and then come back and tell you the score. There's only one way out of here and Oddjob, that Korean ape, is guarding it. Now then, breakfast or lunch?'

She unbent an inch. 'Thank you. Scrambled eggs and coffee, please. And toast and marmalade.'

'Cigarettes?'

'No, thank you. I don't smoke.'

Bond went back to his room and knocked on the door. It opened an inch. Bond said, 'All right, Oddjob. I'm not going to kill you yet.'

The door opened farther. Oddjob's face was impassive. Bond gave the order. The door closed. Bond poured himself a bourbon and soda. He sat on the edge of the bed and wondered how he was going to get the girl on his side. From the beginning she had resented him. Was that only because of her sister? Why had Goldfinger made that cryptic remark about her 'inclinations'? What was there about her that he himself felt–something withdrawn, inimical. She was beautiful–physically desirable. But there was a cold, hard centre to her that Bond couldn't understand or define. Oh well, the main thing was to get her to go along. Otherwise life in prison would be intolerable.

Bond went back into her room. He left both doors open so that he could hear. She was still sitting on the bed wrapped in a coiled immobility. She watched Bond carefully. Bond leaned against the jamb of the door. He took a long pull at his whisky. He said, looking her in the eye, 'You'd better know that I'm from Scotland Yard'–the euphemism would serve. 'We're after this man Goldfinger. He doesn't mind. He thinks no one can find us for at least a week. He's probably right. He saved our lives because he wants us to work for him on a crime. It's big business. Pretty scatter-brained. But there's a lot of planning and paperwork. We've got to look after that side. Can you do shorthand and typing?'

'Yes.' Her eyes were alight. 'What's the crime?'

Bond told her. He said, 'Of course it all sounds ridiculous and I daresay a few questions and answers will show these gangsters, if they don't show Goldfinger, that the whole thing's impossible. But I don't know. Goldfinger's an extraordinary man. From what I know about him, he never moves unless the odds are right. And I don't think he's mad–at least not madder than other kinds of geniuses–scientists and so on. And there's no doubt he's a genius in his particular field.'

'So what are you going to do about it?'

Bond lowered his voice. He said, 'What are *we* going to do about it, you mean. *We* are going to play along. And to the hilt. No shirking and no funny business. We're going to be greedy for the money and we're going to give him absolutely top-notch service. Apart from saving our lives, which means less than nothing to him, it's the only hope we, or rather I because that's my line of country, can have of a chance to queer his pitch.'

'How are you going to do that?'

'I haven't the faintest idea. Something may turn up.'

'And you expect me to go along with you?'

'Why not? Any other suggestions?'

She pursed her lips obstinately. 'Why should I do what you say?'

Bond sighed. 'There's no point in being a suffragette about this. It's either that or get yourself killed after breakfast. It's up to you.'

The mouth turned down with distaste. She shrugged her shoulders. She said ungraciously, 'Oh, all right then.' Suddenly her eyes flared. 'Only don't ever touch me or I shall kill you.'

There came the click of Bond's bedroom door. Bond looked mildly down at Tilly Masterton. 'The challenge is attractive. But don't worry. I won't take it up.' He turned and strolled out of the room.

One of the Koreans passed him carrying the girl's breakfast. In his room another Korean had brought in a typist's desk and chair and a Remington portable. He arranged them in the corner away from the bed. Oddjob was standing in the doorway. He held out a sheet of paper. Bond went up to him and took it.

It was a foolscap memo sheet. The writing, with a ball point, was neat, careful, legible, undistinguished. It said:

Prepare ten copies of this agenda.

Meeting held under the chairmanship of Mr Gold

Secretaries: J. Bond
Miss Tilly Masterton

Present

Helmut M. Springer	The Purple Gang. Detroit
Jed Midnight	Shadow Syndicate. Miami and Havana
Billy (The Grinner) Ring	The Machine. Chicago
Jack Strap	The Spangled Mob. Las Vegas
Mr Solo	Unione Siciliano
Miss Pussy Galore	The Cement Mixers. Harlem. New York City

Agenda

A project with the code name OPERATION GRAND SLAM.

(Refreshments.)

At the end of this was written, 'You and Miss Masterton will be fetched at 2.20. Both will be prepared to take notes. Formal dress, please.'

Bond smiled. The Koreans left the room. He sat down at the desk, slipped paper and carbons into the typewriter and set to. At least he would show the girl that he was prepared to do his stint. Gosh, what a crew! Even the Mafia had come in. How had Goldfinger persuaded them all to come? And who in heaven's name was Miss Pussy Galore?

Bond had the copies finished by two o'clock. He went into the girl's room and gave them to her together with a shorthand notebook and pencils. He also read her Goldfinger's note. He said, 'You'd better get these names in your head. They probably won't be hard to identify. We can ask if we get stuck. I'll go and get into my formal dress.' He smiled at her. 'Twenty minutes to go.'

She nodded.

Walking down the corridor behind Oddjob, Bond could hear the sounds of the river–the slapping of water on the piles below the warehouse, the long mournful hoot of a ferry clearing her way, the distant thump of diesels. Somewhere beneath his feet a truck started up, revved and then growled away presumably towards the West Side Highway. They must be on the top tier of the long two-tiered building. The grey paint in the corridor smelled new. There were no side doors. Light came from bowls in the ceiling. They reached the end. Oddjob knocked. There was the sound of a Yale key being turned and two lots of bolts being pulled and they walked through and into a large bright sunlit room. The room was over the end of the warehouse and a wide picture window, filling most of the facing wall, framed the river and the distant brown muddle of Jersey City. The room had been dressed for the conference. Goldfinger sat with his back to the window at a large round table with a green baize cloth, carafes of water, yellow scratch-pads and pencils. There were nine comfortable armchairs and on the scratch-pads in front of six of them were small oblong white parcels sealed with red wax. To the right, against the wall, was a long buffet table gleaming with silver and cut glass. Champagne stood in silver coolers and there was a row of other bottles. Among the various foods Bond noticed two round five-pound tins of Beluga caviar and several terrines of foie gras. On the wall opposite the buffet hung a blackboard above a table on which there were papers and one large oblong carton.

Goldfinger watched them come towards him across the thick wine-red carpet. He gestured to the chair on his left for Tilly Masterton and to the one on the right for Bond. They sat down.

'The agenda?' Goldfinger took the copies, read the top one and handed them back to the girl. He gave a circular wave of the hand and she got up and distributed the copies round the table. He put his hand beneath the table and pressed a hidden bell. The door at the back of the room opened. One of the Koreans came in and stood waiting. 'Is everything ready?' The man nodded. 'You understand that no one is to come into this room but the people on your list. Good. Some of them, perhaps all, will bring a companion. The companions will remain in the anteroom. See that they have everything they wish. The cards are there and the dice? Oddjob.' Goldfinger glanced up at the Korean who had remained behind Bond's chair. 'Go and take up your position. What is the signal?' Oddjob held up two fingers. 'Right. Two rings on the bell. You may go. See that all the staff carry out their duties to perfection.'

Bond said casually, 'How many staff have you got?'

'Twenty. Ten Koreans and ten Germans. They are all excellent men, hand picked. Much goes on in this building. It is like below-decks in a man-of-war.' Goldfinger laid his hands flat on the table in front of him. 'And now, your duties. Miss Masterton, you will take notes of any practical points that arise, anything that is likely to require action by me. Do not bother with the argument and chatter. Right?'

Bond was glad to see that Tilly Masterton now looked bright and businesslike. She nodded briskly, 'Certainly.'

'And, Mr Bond, I shall be interested in any reactions you may have to the speakers. I know a great deal about all these people. In their own territories they are paramount chiefs. They are only here because I have bribed them to come. They know nothing of me and I need to persuade them that I know what I am talking about and will lead them to success. Greed will do the rest. But there may be one or more who wish to back out. They will probably reveal themselves. In their cases I have made special arrangements. But there may be doubtful ones. During the talk, you will scribble with your pencil on this agenda. Casually you will note with a plus or a minus sign opposite the names whether you consider each one for or against the project. I shall be able to see what sign you have made. Your views may be useful. And do not forget, Mr Bond, that one traitor among them, one backslider, and we could quickly find ourselves either dead or in prison for life.'

'Who is this Pussy Galore from Harlem?'

'She is the only woman who runs a gang in America. It is a gang of women. I shall need some women for this operation. She is entirely reliable. She was a trapeze artiste. She had a team. It was called "Pussy Galore and her Abrocats".' Goldfinger did not smile. 'The team was unsuccessful, so she trained them as burglars, cat burglars. It grew into a gang of outstanding ruthlessness. It is a Lesbian organization which now calls itself "The Cement Mixers". Even the big American gangs respect them. She is a remarkable woman.'

A buzzer sounded very softly beneath the table. Goldfinger straightened himself. The door at the end of the room opened briskly and five men came in. Goldfinger rose in his chair and ducked his head in welcome. He said, 'My name is Gold. Will you please be seated.'

There was a careful murmur. Silently the men closed round the table, pulled out chairs and sat down. Five pairs of eyes looked coldly, warily at Goldfinger. Goldfinger sat down. He said quietly, 'Gentlemen, in the parcels before you you will find one twenty-four-carat gold bar, value fifteen thousand dollars. I thank you for the courtesy of your attendance. The agenda is self-explanatory. Perhaps, while we wait for Miss Galore, I could run through your names for the information of my secretaries, Mr Bond here, and Miss Masterton. No notes will be made of this meeting, except on action you may wish me to take, and I can assure you there are no microphones. Now then, Mr Bond, on your right is Mr Jed Midnight of the Shadow Syndicate operating out of Miama and Havana.'

Mr Midnight was a big, good-living man with a jovial face but slow careful eyes. He wore a light blue tropical suit over a white silk shirt ornamented with small green palm trees. The complicated gold watch on his wrist must have weighed nearly half a pound. He smiled tautly at Bond and said, 'Howdo.'

'Then we have Mr Billy Ring who controls the famous Chicago "Machine".'

Bond thought he had never seen anyone who was less of a 'Billy'. It was a face out of a nightmare and, as the face turned towards Bond, it knew it was, and watched Bond for his reactions. It was a pale, pear-shaped, baby face with downy skin and a soft thatch of straw-coloured hair, but the eyes, which should have been pale blue, were a tawny brown. The whites showed all round the pupils and gave a mesmeric quality to the hard thoughtful stare, unsoftened by a tic in the right eyelid which made the right eye wink with the heart-beat. At some early stage in Mr Ring's career someone had cut off Mr Ring's lower lip–perhaps he had talked too much–and this had given him a permanent false smile like the grin of a Hallowe'en pumpkin. He was about forty years old. Bond summed him up as a merciless killer. Bond smiled cheerfully into the hard stare of Mr Ring's left eye and looked past him at the man Goldfinger introduced as Mr Helmut Springer of the Detroit Purple Gang.

Mr Springer had the glazed eyes of someone who is either very rich or very dead. The eyes were pale blue opaque glass marbles which briefly recognized Bond and then turned inwards again in complete absorption with self. The rest of Mr Springer was a 'man of distinction'–casually pin-striped, Hathaway-shirted, Aqua-Velva'd. He gave the impression of someone who found himself in the wrong company–a first-class ticket holder in a third-class compartment, a man from the stalls who has been shown by mistake to a seat in the pit.

Mr Midnight put his hand up to his mouth and said softly for Bond's benefit, 'Don't be taken in by the Duke. My friend Helmut was the man who put the piquéd shirt on the hood. Daughter goes to Vassar, but it's protection money that pays for her hockey-sticks.' Bond nodded his thanks.

'And Mr Solo of the Unione Siciliano.'

Mr Solo had a dark heavy face, gloomy with the knowledge of much guilt and many sins. His thick horn-rimmed spectacles helioed briefly in Bond's direction and then bent again to the business of cleaning Mr Solo's nails with a pocket knife. He was a big, chunky man, half boxer, half head waiter, and it was quite impossible to tell what was on his mind or where his strength lay. But there is only one head of the Mafia in America and, if Mr Solo had the job, thought Bond, he had got it by strength out of terror. It would be by the exercise of both that he kept it.

'Howdy.' Mr Jack Strap of the Spangled Mob had the synthetic charm of a front man for the Las Vegas casinos, but Bond guessed he had inherited from the late lamented brothers Spang thanks to other qualities. He was an expansive, showily dressed man of about fifty. He was coming to the end of a cigar. He smoked it as if he was eating it, munching hungrily. From time to time he turned his head sideways and discreetly spat a scrap of it out on to the carpet behind him. Behind this compulsive smoking there would be a lot of tension. Mr Strap had quick conjuror's eyes. He seemed to know that his eyes frightened people because now, presumably not wanting to frighten Bond, he gave them charm by crinkling them at the corners.

The door at the back of the room opened. A woman in a black masculine-cut suit with a high coffee-coloured lace jabot stood in the doorway. She walked slowly, unselfconsciously down the room and stood behind the empty chair. Goldfinger had got to his feet. She examined him carefully and then ran her eyes round the table. She said a collective, bored 'Hi' and sat down. Mr Strap said 'Hi Pussy,' and the others, except Mr Springer who merely bowed, made careful sounds of welcome.

Goldfinger said, 'Good afternoon, Miss Galore. We have just been through the formality of introductions. The agenda is before you, together with the fifteen-thousand-dollar gold bar I asked you to accept to meet the expense and inconvenience of attending this meeting.'

Miss Galore reached for her parcel and opened it. She weighed the gleaming yellow brick in her hand. She gave Goldfinger a direct, suspicious look. 'All the way through?'

'All the way through.'

Miss Galore held his eyes. She said 'Pardon my asking' with the curt tone of a hard woman shopper at the sales.

Bond liked the look of her. He felt the sexual challenge all beautiful Lesbians have for men. He was amused by the uncompromising attitude that said to Goldfinger and to the room, 'All men are bastards and cheats. Don't try any masculine hocus on me. I don't go for it. I'm in a separate league.' Bond thought she would be in her early thirties. She had pale, Rupert Brooke good looks with high cheekbones and a beautiful jawline. She had the only violet eyes Bond had ever seen. They were the true deep violet of a pansy and they looked candidly out at the world from beneath straight black brows. Her hair, which was as black as Tilly Masterton's, was worn in an untidy urchin cut. The mouth was a decisive slash of deep vermilion. Bond thought she was superb and so, he noticed, did Tilly Masterton who was gazing at Miss Galore with worshipping eyes and lips that yearned. Bond decided that all was now clear to him about Tilly Masterton.

Goldfinger said, 'And now I must introduce myself. My name is not Gold. My credentials are as follows. By various operations, most of them illegitimate, I have made a large sum of money in twenty years. That sum now stands at sixty million dollars.' (A respectful hm-ing went round the table.) 'My operations have, for the most part, been confined to Europe, but you may be interested to know that I founded and subsequently disposed of the "Golden Poppy Distributors" who operated out of Hongkong.' (Mr Jack Strap whistled softly.) 'The Happy Landings Travel Agency", which some of you may have employed in emergency, was organized and owned by me until I disbanded it.' (Mr Helmut Springer screwed a rimless monocle into one glazed eye so that he could examine Goldfinger more closely.) 'I mention these minor concerns to show you that, although you may not know me, I have, in the past, acted at many removes on, I believe, all your behalfs.' ('Well, whaddya know!' muttered Mr Jed Midnight with something like awe in his voice.) 'That, gentleman and–er–madam, is how I knew of you and how I came to invite here tonight what I have learned through my own experience to be the aristocracy, if I may so describe it, of American crime.'

Bond was impressed. Goldfinger had, in three minutes flat, got the meeting on his side. Now everyone was looking towards Goldfinger with profound attention. Even Miss Pussy Galore's eyes were rapt. Bond knew nothing about the Golden Poppy Distributors or the Happy Landings Agency, but they must have run like clockwork from the expressions on their former customers' faces. Now everyone was hanging on Goldfinger's words as if he was Einstein.

Goldfinger's face showed no emotion. He made a throwaway gesture of his right hand. He said flatly, 'I have mentioned two projects of mine that were successful. They were small. There have been many others of a higher calibre. Not one of them has failed, and, so far as I know, my name is on the police files of no country. I say this to show you that I thoroughly understand my–our–profession. And now, gentlemen and madam, I propose to offer you partnership in an undertaking that will assuredly place in each of your treasuries, within one week, the sum of one billion dollars.' Mr Goldfinger held up his hand. 'We have different views in Europe and America as to what constitutes the arithmetical expression "a billion". I use the word in the sense of one thousand million. Do I make myself clear?'

Chapter Eighteen

Crime de la Crime

A tug hooted on the river. Another answered. A flurry of engine noises receded.

Mr Jed Midnight, on Bond's right, cleared his throat. He said emphatically, 'Mister Gold, or whatever your name is, don't you worry about definitions. A billion dollars is a lot of money whichever way you say it. Keep talking.'

Mr Solo raised slow black eyes and looked across the table at Goldfinger. He said, 'Is very moch money, yess. But how moch your cut, mister?'

'Five billion.'

Jack Strap from Las Vegas gave a short boisterous laugh. 'Listen fellers, what's a few billion between friends. If Mister–er–Whoosis can lead me to a billion dollars I'll be glad to slip him a fin or even maybe a mega-fin for his trouble. Don't let's be small-minded about this, huh?'

Mr Helmut Springer tapped his monocle on the gold brick in front of him. Everyone looked towards him. 'Mister–ah–Gold.' It was the grave voice of the family lawyer. 'These are big figures you mention. As I understand it, a total of some eleven billion dollars is involved.'

Mr Goldfinger said with precision, 'The exact figure will be nearer fifteen billion. For convenience I referred only to the amounts I thought it would be possible for us to carry away.'

A sharp excited giggle came from Mr Billy Ring.

'Quite, quite, Mr Gold.' Mr Springer screwed his monocle back into his eye to observe Goldfinger's reactions. 'But quantities of bullion or currency to that amount are to be gathered together in only three depositories in the United States. They are the Federal Mint in Washington, the Federal Reserve Bank in New York City, and Fort Knox in Kentucky. Do you intend that we should–er–"knock off" one of these? And if so which?'

'Fort Knox.'

Amid the chorus of groans, Mr Midnight said resignedly, 'Mister, I never met any guy outside Hollywood that had what you've got. There it's called "vision". And vision, mister, is a talent for mistaking spots before the eyes for fabulous projects. You should have a talk with your head-shrinker or get yourself Miltownized.' Mr Midnight shook his head sorrowfully. 'Too bad. That billion sure felt good while I had it.'

Miss Pussy Galore said in a deep, bored voice, 'Sorry mister, none of my set of bent pins could take that kind of piggy-bank.' She made to get up.

Goldfinger said amiably, 'Now hear me through, gentlemen and–er–madam. Your reaction was not unexpected. Let me put it this way: Fort Knox is a bank like any other bank. But it is a much bigger bank and its protective devices are correspondingly stronger and more ingenious. To penetrate them will require corresponding strength and ingenuity. That is the only novelty in my project–that it is a big one. Nothing else. Fort Knox is no more impregnable than other fortresses. No doubt we all thought the Brink organization was unbeatable until half a dozen determined men robbed a Brink-armoured car of a million dollars back in 1950. It is impossible to escape from Sing Sing and yet men have found ways of escaping from it. No, no, gentlemen. Fort Knox is a myth like other myths. Shall I proceed to the plan?'

Billy Ring hissed through his teeth, like a Japanese, when he talked. He said harshly, 'Listen, shamus, mebbe ya didn't know it, but the Third Armoured is located at Fort Knox. If that's a myth, why don't the Russkis come and take the United States the next time they have a team over here playing ice-hockey?'

Goldfinger smiled thinly. 'If I may correct you without weakening your case, Mr Ring, the following is the order of battle of the military units presently quartered at Fort Knox. Of the Third Armoured Division, there is only the Spearhead, but there are also the 6th Armoured Cavalry Regiment, the 15th Armoured Group, the 160th Engineer Group and approximately half a division from all units of the United States Army currently going through the Armoured Replacement Training Centre and Military Human Research Unit No. 1. There is also a considerable body of men associated with Continental Armoured Command Board No. 2, the Army Maintenance Board and various activities connected with the Armoured Centre. In addition there is a police force consisting of twenty officers and some four hundred enlisted men. In short, out of a total population of some sixty thousand, approximately twenty thousand are combat troops of one sort or another.'

'And who's going to say boo to them?' jeered Mr Jack Strap through his cigar. Without waiting for an answer he disgustedly tore the tattered stump out of his mouth and mashed it to fragments in the ash-tray.

Next to him Miss Pussy Galore sucked her teeth sharply with the incisiveness of a parrot spitting. She said, 'Go buy yourself some better smokes, Jacko. That thing smells like burning wrestlers' trunks.'

'Shove it, Puss,' said Mr Strap inelegantly.

Miss Galore was determined to have the last word. She said sweetly, 'Know what, Jacko? I could go for a he-man like you. Matter of fact I wrote a song about you the other day. Care to hear its title? It's called "If I had to do it all over again, I'd do it all over you".'

A bray of laughter came from Mr Midnight, a high giggle from Mr Ring. Goldfinger tapped lightly for order. He said patiently, 'Now hear me through, please, gentlemen.' He got up and walked to the blackboard and pulled a roll map down over it. It was a detailed town map of Fort Knox including the Godman Army Airfield and the roads and railway tracks leading into the town. The committee members on the right of the table swivelled their chairs. Goldfinger pointed to the Bullion Depository. It was down on the left-hand corner enclosed in a triangle formed by the Dixie

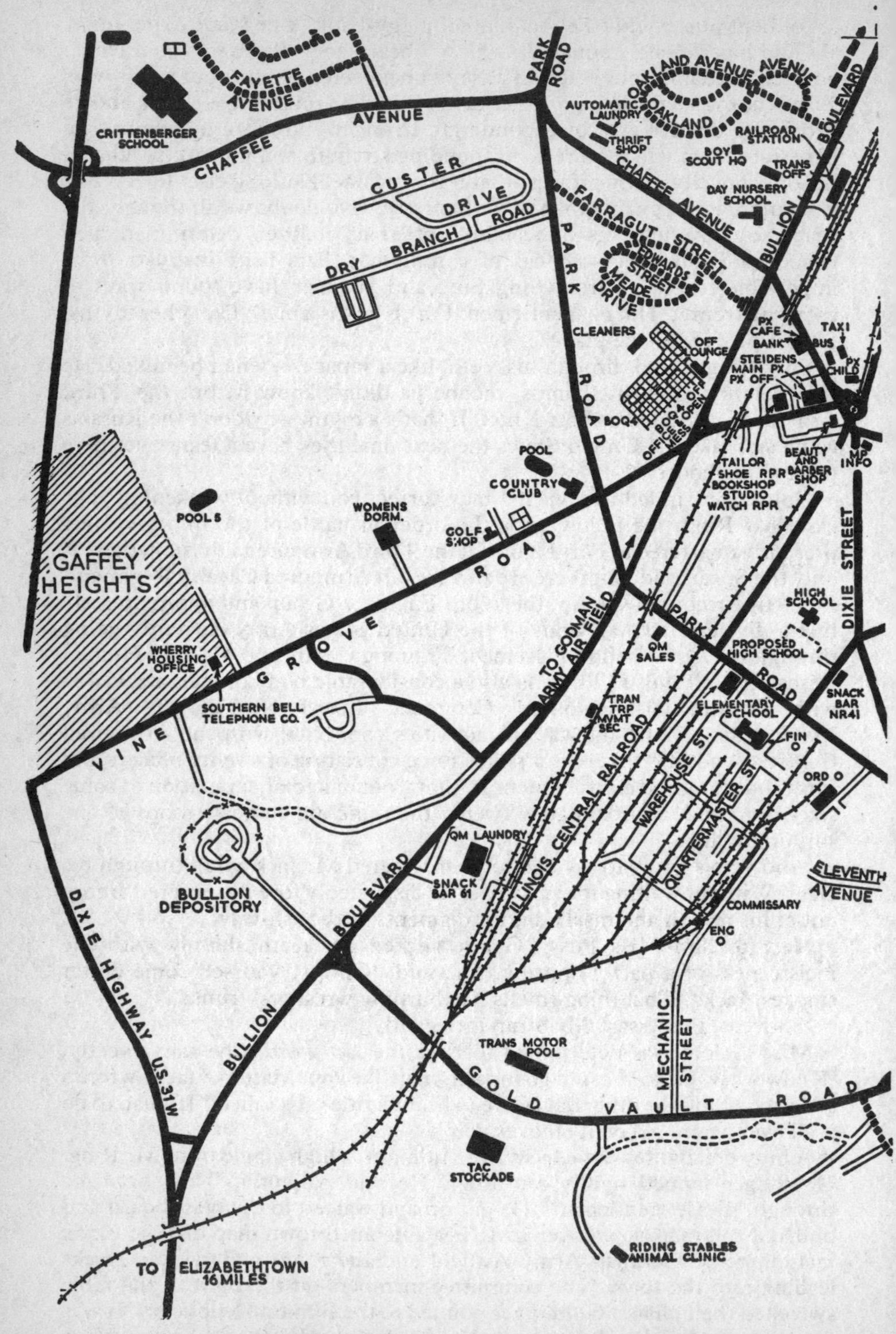

FAYETTE AVENUE
CRITTENBERGER SCHOOL
CHAFFEE AVENUE
PARK ROAD
OAKLAND AVENUE
AVENUE
OAKLAND
AUTOMATIC LAUNDRY
THRIFT SHOP
BOY SCOUT HQ
RAILROAD STATION
TRANS OFF
BOULEVARD
CUSTER DRIVE
DRY BRANCH ROAD
FARRAGUT STREET
CHAFFEE AVENUE
DAY NURSERY SCHOOL
BULLION
EDWARDS STREET
MEADE DRIVE
PARK ROAD
CLEANERS
OFF LOUNGE
PX CAFE
BANK
TAXI
BUS
PX CHILD
STEIDENS MAIN PX
PX OFF
BOQ4
OFFICE BOQ 4 MESS
ICE OPEN
BEAUTY AND BARBER SHOP
MP INFO
TAILOR
SHOE RPR
BOOKSHOP
STUDIO
WATCH RPR
POOL
COUNTRY CLUB
POOL 5
WOMENS DORM.
GOLF SHOP
GAFFEY HEIGHTS
ROAD
GROVE
VINE
DIXIE STREET
HIGH SCHOOL
PROPOSED HIGH SCHOOL
QM SALES
PARK ROAD
WHERRY HOUSING OFFICE
SOUTHERN BELL TELEPHONE CO.
TO GODMAN ARMY AIR FIELD
TRAN TRP MVMT SEC
ELEMENTARY SCHOOL
SNACK BAR NR41
FIN
ORD
WAREHOUSE ST.
QUARTERMASTER ST
ILLINOIS CENTRAL RAILROAD
QM LAUNDRY
SNACK BAR 61
BULLION DEPOSITORY
BOULEVARD
ELEVENTH AVENUE
COMMISSARY
ENG
DIXIE HIGHWAY
US. 31W
BULLION
TRANS MOTOR POOL
MECHANIC STREET
GOLD VAULT ROAD
TAC STOCKADE
RIDING STABLES
ANIMAL CLINIC
TO ELIZABETHTOWN 16 MILES

Highway, Bullion Boulevard and Vine Grove Road. Goldfinger said, 'I will show you a detailed plan of the depository in just a moment.' He paused. 'Now, gentlemen, allow me to point out the main features of this fairly straightforward township. Here'–he ran his finger from the top centre of the map down through the town and out beyond the Bullion Depository–'runs the line of the Illinois Central Railroad from Louisville, thirty-five miles to the north, through the town and on to Elizabethtown eighteen miles to the south. We are not concerned with Brandenburg Station in the centre of the town, but with this complex of sidings adjoining the Bullion Vault. That is one of the loading and unloading bays for the bullion from the Mint in Washington. Other methods of transport to the vault, which are varied in no particular rotation for security reasons, are by truck convoy down the Dixie Highway or by freight plane to Godman Airfield. As you can see, the vault is isolated from these routes and stands alone without any natural cover whatsoever in the centre of approximately fifty acres of grassland. Only one road leads to the vault, a fifty-yard driveway through heavily armed gates on Bullion Boulevard. Once inside the armoured stockade, the trucks proceed on to this circular road which runs round the vault to the rear entrance where the bullion is unloaded. That circular road, gentlemen, is manufactured out of steel plates or flaps. These plates are on hinges and in an emergency the entire steel surface of the road can be raised hydraulically to create a second internal stockade of steel. Not so obvious to the eye, but known to me, is that an underground delivery tunnel runs below the plain between Bullion Boulevard and Vine Grove Road. This serves as an additional means of access to the vault through steel doors that lead from the wall of the tunnel to the first sub-ground floor of the depository.'

Goldfinger paused and stood away from the map. He looked round the table. 'All right, gentlemen. There is the vault and those are the main approaches to it with the exception of its front door which is purely an entrance to the reception hall and offices. Any questions?'

There were none. All eyes were on Goldfinger, waiting. Once again the authority of his words had gripped them. This man seemed to know more about the secrets of Fort Knox than had ever been released to the outside world.

Goldfinger turned back to the blackboard and pulled down a second map over the first. This was the detailed plan of the Gold Vault. Goldfinger said, 'Well, gentlemen, you can see that this is an immensely solid two-storey building somewhat like a square, two-layered cake. You will notice that the roof has been stepped for bomb protection, and you will observe the four pill boxes on the ground at the four corners. These are of steel and are connected with the interior of the building. The exterior dimensions of the vault are a hundred and five by a hundred and twenty-one feet. The height from ground level is forty-two feet. The construction is of Tennessee granite, steel-lined. The exact constituents are: sixteen thousand cubic feet of granite, four thousand cubic yards of concrete, seven hundred and fifty tons of reinforcing steel and seven hundred and sixty tons of structural steel. Right? Now, within the building, there is a two-storey steel and concrete vault divided into compartments. The vault door weighs more than twenty tons and the casing of the vault is of steel plates, steel I-beams and steel cylinders laced with hoop-bands and encased in concrete. The roof is of similar construction and is independent of the roof of the building. A corridor encircles the vault at both levels and gives access both to the vault and to the offices and storerooms that are housed in the outer wall of the building. No one person is entrusted with the combination to the door of the vault. Various senior members of the depository staff must separately dial combinations known only to each of them. Naturally the building is equipped with the latest and finest protective devices. There is a strong guard-post within the building and immensely powerful reinforcements are at all times available from the Armoured Centre less than a mile distant. Do you follow me? Now, as to the actual content of the vault–these amount, as I said earlier, to some fifteen billion dollars' worth of standard mint bars one thousand fine. Each bar is double the size of the one before you and contains four hundred Troy ounces, the avoirdupois weight being some twenty-seven and a half pounds. These are stored without wrappings in the compartments of the vault.' Goldfinger glanced round the table. 'And that, gentlemen and madam,' he concluded flatly, 'is all I can tell you, and all I think we need to know, about the nature and contents of Fort Knox Depository. Unless there are any questions at this stage, I will proceed to a brief explanation of how this depository may be penetrated and its contents seized.'

There was silence. The eyes round the table were rapt, intent. Nervously, Mr Jack Strap took a medium-sized cigar out of his vest pocket and stuffed it in the corner of his mouth.

Pussy Galore said sternly, 'If you set fire to that thing I swear I'll kayo you with my gold brick.' She took a threatening hold of the bar.

'Take it easy, kid,' said Mr Strap out of the corner of his mouth.

Mr Jed Midnight commented decisively, 'Mister, if you can heist that joint, you got yourself a summum cum laude. Go ahead and tell. This is either a bust or the Crime de la Crime.'

Goldfinger said indifferently, 'Very well, gentlemen. You shall hear the plan.' He paused and looked carefully round the table and into each pair of eyes in turn. 'But I hope you understand that total security must now prevail. What I have said so far, if repeated, would be taken for the maunderings of a lunatic. What I am about to say will involve all of us in the greatest peace-time conspiracy in the history of the United States. May I take it that we are all bound by an oath of absolute secrecy?'

Almost instinctively, Bond watched the eyes of Mr Helmut Springer from Detroit. While affirmatives in various tones of voice came from the others, Mr Springer veiled his eyes. His portentous 'You have my solemn word' rang hollow. To Bond, the candour was as false as a second-hand motor salesman's. Casually he drew a short straight minus line beside Mr Springer's name on the agenda.

'Very well then.' Goldfinger returned to his seat at the table. He sat down, picked up his pencil and began talking to it in a thoughtful, conversational voice. 'First, and in some ways most difficult, is the question of disposal. One billion dollars of gold bullion weighs approximately one thousand tons. To transport this amount would require one hundred ten-ton trucks or some twenty six-wheel heavy industry road transporters. I recommend the latter vehicles. I have a list of the charter companies who hire out this type of vehicle and I recommend that, if we are to be partners, you should proceed immediately after this meeting to contracting with the relevant companies in your territories. For obvious reasons you will all wish to engage your own drivers and this I must leave in your hands. No doubt'–Mr Goldfinger allowed himself the ghost of a smile–'the Teamsters' Union will prove a fruitful source for reliable men and you will perhaps consider recruiting ex-drivers from the Negro Red Ball Express that served the American armies during the war. However, these are details requiring exact planning and co-ordination. There will also be a traffic control problem and no doubt you will make arrangements among yourselves for sharing out the available roads. Transport aircraft will be a subsidiary source of mobility and arrangements will be made to keep open the north-south runway on the Godman Airfield. Your subsequent disposal of the bullion will, of course, be your own affair. For my part'–Goldfinger looked coolly round the table–'I shall initially be using the railroad and, since I have a bulkier transport problem, I trust you will allow me to reserve this means of egress for my own.' Goldfinger did not wait for comment. He continued in an even tone: 'Compared with this problem of transport, the other arrangements will be relatively simple. To begin with, on D – 1, I propose to put the entire population, military and civilian, of Fort Knox temporarily out of action. Exact arrangements have been made and only await my signal. Briefly, the town is supplied with all drinking and other water-supplies by two wells and two filter plants yielding just under seven million gallons per day. These are under the control of the Post Engineer. This gentleman has been pleased to accept a visit from the Superintendent and Deputy Superintendent of the Tokyo Municipal Waterworks who wish to study the workings of a plant of this size for installation in a new suburb planned for the environs of Tokyo. The Post Engineer has been much flattered by this request and the Japanese gentlemen will be accorded all facilities. These two gentlemen, who are, of course, members of my staff, will be carrying on their persons relatively small quantities of a highly concentrated opiate devised by the German chemical warfare experts for just this purpose during the last war. This substance disseminates rapidly through a volume of water of this magnitude, and, in its consequent highly diluted form, has the effect of instant but temporary narcosis of any person drinking half a tumbler of the infected water. The symptoms are a deep and instant sleep from which the victim awakens much refreshed in approximately three days. Gentlemen–' Goldfinger held out one hand palm upwards–'in the month of June in Kentucky I consider it out of the question that a single resident is able to go through twenty-four hours without consuming half a glass of water. There may perhaps be a handful of confirmed alcoholics on their feet on D-Day, but I anticipate that we shall enter a town in which virtually the entire population has fallen into a deep sleep where they stand.'

'What was that fairy-tale?' Miss Galore's eyes were shining with the vision.

'*Puss in Boots*,' said Mr Jack Strap in a surly voice. 'Go ahead, mister. This is good. How do we get into the town?'

'We come in,' said Goldfinger, 'on a special train that will have left New York City on the night of D – 1. There will be approximately one hundred of us and we shall be attired as Red Cross workers. Miss Galore will, I hope, provide the necessary contingent of nurses. It is to fill this minor but important role that she has been invited to this meeting.'

Miss Galore said enthusiastically, 'Wilco, Roger, over and out! My girls'll look sweet in starch. Whaddya say, Jacko?' She leant sideways and nudged Mr Strap in the ribs.

'I say they'd look better in cement overcoats,' said Mr Strap impatiently. 'Whaddya have to keep on butting in for? Keep going, mister.'

'At Louisville, thirty-five miles from Fort Knox, I myself and an assistant will ask to be allowed to ride in the leading diesel. We shall have delicate instruments. We shall say that it will be necessary for us to sample the air as we approach Fort Knox for, by this time, news of the mysterious affliction that has struck down the inhabitants will have reached the outer world and there is likely to be some panic in the surrounding area, and indeed in the country as a whole. Rescue planes may be expected to approach shortly after our arrival at dawn and an early task will be to man the control tower at Godman Airfield, declare the base closed and re-route all planes to Louisville. But, to go back for a moment, shortly after leaving Louisville, my assistant and I will dispose of the driver and fireman by as humane methods as are possible' (I bet, thought Bond) 'and I shall personally bring the train–I may say that I have the requisite knowledge of these locomotives–through Fort Knox to the bullion sidings alongside the depository.' Goldfinger paused. He looked with slow, grave eyes round the circle. Satisfied with what he saw, he continued in the same even tone. 'By this time, gentlemen and madam, your transport convoys should be arriving. The traffic controller will dispose them in the neighbourhood of the depository according to a pre-arranged plan, the airport staff will proceed by truck to Godman Airfield and take over, and we shall enter the depository, paying no heed to the sleeping bodies with which the landscape will be–er–decorated. Right?'

Mr Solo's dark eyes burned across the table. He said softly, 'Sure, is right so far. Now mebbe you–' he blew out his cheeks and gave a quick hard puff towards Goldfinger–'like this and the twenty-ton door he fall down. Yes?'

'Yes,' said Goldfinger equably. 'Almost exactly like that.' He rose and went to the table under the blackboard, lifted up the big ungainly carton and carried it carefully back and placed it on the table in front of him. It seemed to be very heavy.

He sat down and continued, 'While ten of my trained assistants are making preparations for the vault to be opened, stretcher teams will enter the depository and remove to safety as many of the inmates as can be located.' Bond thought he noticed a treacherous purr underlying Goldfinger's next words. 'I am sure you will all agree, gentlemen and madam, that all unnecessary loss of life should be avoided. Thus far, I hope you notice that there have been no casualties with the exception of two employees of the Illinois Central Railroad who have received sore heads.' Goldfinger didn't wait for comment but went on. 'Now,' he reached out and placed his hand on the carton, 'when you, gentlemen, and your associates have needed weapons, other than the conventional small arms, where have you found them? At military establishments, gentlemen. You have purchased sub-machine guns and other heavy equipment from quarter-master storekeepers at near-by military bases. You have achieved this by the use of pressure, blackmail or money. I have done the same. Only one weapon would be powerful enough to blast open the Bullion Vault at Fort Knox and I obtained one, after much seeking, from a certain allied military base in Germany. It cost me exactly one million dollars. This, gentlemen, is an atomic warhead designed for use with the Corporal Intermediate Range Guided Missile.'

'Cheesus Kerist.' Jed Midnight's hands reached for the edge of the table beside Bond and gripped it.

All the faces round the table were pale. Bond could feel the skin taut over his own tensed jaw. To break his tension he reached inside his coat pocket for the Chesterfields and lit one. He slowly blew out the flame and put the lighter back in his pocket. God Almighty! What had he got himself into? Bond looked back down the vista of his knowledge of Goldfinger. The first meeting with the naked brown body on the roof of the Floridiana Cabana Club. The casual way he had rapped Goldfinger's knuckles. The interview with M. The meeting at the bank at which it had been a question of tracking down a gold smuggler–admittedly a big one and one who worked for the Russians–but still only a man-sized criminal, someone Bond had taken trouble to beat at golf and then had pursued coolly, efficiently, but still as only one more quarry like so many others. And now! Now it was not a rabbit in the rabbit hole, not even a fox, it was a king cobra–the biggest, most deadly inhabitant of the world! Bond sighed wearily. Once more into the breach, dear friends! This time it really was St George and the dragon. And St George had better get a move on and do something before the dragon hatched the little dragon's egg he was now nesting so confidently. Bond smiled tautly. Do what? What in God's name was there he could do?

Goldfinger held up his hand. 'Gentlemen and madam, believe me, this object is an entirely harmless lump of machinery. It is not armed. If I hit it with a hammer it would not explode. Nothing can make it explode until it is armed and that will not happen until The Day.'

Mr Billy Ring's pale face was shiny with sweat. The words trembled slightly as they hissed out through the false grin. 'Mister, what . . . what about this thing they call–er–fall-out?'

'Fall-out will be minimal, Mr Ring, and extremely localized. This is the latest model–the so-called "clean" atomic bomb. But protection suits will be issued to the squad that first enters the ruins of the building. They will form the first in the human chain that will remove the gold and pass it to the waiting trucks.'

'Flying debris, Mister? Chunks of concrete and steel and so forth?' Mr Midnight's voice came from somewhere in his stomach.

'We shall take shelter behind the outer steel stockade of the depository, Mr Midnight. All personnel will wear ear-plugs. There may be minor damage to some of the trucks, but that hazard must be accepted.'

'Da sleeping guys?' Mr Solo's eyes were greedy. 'Mebbe dey jess sleeps a liddle longer?' Mr Solo obviously didn't worry too much about the sleeping guys.

'We shall move as many as possible to safety. We must, I am afraid, accept minor damage to the town. I estimate that casualties among the population will approximately equal three days' toll on the roads of Fort Knox. Our operation will merely serve to keep road accident statistics at a steady level.'

'Damn nice of us.' Mr Midnight's nerves had now recovered.

'Any more questions?' Goldfinger's voice was bland. He had read out the figures, estimated the prospects for the business. Now it was time to put the meeting to the vote. 'Details remain to be worked out exactly. In that, my staff here'–he turned first to Bond and then to Miss Masterton–'will be assisting me. This room will be our operations room to which you will all have access by day or by night. The code word for the project is "Operation

Grand Slam", which will always be used in referring to the project. May I suggest that those of you who wish to participate should brief one, and only one, of your most trusted lieutenants. Other staff can be trained for their functions as if this were a run-of-the-mill bank robbery. On D–1 a slightly wider briefing of staff will be necessary. I know I can rely on you, gentlemen and madam, if you decide to participate, to treat this whole project as an operation of war. Inefficiency or insecurity will of course have to be dealt with decisively. And now, gentlemen and madam, I will ask you to reply on behalf of your respective organizations. Which of you wishes to enter this race? The prize is gigantic. The risks are minimal. Mr Midnight?' Goldfinger turned his head an inch to the right. Bond saw the wide open X-ray gaze devour his neighbour. 'Yes?' There was a pause. 'Or no?'

Chapter Nineteen

Secret Appendix

'Mr Gold,' Jed Midnight pronounced sonorously, 'you are undoubtedly the greatest thing in crime since Cain invented murder and used it on Abel.' He paused and added emphatically, 'I shall count it an honour to be associated with you in this enterprise.'

'Thank you, Mr Midnight. And you, Mr Ring?'

Bond was doubtful about Mr Billy Ring. He had scrawled plusses against all the names except Ring and Helmut Springer. To Mr Ring he had allotted a nought, to Springer a minus sign. He had come to his conclusions by watching eyes, mouths, hands, but nothing had been betrayed by The Grinner's unwavering false smile. The wink in his right eye had been as steady on the pulse-beat as a metronome and he had kept his hands below the table.

Now Billy Ring brought his hands up from below the table and formed a cat's cradle with them on the green baize in front of him. For a moment he watched the two thumbs twirling, then he raised his nightmare face to Goldfinger's. The tic in his right eye had stopped. The two rows of teeth began to operate like a ventriloquist's dummy. 'Mister–' he found difficulty with his b's, m's and p's and produced them by bringing his upper lip down over his teeth like a horse does when it takes sugar out of your hand–'long time now my friends and I been back in legal. What I mean, the old days of leaving corpses strewn all over the landscape went out with the 'forties. Me and my associates, we do all right with the girls, the hemp, and the racetrack, and when we're short there's our good friends the Unions to slip us the odd fin. Ya see, mister–' The Grinner opened his hands and then put them back into the cradle–'we figger the old days are gone. Big Jim Colossimo, Johnny Torrio, Dion O'Bannion, Al Capone–where are those guys today, huh? Mister, they're pushing up the morning glory by the fence. Mebbe you weren't around in the days when we used to hide up between fights in Little Bohemia up behind Milwaukee? Well, siree, in those days, people were shooting at each other so fast you'd often need a programme to tell the act from the spectators. So all right, people got tired of it–those that hadn't already got tired to death, if you get my meaning–and when the 'fifties come along and I take over the team, it's unanimous that we get out of the fireworks business. And now what, mister? Now you come along and put it to me that me and my friends assist you to let off the biggest fizzbang in history! So what do I figger to say to your proposition, Mister–er–Whoosis? Well, I tell you, mister. Everybody's got his price, see?–and for a billion dollars it's a deal. We'll put away the marbles and bring out the sling-shots. We're in.'

'Grinner, you sure take one hell of a long time to say yes,' commented Mr Midnight sourly.

Goldfinger said cordially, 'Thank you for your most interesting statement, Mr Ring. I am very happy to welcome you and your associates. Mr Solo?'

Mr Solo prefaced his reply by reaching into his coat pocket and taking out a battery shaver. He switched it on. The room filled with the noise of angry bees. Mr Solo leant his head back and began running the machine thoughtfully up the right side of his face while his uptilted eyes sought decision in the ceiling. Suddenly he switched the razor off, put it down on the table in front of him and jerked his head down and forward like a snake striking. The black gun-muzzles of his eyes pointed threateningly across the table at Goldfinger and moved slowly from feature to feature of the big moon-face. Half Mr Solo's own face now looked naked. The other half was dark with the Italian swarthiness that comes from an uncontrollable beard growth. Bond guessed that he probably had to shave every three or four hours. Now Mr Solo decided to speak. He spoke in a voice that brought chill into the room. He said softly, 'Mister, I been watching you. You are a very relaxed man for someone who speaks such big things. Last man I knew was so much relaxed he got himself totally relaxed by a quick burst of the chopper. Okay, okay.' Mr Solo sat back. He spread open palms in reluctant surrender. 'So I come in, yes. But mister–' there was a pause for emphasis–'either we get that billion or you get dead. Is okay with you?'

Goldfinger's lips bent ironically. 'Thank you, Mr Solo. Your conditions are quite acceptable. I have every wish to stay alive. Mr Helmut Springer?'

Mr Springer's eyes looked deader than ever. He said pompously. 'I am still giving the matter my full consideration. Pray consult my colleagues while I deliberate.'

Mr Midnight commented impatiently, 'Same old Hell. Waits for what he calls inspiration. He's guided–messages from the Almighty on the angels' wavelength. I guess he hasn't heard a human voice in twenty years.'

'And Mr Strap?'

Mr Jack Strap crinkled his eyes at Goldfinger. He said smoothly, 'Mister, I figure you know the odds and you surely pay the best since one of our machines at Vegas got the trots and gave continuous jackpots. I guess if we provide the muscles and the guns this caper'll pay off. You can count me in.' Mr Strap turned off the charm. His eyes, now frightening again, turned, with Goldfinger's, to Miss Pussy Galore.

Miss Galore veiled her violet eyes so as not to have to look at either of them. She said indifferently to the room at large, 'Business ain't been so brisk in my corner of the woods.' She tapped with long, silver-painted finger-nails on the gold bar before her. 'Mind you, I won't say I'm overdrawn at the bank. Let's put it I'm just a shade under-deposited. Yup. Sure I'll come in. Me and my gals got to eat.'

Goldfinger allowed himself a half-smile of sympathy. 'That is excellent news, Miss Galore. And now,' he turned to face across the table, 'Mr Springer, might we ask if you have made up your mind?'

Slowly Mr Springer rose to his feet. He gave the controlled yawn of an opera-goer. He followed the yawn with a small belch. He took out a fine linen handkerchief and patted his lips. His glazed eyes moved round the table and finally rested on Goldfinger. Slowly his head moved from side to side as if he was trying to exercise fibrositis in his neck muscles. He said gravely, like a bank manager refusing a loan, 'Mr Gold, I fear your proposal would not find favour with my colleagues in Detroit.' He gave a little bow which included everyone. 'It only remains for me to thank you for a most interesting occasion. Good afternoon, gentlemen and madam.' In the chilly silence, Mr Springer tucked his handkerchief carefully into the left-hand cuff of his immaculate pin-stripe, turned and walked softly to the door and let himself out.

The door closed with a sharp click. Bond noticed Goldfinger's hand slip casually below the table. He guessed that Oddjob was getting his signal. Signal for what?

Mr Midnight said nastily, 'Glad he's out. He's strictly a four-ulcer man. Now then–' he got up briskly and turned to Bond–'how about a little drink?'

They all rose and gathered round the buffet. Bond found himself between Miss Pussy Galore and Tilly Masterton. He offered them champagne. Miss Galore looked at him coldly and said, 'Move over, Handsome. Us girls want to talk secrets. Don't we, yummy?' Miss Masterton blushed and then turned very pale. She whispered adoringly, 'Oh yes please, Miss Galore.'

Bond smiled sourly at Tilly Masterton and moved down the room.

Jed Midnight had witnessed the snub. He got close to Bond and said earnestly, 'Mister, if that's your doll, you better watch her. Pussy gets the girls she wants. She consumes them in bunches–like grapes, if you follow me.' Mr Midnight sighed wearily. 'Cheesus how they bore me, the lizzies! You'll see, she'll soon have that frail parting her hair three ways in front of the mirror.'

Bond said cheerfully, 'I'll watch out. There's nothing much I can do. She's an independent sort of a girl.'

'That so?' said Mr Midnight with a spark of interest. 'Well mebbe I can help to break it up.' He straightened his tie. 'I could go for that Masterton. She's sure got natural resources. See you around.' He grinned at Bond and moved off down the room.

Bond was having a quiet square meal off caviar and champagne and thinking how well Goldfinger had handled the meeting when the door at the end of the room opened and one of the Koreans hurried in and went up to Goldfinger. Goldfinger bent his head to the whispered words. His face became grave. He rapped a fork on his glass of Saratoga Vichy.

'Gentlemen and madam.' He looked sadly round the group. 'I have received bad news. Our friend Mr Helmut Springer has met with an accident. He fell down the stairs. Death was instantaneous.'

'Ho, ho!' Mr Ring's laugh was not a laugh. It was a hole in the face. 'And what does that Slappy Hapgood, his torpedo, have to say about it?'

Goldfinger said gravely, 'Alas, Mr Hapgood also fell down the stairs and has succumbed to his injuries.'

Mr Solo looked at Goldfinger with new respect. He said softly, 'Mister, you better get those stairs fixed before me and my friend Giulio come to use them.'

Goldfinger said seriously, 'The fault has been located. Repairs will be put in hand at once.' His face grew thoughtful. 'I fear these accidents may be misconstrued in Detroit.'

Jed Midnight said cheerfully, 'Don't give it a thought, mister. They love funerals up there. And it'll take a load off their minds. Old Hell wouldn't have lasted much longer. They been stoking the fires under him these twelve months.' He appealed to Mr Strap who stood next to him. 'Am I right, Jacko?'

'Sure, Jed,' said Mr Strap sagely. 'You got the score. Mr Helmut M. Springer had to be hit.'

'Hit'–mobese for murder. When Bond at last got to bed that night, he couldn't wipe the word out of his mind. Oddjob had got the signal, a double ring, and Springer and his guard had got hit. There had been nothing Bond could have done about it–even if he had wanted to, and Mr Helmut Springer meant nothing to him, probably richly deserved to be hit anyway–but now some 59,998 other people were going to get hit unless he, and only he, could do something about it.

When the meeting of paramount hoods had broken up to go about their various duties, Goldfinger had dismissed the girl and kept Bond in the room. He told Bond to take notes and then for more than two hours went over the operation down to the smallest detail. When they came to the doping of the two reservoirs (Bond had to work out an exact timetable to ensure that the people of Fort Knox would all be 'under' in good time) Bond had asked for details of the drug and its speed of action.

'You won't have to worry about that.'

'Why not? Everything depends on it.'

'Mr Bond.' Goldfinger's eyes had a faraway, withdrawn look. 'I will tell you the truth because you will have no opportunity of passing it on. From now, Oddjob will not be more than a yard from your side and his orders will be strict and exact. So I can tell you that the entire population of Fort Knox will be dead or incapacitated by midnight on D–1. The substance that will be inserted in the water supply, outside the filter plant, will be a highly concentrated form of GB.'

'You're mad! You don't really mean you're going to kill sixty thousand people!'

'Why not? American motorists do it every two years.'

Bond stared into Goldfinger's face in fascinated horror. It couldn't be true! He couldn't mean it! He said tensely, 'What's this GB?'

'GB is the most powerful of the Trilone group of nerve poisons. It was perfected by the Wehrmacht in 1943, but never used for fear of reprisals. In fact, it is a more effective instrument of destruction than the hydrogen bomb. Its disadvantage lies in the difficulty of applying it to the populace. The Russians captured the entire German stocks at Dyhernfurth on the Polish frontier. Friends of mine were able to supply me with the necessary quantities. Introduction through the water supply is an ideal method of applying it to a densely populated area.'

Bond said, 'Goldfinger, you're a lousy, —— bastard.'

'Don't be childish. We have work to do.'

Later, when they had got to the problem of transporting the tons of gold out of the town, Bond had had one last try. He said, 'Goldfinger, you're not going to get this stuff away. Nobody's going to get their hundred tons of gold out of the place–let alone five hundred. You'll find yourself tearing down the Dixie Highway in a truck with a few gold bars loaded with gamma rays and the American Army on your tail. And you'll have killed sixty thousand people for that? The thing's farcical. Even if you do get a ton or two away, where the hell do you think you're going to hide it?'

'Mr Bond.' Goldfinger's patience was infinite. 'It just happens that a Soviet cruiser of the *Sverdlovsk* class will be visiting Norfolk, Virginia, on a goodwill cruise at that time. It sails from Norfolk on D+1. Initially by train and then by transporter convoy, my gold will arrive on board the cruiser by midnight on D-Day. I shall sail in the cruiser for Kronstadt. Everything has been carefully planned, every possible hitch has been foreseen. I have lived with this operation for five years. Now the time has come for the performance. I have tidied up my activities in England and Europe. Such small debris as remains of my former life can go to the scavengers who will shortly be sniffing on my trail. I shall be gone. I shall have emigrated and, Mr Bond, I shall have taken the golden heart of America with me. Naturally'–Goldfinger was indulgent–'this unique performance will not be immaculate. There has not been enough time for rehearsals. I need these clumsy gangsters with their guns and their men, but I could not bring them into the plan until the last moment. They will make mistakes. Conceivably they will have much trouble getting their own loot away. Some will be caught, others killed. I couldn't care less. These men are amateurs who were needed, so to speak, for the crowd scenes. They are extras, Mr Bond, brought in off the streets. What happens to them after the play is of no interest to me whatsoever. And now, on with the work. I shall need seven copies of all this by nightfall. Where were we . . .?'

So in fact, reflected Bond feverishly, this was not only a Goldfinger operation with SMERSH in the background. SMERSH had even got the High Praesidium to play. This was Russia versus America with Goldfinger as the spearhead! Was it an act of war to steal something from another country? But who would know that Russia had the gold? No one, if the plan went off as Goldfinger intended. None of the gangsters had an inkling. To them Goldfinger was just another of them, another gangster, slightly larger than life-size. And Goldfinger's staff, his drivers for the golden convoy to the coast? Bond himself, and Tilly Masterton? Some would be killed, including him and the girl. Some, the Koreans for instance, would no doubt sail in the cruiser. Not a trace would be left, not a witness. It was modern piracy with all the old-time trimmings. Goldfinger was sacking Fort Knox as Bloody Morgan had sacked Panama. There was no difference except that the weapons and the techniques had been brought up to date.

And there was only one man in the whole world who could stop it. But how?

The next day was an unending blizzard of paper-work. Every half-hour a note would come in from Goldfinger's operations room asking for schedules of this, copies of that, estimates, timetables, lists of stores. Another typewriter was brought in, maps, reference books–anything that Bond requisitioned. But not once did Oddjob relax the extreme care with which he opened the door to Bond's knock, not once did his watchful eyes wander from Bond's eyes, hands, feet when he came into the room to bring meals or notes or supplies. There was no question of Bond and the girl being part of the team. They were dangerous slaves and nothing else.

Tilly Masterton was equally reserved. She worked like a machine–quick, willing, accurate, but uncommunicative. She responded with cool politeness to Bond's early attempts to make friends, share his thoughts with her. By the evening, he had learnt nothing about her except that she had been a successful amateur ice-skater in between secretarial work for Unilevers. Then she had started getting star parts in ice-shows. Her hobby had been indoor pistol and rifle shooting and she had belonged to two marksman clubs. She had few friends. She had never been in love or engaged. She lived by herself in two rooms in Earls Court. She was twenty-four. Yes, she realized that they were in a bad fix. But something would turn up. This Fort Knox business was nonsense. It would certainly go wrong. She thought Miss Pussy Galore was 'divine'. She somehow seemed to count on her to get her out of this mess. Women, with a sniff, were rather good at things that needed finesse. Instinct told them what to do. Bond was not to worry about her. She would be all right.

Bond came to the conclusion that Tilly Masterton was one of those girls whose hormones had got mixed up. He knew the type well and thought they and their male counterparts were a direct consequence of giving votes to women and 'sex equality'. As a result of fifty years of emancipation, feminine qualities were dying out or being transferred to the males. Pansies of both sexes were everywhere, not yet completely homosexual, but confused, not knowing what they were. The result was a herd of unhappy sexual misfits–barren and full of frustrations, the women wanting to dominate and the men to be nannied. He was sorry for them, but he had no time for them. Bond smiled sourly to himself as he remembered his fantasies about this girl as they sped along the valley of the Loire. Entre Deux Seins indeed!

At the end of the day, there was a final note from Goldfinger:

> Five principals and myself will leave La Guardia Airport tomorrow at 11 a.m. in chartered plane flown by my pilots for aerial survey of Grand Slam. You will accompany. Masterton will remain. G.

Bond sat on the edge of his bed and looked at the wall. Then he got up and went to the typewriter. He worked for an hour, typing, single-spaced, on both sides of the sheet, exact details of the operation. He folded the sheet, rolled it to a small cylinder about the size of his little finger and sealed it carefully with gum. Next he typed on a slip of paper:

> URGENT AND VITAL. REWARD OF FIVE THOUSAND DOLLARS IS GUARANTEED WITH NO QUESTIONS ASKED TO THE FINDER WHO DELIVERS THIS MESSAGE UNOPENED TO FELIX LEITER CARE PINKERTON'S DETECTIVE AGENCY, 154 NASSAU STREET, NEW YORK CITY. IMMEDIATE CASH ON DELIVERY.

Bond rolled this message round the cylinder, wrote $5,000 REWARD in red ink on the outside, and stuck the little package down the centre of three inches of Scotch tape. Then he sat down again on the edge of the bed and carefully strapped the free ends of the Scotch tape down the inside of his thigh.

Chapter Twenty

Journey into Holocaust

'Mister, Flying Control is buzzing us. Wants to know who we are. They say this is restricted air.'

Goldfinger got up from his seat and went forward into the cockpit. Bond watched him pick up the hand microphone. His voice came back clearly over the quiet hum of the ten-seater Executive Beechcraft. 'Good morning. This is Mr Gold of Paramount Pictures Corporation. We are carrying out an authorized survey of the territory for a forthcoming 'A' picture of the famous Confederate raid of 1861 which resulted in the capture of General Sherman at Muldraugh Hill. Yes, that's right. Cary Grant and Elizabeth Taylor in the lead. What's that? Clearance? Sure we've got clearance. Let me see now' (Goldfinger consulted nothing) '–yes, here it is. Signed by Chief of Special Services at the Pentagon. Sure, the Commanding Officer at the Armoured Centre will have a copy. Okay and thanks. Hope you'll enjoy the picture. 'Bye.'

Goldfinger wiped the breezy expression off his face, handed over the microphone and came back into the cabin. He braced his legs and stood looking down at his passengers. 'Well, gentlemen and madam, do you think you've seen enough? I think you'll agree it's all pretty clear and conforms with your copies of the town plan. I don't want to go much lower than six thousand. Perhaps we could make one more circuit and be off. Oddjob, get out the refreshments.'

There was a mumble of comment and questions which Goldfinger dealt with one by one. Oddjob got up from Bond's side and walked down to the rear. Bond followed him and, under his hard, suspicious stare, went into the little lavatory and locked the door.

He sat down calmly and thought. There hadn't been a chance on the way down to La Guardia. He had sat with Oddjob in the back of an unobtrusive Buick saloon. The doors had been locked on them by the driver and the windows tightly closed. Goldfinger had ridden in front, the partition closed behind him. Oddjob had sat slightly sideways, his horn-ridged hands held ready on his thighs like heavy tools. He had not taken his eyes off Bond until the car had driven round the boundary to the charter hangars and come up alongside the private plane. Sandwiched between Goldfinger and Oddjob, Bond had had no alternative but to climb up the steps into the plane and take his seat with Oddjob beside him. Ten minutes later, the others had arrived. There was no communication with them except an exchange of curt greetings. They were all different now–no smart remarks, no unnecessary talk. These were men who had gone to war. Even Pussy Galore, in a black

Dacron macintosh with a black leather belt, looked like some young S.S. guardsman. Once or twice in the plane she had turned and looked at Bond rather thoughtfully. But she hadn't answered his smile. Perhaps she just couldn't understand where Bond fitted in, who he was. When they got back to La Guardia there would be the same routine. It was now or never. But where? Among the leaves of lavatory paper? But they might be disturbed too soon or not for weeks. Would the ash-tray be emptied? Possibly not. But one thing would.

There was a rattle at the door-handle. Oddjob was getting restless. Perhaps Bond was setting fire to the plane. Bond called, 'Coming, ape.' He got up and lifted the seat. He tore the little package off the inside of his thigh and transferred it to the underside of the fore-edge of the seat. The seat would have to be lifted to get at the Elsan and that would certainly be looked to as soon as the plane got back to the hangar. The $5,000 REWARD stared back at him boldly. Not even the most hasty cleaner could miss it. So long as no one preceded the cleaner. But Bond didn't think any of the passengers would lift the seat. The little compartment was too cramped to stand comfortably in. He softly put the seat down, ran some water in the basin, washed his face and smoothed his hair and walked out.

Oddjob was waiting angrily. He pushed past Bond, looked carefully round the lavatory and came out again, shutting the door. Bond walked back to his seat. Now the SOS was in the bottle and the bottle had been committed to the waves. Who would be the finder? How soon?

Everyone, down to the pilot and co-pilot, went to the blasted little lavatory before they got back on the ground. As each one came out, Bond expected to feel the cold nose of a gun in his neck, the harsh suspicious words, the crackle of paper being unfolded. But at last they were back in the Buick and speeding over the Triborough into uptown Manhattan and then down the river on the parkway and in through the well-guarded doors of the warehouse and back to work.

Now it was a race–a race between Goldfinger's calm, unhurried, efficient machine and the tiny gunpowder trail Bond had lit. What was going on outside? During every hour of the next three days Bond's imagination followed what might be happening–Leiter telling his chief, the conference, the quick flight down to Washington, the F.B.I. and Hoover, the Army, the President. Leiter insisting that Bond's conditions be adhered to, that no suspicious moves be made, no inquiries started, that no one moved an inch except according to some master plan that would operate on the day and get the whole gang into the bag so that not one of them escaped. Would they accept Bond's conditions or would they not dare take the chance? Had they talked across the Atlantic with M? Had M insisted that Bond should be somehow pulled out? No, M would see the point. He would agree that Bond's life must be disregarded. That nothing must jeopardize the big clean-up. They would have to get the two 'Japanese', of course, somehow beat out of them the code message Goldfinger would be waiting for on D–1.

Was that how it was going, or was it all a shambles? Leiter away on another assignment. 'Who is this 007? What does it stand for? Some crazy loon. Hi, Smith, check on this, could you? Get down to the warehouse and take a look. Sorry, mister, no five grand for you. Here's car fare back to La Guardia. Afraid you've been hoaxed.'

Or, worse still, had none of these things happened? Was the plane still standing in a corner of the field, unserviced?

Night and day, the torment of thoughts went through Bond's head while the work got cleared and the hours ticked by and the deadly machine whirred quietly on. D–1 came and flashed by in a last fever of activity. Then, in the evening, came the note from Goldfinger.

> First phase of operation successful. Entrain as planned at midnight. Bring copies of all maps, schedules, operation orders. G.

In close formation, with Bond and Tilly Masterton–he in a white surgeon's coat, she dressed as a nurse–wedged in the middle, the Goldfinger contingent marched swiftly through the almost empty Concourse of Pennsylvania station and down to the waiting Special. Everyone, including Goldfinger, was wearing the conventional white garb and armbands of a medical field force and the dim platform was crowded with the ghostly waiting figures of the posses from the gangs. The silence and tension was appropriate for an emergency force hurrying to the scene of a disaster, and the stretchers and decontamination suits being loaded into the compartments added drama to the scene. The Superintendent was talking quietly with the senior physicians in the shape of Midnight, Strap, Solo and Ring. Near by stood Miss Galore with a dozen pale-faced nurses who waited with eyes bent as if they stood beside an open grace. Without make-up, their exotic hair-do's tucked into dark blue Red Cross caps, they had been well rehearsed. They were giving an excellent performance–dutiful, merciful, dedicated to the relief of human suffering.

When the Superintendent saw Goldfinger and his party approaching he hurried up. 'Dr Gold?' his face was grave. 'I'm afraid the news coming through isn't too good. Guess it'll all be in the papers tonight. All trains held at Louisville, no reply from the depot at Fort Knox. But we'll get you through all right. God Almighty, Doctor! What's going on down there? People coming through from Louisville are talking about the Russians spraying something from the air. Of course'–the Superintendent looked keenly at Goldfinger–'I'm not believing *that* kind of stuff. But what is it? Food poisoning?'

Goldfinger's face was solemn. He said in a kindly voice, 'My friend, that's what we've got to find out. That's why we're being rushed down. If you want me to make a guess, but mark you it's only a guess, it's a form of sleeping sickness–trypanosomiasis we call it.'

'That so?' the Superintendent was impressed by the sound of the malady. 'Well, believe you me, Doctor, we're all mighty proud of you and your folks of the Emergency Force.' He held out his hand, Goldfinger took it. 'Best of luck, Doc; and now, if you'll get your men and the nurses on board, I'll have this train on its way just as quick as may be.'

'Thank you, Superintendent. My colleagues and I will not forget your services.' Goldfinger gave a short bow. His contingent moved on.

'Board!'

Bond found himself in a Pullman with Tilly Masterton across the aisle and the Koreans and Germans all around them. Goldfinger was in the front of the car talking cheerfully with his satraps. Miss Pussy Galore strolled by. She ignored the upturned face of Tilly Masterton but gave Bond the usual searching glance. There was a banging of doors being closed. Pussy Galore stopped and rested an arm on the back of the seat in front of Bond. She looked down at him. 'Hullo, Handsome. Long time no see. Uncle doesn't seem to let you off the lead much.'

Bond said, 'Hullo, Beautiful. That outfit suits you fine. I'm feeling rather faint. How about doing a bit of nursing?'

The deep violet eyes examined him carefully. She said softly, 'You know what, Mister Bond? I got a feeling there's something phoney about you. I got instincts, see? Just what are you and that doll'–she jerked her head back–'doing in this outfit?'

'We do all the work.'

The train began to move. Pussy Galore straightened herself. She said, 'Mebbe you do. But if any little thing goes wrong with this caper, for my money it'll be Handsome who knows why. Get me?'

She didn't wait for Bond's answer, but moved on down and joined the Chiefs of Staff meeting.

It was a confused, busy night. Appearances had to be kept up before the inquisitive, sympathetic eyes of the conductors. Last-minute conferences up and down the train had to wear the appearance of serious medical conclaves–no cigar-smoking; no swearing, no spitting. Jealousies and competition between the gangs had to be kept under rigid control. The cold superiority of the Mafia, particularly vis-à-vis Jack Strap and his soft, easy-living crowd from the West, might have led to gunplay if the chiefs hadn't been ready for trouble and constantly on the look-out for it. All these minor psychological factors had been foreseen by Goldfinger and prepared for. The women from the Cement Mixers were carefully segregated, there was no drinking and the gang chiefs kept their men occupied with further exact briefings, dummy exercises with maps and lengthy discussions about their escape plans with the gold. There was casual spying on each other's plans and Goldfinger was often called in to judge who should have which routes to the Mexican border, to the desert, to Canada. To Bond it was amazing that a hundred of the toughest crooks in America, on edge with excitement and greed, could be kept as quiet as they were. It was Goldfinger who had achieved the miracle. Apart from the calm, dangerous quality of the man, it was the minuteness of the planning and the confidence he exuded that calmed the battle nerves and created some sort of a team-spirit among the rival mobs.

As the iron gallop of the train stretched itself out through the flat lands of Pennsylvania, gradually the passengers fell into an uneasy, troubled sleep. But not Goldfinger or Oddjob. They remained awake and watchful and soon Bond gave up any idea he might have had of using one of his hidden knives on Oddjob and making a bid for freedom when the train slowed through a station or on an up-gradient.

Bond dozed fitfully, wondering, imagining, puzzling over the Superintendent's words. The Superintendent had certainly thought they were the truth, knew that Fort Knox was in emergency. Was his news from Louisville the truth or part of the giant cover plan that would be necessary to get every member of the conspiracy in the bag? If it was a cover plan, how meticulously had it been prepared? Would someone slip up? Would there be some ghastly bungle that would warn Goldfinger in time? Or if the news was true, if the poison had been successful, what did there remain for Bond to do?

Bond had made up his mind on one score. Somehow, in the excitement of

H-Hour, he would get close to Goldfinger and cut his throat with one of his hidden knives. How much would that achieve apart from an act of private vengeance? Would Goldfinger's squad accept another man's order to arm the warhead and fire it? Who would be strong enough, cool enough to take over? Mr Solo? Probably. The operation would perhaps be half successful, they would get away with plenty of gold–except Goldfinger's men who would be lost without him to lead them. And in the meantime, whatever else Bond could now do, had sixty thousand people already died? Was there anything he could have done to prevent that? Had there ever been a chance to kill Goldfinger? Would it have done any good to make a scene at Pennsylvania Station? Bond stared at his dark reflection in the window, listened to the sweet ting of the grade-crossing bells and the howl of the windhorn clearing their way, and shredded his nerves with doubts, questions, reproaches.

Chapter Twenty-one

The Richest Man in History

Slowly the red dawn broke over the endless plain of black grass that gradually turned to the famous Kentucky blue as the sun ironed out the shadows. At six o'clock the train began to slacken speed and soon they were gliding gently through the waking suburbs of Louisville to come to rest with a sigh of hydraulics in the echoing, almost deserted station.

A small, respectful group was awaiting them. Goldfinger, his eyes black-ringed with lack of sleep, beckoned to one of the Germans, picked up his authoritative little black bag and stepped down on to the platform. There was a short, serious conclave, the Louisville Superintendent doing the talking and Goldfinger interjecting a few questions and nodding gravely at the answers. Goldfinger turned wearily back to the train. Mr Solo had been deputed to take his report. He stood at the open door at the end of the Pullman. Bond heard Goldfinger say sorrowfully, 'I am afraid, Doctor, the situation is as bad as we feared. I will now go forward to the leading diesel with this,' he held up the black bag, 'and we will proceed slowly into the infected area. Would you please tell all personnel to be prepared to put on their masks? I have masks for the driver and fireman. All other railway personnel will leave the train here.'

Mr Solo nodded solemnly. 'Right, Professor.' He closed his door. Goldfinger walked off down the platform followed by his German strong-arm man and the respectful, head-shaking group.

There was a short pause and then silently, almost reverently, the long train whispered its way out of the station leaving the little group of officials, now reinforced by four rather shamefaced conductors, with hands raised in benediction.

Thirty-five miles, half an hour, to go! Coffee and doughnuts were brought round by the nurses, and (Goldfinger thought of everything) for those whose nerves needed it, two grains of dexedrine. The nurses were pale, silent. There were no jokes, no smart remarks. The train was electric with tension.

After ten minutes there was a sudden slackening of speed and a sharp hiss from the brakes. Coffee was spilled. The train almost stopped. Then there was a jerk and it gathered speed again. A new hand had taken over on the dead man's handle.

A few minutes later, Mr Strap came hurrying through the train. 'Ten minutes to go! On your toes, folks! Squads A, B and C get their equipment on. Everything's going fine. Stay calm. Remember your duties.' He hurried through to the next compartment and Bond heard the voice repeating its message.

Bond turned to Oddjob. 'Listen, you ape, I'm going to the lavatory and probably Miss Masterton will too.' He turned to the girl. 'What about it, Tilly?'

'Yes,' she said indifferently, 'I suppose I'd better.'

Bond said, 'Well, go ahead.'

The Korean beside the girl looked inquiringly at Oddjob. Oddjob shook his head.

Bond said, 'Unless you leave her alone I'm going to start a fight. Goldfinger won't like that.' He turned to the girl. 'Go ahead, Tilly. I'll see to these apes.'

Oddjob uttered a series of barks and snarls which the other Korean seemed to understand. The guard got up and said, 'Okay, but not locking the door.' He followed the girl down the Pullman and stood and waited for her to come out.

Oddjob carried out the same routine with Bond. Once inside, Bond took off his right shoe, slid out the knife and slipped it down inside the waist-band of his trousers. One shoe would now have no heel, but no one was going to notice that this morning. Bond washed himself. The face in the mirror was pale and the blue-grey eyes dark with tension. He went out and back to his seat.

Now there was a distant shimmer away to the right and a hint of low buildings rising like a mirage in the early morning ground-mist. They slowly defined themselves as hangars with a squat control tower. Godman Field! The soft pounding howl of the train slackened. Some trim modern villas, part of a new housing development, slid by. They seemed to be unoccupied. Now, on the left, there was the black ribbon of Brandenburg Station Road. Bond craned. The gleaming modern sprawl of Fort Knox looked almost soft in the light mist. Above its jagged outline the air was clear as crystal–not a trace of smoke, no breakfasts cooking! The train slowed to a canter. On Station Road there had been a bad motor accident. Two cars seemed to have met head on. The body of a man sprawled half out of a smashed door. The other car lay on its back like a dead beetle. Bond's heart pounded. The main signal box came and went. Over the levers something white was draped. It was a man's shirt. Inside the shirt the body hung down, its head below the level of the window. A row of modern bungalows. A body clad in singlet and trousers flat on its face in the middle of a trim lawn. The lines of mown grass were beautifully exact until, near the man, the mower had written an ugly flourish and had then come to rest on its side in the newly turned earth of the border. A line of washing that had broken when the woman had grasped it. The woman lay in a white pile at one end of the sagging string of family underclothes, cloths and towels. And now the train was moving at walking pace into the town and everywhere, down every street, on every sidewalk, there were the sprawling figures–singly, in clumps, in rocking-chairs on the porches, in the middle of intersections where the traffic lights still unhurriedly ticked off their coloured signals, in cars that had managed to pull up and in others that had smashed into shop windows. Death! Dead people everywhere. No movement, no sound save the click of the murderer's iron feet as his train slid through the graveyard.

Now there was bustle in the carriages. Billy Ring came through grinning hugely. He stopped by Bond's chair. 'Oh boy!' he said delightedly, 'old Goldie certainly slipped them the Micky Finn! Too bad some people were out for a ride when they got hit. But you know what they say about omelettes: can't make 'em without you break some eggs, right?'

Bond smiled tightly. 'That's right.'

Billy Ring made his silent O of a laugh and went on his way.

The train trundled through Brandenburg Station. Now there were scores of bodies–men, women, children, soldiers. The platform was scribbled with them, faces upwards to the roof, down in the dust, cradled sideways. Bond searched for movement, for an inquisitive eye, for a twitching hand. Nothing! Wait! What was that? Thinly through the closed window there came a soft, mewing wail. Three perambulators stood against the ticket office, the mothers collapsed beside them. Of course! The babies in the perambulators would have drunk milk, not the deadly water.

Oddjob got to his feet. So did the whole of Goldfinger's team. The faces of the Koreans were indifferent, unchanged, only their eyes flickered constantly like nervous animals. The Germans were pale, grim. Nobody looked at anyone else. Silently they filed towards the exit and lined up, waiting.

Tilly Masterton touched Bond's sleeve. Her voice trembled. 'Are you sure they're only asleep? I thought I saw some sort of . . . sort of froth on some of the lips.'

Bond had seen the same thing. The froth had been pink. He said, 'I expect some of them were eating sweets or something when they fell asleep. You know what these Americans are–always chewing something.' He softly mouthed the next words. 'Stay away from me. There may be shooting.' He looked hard at her to see she understood.

She nodded dumbly, not looking at him. She whispered out of the corner of her mouth, 'I'm going to get near Pussy. She'll look after me.'

Bond gave her a smile and said 'Good', encouragingly.

The train clicked slowly over some points and slid to rest. There came one blast of the diesel's windhorn. The doors swung open and the different groups piled out on to the platform of the Bullion Depository siding.

Now everything went with military precision. The various squads formed up in their battle order–first an assault group with sub-machine guns, then the stretcher-bearers to get the guard and other personnel out of the vault (surely an unnecessary refinement now, thought Bond) then Goldfinger's demolition team–ten men with their bulky tarpaulin-covered package–then a mixed group of spare drivers and traffic-control men, then the group of nurses, now all armed with pistols, who were to stay in the background with a heavily armed reserve group that was to deal with any unexpected interference from anybody who, as Goldfinger had put it, 'might wake up'.

Bond and the girl had been included in the Command Group which consisted of Goldfinger, Oddjob and the five gang leaders. They were to be stationed on the flat roofs of the two diesel locomotives which now stood, as planned, beyond the siding buildings and in full view of the objective and its approaches. Bond and the girl were to handle the maps, the timetables and the stop-watch, and Bond was to watch out for fumbles and delays and bring them at once to Goldfinger's attention to be rectified by walkie-talkie with the squad leaders. When the bomb was due to be fired, they would take shelter behind the diesels.

There came a double blast from the windhorn and, as Bond and the girl climbed to their position on the roof of the first diesel, the assault squad, followed by the other sections, doubled across the twenty yards of open ground between the railway and Bullion Boulevard. Bond edged as close as he could to Goldfinger. Goldfinger had binoculars to his eyes. His mouth was close to the microphone strapped to his chest. But Oddjob stood between them, a solid mountain of flesh, and his eyes, uninterested in the drama of the assault, never flickered from Bond and the girl.

Bond, under cover of scanning his plastic map-case and keeping an eye on the stop-watch, measured inches and angles. He glanced at the next-door group of the four men and the woman. They were gazing, in frozen attention, at the scene before them. Now Jack Strap said excitedly, 'They're through the first gates.' Bond, putting half his mind to work on his own plans, took a quick look at the battlefield.

It was an extraordinary scene. In the centre stood the huge squat mausoleum, the sun glinting off the polished granite of its walls. Outside the big open field in which it stood, the roads–the Dixie Highway, Vine Grove and Bullion Boulevard–were lined with trucks and transporters two deep with the recognition flags of the gangs flying from the first and last vehicle of each convoy. Their drivers lay piled up outside the shelter of the surrounding guard wall of the vault while, through the main gate, poured the tidy disciplined squads from the train. Outside this world of movement there was absolute stillness and silence as if the rest of America was holding its breath at the committal of this gigantic crime. And outside lay the bodies of the soldiers, sprawling where they had fallen–the sentries by their pill boxes, still clutching their automatic pistols, and, inside the protecting wall, two ragged squads of soldiers in battle-dress. They lay in vague, untidy heaps, some bodies athwart or on top of their neighbours. Outside, between Bullion Boulevard and the main gate, two armoured cars had crashed into each other and now stood locked, their heavy machine guns pointing, one at the ground and the other at the sky. A driver's body sprawled out of the turret of one of the vehicles.

Desperately Bond looked for a sign of life, a sign of movement, a hint that all this was a careful ambush. Nothing! Not a cat moved, not a sound came out of the crowded buildings that formed a backdrop to the scene. Only the squads hurried about their tasks or now stood waiting in their planned dispositions.

Goldfinger spoke quietly into his microphone. 'Last stretcher out. Bomb squad ready. Prepare to take cover.'

Now the covering troops and the stretcher-bearers were hurrying for the exit, getting down under cover of the guard wall. There would be five minutes' delay to clear the area before the bomb squad, now waiting bunched at the main gate, would go in.

Bond said efficiently, 'They're a minute ahead of time.'

Goldfinger looked past Oddjob's shoulder. The pale eyes were aflame. They stared into Bond's. Goldfinger's mouth twisted into a harsh snarl. He said through his teeth, 'You see, Mr Bond. You were wrong and I was right. Ten more minutes and I shall be the richest man in the world, the richest man in history! What do you say to that?' His mouth spat out the words.

Bond said equably, 'I'll tell you after those ten minutes are up.'

'Will you?' said Goldfinger. 'Maybe.' He looked at his watch and spoke rapidly into his microphone. The Goldfinger squad loped slowly through the main gate, their heavy burden slung from four shoulders in a cradle of webbing.

Goldfinger looked past Bond at the group on the roof of the second diesel. He called out triumphantly, 'Another five minutes, gentlemen, and then we must take cover.' He turned his eyes on Bond and added softly, 'And then we will say goodbye, Mr Bond. And thank you for the assistance you and the girl have given me.'

Out of the corner of his eye, Bond saw something moving–moving in the sky. It was a black, whirling speck. It reached the top of its trajectory, paused and then came the ear-splitting crack of a maroon signal.

Bond's heart leapt. A quick glance showed him the ranks of dead soldiers springing to life, the machine guns on the locked armoured cars swinging to cover the gates. A loud-speaker roared from somewhere, 'Stand where you are. Lay down your arms.' But there came a futile crackle of fire from one of the rearguard covering party and then all hell broke loose.

Bond seized the girl round the waist and jumped with her. It was a ten-foot drop to the platform. Bond broke his fall with his left hand and hoisted the girl to her feet with a jerk of his hip. As he began to run, close to the train for cover, he heard Goldfinger shout, 'Get them and kill them.' A splatter of lead from Goldfinger's automatic whipped at the cement to his left. But Goldfinger would have to shoot left-handed. It was Oddjob that Bond feared. Now, as Bond tore down the platform with the girl's hand in his, he heard the lightning scuffle of the running feet.

The girl's hand tugged at him. She screamed angrily, 'No, No. Stop! I want to stay close to Pussy. I'll be safe with her.'

Bond shouted back, 'Shut up, you little fool! Run like hell!' But now she was dragging at him, checking his speed. Suddenly she tore her hand out of his and made to dart into an open Pullman door. Christ, thought Bond, that's torn it! He whipped the knife out of his belt and swirled to meet Oddjob.

Ten yards away Oddjob hardly paused in his rush. One hand whipped off his ridiculous, deadly hat, a glance to take aim and the black steel half-moon sang through the air. Its edge caught the girl exactly at the nape of the neck. Without a sound she fell backwards on to the platform in Oddjob's path. The hurdle was just enough to put Oddjob off the flying high kick he had started to launch at Bond's head. He turned the kick into a leap, his left hand cutting the air towards Bond like a sword. Bond ducked and struck upwards and sideways with his knife. It got home somewhere near the ribs but the momentum of the flying body knocked the knife out of his hand. There was a tinkle on the platform. Now Oddjob was coming back at him, apparently unharmed, his hands outstretched and his feet splayed back ready for another leap or a kick. His blood was up. The eyes were red and there was a fleck of saliva at the open, panting mouth.

Above the boom and rattle of the guns outside the station, three blasts sounded on the diesel's windhorn. Oddjob snarled angrily and leapt. Bond dived at full length sideways. Something hit him a gigantic blow on the shoulder and sent him sprawling. Now, he thought as he hit the ground, now the death stroke! He scrambled clumsily to his feet, his neck hunched into his shoulders to break the impact. But no blow came and Bond's dazed eyes took in the figure of Oddjob flying away from him up the platform.

Already the leading diesel was on the move. Oddjob got to it and leapt for the footplate. For a moment he hung, his legs scrabbling for a foothold. Then he had disappeared into the cabin and the huge streamlined engine gathered speed.

Behind Bond the door of the quartermaster's office burst open. There was the hammer of running feet and a yell 'Santiago!' – St James, the battle-cry of Cortez that Leiter had once jokingly allotted to Bond.

Bond swivelled. The straw-haired Texan, clad in his war-time Marine Corps battle-dress, was pounding up the platform followed by a dozen men in khaki. He carried a one-man bazooka by the steel hook he used for a right hand. Bond ran to meet him. He said, 'Don't shoot my fox, you bastard. Give over.' He snatched the bazooka out of Leiter's hand and threw himself down on the platform, splaying out his legs. Now the diesel was two hundred yards away and about to cross the bridge over the Dixie Highway. Bond shouted 'Stand clear!' to get the men out of line of the recoil flash, clicked up the safe and took careful aim. The bazooka shuddered slightly and the ten-pound armour-piercing rocket was on its way. There was a flash and a puff of blue smoke. Some bits of metal flew off the rear of the flying engine. But then it had crossed the bridge and taken the curve and was away.

'Not bad for a rookie,' commented Leiter. 'May put the rear diesel out, but those jobs are twins and he can make it on the forward engine.'

Bond got to his feet. He smiled warmly into the hawk-like, slate-grey eyes. 'You bungling oaf,' he said sarcastically, 'why in hell didn't you block that line?'

'Listen, shamus. If you've got any complaints about the stage management you can tell them to the President. He took personal command of this operation and it's a honey. There's a spotter plane overhead now. They'll pick up the diesel and we'll have old Goldilocks in the hoosegow by midday. How were we to know he was going to stay aboard the train?' He broke off and thumped Bond between the shoulder-blades. 'Hell, I'm glad to see you. These men and I were detailed off to give you protection. We've been dodging around looking for you and getting shot at by both sides for our pains.' He turned to the soldiers. 'Ain't that right, men?'

They laughed. 'Sure is, Cap'n.'

Bond looked affectionately at the Texan with whom he had shared so many adventures. He said seriously, 'Bless you, Felix. You've always been good at saving my life. It was darn nearly too late this time. I'm afraid Tilly Masterton's had it.' He walked off up the train with Felix at his heels. The little figure still lay sprawled where she had fallen. Bond knelt beside her. The broken-doll angle of the head was enough. He felt for her pulse. He got up. He said softly, 'Poor little bitch. She didn't think much of men.' He looked defensively at Leiter. 'Felix, I could have got her away if she'd only followed me.'

Leiter didn't understand. He put his hand on Bond's arm and said, 'Sure kid. Take it easy.' He turned to his men. 'Two of you carry the girl into the Q.M.'s office over there. O'Brien, you go for the ambulance. When you've done that, stop over at the Command post and give 'em the facts. Say we've got Commander Bond and I'll bring him right over.'

Bond stood and looked down at the little empty tangle of limbs and clothes. He saw the bright, proud girl with the spotted handkerchief round her hair in the flying TR3. Now she had gone.

High up over his head a whirling speck soared into the sky. It reached the top of its flight and paused. There came the sharp crack of the maroon. It was the cease-fire.

Chapter Twenty-two

The Last Trick

It was two days later. Felix Leiter was weaving the black Studillac fast through the lanes of dawdling traffic on the Triborough bridge. There was plenty of time to catch Bond's plane, the evening B.O.A.C. Monarch to London, but Leiter enjoyed shaking up Bond's low opinion of American cars. Now the steel hook that he used for a right hand banged the gear lever into second and the low black car leapt for a narrow space between a giant refrigerator truck and a mooning Oldsmobile whose rear window was almost obscured by holiday stickers.

Bond's body jerked back with the kick of the 300 b.h.p. and his teeth snapped shut. When the manœuvre was completed, and the angry hooting had vanished behind them, Bond said mildly, 'It's time you graduated out of the Kiddicar class and bought yourself an express carriage. You want to get cracking. This pedalling along ages one. One of these days you'll stop moving altogether and when you stop moving is when you start to die.'

Leiter laughed. He said, 'See that green light ahead? Bet I can make it before it goes red.' The car leapt forward as if it had been kicked. There was a brief hiatus in Bond's life, an impression of snipe-like flight and of a steel wall of cars that somehow parted before the whiplash of Leiter's triple klaxons, a hundred yards when the speedometer touched ninety and they were across the lights and cruising genteelly along in the centre lane.

Bond said calmly. 'You meet the wrong traffic cop and that Pinkerton card of yours won't be good enough. It isn't so much that you drive slowly, it's holding back the cars behind they'll book you for. The sort of car you need is a nice elderly Rolls Royce Silver Ghost with big plate-glass windows so you can enjoy the beauties of nature'–Bond gestured towards a huge automobile junk heap on their right. 'Maximum fifty and it can stop and even go backwards if you want to. Bulb horn. Suit your sedate style. Matter of fact there should be one on the market soon–Goldfinger's. And by the same token, what the hell's happened to Goldfinger? Haven't they caught up with him yet?'

Leiter glanced at his watch and edged into the outside lane. He brought the car down to forty. He said seriously, 'Tell you the truth, we're all a bit worried. The papers are needling us, or rather Edgar Hoover's crowd, like hell. First they had a gripe at the security clamp-down on you. We couldn't tell them that wasn't our fault and that someone in London, an old limey called M, had insisted on it. So they're getting their own back. Say we're dragging our feet and so forth. And I'm telling you, James'–Leiter's voice was glum, apologetic–'we just haven't a clue. They caught up with the diesel. Goldfinger had fixed the controls at thirty and had let it run on down the line. Somewhere he and the Korean had got off and probably this Galore girl and the four hoods as well because they've vanished too. We found his truck convoy, of course, waiting on the eastbound highway out of Elizabethville. But never a driver. Most probably scattered, but somewhere there's Goldfinger and a pretty tough team hiding up. They didn't get to the *Sverdlovsk* cruiser at Norfolk. We had a plain-clothes guard scattered round the docks and they report that she sailed to schedule without any strangers going aboard. Not a cat's been near that warehouse on East River and no one's shown at Idlewild or the frontiers–Mexico and Canada. For my money, that Jed Midnight has somehow got them out to Cuba. If they'd taken two or three trucks from the convoy and driven like hell they could have got down to Florida, somewhere like Daytona Beach, by the early hours of D+1. And Midnight's darn well organized down there. The Coast Guards and the Air Force have put out all they've got, but nothing's shown yet. But they could have hidden up during the day and got over to Cuba during the night. It's got everybody worried as hell and it's no help that the President's hopping mad.'

Bond had spent the previous day in Washington treading the thickest, richest red carpet. There had been speeches at the Bureau of the Mint, a big brass lunch at the Pentagon, an embarrassing quarter of an hour with the President, and the rest of the day had been hard work with a team of stenographers in Edgar Hoover's suite of offices with a colleague of Bond's from Station A sitting in. At the end of that, there had been a brisk quarter of an hour's talk with M on the Embassy transatlantic scrambler. M had told him what had been happening on the European end of the case. As Bond had expected, Goldfinger's cable to Universal Export had been treated as emergency. The factories at Reculver and Coppet had been searched and extra evidence of the gold-smuggling racket had been found. The Indian Government had been warned about the Mecca plane that was already en route for Bombay and that end of the operation was on the way to being cleaned up. The Swiss Special Brigade had quickly found Bond's car and had got on to the route by which Bond and the girl had been taken to America, but there, at Idlewild, the F.B.I. had lost the scent. M seemed pleased with the way Bond had handled Operation Grand Slam, but he said the Bank of England were worrying him about Goldfinger's twenty million pounds in gold. Goldfinger had assembled all this at the Paragon Safe Deposit Co in New York but had withdrawn it on D–1. He and his men had driven it away in a covered truck. The Bank of England had ready an Order in Council to impound the gold when it was found and there would then be a case to prove that it had been smuggled out of England, or at least that it was originally smuggled gold whose value had been increased by various doubtful means. But this was now being handled by the U.S. Treasury and the F.B.I. and, since M had no jurisdiction in America, Bond had better come home at once and help tidy things up. Oh yes–at the end of the conversation M's voice had sounded gruff–there had been a very kind request to the P.M. that Bond should be allowed to accept the American Medal of Merit. Of course M had had to explain via the P.M. that the Service didn't go in for those sort of things–particularly from foreign countries, however friendly they were. Too bad, but M knew that this was what Bond would have expected. He knew the rules. Bond had said yes of course and thank you very much and he'd take the next plane home.

Now, as they motored quietly down the Van Wyck Expressway, Bond was feeling vaguely dissatisfied. He didn't like leaving ragged ends to a case. None of the big gangsters had been put in the bag and he had failed in the two tasks he had been given, to get Goldfinger and get Goldfinger's bullion. It was nothing but a miracle that Operation Grand Slam had been broken. It had been two days before the Beechcraft had been serviced and the cleaner who found the note had got to Pinkerton's only half an hour before Leiter was due to go off to the Coast on a big racing scandal. But then Leiter had really got cracking–to his chief, then to the F.B.I. and the Pentagon. The F.B.I.'s knowledge of Bond's record, plus contact with M through the Central Intelligence Agency, had been enough to get the whole case up to the President within an hour. After that it had just been a case of building up the gigantic bluff in which all the inhabitants of Fort Knox had participated in one way or another. The two 'Japanese' had been taken easily enough and it was confirmed by Chemical Warfare that the three pints of GB carried as gin in their briefcases would have been enough to slay the entire population of Fort Knox. The two men had been quickly and forcibly grilled into explaining the form of the all-clear cable to Goldfinger. The cable had been sent. Then the Army had declared emergency. Road and rail and air blocks had turned back all traffic to the Fort Knox area with the exception of the gangster convoys which had not been hindered. The rest was play-acting right down to the pink froth and the squalling babies which it was thought would add nice touches of verisimilitude.

Yes, it had all been very satisfactory so far as Washington was concerned, but what about the English end? Who in America cared about the Bank of England's gold? Who cared that two English girls had been murdered in the course of this business? Who really minded that Goldfinger was still at liberty now that America's bullion was safe again?

They idled across the drab plain of Idlewild, past the ten-million-dollar steel and cement skeletons that would one day be an adult airport, and pulled up outside the makeshift huddle of concrete boxes that Bond knew so well. Already the well-mannered iron voices were reaching out to them. 'Pan American World Airways announces the departure of its President Flight PA 100', 'Transworld Airways calling Captain Murphy. Captain Murphy, please.' And the pear-shaped vowels and fluted diction of B.O.A.C., 'B.O.A.C. announces the arrival of its Bermudan Flight BA 491. Passengers will be disembarking at gate number neyne.'

Bond took his bag and said goodbye to Leiter. He said, 'Well, thanks for everything, Felix. Write to me every day.'

Leiter gripped his hand hard. He said, 'Sure thing, kid. And take it easy.

Tell that old bastard M to send you back over soon. Next visit we'll take some time off from the razzmatazz. Time you called in on my home state. Like to have you meet my oil-well. 'Bye now.'

Leiter got into his car and accelerated away from the arrival bay. Bond raised his hand. The Studillac dry-skidded out on to the approach road. There was an answering glint from Leiter's steel hook out of the window and he was gone.

Bond sighed. He picked up his bag and walked in and over to the B.O.A.C. ticket counter.

Bond didn't mind airports so long as he was alone in them. He had half an hour to wait and he was quite content to wander through the milling crowds, have a bourbon and soda at the restaurant and spend some time choosing something to read at the bookstore. He bought Ben Hogan's *Modern Fundamentals of Golf* and the latest Raymond Chandler and sauntered along to the Souvenir Shop to see if he could find an amusing gimmick to take back to his secretary.

Now there was a man's voice on the B.O.A.C. announcing system. It called out a long list of Monarch passengers who were required at the ticket counter. Ten minutes later Bond was paying for one of the latest and most expensive ball-point pens when he heard his own name being called. 'Will Mr James Bond, passenger on B.O.A.C. Monarch flight No. 510 to Gander and London, please come to the B.O.A.C. ticket counter. Mr James Bond, please.' It was obviously that infernal tax form to show how much he had earned during his stay in America. On principle Bond never went to the Internal Revenue Office in New York to get clearance and he had only once had to argue it out at Idlewild. He went out of the shop and across to the B.O.A.C. counter. The official said politely, 'May I see your health certificate, please, Mr Bond?'

Bond took the form out of his passport and handed it over.

The man looked at it carefully. He said, 'I'm very sorry, sir, but there's been a typhoid case at Gander and they're insisting that all transit passengers who haven't had their shots in the last six months should be topped up. It's most annoying, sir, but Gander's very touchy about these things. Too bad we couldn't have managed a direct flight, but there's a strong head-wind.'

Bond hated inoculations. He said irritably, 'But look here, I'm stuffed with shots of one kind or another. Been having them for twenty years for one damned thing or another!' He looked round. The area near the B.O.A.C. departure gate seemed curiously deserted. He said, 'What about the other passengers? Where are they?'

'They've all agreed, sir. Just having their shots now. It won't take a minute, sir, if you'll come this way.'

'Oh well.' Bond shrugged his shoulders impatiently. He followed the man behind the counter and through a door to the B.O.A.C. station manager's office. There was the usual white-clothed doctor, a mask over the bottom of his face, the needle held ready. 'Last one?' he asked of the B.O.A.C. official.

'Yes, Doctor.'

'Okay. Coat off and left sleeve up, please. Too bad they're so sensitive up at Gander.'

'Damned sight too bad,' said Bond. 'What are they afraid of? Spreading the black death?'

There came the sharp smell of the alcohol and the jab of the needle.

'Thanks,' said Bond gruffly. He pulled down his sleeve and made to pick his coat up from the back of the chair. His hand went down for it, missed it, went on down, down towards the floor. His body dived after the hand, down , down, down . . .

All the lights were on in the plane. There seemed to be plenty of spare places. Why did he have to get stuck with a passenger whose arm was hogging the central arm-rest. Bond made to get up and change his seat. A wave of nausea swept over him. He closed his eyes and waited. How extraordinary! He was never air-sick. He felt the cold sweat on his face. Handkerchief. Wipe it off. He opened his eyes again and looked down at his arms. The wrists were bound to the arms of his chair. What had happened? He had had his shot and then passed out or something. Had he got violent? What the hell was all this about? He glanced to his right and then stared, aghast. Oddjob was sitting there. Oddjob! Oddjob in B.O.A.C. uniform!

Oddjob glanced incuriously at him and reached for the steward's bell. Bond heard the pretty ding-dong back in the pantry. There was the rustle of a skirt beside him. He looked up. It was Pussy Galore, trim and fresh in the blue uniform of a stewardess! She said, 'Hi, Handsome.' She gave him the deep, searching look he remembered so well from when? From centuries ago, in another life.

Bond said desperately, 'For Christ's sake, what's going on? Where did you come from?'

The girl smiled cheerfully, 'Eating caviar and drinking champagne. You Britishers sure live the life of Reilly when you get up twenty thousand feet. Not a sign of a Brussels sprout and if there's tea I haven't got around to it yet. Now, you take it easy. Uncle wants to talk to you.' She sauntered up the aisle, swinging her hips, and disappeared through the cockpit door.

Now nothing could surprise Bond. Goldfinger, in a B.O.A.C. captain's uniform that was rather too large for him, the cap squarely on the centre of his head, closed the cockpit door behind him and came down the aisle.

He stood and looked grimly down at Bond. 'Well, Mr Bond. So Fate wished us to play the game out. But this time, Mr Bond, there cannot possibly be a card up your sleeve. Ha!' The sharp bark was a mixture of anger, stoicism and respect. 'You certainly turned out to be a snake in my pastures.' The great head shook slowly. 'Why I kept you alive! Why I didn't crush you like a beetle! You and the girl were useful to me. Yes, I was right about that. But I was mad to have taken the chance. Yes, mad.' The voice dropped and went slow. 'And now tell me, Mr Bond. How did you do it? How did you communicate?'

Bond said equably, 'We will have a talk, Goldfinger. And I will tell you certain things. But not until you have taken off these straps and brought me a bottle of bourbon, ice, soda water and a packet of Chesterfields. Then, when you have told me what I wish to know, I will decide what to tell you. As you say, my situation is not favourable, or at least it doesn't appear to be. So I have nothing to lose and if you want to get something out of me it will be on my own terms.'

Goldfinger looked gravely down. 'I have no objection to your conditions. Out of respect for your abilities as an opponent, you shall spend your last journey in comfort. Oddjob'–the voice was sharp. 'Ring the bell for Miss

Galore and undo those straps. Get into the seat in front. There is no harm he can do at the rear of the plane but he is not to approach the cockpit door. If need be, kill him at once, but I prefer to get him to our destination alive. Understood?'

'Arrgh.'

Five minutes later Bond had what he wanted. The tray in front of him was down and on it were his whisky and cigarettes. He poured himself a stiff bourbon. Goldfinger was seated in the chair across the aisle, waiting. Bond picked up his drink and sipped it. He was about to take a deeper drink when he saw something. He put the glass carefully down without disturbing the little round paper coaster that had stuck to the bottom of his glass. He lit a cigarette, picked up his drink again and removed the ice-cubes and put them back in the ice bucket. He drank the whisky down almost to the end. Now he could read the words through the bottom of the glass. He carefully put the glass down without disturbing the coaster. The message had read, 'I'm with you. XXX. P.'

Bond turned and made himself comfortable. He said, 'Now then, Goldfinger. First of all, what's going on, how did you get this plane, where are we heading?'

Goldfinger crossed one leg over the other. He gazed away from Bond, up the aisle. He said in a relaxed, conversational tone, 'I took three trucks and drove across country to the vicinity of Cape Hatteras. One of the trucks contained my personal hoard of gold bullion. The other two contained my drivers, spare personnel and those gangsters. I required none of them except Miss Galore. I kept a nucleus of the staff I would need, paid off the others with huge sums and dispersed them gradually along the route. At the coast I held a meeting with the four gang leaders in a deserted place, having left Miss Galore under some pretext with the trucks. I shot the four men in my usual fashion–one bullet for each. I went back to the trucks and explained that the four men had chosen money and independent action. I was now left with six men, the girl and the bullion. I hired a plane and flew to Newark, New Jersey, the crates of gold being passed off as lead for X-ray plates. From there I proceeded alone to a certain address in New York from which I talked with Moscow by radio and explained the mishap to Operation Grand Slam. In the course of the talk I mentioned your name. My friends, whom I believe you know,' Goldfinger looked hard at Bond, 'pass under the generic name of SMERSH. They recognized the name of Bond and told me who you were. I at once understood a great deal of what had previously been hidden from me. SMERSH said they would greatly like to interview you. I pondered the matter. In due course I conceived the plan which you now see in operation. Posing as a friend of yours, I had no difficulty in finding out the flight on which you were booked. Three of my men were formerly of the Luftwaffe. They assured me there would be no difficulty in flying this plane. The rest was mere detail. By cool bluffing, impersonation and the use of a certain amount of force, all the B.O.A.C. personnel at Idlewild, the crew of this plane and the passengers were given the necessary injections from which they will now be recovering. We changed clothes with the unconscious crew, the bullion was loaded on the plane, you were dealt with and carried out on a stretcher and in due course the new B.O.A.C. crew, with their stewardess, boarded the plane and we took to the air.'

Goldfinger paused. He lifted a hand resignedly. 'Of course there were small hitches. We were told to "follow taxiway Alpha to runway four", and it was only by following a KLM plane that we were successful. The Idlewild routine was not easy to master and we must have seemed somewhat clumsy and inexperienced, but, Mr Bond, with assurance, strong nerves and a gruff, intimidating manner it is never difficult to override the Civil Service mentality of what, after all, are minor employees. I understand from the wireless operator that a search for this plane is under way. They were already questioning us before we were out of VHF range at Nantucket. Then the Distant Early Warning system queried us on high frequency. That did not disturb me. We have enough fuel. We have already had clearance from Moscow for East Berlin, Kiev or Murmansk. We shall take whichever route the weather dictates. There should be no trouble. If there is, I shall talk my way out of it on the radio. No one is going to shoot down a valuable B.O.A.C. plane. The mystery and confusion will protect us until we are well within Soviet territory and then, of course, we shall have disappeared without trace.'

To Bond there had been nothing fantastic, nothing impossible about Goldfinger since he had heard the details of Operation Grand Slam. The theft of a Stratocruiser, as Goldfinger had explained it, was preposterous, but no more so than his methods of smuggling gold, his purchase of an atomic warhead. When one examined these things, while they had a touch of magic, of genius even, they were logical exercises. They were bizarre only in their magnitude. Even the tiny manœuvre of cheating Mr Du Pont had been quite brilliantly contrived. There was no doubt about it, Goldfinger was an artist–a scientist in crime as great in his field as Cellini or Einstein in theirs.

'And now, Mr Bond of the British Secret Service, we made a bargain. What have you to tell me? Who put you on to me? What did they suspect? How did you manage to interfere with my plans?' Goldfinger sat back, placed his hands across his stomach and looked at the ceiling.

Bond gave Goldfinger a censored version of the truth. He mentioned nothing about SMERSH or the location of the post box and he said nothing about the secrets of the Homer, a device that might be new to the Russians. He concluded, 'So you see, Goldfinger, you only just got away. But for Tilly Masterton's intervention at Geneva, you'd have been in the bag by now. You'd be sitting picking your teeth in a Swiss prison waiting to be sent to England. You underestimate the English. They may be slow, but they get there. You think you'll be pretty safe in Russia? I wouldn't be too sure. We've got people even out of there before now. I'll give you one last aphorism for your book, Goldfinger: "Never go a bear of England."'

Chapter Twenty-three

T.L.C. Treatment

The plane throbbed on, high above the weather, over the great moonlit landscape. The lights had been turned out. Bond sat quietly in the darkness and sweated with fear at what he was going to do.

An hour before, the girl had brought him dinner. There was a pencil hidden in the napkin. She had made some tough remarks for the benefit of Oddjob and gone away. Bond had eaten some scraps of food and drunk a good deal of bourbon while his imagination hunted round the plane wondering what he could conceivably do to force an emergency landing at Gander or somewhere else in Nova Scotia. As a last resort, could he set fire to the plane? He toyed with the idea, and with the possibility of forcing the entrance hatch open. Both ideas seemed impracticable and suicidal. To save him the trouble of pondering over them, the man whom Bond had seen before at the B.O.A.C. ticket counter, one of the Germans, came through and stopped by Bond's chair.

He grinned down at Bond. 'B.O.A.C. takes good care of you, isn't it? Mister Goldfinger thinks you might have foolish notions. I am to keep an eye on the rear of the plane. So just sit back and enjoy the ride, isn't it?'

When Bond didn't answer, the man went on back to the rear section.

Something was nagging at Bond's mind, something connected with his previous thoughts. That business about forcing the hatch. Now what was it that had happened to that plane, flying over Persia back in '57? Bond sat for a while and stared with wide, unseeing eyes at the back of the seat in front of him. It might work! It just conceivably might!

Bond wrote on the inside of the napkin, 'I'll do my best. Fasten your seat belt. XXX. J.'

When the girl came to take his tray Bond dropped the napkin and then picked it up and handed it to her. He held her hand and smiled up into the searching eyes. She bent to pick up the tray. She kissed him quickly on the cheek. She straightened herself. She said toughly, 'I'll see you in my dreams, Handsome,' and went off to the galley.

And now Bond's mind was made up. He had worked out exactly what had to be done. The inches had been measured, the knife from his heel was under his coat and he had twisted the longest end of his seat belt round his left wrist. All he needed was one sign that Oddjob's body was turned away from the window. It would be too much to expect Oddjob to go to sleep, but at least he could make himself comfortable. Bond's eyes never left the dim profile he could see reflected in the Perspex oblong of the window of the seat in front, but Oddjob sat stolidly under the reading light he had prudently kept burning, his eyes staring at the ceiling, his mouth slightly open and his hands held ready and relaxed on the arms of his chair.

One hour, two hours. Bond began to snore, rhythmically, drowsily, he hoped hypnotically. Now Oddjob's hands had moved to his lap. The head nodded once and pulled itself up, shifted to get more comfortable, turned away from the piercing eye of light in the wall, rested on its left cheek away from the window!

Bond kept his snores exactly even. Getting under the Korean's guard would be as difficult as getting past a hungry mastiff. Slowly, inch by inch, he crouched forward on the balls of his feet and reached with his knife hand between the wall and Oddjob's seat. Now his hand was there. Now the needle-sharp tip of the dagger was aimed at the centre of the square inch of Perspex he had chosen. Bond grasped the end of his seat belt tightly in his hand, drew the knife back two inches and lunged.

Bond had had no idea what would happen when he cut through the window. All he knew from the Press reports of the Persian case was that the suction out of the pressurized cabin had whirled the passenger next to the window out through the window and into space. Now, as he whipped back his dagger, there was a fantastic howl, almost a scream of air, and Bond was sucked violently against the back of Oddjob's seat with a force that tore the end of the seat belt from his hand. Over the back of the seat he witnessed a miracle. Oddjob's body seemed to elongate towards the howling black aperture. There was a crash as his head went through and his shoulders hit the frame. Then, as if the Korean's body was toothpaste, it was slowly, foot by foot, sucked with a terrible whistling noise through the aperture. Now Oddjob was out to his waist. Now the huge buttocks stuck and the human paste moved only inch by inch. Then, with a loud boom, the buttocks got through and the legs disappeared as if shot from a gun.

After that came the end of the world. With an appalling crash of crockery from the galley, the huge plane stood on its nose and dived. The last thing Bond knew before he blacked out was the high scream of the engines through the open window and a fleeting vision of pillows and rugs whipping out into space past his eyes. Then, with a final desperate embrace of the seat in front, Bond's oxygen-starved body collapsed in a sear of lung-pain.

The next thing Bond felt was a hard kick in the ribs. There was a taste of blood in his mouth. He groaned. Again the foot smashed into his body. Painfully he dragged himself to his knees between the seats and looked up through a red film. All the lights were on. There was a thin mist in the cabin. The sharp depressurization had brought the air in the cabin down below the dew-point. The roar of the engines through the open window was gigantic. An icy wind seared him. Goldfinger stood over him, his face fiendish under the yellow light. There was a small automatic dead steady in his hand. Goldfinger reached back his foot and kicked again. Bond lit with a blast of hot rage. He caught the foot and twisted it sharply, almost breaking the ankle. There came a scream from Goldfinger and a crash that shook the plane. Bond leapt for the aisle and threw himself sideways and down on to the heap of body. There was an explosion that burned the side of his face. But then his knee thudded into Goldfinger's groin and his left hand was over the gun.

For the first time in his life, Bond went berserk. With his fists and knees he pounded the struggling body while again and again he crashed his forehead down on to the glistening face. The gun came quavering towards him again. Almost indifferently Bond slashed sideways with the edge of his hand and heard the clatter of metal among the seats. Now Goldfinger's hands were at his throat and Bond's at Goldfinger's. Down, down went Bond's thumbs into the arteries. He threw all his weight forward, gasping for breath. Would he black out before the other man died? Would he? Could he stand the pressure of Goldfinger's strong hands? The glistening moon-face was changing. Deep purple showed through the tan. The eyes began to flicker up. The pressure of the hands on Bond's throat slackened. The hands fell away. Now the tongue came out and lolled from the open mouth and there came a terrible gargling from deep in the lungs. Bond sat astride the silent chest and slowly, one by one, unhinged his rigid fingers.

Bond gave a deep sigh and knelt and then stood slowly up. Dazedly he looked up and down the lighted plane. By the galley, Pussy Galore lay strapped in her seat like a heap of washing. Farther down, in the middle of the aisle, the guard lay spreadeagled, one arm and the head at ridiculous angles. Without a belt to hold him when the plane dived, he must have been tossed at the roof like a rag doll.

Bond brushed his hands over his face. Now he felt the burns on his palm and cheeks. Wearily he went down on his knees again and searched for the little gun. It was a Colt ·25 automatic. He flicked out the magazine. Three rounds left and one in the chamber. Bond half walked, half felt his way down the aisle to where the girl lay. He unbuttoned her jacket and put his hand against her warm breast. The heart fluttered like a pigeon under his palm. He undid the seat belt and got the girl face down on the floor and knelt astride her. For five minutes he pumped rhythmically at her lungs. When she began to moan, he got up and left her and went on down the aisle and took a fully loaded Luger out of the dead guard's shoulder holster. On the way back past the shambles of the galley he saw an unbroken bottle of bourbon rolling gently to and fro among the wreckage. He picked it up and pulled the cork and tilted it into his open mouth. The liquor burned like disinfectant. He put the cork back and went forward. He stopped for a minute outside the cockpit door, thinking. Then, with a gun in each hand, he knocked the lever down and went through.

The five faces, blue in the instrument lights, turned towards him. The mouths made black holes and the eyes glinted white. Here the roar of the engines was less. There was a smell of fright-sweat and cigarette smoke. Bond stood with his legs braced, the guns held unwavering. He said, 'Goldfinger's dead. If anyone moves or disobeys an order I shall kill him. Pilot, what's your position, course, height and speed?'

The pilot swallowed. He had to gather saliva before he could speak. He said, 'Sir, we are about five hundred miles east of Goose Bay. Mr Goldfinger said we would ditch the plane as near the coast north of there as we could get. We were to reassemble at Montreal and Mr Goldfinger said we would come back and salvage the gold. Our ground speed is two hundred and fifty miles per hour and our height two thousand.'

'How much flying can you do at that altitude? You must be using up fuel pretty fast.'

'Yes, sir. I estimate that we have about two hours left at this height and speed.'

'Get me a time signal.'

The navigator answered quickly, 'Just had one from Washington, sir. Five minutes to five a.m. Dawn at this level will be in about an hour.'

'Where is Weathership Charlie?'

'About three hundred miles to the north-east, sir.'

'Pilot, do you think you can make Goose Bay?'

'No, sir, by about a hundred miles. We can only make the coast north of there.'

'Right. Alter course for Weathership Charlie. Operator, call them up and give me the mike.'

'Yes, sir.'

While the plane executed a wide curve, Bond listened to the static and broken snatches of voice that sounded from the amplifier above his head.

The operator's voice came softly to him, 'Ocean Station Charlie. This is Speedbird 510. G-ALGY calling C for Charlie, G-ALGY calling Charlie, G-ALGY . . .'

A sharp voice broke in. 'G-ALGY give your position. G-ALGY give your position. This is Gander Control. Emergency. G-ALGY . . .'

London came over faintly. An excited voice began chattering. Now voices were coming at them from all directions. Bond could imagine the fix being quickly co-ordinated at all flying control stations, the busy men under the arcs working on the big plot, telephones being lifted, urgent voices talking to each other across the world. The strong signal of Gander Control smothered all other transmissions. 'We've located G-ALGY. We've got them at about 50 N by 70 E. All stations stop transmitting. Priority. I repeat, we have a fix on G-ALGY . . .'

Suddenly the quiet voice of C for Charlie came in. 'This is Ocean Station Charlie calling Speedbird 510. Charlie calling G-ALGY. Can you hear me? Come in Speedbird 510.'

Bond slipped the small gun into his pocket and took the offered microphone. He pressed the transmitter switch and talked quietly into it, watching the crew over the oblong of plastic.

'C for Charlie this is G-ALGY Speedbird hi-jacked last evening at Idlewild. I have killed the man responsible and partly disabled the plane by depressurizing the cabin. I have the crew at gunpoint. Not enough fuel to make Goose so propose to ditch as close to you as possible. Please put out line of flares.'

A new voice, a voice of authority, perhaps the captain's, came over the air. 'Speedbird this is C for Charlie. Your message heard and understood. Identify the speaker. I repeat identify the speaker over.'

Bond said and smiled at the sensation his words would cause, 'Speedbird to C for Charlie. This is British Secret Service agent Number 007, I repeat Number 007. Whitehall Radio will confirm. I repeat check with Whitehall Radio over.'

There was a stunned pause. Voices from round the world tried to break in. Some control, presumably Gander, cleared them off the air. C for Charlie came back, 'Speedbird this is C for Charlie alias the Angel Gabriel speaking okay I'll check with Whitehall and Wilco the flares but London and Gander want more details . . .'

Bond broke in, 'Sorry C for Charlie but I can't hold five men in my sights and make polite conversation just give me the sea conditions would you and then I'm going off the air till we come in to ditch over.'

'Okay Speedbird I see the point wind here force two sea conditions long smooth swell no broken crests you should make it okay I'll soon have you on the radar and we'll keep constant watch on your wavelength have whisky for one and irons for five waiting good luck over.'

Bond said, 'Thanks C for Charlie add a cup of tea to that order would you I've got a pretty girl on board this is Speedbird saying over and out.'

Bond released the switch and handed the microphone to the radio officer. He said, 'Pilot, they're putting down flares and keeping constant watch on our wavelength. Wind force two, long smooth swell with no broken crests. Now take it easy and let's try and get out of this alive. As soon as we hit the water I'll get the hatch open. Until then if anyone comes through the cockpit door he gets shot. Right?'

The girl's voice sounded from the door behind Bond. 'I was just coming to join the party but I won't now. Getting shot doesn't agree with me. But you might call that man back and make it two whiskies. Tea makes me hiccup.'

Bond said, 'Pussy, get back to your basket.' He gave a last glance round the cockpit and backed out of the door.

Two hours, two years, later Bond was lying in the warm cabin in Weathership Charlie listening dreamily to an early morning radio programme from Canada. Various parts of his body ached. He had got to the tail of the plane and made the girl kneel down with her head cradled in her arms on the seat of a chair. Then he had wedged himself in behind and over her and had held her life-jacketed body tightly in his arms and braced his back against the back of the seat behind him.

She had been nervously making facetious remarks about the indelicacy of this position when the belly of the Stratocruiser had thudded into the first mountain of swell at a hundred miles an hour. The huge plane skipped once and then crashed nose first into a wall of water. The impact had broken the back of the plane. The leaden weight of the bullion in the baggage compartment had torn the plane in half, spewing Bond and the girl out into the icy swell, lit red by the line of flares. There they had floated, half stunned, in their yellow life-jackets until the lifeboat got to them. By then there were only a few chunks of wreckage on the surface and the crew, with three tons of gold round their necks, were on their way down to the bed of the Atlantic. The boat hunted for ten minutes but when no bodies came to the surface they gave up the search and chugged back up the searchlight beam to the blessed wall of iron of the old frigate.

They had been treated like a mixture of royalty and people from Mars. Bond had answered the first, most urgent questions and then it had all suddenly seemed to be too much for his tired mind to cope with. Now he was lying luxuriating in the peace and the heat of the whisky and wondering about Pussy Galore and why she had chosen shelter under his wing rather than under Goldfinger's.

The connecting door with the next cabin opened and the girl came in. She was wearing nothing but a grey fisherman's jersey that was decent by half an inch. The sleeves were rolled up. She looked like a painting by Vertes. She said, 'People keep on asking if I'd like an alcohol rub and I keep on saying that if anyone's going to rub me it's you, and if I'm going to be rubbed with anything it's you I'd like to be rubbed with.' She ended lamely. 'So here I am.'

Bond said firmly, 'Lock that door, Pussy, take off that sweater and come into bed. You'll catch cold.'

She did as she was told, like an obedient child.

She lay in the crook of Bond's arm and looked up at him. She said, not in a gangster's voice, or a Lesbian's, but in a girl's voice, 'Will you write to me in Sing Sing?'

Bond looked down into the deep blue-violet eyes that were no longer hard, imperious. He bent and kissed them lightly. He said, 'They told me you only liked women.'

She said, 'I never met a man before.' The toughness came back into her voice. 'I come from the South. You know the definition of a virgin down there? Well, it's a girl who can run faster than her brother. In my case I couldn't run as fast as my uncle. I was twelve. That's not so good, James. You ought to be able to guess that.'

Bond smiled down into the pale, beautiful face. He said, 'All you need is a course of T.L.C.'

'What's T.L.C.?'

'Short for Tender Loving Care treatment. It's what they write on most papers when a waif gets brought in to a children's clinic.'

'I'd like that.' She looked at the passionate, rather cruel mouth waiting above hers. She reached up and brushed back the comma of black hair that had fallen over his right eyebrow. She looked into the fiercely slitted grey eyes. 'When's it going to start?'

Bond's right hand came slowly up the firm, muscled thighs, over the flat soft plain of the stomach to the right breast. Its point was hard with desire. He said softly, 'Now.' His mouth came ruthlessly down on hers.

THUNDERBALL

THUNDERBALL

The story is based on a screen treatment by
Kevin McClory, Jack Whittingham
and Ian Fleming

To
Ernest Cuneo
Muse

Chapter One

'Take it easy, Mr Bond'

It was one of those days when it seemed to James Bond that all life, as someone put it, was nothing but a heap of six to four against.

To begin with he was ashamed of himself–a rare state of mind. He had a hangover, a bad one, with an aching head and stiff joints. When he coughed–smoking too much goes with drinking too much and doubles the hangover–a cloud of small luminous black spots swam across his vision like amoebae in pond water. The one drink too many signals itself unmistakably. His final whisky and soda in the luxurious flat in Park Lane had been no different from the ten preceding ones, but it had gone down reluctantly and had left a bitter taste and an ugly sensation of surfeit. And, although he had taken in the message, he had agreed to play just one more rubber. Five pounds a hundred as it's the last one? He had agreed. And he had played the rubber like a fool. Even now he could see the queen of spades, with that stupid Mona Lisa smile on her fat face, slapping triumphantly down on his knave–the queen, as his partner had so sharply reminded him, that had been so infallibly marked with South, and that had made the difference between a grand slam redoubled (drunkenly) for him, and four hundred points above the line for the opposition. In the end it had been a twenty-point rubber, £100 against him–important money.

Again Bond dabbed with the bloodstained styptic pencil at the cut on his chin and despised the face that stared sullenly back at him from the mirror above the washbasin. Stupid, ignorant bastard! It all came from having nothing to do. More than a month of paper-work–ticking off his number on stupid dockets, scribbling minutes that got spikier as the weeks passed, and snapping back down the telephone when some harmless section officer tried to argue with him. And then his secretary had gone down with the flu and he had been given a silly, and, worse, ugly bitch from the pool who called him 'sir' and spoke to him primly through a mouth full of fruit stones. And now it was another Monday morning. Another week was beginning. The May rain thrashed at the windows. Bond swallowed down two Phensics and reached for the Enos. The telephone in his bedroom rang. It was the loud ring of the direct line with Headquarters.

James Bond, his heart thumping faster than it should have done, despite the race across London and a fretful wait for the lift to the eighth floor, pulled out the chair and sat down and looked across into the calm, grey, damnably clear eyes he knew so well. What could he read in them?

'Good morning, James. Sorry to pull you along a bit early in the morning.

Got a very full day ahead. Wanted to fit you in before the rush.'

Bond's excitement waned minutely. It was never a good sign when M addressed him by his Christian name instead of by his number. This didn't look like a job–more like something personal. There was none of the tension in M's voice that heralded big, exciting news. M's expression was interested, friendly, almost benign. Bond said something noncommittal.

'Haven't seen much of you lately, James. How have you been? Your health, I mean.' M picked up a sheet of paper, a form of some kind, from his desk, and held it as if preparing to read.

Suspiciously, trying to guess what the paper said, what all this was about, Bond said, 'I'm all right, sir.'

M said mildly, 'That's not what the M.O. thinks, James. Just had your last Medical. I think you ought to hear what he has to say.'

Bond looked angrily at the back of the paper. Now what the hell! He said with control, 'Just as you say, sir.'

M gave Bond a careful, appraising glance. He held the paper closer to his eyes. '"This officer",' he read, '"remains basically physically sound. Unfortunately his mode of life is not such as is likely to allow him to remain in this happy state. Despite many previous warnings, he admits to smoking sixty cigarettes a day. These are of a Balkan mixture with a higher nicotine content than the cheaper varieties. When not engaged upon strenuous duty, the officer's average daily consumption of alcohol is in the region of half a bottle of spirits of between sixty and seventy proof. On examination, there continues to be little definite sign of deterioration. The tongue is furred. The blood pressure a little raised at 160/90. The liver is not palpable. On the other hand, when pressed, the officer admits to frequent occipital headaches and there is spasm in the trapezius muscles and so-called 'fibrositis' nodules can be felt. I believe these symptoms to be due to this officer's mode of life. He is not responsive to the suggestion that over-indulgence is no remedy for the tensions inherent in his professional calling and can only result in the creation of a toxic state which could finally have the effect of reducing his fitness as an officer. I recommend that No. 007 should take it easy for two to three weeks on a more abstemious regime, when I believe he would make a complete return to his previous exceptionally high state of physical fitness."'

M reached over and slid the report into his OUT tray. He put his hands flat down on the desk in front of him and looked sternly across at Bond. He said, 'Not very satisfactory is it, James?'

Bond tried to keep impatience out of his voice. He said, 'I'm perfectly fit, sir. Everyone has occasional headaches. Most week-end golfers have fibrositis. You get it from sweating and then sitting in a draught. Aspirin and embrocation get rid of them. Nothing to it, really, sir.'

M said severely, 'That's just where you're making a big mistake, James. Taking medicine only suppresses these symptoms of yours. Medicine doesn't get to the root of the trouble. It only conceals it. The result is a more highly poisoned condition which may become chronic disease. All drugs are harmful to the system. They are contrary to nature. The same applies to most of the food we eat–white bread with all the roughage removed, refined sugar with all the goodness machined out of it, pasteurized milk which has had most of the vitamins boiled away, everything overcooked and denaturized. Why,' M reached into his pocket for his notebook and consulted it, 'do you know what our bread contains apart from a bit of overground flour?' M looked accusingly at Bond. 'It contains large quantities of chalk, also benzol peroxide powder, chlorine gas, sal ammoniac, and alum.' M put the notebook back in his pocket. 'What do you think of that?'

Bond, mystified by all this, said defensively, 'I don't eat all that much bread, sir.'

'Maybe not,' said M impatiently. 'But how much stone-ground whole wheat do you eat? How much yoghurt? Uncooked vegetables, nuts, fresh fruit?'

Bond smiled. 'Practically none at all, sir.'

'It's no laughing matter.' M tapped his forefinger on the desk for emphasis. 'Mark my words. There is no way to health except the natural way. All your troubles'–Bond opened his mouth to protest, but M held up his hand–'the deep-seated toxaemia revealed by your Medical, are the result of a basically unnatural way of life. Ever heard of Bircher-Brenner, for instance? Or Kneipp, Preissnitz, Rikli, Schroth, Gossman, Bilz?'

'No, sir.'

'Just so. Well those are the men you would be wise to study. Those are the great naturopaths–the men whose teaching we have foolishly ignored. Fortunately,' M's eyes gleamed enthusiastically, 'there are a number of disciples of these men practising in England. Nature cure is not beyond our reach.'

James Bond looked curiously at M. What the hell had got into the old man? Was all this the first sign of senile decay? But M looked fitter than Bond had ever seen him. The cold grey eyes were clear as crystal and the skin of the hard, lined face was luminous with health. Even the iron-grey hair seemed to have new life. Then what was all this lunacy?

M reached for his IN tray and placed it in front of him in a preliminary gesture of dismissal. He said cheerfully, 'Well, that's all, James. Miss Moneypenny has made the reservation. Two weeks will be quite enough to put you right. You won't know yourself when you come out. New man.'

Bond looked across at M, aghast. He said in a strangled voice, 'Out of where, sir?'

'Place called "Shrublands". Run by quite a famous man in his line–Wain, Joshua Wain. Remarkable chap. Sixty-five. Doesn't look a day over forty. He'll take good care of you. Very up-to-date equipment, and he's even got his own herb garden. Nice stretch of country. Near Washington in Sussex. And don't worry about your work here. Put it right out of your mind for a couple of weeks. I'll tell 009 to take care of the Section.'

Bond couldn't believe his ears. He said, 'But, sir. I mean, I'm perfectly all right. Are you sure? I mean, is this really necessary?'

'No,' M smiled frostily. 'Not necessary. Essential. If you want to stay in the double-O Section, that is. I can't afford to have an officer in that section who isn't one hundred per cent fit.' M lowered his eyes to the basket in front of him and took out a signal file. 'That's all, 007.' He didn't look up. The tone of voice was final.

Bond got to his feet. He said nothing. He walked across the room and let himself out, closing the door with exaggerated softness.

Outside the door, Miss Moneypenny looked sweetly up at him.

Bond walked over to her desk and banged his fist down so that the typewriter jumped. He said furiously, 'Now what the hell, Penny? Has the old man gone off his rocker? What's all this bloody nonsense? I'm damned if I'm going. He's absolutely nuts.'

Miss Moneypenny smiled happily. 'The manager's been terribly helpful and kind. He says he can give you the Myrtle room, in the Annex. He says it's a lovely room. It looks right over the herb garden. They've got their own herb garden, you know.'

'I know all about their bloody herb garden. Now look here, Penny,' Bond pleaded with her, 'be a good girl and tell me what it's all about. What's eating him?'

Miss Moneypenny, who often dreamed hopelessly about Bond, took pity on him. She lowered her voice conspiratorially. 'As a matter of fact, I think it's only a passing phase. But it *is* rather bad luck on you getting caught up in it before it's passed. You know he's always apt to get bees in his bonnet about the efficiency of the Service. There was the time when all of us had to go through that physical exercise course. Then he had the head-shrinker in, the psycho-analyst man–you missed that. You were somewhere abroad. All the Heads of Section had to tell him their dreams. He didn't last long. Some of their dreams must have scared him off or something. Well, last month M got lumbago and some friend of his at Blades, one of the fat, drinking ones I suppose,' Miss Moneypenny turned down her desirable mouth, 'told him about this place in the country. This man swore by it. Told M that we were all like motor-cars and that all we needed from time to time was to go to a garage and get decarbonized. He said he went there every year. He said it only cost twenty guineas a week which was less than what he spent in Blades in one day and it made him feel wonderful. Well, you know M always likes trying new things, and he went there for ten days and came back absolutely sold on the place. Yesterday he gave me a great talking-to all about it and this morning in the post I got a whole lot of tins of treacle and wheat germ and heaven knows what all. I don't know what to do with the stuff. I'm afraid my poor poodle'll have to live on it. Anyway, that's what's happened and I must say I've never seen him in such wonderful form. He's absolutely rejuvenated.'

'He looks like that blasted man in the old Kruschen Salts advertisements. But why does he pick on me to go to this nuthouse?'

Miss Moneypenny gave a secret smile. 'You know he thinks the world of you–or perhaps you don't. Anyway, as soon as he saw your Medical he told me to book you in.' Miss Moneypenny screwed up her nose. 'But, James, do you really drink and smoke as much as that? It can't be good for you, you know.' She looked up at him with motherly eyes.

Bond controlled himself. He summoned a desperate effort at nonchalance, at the throw-away phrase, 'It's just that I'd rather die of drink than of thirst. As for the cigarettes, it's really only that I don't know what to do with my hands.' He heard the stale, hangover words fall like clinker in a dead grate. Cut out the schmalz! What you need is a double brandy and soda.

Miss Moneypenny's warm lips pursed into a disapproving line. 'About the hands–that's not what I've heard.'

'Now don't you start on me, Penny.' Bond walked angrily towards the door. He turned round. 'Any more ticking-off from you and when I get out of this place I'll give you such a spanking you'll have to do your typing off a block of Dunlopillo.'

Miss Moneypenny smiled sweetly at him. 'I don't think you'll be able to do much spanking after living on nuts and lemon juice for two weeks, James.'

Bond made a noise between a grunt and a snarl and stormed out of the room.

Chapter Two

Shrublands

James Bond slung his suitcase into the back of the old chocolate-brown Austin taxi and climbed into the front seat beside the foxy, pimpled young man in the black leather windcheater. The young man took a comb out of his breast pocket, ran it carefully through both sides of his duck-tail haircut, put the comb back in his pocket, then leaned forward and pressed the self-starter. The play with the comb, Bond guessed, was to assert to Bond that the driver was really only taking him and his money as a favour. It was typical of the cheap self-assertiveness of young labour since the war. This youth, thought Bond, makes about twenty pounds a week, despises his parents, and would like to be Tommy Steele. It's not his fault. He was born into the buyers' market of the Welfare State and into the age of atomic bombs and space flight. For him, life is easy and meaningless. Bond said, 'How far is it to "Shrublands"?'

The young man did an expert but unnecessary racing change round an island and changed up again. ''Bout half an hour.' He put his foot down on the accelerator and neatly but rather dangerously overtook a lorry at an intersection.

'You certainly get the most out of your Bluebird.'

The young man glanced sideways to see if he was being laughed at. He decided that he wasn't. He unbent fractionally. 'My dad won't spring me something better. Says this old crate was okay for him for twenty years so it's got to be okay for me for another twenty. So I'm putting money by on my own. Half way there already.'

Bond decided that the comb-play had made him over-censorious. He said, 'What are you going to get?'

'Volkswagen Minibus. Do the Brighton races.'

'That sounds a good idea. Plenty of money in Brighton.'

'I'll say.' The young man showed a trace of enthusiasm. 'Only time I ever got there, a couple of bookies had me take them and a couple of tarts to London. Ten quid and a fiver tip. Piece of cake.'

'Certainly was. But you can get both kinds at Brighton. You want to watch out for being mugged and rolled. There are some tough gangs operating out of Brighton. What's happened to the Bucket of Blood these days?'

'Never opened up again after that case they had. The one that got in all the papers.' The young man realized that he was talking as if to an equal. He glanced sideways and looked Bond up and down with a new interest. 'You going into the Scrubs or just visiting?'

'Scrubs?'

'Shrublands–Wormwood Scrubs–Scrubs,' said the young man laconically. 'You're not like the usual ones I get to take there. Mostly fat women and old geezers who tell me not to drive so fast or it'll shake up their sciatica or something.'

Bond laughed. 'I've got fourteen days without the option. Doctor thinks it'll do me good. Got to take it easy. What do they think of the place round here?'

The young man took the turning off the Brighton road and drove westwards under the Downs through Poynings and Fulking. The Austin whined stolidly through the inoffensive countryside. 'People think they're a lot of crackpots. Don't care for the place. All those rich folk and they don't spend any money in the area. Tea-rooms make a bit out of them–specially out of the cheats.' He looked at Bond. 'You'd be surprised. Grown people, some of them pretty big shots in the City and so forth, and they motor around in their Bentleys with their bellies empty and they see a tea-shop and go in just for their cups of tea. That's all they're allowed. Next thing, they see some guy eating buttered toast and sugar cakes at the next table and they can't stand it. They order mounds of the stuff and hog it down just like kids who've broken into the larder–looking round all the time to see if they've been spotted. You'd think people like that would be ashamed of themselves.'

'Seems a bit silly when they're paying plenty to take the cure or whatever it is.'

'And that's another thing,' the young man's voice was indignant. 'I can understand charging twenty quid a week and giving you three square meals a day, but how do they get away with charging twenty quid for giving you nothing but hot water to eat? Doesn't make sense.'

'I suppose there are the treatments. And it must be worth it to the people if they get well.'

'Guess so,' said the young man doubtfully. 'Some of them do look a bit different when I come to take them back to the station.' He sniggered. 'And some of them change into real old goats after a week of nuts and so forth. Guess I might try it myself one day.'

'What do you mean?'

The young man glanced at Bond. Reassured and remembering Bond's worldly comments on Brighton, he said, 'Well, you see we got a girl here in Washington. Racy bird. Sort of local tart if you see what I mean. Waitress at a place called the Honey Bee Tea Shop–or was, rather. She started most of us off, if you get my meaning. Quid a go and she knows a lot of French tricks. Regular sport. Well, this year the word got round up at the Scrubs and some of these old goats began patronizing Polly–Polly Grace, that's her name. Took her out in their Bentleys and gave her a roll in a deserted quarry up on the Downs. That's been her pitch for years. Trouble was they paid her five, ten quid and she soon got too good for the likes of us. Priced her out of our market, so to speak. Inflation, sort of. And a month ago she chucked up her job at the Honey Bee, and you know what?' The young man's voice was loud with indignation. 'She bought herself a beat-up Austin Metropolitan for a couple of hundred quid and went mobile. Just like the London tarts in Curzon Street they talk about in the papers. Now she's off to Brighton, Lewes–anywhere she can find the sports, and in between whiles she goes to work in the quarry with these old goats from the Scrubs! Would you believe it!' The young man gave an angry blast on his klaxon at an inoffensive couple on a tandem bicycle.

Bond said seriously, 'That's too bad. I wouldn't have thought these people would be interested in that sort of thing on nut cutlets and dandelion wine or whatever they get to eat at this place.'

The young man snorted. 'That's all you know. I mean'–he felt he had been too emphatic–'that's what we all thought. One of my pals, he's the son of the local doctor, talked the thing over with his dad–in a roundabout way, sort of. And his dad said no. He said that this sort of diet and no drink and plenty of rest, what with the massage and the hot and cold Sitz baths and what have you, he said that all clears the blood-stream and tones up the system, if you get my meaning. Wakes the old goats up–makes 'em want to start cutting the mustard again, if you know the song by that Rosemary Clooney.'

Bond laughed. He said, 'Well, well. Perhaps there's something to the place after all.'

A sign on the right of the road said '"*Shrublands*". *Gateway to Health. First right. Silence please.*' The road ran through a wide belt of firs and evergreens in a fold of the Downs. A high wall appeared and then an imposing, mock-battlemented entrance with a Victorian lodge from which a thin wisp of smoke rose straight up among the quiet trees. The young man turned in and followed a gravel sweep between thick laurel bushes. An elderly couple cringed off the drive at a blare from his klaxon and then on the right there were broad stretches of lawn and neatly flowered borders and a sprinkling of slowly moving figures, alone and in pairs, and behind them a red brick Victorian monstrosity from which a long glass sun-parlour extended to the edge of the grass.

The young man pulled up beneath a heavy portico with a crenellated roof. Beside a varnished, iron-studded arched door stood a tall glazed urn above which a notice said: '*No smoking inside. Cigarettes here please.*' Bond got down from the taxi and pulled his suitcase out of the back. He gave the young man a ten-shilling tip. The young man accepted it as no less than his due. He said, 'Thanks. You ever want to break out, you can call me up. Polly's not the only one. And there's a tea-shop on the Brighton road has buttered muffins. So long.' He banged the gears into bottom and ground off back the way he had come. Bond picked up his suitcase and walked resignedly up the steps and through the heavy door.

Inside it was very warm and quiet. At the reception desk in the big oak-panelled hall a severely pretty girl in starched white welcomed him briskly. When he had signed the register she led him through a series of sombrely furnished public rooms and down a neutral-smelling white corridor to the back of the building. Here there was a communicating door with the annex, a long low cheaply-built structure with rooms on both sides of a central passage. The doors bore the names of flowers and shrubs. She showed him into Myrtle, told him that 'The Chief' would see him in an hour's time, at six o'clock, and left him.

It was a room-shaped room with furniture-shaped furniture and dainty curtains. The bed was provided with an electric blanket. There was a vase containing three marigolds beside the bed and a book called *Nature Cure Explained* by Alan Moyle, M.N.B.A. Bond opened it and ascertained that the initials stood for 'Member: British Naturopathic Association'. He turned off the central heating and opened the windows wide. The herb garden, row upon row of small nameless plants round a central sundial, smiled up at him. Bond unpacked his things and sat down in the single armchair and read about eliminating the waste products from his body. He learned a great deal about foods he had never heard of, such as Potassium Broth, Nut Mince, and the mysteriously named Unmalted Slippery Elm. He had got as far as the chapter on massage and was reflecting on the injunction that this art should be divided into Effleurage, Stroking, Friction, Kneading, Petrissage, Tapotement, and Vibration, when the telephone rang. A girl's voice said that Mr Wain would be glad to see him in Consulting Room A in five minutes.

Mr Joshua Wain had a firm, dry handshake and a resonant, encouraging voice. He had a lot of bushy grey hair above an unlined brow, soft, clear brown eyes, and a sincere and Christian smile. He appeared to be genuinely pleased to see Bond and to be interested in him. He wore a very clean smock-like coat with short sleeves from which strong hairy arms hung relaxed. Below were rather incongruous pin-stripe trousers. He wore sandals over socks of conservative grey and when he moved across the consulting room his stride was a springy lope.

Mr Wain asked Bond to remove all his clothes except his pants. When he saw the many scars he said politely, 'Dear me, you do seem to have been in the wars, Mr Bond.'

Bond said indifferently, 'Near miss. During the war.'

'Really! War between peoples is a terrible thing. Now, just breathe in deeply, please.' Mr Wain listened at Bond's back and chest, took his blood pressure, weighed him and recorded his height, and then, after asking him to lie face down on a surgical couch, handled his joints and vertebrae with soft, probing fingers.

While Bond replaced his clothes, Mr Wain wrote busily at his desk. Then he sat back. 'Well, Mr Bond, nothing much to worry about here, I think. Blood pressure a little high, slight osteopathic lesions in the upper vertebrae–they'll probably be causing your tension headaches, by the way–and some right sacroiliac strain with the right ilium slightly displaced backwards. Due to a bad fall some time, no doubt.' Mr Wain raised his eyebrows for confirmation.

Bond said, 'Perhaps.' Inwardly he reflected that the 'bad fall' had probably been when he had had to jump from the Arlberg Express after Heinkel and his friends had caught up with him around the time of the Hungarian uprising in 1956.

'Well now.' Mr Wain drew a printed form towards him and thoughtfully ticked off items on a list. 'Strict dieting for one week to eliminate the toxins in the blood-stream. Massage to tone you up, irrigation, hot and cold Sitz baths, osteopathic treatment, and a short course of Traction to get rid of the lesions. That should put you right. And complete rest, of course. Just take it easy, Mr Bond. You're a civil servant, I understand. Do you good to get away from all that worrying paper-work for a while.' Mr Wain got up and handed the printed form to Bond. 'Treatment rooms in half an hour, Mr Bond. No harm in starting right away.'

'Thank you.' Bond took the form and glanced at it. 'What's Traction, by the way?'

'A mechanical device for stretching the spine. Very beneficial.' Mr Wain smiled indulgently. 'Don't be worried by what some of the other patients tell you about it. They call it "The Rack". You know what wags some people are.'

'Yes.'

Bond walked out and along the white painted corridor. People were sitting about, reading or talking in soft tones in the public rooms. They were all elderly, middle-class people, mostly women, many of whom wore unattractive quilted dressing-gowns. The warm, close air and the frumpish women gave Bond claustrophobia. He walked through the hall to the main door and let himself out into the wonderful fresh air.

Bond walked thoughtfully down the trim narrow drive and smelled the musty smell of the laurels and the laburnums. Could he stand it? Was there any way out of this hell-hole short of resigning from the Service? Deep in thought, he almost collided with a girl in white who came hurrying round a sharp bend in the thickly hedged drive. At the same instant as she swerved out of his path and flashed him an amused smile, a mauve Bentley, taking the corner too fast, was on top of her. At one moment she was almost under its wheels, at the next, Bond, with one swift step, had gathered her up by the waist and, executing a passable Veronica, with a sharp swivel of his hips had picked her body literally off the bonnet of the car. He put the girl down as the Bentley dry-skidded to a stop in the gravel. His right hand held the memory of one beautiful breast. The girl said 'Oh!' and looked up into his eyes with an expression of flurried astonishment. Then she took in what had happened and said breathlessly, 'Oh, thank you.' She turned towards the car. A man had climbed unhurriedly down from the driving seat. He said calmly, 'I am so sorry. Are you all right?' Recognition dawned on his face. He said silkily, 'Why, if it isn't my friend Patricia? How are you, Pat? All ready for me?'

The man was extremely handsome–a dark bronzed woman-killer with a neat moustache above the sort of callous mouth women kiss in their dreams. He had regular features that suggested Spanish or South American blood and bold, hard brown eyes that turned up oddly, or, as a woman would put it, intriguingly, at the corners. He was an athletic-looking six foot, dressed in the sort of casually well-cut beige herring-bone tweed that suggests Anderson and Sheppard. He wore a white silk shirt and a dark red polka-dot tie, and the soft dark brown V-necked sweater looked like vicuna. Bond summed him up as a good-looking bastard who got all the women he wanted and probably lived on them–and lived well.

The girl had recovered her poise. She said severely, 'You really ought to be more careful, Count Lippe. You know there are always patients and staff walking down this drive. If it hadn't been for this gentleman,' she smiled at Bond, 'you'd have run me over. After all, there *is* a big sign asking drivers to take care.'

'I am so sorry, my dear. I was hurrying. I am late for my appointment with the good Mr Wain. I am as usual in need of decarbonization–this time after two weeks in Paris.' He turned to Bond. He said with a hint of condescension, 'Thank you, my dear sir. You have quick reactions. And now, if you will forgive me—' He raised a hand, got back into the Bentley, and purred off up the drive.

The girl said, 'Now I really must hurry. I'm terribly late.' Together they turned and walked after the Bentley.

Bond said, examining her, 'Do you work here?' She said that she did. She had been at Shrublands for three years. She liked it. And how long was he staying? The small-talk continued.

She was an athletic-looking girl whom Bond would have casually associated with tennis, or skating, or show-jumping. She had the sort of firm, compact figure that always attracted him and a fresh open-air type of prettiness that would have been common-place but for a wide, rather passionate mouth and a hint of authority that would be a challenge to men. She was dressed in a feminine version of the white smock worn by Mr Wain, and it was clear from the undisguised curves of her breasts and hips that she had little on underneath it. Bond asked her if she didn't get bored. What did she do with her time off?

She acknowledged the gambit with a smile and a quick glance of appraisal. 'I've got one of those bubble cars. I get about the country quite a lot. And there are wonderful walks. And one's always seeing new people here. Some of them are very interesting. That man in the car, Count Lippe. He comes here every year. He tells me fascinating things about the Far East–China and so on. He's got some sort of business in a place called Macao. It's near Hong Kong, isn't it?'

'Yes, that's right.' So those turned-up eyes were a dash of Chinaman. It would be interesting to know his background. Probably Portuguese blood if he came from Macao.

They had reached the entrance. Inside the warm hall the girl said, 'Well, I must run. Thank you again.' She gave him a smile that, for the benefit of the watching receptionist, was entirely neutral. 'I hope you enjoy your stay.' She hurried off towards the treatment rooms. Bond followed, his eyes on the taut swell of her hips. He glanced at his watch and also went down the stairs and into a spotlessly white basement that smelled faintly of olive oil and Aerosol disinfectant.

Beyond a door marked 'Gentlemen's Treatment' he was taken in hand by an indiarubbery masseur in trousers and singlet. Bond undressed and with a towel round his waist followed the man down a long room divided into compartments by plastic curtains. In the first compartment, side by side, two elderly men lay, the perspiration pouring down their strawberry faces, in electric blanket-baths. In the next were two massage tables. On one, the pale, dimpled body of a youngish but very fat man wobbled obscenely beneath the pummelling of his masseur. Bond, his mind recoiling from it all, took off his towel and lay down on his face and surrendered himself to the toughest deep massage he had every experienced.

Vaguely, against the jangling of his nerves and the aching of muscles and tendons, he heard the fat man heave himself off his table and, moments later, another patient take his place. He heard the man's masseur say, 'I'm afraid we'll have to have the wrist-watch off, sir.'

The urbane, silky voice that Bond at once recognized said with authority, 'Nonsense, my dear fellow. I come here every year and I've always been allowed to keep it on before. I'd rather keep it on, if you don't mind.'

'Sorry, sir.' The masseur's voice was politely firm. 'You must have had someone else doing the treatment. It interferes with the flow of blood when I come to treat the arm and hand. If you don't mind, sir.'

There was a moment's silence. Bond could almost feel Count Lippe controlling his temper. The words, when they came, were spat out with what seemed to Bond ludicrous violence. 'Take it off then.' The 'Damn you' didn't have to be uttered. It hung in the air at the end of the sentence.

'Thank you, sir.' There was a brief pause and then the massage began.

The small incident seemed odd to Bond. Obviously one had to take off one's wrist-watch for a massage. Why had the man wanted to keep it on? It seemed very childish.

'Turn over, please sir.'

Bond obeyed. Now his face was free to move. He glanced casually to his right. Count Lippe's face was turned away from him. His left arm hung down towards the floor. Where the sunburn ended, there was a bracelet of almost white flesh at the wrist. In the middle of the circle where the watch had been there was a sign tattooed in red on the skin. It looked like a small zigzag crossed by two vertical strokes. So Count Lippe had not wanted this sign to be seen! It would be amusing to ring up Records and see if they had a line on what sort of people wore this little secret recognition sign under their wrist-watches.

Chapter Three

The Rack

At the end of the hour's treatment Bond felt as if his body had been eviscerated and then run through a wringer. He put on his clothes and, cursing M, climbed weakly back up the stairs into what, by comparison with the world of nakedness and indignities in the basement, were civilized surroundings. At the entrance to the main lounge were two telephone booths. The switchboard put him through to the only Headquarters number he was allowed to call on an outside line. He knew that all such outside calls were monitored. As he asked for Records, he recognized the hollowness on the line that meant the line was bugged. He gave his number to Head of Records and put his question, adding that the subject was an Oriental probably of Portuguese extraction. After ten minutes Head of Records came back to him.

'It's a Tong sign.' His voice sounded interested. 'The Red Lightning Tong. Unusual to find anyone but a full-blooded Chinaman being a member. It's not the usual semi-religious organization. This is entirely criminal. Station H had dealings with it once. They're represented in Hong Kong, but their headquarters are across the bay in Macao. Station H paid big money to get a courier service running into Pekin. Worked like a dream, so they gave the line a trial with some heavy stuff. It bounced, badly. Lost a couple of H's top men. It was a double-cross. Turned out that Redland had some sort of a deal with these people. Hell of a mess. Since then they've cropped up from time to time in drugs, gold smuggling to India, and top-bracket White Slavery. They're big people. We'd be interested if you've got any kind of a line.'

Bond said, 'Thanks, Records. No, I've got nothing definite. First time

I've heard of these Red Lightning people. Let you know if anything develops. So long.'

Bond thoughtfully put back the receiver. How interesting! Now what the hell could this man be doing at Shrublands? Bond walked out of the booth. A movement in the next booth caught his eye. Count Lippe, his back to Bond, had just picked up the receiver. How long had he been in there? Had he heard Bond's inquiry? Or his comment? Bond had the crawling sensation at the pit of his stomach he knew so well–the signal that he had probably made a dangerous and silly mistake. He glanced at his watch. It was seven thirty. He walked through the lounge to the sun-parlour where 'dinner' was being served. He gave his name to the elderly woman with a wardress face behind a long counter. She consulted a list and ladled hot vegetable soup into a plastic mug. Bond took the mug. He said anxiously, 'Is that all?'

The woman didn't smile. She said severely, 'You're lucky. You wouldn't be getting as much on Starvation. And you may have soup every day at midday and two cups of tea at four o'clock.'

Bond gave her a bitter smile. He took the horrible mug over to one of the little café tables near the windows overlooking the dark lawn and sat down and sipped the thin soup while he watched some of his fellow inmates meandering aimlessly, weakly, through the room. Now he felt a grain of sympathy for the wretches. Now he was a member of their club. Now he had been initiated. He drank the soup down to the last neat cube of carrot and walked abstractedly off to his room, thinking of Count Lippe, thinking of sleep, but above all thinking of his empty stomach.

After two days of this, Bond felt terrible. He had a permanent slight nagging headache, the whites of his eyes had turned rather yellow, and his tongue was deeply furred. His masseur told him not to worry. This was as it should be. These were the poisons leaving his body. Bond, now a permanent prey to lassitude, didn't argue. Nothing seemed to matter any more but the single orange and hot water for breakfast, the mugs of hot soup, and the cups of tea which Bond filled with spoonfuls of brown sugar, the only variety that had Mr Wain's sanction.

On the third day, after the massage and the shock of the Sitz baths, Bond had on his programme 'Osteopathic Manipulation and Traction'. He was directed to a new section of the basement, withdrawn and silent. When he opened the designated door he expected to find some hairy H-man waiting for him with flexed muscles. (H-man, he had discovered, stood for Health-man. It was the smart thing to call oneself if you were a naturopath.) He stopped in his tracks. The girl, Patricia something, whom he had not set eyes on since his first day, stood waiting for him beside the couch. He closed the door behind him and said, 'Good lord. Is this what you do?'

She was used to this reaction of the men patients and rather touchy about it. She didn't smile. She said in a businesslike voice, 'Nearly twenty per cent of osteopaths are women. Take off your clothes, please. Everything except your pants.' When Bond had amusedly obeyed she told him to stand in front of her. She walked round him, examining him with eyes in which there was nothing but professional interest. Without commenting on his scars she told him to lie face downwards on the couch and, with strong, precise, and thoroughly practised holds, went through the handling and joint-cracking of her profession.

Bond soon realized that she was an extremely powerful girl. His muscled body, admittedly unresistant, seemed to be easy going for her. Bond felt a kind of resentment at the neutrality of this relationship between an attractive girl and a half naked man. At the end of the treatment she told him to stand up and clasp his hands behind her neck. Her eyes, a few inches away from his, held nothing but professional concentration. She hauled strongly away from him, presumably with the object of freeing his vertebrae. This was too much for Bond. At the end of it, when she told him to release his hands, he did nothing of the sort. He tightened them, pulled her head sharply towards him, and kissed her full on the lips. She ducked quickly down through his arms and straightened herself, her cheeks red and her eyes shining with anger. Bond smiled at her, knowing that he had never missed a slap in the face, and a hard one at that, by so little. He said, 'It's all very well, but I just had to do it. You shouldn't have a mouth like that if you're going to be an osteopath.'

The anger in her eyes subsided a fraction. She said, 'The last time that happened, the man had to leave by the next train.'

Bond laughed. He made a threatening move towards her. 'If I thought there was any hope of being kicked out of this damn place I'd kiss you again.'

She said, 'Don't be silly. Now pick up your things. You've got half an hour's Traction.' She smiled grimly. 'That ought to keep you quiet.'

Bond said morosely, 'Oh, all right. But only on condition you let me take you out on your next day off.'

'We'll see about that. It depends how you behave at the next treatment.' She held open the door. Bond picked up his clothes and went out, almost colliding with a man coming down the passage. It was Count Lippe, in slacks and a gay windcheater. He ignored Bond. With a smile and a slight bow he said to the girl, 'Here comes the lamb to the slaughter. I hope you're not feeling too strong today.' His eyes twinkled charmingly.

The girl said briskly, 'Just get ready, please. I shan't be a moment putting Mr Bond on the Traction table.' She moved off down the passage with Bond following.

She opened the door of a small anteroom, told Bond to put his things down on a chair, and pulled aside plastic curtains that formed a partition. Just inside the curtains was an odd-looking kind of surgical couch in leather and gleaming aluminium. Bond didn't like the look of it at all. While the girl fiddled with a series of straps attached to three upholstered sections that appeared to be on runners, Bond examined the contraption suspiciously. Below the couch was a stout electric motor on which a plate announced that this was the Hercules Motorized Traction Table. A power drive in the shape of articulated rods stretched upwards from the motor to each of the three cushioned sections of the couch and terminated in tension screws to which the three sets of straps were attached. In front of the raised portion where the patient's head would lie, and approximately level with his face, was a large dial marked in lbs.-pressure up to 200. After 150 lbs. the numerals were in red. Below the headrest were grips for the patient's hands. Bond noted gloomily that the leather on the grips was stained with, presumably, sweat.

'Lie face downwards here, please.' The girl held the straps ready.

Bond said obstinately, 'Not until you tell me what this thing does. I don't like the look of it.'

The girl said patiently, 'This is simply a machine for stretching your spine. You've got some mild spinal lesions. It will help to free those. And at the base of your spine you've got some right sacroiliac strain. It'll help that too. You won't find it bad at all. Just a stretching sensation. It's very soothing really. Quite a lot of patients fall asleep.'

'This one won't,' said Bond firmly. 'What strength are you going to give me? Why are those top figures in red? Are you sure I'm not going to be pulled apart?'

The girl said with a touch of impatience, 'Don't be silly. Of course if there was too much tension it might be dangerous. But I shall be starting you only at 90 lbs. and in a quarter of an hour I shall come and see how you're getting on and probably put you up to 120. Now come along. I've got another patient waiting.'

Reluctantly Bond climbed up on the couch and lay on his face with his nose and mouth buried in a deep cleft in the headrest. He said, his voice muffled by the leather, 'If you kill me, I'll sue.'

He felt the straps being tightened round his chest and then round his hips. The girl's skirt brushed the side of his face as she bent to reach the control lever beside the big dial. The motor began to whine. The straps tightened and then relaxed, tightened and relaxed. Bond felt as if his body was being stretched by giant hands. It was a curious sensation, but not unpleasant. With difficulty Bond raised his head. The needle on the dial stood at ninety. Now the machine was making a soft iron hee-hawing, like a mechanical donkey, as the gears alternatively engaged and disengaged to produce the rhythmic traction.

'Are you all right?'

'Yes.' He heard the girl pass through the plastic curtains and then the click of the outer door. Bond abandoned himself to the soft feel of the leather at his face, to the relentless intermittent haul on his spine and to the hypnotic whine and drone of the machine. It really wasn't too bad. How silly to have had nerves about it!

A quarter of an hour later he heard again the click of the outside door and the swish of the curtains.

'All right?'

'Fine.'

The girl's hand came into his line of vision as she turned the lever. Bond raised his head. The needle crept up to 120. Now the pull was really hard and the voice of the machine was much louder.

The girl put her head down to his. She laid a reassuring hand on his shoulder. She said, her voice loud above the noise of the gears, 'Only another quarter of an hour to go.'

'All right.' Bond's voice was careful. He was probing the new strength of the giant haul on his body. The curtains swished. Now the click of the outside door was drowned by the noise of the machine. Slowly Bond relaxed again into the arms of the rhythm.

It was perhaps five minutes later when a tiny movement of the air against his face made Bond open his eyes. In front of his eyes was a hand, a man's hand, reaching softly for the lever of the accelerator. Bond watched it, at first fascinated, and then with dawning horror as the lever was slowly depressed and the straps began to haul madly at his body. He shouted–something, he didn't know what. His whole body was racked with a great pain. Desperately he lifted his head and shouted again. On the dial, the needle was trembling at 200! His head dropped back, exhausted. Through a mist of sweat he watched the hand softly release the lever. The hand paused and turned slowly so that the back of the wrist was just below his eyes. In the centre of the wrist was the little red sign of the zigzag and the two bisecting lines. A voice said quietly, close up against his ear, 'You will not meddle again, my friend.' Then there was nothing but the great whine and groan of the machine and the bite of the straps that were tearing his body in half. Bond began to scream, weakly, while the sweat poured from him and dripped off the leather cushions on to the floor.

Then suddenly there was blackness.

Chapter Four

Tea and Animosity

It is just as well that the body retains no memory of pain. Yes, it hurt, that abscess, that broken bone, but just how it hurt, and how much, is soon forgotten by the brain and the nerves. It is not so with pleasant sensations, a scent, a taste, the particular texture of a kiss. These things can be almost totally recalled. Bond, gingerly exploring his sensations as life came flooding back into his body, was astonished that the web of agony that had held his body so utterly had now completely dissolved. It was true that his whole spine ached as if it had been beaten, each vertebra separately, with wooden truncheons, but this pain was recognizable, something within his knowledge and therefore capable of control. The searing tornado that had entered his body and utterly dominated it, replacing his identity with its own, had gone. How had it been? What had it been like? Bond couldn't remember except that it had reduced him to something lower in the scale of existence than a handful of grass in the mouth of a tiger.

The murmur of voices grew more distinct.

'But what told you first that something was wrong, Miss Fearing?'

'It was the noise, the noise of the machine. I had just finished a treatment. A few minutes later I heard it. I'd never heard it so loud. I thought perhaps the door had been left open. I wasn't really worried but I came along to make sure. And there it was. The indicator up to 200! I tore down the lever and got the straps off and ran to the surgery and found the coramine and injected it into the vein–one c.c. The pulse was terribly weak. Then I telephoned you.'

'You seem to have done everything possible, Miss Fearing. And I'm sure you bear no responsibility for this terrible thing.' Mr Wain's voice was doubtful. 'It really is most unfortunate. I suppose the patient must have jerked the lever, somehow. Perhaps he was experimenting. He might easily have killed himself. We must tell the company about this and have some safety arrangement installed.'

A hand gingerly clasped Bond's wrist, feeling for his pulse. Bond thought it was time to re-enter the world. He must quickly get himself a doctor, a real one, not one of these grated-carrot merchants. A sudden wave of anger poured through him. This was all M's fault. M was mad. He would have it out with him when he got back to Headquarters. If necessary he would go higher–to the Chiefs of Staff, the Cabinet, the Prime Minister. M was a dangerous lunatic–a danger to the country. It was up to Bond to save England. The weak, hysterical thoughts whirled through his brain, mixed themselves up with the hairy hand of Count Lippe, the mouth of Patricia Fearing, the taste of hot vegetable soup and, as consciousness slipped away from him again, the diminishing voice of Mr Wain: 'No structural damage. Only considerable surface abrasion of the nerve ends. And of course shock. You will take personal charge of the case, Miss Fearing. Rest, warmth, and effleurage. Is that under . . .?'

Rest, warmth, and effleurage. When Bond came round again, he was lying face downward on his bed and his whole body was bathed in exquisite sensation. Beneath him was the soft warmth of an electric blanket, his back glowed with the heat from two large sun lamps, and two hands, clad in what felt to be some particularly velvety fur, were rhythmically passing, one after the other, up and down the whole length of his body from his neck to the backs of his knees. It was a most gentle and almost piercingly luxurious experience, and Bond lay and bathed himself in it.

Presently he said sleepily, 'Is that what they call effleurage?'

The girl's voice said softly, 'I thought you'd come round. The whole tone of your skin suddenly changed. How are you feeling?'

'Wonderful. I'd be still better for a double whisky on the rocks.'

The girl laughed. 'Mr Wain did say dandelion tea would be best for you. But I thought a little stimulant might be good, I mean just this once. So I brought the brandy with me. And there's plenty of ice as I'm going to give you an ice-pack presently. Would you really like some? Wait, I'll put your dressing-gown over you and then you can see if you can turn over. I'll look the other way.'

Bond heard the lamps being pulled away. Gingerly, he turned on his side. The dull ache returned, but it was already wearing off. He cautiously slipped his legs over the side of the bed and sat up.

Patricia Fearing stood in front of him, clean, white, comforting, desirable. In one hand was a pair of heavy mink gloves, but with the fur covering the palm instead of the back. In the other was a glass. She held out the glass. As Bond drank and heard the reassuring, real-life tinkle of the ice, he thought: this is a most splendid girl. I will settle down with her. She will give me effleurage all day long and from time to time a good tough drink like this. It will be a life of great beauty. He smiled at her and held out the empty glass and said, 'More.'

She laughed, mostly with relief that he was completely alive again. She took the glass and said, 'Well, just one more then. But don't forget it's on an empty stomach. It may make you dreadfully tight.' She paused with the brandy bottle in her hand. Suddenly her gaze was cool, clinical. 'And now you must try and tell me what happened. Did you accidentally touch the lever or something? You gave us all a dreadful fright. Nothing like that has ever happened before. The Traction table's really perfectly safe, you know.'

Bond looked candidly into her eyes. He said reassuringly, 'Of course. I was just trying to get more comfortable. I heaved about and I do remember that my hand hit something rather hard. I suppose it must have been the lever. Then I don't remember any more. I must have been awfully lucky you came along so quickly.'

She handed him the fresh drink. 'Well, it's all over now. And thank heavens nothing's badly strained. Another two days of treatment and you'll be right as rain.' She paused. She looked rather embarrassed. 'Oh, and Mr Wain asks if you could possibly keep all this, all this trouble, to yourself. He doesn't want the other patients to get worried.'

I should think not, thought Bond. He could see the headlines. 'PATIENT TORN NEARLY LIMB FROM LIMB AT NATURE CLINIC. RACK MACHINE GOES BERSERK. MINISTRY OF HEALTH STEPS IN.' He said, 'Of course I won't say anything. It was my fault anyway.' He finished his drink, handed back the glass, and cautiously lay back on the bed. He said, 'That was marvellous. Now how about some more of the mink treatment. And by the way. Will you marry me? You're the only girl I've ever met who knows how to treat a man properly.'

She laughed. 'Don't be silly. And turn over on your face. It's your back that needs treatment.'

'How do you know?'

Two days later, Bond was once more back in the half-world of the nature cure. The routine of the early morning glass of hot water, the orange, carefully sliced into symmetrical pigs by some ingenious machine wielded, no doubt, by the wardress in charge of diets, then the treatments, the hot soup, the siesta, and the blank, aimless walk or bus ride to the nearest tea-shop for the priceless strength-giving cups of tea laced with brown sugar. Bond loathed and despised tea, that flat, soft, time-wasting opium of the masses, but on his empty stomach, and in his febrile state, the sugary brew acted almost as an intoxicant. Three cups he reckoned had the effect, not of hard liquor, but of just about half a bottle of champagne in the outside world, in real life. He got to know them all, these dainty opium dens–Rose Cottage, which he avoided after the woman charged him extra for emptying the sugar bowl; The Thatched Barn, which amused him because it was a real den of iniquity–large plates of sugar cakes put on one's table, the piercing temptation of the smell of hot scones–the Transport Café, where the Indian tea was black and strong and the lorry drivers brought in a smell of sweat and petrol and the great world (Bond found that all his senses, particularly his palate and nose, had miraculously become sharpened), and a dozen other cottagey, raftery nooks where elderly couples with Ford Populars and Morris Minors talked in muted tones about children called Len and Ron and Pearl and Ethel, and ate in small mouthfuls with the points of their teeth and made not a sound with the tea things. It was all a world whose ghastly daintiness and propriety would normally have sickened him. Now, empty, weak, drained of all the things that belonged to his tough, fast, basically dirty life, through banting, he had somehow regained some of the innocence and purity of childhood. In this frame of mind, the naivety and total lack of savour, surprise, excitement, of the dimity world of the Nice-Cup-of-Tea, of the Home-made Cakes, and the One-Lump-or-Two, were perfectly acceptable.

And the extraordinary thing was that he could not remember when he had felt so well–not strong, but without any aches and pains, clear of eye and skin, sleeping ten hours a day and, above all, without the nagging sense of morning guilt that one is slowly wrecking one's body. It was really quite disturbing. Was his personality changing? Was he losing his edge, his point, his identity? Was he losing the vices that were so much part of his ruthless, cruel, fundamentally tough character? Who was he in process of becoming? A soft, dreaming, kindly idealist who would naturally leave the Service and become instead a prison visitor, interest himself in youth clubs, march with the H-bomb marchers, eat nut cutlets, try and change the world for the better?

James Bond would have been more worried, as day by day the H-cure drew his teeth, if it had not been for three obsessions which belonged to his former life and which would not leave him–a passionate longing for a large dish of Spaghetti Bolognese containing plenty of chopped garlic and accompanied by a whole bottle of the cheapest, rawest Chianti (bulk for his empty stomach and sharp tastes for his starved palate), an overwhelming desire for the strong, smooth body of Patricia Fearing, and a deadly concentration on ways and means to wring the guts of Count Lippe.

The first two would have to wait, though tantalizing schemes for consuming both dishes on the day of his release from Shrublands occupied much of his mind. So far as Count Lippe was concerned, work had started on the project from the moment Bond took up again the routine of the cure.

With the cold intensity he would have employed against an enemy agent, say in a hotel in Stockholm or Lisbon during the war, James Bond set about spying on the other man. He became garrulous and inquisitive, chatting with Patricia Fearing about the various routines at Shrublands. 'But when do the staff find time to have lunch?' 'That man Lippe looks very fit. Oh, he's worried about his waist-line! Aren't the electric blanket baths good for that? No, I haven't seen the Turkish Bath Cabinet. Must have a look at it some time.' And to his masseur: 'Haven't seen that big chap about lately, Count something–Ripper? Hipper? Oh yes, Lippe. Oh, noon every day? I think I must try and get that time as well. Nice being clear for the rest of the day. And I'd like to have a spell in the Turkish Bath thing when you've finished the massage. Need a good sweat.' Innocently, fragment by fragment, James Bond built up a plan of operations–a plan that would leave him and Lippe alone among the machinery of the sound-proof treatment rooms.

For there would be no other opportunity. Count Lippe kept to his room in the main building until his treatment time at noon. In the afternoons he swished away in the violet Bentley–to Bournemouth it seemed, where he had 'business'. The night porter let him in around eleven each night. One afternoon–in the siesta hour–Bond slipped the Yale lock on Count Lippe's room with a straight piece of plastic cut off a child's aeroplane he had bought for the purpose in Washington. He went over the room meticulously and drew a blank. All he learned–from the clothes–was that the Count was a much travelled man–shirts from Charvet, ties from Tripler, Dior, and Hardy Amies, shoes from Peel, and raw silk pyjamas from Hong Kong. The dark red morocco suitcase from Mark Cross might have contained secrets, and Bond eyed the silk linings and toyed with the Count's Wilkinson razor. But no! Better that revenge, if it could be contrived, should come out of a clear sky.

That same afternoon, drinking his treacly tea, Bond scraped together the meagre scraps of his knowledge of Count Lippe. He was about thirty, attractive to women, and physically, to judge from the naked body Bond had seen, very strong. His blood would be Portuguese with a dash of Chinaman and he gave the appearance of wealth. What did he do? What was his profession? At first glance Bond would have put him down as a tough *maquereau* from the Ritz bar in Paris, the Palace at St Moritz, the Carlton at Cannes–good at backgammon, polo, water-skiing, but with the yellow streak of the man who lives on women. But Lippe had heard Bond making inquiries about him and that had been enough for an act of violence–an inspired act that he had carried out swiftly and coolly when he finished his treatment with the Fearing girl and knew, from her remark, that Bond would be alone on the Traction table. The act of violence might only have been designed to warn, but equally, since Lippe could only guess at the effect of a 200-lb. pull on the spine, it might have been designed to kill. Why? Who was this man who had so much to hide? And what were his secrets? Bond poured the last of his tea on to a mound of brown sugar. One thing was certain–the secrets were big ones.

Bond never seriously considered telling Headquarters about Lippe and what he had done to Bond. The whole thing, against the background of Shrublands, was so unlikely and so utterly ridiculous. And somehow Bond, the man of action and resource, came out of it all as something of a ninny. Weakened by a diet of hot water and vegetable soup, the ace of the Secret Service had been tied to some kind of a rack and then a man had come along and just pulled a lever up a few notches and reduced the hero of a hundred combats to a quivering jelly! No! There was only one solution–a private solution, man to man. Later perhaps, to satisfy his curiosity, it might be amusing to put through a good Trace on Count Lippe–with S.I.S. Records, with the C.I.D., with the Hong Kong Station. But for the time being Bond would stay quiet, keep out of Count Lippe's way, and plan meticulously for just the right kind of pay-off.

By the time the fourteenth day, the last day, came, Bond had it all fixed–the time, the place, and the method.

At ten o'clock, Mr Joshua Wain received Bond for his final check-up. When Bond came into the consulting room, Mr Wain was standing by the open window doing deep-breathing exercises. With a final thorough exhalation through the nostrils he turned to greet Bond with an Ah! Bisto! expression on his healthily flushed face. His smile was elastic with good-fellowship. 'And how's the world treating you, Mr Bond? No ill effects from that unhappy little accident? No. Quite so. The body is a most remarkable piece of mechanism. Extraordinary powers of recovery. Now then, shirt off, please, and we'll see what Shrublands has managed to do for you.'

Ten minutes later, Bond, blood pressure down to 132/84, weight reduced by ten pounds, osteopathic lesions gone, clear of eye and tongue, was on his way down to the basement rooms for his final treatment.

As usual, it was clammily quiet and neutral-smelling in the white rooms and corridors. From the separate cubicles there came an occasional soft exchange between patient and staff, and, in the background, intermittent plumbing noises. The steady whir of the ventilation system created the impression of the deep innards of a liner in a dead calm. It was nearly twelve thirty. Bond lay face down on the massage table and listened for the authoritative voice and the quick slap of the naked feet of his prey. The door at the end of the corridor sighed open and sighed shut again. 'Morning, Beresford. All ready for me? Make it good and hot today. Last treatment. Three more ounces to lose. Right?'

'Very good, sir.' The gym shoes of the chief attendant, followed by the slapping feet, came down the corridor outside the plastic curtain of the massage room and on to the end room of all, the electric Turkish bath. The door sighed shut and a few minutes later sighed again as the attendant, having installed Count Lippe, came back down the corridor. Twenty minutes went by. Twenty-five. Bond rolled off the table. 'Well, thanks, Sam. You've done me a power of good. I'll be back to see you again one of these days I expect. I'll just go along and have a final salt rub and a Sitz bath. You cut along to your carrot cutlets. Don't worry about me. I'll let myself out when I've finished.' Bond wrapped a towel round his waist and moved off down the corridor. There was a flurry of movement and voices as the attendants got rid of their patients and made their way through the staff door for the luncheon break. The last patient, a reformed drunk, called back from the entrance, 'See you later, Irrigator!' Somebody laughed. Now the petty-officer voice of Beresford sounded down the corridor, making certain that everything was shipshape: 'Windows, Bill? Okay. Your next is Mr Dunbar at two sharp. Len, tell the laundry we shall need more towels after lunch. Ted . . . Ted. You there, Ted? Well, then, Sam, look after Count Lippe, would you, Turkish bath.'

Bond had listened to this routine for a whole week, noting the men that cut minutes off their duty and got off early to lunch, noting the ones that stayed to do their full share of the last chores. Now, from the open door of the empty shower room, he called back, in Sam's deep voice, 'Okay, Mr Beresford,' and waited for the crisp squeak of the gym shoes on the linoleum. There it was! The brief pause half way down the corridor and then the double sigh as the staff door opened and shut. Now there was dead silence save for the hum of the fans. The treatment rooms were empty. Now there was only James Bond and Count Lippe.

Bond waited a moment and then came out of the shower room and softly opened the door to the Turkish bath. He had had one session in the place, just to get the geography clear in his mind, and the scene was exactly as he remembered.

It was a white cubicle treatment-room like all the others, but in this one the only object was a big cream metal and plastic box about five feet tall by four feet square. It was closed on all sides but the top. The front of the big cabinet was hinged to allow a patient to climb in and sit inside and there was a hole in the top with a foam rubber support for the nape of the neck and the chin, through which the patient's head emerged. The rest of his body was exposed to the heat from many rows of naked electric bulbs inside the cabinet and the degree of heat was thermostatically controlled by a dial at the back of the cabinet. It was a simple sweat-box, designed, as Bond had noticed on his previous visit to the room, by the Medikalischer Maschinenbau G.m.b.H., 44 Franziskanerstrasse, Ulm, Bavaria.

The cabinet faced away from the door. At the hiss of the hydraulic fastener, Count Lippe said angrily, 'Goddammit, Beresford. Let me out of this thing. I'm sweating like a pig.'

'You said you wanted it hot, sir.' Bond's amiable voice was a good approximation to the chief attendant's.

'Don't argue, goddammit. Let me out of here.'

'I don't think you quite realize the value of heat in the H-Cure, sir. Heat resolves many of the toxins in the blood-stream and for the matter of that in the muscle tissue also. A patient suffering from your condition of pronounced toxaemia will find much benefit from the heat treatment.' Bond found the H-lingo rattling quite easily off the tongue. He was not worried about the consequences to Beresford. He would have the solid alibi of luncheon in the staff canteen.

'Don't give me that crap. I tell you, let me out of here.'

Bond examined the dial on the back of the machine. The needle stood at 120. What should he give the man? The dial ran up to 200 degrees. That much might roast him alive. This was only to be a punishment, not a murder. Perhaps 180 would be a just retribution. Bond clicked the knob up to 180. He said: 'I think just half an hour of real heat will do you the world of good, sir.' Bond dropped the sham voice. He added sharply, 'And if you catch fire you can sue.'

The dripping head tried to turn, failed. Bond moved towards the door. Count Lippe now had a new voice, controlled but desperate. He said woodenly, concealing the knowledge and the hate, 'Give you a thousand pounds and we're quits.' He heard the hiss of the opening door. 'Ten thousand. All right then, fifty.'

Bond closed the door firmly behind him and walked quickly down the corridor to put on his clothes and get out. Behind him, deeply muffled, came the first shout for help. Bond closed his ears. There was nothing that a painful week in hospital and plenty of Gentian Violet or Tannic Acid jelly wouldn't cure. But it did cross his mind that a man who could offer a bribe of fifty thousand pounds must be either very rich or have some very urgent reason for needing freedom of movement. It was surely too much to pay just for avoidance of pain.

James Bond was right. The outcome of this rather childish trial of strength between two extremely tough and ruthless men, in the bizarre surroundings of a nature clinic in Sussex, was to upset, if only in a minute fashion, the exactly-timed machinery of a plot that was about to shake the governments of the Western world.

Chapter Five

S.P.E.C.T.R.E.

The Boulevard Haussmann, in the VIIIth and IXth Arrondissements, stretches from the Rue du Faubourg St Honoré to the Opéra. It is very long and very dull, but it is perhaps the solidest street in the whole of Paris. Not the richest–the Avenue d'Iéna has that distinction–but rich people are not necessarily solid people and too many of the landlords and tenants in the Avenue d'Iéna have names ending in 'escu', 'ovitch', 'ski', and 'stein', and these are sometimes not the endings of respectable names. Moreover, the Avenue d'Iéna is almost entirely residential. The occasional discreet brass plate giving the name of a holding company in Liechtenstein or in the

Bahamas or the Canton de Vaud in Switzerland are there for tax purposes only–the cover names for private family fortunes seeking alleviation from the punitive burden of the Revenue, or, more briefly, tax-dodging. The Boulevard Haussmann is not like that. The massive, turn-of-the-century, bastard Second Empire buildings in heavily ornamented brick and stucco are the 'sièges', the seats, of important businesses. Here are the head offices of the *gros industriels* from Lille, Lyons, Bordeaux, Clermont Ferrand, the 'locaux' of the *grosses légumes*, the 'big vegetables' in cotton, artificial silk, coal, wine, steel, and shipping. If, among them, there are some fly-by-nights concealing a lack of serious capital–*des fonds sérieux*–behind a good address, it would only be fair to admit that such men of paper exist also behind the even solider frontages of Lombard and Wall Streets.

It is appropriate that among this extremely respectable company of tenants, suitably diversified by a couple of churches, a small museum and the French Shakespeare Society, you should also find the headquarters of charitable organizations. At No. 136 bis, for instance, a discreetly glittering brass plate says '*F.I.R.C.O.*' and, underneath, '*Fraternité Internationale de la Résistance Contre l'Oppression*'. If you were interested in this organization, either as an idealist or because you were a salesman of, say, office furniture, and you pressed the very clean porcelain bell button, the door would in due course be opened by an entirely typical French concierge. If your business was serious or obviously well-meaning, the concierge would show you across a rather dusty hall to tall, bogus Directoire double doors adjoining the over-ornamented cage of a shaky-looking lift. Inside the doors you would be greeted by exactly what you had expected to see–a large dingy room needing a fresh coat of its café-au-lait paint, in which half a dozen men sat at cheap desks and typed or wrote amidst the usual accoutrements of a busy organization–IN and OUT baskets, telephones, in this case the old-fashioned standard ones that are typical of such an office in this part of Paris, and dark green metal filing cabinets in which drawers stand open. If you were observant of small details, you might register that all the men were of approximately the same age-group, between thirty and forty, and that in an office where you would have expected to find women doing the secretarial work, there were none.

Inside the tall door you would receive the slightly defensive welcome appropriate to a busy organization accustomed to the usual proportion of cranks and time-wasters but, in response to your serious inquiry, the face of the man at the desk near the door would clear and become cautiously helpful. The aims of the Fraternity? We exist, monsieur, to keep alive the ideals that flourished during the last war among members of all Resistance groups. No, monsieur, we are entirely unpolitical. Our funds? They come from modest subscriptions from our members and from certain private persons who share our aims. You have perhaps a relative, a member of a Resistance group, whose whereabouts you seek? Certainly, monsieur. The name? Gregor Karlski, last heard of with Mihailovitch in the summer of 1943. Jules! (He might turn to a particular man and call out.) Karlski, Gregor. Mihailovitch, 1943. Jules would go to a cabinet and there would be a brief pause. Then the reply might come back, Dead. Killed in the bombing of the General's headquarters, October 21st, 1943. I regret, monsieur. Is there anything further we can do for you? Then perhaps you would care to have some of our literature. Forgive me for not having time to spare to give you more details of

FIRCO myself. But you will find everything there. This happens to be a particularly busy day. This is the International Refugee Year and we have many inquiries such as yours from all over the world. Good afternoon, monsieur. *Pas de quoi*.

So, or more or less so, it would be and you would go out on to the Boulevard satisfied and even impressed with an organization that was doing its excellent if rather vague work with so much dedication and efficiency.

On the day after James Bond had completed his nature cure and had left for London after, the night before, scoring a most satisfactory left and right of Spaghetti Bolognese and Chianti at Lucien's in Brighton and of Miss Patricia Fearing on the squab seats from her bubble car high up on the Downs, an emergency meeting of the Trustees of FIRCO was called for seven o'clock in the evening. The men, for they were all men, came from all over Europe, by train or car or aeroplane, and they entered No. 136 bis singly or in pairs, some by the front door and some by the back, at intervals during the late afternoon and evening. Each man had his allotted time for arriving at these meetings–so many minutes, up to two hours, before zero hour–and each man alternated between the back and the front door from meeting to meeting. Now there were two 'concierges' for each door and other less obvious security measures–warning systems, closed circuit television scanning of the two entrances, and complete sets of dummy FIRCO minutes, backed up one hundred per cent by the current business of the FIRCO organization on the ground floor. Thus, if necessary, the deliberations of the 'Trustees' could, in a matter only of seconds, be switched from clandestine to overt–as solidly overt as any meeting of principals in the Boulevard Haussmann could possibly be.

At seven o'clock precisely the twenty men who made up this organization strode, lounged or sidled, each according to his character, into the workmanlike boardroom on the third floor. Their chairman was already in his seat. No greetings were exchanged. They were ruled by the chairman to be a waste of breath and, in an organization of this nature, hypocritical. The men filed round the table and took their places at their numbers, the numbers from one to twenty-one that were their only names and that, as a small security precaution, advanced round the rota by two digits at midnight on the first of every month. Nobody smoked–drinking was taboo and smoking frowned upon–and nobody bothered to glance down at the bogus FIRCO agenda on the table in front of him. They sat very still and looked up the table at the chairman with expressions of the sharpest interest and what, in lesser men, would have been obsequious respect.

Any man seeing No. 2, for that was the chairman's number of the month, even for the first time would have looked at him with some degree of the same feelings, for he was one of those men–one meets perhaps only two or three in a lifetime–who seem almost to suck the eyes out of your head. These rare men are apt to possess three basic attributes–their physical appearance is extraordinary, they have a quality of relaxation, of inner certainty, and they exude a powerful animal magnetism. The herd has always recognized the other-worldliness of these phenomena and in primitive tribes you will find that any man singled out by nature in this fashion will also have been chosen by the tribe to be their chief. Certain great men of history, perhaps Genghis Khan, Alexander the Great, Napoleon, among the politicians, have had these qualities. Perhaps they even explain the hypnotic sway of an altogether more meagre individual, the otherwise inexplicable Adolf Hitler, over eighty million of the most gifted nation in Europe. Certainly, No. 2 had these qualities and any man in the street would have recognized them–let alone these twenty chosen men. For them, despite the deep cynicism ingrained in their respective callings, despite their basic insensitivity towards the human race, he was, however reluctantly, their Supreme Commander–almost their god.

This man's name was Ernst Stavro Blofeld and he was born in Gdynia of a Polish father and a Greek mother on May 28th, 1908. After matriculating in economics and political history at the University of Warsaw he studied engineering and radionics at the Warsaw Technical Institute and at the age of twenty-five obtained a modest post in the central administration of the Ministry of Posts and Telegraphs. This would seem a curious choice for such a highly gifted youth, but Blofeld had come to an interesting conclusion about the future of the world. He had decided that fast and accurate communication lay, in a contracting world, at the very heart of power. Knowledge of the truth before the next man, in peace or war, lay, he thought, behind every correct decision in history and was the source of all great reputations. He was doing very well on this theory, watching the cables and radiograms that passed through his hands at the Central Post Office and buying or selling on margin on the Warsaw Bourse–only occasionally, when he was absolutely certain, but then very big–when the basic nature of the postal traffic changed. Now Poland was mobilizing for war and a spate of munition orders and diplomatic cables poured through his department. Blofeld changed his tactics. This was valuable stuff, worth nothing to him, but priceless to the enemy. Clumsily at first, and then more expertly, he contrived to take copies of cables, choosing, for the ciphers hid their contents from him, only those prefixed 'MOST IMMEDIATE' or 'MOST SECRET'. Then, working carefully, he built up in his head a network of fictitious agents. These were real but small people in the various embassies and armament firms to whom most of the traffic was addressed–a junior cipher clerk in the British Embassy, a translator working for the French, private secretaries–real ones–in the big firms. These names were easily obtained from the diplomatic lists, by ringing up a firm and asking Enquiries for the name of the chairman's private secretary. He was speaking for the Red Cross. They wished to discuss the possibility of a donation from the chairman. And so on. When Blofeld had all his names right, he christened his network TARTAR and made a discreet approach to the German Military Attaché with one or two specimens of its work. He was rapidly passed on to the representative of AMT IV of the Abwehr, and from then on things were easy. When this pot was bubbling merrily, and the money (he refused to accept payment except in American dollars) coming in (it came in fast; he explained that he had so many agents to pay off), he proceeded to widen his market. He considered the Russians but dismissed them, and the Czechs, as probable non-, or at any rate slow, payers. Instead he chose the Americans and the Swedes, and money positively showered in on him. He soon realized, for he was a man of almost mimosaic sensibility in matters of security, that the pace could not possibly last. There would be a leak: perhaps between the Swedish and German secret services, who he knew (for through his contacts with their spies he was picking up the gossip of his new trade) were working closely together in some territories; or through Allied counter-espionage or their cryptographic services; or else one of his national agents would die or be transferred without his knowledge while he continued to use the name as a source. Anyway, by now he had two hundred thousand dollars and there was the added spur that the war was getting too close for comfort. It was time for him to be off into the wide world–into one of the safe bits of it.

Blofeld carried out his withdrawal expertly. First he slowly petered off the service. Security, he explained, was being tightened up by the English and the French. Perhaps there had been a leak–he looked with mild reproof into the eyes of his contact–this secretary had had a change of heart, that one was asking too much money. Then he went to his friend on the Bourse and, after sealing his lips with a thousand dollars, had all his funds invested in Shell Bearer Bonds in Amsterdam and thence transferred to a Numbered Safe Deposit box with the Diskonto Bank in Zurich. Before the final step of telling his contacts that he was brulé and that the Polish Deuxième Bureau was sniffing at his heels, he paid a visit to Gdynia, called on the Registrar and on the Church where he had been baptized and, on the pretext of looking up details of an invented friend, neatly cut out the page recording his own name and birth. It remained only to locate the passport factory that operates in every big seaport and purchase a Canadian seaman's passport for 2,000 dollars. Then he was off to Sweden by the next boat. After a pause in Stockholm for a careful look round the world and some cool thinking about the probable course of the war, he flew to Turkey on his original Polish passport, transferred his money from Switzerland to the Ottoman Bank in Istanbul, and waited for Poland to fall. When, in due course, this happened, he claimed refuge in Turkey and spent a little money amongst the right officials in order to get his claim established. Then he settled down. Ankara Radio was glad to have his expert services and he set up RAHIR, another espionage service built on the lines of TARTAR, but rather more solidly. Blofeld wisely waited to ascertain the victor before selling his wares, and it was only when Rommel had been kicked out of Africa that he plumped for the Allies. He finished the war in a blaze of glory and prosperity and with decorations or citations from the British, Americans, and French. Then, with half a million dollars in Swiss banks and a Swedish passport in the name of Serge Angstrom, he slipped off to South America for a rest, some good food, and a fresh think.

And now Ernst Blofeld, the name to which he had decided it was perfectly safe to return, sat in the quiet room in the Boulevard Haussmann, gazed slowly round the faces of his twenty men, and looked for eyes that didn't squarely meet his. Blofeld's own eyes were deep black pools surrounded–totally surrounded, as Mussolini's were–by very clear whites. The doll-like effect of this unusual symmetry was enhanced by long silken black eyelashes that should have belonged to a woman. The gaze of these soft doll's eyes was totally relaxed and rarely held any expression stronger than a mild curiosity in the object of their focus. They conveyed a restful certitude in their owner and in their analysis of what they observed. To the innocent, they exuded confidence, a wonderful cocoon of confidence in which the observed one could rest and relax knowing that he was in comfortable, reliable hands. But they stripped the guilty or the false and made him feel transparent–as transparent as a fishbowl through whose sides Blofeld examined, with only the most casual curiosity, the few solid fish, the grains of truth, suspended in the void of deceit or attempted obscurity. Blofeld's gaze was a microscope, the window on the world of a superbly clear brain, with a focus that had been sharpened by thirty years of danger and of keeping just one step ahead of it, and of an inner self-assurance built up on a lifetime of success in whatever he had attempted.

The skin beneath the eyes that now slowly, mildly, surveyed his colleagues was unpouched. There was no sign of debauchery, illness, or old age on the large, white, bland face under the square, wiry black crew-cut. The jawline, going to the appropriate middle-aged fat of authority, showed decision and independence. Only the mouth, under a heavy, squat nose, marred what might have been the face of a philosopher or a scientist. Proud and thin, like a badly healed wound, the compressed, dark lips, capable only of false, ugly smiles, suggested contempt, tyranny, and cruelty. But to an almost Shakespearian degree. Nothing about Blofeld was small.

Blofeld's body weighed about twenty stone. It had once been all muscle–he had been an amateur weightlifter in his youth–but in the past ten years it had softened and he had a vast belly that he concealed behind roomy trousers and well-cut double-breasted suits, tailored, that evening, out of beige doeskin. Blofeld's hands and feet were long and pointed. They were quick-moving when they wanted to be, but normally, as now, they were still and reposed. For the rest, he didn't smoke or drink and he had never been known to sleep with a member of either sex. He didn't even eat very much. So far as vices or physical weaknesses were concerned, Blofeld had always been an enigma to everyone who had known him.

The twenty men who looked up the long table at this man and waited patiently for him to speak were a curious mixture of national types. But they had certain characteristics in common. They were all in the thirty-to-forty age-group, they all looked extremely fit, and nearly all of them–there were two who were different–had quick, hard, predatory eyes, the eyes of the wolves and the hawks that prey upon the herd. The two who were different were both scientists with scientists' other-worldly eyes–Kotze, the East German physicist who had come over to the West five years before and had exchanged his secrets for a modest pension and retirement in Switzerland, and Maslov, formerly Kandinsky, the Polish electronics expert who, in 1956, had resigned as head of the radio research department of Philips AG of Eindhoven and had then disappeared into obscurity. The other eighteen men consisted of cells of three (Blofeld accepted the Communist triangle system for security reasons) from six national groups and, within these groups, from six of the world's great criminal and subversive organizations. There were three Sicilians from the top echelon of the Unione Siciliano, the Mafia; three Corsican Frenchmen from the Union Corse, the secret society, contemporary with and similar to the Mafia, that runs nearly all organized crime in France; three former members of SMERSH, the Soviet organization for the execution of traitors and enemies of the State that had been disbanded on the orders of Khruschev in 1958 and replaced by the Special Executive Department of the M.W.D.; three of the top surviving members of the former Sonderdienst of the Gestapo; three tough Yugoslav operatives who had resigned from Marshal Tito's Secret Police, and three highland Turks (the Turks of the plains are no good), formerly members of Blofeld's RAHIR and subsequently responsible for KRYSTAL, the important Middle East heroin pipeline whose outlet is Beirut. These eighteen men, all experts in conspiracy, in the highest ranges of secret communication and action and, above all, of silence, also shared one supreme virtue–every man had a solid cover. Every man possessed a valid passport with up-to-date visas for the principal countries in the world, and an entirely clean sheet with Interpol and with their respective national police forces. That factor alone, the factor of each man's cleanliness after a lifetime in big crime, was his highest qualification for membership of S.P.E.C.T.R.E.–The Special Executive for Counterintelligence, Terrorism, Revenge, and Extortion.

The founder and chairman of this private enterprise for private profit was Ernst Stavro Blofeld.

Chapter Six

Violet-scented Breath

Blofeld completed his inspection of the faces. As he had anticipated, only one pair of eyes had slid away from his. He had known he was right. The double-checked reports had been entirely circumstantial, but his own eyes and his intuition had to be the seal. He slowly put both hands under the table. One hand remained flat on his thigh. The other went to a side-pocket and drew out a thin gold vinaigrette and placed it on the table in front of him. He prised open the lid with his thumbnail, took out a violet-scented cachou, and slipped it into his mouth. It was his custom, when unpleasant things had to be said, to sweeten his breath.

Blofeld tucked the cachou under his tongue and began to talk in a soft, resonant, and very beautifully modulated voice.

'I have a report to make to members about The Big Affair, about Plan Omega.' (Blofeld never prefixed his words with 'Gentlemen', 'Friends', 'Colleagues', or the like. These were fripperies.) 'But before I proceed to that matter, for security's sake I propose to touch upon another topic.' Blofeld looked mildly round the table. The same pair of eyes evaded his. He continued in a narrative tone of voice: 'The Executive will agree that the first three years of our experience have been successful. Thanks in part to our German section, the recovery of Himmler's jewels from the Mondsee was successfully accomplished in total secrecy and the stones disposed of, by our Turkish section, in Beirut. Income: £750,000. The disappearance of the safe with its contents intact from the M.W.D. headquarters in East Berlin has never been traced to our Russian section, and the subsequent sale to the American Central Intelligence Agency yielded 500,000 dollars. The interception of one thousand ounces of heroin in Naples, the property of the Pastori circuit, when sold to the Firpone interests in Los Angeles, brought in 800,000 dollars. The British Secret Service paid £100,000 for the Czech germ warfare phials from the State chemical factory in Pilsen. The successful blackmail of former S.S. Gruppenführer Sonntag, living under the name of Santos in Havana, yielded a meagre 100,000 dollars–unfortunately all the man possessed–and the assassination of

Peringue, the French heavy-water specialist who went over to the Communists through Berlin, added, thanks to the importance of his knowledge and the fact that we got him before he had talked, one billion francs from the Deuxième Bureau. In round sums, as the Special Executive knows from our accounts, the total income to date, not counting our last and undistributed dividend, has amounted to approximately one and a half million pounds sterling in the Swiss francs and Venezuelan bolivars in which for reasons of prudence–they continue to be the hardest currencies in the world–we convert all our takings. This income, as the Special Executive will be aware, has been distributed in accordance with our charter as to ten per cent for overheads and working capital, ten per cent to myself, and the remainder in equal shares of four per cent to the members–a profit to each member of approximately £60,000. This amount I regard as a barely adequate remuneration for members' services–£20,000 a year is not in accordance with our expectations–but you will be aware that Plan Omega will yield sufficient to provide each of us with a considerable fortune and will allow us, if we wish to do so, to wind up our organization and transfer our respective energies to other pursuits.' Blofeld looked down the table. He said amiably, 'Any questions?'

The twenty pairs of eyes, on this occasion all of them, gazed stolidly, unemotionally back at their chairman. Each man had made his own calculation, knew his own mind. There was no comment to be extracted from these good, though narrow, minds. They were satisfied, but it was not a part of their harsh personalities to say so. These were known things that their chairman had spoken. It was time for the unknown.

Blofield slipped a second cachou into his mouth, manoeuvred it under his tongue, and continued.

'Then so be it. And now to the last operation, completed a month ago and yielding one million dollars.' Blofeld's eyes moved down the left-hand rank of members to the end of the row. He said softly, 'Stand up No. 7.'

Marius Domingue of the Union Corse, a proud, chunky man with slow eyes, who was wearing ready-made, rather sharp clothes that probably came from the Galleries Barbes in Marseilles, got slowly to his feet. He looked squarely down the table at Blofeld. His big, rough hands hung relaxed at the seam of his trousers. Blofeld appeared to answer his gaze, but in fact he was noting the reaction of the Corsican next to No. 7, No. 12, Pierre Borraud. This man sat directly facing Blofeld at the far end of the long table. It was his eyes that had been evasive during the meeting. Now they were not. Now they were relaxed, assured. Whatever the eyes had feared had passed.

Blofeld addressed the company. 'This operation, you will recall, involved the kidnapping of the seventeen-year-old daughter of Magnus Blomberg, owner of the Principality Hotel in Las Vegas and participant in other American enterprises through his membership of the Detroit Purple Gang. The girl was abducted from her father's suite in the Hotel de Paris in Monte Carlo and taken by sea to Corsica. This part of the operation was executed by the Corsican section. One million dollars ransom was demanded. Mr Blomberg was willing and, in accordance with the instructions of SPECTRE, the money, in an inflated life raft, was dropped at dusk off the Italian coast near San Remo. At nightfall the raft was recovered by the ship operated by our Sicilian section. This section is to be commended for detecting the transistorized radio transmitter concealed in the raft which it was intended should allow a unit of the French Navy to direction-find our ship and hunt it down. On receipt of the ransom money, and in accordance with our undertaking, the girl was returned to her parents apparently suffering from no ill effects except for the hair-dye that had been necessary to transfer her from Corsica to a wagon-lit in the Blue Train from Marseilles. I say "apparently". From a source in the police commissariat at Nice, I now learn that the girl was violated during her captivity in Corsica.' Blofeld paused to allow this intelligence time to sink in. He continued. 'It is the parents who maintain that she was violated. It is possible that only carnal knowledge, with her consent, was involved. No matter. This organization undertook that the girl would be returned undamaged. Without splitting hairs about the effect of sexual knowledge on a girl, I am of the opinion that, whether the act was voluntary or involuntary on the girl's part, she was returned to her parents in a damaged, or at least used, condition.' Blofeld rarely employed gestures. Now he slowly opened the left hand that lay on the table. He said, in the same even tone of voice, 'We are a large and very powerful organization. I am not concerned with morals or ethics, but members will be aware that I desire, and most strongly recommend, that SPECTRE shall conduct itself in a superior fashion. There is no discipline in SPECTRE except self-discipline. We are a dedicated fraternity whose strength lies entirely in the strength of each member. Weakness in one member is the death-watch beetle in the total structure. You are aware of my views in this matter, and on the occasions when cleansing has been necessary you have approved my action. In this case, I have already done what I considered necessary vis-à-vis this girl's family. I have returned half a million dollars with an appropriate note of apology. This despite the matter of the radio transmitter which was a breach of our contract with the family. I dare say they knew nothing of the ruse. It was typical police behaviour–a pattern that I was expecting. The dividend for all of us from this operation will be correspondingly reduced. Regarding the culprit, I have satisfied myself that he is guilty. I have decided on the appropriate action.'

Blofeld looked down the table. His eyes were fixed on the man standing–on No. 7. The Corsican, Marius Domingue, looked back at him steadily. He knew he was innocent. He knew who was guilty. His body was still with tension. But it was not fear. He had faith, as they all had, in the rightness of Blofeld. He could not understand why he had been singled out as a target for all the eyes that were now upon him, but Blofeld had decided, and Blofeld was always right.

Blofeld noted the man's courage and sensed the reasons for it. He also observed the sweat shining on the face of No. 12, the man alone at the head of the table. Good! The sweat would improve the contact.

Under the table, Blofeld's right hand came up off his thigh, found the knob, and pulled the switch.

The body of Pierre Borraud, seized in the iron fist of 3,000 volts, arced in the armchair as if it had been kicked in the back. The rough mat of black hair rose sharply straight up on his head and remained upright, a gollywog fringe for the contorted, bursting face. The eyes glared wildly and then faded. A blackened tongue slowly protruded between the snarling teeth and remained hideously extended. Thin wisps of smoke rose from under the hands, from the middle of the back, and from under the thighs where the concealed electrodes in the chair had made contact. Blofeld pulled back the switch. The lights in the room that had dimmed to orange, making a dull supernatural glow, brightened to normal. The roasted meat and burned fabric smell spread slowly. The body of No. 12 crumpled horribly. There was a sharp crack as the chin hit the edge of the table. It was all over.

Blofeld's soft, even voice broke the silence. He looked down the table at No. 7. He noted that the staunch, impassive stance had not quavered. This was a good man with good nerves. Blofeld said, 'Sit down No. 7. I am satisfied with your conduct.' (Satisfaction was Blofeld's highest expression of praise.) 'It was necessary to distract the attention of No. 12. He knew that he was under suspicion. There might have been an untidy scene.'

Some of the men round the table nodded their understanding. As usual, Blofeld's reasoning made good sense. No one was greatly perturbed or surprised by what they had witnessed. Blofeld always exercised his authority, meted out justice, in full view of the members. There had been two previous occasions of this nature, both at similar meetings and both on security or disciplinary grounds which affected the cohesion, the inner strength, of the whole team. In one, the offender had been shot by Blofeld through the heart with a thick needle fired from a compressed air pistol–no mean feat at around twelve paces. In the other, the guilty man, who had been seated next to Blofeld on his left hand, had been garrotted with a wire noose casually flicked over his head and then, with two swift steps by Blofeld, pulled tight over the back of the man's chair. Those two deaths had been just, necessary. So had this death, the third. Now, the members, ignoring the heap of death at the end of the table, settled in their chairs. It was time to get back to business.

Blofeld snapped shut the gold vinaigrette and slipped it into a waistcoat pocket. 'The Corsican section,' he said softly, 'will put forward recommendations for a replacement for No. 12. But that can wait until after completion of Plan Omega. On this matter, there are certain details to be discussed. Sub-operator G, recruited by the German section, has made an error, a serious error which radically affects our time-table. This man, whose membership of the Red Lightning Tong in Macao should have made him expert in conspiracy, was instructed to make his headquarters at a certain clinic in the south of England, an admirable refuge for his purposes. His instructions were to keep intermittent contact with the airman Petacchi at the not-far-distant Boscombe Down airfield where the bomber squadron is under training. He was to report at intervals on the airman's fitness and morale. His reports have been satisfactory, and the airman, by the way, continues to be willing. But Sub-operator G was also required to post The Letter on D plus One, or three days from now. Unfortunately this foolish man took it upon himself to become embroiled in a hotheaded fashion with some fellow patient at the clinic, as a result of which, and I need not go into details, he is now in Brighton Central Hospital suffering from second-degree burns. He is thus out of action for at least a week. This will involve an irritating but fortunately not a serious delay in Plan Omega. Fresh instructions have been issued. The airman Petacchi has been provided with a phial of influenza virus of sufficient strength for him to remain on the sick list for one week during which he will be unable to accept his test flight. He will take the first flight after his recovery and alert us accordingly. The date of his flight will be communicated to Sub-operator G and he will by that time be recovered and will post The Letter according to plan. the Special

Executive,' Blofeld glanced round the table, 'will readjust their flight schedules to Area Zeta in accordance with the new operational schedule. As for Sub-operator G'–Blofeld bent his gaze, one by one, on the three ex-Gestapo men–'this is an unreliable agent. The German section will make arrangements for his elimination within twenty-four hours of the posting of The Letter. Is that understood?'

The three German faces stood unanimously to attention, 'Yes, sir.'

'For the rest,' continued Blofeld, 'all is in order. No. 1 has solidly established his cover in Area Zeta. The treasure-hunting myth continues to be built up and has already gained full credence. The crew of the yacht, all hand-picked sub-operators, are accepting the discipline and the security regulations better than had been expected. A suitable land base has been secured. It is remote and not easily accessible. It belongs to an eccentric Englishman, the nature of whose friends and personal habits demands seclusion. Your arrival in Area Zeta continues to be minutely planned. Your wardrobe awaits you in Areas F and D, according to your various flight plans. This wardrobe, down to the smallest detail, will be in accordance with your identities as financial backers of the treasure hunt who have demanded to visit the scene and take part in the adventure. You are not gullible millionaires. You are the kind of rich, middle-class rentiers and businessmen who might be expected to be taken in by such a scheme. You are all shrewd, so you have come to watch over your investment and ensure that not one doubloon goes astray.' (Nobody smiled.) 'You are all aware of the part you have to play and I trust that you have studied your respective roles with close attention.'

There was a careful nodding of heads around the table. These men were all satisfied that not too much had been asked of them in the matter of their cover. This one was a rich café proprietor from Marseilles. (He had been one. He could talk to anyone about the business.) That one had vineyards in Yugoslavia. (He had been brought up in Bled. He could talk vintages and crop-sprays with a Calvet from Bordeaux.) That one had smuggled cigarettes from Tangier. (He had done so and would be just sufficiently discreet about it.) All of them had been given covers that would stand up at least to second degree inspection.

'In the matter of aqualung training,' continued Blofeld, 'I would like reports from each section.' Blofeld looked at the Yugoslav section on his left.

'Satisfactory.' 'Satisfactory,' echoed the German section, and the word was repeated round the table.

Blofeld commented, 'The safety factor is paramount in all underwater operations. Has this factor received sufficient attention in your respective training schedules?' Affirmative. 'And exercises with the new CO_2 underwater gun?' Again all sections reported favourably. 'And now,' continued Blofeld, 'I would like a report from the Sicilian section on the preparations for the bullion drop.'

Fidelio Sciacca was a gaunt, cadaverous Sicilian with a closed face. He might have been, and had been, a schoolmaster with communist leanings. He spoke for the section because his English, the compulsory language of the Special Executive, was the best. He said, in a careful, expository tone of voice, 'The chosen area has been carefully reconnoitred. It is satisfactory. I have here,' he touched the briefcase on his lap, 'the plans and detailed time-table for the information of the Chairman and members. Briefly, the designated area, Area T, is on the north-west slopes of Mount Etna, above the tree line–that is to say between the altitudes of 2,000 and 3,000 metres. This is an uninhabited and uncultivated area of black lava on the upper slopes of the volcano more or less above the small town of Bronte. For the purpose of the drop, an area approximately two kilometres square will be marked out by the torches of the recovery team. In the centre of this area will be positioned a Decca Aircraft Homing Signal as an additional navigational aid. The bullion flight, which I estimate conservatively will consist of five Mark IV Transport Comets, should make their run in at ten thousand feet at an air speed of 300 m.p.h. Having regard to the weight of each consignment, multiple parachutes will be needed, and, owing to the harsh nature of the terrain, very careful packing in foam rubber will be essential. The parachutes and the packings should be coated in Dayglo or some phosphorescent paint to assist recovery. No doubt,' the man opened his hands, 'the SPECTRE memorandum of dropping instructions will include these and other details, but very careful planning and co-ordination by those responsible for the flight will be necessary.'

'And the recovery team?' Blofeld's voice probed softly but with an urgent edge to it.

'The Capo Mafiosi of the district is my uncle. He has eight grandchildren, to whom he is devoted. I have made it clear that the whereabouts of these children is known to my associates. The man understood. At the same time, as instructed, I made him the offer of one million pounds for total recovery and safe delivery to the depot at Catania. This is a most important sum for the funds of the Unione. The Capo Mafiosi agreed to these terms. He understands that the robbery of a bank is in question. He wishes to know no more. The delay that has been announced will not affect the arrangements. It will still be within the full moon period. Sub-operator 52 is a most capable man. He has been provided with the Hallicraftor set issued to me for the purpose and he will listen on 18 megacycles in accordance with the schedule. Meanwhile he remains in touch with the Capo Mafiosi, to whom he is related by marriage.'

Blofeld was silent for a long two minutes. He slowly nodded. 'I am satisfied. So far as the next step is concerned, the disposal of the bullion, this will be in the hands of Sub-operator 201, of whom we have had full experience. He is a man to be trusted. The M.V. *Mercurial* will load at Catania and proceed through the Suez Canal to Goa, in Portuguese India. En route, at a designated cross-bearing in the Arabian Gulf, she will rendezvous with a merchant ship owned by a consortium of the chief Bombay bullion brokers. The bullion will be transferred to this ship in exchange for the equivalent value, at the ruling gold bullion price, in used Swiss francs, dollars, and bolivars. These large amounts of currency will be broken up into the allotted percentages and will then be transferred from Goa by chartered plane to twenty-two different Swiss banks in Zurich, where they will be placed in deposit boxes. The keys to these numbered boxes will be distributed to members after this meeting. From that moment on, and subject of course to the usual security regulations regarding injudicious spending and display, these deposits will be entirely at the disposal of members.' Blofeld's slow, calm eyes surveyed the meeting. 'Is this procedure considered satisfactory?'

There were cautious nods. No. 18, Kandinsky, the Polish electronics expert, spoke up. He spoke without diffidence. There was no diffidence between these men. 'This is not my province,' he said seriously. 'But is there not danger that one of the navies concerned will intercept this ship, the *Mercurial*, and remove the bullion? It will be clear to the Western powers that the bullion will have to be removed from Sicily. Various patrols of the air and sea would be an easy matter.'

'You forget,' Blofeld's voice was patient, 'that neither the first, nor if need be the second, bomb will be rendered safe until the money is in the Swiss banks. There will be no risk on that score. Nor, another possibility that I had envisaged, is there likely to be danger of our ship being pirated on the high seas by some independent operator. I envisage that complete secrecy will be enforced by the Western powers. Any leakage would result in panic. Any other questions?'

Bruno Bayer, one of the German Section, said stiffly, 'It is fully understood that No. 1 will be in immediate control in Area Zeta. Is it correct that he will have full powers delegated by yourself? Is it that he will, so to speak, be Supreme Commander in the field?'

How typical, thought Blofeld. The Germans will always obey orders, but they wish to be quite clear where final authority resides. The German generals would only obey the Supreme Command if they knew Hitler approved the Supreme Command. He said firmly, 'I have made it clear to the Special Executive, and I repeat: No. 1 is already, by your unanimous vote, my successor in case of my death or incapacity. So far as Plan Omega is concerned, he is deputy Supreme Commander of SPECTRE, and since I shall remain at Headquarters to keep watch over reactions to The Letter, No. 1 will be Supreme Commander in the field. His orders will be obeyed as if they were my own. I hope we are fully agreed in this matter.' Blofeld's eyes, sharply focused, swept the meeting. Everyone signified his agreement.

'So,' said Blofeld. 'Then the meeting is now closed. I will instruct the disposal squad to take care of the remains of No. 12. No. 18, please connect me with No. 1 on 20 megacycles. That waveband will have been unoccupied by the French Post Office since eight o'clock.'

Chapter Seven

'Fasten your lap-strap'

James Bond scraped the last dregs of yoghurt out of the bottom of the carton that said '*Goat-milk culture. From our own Goat Farm at Stanway, Glos. The Heart of the Cotswolds. According to an authentic Bulgarian recipe.*' He took an Energen roll, sliced it carefully–they are apt to crumble–and reached for the black treacle. He masticated each mouthful thoroughly. Saliva contains ptyalin. Thorough mastication creates ptyalin which helps to convert starches into sugar to supply energy for the body. Ptyalin is an enzyme. Other enzymes are pepsin, found in the stomach, and trypsin and erepsin found in the intestine. These and other enzymes are chemical substances that break up the food as it passes through the mouth, the stomach, and the digestive tract and help absorb it directly into the blood-stream. James Bond now had all these important facts at his finger-tips. He couldn't understand why no one had told him these things before. Since leaving Shrublands ten days before, he had never felt so well in his life. His energy had doubled. Even the paper-work he had always found an intolerable drudgery was now almost a pleasure. He ate it up. Sections, after a period of being only surprised, were now becoming slightly irritated by the forceful, clear-headed minutes that came shooting back at them from the Double-O Section. Bond awoke so early and so full of beans that he had taken to arriving at his office early and leaving late, much to the irritation of his secretary, the delectable Loelia Ponsonby, who found her own private routines being put seriously out of joint. She also was beginning to show signs of irritation and strain. She had even taken upon herself to have a private word with Miss Moneypenny, M's private secretary and her best friend in the building. Miss Moneypenny, swallowing her jealousy of Loelia Ponsonby, had been encouraging. 'It's all right, Lil,' she had said over coffee in the canteen. 'The Old Man was like that for a couple of weeks after he had got back from that damned nature cure place. It was like working for Gandhi or Schweitzer or someone. Then a couple of bad cases came up and rattled him and one evening he went to Blades–to take his mind off things I suppose–and the next day he felt awful, and looked it, and from then on he's been all right again. I suppose he got back on the champagne cure or something. It's really the best for men. It makes them awful, but at least they're human like that. It's when they get godlike one can't stand them.'

May, Bond's elderly Scottish treasure, came in to clear the breakfast things away. Bond had lit up a Duke of Durham, king-size, with filter. The authoritative Consumers Union of America rates this cigarette the one with the smallest tar and nicotine content. Bond had transferred to the brand from the fragrant but powerful Morland Balkan mixture with three gold rings round the paper he had been smoking since his teens. The Dukes tasted of almost nothing, but they were at least better than Vanguards, the new 'tobaccoless' cigarette from America that, despite its health-protecting qualities, filled the room with a faint 'burning leaves' smell that made visitors to his office inquire whether 'something was on fire somewhere'.

May was fiddling about with the breakfast things–her signal that she had something to say. Bond looked up from the centre news page of *The Times*. 'Anything on your mind, May?'

May's elderly, severe features were flushed. She said defensively, 'I have that.' She looked straight at Bond. She was holding the yoghurt carton in her hand. She crumpled it in her strong fingers and dropped it among the breakfast things on the tray. 'It's not my place to say it, Mister James, but ye're poisoning yersel'.'

Bond said cheerfully, 'I know, May. You're quite right. But at least I've got them down to ten a day.'

'I'm not talking about yer wee bitty smoke. I'm talking 'bout this,' May gestured at the tray, 'this pap.' The word was spat out with disdain. Having got this off her chest, May gathered steam. 'It's no recht for a man to be eating bairns' food and slops and suchlike. Ye needn't worry that I'll talk, Mister James, but I'm knowing more about yer life than mebbe ye were wishing I did. There's been times when they've brought ye home from hospital and there's talk you've been in a motoring accident or some such. But I'm not the old fule ye think I am, Mister James. Motoring accidents don't make one small hole in yer shoulder or yer leg or somewhere. Why, ye've got scars on ye the noo–ach ye needn't grin like that, I've seen them–that could only be made by buellets. And these guns and knives and things ye carry around when ye're off abroad. Ach!' May put her hands on her hips. Her eyes were bright and defiant. 'Ye can tell me to mind my ain business and pack me off back to Glen Orchy, but before I go I'm telling ye, Mister James, that if ye get yourself into anuither fight and ye've got nothing but yon muck in yer stomach, they'll be bringing ye home in a hearse. That's what they'll be doing.'

In the old days, James Bond would have told May to go to hell and leave him in peace. Now, with infinite patience and good humour, he gave May a quick run through the basic tenets of 'live' as against 'dead' foods. 'You see, May,' he said reasonably, 'all these denaturized foods–white flour, white sugar, white rice, white salts, whites of egg–these are dead foods. Either they're dead anyway like whites of egg or they've had all the nourishment refined out of them. They're slow poisons, like fried foods and cakes and coffee and heaven knows how many of the things I used to eat. And anyway, look how wonderfully well I am. I feel absolutely a new man since I took to eating the right things and gave up drink and so on. I sleep twice as well. I've got twice as much energy. No headaches. No muscle pains. No hangovers. Why, a month ago there wasn't a week went by but that on at least one day I couldn't eat anything for breakfast but a couple of aspirins and a prairie oyster. And you know quite well that that used to make you cluck and tut-tut all over the place like an old hen. Well,' Bond raised his eyebrows amiably, 'what about that?'

May was defeated. She picked up the tray and, with a stiff back, made for the door. She paused on the threshold and turned round. Her eyes were bright with angry tears. 'Well, all I can say is, Mister James, that mebbe ye're right and mebbe ye're wrong. What worries the life out of me is that ye're not yersel' any more.' She went out and banged the door.

Bond sighed and picked up the paper. He said the magical words that all men say when a middle-aged woman makes a temperamental scene, 'change of life', and went back to reading about the latest reasons for not having a Summit meeting.

The telephone, the red one that was the direct line with Headquarters, gave its loud, distinctive jangle. Bond kept his eyes on the page and reached out a hand. With the Cold War easing off, it was not like the old days. This would be nothing exciting. Probably cancelling his shoot at Bisley that afternoon with the new F.N. rifle. 'Bond speaking.'

It was the Chief of Staff. Bond dropped his paper on the floor. He pressed the receiver to his ear, trying, as in the old days, to read behind the words.

'At once please, James. M.'

'Something for me?'

'Something for everyone. Crash-dive, and Ultra Hush. If you've got any dates for the next few weeks, better cancel them. You'll be off tonight. See you.' The line went dead.

Bond had the most selfish car in England. It was a Mark II Continental Bentley that some rich idiot had married to a telegraph pole on the Great West Road. Bond had bought the bits for £1,500 and Rolls had straightened the bend in the chassis and fitted new clockwork–the Mark IV engine with 9·5 compression. Then Bond had gone to Mulliners with £3,000, which was half his total capital, and they had sawn off the old cramped sports saloon body and had fitted a trim, rather square convertible two-seater affair, power-operated, with only two large armed bucket seats in black leather. The rest of the blunt end was all knife-edged, rather ugly, boot. The car was painted in rough, not gloss, battleship grey and the upholstery was black morocco. She went like a bird and a bomb and Bond loved her more than all the women at present in his life rolled, if that were feasible, together.

But Bond refused to be owned by any car. A car, however splendid, was a means of locomotion (he called the Continental 'The Locomotive' . . . 'I'll pick you up in my locomotive') and it must at all times be ready to locomote–no garage doors to break one's nails on, no pampering with mechanics except for the quick monthly service. The locomotive slept out of doors in front of his flat and was required to start immediately, in all weathers, and, after that, stay on the road.

The twin exhausts–Bond had demanded two-inch pipes; he hadn't liked the old soft flutter of the marque–growled solidly as the long grey nose topped by a big octagonal silver bolt instead of the winged B, swerved out of the little Chelsea square and into King's Road. It was nine o'clock, too early for the bad traffic, and Bond pushed the car fast up Sloane Street and into the park. It would also be too early for the traffic police, so he did some fancy driving that brought him to the Marble Arch exit in three minutes flat. Then there came the slow round-the-houses into Baker Street and so into Regent's Park. Within ten minutes of getting the Hurry call he was going up in the lift of the big square building to the eighth and top floor.

Already, as he strode down the carpeted corridor, he smelled emergency. On this floor, besides M's offices, was house Communications, and from behind the grey closed doors there came a steady zing and crackle from the banks of transmitters and a continuous machine-gun rattle and clack from the cipher machines. It crossed Bond's mind that a General Call was going out. What the hell had happened?

The Chief of Staff was standing over Miss Moneypenny. He was handing her signals from a large sheaf and giving her routing instructions. 'CIA Washington, Personal for Dulles. Cipher Triple X by Teleprinter. Mathis. Deuxième Bureau. Same prefix and route. Station F for Head of NATO Intelligence. Personal. Standard route through Head of Section. This one by Safe Hand to Head of M.I.5, Personal, copy to Commissioner of Police, Personal, and these,' he handed over a thick batch, 'Personal to Heads of Stations from M. Cipher Double X by Whitehall Radio and Portishead. All right? Clear them as quick as you can, there's a good girl. There'll be more coming. We're in for a bad day.'

Miss Moneypenny smiled cheerfully. She liked what she called the shot-and-shell days. It reminded her of when she had started in the Service as a junior in the Cipher Department. She leant over and pressed the switch on the intercom. '007's here, sir.' She looked up at Bond. 'You're off.' The Chief of Staff grinned and said, 'Fasten your lap-strap.' The red light went on above M's door. Bond walked through.

Here it was entirely peaceful. M sat relaxed, sideways to his desk, looking out of the broad window at the distant glittering fretwork of London's skyline. He glanced up. 'Sit down, 007. Have a look at these.' He reached out and slid some foolscap-sized photostats across the desk. 'Take your time.' He picked up his pipe and began to fill it, absent-minded fingers dipping into the shell-based tobacco jar at his elbow.

Bond picked up the top photostat. It showed the front and back of an addressed envelope, dusted for finger-prints, which were all over its surface.

M glanced sideways. 'Smoke if you like.'

Bond said, 'Thanks, sir. I'm trying to give it up.'

M said, 'Humpf,' put his pipe in his mouth, struck a match, and inhaled a deep lungful of smoke. He settled himself deeper in his chair. The grey sailor's eyes gazed through the window introspectively, seeing nothing.

The envelope, prefixed 'PERSONAL AND MOST IMMEDIATE', was addressed to the Prime Minister, by name, at No. 10, Downing Street, Whitehall, London, SW1. Every detail of the address was correct down to the final 'P.C.' to denote that the Prime Minister was a Privy Councillor. The punctuation was meticulous. The stamp was postmarked Brighton, 8.30 a.m. on June 3rd. It crossed Bond's mind that the letter might therefore have been posted under cover of night and that it would probably have been delivered some time in the early afternoon of the same day, yesterday. A typewriter with a bold, rather elegant type had been used. This fact together with the generous 5-by-7½-inch envelope and the spacing and style of the address gave a solid, businesslike impression. The back of the envelope showed nothing but fingerprints. There was no sealing wax.

The letter, equally correct and well laid-out, ran as follows:

> Mr Prime Minister,
>
> You should be aware, or you will be if you communicate with the Chief of the Air Staff, that, since approximately 10 p.m. yesterday, 2nd June, a British aircraft carrying two atomic weapons is overdue on a training flight. The aircraft is Villiers Vindicator O/NBR from No. 5 R.A.F. Experimental Squadron based at Boscombe Down. The Ministry of Supply Identification Numbers on the atomic weapons are MOS/bd/654/Mk V. and MOS/bd/655/Mk V. There are also U.S.A.F. Identification Numbers in such profusion and of such prolixity that I will not weary you with them.
>
> This aircraft was on a NATO training flight with a crew of five and one observer. It carried sufficient fuel for ten hours' flying at 600 m.p.h. at a mean altitude of 40,000 feet.
>
> This aircraft, together with the two atomic weapons, is now in the possession of this organization. The crew and the observer are deceased and you have our authority to inform the next-of-kin accordingly, thus assisting you in preserving, on the grounds that the aircraft has crashed, the degree of secrecy you will no doubt wish to maintain and which will be equally agreeable to ourselves.
>
> The whereabouts of this aircraft and of the two atomic weapons, rendering them possible of recovery, will be communicated to you in exchange for the equivalent of £100,000,000 in gold bullion, one thousand, or not less than nine hundred and ninety-nine, fine. Instructions for the delivery of the gold are contained in the attached memorandum. A further condition is that the recovery and disposal of the gold will not be hampered and that a free pardon, under your personal signature and that of the President of the United States, will be issued in the name of this organization and all its members.
>
> Failure to accept these conditions within seven days from 5 p.m. G.M.T. on June 3rd, 1959–i.e. not later than 5 p.m. G.M.T. on June 10th, 1959–will have the following consequences. Immediately after that date a piece of property belonging to the Western Powers, valued at not less than the aforesaid

£100,000,000, will be destroyed. There will be loss of life. If, within 48 hours after this warning, willingness to accept our terms is still not communicated, there will ensue, without further warning, the destruction of a major city situated in an undesignated country of the world. There will be very great loss of life. Moreover, between the two occurrences, this organization will reserve to itself the right to communicate to the world the 48-hour time limit. This measure, which will cause widespread panic in every major city, will be designed to hasten your hand.

This, Mr Prime Minister, is a single and final communication. We shall await your reply, every hour on the hour G.M.T., on the 16-megacycle waveband.

Signed

S.P.E.C.T.R.E.

The Special Executive for Counterintelligence,
Terrorism, Revenge, and Extortion

James Bond read through the letter again and put it carefully down on the desk in front of him, He then turned to the second page, a detailed memorandum for the delivery of the gold. 'North-western slopes of Mount Etna in Sicily . . . Decca Navigational Aid transmitting on . . . Full moon period . . . between midnight and 0100 G.M.T. . . . individual quarter-ton consignments packed in one-foot-thick foam rubber . . . minimum of three parachutes per consignment . . . nature of planes and flight schedule to be communicated on the 16-megacycle waveband not later than 24 hours before the operation . . . Any counter measures initiated will be considered a breach of contract and will result in the detonation of Atomic Weapon No. 1 or No. 2 as the case may be.' The typed signature was the same. Both pages had one last line: 'Copy to the President of the United States of America, by Registered Airmail, posted simultaneously.'

Bond laid the photostat quietly down on top of the others. He reached into his hip-pocket for the gunmetal cigarette case that now contained only nine cigarettes, took one and lit it, drawing the smoke deep down into his lungs and letting it out with a long reflective hiss.

M swivelled his chair round so they were facing each other. 'Well?'

Bond noticed that M's eyes, three weeks before so clear and vital, were now bloodshot and strained. No wonder! He said: 'If this plane, and the weapons, really are missing, I think it stands up, sir. I think they mean it. I think it's a true bill.'

M said, 'So does the War Cabinet. So do I.' He paused. 'Yes, the plane with the bombs is missing. And the stock numbers on the bombs are correct.'

Chapter Eight

'Big Fleas have Little Fleas . . .'

Bond said, 'What is there to go on, sir?'

'Damned little, practically speaking nothing. Nobody's ever heard of these SPECTRE people. We know there's some kind of independent unit working in Europe–we've bought some stuff from them, so have the Americans, and Mathis admits now that Goltz, that French heavy-water scientist who went over last year, was assassinated by them, for big money, as a result of an offer he got out of the blue. No names were mentioned. It was all done on the radio, the same 16 megacycles that's mentioned in the letter. To the Deuxième Communications section. Mathis accepted on the off-chance. They did a neat job. Mathis paid up–a suitcase full of money left at a Michelin road sign in N1. But no one can tie them in with these SPECTRE people. When we and the Americans dealt, there were endless cutouts, really professional ones, and anyway we were more interested in the end product than the people involved. We both paid a lot of money, but it was worth it. If it's the same group working this, they're a serious outfit and I've told the P.M. so. But that's not the point. The plane is missing and the two bombs, just as the letter says. All details exactly correct. The Vindicator was on a NATO training flight south of Ireland and out into the Atlantic.' M reached for a bulky folder and turned over some pages. He found what he wanted. 'Yes, it was to be a six-hour flight leaving Boscombe Down at eight p.m. and due back at two a.m. There was an R.A.F. crew of five and a NATO observer, an Italian, man called Petacchi, Giuseppi Petacchi, squadron leader in the Italian Air Force, seconded to NATO. Fine flyer, apparently, but they're checking on his background now. He was sent over here on a normal tour of duty. The top pilots from NATO have been coming over for months to get used to the Vindicator and the bomb-release routines. This plane's apparently going to be used for the NATO long range striking force. Anyway,' M turned over a page, 'the plane was watched on the screen as usual and all went well until it was west of Ireland at about 40,000 feet. Then, contrary to the drill, it came down to around 30,000 and got lost in the transatlantic air traffic. Bomber Command tried to get in touch, but the radio couldn't or wouldn't answer. The immediate reaction was that the Vindicator had hit one of the transatlantic planes and there was something of a panic. But none of the companies reported any trouble or even a sighting.' M looked across at Bond. 'And that was the end of it. The plane just vanished.'

Bond said, 'Did the American DEW line pick it up–their Distant Early Warning system?'

'There's a query on that. The only grain of evidence we've got. Apparently about five hundred miles east of Boston there was some evidence that a plane had peeled off the inward route to Idlewild and turned south. But that's another big traffic lane–for the northern traffic from Montreal and Gander down to Bermuda and the Bahamas and South America. So these DEW operators just put it down as a B.O.A.C. or Trans-Canada plane.'

'It certainly sounds as if they've got the whole thing worked out pretty well, hiding in these traffic lanes. Could the plane have turned northwards in the middle of the Atlantic and made for Russia?'

'Yes, or southwards. There's a big block of space about 500 miles out from both shores that's out of radar range. Better still, it could have turned on its tracks and come back in to Europe on any of two or three air-lanes. In fact it could be almost anywhere in the world by now. That's the point.'

'But it's a huge plane. It must need special runways and so on. It must have come down somewhere. You can't hide a plane of that size.'

'Just so. All these thing are obvious. By midnight last night the R.A.F. had checked with every single airport, every one in the world, that could have taken it. Negative. But the C.A.S. says of course it could be crash-landed in the Sahara for instance, or on some other desert, or in the sea, in shallow water.'

'Wouldn't that explode the bombs?'

'No. They're absolutely safe until they're armed. Apparently even a direct drop, like that one from the B-47 over North Carolina in 1958, would only explode the T.N.T. trigger to the thing. Not the plutonium.'

'How are these SPECTRE people going to explode them then?'

M spread his hands. 'They explained all this at the War Cabinet meeting. I don't understand it all, but apparently an atomic bomb looks just like any other bomb. The way it works is that the nose is full of ordinary T.N.T. with the plutonium in the tail. Between the two there's a hole into which you screw some sort of a detonator, a kind of plug. When the bomb hits, the T.N.T. ignites the detonator and the detonator sets off the plutonium.'

'So these people would have to drop the bomb to set it off?'

'Apparently not. They would need a man with good physics knowledge who understood the thing, but then all he'd have to do would be to unscrew the nose cone on the bomb–the ordinary detonator that sets off the T.N.T.–and fix on some kind of time fuse that would ignite the T.N.T. without it being dropped. That would set the thing off. And it's not a very bulky affair. You could get the whole thing into something only about twice the size of a big golf-bag. Very heavy, of course. But you could put it into the back of a big car, for instance, and just run the car into a town and leave it parked with the time fuse switched on. Give yourself a couple of hours' start to get out of range–at least 100 miles away–and that would be that.'

Bond reached in his pocket for another cigarette. It couldn't be, yet it was so. Just what his Service and all the other intelligence services in the world had been expecting to happen. The anonymous little man in the raincoat with a heavy suitcase–or golf bag, if you like. The left luggage office, the parked car, the clump of bushes in a park in the centre of a big town. And there was no answer to it. In a few years' time, if the experts were right, there would be even less answer to it. Every tin-pot little nation would be making atomic bombs in their backyards, so to speak. Apparently there was no secret now about the things. It had only been the prototypes that had been difficult–like the first gun-powder weapons for instance, or machine-guns or tanks. Today these were everybody's bows and arrows. Tomorrow, or the day after, the bows and arrows would be atomic bombs. And this was the first blackmail case. Unless SPECTRE was stopped, the word would get round and soon every criminal scientist with a chemical set and some scrap iron would be doing it. If they couldn't be stopped in time there would be nothing for it but to pay up. Bond said so.

'That's about it,' commented M. 'From every point of view, including politics, not that they matter all that much. But neither the P.M. nor the President would last five minutes if anything went wrong. But whether we pay or don't pay, the consequences will be endless–and all bad. That's why absolutely everything has got to be done to find these people and the plane and stop the thing in time. The P.M. and the President are entirely agreed. Every intelligence man all over the world who's on our side is being put on to this operation–Operation *Thunderball* they're calling it. Planes, ships, submarines–and of course money's no object. We can have everything, whenever we want it. The Cabinet have already set up a special staff and a war-room. Every scrap of information will be fed into it. The Americans have done the same. Some kind of a leak can't be helped. It's being put about that all the panic, and it is panic, is because of the loss of the Vindicator–bombs included, whatever fuss that may cause politically. Only the letter will be absolutely secret. All the usual detective work–finger-prints, Brighton, writing paper–these'll be looked after by Scotland Yard with the F.B.I., Interpol, and all the NATO intelligence organizations helping where they can. Only a segment of the paper and the typing will be used–a few innocent words. This will all be quite separate from the search for the plane. That'll be handled as a top espionage matter. No one should be able to connect the two investigations. M.I.5 will handle the background to all the crew members and the Italian observer. That will be a natural part of the search for the plane. As for the Service, we've teamed up with the C.I.A. to cover the world. Allen Dulles is putting every man he's got on to it and so am I. Just sent out a General Call. Now all we can do is sit back and wait.'

Bond lit another cigarette, his sinful third in one hour. He said, putting unconcern into his voice, 'Where do I come in, sir?'

M looked vaguely at Bond, as if seeing him for the first time. Then he swivelled his chair and gazed again through the window at nothing. Finally he said, in a conversational tone of voice, 'I have committed a breach of faith with the P.M. in telling you all this, 007. I was under oath to tell no one what I have just told you. I decided to do what I have done because I have an idea, a hunch, and I wish this idea to be pursued by a'–he hesitated–'by a reliable man. It seemed to me that the only grain of possible evidence in this case was the DEW radar plot, a doubtful one I admit, of the plane that left the East–West air channel over the Atlantic and turned south towards Bermuda and the Bahamas. I decided to accept this evidence, although it has not aroused much interest elsewhere. I then spent some time studying a map and charts of the Western Atlantic and I endeavoured to put myself in the minds of SPECTRE–or rather, for there is certainly a master mind behind all this, in the mind of the chief of SPECTRE: my opposite number, so to speak. And I came to certain conclusions. I decided that a favourable target for Bomb No. 1, and for Bomb No. 2, if it comes to that, would be in America rather than in Europe. To begin with, the Americans are more bomb-conscious than we in Europe and therefore more susceptible to persuasion if it came to using Bomb No. 2. Installations worth more than £100,000,000, and thus targets for Bomb No. 1, are more numerous in America than in Europe, and finally, guessing that SPECTRE is a European organization, from the style of the letter and from the paper, which is Dutch by the way, and also from the ruthlessness of the plot, it seemed to me at least possible that an American rather than a European target might have been chosen. Anyway, going on these assumptions, and assuming that the plane could not have landed in America itself or off American shores–the coastal radar network is too good–I looked for a neighbouring area which might be suitable. And,' M glanced round at Bond and away again, 'I decided on the Bahamas, the group of islands, many of them uninhabited, surrounded mostly by shoal water over sand and possessing only one simple radar station–and that one concerned only with civilian air traffic and manned by local civilian personnel. South, towards Cuba, Jamaica, and the Caribbean, offers no worthwhile targets. Anyway it is too far from the American coastline. Northwards towards Bermuda has the same disadvantages. But the nearest of the Bahama group is only 200 miles–only six or seven hours in a fast motor-boat or yacht–from the American coastline.'

Bond interrupted. 'If you're right, sir, why didn't SPECTRE send their letter to the President instead of the P.M.?'

'For the sake of obscurity. To make us do what we are doing–hunting all round the world instead of only in one part of it. And for maximum impact. SPECTRE would realize that the arrival of the letter right on top of the loss of the bomber would hit us in the solar plexus. It might, they would reason, even shake the money out of us without any further effort. The next stage of their operation, attacking target No. 1, is going to be a nasty business for them. It's going to expose their whereabouts to a considerable extent. They'd like to collect the money and close the operation as quickly as possible. That's what we've got to gamble on. We've got to push them as close to the use of No. 1 bomb as we dare in the hope that something will betray them in the next six and three-quarter days. It's a slim chance. I'm pinning my hopes on my guess'–M swung his chair round to the desk–'and on you. Well,' he looked hard at Bond. 'Any comments? If not you'd better get started. You're booked on all New York planes from now until midnight. Then on by B.O.A.C. I thought of using an R.A.F. Canberra, but I don't want your arrival to make any noise. You're a rich young man looking for some property in the islands. That'll give you an excuse to do as much prospecting as you want. Well?'

'All right, sir.' Bond got to his feet. 'I'd rather have had somewhere more interesting–the Iron Curtain beat for instance. I can't help feeling this is a bigger operation than a small unit could take on. For my money this looks more like a Russian job. They get the experimental plane and the bombs–they obviously want them–and throw dust in our eyes with all this SPECTRE ballyhoo. If SMERSH was still in business, I'd say they'd got a finger in it somewhere. Just their style. But the Eastern Stations may pick up something on that if there's anything in the idea. Anything else, sir? Who do I co-operate with in Nassau?'

'The Governor knows you're coming. They've got a well-trained police force. C.I.A. are sending down a good man, I gather. With a communications outfit. They've got more of that sort of machinery than we have. Take a cipher machine with the Triple X setting. I want to hear every single detail you turn up. Personal to me. Right?'

'Right, sir.' Bond went to the door and let himself out. There was nothing more to be said. This looked like the biggest job the Service had ever been given and, in Bond's opinion, for he didn't give much for M's guess, he had been relegated to the back row of the chorus. So be it. He would get himself a good sunburn and watch the show from the wings.

When Bond walked out of the building, carrying the neat leather cipher case, an expensive movie camera perhaps, slung over his shoulder, the man in the beige Volkswagen stopped scratching the burn-scab under his shirt, loosed, for the tenth time, the long-barrelled forty-five in the holster under his arm, started the car and put it in gear. He was twenty yards behind Bond's parked Bentley. He had no idea what the big building was. He had simply obtained Bond's home address from the receptionist at Shrublands and, as soon as he got out of the Brighton hospital, he had carefully tailed Bond. The car was hired, under an assumed name. When he had done what had to be done he would go straight to London Airport and take the first plane out to any country on the Continent. Count Lippe was a sanguine individual. The job, the private score he had to settle, presented no problem to him. He was a ruthless, vengeful man and he had eliminated many obstreperous and perhaps dangerous people in his life. He reasoned that, if they ever came to hear of this, SPECTRE would not object. The overheard telephone conversation on that first day at the clinic showed that his cover had been broached, however slightly, and it was just conceivable that he could be traced through his membership of the Red Lightning Tong. From there to SPECTRE was a long step, but Sub-operator G knew that once a cover began to run, it ran like an old sock. Apart from that, this man must be paid off. Count Lippe had to be quits with him.

Bond was getting into his car. He had slammed the door. Sub-operator G watched the blue smoke curl from the twin exhausts. He got moving.

On the other side of the road, and a hundred yards behind the Volkswagen, SPECTRE No. 6 slipped his goggles down over his eyes, stamped the 500-c.c. Triumph into gear and accelerated down the road. He swerved neatly through the traffic–he had been a test rider for D.K.W. at one time in his post-war career–and stationed himself ten yards behind the off rear wheel of the Volkswagen and just out of the driver's line of vision in the windscreen mirror. He had no idea why Sub-operator G was following the Bentley, nor who the Bentley belonged to. His job was to kill the driver of the Volkswagen. He put his hand into the leather satchel he carried slung over his shoulder, took out the heavy grenade–it was twice the normal military size–and watched the traffic ahead for the right pattern to allow his getaway.

Sub-operator G was watching for a similar pattern. He also noted the spacing on the lamp-posts on the pavement in case he might be blocked and have to run off the road. Now the cars ahead were sparse. He stamped his foot into the floor and, driving with his left hand, drew out the Colt with his right. Now he was up with the Bentley's rear bumper. Now he was alongside. The dark profile was a sitting target. With a last quick glance ahead, he raised the gun.

It was the cheeky iron rattle of the Volkswagen's air-cooled engine that made Bond turn his head, and it was this minute reduction of the target area that saved his jaw. If he had then accelerated, the second bullet would have got him, but some blessed instinct made his foot stamp the brake at the same time as his head ducked so swiftly that his chin hit the horn button, nearly knocking him out. Almost simultaneously, instead of a third shot, there came the roar of an explosion and the remains of his windshield, already shattered, cascaded around him. The Bentley had stopped, the engine stalled. Brakes screamed. There were shouts and the panicky screams of horns. Bond shook his head and cautiously raised it. The Volkswagen, one wheel still spinning, lay on its side in front and broadside to the Bentley. Most of the roof had been blown off. Inside, and half sprawling into the road, was a horrible, glinting mess. Flames were licking at the blistered paintwork. People were gathering. Bond pulled himself together and got quickly out of his car. He shouted, "Stand back. The petrol tank'll go.' Almost as he said the words there came a dull boom and a cloud of black smoke. The flames spurted. In the distance, sirens sounded. Bond edged through the people and strode quickly back towards his headquarters, his thoughts racing.

The inquiry made Bond lose two planes to New York. By the time the police had put out the fire and had transported the bits of man and the bits of machinery and bomb casing to the morgue it was quite clear that they would have nothing to go on but the shoes, the number on the gun, some fibres and shreds of clothing, and the car. The car-hire people remembered nothing but a man with dark glasses, a driver's licence in the name of Johnston, and a handful of fivers. The car had been hired three days before for one week. Plenty of people remembered the motor cyclist, but it seemed that he had no rear number plate. He had gone like a bat out of hell towards Baker Street. He wore goggles. Medium build. Nothing else.

Bond had not been able to help. He had seen nothing of the Volkswagen driver. The roof of the Volkswagen had been too low. There had only been a hand and the glitter of a gun.

The Secret Service asked for a copy of the police report and M instructed that this should be sent to the Thunderball war-room. He saw Bond briefly again, rather impatiently, as if it had all been Bond's fault. Then he told Bond to forget about it–it was probably something to do with one of his past cases. A hangover of some kind. The police would get to the bottom of it in time. The main thing was operation Thunderball. Bond had better get a move on.

By the time Bond left the building for the second time, it had begun to rain. One of the mechanics from the car pool at the back of the building had done what he could, knocking out the remains of the Bentley's windscreen and cleaning the bits out of the car, but when he got home at lunch time Bond was soaked to the skin. He left the car in a near-by garage, telephoned Rolls and his insurance company (he had got too close to a lorry carrying steel lengths, for reinforced concrete presumably. No, he had not got the lorry's number. Sorry, but you know how it is when these things happen all of a sudden), and then went home and had a bath and changed into his dark blue tropical worsted. He packed carefully–one large suitcase and a holdall for his underwater swimming gear–and went through to the kitchen.

May was looking rather contrite. It seemed as if she might make another speech. Bond held up his hand. 'Don't tell me, May. You were right. I can't do my work on carrot juice. I've got to be off in an hour and I need some proper food. Be an angel and make me your kind of scrambled eggs–four eggs. Four rashers of that American hickory-smoked bacon if we've got any left, hot buttered toast–your kind, not wholemeal–and a big pot of coffee, double strength. And bring in the drink tray.'

May looked at him, relieved but aghast. 'Whatever happened, Mister James?'

Bond laughed at the expression on her face. 'Nothing, May. It just occurred to me that life's too short. Plenty of time to watch the calories when one gets to heaven.'

Bond left May tut-tutting at this profanity, and went off to look to his armament.

Chapter Nine

Multiple Requiem

So far as SPECTRE was concerned, Plan Omega had gone exactly as Blofeld had known it would and Phases I to III in their entirety had been completed on schedule and without a hitch.

Giuseppe Petacchi, the late Giuseppe Petacchi, had been well chosen. At the age of eighteen he had been co-pilot of a Focke-Wulf 200 from the Adriatic anti-submarine patrol, one of the few hand-picked Italian airmen who had been allowed to handle these German planes. The group was issued with the latest German pressure mines charged with the new Hexogen explosive just when the tide had turned in the Allied battle up the spine of Italy. Petacchi had known where his destiny lay and had gone into business for himself. On a routine patrol, he had shot the pilot and the navigator, very carefully, with one ·38 bullet in the back of the head for each of them, and had brought the big plane skimming in, just above the waves to avoid the anti-aircraft fire, to the harbour of Bari. Then he had hung his shirt out of the cockpit as a token of surrender and had waited for the R.A.F. launch. He had been decorated by the English and the Americans for this exploit and had been awarded £10,000 from special funds for his presentation to the Allies of the pressure mine. He had told a highly coloured story to the Itelligence people of having been a one-man resistance ever since he had been old enough to join the Italian Air Force, and he emerged at the end of the war as one of Italy's most gallant resistance heroes. From then on life had been easy–pilot and later captain in Alitalia when it got going again, and then back into the new Italian Air Force as colonel. His secondment to NATO followed and then his appointment as one of the six Italians chosen for the Advance Striking Force. But he was now thirty-four, and it occurred to him that he had had just about enough of flying. He especially did not care for the idea of being part of the spearhead of NATO defences. It was time for younger men to provide the heroics. And all his life he had had a passion for owning things–flashy, exciting, expensive things. He had most of what he desired–a couple of gold cigarette cases, a solid gold Rolex Oyster Perpetual Chronometer on a flexible gold bracelet, a white convertible Lancia Gran Turismo, plenty of sharp clothes, and all the girls he wanted (he had once been briefly married but it had not been a success). Now he desired, and what he desired he often got, a particular Ghia-bodied 3,500 G.T. Maserati he had seen at the Milan motor show. He also wanted Out–out of the pale green corridors of NATO, out of the air force and, therefore, off to new worlds with a new name. Rio de Janeiro sounded just right. But all this meant a new passport, plenty of money, and 'organismo'–the vital 'organismo'.

The organismo turned up, and turned up bearing just those gifts that Petacchi lusted for. It came in the shape of an Italian named Fonda who was at that time No. 4 in SPECTRE and who had been casing the personnel of NATO, via Versailles and Paris night-clubs and restaurants, for just such a man. It had taken one whole very careful month to prepare the bait and inch it forward towards the fish and, when it was finally presented, No. 4 had been almost put off by the greed with which it had been gobbled. There was delay while the possibility of a double-cross was probed by SPECTRE, but finally all the lights were green and the full proposition was laid out for inspection. Petacchi was to get on the Vindicator training course and hi-jack the plane. (There was no mention of atomic weapons. This was a Cuban revolutionary group who wanted to call attention to its existence and aims by a dramatic piece of self-advertisement. Petacchi closed his ears to this specious tale. He didn't mind in the least who wanted the plane so long as he was paid.) In exchange, Petacchi would receive one million dollars, a new passport in any name and nationality he chose, and immediate onward passage from the point of delivery to Rio de Janeiro. Many details were discussed and perfected, and when, at eight o'clock in the evening of that June 2nd, the Vindicator screamed off down the runway and out over St Alban's Head, Petacchi was tense but confident.

For the training flights, a couple of ordinary civil aircraft seats had been fixed inside the roomy fuselage just back of the large cockpit, and Petacchi sat quietly for a whole hour and watched the five men at work at the crowded dials and instruments. When it came to his turn to fly the plane he was quite satisfied that he could dispense with all five of them. Once he had set George, there would be nothing to do but stay awake and make certain from time to time that he was keeping exactly at 32,000 feet, just above the transatlantic air-channel. There would be a tricky moment when he turned off the East-West channel on to the North-South for the Bahamas, but this had all been worked out for him and every move he would have to make was written down in the notebook in his breast pocket. The landing was going to need very steady nerves, but for one million dollars the steady nerves would be summoned.

For the tenth time Petacchi consulted the Rolex. Now! He verified and tested the oxygen mask in the bulkhead beside him and laid it down ready. Next he took the little red-ringed cylinder out of his pocket and remembered exactly how many turns to give the release valve. Then he put it back in his pocket and went through into the cockpit.

'Hullo, Seppy. Enjoying the flight?' The pilot liked the Italian. They had gone out together on one or two majestic thrashes in Bournemouth.

'Sure, sure.' Petacchi asked some questions, verified the course set on George, checked the air-speed and altitude. Now everyone in the cockpit was relaxed, almost drowsy. Five more hours to go. Rather a bind missing *North by North-West* at the Odeon. But one would catch up with it at Southampton. Petacchi stood with his back to the metal map-rack that held the log and the charts. His right hand went to his pocket, felt for the release valve, and gave it three complete turns. He eased the cylinder out of his pocket and slipped it behind him and down behind the books.

Petacchi stretched and yawned. 'Is time for a zizz,' he said amiably. He had got the slang phrase pat. It rolled easily off the tongue.

The navigator laughed. 'What do they call it in Italian–"Zizzo"?'

Petacchi grinned cheerfully. He went through the open hatch, got back to his chair, clamped on his oxygen mask, and turned the control regulator to 100 per cent oxygen to cut out the air bleed. Then he made himself comfortable and watched.

They had said it would take under five minutes. Sure enough, in about two minutes, the man nearest to the map rack, the navigator, suddenly clutched his throat and fell forward, gargling horribly. The radio operator dropped his earphones and started forward, but with his second step he was down on his knees. He lurched sideways and collapsed. Now the three other men began to fight for air, briefly, terribly. The co-pilot and the flight engineer writhed off their stools together. They clawed vaguely at each other and then fell back, spreadeagled. The pilot groped up towards the microphone above his head, said something indistinctly, got half to his feet, turned slowly so that his bulging eyes, already dead, seemed to stare through the hatchway into Petacchi's, and then thudded down on top of the body of his co-pilot.

Petacchi glanced at his watch. Four minutes flat. Give them one more minute. When the minute was up, he took rubber gloves out of his pocket, put them on and, pressing the oxygen mask tight against his face and trailing the flexible tube behind him, he went forward, reached down into the map rack, and closed the valve on the cylinder of cyanide. He verified George and adjusted the cabin pressurization to help clear the poison gas. He then went back to his seat to wait for fifteen minutes.

They had said fifteen would be enough, but at the last moment he gave it another ten and then, still with his oxygen mask on, he went forward again and began slowly, for the oxygen made him rather breathless, to pull the bodies back into the fuselage. When the cockpit was clear, he took a small phial of crystals out of his trousers pocket, took out the cork, and sprinkled the cabin floor with them. He went down on his knees and watched the crystals. They kept their white colour. He eased his oxygen mask away and took a small cautious sniff. There was no smell. But still, when he took over the controls and began easing the plane down to 32,000 and then slightly north-west-by-west to get into the traffic lane, he kept the mask on.

The giant plane whispered on into the night. The cockpit, bright with the yellow eyes of the dials, was quiet and warm. In the deafening silence in the cockpit of a big jet in flight there was only the faint buzz of an invector. As he verified the dials, the click of each switch as loud as a small-calibre pistol-shot.

Petacchi again checked George with the gyro and verified each fuel tank to see that they were all feeding evenly. One tank pump needed adjustment. The jet pipe temperatures were not overheating.

Satisfied, Petacchi settled himself comfortably in the pilot's seat and swallowed a benzedrine tablet and thought about the future. One of the headphones scattered on the floor of the cockpit began to chirrup loudly. Petacchi glanced at his watch. Of course! Boscombe Air Traffic Control was trying to raise the Vindicator. He had missed the third of the half-hourly calls. How long would Air Control wait before alerting Air Sea Rescue, Bomber Command, and the Air Ministry? There would first be checks and double-checks with the Southern Rescue Centre. They would probably take another half-hour and by that time he would be well out over the Atlantic.

The chirrup of the headphones went quiet. Petacchi got up from his seat and took a look at the radar screen. He watched it for some time, noting the occasional 'blip' of planes being overhauled below him. Would his own swift passage above the air corridor be noted by the planes as he passed above them? Unlikely. The radar on commercial planes has a limited field of vision in a forward cone. He would almost certainly not be spotted until he crossed the Defence Early Warning line, and DEW would probably put him down as a commercial jet that had strayed above its normal channel.

Petacchi went back to the pilot's seat and again minutely checked the dials. He weaved the plane gently to get the feel of the controls. Behind him, the bodies on the floor of the fuselage stirred uneasily. The plane answered perfectly. It was like driving a beautiful quiet motor-car. Petacchi dreamed briefly of the Maserati. What colour? Better not his usual white, or anything spectacular. Dark blue with a thin red line along the coachwork. Something quiet and respectable that would fit in with his new, quiet identity. It would be fun to run her in some of the trials and road races–even the Mexican '2,000'. But that would be too dangerous. Supposing he won and his picture got into the papers! No. He would have to cut out anything like that. He would only drive the car really fast when he wanted to get a girl. They melted in a fast car. Why was that? The sense of surrender to the machine, to the man whose strong, sunburned hands were on the wheel? But it was always so. You turned the car into a wood after ten minutes at 150 and you would almost have to lift the girl out and lay her down on the moss, her limbs would be so trembling and soft.

Petacchi pulled himself out of the daydream. He glanced at his watch. The Vindicator was already four hours out. At 600 m.p.h. one certainly covered the miles. The coastline of America should be on the screen by now. He got up and had a look. Yes, there, 500 miles away, was the coastline map already in high definition, the bulge that was Boston, and the silvery creek of the Hudson River. No need to check his position with weather ships Delta or Echo that would be somewhere below him. He was dead on course and it would soon be time to turn off the East-West channel.

Petacchi went back to his seat, munched another benzedrine tablet, and consulted his chart. He got his hands to the controls and watched the eerie glow of the gyro compass. Now! He eased the controls gently round in a fairly tight curve, then he flattened out again, edged the plane exactly on to its new course, and re-set George. Now he was flying due south, now he was on the last lap, a bare three hours to go. It was time to start worrying about the landing.

Petacchi took out his little notebook. 'Watch for the lights of Grand Bahama to port, and Palm Beach to starboard. Be ready to pick up the navigational aids from No. 1's yacht–dot-dot-dash; dot-dot-dash, jettison fuel, lose height to around 1,000 feet for the last quarter of an hour, kill speed with the air brakes, and lose more height. Watch out for flashing red beacon and prepare for the final approach. Flaps down only at the check altitude with about 140 knots indicated. Depth of water will be forty feet. You will have plenty of time to get out of the escape hatch. You will be taken on board No. 1's yacht. There is a Bahamas Airways flight to Miami at 8.30 on the next morning and then Braniff or Real Airlines for the rest of the way. No. 1 will give you the money in 1,000-dollar bills or in Travellers Cheques. He will have both available, also the passport in the name of Enrico Valli, Company Director.'

Petacchi checked his position, course, and speed. Only one more hour to go. It was three a.m. G.M.T., nine p.m. Nassau time. A full moon was coming up and the carpet of clouds 10,000 feet below was a snowfield.

Petacchi dowsed the collision lights on his wing tips and fuselage. He checked the fuel: 2,000 gallons including the reserve tanks. He would need 500 for the last four hundred miles. He pulled the release valve on the reserve tanks and lost 1,000 gallons. With the loss of weight the plane began to climb slowly and he corrected back to 32,000. Now there was twenty minutes to go–time to begin the long descent . . .

Down through the cloud base, the moments of blindness and then, far below, the sparse lights of North and South Bimini winked palely against the silver sheen of the moon on the quiet sea. There were no whitecaps. The met. report he had picked up from Vero Beach on the American mainland had been right: 'Dead calm, light airs from the north-east, visibility good, no immediate likelihood of change' and a check on the fainter Nassau Radio had confirmed. The sea looked as smooth and as solid as steel. This was going to be all right. Petacchi dialled Channel 67 on the pilot's command set to pick up No. 1's navigational aid. He had a moment's panic when he didn't hit it at once, but then he got it, faint but clear–dot-dot-dash, dot-dot-dash. It was time to get right down. Petacchi began to kill his speed with the air brakes and cut down the four jets. The great plane began a shallow dive. The radio altimeter became vocal, threatening. Petacchi watched it and the sea of quicksilver below him. He had a moment when the horizon was lost. There was so much reflection off the moonlit water. Then he was on and over a small dark island. It gave him confidence in the 2,000 feet indicated on the altimeter. He pulled out of the shallow dive and held the plane steady.

Now No. 1's beacon was coming in loud and clear. Soon he would see the red flashing light. And there it was, perhaps five miles dead ahead. Petacchi inched the great nose of the plane down. Any moment now! It was going to be easy! His fingers played with the controls as delicately as if they were the erotic trigger points on a woman. Five hundred feet, four hundred, three, two . . . there was the pale shape of the yacht, lights dowsed. He was dead on line with the red flash of the beacon. Would he hit it? Never mind. Inch her down, down, down. Be ready to switch off at once. The belly of the plane gave a jolt. Up with the nose! Crash! A leap in the air and then . . . Crash again!

Petacchi unhinged his cramped fingers from the controls, and gazed numbly out of the window at the foam and small waves. By God he had done it! He, Giuseppe Petacchi, had done it!

Now for the applause! Now for the rewards!

The plane was settling slowly and there was a hiss of steam from the submerging jets. From behind him came the rip and crack of tearing metal as the tail section gaped open where the back of the plane had broken. Petacchi went through into the fuselage. The water swirled around his feet. The filtering moonlight glittered white on the upturned face of one of the corpses now soggily awash at the rear of the plane. Petacchi broke the perspex cover to the handle of the port side emergency exit and jerked the handle down. The door fell outwards and Petacchi stepped through and walked out along the wing.

The big jolly-boat was almost up with the plane. There were six men in it. Petacchi waved and shouted delightedly. One man raised a hand in reply. The faces of the men, milk-white under the moon, looked up at him quietly, curiously. Petacchi thought: these men are very serious, very businesslike. It is right so. He swallowed his triumph and also looked grave.

The boat came alongside the wing, now almost awash, and one man climbed up on to the wing and walked towards him. He was a short, thick man with a very direct gaze. He walked carefully, his feet well apart and his knees flexed to keep his balance. His left hand was hooked in his belt.

Petacchi said happily, 'Good evening. Good evening. I am delivering one plane in good condition.' (He had thought the joke out long before.) 'Please sign here.' He held out his hand. The man from the jolly-boat took the hand in a strong grasp, braced himself, and pulled sharply. Petacchi's head was flung back by the quick jerk and he was looking full into the eyes of the moon as the stiletto flashed up and under the offered chin, through the roof of the mouth, into the brain. He knew nothing but a moment's surprise, a sear of pain, and an explosion of brilliant light.

The killer held in the knife for a moment, the back of his hand feeling the stubble on Petacchi's chin, then he lowered the body on to the wing and withdrew the knife. He carefully rinsed the knife in the sea water and wiped the blade on Petacchi's back and put the knife away. Then he hauled the body along the wing and thrust it under water beside the escape hatch.

The killer waded back along the wing to the waiting jolly-boat and laconically raised a thumb. By now four of the men had pulled on their aqualungs. One by one, with a last adjustment of their mouthpieces, they clumsily heaved themselves over the side of the rocking boat and sank in a foam of small bubbles. When the last man had gone the mechanic at the engine carefully lowered a huge underwater searchlight over the side and paid out the cable. At a given moment he switched the light on and the sea and the great sinking hulk of the plane were lit up with a mist of luminescence. The mechanic slipped the idling motor into gear and backed away, paying out cable as he went. At twenty yards, out of range of the suction of the sinking plane, he stopped and switched off his engine. He reached into his overalls and took out a packet of Camels. He offered one to the killer, who took it, broke it carefully in half, put one half behind his ear and lit the other half.

The killer was a man who rigidly controlled his weaknesses.

Chapter Ten

The Disco Volante

On board the yacht, No. 1 put down his night glasses, took a Charvet handkerchief out of the breast pocket of his white shark-skin jacket and dabbed gently at his forehead and temples. The musky scent of Schiaparelli's Snuff was reassuring, reminding him of the easy side of life, of Dominetta who would now be sitting down to dinner–everyone kept Spanish hours in Nassau and cocktails would not have finished before ten–with the raffish but rather gay Saumurs and their equally frivolous guests; of the early game that would already be under way at the Casino; of the calypsos thudding into the night from the bars and night-clubs on Bay Street. He put the handkerchief back in his pocket. But this also was good–this wonderful operation! Like clockwork! He glanced at his watch. Just ten fifteen. The plane had been a bare thirty minutes late, a nasty half-hour to have to wait, but the landing had been perfect. Vargas had done a good quick job on the Italian pilot–what was his name?–so that now they were running only fifteen minutes late. If the recovery group didn't have to use oxy-acetylene cutters to get out the bombs, they would soon make that up. But one mustn't expect no hitch at all. There was a good eight hours of darkness to go. Calm, method, efficiency, in that order. Calm, method, efficiency. No. 1 ducked down off the bridge and went into the radio cabin. It smelled of sweat and tension. Anything from the Nassau control tower? Any report of a low-flying plane? Of a possible crash into the sea off Bimini? Then keep watching and get me No. 2. Quick, please. It's just on the quarter.

No. 1 lit a cigarette and watched the yacht's big brain get to work, scanning the ether, listening, searching. The operator played the dials with insect fingers, pausing, verifying, hastening on through the sound waves of the world. Now he suddenly stopped, checked, minutely adjusted the volume. He raised his thumb. No. 1 spoke into the little sphere of wire mesh that rose in front of his mouth from the base of the head set. 'No. 1 speaking.'

'No. 2 listening.' The voice was hollow. The words waxed and waned. But it was Blofeld, all right. No. 1 knew that voice better than he remembered his father's.

'Successful. Ten fifteen. Next phase ten forty-five. Continuing. Over.'

'Thank you. Out.' The sound waves went dead. The interchange had taken forty-five seconds. No conceivable fear of interception in that time, on that waveband.

No. 1 went through the big stateroom and down into the hold. The four men of B team, their aqualungs beside them, were sitting around smoking. The wide underwater hatch just above the keel of the yacht was open. Moonlight, reflected off the white sand under the ship, shone up through the six feet of water in the hold. Stacked on the grating beside the men was the thick pile of tarpaulin painted a very pale café-au-lait with occasional irregular blotches of dark green and brown. No. 1 said, 'All is going very well. The recovery team is at work. It should not be long now. How about the chariot and the sled?'

One of the men jerked his thumb downwards. 'They are down there. Outside on the sand. So it will be quicker.'

'Correct.' No. 1 nodded towards a crane-like contraption fastened to a bulkhead above the hold. 'The derrick took the strain all right?'

'The chain could handle twice the weight.'

'The pumps?'

'In order. They will clear the hold in seven minutes.'

'Good. Well, take it easy. It will be a long night.' No. 1 climbed the iron ladder out of the hold and went up on deck. He didn't need his night glasses. Two hundred yards away to starboard the sea was empty save for the jolly-boat riding at anchor above the golden submarine glow. The red marker light had been taken in to the boat. The rattle of the little generator making current for the big searchlight was loud. It would carry far across a sea as still as this. But accumulators would have been too bulky and might have exhausted themselves before the work was finished. The generator was a calculated risk and a small one at that. The nearest island was five miles away and uninhabited unless someone was having a midnight picnic on it. The yacht had stopped and searched it on the way to the rendezvous. Everything had been done that could be done, every precaution taken. The wonderful machine was running silently and full out. There was nothing to worry about now except the next step. No. 1 went through the hatch into the enclosed bridge and bent over the lighted chart table.

Emilio Largo, No. 1, was a big, conspicuously handsome man of about forty. He was a Roman and he looked like a Roman, not from the Rome of today, but from the Rome of the ancient coins. The large, long face was sunburned a deep mahogany brown and the light glinted off the strong rather hooked nose and the clean-cut jaw that had been meticulously shaved before he had started out late that afternoon. In contrast to the hard, slow-moving brown eyes, the mouth, with its thick, rather down-curled lips, belonged to a satyr. Ears that, from dead in front, looked almost pointed, added to an animalness that would devastate women. The only weakness in the fine centurion face lay in the overlong sideburns and the too carefully waved black hair that glistened so brightly with pomade that it might almost have been painted on to the skull. There was no fat on the big-boned frame–Largo had fought for Italy in the Olympic foils, was almost an Olympic class swimmer with the Australian crawl, and only a month before had won the senior class in the Nassau water-ski championships–and the muscles bulged under the exquisitely cut shark-skin jacket. An aid to his athletic prowess were his hands. They were almost twice the normal size, even for a man of his stature, and now, as they walked across the chart holding a ruler and a pair of dividers, they looked, extruding from the white sleeves that rested on the white chart, almost like large brown furry animals quite separate from their owner.

Largo was an adventurer, a predator on the herd. Two hundred years before, he would have been a pirate–not one of the jolly ones of the story books, but a man like Blackbeard, a blood-stained cut-throat who scythed his way through people towards gold. But Blackbeard had been too much of a bully and a rough-neck and wherever he went in the world he left behind a tell-tale shambles. Largo was different. There was a cool brain and an exquisite finesse behind his actions that had always saved him from the herd's revenge–from his post-war debut as head of the black market in Naples, through five lucrative years smuggling from Tangier, five more masterminding the wave of big jewel robberies on the French Riviera, down to his last five with SPECTRE. Always he got away with it. Always he had seen the essential step ahead that would have been hidden from lesser men. He was the epitome of the gentleman crook–a man of the world, a great womanizer, a high liver, with the entrée to café society in four continents, and the last survivor, conveniently enough, of a once famous Roman family whose fortune, so he said, he had inherited. He also benefited from having no wife, a spotless police record, nerves of steel, a heart of ice, and the ruthlessness of a Himmler. He was the perfect man for SPECTRE, and the perfect man, rich Nassau playboy and all, to be Supreme Commander of Plan Omega.

One of the crew knocked on the hatch and came in. 'They have signalled. The chariot and sled are on the way.'

'Thank you.' In the heat and excitement of any operation, Largo always created calm. However much was at stake, however great the dangers and however urgent the need for speed and quick decisions, he made a fetish of calm, of the pause, of an almost judolike inertia. This was an act to which he had trained himself. He found it had an extraordinary effect on his accomplices. It tied them to him and invoked their obedience and loyalty more than any other factor in leadership. That he, a clever and cunning man, should show unconcern at particularly bad, or, as in this case, particularly good news, meant that he already knew that what had happened would happen. With Largo, consequences were foreseen. One could depend on him. He never lost balance. So now, at this splendid news, Largo deliberately picked up his dividers again and made a trace, an imaginary trace, on the chart for the sake of the crew member. He then put down the dividers and strolled out of the air-conditioning into the warm night.

A tiny worm of underwater light was creeping out towards the jolly-boat. It was a two-man underwater chariot identical with those used by the Italians during the war and bought, with improvements, from Ansaldo, the firm that had originally invented the one-man submarine. It was towing an underwater sled, a sharp-prowed tray with negative buoyancy used for the recovery and transport of heavy objects under the sea. The worm of light merged with the luminescence from the searchlight and, minutes later, re-emerged on its way back to the ship. It would have been natural for Largo to have gone down to the hold to witness the arrival of the two atomic weapons. Typically, he did nothing of the sort. In due course the little headlight reappeared, going back over its previous course. Now the sled would be loaded with the huge tarpaulin, camouflaged to merge in with just this piece of underwater terrain, with its white sand and patches of coral outcrop, that would be spread so as to cover every inch of the wrecked plane and pegged all round with corkscrew iron stanchions that would not be shifted by the heaviest surface storm or groundswell. In his imagination, Largo saw every move of the eight men who would now be working far below the surface on the reality for which there had been so much training, so many dummy exercises. He marvelled at the effort, the incredible ingenuity, that had gone into Plan Omega. Now all the months of preparation, of sweat and tears, were being repaid.

There came a bright blink of light on the surface of the water not far from the jolly-boat–then another and another. The men were surfacing. As they did so, the moon caught the glass of their masks. They swam to the boat–Largo verified that all eight were there–and clumsily heaved up the short ladder and over the side. The mechanic and Brandt, the German killer, helped them off with their gear, the underwater light was switched off and hauled inboard and, instead of the rattle of the generator, there came the muffled roar of the twin Johnstons. The boat sped back to the yacht and to the waiting arms of the derricks. The couplings were made firm and verified and, with a shrill electric whine, the boat, complete with passengers, was swung up and inboard.

The captain came and stood at Largo's side. He was a big, sullen, rawboned man who had been cashiered from the Canadian Navy for drunkenness and insubordination. He had been a slave to Largo ever since Largo had called him to the stateroom one day and broken a chair over his head on account of a questioned command. That was the kind of discipline he understood. Now he said, 'The hold's clear. Okay to sail?'

'Are both the teams satisfied?'

'They say so. Not a hitch.'

'First see they all get one full jigger of whisky. Then tell them to rest. They will be going out again in just about an hour. Ask Kotze to have a word with me. Be ready to sail in five minutes.'

'Okay.'

The eyes of the physicist, Kotze, were bright under the moon. Largo noticed that he was trembling slightly as if with fever. He tried to instil calm into the man. He said cheerfully, 'Well, my friend. Are you pleased with your toys? The toy-shop has sent you everything you want?'

Kotze's lips trembled. He was on the verge of excited tears. He said, his voice high, 'It is tremendous! You have no idea. Weapons such as I had never dreamed of. And of a simplicity–a safety! Even a child could handle these things without danger.'

'The cradles were big enough for them? You have room to do your work?'

'Yes, yes.' Kotze almost flapped his hands with enthusiasm. 'There are no problems, none at all. The fuses will be off in no time. It will be a simple matter to replace them with the time mechanism. Maslov is already at work correcting the threads. I am using lead screws. They are more easy to machine.'

'And the two plugs–these ignitors you were telling me about? They are safe? Where did the divers find them?'

'They were in a leaden box under the pilot's seat. I have verified them. Perfectly simple when the time comes. They will of course be kept apart in the hiding place. The rubber bags are splendid. Just what was needed. I have verified that they seal completely watertight.'

'No danger from radiation?'

'Not now. Everything is in the leaden cases.' Kotze shrugged. 'I may have picked up a little while I was working on the monsters but I wore the harness. I will watch for signs. I know what to do.'

'You are a brave man, Kotze. I won't go near the damned things until I have to. I value my sex-life too much. So you are satisfied with everything? You have no problems? Nothing has been left on the plane?'

Kotze had got himself under control. He had been bursting with the news, with his relief that the technical problems were within his power. Now he felt empty, tired. He had voided himself of the tensions that had been with him for weeks. After all this planning, all these dangers, supposing his knowledge had not been enough! Supposing the bloody English had invented some new safety device, some secret control, of which he knew nothing! But when the time came, when he unwrapped the protective webbing and got to work with his jeweller's tools, then triumph and gratitude had flooded into him. No, now there were no problems. Everything was all right. Now there was only routine. Kotze said dully, 'No. There are no problems. Everything is there. I will go and get the job finished.'

Largo watched the thin figure shamble off along the deck. Scientists were queer fish. They saw nothing but science. Kotze couldn't visualize the risks that still had to be run. For him the turning of a few screws was the end of the job. For the rest of the time he would be a useless supercargo. It would be easier to get rid of him. But that couldn't be done yet. He would have to be kept on just in case the weapons had to be used. But he was a depressing little man and a near hysteric. Largo didn't like such people near him. They lowered his spirits. They smelled of bad luck. Kotze would have to be found some job in the engine room where he would be kept busy and, above all, out of sight.

Largo went into the cockpit bridge. The captain was sitting at the wheel, a light aluminium affair consisting only of the bottom half of a circle. Largo said, 'Okay. Let's go.' The captain reached out his hand to the bank of buttons at his side and pressed the one that said '*Start Both*'. There came a low, hollow rumble from amidships. A light blinked on the panel to show that both engines were firing properly. The captain pulled the electro-magnetic gear shift to '*Slow Ahead Both*' and the yacht began to move. The captain made it '*Full Ahead Both*' and the yacht trembled and settled a little in the stern. The captain watched the revolution counter, his hand on a squat lever at his side. At twenty knots the counter showed 5,000. The captain inched back the lever that depressed the great steel scoop below the hull. The revolutions remained the same, but the finger of the speedometer crawled on round the dial until it said forty knots. Now the yacht was half-flying, half-planing across the glittering sheet of still water, the hull supported four feet above the surface on the broad, slightly uptilted metal skid and with only a few feet of the stern and the two big screws submerged. It was a glorious sensation and Largo, as he always did, thrilled to it.

The motor yacht, *Disco Volante*, was a hydrofoil craft, built for Largo with SPECTRE funds by the Italian constructors, Leopoldo Rodrigues, of Messina, the only firm in the world to have successfully adapted the Shertel-Sachsenberg system to commercial use. With a hull of aluminium and magnesium alloy, two Daimler-Benz four-stroke diesels supercharged by twin Brown-Boveri turbo superchargers, the *Disco Volante* could move her 100 tons at around fifty knots, with a cruising range at that speed of around four hundred miles. She had cost £200,000, but she had been the only craft in the world with the speed, cargo- and passenger-space, and with the essential shallow draft for the job required of her in Bahamian waters.

The constructors claim of this type of craft that it has a particular refinement that SPECTRE had appreciated. Having high stability and a shallow draft, *Aliscafos*, as they are called in Italy, do not determine magnetic field variation, nor do they cause pressure waves–both desirable characteristics, in case the *Disco Volante* might wish, some time in her career, to escape detection.

Six months before, the *Disco* had been shipped out to the Florida Keys by the South Atlantic route. She had been a sensation in Florida waters and among the Bahamas, and had vastly helped to make Largo the most popular 'millionaire' in a corner of the world that crawls with millionaires who 'have everything'. And the fast and mysterious voyages he made in the *Disco*, with all those underwater swimmers and occasionally with a two-seater Lycoming-engined folding-wing amphibian mounted on the roof of the streamlined superstructure had aroused just the right amount of excited comment. Slowly, Largo had let the secret leak out–through his own indiscretions at dinners and cocktail parties, through carefully primed members of the crew in the Bay Street bars. This was a treasure hunt, an important one. There was a pirates' map, a sunken galleon thickly overgrown with coral. The wreck had been located. Largo was only waiting for the end of the winter tourist season and for the calms of early summer and then his shareholders would be coming out from Europe and work would begin in earnest. And two days before, the shareholders, nineteen of them, had duly come trickling in to Nassau by different routes–from Bermuda, from New York, from Miami. Rather dull looking people to be sure, just the sort of hard-headed, hard-working businessmen who would be amused by a gamble like this, a pleasant sunshine gamble with a couple of weeks' holiday in Nassau to make up for it if the doubloons were after all not in the wreck. And that evening, with all the visitors on board, the engines of the *Disco* had begun to murmur, just when they should have, the harbour folk agreed, just when it was getting dark, and the beautiful dark blue and white yacht had slid out of harbour. Once in the open sea, the engines had started up their deep booming that had gradually diminished to the south-east, towards, the listeners agreed, an entirely appropriate hunting ground.

The southerly course was considered appropriate because it is among the Southern Bahamas that the great local treasure troves are expected to be found. It was through the southerly passages through these islands–the Crooked Island, the Mayaguana and the Caicos passages–that the Spanish treasure ships would try to dodge the pirates and the French and British fleets as they made for home. Here, it is believed, lie the remains of the *Porto Pedro*, sunk in 1668, with a million pounds of bullion on board. The *Santa Cruz*, lost in 1694, carried twice as much, and the *El Capitan* and *San Pedro*, both sunk in 1719, carried a million, and half a million, pounds of treasure respectively.

Every year, treasure hunts for these and other ships are carried out among the Southern Bahamas. No one can guess how much, if anything, has been recovered, but everyone in Nassau knows of the 72-lb. silver bar recovered by two Nassau businessmen off Gorda Cay in 1950, and since presented to the Nassau Development Board, in whose offices it is permanently on view. So all Bahamians know that treasure is there for the finding, and when the harbour folk of Nassau heard the deep boom of the *Disco*'s engines dying away to the south, they nodded wisely.

But once the *Disco* was well away and the moon had not yet risen, with all lights doused, she swung away in a wide circle towards the west and towards the rendezvous point she was now leaving. Now she was a hundred miles, two hours, away from Nassau. But it would be almost dawn when, after one more vital call, Nassau would again hear the boom of her engines coming in from the false southern trail.

Largo got up and bent over the chart table. They had covered the course many times and in all weathers. It was really no problem. But Phases I and II had gone so well that double care must be taken over Phase III. Yes, all was well. They were dead on course. Fifty miles. They would be there in an hour. He told the captain to keep the yacht as she was, and went below to the radio room. Eleven fifteen was just coming up. It was call time.

The small island, Dog Island, was no bigger than two tennis courts. It was a hunk of dead coral with a smattering of seagrape and battered screw palm that grew on nothing but pockets of brackish rainwater and sand. It was the point where the Dog Shoal broke the surface, a well-known navigational hazard that even the fishing boats kept well away from. In daylight, Andros Island showed to eastwards, but at night it was as safe as houses.

The *Disco* came up fast and then slowly lowered herself back into the water and slid up to within a cable's length of the rock. Her arrival brought small waves that lapped and sucked at the rock and then were still. The anchor slipped silently down forty feet and held. Down in the hold, Largo and the disposal team of four waited for the underwater hatch to be opened.

The five men wore aqualungs. Largo held nothing but a powerful underwater electric torch. The four others were divided into two pairs. They wore webbing slung between them and they sat on the edge of the iron grating with their frogman's feet dangling, waiting for the water to swirl in and give them buoyancy. On the webbing, between each pair, rested a six-foot-long tapering object in an obscene grey rubber envelope.

The water seeped, rushed, and then burst into the hold, submerging the five men. They slipped off their seats and trudged out through the hatchway, Largo in the lead and the two pairs behind him at precisely tested intervals.

Largo did not at first switch on his torch. It was not necessary and it would bring stupid, dazed fish that were a distraction. It might even bring shark or barracuda and, though they would be no more than a nuisance, one of the team, despite Largo's assurances, might lose his nerve.

They swam on in the soft moonlit mist of the sea. At first there was nothing but a milky void below them, but then the coral shelf of the island showed up, climbing steeply towards the surface. Sea fans, like small shrouds in the moonlight, waved softly, beckoning, and the clumps and trees of coral were grey and enigmatic. It was because of these things, the harmless underwater mysteries that make the skin crawl on the inexperienced, that Largo had decided to lead the disposal teams himself. Out in the open, where the plane had foundered, the eye of the big searchlight made, with the known object of the plane itself, the underwater world into the semblance of a big room. But this was different. This grey-white world needed the contempt of a swimmer who had experienced these phantom dangers a thousand times before. That was the main reason why Largo led the teams. He also wanted to know exactly how the two grey sausages were stored away. It could happen, if things went wrong, that he would have to salvage them himself.

The underpart of the small island had been eroded by the waves so that, seen from below, it resembled a thick mushroom. Under the umbrella of coral there was a wide fissure, a dark wound in the side of the stem. Largo made for it and, when he was close, switched on his torch. Beneath the umbrella of coral it was dark. The yellow light of the torch showed up the minute life of an inshore coral community–the pale sea urchins and the fierce black spines of sea-eggs, the shifting underbrush of seaweeds, the yellow and blue seeking antennae of a langouste, the butterfly and angel fish, fluttering like moths in the light, a coiled bêche de mer, a couple of meandering sea-caterpillars and the black and green jelly of a sea-hare.

Largo lowered the black fins on his feet, got his balance on a ledge, and looked round, shining his torch on the rock so that the two teams could get a foothold. Then he waved them on and into the smooth broad fissure that showed a glimmer of moonlight at its far end inside the centre of the rock. The underwater cave was only about ten yards long. Largo led the teams one after the other through and into the small chamber that might once perhaps have been a wonderful repository for a different kind of treasure. From the chamber a narrow fissure led to the upper air and this would certainly become a fine blow-hole in a storm, though it would be unlikely that fishermen would be close enough to the Dog Shoal in a storm to see the water fountaining out of the centre of the island. Above the present waterline in the chamber, Largo's men had hammered stanchions into the rock to form cradles for the two atomic weapons with leather straps to hold them secure against any weather. Now, one by one, the two teams lifted the rubber packages up on to the iron bars and made them secure. Largo examined the result and was satisfied. The weapons would be ready for him when he needed them. In the meantime such radiation as there was would be quarantined within this tiny rock a hundred miles from Nassau and his men and his ship would be clean and innocent as snow.

The five men trudged calmly back to the ship and into the hold through the hatch. To the boom of the engines the bows of the *Disco* lifted slowly out of the water and the beautiful ship, streamlined like the gondola of some machine of the air rather than of the sea, skimmed off on the homeward journey.

Largo stripped off his equipment and, with a towel round his slim waist, went forrard to the radio cabin. He had missed the midnight call. It was now one fifteen–seven fifteen in the morning for Blofeld.

Largo thought of this while contact was being made. Blofeld would be sitting there, haggard perhaps, probably unshaven. There would be coffee beside him, the last of an endless chain of cups. Largo could smell it. Now Blofeld would be able to take a taxi to the Turkish baths in the Rue Aubert, his resort when there were tensions to be dissipated. And there, at last, he would sleep.

'Number 1 speaking.'

'Number 2 listening.'

'Phase III completed. Phase III completed. Successful. One a.m. here. Closing down.'

'I am satisfied.'

Largo stripped off the earphones. He thought to himself, 'So am I! We are more than three-quarters home. Now only the devil can stop us.'

He went in to the stateroom and carefully made himself a tall glass of his favourite drink–crème de menthe frappé with a maraschino cherry on top.

He sipped it delicately to the end and ate the cherry. Then he took one more cherry out of the bottle, slipped it into his mouth, and went up on the bridge.

Chapter Eleven

Domino

The girl in the sapphire blue MG two-seater shot down the slope of Parliament Street and at the junction with Bay Street executed an admirable change through third into second. She gave a quick glance to the right, correctly estimated the trot of the straw-hatted horse in the shafts of the rickety cab with the gay fringe, and swerved out of the side street left-handed. The horse jerked back his head indignantly and the coachman stamped his foot up and down on the big Bermuda bell. The disadvantage of the beautiful deep ting-tong, ting-tong of the Bermuda carriage bell is that it cannot possibly sound angry, however angrily you may sound it. The girl gave a cheerful wave of a sunburned hand, raced up the street in second, and stopped in front of The Pipe of Peace, the Dunhills of Nassau.

Not bothering to open the low door of the MG, the girl swung one brown leg and then the other over the side of the car, showing her thighs under the pleated cream cotton skirt almost to her waist, and slipped to the pavement. By now the cab was alongside. The cabby reined in. He was mollified by the gaiety and beauty of the girl. He said, 'Missy, you done almost shaved de whiskers off of Old Dreamy here. You wanna be more careful.'

The girl put her hands on her hips. She didn't like being told anything by anyone. She said sharply, 'Old Dreamy yourself. Some people have got work to do. Both of you ought to be put out to grass instead of cluttering up the streets getting in everyone's way.'

The ancient Negro opened his mouth, thought better of it, said a pacifying 'Hokay, Missy. Hokay,' flicked at his horse and moved on, muttering to himself. He turned on his seat to get another look at the she-devil, but she had already disappeared into the shop. 'Dat's a fine piece of gal,' he said inconsequentially, and put his horse into an ambling trot.

Twenty yards away, James Bond had witnessed the whole scene. He felt the same way about the girl as the cabby did. He also knew who she was. He quickened his step and pushed through the striped sun-blinds into the blessed cool of the tobacconist's.

The girl was standing at a counter arguing with one of the assistants. 'But I tell you I don't want Senior Service. I tell you I want a cigarette that's so disgusting that I shan't want to smoke it. Haven't you got a cigarette that stops people smoking? Look at all that.' She waved a hand towards the stacked shelves. 'Don't tell me some of those don't taste horrible.'

The man was used to crazy tourists and anyway the Nassavian doesn't get excited. He said, 'Well, Mam . . .' and turned and languidly looked along the shelves.

Bond said sternly to the girl, 'You can choose between two kinds of cigarette if you want to smoke less.'

She looked sharply up at him. 'And who might you be?'

'My name's Bond, James Bond. I'm the world's authority on giving up smoking. I do it constantly. You're lucky I happen to be handy.'

The girl looked him up and down. He was a man she hadn't seen before in Nassau. He was about six feet tall and somewhere in his middle thirties. He had dark, rather cruel good looks and very clear blue-grey eyes that were now observing her inspection sardonically. A scar down his right cheek showed pale against a tan so mild that he must have only recently come to the island. He was wearing a very dark blue lightweight single-breasted suit over a cream silk shirt and a black knitted silk tie. Despite the heat, he looked cool and clean, and his only concession to the tropics appeared to be the black saddle-stitched sandals on his bare feet.

It was an obvious attempt at a pick-up. He had an exciting face, and authority. She decided to go along. But she wasn't going to make it easy. She said coldly, 'All right. Tell me.'

'The only way to stop smoking is to stop it and not start again. If you want to *pretend* to stop for a week or two, it's no good trying to ration yourself.

You'll become a bore and think about nothing else. And you'll snatch at a cigarette every time the hour strikes or whatever the intervals may be. You'll behave greedily. That's unattractive. The other way is to have cigarettes that are either too mild or too strong. The mild ones are probably the best for you.' Bond said to the attendant, 'A carton of Dukes, king-size with filter.' Bond handed them to the girl. 'Here, try these. With the compliments of Faust.'

'Oh, but I can't. I mean . . .'

But Bond had already paid for the carton and for a packet of Chesterfields for himself. He took the change and followed her out of the shop. They stood together under the striped awning. The heat was terrific. The white light on the dusty street, the glare reflected back off the shop fronts opposite and off the dazzling limestone of the houses made them both screw up their eyes. Bond said, 'I'm afraid smoking goes with drinking. Are you going to give them both up or one by one?'

She looked at him quizzically. 'This is very sudden, Mr–er–Bond. Well, all right. But somewhere out of the town. It's too hot here. Do you know The Wharf out beyond the Fort Montague? Bond noticed that she looked quickly up and down the street. 'It's not bad. Come on. I'll take you there. Mind the metal. It'll raise blisters on you.'

Even the white leather of the upholstery burned through to Bond's thighs. But he wouldn't have minded if his suit had caught fire. This was his first sniff at the town and already he had got hold of the girl. And she was a fine girl at that. Bond caught hold of the leather-bound safety grip on the dashboard as the girl did a sharp turn up Frederick Street and another one on to Shirley.

Bond settled himself sideways so that he could look at her. She wore a gondolier's broadrimmed straw hat, tilted impudently down over her nose. The pale blue tails of its ribbon streamed out behind. On the front of the ribbon was printed in gold 'M/Y DISCO VOLANTE'. Her short-sleeved silk shirt was in half-inch vertical stripes of pale blue and white and, with the pleated cream skirt, the whole get-up reminded Bond vaguely of a sunny day at Henley Regatta. She wore no rings and no jewellery except for a rather masculine square gold wrist-watch with a black face. Her flat-heeled sandals were of white doeskin. They matched her broad white doeskin belt and the sensible handbag that lay, with a black and white striped silk scarf, on the seat between them. Bond knew a good deal about her from the immigration form, one among a hundred, which he had been studying that morning. Her name was Dominetta Vitali. She had been born in Bolzano in the Italian Tyrol and therefore probably had as much Austrian as Italian blood in her. She was twenty-nine and gave her profession as 'actress'. She had arrived six months before in the *Disco* and it was entirely understood that she was mistress to the owner of the yacht, an Italian called Emilio Largo. 'Whore', 'tart', 'prostitute' were not words Bond used about women unless they were professional streetwalkers or the inmates of a brothel, and when Harling, the Commissioner of Police, and Pitman, Chief of Immigration and Customs, had described her as an 'Italian tart' Bond had reserved judgment. Now he knew he had been right. This was an independent, a girl of authority and character. She might like the rich, gay life but, so far as Bond was concerned, that was the right kind of girl. She might sleep with men, obviously did, but it would be on her terms and not on theirs.

Women are often meticulous and safe drivers, but they are very seldom first-class. In general Bond regarded them as a mild hazard and he always gave them plenty of road and was ready for the unpredictable. Four women in a car he regarded as the highest danger potential, and two women as nearly as lethal. Women together cannot keep silent in a car, and when women talk they have to look into each other's faces. An exchange of words is not enough. They have to see the other person's expression, perhaps in order to read behind the other's words or to analyse the reaction to their own. So two women in the front seat of a car constantly distract each other's attention from the road ahead and four women are more than doubly dangerous, for the driver not only has to hear, and see, what her companion is saying but also, for women are like that, what the two behind are talking about.

But this girl drove like a man. She was entirely focused on the road ahead and on what was going on in her driving mirror, an accessory rarely used by women except for making up their faces. And, equally rare in a woman, she took a man's pleasure in the feel of her machine, in the timing of her gear changes, and the use of her brakes.

She didn't talk to Bond or seem to be aware of him, and this allowed him to continue his inspection without inhibition. She had a gay, to-hell-with-you face that, Bond thought, would become animal in passion. In bed she would fight and bite and then suddenly melt into hot surrender. He could almost see the proud, sensual mouth bare away from the even white teeth in a snarl of desire and then, afterwards, soften into a half-pout of loving slavery. In profile the eyes were soft charcoal slits such as you see on some birds, but in the shop Bond had seen them full face. Then they had been fierce and direct with a golden flicker in the dark brown that held much the same message as the mouth. The profile, the straight, small uptilted nose, the determined set of the chin, and the clean-cut sweep of the jawline were as decisive as a royal command, and the way the head was set on the neck had the same authority–the poise one associates with imaginary princesses. Two features modified the clean-cut purity of line–a soft, muddled Brigitte Bardot haircut that escaped from under the straw hat in an endearing disarray, and two deeply cut but soft dimples which could only have been etched by a sweet if rather ironic smile that Bond had not yet seen. The sunburn was not overdone and her skin had none of that dried, exhausted sheen that can turn the texture of even the youngest skin into something more like parchment. Beneath the gold, there was an earthy warmth in the cheeks that suggested a good healthy peasant strain from the Italian Alps and her breasts, high-riding and deeply V-ed, were from the same stock. The general impression, Bond decided, was of a wilful, high-tempered, sensual girl–a beautiful Arab mare who would only allow herself to be ridden by a horseman with steel thighs and velvet hands, and then only with curb and saw-bit–and then only when he had broken her to bridle and saddle. Bond thought that he would like to try his strength against hers. But that must be for some other time. For the moment another man was in the saddle. He would first have to be unhorsed. And anyway, what the hell was he doing fooling with these things? There was a job to be done. The devil of a job.

The MG swept out of Shirley Street on to Eastern Road and followed the coast. Across the wide harbour entrance were the emerald and turquoise shoals of Athol Island. A deep-sea fishing boat was passing over them, the two tall antennae of her twelve-foot rods streaming their lines astern. A fast motorboat came hammering by close in shore, the water-skier on the line behind her executing tight slaloms across the waves of her wake. It was a sparkling, beautiful day and Bond's heart lifted momentarily from the trough of indecision and despondency created by an assignment that, particularly since his arrival at dawn that day, seemed increasingly time-wasting and futile.

The Bahamas, the string of a thousand islands that straggle five hundred miles south-east from just east of the coast of Florida to just north of Cuba, from latitude 27° down to latitude 21°, were, for most of three hundred years, the haunt of every famous pirate of the Western Atlantic, and today tourism makes full use of the romantic mythology. A road-sign said '*Blackbeard's Tower 1 mile*' and another '*Gunpowder Wharf. Sea Food. Native Drinks. Shady Garden. First Left*'.

A sand track showed on their left. The girl took it and pulled up in front of a ruined stone warehouse against which leant a pink clapboard house with white window-frames and a white Adam style doorway over which hung a brightly painted inn sign of a powder keg with a skull and crossbones on it. The girl drove the MG into the shade of a clump of casuarinas and they got out and went through the door and through a small dining-room with red and white checked covers and out on to a terrace built on the remains of a stone wharf. The terrace was shaded by sea-almond trees trimmed into umbrellas. Trailed by a shuffling coloured waiter with soup stains down his white coat, they chose a cool table on the edge of the terrace looking over the water. Bond glanced at his watch. He said to the girl, 'It's exactly midday. Do you want to drink solid or soft?'

The girl said, 'Soft. I'll have a double Bloody Mary with plenty of Worcester sauce.'

Bond said, 'What do you call hard? I'll have a vodka and tonic with a dash of bitters.' The waiter said, 'Yassuh,' and mooched away.

'I call vodka-on-the-rocks hard. All that tomato juice makes it soft.' She hooked a chair towards her with one foot and stretched our her legs on it so that they were in the sun. The position wasn't comfortable enough. She kicked off her sandals and sat back, satisfied. She said, 'When did you arrive? I haven't seen you about. When it's like this, at the end of the season, one expects to know most of the faces.'

'I got in this morning. From New York. I've come to look for a property. It struck me that now would be better than in the season. When all the millionaires are here the prices are hopeless. They may come down a bit now they're gone. How long have you been here?'

'About six months. I came out in a yacht, the *Disco Volante*. You may have seen her. She's anchored up the coast. You probably flew right over her coming in to land at Windsor Field.'

'A long low streamlined affair? Is she yours? She's got beautiful lines.'

'She belongs to a relative of mine.' The eyes watched Bond's face.

'Do you stay on board?'

'Oh no. We've got a beach property. Or rather we've taken it. It's a place called Palmyra. Just opposite where the yacht is. It belongs to an Englishman. I believe he wants to sell it. It's very beautiful. And it's a long way away from the tourists. It's at a place called Lyford Key.'

'That sounds the sort of place I'm looking for.'

'Well, we'll be gone in about a week.'

'Oh.' Bond looked into her eyes. 'I'm sorry.'

'If you've got to flirt, don't be obvious.' Suddenly the girl laughed. She looked contrite. The dimples remained. 'I mean, I didn't really mean that–not the way it sounded. But I've spent six months listening to that kind of thing from these silly old rich goats and the only way to shut them up is to be rude. I'm not being conceited. There's no one under sixty in this place. Young people can't afford it. So any woman who hasn't got a harelip or a moustache–well not even a moustache would put them off. They'd probably like it. Well I mean absolutely any girl makes these old goats get their bifocals all steamed up.' She laughed again. She was getting friendly. 'I expect you'll have just the same effect on the old women with pince-nez and blue rinses.'

'Do they eat boiled vegetables for lunch?'

'Yes, and they drink carrot juice and prune juice.'

'We won't get on then. I won't sink lower than conch chowder.'

She looked at him curiously. 'You seem to know a lot about Nassau.'

'You mean about conch being an aphrodisiac? That's not only a Nassau idea. It's all over the world where there are conchs.'

'Is it true?'

'Island people have it on their wedding night. I haven't found it have any effect on me.'

'Why?' She looked mischievous. 'Are you married?'

'No.' Bond smiled across into her eyes. 'Are you?'

'No.'

'Then we might both try some conch soup some time and see what happens.'

'That's only a little better than the millionaires. You'll have to try harder.'

The drinks came. The girl stirred hers with a finger, to mix in the brown sediment of Worcester sauce, and drank half of it. She reached for the carton of Dukes, broke it open, and slit a packet with her thumbnail. She took out a cigarette, sniffed it cautiously, and lit it with Bond's lighter. She inhaled deeply and blew out a long plume of smoke. She said doubtfully, 'Not bad. At least the smoke looks like smoke. Why did you say you were such an expert on giving up smoking?'

'Because I've given it up so often.' Bond thought it time to get away from the small-talk. He said, 'Why do you talk such good English? Your accent sounds Italian.'

'Yes, my name's Dominetta Vitali. But I was sent to school in England. To the Cheltenham Ladies College. Then I went to RADA to learn acting. The English kind of acting. My parents thought that was a ladylike way to be brought up. Then they were both killed in a train crash. I went back to Italy to earn my living. I remembered my English but'–she laughed without bitterness–'I soon forgot most of the rest. You don't get far in the Italian theatre by being able to walk about with a book balanced on your head.'

'But this relative with the yacht.' Bond looked out to sea. 'Wasn't he there to look after you?'

'No.' The answer was curt. When Bond made no comment she added. 'He's not exactly a relative, not a close one. He's a sort of close friend. A guardian.'

'Oh yes.'

'You must come and visit us on the yacht.' She felt that a bit of gush was needed. 'He's called Largo, Emilio Largo. You've probably heard. He's here on some kind of a treasure hunt.'

'Really?' Now it was Bond's turn to gush. 'That sounds rather fun. Of course I'd like to meet him. What's it all about? Is there anything in it?'

'Heaven knows. He's very secretive about it. Apparently there's some kind of a map. But I'm not allowed to see it and I have to stay ashore when he goes off prospecting or whatever he does. A lot of people have put up money for it, sort of shareholders. They've all just arrived. As we're going in a week or so, I suppose everything's ready and the real hunt's going to start any moment now.'

'What are the shareholders like? Do they seem sensible sort of people? The trouble with most treasure hunts is that either someone's been there before and sneaked off with the treasure or the ship's so deep in the coral you can't get at it.'

'They seem all right. Very dull and rich. Terribly serious for something as romantic as treasure hunting. They seem to spend all their time with Largo. Plotting and planning I suppose. And they never seem to go out in the sun or go bathing or anything. It's as if they didn't want to get sunburned. As far as I can gather, none of them have ever been in the tropics before. Just a typical bunch of stuffy businessmen. They're probably better than that. I haven't seen much of them. Largo's giving a party for them at the Casino tonight.'

'What do you do all day?'

'Oh, I fool around. Do a bit of shopping for the yacht. Drive around in the car. Bathe on other people's beaches when their houses are empty. I like underwater swimming. I've got an aqualung and I take one of the crew out or a fisherman. The crew are better. They all do it.'

'I used to do a bit. I've brought my gear. Will you show me some good bits of reef some time?'

The girl looked pointedly at her watch. 'I might do. It's time I went.' She got up. 'Thanks for the drink. I'm afraid I can't take you back. I'm going the other way. They'll get you a taxi here.' She shuffled her feet into her sandals.

Bond followed the girl through the restaurant to her car. She got in and pressed the starter. Bond decided to risk another snub. He said, 'Perhaps I'll see you at the Casino tonight, Dominetta.'

'P'raps.' She put the car pointedly into gear. She took another look at him. She decided that she did want to see him again. She said, 'But for God's sake don't call me Dominetta. I'm never called that. People call me Domino.' She gave him a brief smile, but it was a smile into the eyes. She raised a hand. The rear wheels spat sand and gravel and the little blue car whirled out along the driveway to the main road. It paused at the intersection and then, as Bond watched, turned right-handed towards Nassau.

Bond smiled. He said, 'Bitch,' and walked back into the restaurant to pay his bill and have a taxi called.

Chapter Twelve

The Man from the C.I.A.

The taxi took Bond out to the airport at the other end of the island by the Interfield Road. The man from the Central Intelligence Agency was due in by Pan American at 1.15. His name was Larkin, F. Larkin. Bond hoped he wouldn't be a muscle-bound ex-college man with a crew-cut and a desire to show up the incompetence of the British, the backwardness of their little Colony, and the clumsy ineptitude of Bond, in order to gain credit with his chief in Washington. Bond hoped that at any rate he would bring the equipment he had asked for before he left London through Section A, who looked after the liaison with C.I.A. This was the latest transmitter and receiver for agents in the field, so that the two of them could be independent of cable offices and have instant communication with London and Washington, and the most modern portable Geiger counters for operating both on land and under water. One of the chief virtues of C.I.A., in Bond's estimation, was the excellence of their equipment, and he had no false pride about borrowing from them.

New Providence, the island containing Nassau, the capital of the Bahamas, is a drab sandy slab of land fringed with some of the most beautiful beaches in the world. But the interior is nothing but a waste of low-lying scrub, casuarinas, mastic, and poison-wood with a large brackish lake at the western end. There are birds and tropical flowers and palm trees, imported fully grown from Florida, in the beautiful gardens of the millionaires round the coast, but in the middle of the island there is nothing to attract the eye but the skeleton fingers of spidery windmill pumps sticking up above the pine barrens, and Bond spent the ride to the airport reviewing the morning.

He had arrived at seven a.m. to be met by the Governor's A.D.C.–a mild error of security–and taken to the Royal Bahamian, a large old-fashioned hotel to which had recently been applied a thin veneer of American efficiency and tourist gimmicks–iced water in his room, a Cellophane- wrapped basket of dingy fruit 'with the compliments of the Manager', and a strip of 'sanitized' paper across the lavatory seat. After a shower and a tepid, touristy breakfast on his balcony overlooking the beautiful beach, he had gone up to Government House at nine o'clock for a meeting with the Commissioner of Police, the Chief of Immigration and Customs, and the Deputy Governor. It was exactly as he had imagined it would be. The MOST IMMEDIATES and the TOP SECRETS had made a superficial impact and he was promised full co-operation in every aspect of his assignment, but the whole business was clearly put down as a ridiculous flap and something that must not be allowed to interfere with the normal routine of running a small, sleepy colony, nor with the comfort and happiness of the tourists. Roddick, the Deputy Governor, a careful, middle-of-the-way man with a ginger moustache and gleaming pince-nez, had put the whole affair in a most sensible light. 'You see, Commander Bond, in our opinion–and we have most carefully debated all the possibilities, all the, er, angles, as our American friends would say–it is inconceivable that a large four-engined plane could have been hidden anywhere within the confines of the Colony. The only airstrip capable of taking such a plane–am I right, Harling?–is here in Nassau. So far as a landing on the sea is concerned, a, er, ditching I think they call it, we have been in radio contact with the Administrators on all the larger outer islands and the replies are all negative. The radar people at the meteorological station . . .'

Bond had interrupted at this point. 'Might I ask if the radar screen is manned round the clock? My impression is that the airport is very busy during the day, but that there is very little traffic at night. Would it be possible that the radar is not so closely watched at night?'

The Commissioner of Police, a pleasant, very military looking man in his forties, the silver buttons and insignia on whose dark blue uniform glittered as they only can when spit and polish is a main activity and there are plenty of batmen around, said judiciously, 'I think the Commander has a point there, sir. The Airport commandant admits that things do slacken off a bit when there's nothing scheduled. He hasn't got all that amount of staff and of course most of them are locals, sir. Good men, but hardly up to London Airport standards. And the radar at the met. station is only a G.C.A. set with a low horizon and range–mostly used for shipping.'

'Quite, quite.' The Deputy Governor didn't want to be dragged into a discussion about radar sets or the merits of Nassavian labour. 'There's certainly a point there. No doubt Commander Bond will be making his own inquiries. Now there was a request from the Secretary of State,' the title rolled sonorously forth, 'for details and comments on recent arrivals in the island, suspicious characters, and so forth. Mr Pitman?'

The Chief of Immigration and Customs was a sleek Nassavian with quick brown eyes and an ingratiating manner. He smiled pleasantly. 'Nothing out of the ordinary, sir. The usual mixture of tourists and businessmen and local people coming home. We were asked to have details for the past two weeks, sir.' He touched the briefcase on his lap. 'I have all the immigration forms here, sir. Perhaps Commander Bond would care to go through them with me.' The brown eyes flicked towards Bond and away. 'All the big hotels have house detectives. I could probably get him further details on any particular name. All passports were checked in the normal manner. There were no irregularities and none of these people was on our Wanted List.'

Bond said, 'Might I ask a question?'

The Deputy Governor nodded enthusiastically. 'Of course. Of course. Anything you like. We're all here to help.'

'I'm looking for a group of men. Probably ten or more. They probably stick together a good deal. Might be as many as twenty or thirty. I guess they would be Europeans. They probably have a ship or a plane. They may have been here for months or only a few days. I gather you have plenty of conventions coming to Nassau–salesmen, tourist associations, religious groups, heaven knows what all. Apparently they take a block of rooms in some hotel and hold meetings and so forth for a week or so. Is there anything like that going on at the moment?'

'Mr Pitman?'

'Well, of course we do have plenty of those sort of gatherings. Very welcome to the Tourist Board.' The Chief of Immigration smiled conspiratorially at Bond as if he had just given away a closely guarded secret. 'But in the last two weeks we've only had a Moral Rearmament Group at the Emerald Wave and the Tiptop Biscuit people at the Royal Bahamian. They've gone now. Quite the usual convention pattern. All very respectable.'

'That's just it, Mr Pitman. The people I'm looking for, the people who may have arranged to steal this plane, will certainly take pains to look respectable and behave in a respectable fashion. We're not looking for a bunch of flashy crooks. We think these must be very big people indeed. Now, is there anything like that on the island, a group of people like that?'

'Well,' the Chief of Immigration smiled broadly, 'of course we've got our annual treasure hunt going on.'

The Deputy Governor barked a quick, deprecating laugh. 'Now steady on, Mr Pitman. Surely we don't want them to get mixed up in all this, or heaven knows where we shall end. I can't believe Commander Bond wants to bother his head over a lot of rich beachcombers.'

The Commissioner of Police said doubtfully, 'The only thing is, sir–they do have a yacht, and a small plane for the matter of that. And I did hear that a lot of shareholders in the swindle had come in lately. Those points do tally with what the Commander was asking about. I admit it's ridiculous, but this man Largo's respectable enough for Commander Bond's requirements and his men have never once given us trouble. Unusual to have not even one case of drunkenness in a ship's crew in nearly six months.'

And Bond had leapt at the flimsy thread and had pursued it for another two hours–in the Customs building and in the Commissioner's office–and, as a result, he had gone walking in the town to see if he could get a look at Largo or any of his party or pick up any other shreds of gossip. As a result he had got a good look at Domino Vitali.

And now?

The taxi had arrived at the airport. Bond told the driver to wait and walked into the long low entrance hall just as the arrival of Larkin's flight was being announced over the Tannoy. He knew there would be the usual delay for customs and immigration. He went to the souvenir shop and bought a copy of the *New York Times*. In its usual discreet headlines it was still leading with the loss of the Vindicator. Perhaps it knew also about the loss of the atom bombs, because Arthur Krock, on the leader page, had a heavyweight column about the security aspects of the NATO alliance. Bond was half way through this when a quiet voice in his ear said, '007? Meet No. 000.'

Bond swung round. It was! It was Felix Leiter!

Leiter, his C.I.A. companion on some of the most thrilling cases in Bond's career, grinned and thrust the steel hook that was his right hand under Bond's arm. 'Take it easy, friend. Dick Tracy will tell all when we get out of here. Bags are out front. Let's go.'

Bond said, 'Well God damn it! You old so-and-so! Did you know it was going to be me?'

'Sure. C.I.A. knows all.'

At the entrance Leiter had his luggage, which was considerable, put aboard Bond's taxi, and told the driver to take it to the Royal Bahamian. A man standing beside an undistinguished-looking black Ford Consul saloon left the car and came up. 'Mr Larkin? I'm from the Hertz company. This is the car you ordered. We hope she's what you want. You did specify something conventional.'

Leiter glanced casually at the car. 'Looks all right. I just want a car that'll go. None of those ritzy jobs with only room for a small blonde with a sponge bag. I'm here to do property work–not jazz it up.'

'May I see your New York licence, sir? Right. Then if you'll just sign here . . . and I'll make a note of the number of your Diner's Club card. When you go, leave the car anywhere you like and just notify us. We'll collect it. Have a good holiday, sir.'

They got into the car. Bond took the wheel. Leiter said that he'd have to practise a bit on what he called 'this Limey south-paw routine' of driving on the left, and anyway he'd be interested to see if Bond had improved his cornering since their last drive together.

When they were out of the airport Bond said, 'Now go ahead and tell. Last time we met you were with Pinkertons. What's the score?'

'Drafted. Just damned well drafted. Hell, anyone would think there was a war on. You see, James, once you've worked for C.I.A., you're automatically put on the reserve of officers when you leave. Unless you've been cashiered for not eating the code-book under fire or something. And apparently my old Chief, Allen Dulles that is, just didn't have the men to go round when the President sounded the fire alarm. So I and twenty or so other guys were just pulled in–drop everything, twenty-four hours to report. Hell! I thought the Russians had landed! And then they tell me the score and to pack my bathing trunks and my spade and bucket and come on down to Nassau. So of course I griped like hell. Asked them if I shouldn't brush up on my Canasta game and take some quick lessons in the Cha-cha. So then they unbuttoned and told me I was to team up with you down here and I thought maybe if that old bastard of yours, N or M or whatever you call him, had sent you down here with your old equalizer, there might be something cooking in the pot after all. So I picked up the gear you'd asked for from Admin., packed the bow and arrows instead of the spade and bucket, and here I am. And that's that. Now you tell, you old sonofabitch. Hell, it's good to see you.'

Bond took Leiter through the whole story, point by point from the moment he had been summoned to M's office the morning before. When he came to the shooting outside his headquarters, Leiter stopped him.

'Now what do you make of that, James? In my book that's a pretty funny coincidence. Have you been fooling around with anybody's wife lately? Sounds more like around The Loop in Chicago than a mile or so from Piccadilly.'

Bond said seriously, 'It makes no sense to me, and none to anyone else. The only man who might have had it in for me, recently that is, is a crazy bastard I met down at a sort of clinic place I had to go to on some blasted medical grounds.' Bond, to Leiter's keen pleasure, rather sheepishly gave details of his 'cure' at Shrublands. 'I bowled this man out as a member of a Chinese Tong, one of their secret societies, the Red Lightning Tong. He must have heard me getting the gen on his outfit from Records–on an open line from a call box in the place. Next thing, he damned near managed to murder me. Just for a lark, and to get even, I did my best to roast him alive.' Bond gave the details. 'Nice quiet place, Shrublands. You'd be surprised how carrot juice seems to affect people.'

'Where was this lunatic asylum?'

'Place called Washington. Modest little place compared with yours. Not far from Brighton.'

'And the letter was posted from Brighton.'

'That's the hell of a long shot.'

'I'll try another. One of the points our chaps brought up was that if a plane was to be stolen at night and landed at night, a full moon would be the hell of an aid to the job. But the plane was taken five days after the full. Just supposing your roast chicken was the letter-sender. And supposing the roasting forced him to delay sending the letter while he recovered. His employers would be pretty angry. Yes?'

'I suppose so.'

'And supposing they gave orders for him to be rubbed for inefficiency. And supposing the killer got to him just as he got to you to settle his private account. From what you tell me he wouldn't have lain down under what you did to him. Well, now. Just supposing all that. It adds up, doesn't it?'

Bond laughed, partly in admiration. 'You been taking mescalin or something. It's a damned good sequence for a comic strip, but these things don't happen in real life.'

'Planes with atom bombs don't get stolen in real life. Except that they do. You're slowing down, James. How many people would believe the files on some of the cases you and I have got mixed up in? Don't give me that crap about real life. There ain't no such animal.'

Bond said seriously, 'Well, look here, Felix. Tell you what I'll do. There's just enough sense in your story, so I'll put it on the machine to M tonight and see if the Yard can get anywhere with it. They could check with the clinic and the hospital in Brighton, if that's where he was taken, and they may be able to get on from there. Trouble is, wherever they get, there's nothing left of the man but his shoes, and I doubt if they'll catch up with the man on the motorbike. It looked a real pro job to me.'

'Why not? These hi-jackers sound like pros. It's a pro plan. It all fits all right. You go ahead and put it on the wire and don't be ashamed of saying it was my idea. My medal collection has got to looking a bit thin since I left the outfit.'

They pulled up under the portico of the Royal Bahamian and Bond gave the keys to the parking attendant. Leiter checked in and they went up to his room and sent for two double dry Martinis on the rocks and the menu.

From the pretentious dishes, 'For Your Particular Consideration', printed in Ornamental Gothic, Bond chose Native Seafood Cocktail Suprême followed by Disjointed Home Farm Chicken, Sauté au Cresson, which was described in italics as 'Tender Farm Chicken, Broiled to a Rich Brown, Basted with Creamery Butter and Disjointed for Your Convenience. Price 38/6 or dollars 5·35.' Felix Leiter went for the Baltic Herring in Sour Cream followed by 'Chopped Tenderloin of Beef, French Onion Rings (Our Renowned Beef is Chef Selected from the Finest Corn-fed, Mid-Western Cattle, and Aged to Perfection to Assure you of the Very Best). Price 40/3 or dollars 5·65.'

When they had both commented sourly and at length about the inflated bogosity of tourist hotel food and particularly the mendacious misuse of the English language to describe materials which had certainly been in various deep-freezes for at least six months, they settled down on the balcony to discuss Bond's findings of the morning.

Half an hour and one more double dry Martini later, their luncheon came. The whole thing amounted to about five shillings' worth of badly cooked rubbish. They ate in a mood of absentminded irritation, saying nothing. Finally Leiter threw down his knife and fork. 'This is Hamburger and bad Hamburger. The French onion rings were never in France and what's more,' he poked at the remains with a fork, 'they're not even rings. They're oval.' He looked belligerently across at Bond. 'All right, Hawkshaw. Where do we go from here?'

'The major decision is to eat out in future. The next is to pay a visit to the *Disco*–now.' Bond got up from the table. 'When we've done that, we'll have to decide whether or not these people are hunting pieces of eight or £100,000,000. Then we'll have to report progress.' Bond waved at the packing cases in a corner of the room. 'I've got the loan of a couple of rooms on the top floor of police headquarters here. The Commissioner's co-operative and a solid character. These Colonial Police are good, and this one's a cut above the rest. We can set up the radio there and make contact this evening. Tonight there's this party at the Casino. We'll go to that and see if any of these faces mean anything to either of us. The first thing's to see if the yacht's clean or not. Can you break that Geiger counter out?'

'Sure. And it's a honey.' Leiter went to the cases, selected one, and opened it. He came back carrying what looked like a Rolleiflex camera in a portable leather case. 'Here, give me a hand.' Leiter took off his wrist-watch and strapped on what appeared to be another watch. He slung the 'camera' by its strap over his left shoulder. 'Now run those wires from the watch up my sleeve and down inside my coat. Right. Now these two small plugs go through these holes in my coat pocket and into the two holes in the box. Got it? Now we're all fixed.' Leiter stood back and posed. 'Man with a camera and a wrist-watch.' He unbuttoned the flap of the camera. 'See? Perfectly good lenses and all that. Even a button to press in case you have to seem to take a picture. But in back of the make-believe there's a metal valve, a circuit, and batteries. Now take a look at this watch. And it is a watch.' He held it under Bond's eyes. 'Only difference is that it's a very small watch mechanism and that sweep second-hand is a meter that takes the radio-active count. Those wires up the sleeve hitch it on to the machine. Now then. You're still wearing that old wrist-watch of yours with the big phosphorous numerals. So I walk round the room for a moment to get the background count. That's basic. All sorts of things give off radiation of some sort. And I take an occasional glance at my watch–nervous type, and I've got an appointment coming up. Now here, by the bathroom, all that metal is giving off something and my watch is registering positive, but very little. Nothing else in the room and I've established the amount of background interference I'll have to discount when I start to get hot. Right? Now I come close up to you and my camera's only a few inches away from your hand. Here, take a look. Put your watch right up against the counter. See! The sweephand is getting all excited. Move your watch away and it loses interest. It's those phosphorous numerals of yours. Remember the other day one of the watch companies withdrew an air-pilots' watch from the market because the Atomic Energy people got fussy? Same thing. They thought this particular pilots' watch, with the big phosphorescent numerals, was giving off too much radiation to be good for the wearer. Of course,' Leiter patted the camera case, 'this is a special job. Most types give off a clicking sound and if you're prospecting for uranium, which is the big market for these machines, you wear earphones to try and pick up the stuff underground. For this job we don't need anything so sensitive. If we get near where those bombs are hidden, this damned sweephand'll go right off the dial. Okay? So let's go hire ourselves a sixpenny sick and pay a call on the ocean greyhound.'

Chapter Thirteen

'My Name is Emilio Largo'

Leiter's 'sixpenny sick' was the hotel launch, a smart Chrysler-engined speedboat that said it would be 20 dollars an hour. They ran out westwards from the harbour, past Silver Cay, Long Cay and Balmoral Island, and round Delaporte Point. Five miles further down the coast, encrusted with glittering seashore properties the boatman said cost £400 per foot of beach frontage, they rounded Old Fort Point and came upon the gleaming white and dark blue ship lying with two anchors out in deep water just outside the reef. Leiter whistled. He said in an awestruck voice, 'Boy, is that a piece of boat! I'd sure like to have one of those to play with in my bath.'

Bond said, 'She's Italian. Built by a firm called Rodrigues at Messina. Thing called an *Aliscafo*. She's got a hydrofoil under the hull and when she gets going you let this sort of skid down and she rises up and practically flies. Only the screws and a few feet of the stern stay in the water. The Police Commissioner says she can do 50 knots in calm water. Only good for inshore work of course, but they can carry upwards of a hundred passengers when they're designed as fast ferries. Apparently this one's been designed for about forty. The rest of the space is taken up with the owner's quarters and cargo space. Must have cost damned near a quarter of a million.'

The boatman broke in. 'They say on Bay Street that she goin' go after the treasure these next few days or so. All the people that own share in the gold come in a few days ago. Then she spen' one whole night doin' a final recce. They say is down Exhuma way, or over by Watlings Island. Guess you folks know that's where Columbus make him first landfall on this side of the Atlantic. Around fourteen ninety somethin'. But could be anywhere down there. They's always been talk of treasure down 'mongst the Ragged Islands–even as far as Crooked Island. Fact is she sail out southward. Hear her myself, right until her engines died away. East by south-east I'da say.' The boatman spat discreetly over the side. 'Must be plenty heap of treasure with the cost of that ship and all the money they throwing 'way. Every time she go to the Hoiling Wharf they say the bill's five hundred pound.'

Bond said casually, 'Which night was it they did the final recce?'

'Night after she hoiled. That'd be two nights ago. Sail round six.'

The blank portholes of the ship watched them approach. A sailor polishing brass round the curve of the enclosed dome that was the bridge walked through the hatch into the bridge and Bond could see him talking into a mouthpiece. A tall man in white ducks and a very wide mesh singlet appeared on deck and observed them through binoculars. He called something to the sailor, who came and stood at the top of the ladder down the starboard side. When their launch came alongside, the man cupped his hands and called down, 'What is your business please? Have you an appointment?'

Bond called back, 'It's Mr Bond, Mr James Bond. From New York. I have my attorney here. I have an inquiry to make about Palmyra, Mr Largo's property.'

'One moment please.' The sailor disappeared and returned accompanied by the man in white ducks and singlet. Bond recognized him from the police description. He called down cheerfully, 'Come aboard, come aboard.' He gestured for the sailor to go down and help fend the launch. Bond and Leiter climbed out of the launch and went up the ladder.

Largo held out a hand. 'My name is Emilio Largo. Mr Bond? And . . .?'

'Mr Larkin, my attorney from New York. Actually I'm English, but I have property in America.' They shook hands. 'I'm sorry to bother you, Mr Largo, but it's about Palmyra, the property I believe you rent from Mr Bryce.'

'Ah yes, of course.' The beautiful teeth gleamed warmth and welcome. 'Come on down to the stateroom, gentlemen. I'm sorry I am not properly dressed to receive you.' The big brown hands caressed his flanks, the wide mouth turned down in deprecation. 'My visitors usually announce themselves on the ship-to-shore. But if you will forgive the informality . . .' Largo allowed the phrase to die on the air and ushered them through a low hatch and down a few aluminium steps into the main cabin. The rubber-lined hatch hissed to behind him.

It was a fine large cabin panelled in mahogany with deep wine-red carpet and comfortable dark blue leather club chairs. The sun shining through the slats of venetian blinds over the broad square ports added a touch of gay light to an otherwise rather sombre and masculine room, its long centre table littered with papers and charts, glass-fronted cabinets containing fishing gear and an array of guns and other weapons, and a black rubber underwater diving suit and aqualung suspended, almost like the skeleton in a sorcerer's den, from a rack in one corner. The air-conditioning made the cabin deliciously cool, and Bond felt his damp shirt slowly freeing itself from his skin.

'Please take a chair, gentlemen.' Largo carelessly brushed aside the charts and papers on the table as if they were of no importance. 'Cigarettes?' He placed a large silver box between them. 'And now what can I get you to drink?' He went to the loaded sideboard. 'Something cool and not too strong perhaps? A Planter's Punch? Gin and tonic. Or there are various beers. You must have had a hot journey in that open launch. I would have sent my boat for you if only I had known.'

They both asked for a plain tonic. Bond said, 'I'm very sorry to barge in like this, Mr Largo. No idea I could have got you on the telephone. We just got in this morning and as I've only a few days I have to get a move on. The point is, I'm looking for a property down here.'

'Oh yes?' Largo brought the glasses and bottles of tonic to the table and sat down so that they formed a comfortable group. 'What a good idea. Wonderful place. I've been here for six months and already I'd like to stay for ever. But the prices they're asking—' Largo threw up his hands. 'These Bay Street pirates. And the millionaires, they are even worse. But you are wise to come at the end of the season. Perhaps some of the owners are disappointed not to have sold. Perhaps they will not open their mouths so wide.'

'That's what I thought.' Bond sat comfortably back and lit a cigarette. 'Or rather what my lawyer, Mr Larkin, advised.' Leiter shook his head pessimistically. 'He had made some inquiries and he frankly advised that real estate values down here have gone mad.' Bond turned politely towards Leiter to bring him into the conversation. 'Isn't that so?'

'Daft, Mr Largo, quite daft. Worse even than Florida. Out of this world. I wouldn't advise any client of mine to invest at these prices.'

'Quite so.' Largo obviously didn't want to get drawn too deeply into these matters. 'You mentioned something about Palmyra. Is there anything I can do to help in that respect?'

Bond said, 'I understand you have a lease of the property, Mr Largo. And there is talk that you may be leaving the house before long. Only gossip of course. You know what they are in these small islands. But it sounds more or less what I'm looking for and I gather the owner, this Englishman, Bryce, might sell if he got the right price. What I was going to ask you,' Bond looked apologetic, 'was whether we might drive out and look the place over. Some time when you weren't there of course. Any time that might suit you.'

Largo flashed his teeth warmly. He spread his hands. 'But of course, of course, my dear fellow. Whenever you wish. There is no one in residence but my niece and a few servants. And she is out most of the time. Please just call her on the telephone. I shall tell her that you will be doing so. It is indeed a charming property–so imaginative. A beautiful piece of design. If only all rich men had such good taste.'

Bond got to his feet and Leiter followed suit. 'Well that's extraordinarily kind of you, Mr Largo. And now we'll leave you in peace. Perhaps we may meet again in the town some time. You must come and have lunch. But,' Bond poured admiration and flattery into his voice, 'with a yacht like this, I don't suppose you ever want to come ashore. Must be the only one on this side of the Atlantic. Didn't one used to run between Venice and Trieste? I seem to remember reading about it somewhere.'

Largo grinned his pleasure. 'Yes, that is right, quite right. They are also on the Italian lakes. For passenger traffic. Now they are buying them in South America. A wonderful design for coastal waters. She only draws four feet when the hydrofoil is operating.'

'I suppose accommodation's the problem?'

It is a weakness of all men, though not necessarily of all women, to love their material possessions. Largo said, with a trace of pricked vanity, 'No, no. I think you will find that is not so. You can spare five minutes? We are rather crowded at the moment. You have heard no doubt of our treasure hunt?' He looked sharply at them as a man would who expects ridicule. 'But we will not discuss that now. No doubt you do not believe in these things. But my associates in the affair are all on board. With the crew, there are forty of us. You will see that we are not cramped. You would like?' Largo gestured to the door in the rear of the stateroom.

Felix Leiter showed reluctance. 'You know, Mr Bond, that we have that meeting with Mr Harold Christie at five o'clock?'

Bond waved the objection aside. 'Mr Christie is a charming man. I know he won't mind if we are a few minutes late. I'd love to see over the ship if you're sure you can spare the time, Mr Largo.'

Largo said, 'Come. It will not take more than a few minutes. The excellent Mr Christie is a friend of mine. He will understand.' He went to the door and held it open.

Bond had been expecting the politeness. It would interfere with Leiter and his apparatus. He said firmly, 'Please go first Mr Largo. You will be able to tell us when to duck our heads.'

With more affabilities, Largo led the way.

Ships, however modern, are more or less the same–the corridors to port and starboard of the engine room, rows of cabin doors, which Largo explained were occupied, the large communal bathrooms, the galley, where two cheerful looking Italians in white smocks laughed at Largo's jokes about the food and seemed pleased with the visitors' interest, the huge engine room where the chief engineer and his mate, Germans it seemed, gave enthusiastic information about the powerful twin diesels and explained the hydraulics of the hydrofoil depressor–it was all exactly like visiting any other ship and saying the right things to the crew, using the right superlatives to the owner.

The short space of afterdeck was occupied by the little two-seater amphibian, painted dark blue and white to match the yacht, its wings now folded and its engine cowled against the sun, a big jolly-boat to hold about twenty men, and an electric derrick to hoist them in- and outboard. Bond, estimating the ship's displacement and her free-board, said casually, 'And the hold? More cabin space?'

'Just storage. And the fuel tanks of course. She is an expensive ship to run. We have to carry several tons. The ballast problem is important with these ships. When her bows come up, the fuel shifts aft. We have to have big lateral tanks to correct these things.' Talking fluently and expertly Largo led them back up the starboard passageway. They were about to pass the radio room when Bond said, 'You said you had ship-to-shore. What else do you carry? The usual Marconi short and long wave, I suppose. Could I have a look? Radio has always fascinated me.'

Largo said politely, 'Some other time, if you don't mind. I'm keeping the operator full time on met. reports. They're rather important to us at the moment.'

'Of course.'

They climbed up into the enclosed dome of the bridge, where Largo briefly explained the controls and then led them out on to the narrow deck space. 'So there you are,' said Largo. 'The good ship *Disco Volante*–the Flying Saucer. And she really does fly, I can assure you. I hope you and Mr Larkin will come for a short cruise one of these days. For the present,' he smiled with the hint of a secret shared, 'as you may have heard, we are rather busy.'

'Very exciting, this treasure business. Do you think you've got a good chance?'

'We like to think so.' Largo was deprecating. 'I only wish I could tell you more,' he waved an apologetic hand. 'Unfortunately, as they say, my lips are sealed. I hope you will understand.'

'Yes of course. You have your shareholders to consider. I only wish I was one so that I could come along. I suppose there's not room for another investor?'

'Alas no. The issue, as they say, is fully subscribed. It would have been very pleasant to have had you with us.' Largo held out a hand. 'Well, I see that Mr Larkin has been looking anxiously at his watch during our brief tour. We must not keep Mr Christie waiting any longer. It has been a great pleasure to meet you, Mr Bond. And you, Mr Larkin.'

With a further exchange of courtesies they went down the ladder to the waiting launch and got under way. There was a last wave from Mr Largo before he vanished through the hatch to the bridge.

They sat in the stern well away from the boatman. Leiter shook his head. 'Absolutely negative. Reaction around the engine room and the radio room, but that's normal. It was all normal, damnably normal. What did you make of him and the whole set up?'

'Same as you–damned normal. He looks what he says he is, and behaves that way. Not much crew about, but the ones we saw were either ordinary crew or wonderful actors. Only two small things struck me. There was no way down to the hold that I could see, but of course it could have been a manhole under the passage carpet. But then how do you get the stores he talked of down there? And there's the hell of a lot of space in that hold even if I don't know much about naval architecture. I'll do a check with the oiling wharf through the customs people and see just how much fuel he does carry. Then it's odd that we didn't see any of these shareholders. It was around three o'clock when we went on board and most of them may have been having siestas. But surely not all nineteen of them. What do they do in their cabins all the time? Another small thing. Did you notice that Largo didn't smoke and that there was no trace of tobacco smell anywhere in the ship? That's odd. Around forty men and not one of them is a smoker. If one had anything else to go on one would say that wasn't coincidence but discipline. The real pros don't drink or smoke. But I admit it's a damned long shot. Notice the Decca Navigator and the echo-sounder? Pretty expensive bits of equipment both of them. Fairly normal on a big yacht of course, but I'd have expected Largo to point them out when he was showing us the bridge. Rich men are proud of their toys. But that's only clutching at straws. I'd have said the whole outfit's as clean as a whistle if it wasn't for all that missing space we weren't shown. That talk about fuel and ballast sounded a bit glib to me. What do you think?'

'Same as you. There's at least half of that ship we didn't see. But then again there's a perfectly good answer to that. He may have got a stack of secret treasure-hunting gear down there he doesn't want anyone to see. Remember that merchant ship off Gibraltar during the war? The Italian frogmen used it as a base. Big sort of trap door affair cut in the hull below the waterline. I suppose he hasn't got something like that?'

Bond looked sharply at Leiter. 'The *Olterra*. One of the blackest marks against Intelligence during the whole war.' He paused. 'The *Disco* was anchored in about forty feet of water. Supposing they'd got the bombs buried in the sand below her. Would your Geiger counter have registered?'

'Doubt it. I've got an underwater model and we could go and have a sniff round when it gets dark. But really, James,' Leiter frowned impatiently, 'aren't we getting a bit off beam–seeing burglars under the bed? We've got damn-all to go on. Largo's a powerful looking piratical sort of chap, probably a bit of a crook where women are concerned. But what the hell have we got against him? Have you put a Trace through on him and on these shareholders and the crew members?'

'Yes. Put them all on the wire from Government House, Urgent Rates. We should get an answer by this evening. But look here, Felix,' Bond's voice was stubborn, 'there's a damned fast ship with a plane and forty men no one knows anything about. There's not another group or even an individual in the area who looks in the least promising. All right, so the outfit looks all right and its story seems to stand up. But just supposing the whole thing was a phoney–a damned good one of course, but then so it ought to be with all that's at stake. Take another look at the picture. These so-called shareholders all arrive just in time for June 3rd. On that night the *Disco* goes to sea and stays out till morning. Just supposing she rendezvous'd that plane in shallow water somewhere. Just suppose she picked up the bombs and put them away–in the sand under the ship, if you like. Anyway, somewhere safe and convenient. Just suppose all that and what sort of a picture do you get?'

'A B picture so far as I'm concerned, James.' Leiter shrugged resignedly. 'But I guess there's just enough to make it a lead.' He laughed sardonically. 'But I'd rather shoot myself than put it in tonight's report. If we're going to make fools of ourselves, we'd better do it well out of sight and sound of our chiefs. So what's on your mind? What comes next?'

'While you get our communications going, I'm going to check with the oiling wharf. Then we'll call up this Domino girl and try and get ourselves asked for a drink and have a quick look at Largo's shore base–this Palmyra. Then we go to the casino and look over the whole of Largo's group. And then,' Bond looked stubbornly at Leiter, 'I'm going to borrow a good man from the Police Commissioner to give me a hand, put on an aqualung and go out and have a sniff round the *Disco* with your other Geiger machine.'

Leiter said laconically, 'Destry Rides Again! Well, I'll go along with that, James. Just for old times' sake. But don't go and stub your toe on a sea-urchin or anything. I see there are free Cha-cha lessons in the ballroom of the Royal Bahamian tomorrow. We've got to keep fit for those. I guess there'll be nothing else in this trip for my memory book.'

Back in the hotel, a dispatch rider from Government House was waiting for Bond. He saluted smartly, handed over an O.H.M.S. envelope and got Bond's signed receipt in exchange. It was a cable from the Colonial Office 'Personal to the Governor'. The text was prefixed PROBOND. The cable read: 'YOUR 1107 RECORDS HAVE NOTHING REPEAT NOTHING ON THESE NAMES STOP INFORMATIVELY ALL STATIONS REPORT NEGATIVELY ON OPERATION THUNDERBALL STOP WHAT HAVE YOU QUERY.' The message was signed 'PRISM', which meant that M had approved it.

Bond handed the cable to Leiter.

Leiter read it. He said, 'See what I mean? We're on a bum steer. This is a thumb-twiddler. See you later in the Pineapple Bar for a dry Martini that's half a jumbo olive. I'll go send a postcard to Washington and ask them to send down a couple of WAVES. We're going to have time on our hands.'

Chapter Fourteen

Sour Martinis

As it turned out, the first half of Bond's programme for the evening went by the board. On the telephone, Domino Vitali said that it would not be convenient for them to see the house that evening. Her guardian and some of his friends were coming ashore. Yes it was indeed possible that they might meet at the Casino that evening. She would be dining on board and the *Disco* would then sail round and anchor off the Casino. But how would she be able to recognize him in the Casino? She had a very poor memory for faces. Would he perhaps wear a flower in his buttonhole or something?

Bond had laughed. He said that would be all right. He would remember her by her beautiful blue eyes. They were unforgettable. And the blue rinse that matched them. He had put the receiver down half way through the amused, sexy chuckle. He suddenly wanted to see her again very much.

But the movement of the ship altered his plans for the better. It would be much easier to reconnoitre her in the harbour. It would be a shorter swim and he would be able to go into the water under cover of the harbour police wharf. Equally, with her anchorage empty, it would be all the easier to survey the area where she had been lying. But if Largo moved the yacht about so nonchalantly was it likely the bombs, if there were any, would be hidden at the anchorage? If they were, surely the *Disco* would stand watch over them. Bond decided to put a decision aside until he had more, and more expert, information about the ship's hull.

He sat in his room and wrote his negative report to M. He read it through. It would be a depressing signal to get. Should he say anything about the wisp of a lead he was working on? No. Not until he had something solid. Wishful intelligence, the desire to please or reassure the recipient, was the most dangerous commodity in the whole realm of secret information. Bond could imagine the reaction in Whitehall where the *Thunderball* war-room would be ready, anxious to grasp at straws. M's careful 'I think we may conceivably have got a lead in the Bahamas. Absolutely nothing definite, but this particular man doesn't often go wrong on these things. Yes, certainly I'll check back and see if we can get a follow-up.' And the buzz would get around: 'M's on to something. Agent of his thinks he's got a lead. The Bahamas. Yes, I think we'd better tell the P.M.' Bond shuddered. The MOST IMMEDIATES would pour in to him: 'Elucidate your 1806.' 'Flash fullest details.' 'Premier wants detailed grounds for your 1806.' There would be no end to the flood. Leiter would get the same from C.I.A. The whole place would be in an uproar. Then, in answer to Bond's tatty little fragments of gossip and speculation, there would come the blistering: 'Surprised you should take this flimsy evidence seriously.' 'Futurely confine your signals to facts,' and, the final degradation, 'View speculative nature your 1806 and subsequents comma future signals must repeat must be joint and countersigned by CIA representative.'

Bond wiped his forehead. He unlocked the case containing his cipher machine, transposed his text, checked it again and went off to Police Headquarters where Leiter was sitting at his keyboard, the sweat of concentration pouring down his neck. Ten minutes later Leiter took off his earphones and handed over to Bond. He mopped his face with an already drenched handkerchief. 'First it's sunspots and I had to swap over to the emergency wavelength. There I found they'd put a baboon on the other end–you know, one of the ones that can write the whole of Shakespeare if you leave him at it long enough.' He angrily waved several pages of cipher groups. 'Now I've got to unscramble all this. Probably from Accounts about how much extra income tax this sunshine trip will cost me.' He sat down at a table and began cranking away at his machine.

Bond put his short message over quickly. He could see it being punched out on the tapes in one of those busy rooms on the eighth floor, going to the supervisor, being marked 'Personal for M, copy to OO Section and Records', then another girl hurrying off down the passage with the flimsy yellow forms on a clip file. He queried whether there was anything for him and signed off. He left Leiter and went down to the Commissioner's room.

Harling was sitting at his desk with his coat off, dictating to a police sergeant. He dismissed him, pushed a box of cigarettes over his desk to Bond and lit one himself. He smiled quizzically. 'Any progress?'

Bond told him that the Trace on the Largo group had been negative and that they had called on Largo and gone over the *Disco* with a Geiger counter. This also had been negative. Bond still wasn't satisfied. He told the Commissioner what he wanted to know about the fuel capacity of the *Disco* and the exact location of the fuel tanks. The Commissioner nodded amiably and picked up the telephone. He asked for a Sergeant Molony of the Harbour Police. He cradled the receiver and explained, 'We check all fuelling. This is a narrow harbour crammed with small craft, deep sea fishing boats and so on. Quite a fire hazard if something went wrong. We like to know what everyone is carrying and whereabouts in the ship. Just in case there's some fire-fighting to be done or we want a particular ship to get out of range in a hurry.' He went back to the telephone. 'Sergeant Molony?' He repeated Bond's questions, listened, said thank-you, and put the receiver down. 'She carries a maximum of 500 gallons of diesel. Took that amount on on the afternoon of June 2nd. She also carries about forty gallons of lubricating oil and a hundred gallons of drinking water–all carried amidships just forrard of the engine room. That what you want?'

This made nonsense of Largo's talk of lateral tanks and the difficult ballast problem and so forth. Of course he could have wanted to keep some secret treasure-hunting gear out of sight of the visitors, but at least there *was* something on board he wanted to hide, and, for all his show of openness, it was now established that Mr Largo might be a rich treasure hunter, but he was also an unreliable witness. Now Bond's mind was made up. It was the hull of the ship he wanted to have a look at. Leiter's mention of the *Olterra* had been a long shot, but it just might pay off.

Bond passed on a guarded version of his thoughts to the Commissioner. He told him where the *Disco* would be lying that night. Was there on the force a totally reliable man who could give him a hand with his underwater recce, and was there a sound aqualung, fully charged, available?

Harling gently asked if this was wise. He didn't exactly know the laws of trespass, but these seemed to be good citizens and they were certainly good spenders. Largo was very popular with everyone. Any kind of scandal, particularly if the police was involved, would create the hell of a stink in the Colony.

Bond said firmly, 'I'm sorry, Commissioner. I quite see your point. But these risks have to be run and I've got a job to do. Surely the Secretary of State's instructions are sufficient authority,' Bond fired his broadside, 'I could get specific orders from him, or from the Prime Minister for the matter of that, in about an hour if you feel it's necessary.'

The Commissioner shook his head. He smiled. 'No need to use the big guns, Commander. Of course you shall have what you want. I was just giving you the local reaction. I'm sure the Governor would have given you the same warning. This is a small puddle here. We're not used to the crash treatment from Whitehall. No doubt we'll get used to it if this flap lasts long enough. Now then. Yes, we've got plenty of what you want. We've got twenty men in the Harbour Salvage Unit. Have to. You'd be surprised how often a small boat gets wrecked in the fairway, just where some cruise ship's going to anchor. And of course there's the occasional body. I'll have Constable Santos assigned to you. Splendid chap. Native of Eleuthera, where he used to win all the swimming prizes. He'll have the gear you want where you want it. Now just give me the details . . .'

Back in his hotel, Bond took a shower, swallowed a double Bourbon Old Fashioned and threw himself down on his bed. He felt absolutely beat–the plane trip, the heat, the nagging sense that he was making a fool of himself in front of the Commissioner, in front of Leiter, in front of himself, added to the dangers, and probably futile oncs at that, of this ugly night swim, had built up tensions that could only be eased by sleep and solitude. He went out like a light–to dream of Domino being pursued by a shark with dazzling white teeth that suddenly became Largo, Largo who turned on him with those huge hands. They were coming closer, they reached slowly for him, they had him by the shoulder . . . But then the bell rang for the end of the round, and went on ringing.

Bond reached out a drugged hand for the receiver. It was Leiter. He wanted that Martini with the jumbo olive. It was nine o'clock. What the hell was Bond doing? Did he want someone to help with the zip?

The Pineapple Room was panelled in bamboo carefully varnished against termites. Wrought iron pineapples on the tables and against the wall contained segments of thick red candle, and more light was provided by illuminated aquaria let into the walls and by ceiling lights enclosed in pink glass star-fish. The Vinylite banquettes were in ivory white and the barman and the two waiters wore scarlet satin calypso shirts with their black trousers.

Bond joined Leiter at a corner table. They both wore white dinner jackets with their dress trousers. Bond had pointed up his rich, property-seeking status with a wine-red cummerbund. Leiter laughed. 'I nearly tied a gold-plated bicycle chain round my waist in case of trouble, but I remembered just in time that I'm a peaceful lawyer. I suppose it's right that you should get the girls on this assignment. I suppose I just stand by and arrange the marriage settlement and later the alimony. Waiter!'

Leiter ordered two dry Martinis. 'Just watch,' he said sourly.

The Martinis arrived. Leiter took one look at them and told the waiter to send over the barman. When the barman came, looking resentful, Leiter said, 'My friend, I asked for a Martini and not a soused olive.' He picked the olive out of the glass with the cocktail stick. The glass, that had been three-quarters full, was now half full. Leiter said mildly, 'This was being done to me while the only drink you knew was milk. I'd learned the basic economics of your business by the time you'd graduated to Coca Cola. One bottle of Gordon's Gin contains sixteen true measures–double measures that is, the only ones I drink. Cut the gin with three ounces of water and that makes it up to twenty-two. Have a jigger glass with a big steal in the bottom and a bottle of these fat olives and you've got around twenty-eight measures. Bottle of gin here costs only two dollars retail, let's say around a dollar sixty wholesale. You charge eighty cents for a Martini, one dollar sixty for two. Same price as a whole bottle of gin. And with your twenty-eight measures to the bottle, you've still got twenty-six left. That's a clear profit on one bottle of gin of around twenty-one dollars. Give you a dollar for the olives and the drop of vermouth and you've still got twenty dollars in your pocket. Now, my friend, that's too much profit, and if I could be bothered to take this Martini to the management and then to the Tourist Board, you'd be in trouble. Be a good chap and mix us two large dry Martinis without olives and with some slices of lemon peel separately. Okay? Right, then we're friends again.'

The barman's face had run through indignation, respect and then the sullenness of guilt and fear. Reprieved, but clutching at his scraps of professional dignity, he snapped his fingers for the waiter to take away the glasses. 'Okay, suh. Whatever you says. But we've got plenty overheads here and the majority of customers they doan complain.'

Leiter said, 'Well, here's one who's dry behind the ears. A good barman should learn to be able to recognize the serious drinker from the status-seeker who wants just to be seen in your fine bar.'

'Yassuh.' The barman moved away with Negro dignity.

Bond said. 'You got those figures right, Felix? I always knew one got clipped, but I thought only about a hundred per cent–not four or five.'

'Young man, since I graduated from Government service to Pinkertons, the scales have dropped from my eyes. The cheating that goes on in hotels and restaurants is more sinful than all the rest of the sin in the world. Anyone in a tuxedo before seven in the evening is a crocodile, and if he couldn't take a good bite at your pocketbook he'd take a good bite at your ear. The same goes for the rest of the consumer business, even when it's not wearing a tuxedo. Sometimes it gets me real mad to have to eat and drink the muck you get and then see what you're charged for it. Look at our damned lunch today. Six, seven bucks with fifteen per cent added for what's called service. And then the waiter hangs about for another fifty cents for riding up in the elevator with the stuff. Hell,' Leiter ran an angry hand through his mop of straw hair, 'just don't let's talk about it. I'm fit to bust a gut when I think about it.'

The drinks came. They were excellent. Leiter calmed down and ordered a second round. He said, 'Now let's get angry about something else.' He laughed curtly. 'Guess I'm just sore at being back in Government Service again watching all the taxpayers' money going down the drain on this wild goose chase. Mark you, James,' there was apology in Leiter's voice, 'I'm not saying this whole operation isn't a true bill, hell of a —— mess in fact, but what riles me is that we should be a couple of arse-end Charlies stuck down on this sand-spit while the other guys have got the hot spots–you know, places where something really may be happening–or at least likely to happen. Tell you the truth, I felt like a damned fool gumshoeing round that feller's yacht this afternoon with my little Geiger toy.' He looked keenly at Bond. 'You don't find you grow out of these things? I mean it's all right when there's a war on. But it seems kinda childish when peace is bustin' out all over.'

Bond said doubtfully, 'Of course I know what you mean, Felix. Perhaps it's just that in England we don't feel quite as secure as you do in America. The war just doesn't seem to have ended for us–Berlin, Cyprus, Kenya, Suez, let alone these jobs with people like SMERSH that I used to get tangled up in. There always seems to be something boiling up somewhere. Now this damned business. Dare say I'm taking it all too seriously, but there's something fishy going on around here. I checked up on that fuel problem and Largo certainly told us a lie.' Bond gave the details of what he had learned at police headquarters. 'I feel I've got to make sure tonight. You realize there's only about seventy hours to go? If I find anything, I suggest tomorrow we take a small plane and really run a search over as much of the area as we can. That plane's a big thing to hide even under water. You still got your licence?'

'Sure, sure.' Leiter shrugged his shoulders. 'I'll go along with you. Of course I will. If we find anything, perhaps the signal I got this evening won't look so damned silly after all.'

So this was what had put Leiter into such a vile temper! Bond said, 'What was that?'

Leiter took a drink and gazed morosely into his glass. 'Well, for my money it's just so much more attitudinizing by those power-struck fatcats at the Pentagon. But that sheaf of stuff I was waving about was a circular to all our men on this job to say that the Army and the Navy and the Air Force are holding themselves ready to give full support to C.I.A. if anything turns up. Think of that, dammit!' Leiter looked angrily at Bond. 'Think of the waste of fuel and manpower that must be going on all over the world keeping all these units at readiness! Just to show you, know what I've been allocated as my striking force?' Leiter gave a harsh, derisive laugh. 'Half-squadron of Super Sabre fighter bombers from Pensacola, and—' Leiter stabbed at Bond's forearm with a hard finger. 'And, my friend, the *Manta*! The —— *Manta*! Our latest —— atomic submarine!' When Bond smiled at all this vehemence, Leiter continued more reasonably: 'Mark you, it's not quite so idiotic as it sounds. These Sabres are on anti-submarine sweep duties anyway. Carrying depth charges. They have to be at readiness. And the *Manta* happens to be on some sort of a training cruise in the area, getting ready to go under the South Pole for a change I suppose, or some other damned promotion job to help along the Navy Estimates. But I ask you! Here's all these million dollars' worth of material on instant call from Ensign Leiter, commanding Room 201 in the Royal Bahamian Hotel! Not bad!'

Bond shrugged his shoulders. 'Seems to me your President is taking all this a bit more seriously than his Man in Nassau. I suppose our Chiefs of Staff have weighed in with our stuff on the other side of the Atlantic. Anyway, no harm in having the big battalions in the offing just in case Nassau Casino happens to be Target No. 1. By the way, what ideas have your people got about these targets? What have you got in this part of the world that fits in with SPECTRE's letter? We've only got the joint rocket base at a place called North-West Cay at the eastern end of the Grand Bahamas. That's about 150 miles north of here. Apparently the gear and prototypes we and your people have got there would easily be worth £100,000,000.'

'The only possible targets I've been given are Cape Canaveral, the naval base at Pensacola and, if the party really is going to take place in this area, Miami for Target No. 2, with Tampa as a possible runner-up. SPECTRE used the words "a piece of property belonging to the Western Powers". That sounds like some kind of installation to me–something like the uranium mines in the Congo, for instance. But a rocket base would fit all right. If we've got to take this thing seriously, I'd lay odds on Canaveral or this place on Grand Bahama. Only thing I can't understand, if they've got these bombs, how are they going to transport them to the target and set them off?'

'A submarine could do it–just lay one of the bombs offshore through a torpedo tube. Or a sailing dinghy for the matter of that. Apparently exploding these things is no problem so long as they recovered all the parts from the plane. Apparently you'd just have to insert some kind of fuse thing in the right place between the T.N.T. and the plutonium, and screw the impact fuse off the nose and fit a time fuse that would give you time to get a hundred miles away.' Bond added casually, 'Have to have an expert who knows the drill of course, but the trip would be no problem for the *Disco*, for instance. She could lay the bomb off Grand Bahama at midnight and be back at anchor off Palmyra by breakfast time.' He smiled. 'See what I mean? It all adds up.'

'Nuts,' said Leiter succinctly. 'You'll have to do better than that if you want my blood pressure to go up. Anyway, let's get the hell out of here and go have ourselves some eggs and bacon in one of those clip joints on Bay Street. It'll cost us twenty dollars plus tax, but the *Manta* probably burns that every time her screws turn full circle. Then we'll go along to the Casino and see if Mr Fuchs or Signor Pontecorvo is sitting beside Largo at the black jack table.'

Chapter Fifteen

Cardboard Hero

The Nassau Casino is the only legal casino on British soil anywhere in the world. How this is justified under the laws of the Commonwealth no one can quite figure. It is leased each year to a Canadian gambling syndicate and their operating profits in the smart winter season are estimated to average around $100,000. The only games played are roulette, with two zeros instead of one, which increases the take to the house from the European 3·6 to a handsome 5·4; black jack, or 21, on which the house makes between six and seven per cent; and one table of chemin de fer, whose cagnotte yields a modest five per cent. The operation is run as a club in a handsome private house on West Bay Street and there is a pleasant dance and supper room with a three-piece combo that plays old favourites in strict time, and a lounge bar. It is a well run, elegant place that deserves its profit.

The Governor's A.D.C. had presented Bond and Leiter with membership cards, and after they had had coffee and a stinger at the bar they separated and went to the tables.

Largo was playing chemin de fer. He had a fat pile of hundred-dollar plaques in front of him and half a dozen of the big yellow thousand-dollar biscuits. Domino Vitali sat behind him chain-smoking and watching the play. Bond observed the game from a distance. Largo was playing expansively, bancoing whenever he could and letting his own banks run. He was winning steadily, but with excellent manners, and by the way people joked with him and applauded his coups he was obviously a favourite in the Casino. Domino, in black with a square-cut neckline and with one large diamond on a thin chain at her throat, was looking morose and bored. The woman on Largo's right, having bancoed him three times and lost, got up and left the table. Bond went quickly across the room and slid into the empty place. It was a bank of eight hundred dollars–the round sum being due to Largo making up the cagnotte after each play.

It is good for the banker when he has got past the third banco. It often means the bank is going to run. Bond knew this perfectly well. He was also painfully aware that his total capital was only 1,000 dollars. But the fact that everyone was so nervous of Largo's luck made him bold. And, after all, the table has no memory. Luck, he told himself, is strictly for the birds. He said, 'Banco.'

'Ah, my good friend Mr Bond.' Largo held out a hand. 'Now we have the big money coming to the table. Perhaps I should pass the bank. The English know how to play at railway trains. But still,' he smiled charmingly, 'if I have to lose I would certainly like to lose to Mr Bond.'

The big brown hand gave the shoe a soft slap. Largo eased out the pink tongue of playing card and moved it across the baize to Bond. He took one for himself and then pressed out one more for each of them. Bond picked up his first card and flicked it face up into the middle of the table. It was a nine, the nine of diamonds. Bond glanced sideways at Largo. He said, 'That is always a good start–so good that I will also face my second card.' He casually flicked it out to join the nine. It turned over in mid-air and fell beside the nine. It was a glorious ten, the ten of spades. Unless Largo's two cards also added up to nine or nineteen, Bond had won.

Largo laughed, but the laugh had a hard edge to it. 'You certainly make me try,' he said gaily. He threw his cards to follow Bond's. They were the eight of hearts and the king of clubs. Largo had lost by a pip–two naturals, but one just better than the other, the cruellest way to lose. Largo laughed hugely. 'Somebody had to be second,' he said at the table at large. 'What did I say? The English can pull what they like out of the shoe.'

The croupier pushed the chips across to Bond. Bond made a small pile of them. He gestured at the heap in front of Largo: 'So, it seems, can the Italians. I told you this afternoon we should go into partnership.'

Largo laughed delightedly. 'Well, let's just try once again. Put in what you have won and I will banco it in partnership with Mr Snow on your right. Yes, Mr Snow?'

Mr Snow, a tough-looking European who, Bond remembered, was one of the shareholders, agreed. Bond put in the eight hundred and they each put in four against him. Bond won again, this time with a six against a five for the table–once more by one point.

Largo shook his head mournfully. 'Now indeed we have seen the writing on the wall. Mr Snow, you will have to continue alone. This Mr Bond has green fingers against me, I surrender.'

Now Largo was smiling only with his mouth. Mr Snow suivied and pushed forward 1,600 dollars to cover Bond's stake. Bond thought: I have made 1,600 dollars in two coups, over five hundred pounds. And it would be fun to pass the bank and for the bank to go down on the next hand. He withdrew his stake and said, 'La main passe.' There was a buzz of comment. Largo said dramatically, 'Don't do it to me! Don't tell me the bank's going to go down on the next hand! If it does I shoot myself. Okay, okay, I will buy Mr Bond's bank and we will see.' He threw some plaques out on to the table–1,600 dollars' worth.

And Bond heard his own voice say banco! He was bancoing his own bank–telling Largo that he had done it to him once, then twice, and now he was going to do it, inevitably, again!

Largo turned round to face Bond. Smiling with his mouth, he narrowed his eyes and looked carefully, with a new curiosity, at Bond's face. He said quietly, 'But you are hunting me, my dear fellow. You are pursuing me. What is this? Vendetta?'

Bond thought, I will see if an association of words does something to him. He said, 'When I came to the table I saw a spectre.' He said the word casually, with no hint at double meaning.

The smile came off Largo's face as if he had been slapped. It was at once switched on again, but now the whole face was tense, strained, and the eyes had gone watchful and very hard. His tongue came out and touched his lips. 'Really? What do you mean?'

Bond said lightly, 'The spectre of defeat. I thought your luck was on the turn. Perhaps I was wrong.' He gestured at the shoe. 'Let's see.'

The table had gone quiet. The players and spectators felt that a tension had come between these two men. Suddenly there was the smell of enmity where before there had been only jokes. A glove had been thrown down, by the Englishman. Was it about the girl? Probably. The crowd licked its lips.

Largo laughed sharply. He stitched gaiety and bravado back on his face. 'Aha!' His voice was boisterous again, 'My friend wishes to put the evil eye upon my cards. We have a way to deal with that where I come from.' He lifted a hand, and with only the first and little fingers outstretched in a fork, he prodded once, like a snake striking, towards Bond's face. To the crowd it was a playful piece of theatre, but Bond, within the strong aura of the man's animal magnetism, felt the ill-temper, the malevolence behind the old Mafia gesture.

Bond laughed good-naturedly. 'That certainly put the hex on me. But what did it do to the cards? Come on, your spectre against my spectre!'

Again the look of doubt came over Largo's face. Why again the use of this word? He gave the shoe a hefty slap. 'All right, my friend. We are wrestling the best of three falls. Here comes the third.'

Quickly his first two fingers licked out the four cards. The table had hushed. Bond faced his pair inside his hand. He had a total of five–a ten of clubs and a five of hearts. Five is a marginal number. One can either draw or not. Bond folded the cards face down on the table. He said, with the confident look of a man who has a six or a seven, 'No card, thank you.'

Largo's eyes narrowed as he tried to read Bond's face. He turned up his cards, flicked them into the middle of the table with a gesture of disgust. He also had a count of five. Now what was he to do? Draw or not draw? He looked again at the quiet smile of confidence on Bond's face–and drew. It was a nine, the nine of spades. By drawing another card instead of standing on his five and equalling Bond, he had drawn and now had a four to Bond's five.

Impassively Bond turned up his cards. He said, 'I'm afraid you should have killed the evil eye in the pack, not in me.'

There was a buzz of comment round the table. 'But if the Italian had stood on his five . . .' 'I always draw on a five.' 'I never do.' 'It was bad luck.' 'No, it was bad play.'

Now it was an effort for Largo to keep the snarl off his face. But he managed it, the forced smile lost its twist, the balled fists relaxed. He took a deep breath and held out his hand to Bond. Bond took it, folding his thumb inside his palm just in case Largo might give him a bone-crusher with his vast machine-tool of a hand. But it was a firm grasp and no more. Largo said, 'Now I must wait for the shoe to come round again. You have taken all my winnings. I have a hard evening's work ahead of me just when I was going to take my niece for a drink and a dance.' He turned to Domino. 'My dear, I don't think you know Mr Bond, except on the telephone. I'm afraid he has upset my plans. You must find someone else to squire you.'

Bond said, 'How do you do. Didn't we meet in the tobacconist's this morning?'

The girl screwed up her eyes. She said indifferently, 'Ycs? It is possible. I have such a bad memory for faces.'

Bond said, 'Well, could I give you a drink? I can just afford even a Nassau drink now, thanks to the generosity of Mr Largo. And I have finished here. This sort of thing can't last. I mustn't press my luck.'

The girl got up. She said ungraciously, 'If you have nothing better to do.' She turned to Largo: 'Emilio, perhaps if I take this Mr Bond away, your luck will turn again. I will be in the supper room having caviar and champagne. We must try and get as much of your funds as we can back in the family.'

Largo laughed. His spirits had returned. He said, 'You see, Mr Bond, you are out of the frying pan into the fire. In Dominetta's hands you may not fare so well as in mine. See you later, my dear fellow. I must now get back to the salt mines where you have consigned me.'

Bond said, 'Well, thanks for the game. I will order champagne and caviar for three. My spectre also deserves his reward.' Wondering again whether the shadow that flickered in Largo's eyes at the word had more significance than Italian superstition, he got up and followed the girl between the crowded tables to the supper room.

Domino made for a shadowed table in the farthest corner of the room. Walking behind her, Bond had noticed for the first time that she had the smallest trace of a limp. He found it endearing, a touch of childish sweetness beneath the authority and blatant sex appeal of a girl to whom he had been inclined to award that highest, but toughest, French title–a *courtisane de marque*.

When the Clicquot rosé and fifty dollars' worth of Beluga caviar came–anything less, he had commented to her, would be no more than a spoonful–he asked her about the limp. 'Did you hurt yourself swimming today?'

She looked at him gravely. 'No. I have one leg an inch shorter than the other. Does it displease you?'

'No. It's pretty. It makes you something of a child.'

'Instead of a hard old kept woman. Yes?' Her eyes challenged him.

'Is that how you see yourself?'

'It's rather obvious isn't it? Anyway, it's what everyone in Nassau thinks.' She looked him squarely in the eyes, but with a touch of pleading.

'Nobody's told me that. Anyway, I make up my own mind about men and women. What's the good of other people's opinions? Animals don't consult each other about other animals. They look and sniff and feel. In love and hate, and everything in between, those are the only tests that matter. But people are unsure of their own instincts. They want reassurance. So they ask someone else whether they should like a particular person or not. And as the world loves bad news, they nearly always get a bad answer–or at least a qualified one. Would you like to know what I think of you?'

She smiled. 'Every woman likes to hear about herself. Tell me, but make it sound true, otherwise I shall stop listening.'

'I think you're a young girl, younger than you pretend to be, younger than you dress. I think you were carefully brought up, in a red-carpet sort of way, and then the red carpet was suddenly jerked away from under your feet and you were thrown more or less into the street. So you picked yourself up and started to work your own way back to the red carpet you had got used to. You were probably fairly ruthless about it. You had to be. You only had a woman's weapons and you probably used them pretty coolly. I expect you used your body. It would be a wonderful asset. But in using it to get what you wanted, your sensibilities had to be put aside. I don't expect they're very far underground. They certainly haven't atrophied. They've just lost their voice because you wouldn't listen to them. You couldn't afford to listen to them if you were to get back on that red carpet and have the things you wanted. And now you've got the things.' Bond touched the hand that lay on the banquette between them. 'And perhaps you've almost had enough of them.' He laughed. 'But I mustn't get too serious. Now about the smaller things. You know all about them, but just for the record, you're beautiful, sexy, provocative, independent, self-willed, quick-tempered, and cruel.'

She looked at him thoughtfully. 'There's nothing very clever about all that. I told you most of it. You know something about Italian women. But why do you say I'm cruel?'

'If I was gambling and I took a knock like Largo did and I had my woman, a woman, sitting near me watching and she didn't give me one word of comfort or encouragement I would say she was being cruel. Men don't like failing in front of their women.'

She said impatiently, 'I've had to sit there too often and watch him show off. I wanted you to win. I cannot pretend. You didn't mention my only virtue. It's honesty. I love to the hilt and I hate to the hilt. At the present time, with Emilio, I am half way. Where we were lovers, we are now good friends who understand each other. When I told you he was my guardian, I was telling a white lie. I am his kept woman. I am a bird in a gilded cage. I am fed up with my cage and tired of my bargain.' She looked at Bond defensively. 'Yes, it is cruel for Emilio. But it is also human. You can buy the outside of the body, but you cannot buy what is inside–what people call the heart and the soul. But Emilio knows that. He wants women for use. Not for love. He has had thousands in this way. He knows where we both stand. He is realistic. But it is becoming more difficult to keep to my bargain–to, to, let's call it sing for my supper.'

She stopped abruptly. She said, 'Give me some more champagne. All this silly talking has made me thirsty. And I would like a packet of Players—' she laughed–'Please, as they say in the advertisements. I am fed up with just smoking smoke. I need my Hero.'

Bond bought a packet from the cigarette girl. He said, 'What's that about a hero?'

She had entirely changed. Her bitterness had gone, and the lines of strain on her face. She had softened. She was suddenly a girl out for the evening. 'Ah, you don't know! My one true love! The man of my dreams. The sailor on the front of the packet of Players. You have never thought about him as I have.' She came closer to him on the banquette and held the packet under his eyes. 'You don't understand the romance of this wonderful picture–one of the great masterpieces of the world. This man,' she pointed, 'was the first man I ever sinned with. I took him into the woods, I loved him in the dormitory, I spent nearly all my pocket money on him. In exchange, he introduced me to the great world outside the Cheltenham Ladies College. He grew me up. He put me at ease with boys of my own age. He kept me company when I was lonely or afraid of being young. He encouraged me, gave me assurance. Have you never thought of the romance behind this picture? You see nothing, yet the whole of England is there! Listen,' she took his arm eagerly, 'this is the story of Hero, the name on his cap badge. At first he was a young man, a powder monkey or whatever they called it, in that sailing ship behind his right ear. It was a hard time for him. Weevils in the biscuits, hit with marlinspikes and ropes' ends and things, sent up aloft to the top of all that rigging where the flag flies. But he persevered. He began to grow a moustache. He was fair-haired and rather too pretty,' she giggled, 'he may even have had to fight for his virtue, or whatever men call it, among all those hammocks. But you can see from his face–that line of concentration between his eyes–and from his fine head, that he was a man to get on.' She paused and swallowed a glass of champagne. The dimples were now deep holes in her cheeks. 'Are you listening to me? You are not bored having to listen about my hero?'

'I'm only jealous. Go on.'

'So he went all over the world–to India, China, Japan, America. He had many girls and many fights with cutlasses and fists. He wrote home regularly–to his mother and to a married sister who lived at Dover. They wanted him to come home and meet a nice girl and get married. But he wouldn't. You see, he was keeping himself for a dream girl who looked rather like me. And then,' she laughed, 'the first steamships came in and he was transferred to an ironclad–that's the picture of it on the right. And by now he was a bosun, whatever that is, and very important. And he saved up from his pay instead of going out fighting and having girls he grew that lovely beard, to make himself look older and more important, and he set to with a needle and coloured threads to make that picture of himself. You can see how well he did it–his first windjammer and his last ironclad with the lifebuoy as a frame. He only finished it when he decided to leave the Navy. He didn't really like steamships. In the prime of life, don't you agree? And even then he ran out of gold thread to finish the rope round the lifebuoy, so he just had to tail it off. There, you can see on the right where the rope crosses the blue line. So he came back home on a beautiful golden evening after a wonderful life in the Navy and it was so sad and beautiful and romantic that he decided that he would put the beautiful evening into another picture. So he bought a pub at Bristol with his savings and in the mornings before the pub opened he worked away until he had finished and there you can see the little sailing ship that brought him home from Suez with his duffel bag full of silks and seashells and souvenirs carved out of wood. And that's the Needles Lighthouse beckoning him in to harbour on that beautiful calm evening. Mark you,' she frowned, 'I don't like that sort of bonnet thing he's wearing for a hat, and I'd have liked him to have put "H.M.S." before the "*Hero*", but you can see that would have made it lop-sided and he wouldn't have been able to get all the "*Hero*" in. But you must admit it's the most terrifically romantic picture. I cut it off my first packet, when I smoked one in the lavatory and felt terribly sick, and kept it until it fell to pieces. Then I cut off a fresh one. I carried him with me always until things went wrong and I had to go back to Italy. Then I couldn't afford Players. They're too expensive in Italy and I had to smoke things called Nazionales.'

Bond wanted to keep her mood. He said, 'But what happened to the hero's pictures? How did the cigarette people get hold of them?'

'Oh well, you see one day a man with a stove-pipe hat and a frock coat came into the hero's pub with two small boys. Here,' she held the packet sideways, 'those are the ones, "John Player & Sons". You see, it says that their Successors run the business now. Well they had one of the first motor-cars, a Rolls-Royce, and it had broken down outside the hero's pub. The man in the stove-pipe hat didn't drink of course–those sort of people didn't, not the respectable merchants who lived near Bristol. So he asked for ginger beer and bread and cheese while his chauffeur mended the car. And the hero got it for them. And Mr John Player and the boys all admired the two wonderful tapestry pictures hanging on the wall of the pub. Now this Mr Player was in the tobacco and snuff business and cigarettes had just been invented and he wanted to start making them. But he couldn't for the life of him know what to call them or what sort of a picture to put on the packet. And he suddenly had a wonderful idea. When he got back to the factory he talked to his manager and the manager came along to the pub and saw the hero and offered him a hundred pounds to let his two pictures be copied for the cigarette packet. And the hero didn't mind and anyway he wanted just exactly a hundred pounds to get married on.' She paused. Her eyes were far away. 'She was very nice, by the way, only thirty and a good plain cook and her young body kept him warm in bed until he died many years later. And she bore him two children, a boy and a girl. And the boy went into the Navy like his father. Well, anyway, Mr Player wanted to have the hero in the lifebuoy on one side of the packet and the beautiful evening on the other. But the manager pointed out that that would leave no room for all this'–she turned over the packet–'about "Rich, Cool", and "Navy Cut Tobacco" and that extraordinary trade mark of a doll's house swimming in chocolate fudge with Nottingham Castle written underneath. So then Mr Player said, "Well then, we'll put one on top of the other." And that's just exactly what they did and I must say I think it fits in very well, don't you? Though I expect the hero was pretty annoyed at the mermaid being blanked out.'

'The mermaid?'

'Oh yes. Underneath the bottom corner of the lifebuoy where it dips into the sea, the hero had put a tiny mermaid combing her hair with one hand and beckoning him home with the other. That was supposed to be the woman he was going to find and marry. But you can see there wasn't room and anyway her breasts were showing and Mr Player, who was a very strong Quaker, didn't think that was quite proper. But he made it up to the Hero in the end.'

'Oh, how did he do that?'

'Well you see the cigarettes were a great success. It was really the picture that did it. People decided that anything with a wonderful picture like that on the outside must be good and Mr Player made a fortune and I expect his Successors did too. So when the hero was getting old and hadn't got long to live, Mr Player had a copy of the lifebuoy picture drawn by the finest artist of the day. It was just the same as the Hero's except that it wasn't in colour and it showed him very much older, and he promised the Hero that this picture too would always be on his cigarette packets, only on the inside bit. Here.' She pushed out the cardboard container. 'You see how old he looks? And one other thing, if you look closely, the flags on the two ships are flying at half mast. Rather sweet of Mr Player, don't you think, to ask the artist for that. It meant that the Hero's first and last ships were remembering him. And Mr Player and his two sons came and presented it to him just before he died. It must have made it much easier for him don't you think?'

'It certainly must. Mr Player must have been a very thoughtful man.'

The girl was slowly returning from her dreamland. She said in a different, rather prim voice, 'Well thank you anyway for having listened to the story. I know it's all a fairy tale. At least I suppose it is. But children are stupid in that way. They like to have something to keep under the pillow until they're quite grown up–a rag doll or a small toy or something. I know that boys are just the same. My brother hung on to a little metal charm his nanny had given him until he was nineteen. Then he lost it. I shall never forget the scenes he made. Even though he was in the air force by then and it was the middle of the war. He said it brought him luck.' She shrugged her shoulders. There was sarcasm in her voice as she said, 'He needn't have worried. He did all right. He was much older than me, but I adored him. I still do. Girls always love crooks, particularly if they're their brother. He did so well that he might have done something for me. But he never did. He said that life was every man for himself. He said that his grandfather had been so famous as a poacher and a smuggler in the Dolomites that his was the finest tombstone among all the Petacchi graves in the graveyard at Bolzano. My brother said he was going to have a finer one still, and by making money the same way.'

Bond held his cigarette steady. He took a long draw at it and let the smoke out with a quiet hiss. 'Is your family name Petacchi then?'

'Oh yes. Vitali is only a stage name. It sounded better so I changed it. Nobody knows the other. I've almost forgotten it myself. I've called myself Vitali since I came back to Italy. I wanted to change everything.'

'What happened to your brother? What was his first name?'

'Giuseppe. He went wrong in various ways. But he was a wonderful flyer. Last time I heard of him he'd been given some high-up job in Paris. Perhaps that'll make him settle down. I pray every night that it will. He's all I've got. I love him in spite of everything. You understand that?'

Bond stabbed out his cigarette in the ashtray. He called for the bill. He said, 'Yes, I understand that.'

Chapter Sixteen

Swimming the Gauntlet

The dark water below the police wharf sucked and kissed at the rusty iron stanchions. In the latticed shadows cast through the ironwork by the three-quarter moon, Constable Santos heaved the single aqualung cylinder up on to Bond's back and Bond secured the webbing at his waist so that it would not snarl the strap of Leiter's second Geiger counter, the underwater model. He fitted the rubber mouthpiece between his teeth and adjusted the valve release until the air supply was just right. He turned off the supply and took out the mouthpiece. The music of the steel band in the Junkanoo night-club tripped gaily out over the water. It sounded like a giant spider dancing on a tenor xylophone.

Santos was a huge coloured man, naked except for his swimming trunks, with pectoral muscles the size of dinner plates. Bond said, 'What should I expect to see at this time of night? Any big fish about?'

Santos grinned. 'Usual harbour stuff, sah. Some barracuda perhaps. Mebbe a shark. But they's lazy an overfed with the refuse and muck from de drains. Dey won't trouble you–less you bleedin' that is. They'll be night-crawlin' things on the bottom–lobster, crab, mebbe a small pus-feller or two. The bottom's mostly seagrass on bits o' iron from wrecks an plenty of bottle and suchlike. Mucky, if you get me, sah. But the water's clear and you'll be hokay with this moon and the lights from the *Disco* to guide you. Tek you bout twelve, fifteen minute, I'da say. Funny thing. I been lookin' for an hour an dere's no watchman on deck an no one in the wheelhouse. An the bit o' breeze should hide you bubbles. Coulda give you an oxygen re-breather, but ah doan like dem tings. Them dangerous.'

'All right, let's go then. See you in about half an hour.' Bond felt for the knife at his waist, shifted the webbing and put the mouthpiece between his teeth. He turned on the air and, his fins slapping on the muddy sand, walked down and into the water. There he bent down, spat into his mask to prevent it steaming up, washed it out and adjusted it. Then he walked slowly on, getting used to the breathing. By the end of the wharf he was up to his ears. He quietly submerged and launched himself forward into an easy leg crawl, his hands along his flanks.

The mud shelved steeply and Bond kept on going down, until, at about forty feet, he was only a few inches above the bottom. He glanced at the big luminous figures on the dial of his watch–12.10. He untensed himself and put his legs into an easy, relaxed rhythm.

Through the roof of small waves the pale moonlight flickered on the grey bottom, and the refuse–motor tyres, cans, bottles–cast black shadows. A small octopus, feeling his shock-wave, turned from dark brown to pale grey and squeezed itself softly back into the mouth of the oil-drum that was its home. Sea flowers, the gelatinous polyps that grow out of the sand at night, whisked down their holes as Bond's black shadow touched them. Other tiny night things puffed thin jets of silt out of their small volcanoes in the mud as they felt the tremor of Bond's passage, and an occasional hermit crab snapped itself back into its borrowed shell. It was like travelling across a moon landscape, on and under which many mysterious creatures lived minute lives. Bond watched it all, carefully, as if he had been an underwater naturalist. He knew that was the way to keep nerves steady under the sea–to focus the whole attention on the people who lived there and not try and probe the sinister grey walls of mist for imaginary monsters.

The rhythm of his steady progress soon became automatic, and while Bond, keeping the moon at his right shoulder, held to his course, his mind reached back to Domino. So she was the sister of the man who probably hijacked the plane! Probably even Largo, if Largo was in fact involved in the plot, didn't know this. So what did the relationship amount to? Coincidence. It could be nothing else. Her whole manner was so entirely innocent. And yet it was one more thin straw to add to the meagre pile that seemed in some indeterminate way to be adding up to Largo's involvement. And Largo's reaction at the word 'spectre'. That could be put down to Italian superstition–or it could not. Bond had a deadly feeling that all these tiny scraps amounted to the tip of an iceberg–a few feet of ice pinnacle, with, below, a thousand tons of the stuff. Should he report? Or shouldn't he? Bond's mind boiled with indecision. How to put it? How to grade the intelligence so that it would reflect his doubts? How much to say and how much to leave out?

The extrasensory antennae of the human body, the senses left over from the jungle life of millions of years ago, sharpen unconsciously when man knows that he is on the edge of danger. Bond's mind was concentrating on something far away from his present risks, but beneath his conscious thoughts his senses were questing for enemies. Now suddenly the alarm was sounded by a hidden nerve–Danger! Danger! Danger!

Bond's body tensed. His hand went to his knife and his head swivelled sharply to the right–not to the left or behind him. His senses told him to look to the right.

A big barracuda, if it is twenty pounds or over, is the most fearsome fish in the sea. Clean and straight and malevolent, it is all hostile weapon from the long snarling mouth in the cruel jaw that can open like a rattlesnake's to an angle to ninety degrees, along the blue and silver steel of the body to the lazy power of the tail-fin that helps to make this fish one of the five fastest sprinters in the sea. This one, moving parallel with Bond, ten yards away just inside the wall of grey mist that was the edge of visibility, was showing its danger signals. The broad lateral stripes showed vividly–the angry hunting sign–the gold and black tiger's eye was on him, watchful, incurious, and the long mouth was open half an inch so that the moonlight glittered on the sharpest row of teeth in the ocean–teeth that don't bite at the flesh, teeth that tear out a chunk and swallow and then hit and scythe again.

Bond's stomach crawled with the ants of fear and his skin tightened at his groin. Cautiously he glanced at his watch. About three more minutes to go before he was due to come up with the *Disco*. He made a sudden turn and attacked fast towards the great fish, flashing his knife in fast offensive lunges. The giant barracuda gave a couple of lazy wags of its tail and, when Bond turned back on his course, it also turned and resumed its indolent, sneering cruise, weighing him up, choosing which bit–the shoulder, the buttock, the foot–to take first.

Bond tried to recall what he knew about big predator fish, what he had experienced with them before. The first rule was not to panic, to be unafraid. Fear communicates itself to fish as it does to dogs and horses. Establish a quiet pattern of behaviour and stick to it. Don't show confusion or act chaotically. In the sea, untidiness, ragged behaviour, mean that the possible victim is out of control, vulnerable. So keep to a rhythm. A thrashing fish is everyone's prey. A crab or a shell thrown upside down by a wave is offering its underside to a hundred enemies. A fish on its side is a dead fish. Bond trudged rhythmically on, exuding immunity.

Now the pale moonscape changed. A meadow of soft seagrass showed up ahead. In the deep, slow currents it waved languidly, like deep fur. The hypnotic motion made Bond feel slightly seasick. Dotted sparsely in the grass were the big black footballs of dead sponges growing out of the sand like giant puffballs–Nassau's only export until a fungus had got at them and had killed the sponge crop as surely as myxomatosis has killed rabbits. Bond's black shadow flickered across the breathing lawn like a clumsy bat. To the right of his shadow, the thin black lance cast by the barracuda moved with quiet precision.

A dense mass of silvery small fry showed up ahead, suspended in mid-stream as if they had been bottled in aspic. When the two parallel bodies approached, the mass divided sharply, leaving wide channels for the two enemies, and then closing behind them into the phalanx they adopted for an illusory protection. Through the cloud of fish, Bond watched the barracuda. It moved majestically on, ignoring the food around it as a fox creeping up on the chicken run will ignore the rabbits in the warren. Bond sealed himself in the armour of his rhythm, transmitting to the barracuda that he was a bigger, a more dangerous fish, that the barracuda must not be misled by the whiteness of the flesh.

Amongst the waving grass, the black barb of the anchor looked like another enemy. The trailing chain rose from the bottom and disappeared into the upper mists. Bond followed it up, forgetting the barracuda in his relief at hitting the target and in the excitement of what he might find.

Now he swam very slowly, watching the white explosion of the moon on the surface contract and define itself. Once he looked down. There was no sign of the barracuda. Perhaps the anchor and chain had seemed inimical. The long hull of the ship grew out of the upper mists and took shape, a great Zeppelin in the water. The folded mechanism of the hydrofoil looked ungainly, as if it did not belong. Bond clung for a moment to its starboard flange to get his bearings. Far down to his left, the big twin screws, bright in the moonlight, hung suspended, motionless but somehow charged with thrashing speed. Bond moved slowly along the hull towards them, staring upwards for what he sought. He drew in his breath. Yes, it was there, the ridge of a wide hatch below the waterline. Bond groped over it, measuring. About twelve feet square, divided down the centre. Bond paused for a moment, wondering what was inside the closed doors. He pressed the switch of the Geiger counter and held the machine against the steel plates. He watched the dial of the meter on his left wrist. It trembled to show the machine was alive, but it registered only the fraction Leiter had told him to expect from the hull. Bond switched the thing off. So much for that. Now for home.

The clang beside his ear and the sharp impact against his left shoulder were simultaneous. Automatically, Bond sprang back from the hull. Below him the bright needle of the spear wavered slowly down into the depths. Bond whirled. The man, his black rubber suit gleaming like armour in the moonlight, was pedalling furiously in the water while he thrust another spear down the barrel of the CO_2 gun. Bond hurled himself towards him, flailing at the water with his fins. The man pulled back the loading lever and levelled the gun. Bond knew he couldn't make it. He was six strokes away. He stopped suddenly, ducked his head, and jack-knifed down. He felt the small shock-wave of the silent explosion of gas and something hit his foot. Now! He soared up below the man and scythed upwards with his knife. The blade went in. He felt the black rubber against his hand. Then the butt of the gun hit him behind the ear and a white hand came down and scrabbled at his air-pipe. Bond slashed wildly with the knife, his hand moving with terrifying slowness through the water. The point ripped something. The hand let go of the mask, but now Bond couldn't see. Again the butt of the gun crashed down on his head. Now the water was full of black smoke, heavy, stringy stuff that clung to the glass of his mask. Bond backed painfully, slowly away, clawing at the glass. At last it cleared. The black smoke was coming out of the man, out of his stomach. But the gun was coming up again slowly, agonizingly, as if it weighed a ton, and the bright sting of the spear showed at its mouth. Now the webbed feet were hardly stirring, but the man was sinking slowly down to Bond's level. Suspended straight in the water, he looked like one of those little celluloid figures in a Ptolemy jar that rise and fall gracefully with pressure on the rubber top to the jar. Bond couldn't get his limbs to obey. They felt like lead. He shook his head to clear it, but still his hands and flippers moved only half consciously, all speed gone. Now he could see the bared teeth round the other man's rubber mouthpiece. The gun was at his head, at his throat, at his heart. Bond's hands crept up his chest to protect him while his flippers moved sluggishly, like broken wings, below him.

And then, suddenly, the man was hurled towards Bond as if he had been kicked in the back. His arms spread in a curious gesture of embrace for Bond and the gun tumbled slowly away between them and disappeared. A puff of black blood spread out into the sea from behind the man's back and his hands wavered out and up in vague surrender while his head twisted on his shoulders to see what had done this to him.

And now, a few yards behind the man, shreds of black rubber hanging from its jaws, Bond saw the barracuda. It was lying broadside on, seven or eight feet of silver and blue torpedo, and round its jaws there was a thin mist of blood, the taste in the water that had triggered its attack.

Now the great tiger's eye looked coldly at Bond and then downwards at the slowly sinking man. It gave a horrible yawning gulp to rid itself of the shreds of rubber, turned lazily three-quarters on, quivered in all its length and dived like a bolt of white light. It hit the man on the right shoulder with wide open jaws, shook him once, furiously, like a dog with a rat, and then backed away. Bond felt the vomit rising in his gorge like molten lava. He swallowed it down and slowly, as if in a dream, began swimming with languid, sleepy strokes away from the scene.

Bond had not gone many yards when something hit the surface to his left and the moonlight glinted on a silvery kind of egg that turned lazily over and over as it went down. It meant nothing to Bond, but, two strokes later, he received a violent blow in the stomach that knocked him sideways. It also knocked sense into him and he began to move fast through the water, at the same time planing downwards towards the bottom. More buffets hit him in quick succession, but the grenades were bracketing the blood patch near the ship's hull and the shock-waves of the explosions became less.

The bottom showed up–the friendly waving fur, the great black toadstools of the dead sponges and the darting shoals of small fish fleeing with Bond from the explosions. Now Bond swam with all his strength. At any moment a boat would be got over the side and another diver would go down. With any luck he would find no traces of Bond's visit and conclude that the underwater sentry had been killed by shark or barracuda. It would be interesting to see what Largo would report to the harbour police. Difficult to explain the necessity for an armed underwater sentry for a pleasure yacht in a peaceful harbour!

Bond trudged on across the shifting seagrass. His head ached furiously. Gingerly he put up a hand and felt the two great bruises. The skin felt intact. But for the cushion of water, the two blows with the butt of the gun would have knocked him out. As it was, he still felt half stunned and when he came to the end of the seagrass and to the soft white moon landscape with its occasional little volcano puffs from the sea-worms he felt as if he was on the edge of delirium. Wild commotion at the edge of his field of vision shocked him out of the semi-trance. A giant fish, the barracuda, was passing him. It seemed to have gone mad. It was snaking wildly along, biting at its tail, its long body curling and snapping back in a jack-knife motion, its mouth opening wide and shutting again in spasms. Bond watched it hurtle away into the grey mist. He felt somehow sorry to see the wonderful king of the sea reduced to this hideous jiggling automaton. There was something obscene about it, like the blind weaving of a punchy boxer before he finally crashes to the canvas. One of the explosions must have crushed a nerve centre, wrecked some delicate balance mechanism in the fish's brain. It wouldn't last long. A greater predator than itself, a shark, would note the signs, the loss of symmetry that is suicide in the sea. He would follow for a while until the spasms slackened. Then the shark would make a short jabbing run. The barracuda would react sluggishly and that would be the end–in three great grunting bites, the head first and then the still jerking body. And the shark would cruise quietly on, its sickle mouth trailing morsels for the black and yellow pilot fish below his jaws and perhaps for the remora or two, the parasites that travel with the great host, that pick the shark's teeth when it is sleeping and the jaws are relaxed.

And now there were the grey-slimed motor tyres, the bottles, the cans and the scaffolding of the wharf. Bond slid over the shelving sand and knelt in the shallows, his head down, not capable of carrying the heavy aqualung up the beach, an exhausted animal ready to drop.

Chapter Seventeen

The Red-eyed Catacomb

Bond, putting on his clothes, dodged the comments of Constable Santos. It seemed there had been sort of underwater explosions, with eruptions on the surface, on the starboard side of the yacht. Several men had appeared on deck and there had been some kind of commotion. A boat had been lowered on the port side, out of sight of the shore. Bond said he knew nothing of these things. He had cracked his head against the side of the ship. Silly thing to do. He had seen what he had wanted to see and had then swum back. Entirely successful. The Constable had been a great help. Thank you very much and good night. Bond would be seeing the Commissioner in the morning.

Bond walked with careful steadiness up the side street to where he had parked Leiter's Ford. He got to the hotel and telephoned Leiter's room and together they drove to police headquarters. Bond described what had happened and what he had discovered. Now he didn't care what the consequences might be. He was going to make a report. It was eight a.m. in London and there were under forty hours to go to zero hour. All these straws added up to half a haystack. His suspicions were boiling like a pressure cooker. He couldn't sit on the lid any longer.

Leiter said decisively, 'You do just that. And I'll file a copy to C.I.A. and endorse it. What's more I'm going to call up the *Manta* and tell her to get the hell over here.'

'You are?' Bond was amazed at this change of tune. 'What's got into you all of a sudden?'

'Well, I was sculling around the Casino taking a good look at anyone I thought might be a shareholder or a treasure hunter. They were mostly in groups, standing around trying to put up the front of having a good time–sunshine holiday and all that. They weren't succeeding. Largo was doing all the work, being gay and boyish. The others looked like private dicks or the rest of the Torrio gang just after the St Valentine Day massácre. Never seen such a bunch of thugs in my life–dressed up in tuxedos and smoking cigars and drinking champagne and all that–just a glass or two to show the Christmas spirit. Orders, I suppose. But all of them with that smell one gets to know in the Service, or in Pinkertons for the matter of that. You know, careful, cold-fish, thinking-of-something-else kinda look the pros have. Well, none of the faces meant anything to me until I came across a little guy with a furrowed brow and a big egg-head with pebble glasses who looked like a Mormon who's got into a whorehouse by mistake. He was peering about nervously and every time one of these other guys spoke to him he blushed and said what a wonderful place it was and he was having a swell time. I got close enough to hear him say the same thing to two different guys. Rest of the time he just mooned around, sort of helpless and almost sucking a corner of his handkerchief, if you get me. Well that face meant something to me. I knew I'd seen it before somewhere. You know how it is. So after puzzling for a bit I went to the reception and told one of the guys behind the desk in a cheery fashion that I thought I'd located an old classmate who'd migrated to Europe, but I couldn't for the life of me remember his name. Very embarrassing as he seemed to recognize me. Would the guy help? So he came along and I pointed this feller out and he went back to his desk and went through the membership cards and came up with the one I wanted. Seemed he was a man called Traut, Emil Traut. Swiss passport. One of Mr Largo's group from the yacht.' Leiter paused. 'Well I guess it was the Swiss passport that did it.' He turned to Bond. 'Remember a fellow called Kotze, East German Physicist? Came over to the West about five years ago and sang all he knew to the Joint Scientific Intelligence boys? Then he disappeared, thanks to a fat payment for the info, and went to ground in Switzerland. Well, James. Take my word for it. That's the same guy. The file went through my hands when I was still with C.I.A. doing desk work in Washington. All came back to me. It was one hell of a scoop at the time. Only saw his mug on the file, but there's absolutely no doubt about it. That man's Kotze. And now what the hell is a top physicist doing on board the *Disco*? Fits doesn't it?'

They had come to police headquarters. Lights burned only on the ground floor. Bond waited until they had reported to the duty sergeant and had gone up to their room before he answered. He stood in the middle of the room and looked at Leiter. He said, 'That's the clincher, Felix. So now what do we do?'

'With what you got this evening, I'd pull the whole lot in on suspicion. No question at all.'

'Suspicion of what? Largo would reach for his lawyer and they'd be out in five minutes. Democratic processes of the law and so forth. And what single fact have we got that Largo couldn't dodge? All right, so Traut is Kotze. We're hunting for treasure, gentlemen, we need an expert mineralogist. This man offered his services. Said his name was Traut. No doubt he's still worried about the Russians getting after him. Next question? Yes, we've got an underwater compartment on the *Disco*. We're going to hunt treasure through it. Inspect it? Well, if you must. There you are, gentlemen–underwater gear, skids, perhaps even a small bathyscaphe. Underwater sentry? Of course. People have spent six months trying to find out what we're after, how we're going to get it. We're professionals, gentlemen. We like to keep out secrets. And anyway, what was this Mr Bond, this rich gentleman looking for a property in Nassau, doing underneath my ship in the middle of the night? Petacchi? Never heard of him. Don't care what Miss Vitali's family name was. Always known her as Vitali . . .' Bond made a throwaway gesture with one hand. 'See what I mean? This treasure hunting cover is perfect. It explains everything. And what are we left with? Largo pulls himself up to his full height and says, "Thanks, gentlemen. So I may go now? And so I shall, within the hour. I shall find another base for my work and you will be hearing from my lawyers forthwith–wrongful detention and trespass. And good luck to your tourist trade, gentlemen."' Bond smiled grimly. 'See what I mean?'

Leiter said impatiently, 'So what do we do? Limpet mine? Send her to the bottom–in error, so to speak?'

'No. We're going to wait.' At the expression on Leiter's face, Bond held up a hand. 'We're going to send our report, in careful, guarded terms so we don't get an airborne division landing on Windsor Field. And we're going to say the *Manta* is all we need. And so it is. With her, we can keep tabs on the *Disco* just as we please. And we'll stay under cover, keep a hidden watch on the yacht and see what happens. At present we're not suspected. Largo's plan, if there is one, that is, and don't forget this treasure-hunting business still covers everything perfectly well, is going along all right. All he's got to do now is collect the bombs and make for Target No. 1 ready to zero hour in around thirty hours' time. We can do absolutely nothing to him until he's got one or both of those bombs on board or we catch him at their hiding place. Now, that can't be far away. Nor can the Vindicator, if she's hereabouts. So tomorrow we take that amphibian they've got for us and hunt the area inside a radius of a hundred miles. We'll hunt the seas and not the land. She must be in shoal water somewhere and damned well hidden. With this calm weather, we should be able to locate her–if she's here. Now, come on! Let's get those reports off and get some sleep. And say we're out of communication for ten hours. And disconnect your telephone when you get back to your room. However careful we are, this signal is going to set the Potomac on fire as well as the Thames.'

Six hours later, in the crystal light of early morning, they were out at Windsor Field and the ground crew was hauling the little Grumman Amphibian out of the hangar with a jeep. They had climbed on board and Leiter was gunning the engines when a uniformed motorcycle dispatch rider came driving uncertainly towards them across the tarmac.

Bond said, 'Get going! Quick! Here comes paper-work.'

Leiter released the brakes and taxi'd fast towards the single north-south runway. the radio crackled angrily. Leiter took a careful look over the sky. It was clear. He slowly pushed down on the joystick and the little plane snarled its way faster and faster down the concrete and, with a final bump, soared off over the low bush. The radio still crackled. Leiter reached up and switched it off.

Bond sat with the Admiralty chart on his lap. They were flying north. They had decided to start with the Grand Bahama group and have a first look at the possible area of Target No. 1. They flew at a thousand feet. Below them the Berry Islands were a necklace of brown spits set in cream and emerald and turquoise. 'See what I mean?' said Bond. 'You can see anything big through that water down to fifty feet. Anything as big as the Vindicator would have been spotted anywhere on any of the air routes. So I've marked off the areas where there's the minimum traffic. They'd have ditched somewhere well out of the way. Assuming, and it's the hell of an assumption, that, when the *Disco* made off to the south-east on the night of the third, it was a ruse, it'll be reasonable to hunt to the north and the west. She was away eight hours. Two of those would have been at anchor doing the salvage work. That leaves six hours' sailing at around thirty knots. Cut an hour off for laying the false trail, and that leaves five. I've marked off an area from the Grand Bahamas down to south of the Bimini group. That fits–if anything fits.'

'Did you get on to the Commissioner?'

'Yes. He's going to have a couple of good men with day-and-night glasses keeping an eye on the *Disco*. If she moves from her Palmyra anchorage where she's due back at midday, and if we're not back in time, he'll have her shadowed by one of the Bahama Airways charter planes. I got him quite worried with just one or two bits if information. He wanted to go to the Governor with the story. I said not yet. He's a good man. Just doesn't want too much responsibility without someone else's okay. I used the P.M.'s name to keep him quiet until we get back. He'll play all right. When do you think the *Manta* could be here?'

'S'evening, I'd say.' Leiter's voice was uneasy. 'I must have been drunk last night to have sent for her. Christ, we're creating one hell of a flap, James. It doesn't look too good in the cold light of dawn. Anyway, what the hell? There's Grand Bahama coming up dead ahead. Want me to give the rocket base a buzz? Prohibited flying area, but we might as well go in up to our ears while we're about it. Just listen to the bawling out we'll be getting in just a minute or two.' He reached up and switched on the radio.

They flew eastwards along the fifty miles of beautiful coast towards what looked like a small city of aluminium hutments amongst which red and white and silver structures rose like small skyscrapers above the low roofs. 'That's it,' said Leiter. 'See the yellow warning balloons at the corners of the base? Warning to aircraft and fishermen. There's a flight test on this morning. Better get out to sea a bit and keep south. If it's a full test, they'll be firing towards Ascension Island–about five thousand miles east. Off the African coast. Don't want to get an Atlas missile up our backsides. Look over there to the left–sticking up like a pencil beside that red and white gantry! Atlas or a Titan–inter-continental. Or might be a prototype Polaris. The other two gantries'll be for Matador and Snark and perhaps your Thunderbird. That big gun thing, like a howitzer, that's the camera tracker. The two saucer-shaped reflectors are the radar screen. Golly! One of them's turning away towards us! We're going to get hell in a minute. that strip of concrete down the middle of the island. That's the skid strip for bringing in missiles that are recallable. Can't see the central control for telemetering and guidance and destruction of the things if they go mad. That'll be underground–one of those squat block-house things. Some brass hat'll be sitting down there with his staff getting all set for the count-down or whatever's going to happen and telling someone to do something about that goddam little plane that's fouling up the works.'

Above their heads the radio crackled. A metallic voice said, 'N/AKOI, N/AKOI. You're in a prohibited area. Can you hear me. Change course southwards immediately. N/AKOI. This is Grand Bahama Rocket Base. Keep clear. Keep clear.'

Leiter said, 'Oh hell! No use interfering with world progress. Anyway we've seen all we want. No good getting on the Windsor Field report to add to our troubles.' He banked the little plane sharply. 'But you see what I mean? If that little heap of ironmongery isn't worth a quarter of a billion dollars my name's P. Rick. And it's just about a hundred miles from Nassau. Perfect for the *Disco*.'

The radio started again: 'N/AKOI, N/AKOI. You will be reported for entering a prohibited area and for failing to acknowledge. Keep flying south and watch out for sudden turbulence. Over.' The radio went silent.

Leiter said, 'That means they're going to fire a test. Keep an eye on them and let me know when. I'll cut down the revs. No harm in watching ten million dollars of the taxpayer's money being blown off. Look! The radar scanner's turned back to the east. They'll be sweating it out in that blockhouse all right. I've seen 'em at it. Lights'll be blinking all over the big board way down underground. The kibitzers'll be at their periscopes. Voices'll come down over the P.A. System. "Beacon contact . . . Warning balloons up . . . Telemeter contact . . . Tank pressure okay . . . Gyros okay . . . Rocket-tank pressure correct . . . Rocket clear . . . Recorders alive . . . Lights all green . . . Ten, nine, eight, seven, six . . . Fire!"'

Despite Leiter's graphic count-down, nothing happened. Then, through his glasses, Bond saw a wisp of steam coming from the base of the rocket. Then a great cloud of steam and smoke and a flash of bright light that turned red. Breathlessly, for there was something terrible in the sight, Bond gave the blow-by-blow to Leiter. 'It's edging up off the pad. There's a jet of flame. It seems to be sitting on it. Now it's going up like a lift. Now it's off! God, it's going fast! Now there's nothing but a spark of fire in the sky. Now it's gone. Whew!' Bond mopped his brow. 'Remember that Moonraker job I was on a few years back? Interesting to see what the people out front saw.'

'Yeah. You were lucky to get out of that deep fry.' Leiter brushed aside Bond's reminiscences. 'Now then, next stop those spits in the ocean north of Bimini and then a good run down the Bimini Group. Around seventy miles south-west. Keep an eye out. If we miss those dots, we'll end up in the grounds of the Fountain Blue in Miami.'

A quarter of an hour later, the tiny necklet of cays showed up. They were barely above the water line. There was much shoal. It looked an ideal hiding place for the plane. They came down to a hundred feet and slowly cruised in a zig-zag down the group. The water was so clear that Bond could see big fish meandering around the dark clumps of coral and seaweed in the brilliant sand. A big diamond-shaped stingray cowered and buried itself in the sand as the black shadow of the plane pursued and shot over it. There was nothing else and no possibility of concealment. The green shoal waters were as clean and innocent as if they had been open desert. The plane flew on south to North Bimini. Here there were a few houses and some small fishing hotels. Expensive-looking deep-sea fishing craft were out, their tall rods streaming. Gay people in the well-decks waved to the little plane. A girl, sunbathing naked on the roof of a smart cabin cruiser, hastily snatched at a towel. 'Authentic blonde!' commented Leiter. They flew on south to the Cat Cays that trail away south from the Biminis. Here there was still an occasional fishing craft. Leiter groaned. 'What the hell's the good of this? These fishermen would have found it by now if it was here.' Bond told him to keep on south. thirty miles further south there were little unnamed specks on the Admiralty chart. Soon the dark blue water began to shoal again to green. They passed over three sharks circling aimlessly. Then there was nothing–just dazzling sand under the glassy surface, and occasional patches of coral.

They went on carefully down to where the water turned again to blue. Leiter said dully, 'Well, that's that. Fifty miles on there's Andros. Too many people there. Someone would have heard the plane–if there was a plane.' He looked at his watch. '11.30. What next, Hawkshaw? I've only got fuel for another two hours' flying.'

Something was itching deep down in Bond's mind. Something, some small detail, had raised a tiny question-mark. What was it? Those sharks! In about forty feet of water! Circling on the surface! What were they doing there? Three of them. There must be something–something dead that had brought them to that particular patch of sand and coral. Bond said urgently, 'Just go back up once more, Felix. Over the shoals. There's something—'

The little plane made a tight turn. Felix cut down the revs and just kept flying speed about fifty feet above the surface. Bond opened the door and craned out, his glasses at short focus. Yes, there were the sharks, two on the surface with their dorsals out, and one deep down. It was nosing at something. It had its teeth into something and was pulling at it. Among the dark and pale patches, a thin straight line showed on the bottom. Bond shouted, 'Get back over again!' The plane zoomed round and back. Christ! Why did they have to go so fast? But now Bond had seen another straight line on the bottom, leading off at 90 degrees from the first. He flopped back into his seat and banged the door shut. He said quietly, 'Put her down over those sharks, Felix. I think this is it.'

Leiter took a quick glance at Bond's face. He said, 'Christ!' Then, 'Well, I hope I can make it. Damned difficult to get a true horizon. This water's like glass.' He pulled away, curved back and slowly put the nose down. There was a slight jerk and then the hiss of the water under the skids. Leiter cut his engines and the plane came to a quick stop, rocking in the water about ten yards from where Bond wanted. The two sharks on the surface paid no attention. They completed their circle and came slowly back. They passed so close to the plane that Bond could see the incurious, pink button eyes. He peered down through the small ripples cast by the two dorsal fins. Yes! Those 'rocks' on the bottom were bogus. They were painted patches. So were the areas of 'sand'. Now Bond could clearly see the straight edges of the giant tarpaulin. The third shark had nosed back a big section. Now it was shovelling with its flat head trying to get underneath.

Bond sat back. He turned to Leiter. He nodded. 'That's it, all right. Big camouflaged tarpaulin over her. Take a look.'

While Leiter leant across Bond and stared down, Bond's mind was racing furiously. Get the Police Commissioner on the police wavelength and report? Get signals sent off to London? No! If the radio operator on the *Disco* was doing his job, he would be keeping watch on the police frequency. So go on down and have a look. See if the bombs were still there. Bring up a piece of evidence. The sharks? Kill one and the others would go for the corpse.

Leiter sat back. His face was shining with excitement. 'Well, I'll be goddammed! Boy oh boy!' He clapped Bond on the back. 'We've found it! We've found the goddam plane. Whaddya know? Jesus Kerist!'

Bond had taken out the Walther PPK. He checked to see there was a round in the chamber, rested it on his left forearm and waited for the two sharks to come round again. The first was the bigger, a hammerhead, nearly twelve feet long. Its hideously distorted head moved slowly from side to side as it nuzzled through the water, watching what went on below, waiting for a sign of meat. Bond aimed for the base of the dorsal fin that cut through the water like a dark sail. It was fully erect, a sign of tension and awareness in the big fish. Just below it was the spine, unassailable except with a nickel-plated bullet. He pulled the trigger. There was a phut as the bullet hit the surface just behind the dorsal. The boom of the heavy gun rolled away over the sea. The shark paid no attention. Bond fired again. The water foamed as the fish reared itself above the surface, dived shallowly and came up thrashing sideways like a broken snake. It was a brief flurry. The bullet must have severed the spinal cord. Now the great brown shape began moving sluggishly in circles that grew ever wider. The hideous snout came briefly out of the water to show the sickle mouth gasping. For a moment it rolled over on its back, its stomach white to the sun. Then it righted itself and, dead probably, continued its mechanical, disjointed swim.

The following shark had watched all this. Now it approached cautiously. It made a short snapping run and swerved away. Feeling safe, it darted in again, seemed to nuzzle at the dying fish and then lifted its snout above the surface and came down with all its force, scything into the flank of the hammerhead. It got hold, but the flesh was tough. It shook its great brown head like a dog, worrying at the mouthful, and then tore itself away. A cloud of blood poured over the sea. Now the other shark appeared from below and both fish, in a frenzy, tore and tore again at the still moving hulk whose nervous system refused to die.

The dreadful feast moved away on the current and was soon only a distant splashing on the surface of the quiet sea.

Bond handed Leiter the gun. 'I'll get on down. May be rather a long job. They've got enough to keep them busy for half an hour, but if they come back, wing one of them. And if for any reason you want me back on the surface, fire straight down at the water and go on firing. The shock-wave should just about reach me.'

Bond began to struggle out of his clothes and, with Leiter's help, into his aqualung. It was a cramped, difficult business. It would be still worse getting back into the plane and it occured to Bond that he would have to jettison the underwater gear. Leiter said angrily, 'I wish to God I could get down there with you. Trouble with this damned hook, it just won't swim like a hand. Have to think up some rubber webbing gadget. Never occurred to me before.'

Bond said, 'You'll have to keep steam up on this crate. We've already drifted a hundred yards. Get her back up, like a good chap. I don't know who I'm going to find sharing the wreck with me. It's been here a good five days and other visitors may have moved in first.'

Leiter pressed the starter and taxi'd back into position. He said, 'You know the design of the Vindicator? You know where to look for the bombs and these detonator things the pilot has charge of?'

'Yes. Full briefing in London. Well, so long. Tell Mother I died game!' Bond scrambled on to the edge of the cockpit and jumped.

He got his head under and swam leisurely down through the brilliant water. Now he could see that there were swarms of fish over the whole area below him–bill fish, small barracuda, jacks of various types–the carnivores. They parted grudgingly to make room for their big, pale competitor. Bond touched down and made for the edge of the tarpaulin that had been dislodged by the shark. He pulled out a couple of the long corkscrew skewers that secured it to the sand, switched on his waterproof torch and, his other hand on his knife, slipped under the edge.

He had been expecting it, but the foulness of the water made him retch. He clamped his lips more tightly round the mouth-piece and squirmed on to where the bulk of the plane raised the tarpaulin into a domed tent. He stood up. His torch glittered on the underside of a polished wing and then, below it, on to something that lay under a scrabbling mass of crabs, langoustes, sea caterpillars and starfish. This also Bond had been prepared for. He knelt down to his grisly work.

It didn't take long. He unclipped the gold identification disc and unlatched the gold wrist-watch from the horrible wrists and noted the gaping wound under the chin that could not have been caused by sea creatures. He turned his torch on the gold disc. It said 'Giuseppe Petacchi. No. 15932'. He strapped the two bits of evidence to his own wrists and went on towards the fuselage that loomed in the darkness like a huge silver submarine. He inspected the exterior, noted the rent where the hull had been broken on impact, and then climbed up through the open safety hatch into the interior.

Inside, Bond's torch shone everywhere into red eyes that glowed like rubies in the darkness and there was a soft movement and scuttling. He sprayed the light up and down the fuselage. Everywhere there were octopuses, small ones, but perhaps a hundred of them, weaving on the tips of their tentacles, sliding softly away into protecting shadow, changing their camouflage nervously from brown to a pale phosphorescence that gleamed palely in the patches of darkness. The whole fuselage seemed to be crawling with them, evilly, horribly, and as Bond shone his torch on the roof the sight was even worse. There, bumping softly in the slight current, hung the corpse of a crew member. In decomposition, it had risen up from the floor, and octopuses, hanging from it like bats, now let go their hold and shot, jet propelled, to and fro inside the plane–dreadful, glinting, red-eyed comets that slapped themselves into dark corners and stealthily squeezed themselves into cracks and under seats.

Bond closed his mind to the disgusting nightmare and, weaving his torch in front of him, proceeded with his search.

He found the red-striped cyanide canister and tucked it into his belt. He counted the corpses, noted the open hatch to the bomb bay and verified that the bombs had gone. He looked in the open container under the pilot's seat and searched in alternative places for the vital fuses for the bombs. But they also had gone. Finally, having a dozen times had to slash away groping tentacles from his naked legs, he felt his nerve was quickly seeping away. There was much he should have taken with him, the identification discs of the crew, the pulp of the log book that showed nothing but routine flight details and no hint of emergency, readings from the instrument panel, but he couldn't stand another second of the squirming, red-eyed catacomb. He slid out through the escape hatch and swam almost hysterically towards the thin line of light that was the edge of the tarpaulin. Desperately, he scrabbled his way under it, snagged the cylinder on his back in the folds and had to back under again to free himself. And then he was out in the beautiful crystal water and soaring up to the surface. At twenty feet the pain in his ears reminded him to stop and decompress. Impatiently, staring up at the sweet hull of the seaplane above him, he waited until the pain had subsided. Then he was up and clinging to a float and tearing at his equipment to get rid of it and its contamination. He let it all go and watched it tumbling slowly down towards the sand. He rinsed his mouth out with the sweetness of pure salt water and swam to within reach of Leiter's outstretched hand.

Chapter Eighteen

How to Eat a Girl

As they approached Nassau on their way back, Bond asked Leiter to take a look at the *Disco* lying off Palmyra. She was there all right, just where she had been the day before. The only difference, which had little meaning, was that she had only her bow anchor out. There was no movement on board. Bond was thinking that she looked beautiful and quite harmless lying there reflecting her elegant lines in the mirror of the sea, when Leiter said excitedly, 'Say, James, take a look at the beach place. The boathouse alongside the creek. See those double tracks leading up out of the water? Up to the door of the boathouse. They look odd to me. They're deep. What could have made them?'

Bond focused his glasses. The tracks ran parallel. Something, something heavy, had been hauled between the boathouse and the sea. But it couldn't be, surely it couldn't! He said tensely, 'Let's get away quick, Felix.' Then, as they zoomed off overland, 'I'm damned if I can think of anything that could have made those. And dammit, if it was what it might have been, they'd have swept off those tracks pretty quick.'

Leiter said laconically, 'People make mistakes. We'll have to give that place the going over. Ought to have done it before. Nice looking dump. I think I'll take Mr Largo up on his invitation and get out there on behalf of my esteemed client, Mr Rockefeller Bond.'

It was one o'clock by the time they got back to Windsor Field. For half an hour the control tower had been searching for them on the radio. Now they had to face the commandant of the field and, providentially as it happened, the Governor's A.D.C., who gave the Governor's blanket authorization for the string of their misdemeanours and then handed Bond a thick envelope which contained signals for both of them.

The contents began with the expected rockets for breaking communication and demands for further news ('That they'll get!' commented Leiter as they raced towards Nassau in the comfortable back of the Governor's Humber Snipe saloon). E.T.A. for the *Manta* was five o'clock that evening. Inquiries through Interpol and the Italian police confirmed that Giuseppe Petacchi was in fact the brother of Dominetta Vitali, whose personal history as given to Bond stood up in all other respects. The same sources confirmed that Emilio Largo was a big-time adventurer and suspected crook though technically his dossier was clean. The source of his wealth was unknown but did not stem from funds held in Italy. The *Disco* had been paid for in Swiss francs. The constructors confirmed the existence of the underwater compartment. It contained an electric hoist and provision for launching small underwater craft and releasing skin-divers. In Largo's specifications, this modification to the hull had been given as a requirement for underwater research. Further inquiry into the 'shareholders' had yielded no further facts–with the significant exception that most of their backgrounds and professions dated back no further than six years. This suggested the possibility that their identities might be of recent fabrication and, at any rate in theory, this would equate with possible membership of SPECTRE, if such a body did in fact exist. Kotze had left Switzerland for an unknown destination four weeks previously. Latest photographs of the man were on the midday Pan American plane. Nevertheless the Thunderball war-room had to accept the solidity of Largo's cover unless further evidence came to hand, and the present intention was to continue the world-wide search while allotting priority to the Bahamas area. In view of this priority, and the extremely urgent time factor, Brigadier Fairchild, C.B., D.S.O., British Military Attaché in Washington, with Rear Admiral Carlson, U.S.N. Ret., until recently Secretary to the U.S. Chiefs of Staff Committee, would be arriving at 1900 E.S.T. by the President's Boeing 707, 'Columbine', to take joint command of further operations. The full co-operation of Messrs Bond and Leiter was requested and, until the arrival of above named officers, full reports every hour on the hour were to be radio'd to London, copy to Washington, under joint signature.

Leiter and Bond looked at each other in silence. Finally Leiter said, 'James, I propose we disregard the last bit and take formal note of the remainder. We've already missed four hours and I don't propose we spend the rest of the day sweating it out in our radio room. There's just too much to do. Tell you what. I'll do the stint of telling them the latest and then I'll say we're going off the air in view of the new emergency. I then propose to go and look over Palmyra on your behalf, sticking to our cover story. And I propose to have a damned good look at the boathouse and see what those tracks mean. Right? Then, at five, we'll rendezvous with the *Manta* and prepare to intercept the *Disco* if and when she sails. As for the Big Brass in the President's Special, well they can just play pinocle in Government House until tomorrow morning. Tonight's the night and we just can't waste it on the "After you Alphonse" routine. Okay?'

Bond reflected. They were coming in to the outskirts of Nassau, through the shanty-town slums tucked away behind the millionaire façade along the waterfront. He had disobeyed many orders in his life, but this was to disobey the Prime Minister of England and the President of the United States–a mighty left and right. But things were moving a damned sight too fast. M had given him this territory and, right or wrong, M would back him up, as he always backed up his staff, even if it meant M's own head on a charger. Bond said, 'I agree, Felix. With the *Manta* we can manage this on our own. The vital thing is to find out when those bombs go on board the *Disco*. I've got an idea for that. May work, may not. It means giving the Vitali girl a rough time, but I'll try and handle that side. Drop me at the hotel and I'll get cracking. Meet you here again around four thirty. I'll call up Harling and see if he's got anything new on the *Disco* and ask him to pass the word upstairs to you if anything's cooking. You've got all that straight about the plane? Okay. I'll hang on to Petacchi's identification disc for the time being. Be seeing you.'

Bond almost ran through the lobby of the hotel. When he picked up his key at the reception desk they gave him a telephone message. He read it going up in the lift. It was from Domino: 'Please telephone quickly.'

In his room, Bond first ordered a club sandwich and a double Bourbon on the rocks and then called the Police Commissioner. The *Disco* had moved to the oiling wharf at first light and had filled her tanks. Then she had moved back to her anchorage off Palmyra. Half an hour ago, at one thirty precisely, the seaplane had been lowered over the side and, with Largo and one other on board, had taken off eastwards. When the Commissioner had heard this on the walkie-talkie from his watchers he had got on to the control tower at Windsor Field and had asked for the plane to be radar-tracked. But she had flown low, at about 300 feet, and they had lost her among the islands about fifty miles to the south-east. Nothing else had come up except that the harbour authorities had been alerted to expect an American submarine, the *Manta*, the nuclear-powered one, at around five in the evening. That was all. What did Bond know?

Bond said carefully that it was too early to tell. It looked as if the operation was hotting up. Could the watchers be asked to rush the news back as soon as the seaplane was sighted coming back to the *Disco*? This was vital. Would the Commissioner please pass on his news to Felix Leiter who was on his way to the radio room at that moment? And could Bond be lent a car–anything–to drive himself? Yes, a Land Rover would be fine. Anything with four wheels.

Then Bond got on to Domino out at Palmyra. She sounded eager for his voice. 'Where have you been all morning, James?'–it was the first time she had used his Christian name–'I want you to come swimming this afternoon. I have been told to pack and come on board this evening. Emilio says they are going after the treasure tonight. Isn't it nice of him to take me? But it's a dead secret, so don't tell anyone, will you. But he is vague about when we will be back. He said something about Miami. I thought—' she hesitated–'I thought you might have gone back to New York by the time we get back. I have seen so little of you. You left so suddenly last night. What was it?'

'I suddenly got a headache. Touch of the sun I suppose. It had been quite a day. I didn't want to go. And I'd love to come for a swim. Where?'

She gave him careful directions. It was a beach a mile further along the coast from Palmyra. There was a side road and a thatched hut. He couldn't miss it. The beach was sort of better than Palmyra's. The skin-diving was more fun. And of course there weren't so many people. It belonged to some Swedish millionaire who had gone away. When could he get there? Half an hour would be all right. They would have more time. On the reef that is.

Bond's drink came and the sandwich. He sat and consumed them, looking at the wall, feeling excited about the girl, but knowing what he was going to do to her life that afternoon. It was going to be a bad business–when it could have been so good. He remembered her as he had first seen her, the ridiculous straw hat tilted down over the nose, the pale blue ribbons flying as she sped up Bay Street. Oh well . . .

Bond rolled his swimming trunks into a towel, put on a dark blue sea-island cotton shirt over his slacks and slung Leiter's Geiger counter over his shoulder. He glanced at himself in the mirror. He looked like any other tourist with a camera. He felt in his trousers pocket to make sure he had the identification bracelet and went out of the room and down in the lift.

The Land Rover had Dunlopillo cushions, but the ripple-edged tarmac and the pitted bends of Nassau's coastal road were tough on the springs and the quivering afternoon sun was a killer. By the time Bond found the sandy track leading off into the casuarinas and had parked the car on the edge of the beach, all he wanted to do was get into the sea and stay in it. The beach-hut was a Robinson Crusoe affair of plaited bamboo and screwpine with a palm thatch whose wide eaves threw black shadows. Inside were two changing rooms labelled 'HIS' and 'HERS'. HERS contained a small pile of soft clothes and the white doeskin sandals. Bond changed and walked out again into the sun. The small beach was a dazzling half-moon of white sand enclosed on both sides by rocky points. There was no sign of the girl. The beach shelved quickly through green to blue under the water. Bond took a few steps through the shallows and dived through the blood-warm upper water down into the cool depths. He kept down there as long as possible, feeling the wonderful cold caress on his skin and through his hair. Then he surfaced and crawled lazily out to sea, expecting to see the girl skin-diving round one of the headlands. But there was no sign of her, and after ten minutes Bond turned back to the shore, chose a patch of firm sand, and lay down on his stomach, his face cradled in his arms.

Minutes later, something made Bond open his eyes. Coming towards him across the middle of the quiet bay was a thin trail of bubbles. When it passed over the dark blue into the green, Bond could see the yellow single cylinder of the aqualung tank and the glint of a mask with a fan of dark hair streaming out behind. The girl beached herself in the shallows. She raised herself on one elbow and lifted the mask. She said severely, 'Don't lie there dreaming. Come and rescue me.'

Bond got to his feet and walked the few steps to where she lay. He said, 'You oughtn't to aqualung by yourself. What's happened? Has a shark been lunching off you?'

'Don't make silly jokes. I've got some sea-egg spines in my foot. You'll have to get them out somehow. First of all get this aqualung off me. It hurts too much to stand on my foot with all this weight.' She reached for the buckle at her stomach and released the catch. 'Now just lift it off.'

Bond did as he was told and carried the cylinder up into the shade of the trees. Now she was sitting in the shallow water inspecting the sole of her right foot. She said, 'There are only two of them. They're going to be difficult.'

Bond came and knelt beside her. The two black spots, close together, were almost under the curl of the middle toes. He got up and held out a hand. 'Come on. We'll get into the shade. This is going to take time. Don't put your foot down or you'll push them in further. I'll carry you.'

She laughed up at him. 'My hero! All right. But don't drop me.' She held up both arms. Bond reached down and put one arm under her knees and another under her armpits. Her arms closed round his neck. Bond picked her up easily. He stood for a moment in the lapping water and looked down into her upturned face. The bright eyes said yes. He bent his head and kissed her hard on the half-open, waiting mouth.

The soft lips held his and drew slowly away. She said rather breathlessly, 'You shouldn't take your reward in advance.'

'That was only on account.' Bond closed his hand firmly over her right breast and walked out of the water and up the beach into the shade of the casuarinas. He laid her gently down in the soft sand. She put her hands behind her head to keep the sand out of her straggling hair and lay waiting, her eyes half hidden behind the dark mesh of her eyelashes.

The mounded vee of the bikini looked up at Bond and the proud breasts in the tight cups were two more eyes. Bond felt his control going. He said roughly, 'Turn over.'

She did as she was told. Bond knelt down and picked up her right foot. It felt small and soft, like a captured bird, in his hand. He wiped away the specks of sand and uncurled the toes. The small pink pads were like the buds of some multiple flower. Holding them back, he bent and put his lips to where the broken ends of the black spines showed. He sucked hard for about a minute. A small piece of grit from one of the spines came into his mouth and he spat it out. He said, 'This is going to be a long business unless I hurt a bit. Otherwise it'll take all day and I can't waste too much time over just one foot. Ready?'

He saw the muscles of her behind clench to take the pain. She said dreamily, 'Yes.'

Bond sunk his teeth into the flesh round the spines, bit as softly as he could and sucked hard. The foot struggled to get away. Bond paused to spit out some fragments. The marks of his teeth showed white and there were pinpoints of blood at the two tiny holes. He licked them away. There was almost no black left under the skin. He said, 'This is the first time I've eaten a woman. They're rather good.'

She squirmed impatiently but said nothing.

Bond knew how much it would be hurting. He said, 'It's all right, Domino. You're doing fine. Last mouthful.' He gave the sole of her foot a reassuring kiss and then, as tenderly as he could, put his teeth and lips back to work.

A minute or two later and he spat out the last section of spine. He told her it was over and gently laid the foot down. He said, 'Now you mustn't get sand into it. Come on, I'll give you another lift into the hut and you can put your sandals on.'

She rolled over. Her black eyelashes were wet with the tears of small pain. She wiped a hand over them. She said, looking seriously up at him, 'Do you know, you're the first man who's ever made me cry.' She held up her arms and now there was complete surrender.

Bond bent and picked her up. This time he didn't kiss the waiting mouth. He carried her to the door of the hut. HIS OR HERS? He carried her into HIS. He reached out a hand for his shirt and shorts and threw them down to make a scrap of a bed. He put her down softly so that she was standing on his shirt. She kept her arms round his neck while he undid the single button of the brassiere and then the tapes of the taut slip. He stepped out of his bathing trunks and kicked them away.

Chapter Nineteen

When the Kissing Stopped

Bond leant on one elbow and looked down at the beautiful drowned face. There was a dew of sweat below the eyes and at the temples. A pulse beat fast at the base of the neck. The lines of authority had been sponged away by the lovemaking and the face had a soft, sweet, bruised look. The wet eyelashes parted and the tawny eyes, big and faraway, looked up with remote curiosity into Bond's. They focused lazily and examined him as if they were seeing him for the first time.

Bond said, 'I'm sorry. I shouldn't have done that.'

The words amused her. The dimples at each side of the mouth deepened into clefts. She said, 'You talk like a girl who has had it for the first time. Now you are frightened that you will have a baby. You will have to tell your mother.'

Bond leant down and kissed her. He kissed the two corners of her mouth and then the parted lips. He said, 'Come and swim. Then I must talk to you.' He got to his feet and held out his hands. Reluctantly she took them. He pulled her up and against him. Her body flirted with his, knowing it was safe. She smiled impishly up at him and became more wanton. Bond crushed her fiercely to him, to stop her and because he knew they had only a few more minutes of happiness. He said, 'Stop it, Domino. And come on. We don't need any clothes. The sand won't hurt your foot. I was only pretending.'

She said, 'So was I when I came out of the sea. The spines didn't hurt all that much. And I could have cured them if I'd wanted to. Like the fishermen do. You know how?'

Bond laughed. 'Yes I do. Now, into the sea.' He kissed her once and stood back and looked at her body to remember how it had been. Then he turned abruptly and ran to the sea and dived deeply down.

When he got back to shore she was already out and dressing. Bond dried himself. He answered her laughing remarks through the partition with monosyllables. Finally she accepted the change in him. She said, 'What is the matter with you, James? Is anything wrong?'

'Yes, darling.' Pulling on his trousers Bond heard the rattle of the little gold chain against the coins in his pocket. He said, 'Come outside. I've got to talk to you.'

Sentimentally, Bond chose a patch of sand on the other side of the hut from where they had been before. She came and stood in front of him. She examined his face carefully, trying to read it. Bond avoided her eyes. He sat with his arms round his knees and looked out to sea. She sat down beside him, but not close. She said, 'You are going to hurt me. Is it that you too are going away? Be quick. Do it cleanly and I will not cry.'

Bond said, 'I'm afraid it's worse than that, Domino. It's not about me. It's about your brother.'

Bond sensed the stiffening of her body. She said in a low, tense voice, 'Go on. Tell me.'

Bond took the bracelet out of his pocket and silently handed it to her.

She took it. She hardly gave it a glance. She turned a little away from Bond. 'So he is dead. What happened to him?'

'It is a bad story, and a very big one. It involves your friend Largo. It is a very great conspiracy. I am here to find out things for my government. I am really a kind of policeman. I am telling you this and I will tell you the rest because hundreds and perhaps thousands of people will die unless you help to prevent it. That is why I had to show you that bracelet and hurt you so that you would believe me. I am breaking my oath in doing this. Whatever happens, whatever you decide to do, I trust you not to tell what I am going to say.'

'So that is why you made love to me–to make me do what you want. And now you blackmail me with the death of my brother.' The words came out between her teeth. Now in a soft, deadly whisper, she said, 'I hate you, I hate you, I hate you.'

Bond said coldly, in a matter-of-fact voice, 'Your brother was killed by Largo, or on his orders. I came here to tell you that. But then,' he hesitated, 'you were there and I love you and want you. When what happened began to happen I should have had strength to stop it. I hadn't. I knew it was then or perhaps never. Knowing what I knew, it was a dreadful thing to have done. But you looked so beautiful and happy. I wanted to put off hurting you. That is my only excuse.' Bond paused. 'Now listen to what I have to tell you. Try and forget about your hate for me. In a moment you will realize that we are nothing in all this. This is a thing by itself.' Bond didn't wait for her to comment. He began from the beginning and went slowly, minutely, through the whole case, omitting only the advent of the *Manta*, the one factor that could now be of help to Largo and perhaps alter his plans. He ended, 'So you see, there is nothing we can do until those weapons are actually on board the *Disco*. Until that moment comes, Largo has a perfect alibi with his treasure-hunt story. There is nothing to link him with the crashed plane or with SPECTRE. If we interfere with him now, this moment, arrest the ship on some excuse, put a watch on her, prevent her sailing, there will only be a delay in the SPECTRE plan. Only Largo and his men know where the bombs are hidden. If the plane has gone for them, it will be keeping contact with the *Disco* by radio. If there's any hitch, the plane can leave the bombs at the hiding place or at another, dump them in shallow water anywhere, and return for them when the trouble has blown over. Even the *Disco* could be taken off the job and some other ship or plane used any time in the future. SPECTRE headquarters, wherever they are, will inform the Prime Minister that there has been a change of plan, or they can say nothing at all. Then, perhaps weeks from now, they will send another communication. And this time there will perhaps be only twenty-four hour's notice for the money to be dropped. The terms will be tougher. And we shall have to accept them. So long as those bombs are still lost to us, the threat is there. You see that?'

'Yes. So what is to be done?' The voice was harsh. The girl's eyes glittered fiercely as they looked at and through Bond towards some distant target–not, he thought, at Largo the great conspirator, but at Largo who had had her brother killed.

'We have got to know when those bombs are on board the *Disco*. That is all that matters. Then we can act with all our weight. And we have one great factor on our side. We are pretty sure that Largo feels secure. He still believes that the wonderful plan, and it is wonderful, is going exactly as it was meant to do. That is our strength and our only strength. You see that?'

'And how are you to know when the bombs come on board the yacht?'

'You must tell us.'

'Yes.' The monosyllable was dull, indifferent. 'But how am I to know? And how am I to tell you? This man is no fool. He is only foolish in wanting his mistress'–she spat the word out–'when so much else is at stake.' She paused. 'These people have chosen badly. Largo cannot live without a woman within reach. They should have known that.'

'When did Largo tell you to come back on board?'

'Five. The boat is coming to fetch me at Palmyra.'

Bond looked at his watch. 'It is now four. I have this Geiger counter. It is simple to use. It will tell at once if the bombs are on board. I want you to take it with you. If it says there is a bomb on board, I want you to show a light at your porthole–switch the lights on in your cabin several times, anything like that. We have men watching the ship. They will be told to report. Then get rid of the Geiger counter. Drop it overboard.'

She said scornfully, 'That is a silly plan. It is the sort of melodramatic nonsense people write about in thrillers. In real life people don't go into their cabins and switch on their lights in daylight. No. If the bombs are there, I will come up on deck–show myself to your men. that is natural behaviour. If they are not there, I will stay in my cabin.'

'All right. Have it your own way. But will you do this?'

'Of course. If I can prevent myself killing Largo when I see him. But on condition that when you get him you will see that he is killed.' She was entirely serious. She looked at him with matter-of-fact eyes as if he was a travel agent and she was reserving a seat on a train.

'I doubt if that will happen. I should say that every man on board will get a life sentence in prison.'

She considered this. 'Yes. That will do. That is worse than being killed. Now show me how this machine works.' She got to her feet and took a couple of steps up the beach. She seemed to remember something. She looked down at the bracelet in her hand. She turned and walked down to the edge of the sea and stood for a moment looking out across the quiet water. She said some words that Bond couldn't hear. Then she leant back and with all her strength threw the gold chain far out over the shoal into the dark blue. The chain twinkled briefly in the strong sun and there was a small splash. She watched the ripples widen and, when the smashed mirror was whole again, turned and walked back up the sand, her small limp leaving footmarks of uneven depth.

Bond showed her the working of the machine. He eliminated the wrist-watch indicator and told her to depend entirely on the telltale clicking. 'Anywhere in the ship should be all right,' he explained. 'But better near the hold if you can get there. Say you want to take a photograph from the well-deck aft or something. This thing's made up to look like a Rolleiflex. It's got all the Rolleiflex lenses and gadgets on the front, lever to press and all. It just hasn't got a film. You could say that you'd decided to take some farewell pictures of Nassau and the yacht, couldn't you?'

'Yes.' The girl, who had been listening attentively, now seemed distracted. Tentatively she put out a hand and touched Bond's arm. She let the hand fall. She looked up at him and then swiftly away. She said shyly, 'What I said, what I said about hating you. That is not true. I didn't understand. How could I–all this terrible story? I still can't quite believe it, believe that Largo has anything to do with it. We had a sort of an affair in Capri. He is an attractive man. Everyone else wanted him. It was a challenge. to take him from all these other smart women. Then he explained about the yacht and this wonderful trip looking for treasure. It was like a fairy tale. Of course I agreed to come. Who wouldn't have? In exchange, I was quite ready to do what I had to do.' She looked briefly at him and away. 'I am sorry. But that is how it is. When we got to Nassau and he kept me ashore, away from the yacht, I was surprised but I was not offended. The islands are beautiful. There was enough for me to do. But what you have told me explains many small things. I was never allowed in the radio room. The crew were silent and unfriendly–they treated me like someone who was not wanted on board, and they were on curious terms with Largo, more like equals than paid men. And they were tough men and better educated than sailors usually are. So it all fits. I can even remember that, for a whole week before last Thursday, Largo was terribly nervous and irritable. We were already getting tired of each other. I put it down to that. I was even making plans for flying home by myself. But he has been better the last few days and when he told me to be packed and ready to come on board this evening, I thought I might just as well do as he said. And of course I was very excited over this treasure hunt. I wanted to see what it was all about. But then,' she looked out to sea, 'there was you. And this afternoon, after what happened, I had decided to tell Largo I would not go. I would stay here and see where you went and go with you.' For the first time she looked him full in the face and held his eyes. 'Would you have let me do that?'

Bond reached out and put his hand against her cheek. 'Of course I would.'

'But what happens now? When shall I see you again?'

This was the question Bond had dreaded. By sending her back on board, and with the Geiger counter, he was putting her in double danger. She could be found out by Largo, in which case her death would be immediate. If it came to a chase, which seemed almost certain, the *Manta* would sink the *Disco* by gunfire or torpedo, probably without warning. Bond had added up these factors and had closed his mind to them. He kept it closed. He said, 'As soon as this is over. I shall look for you wherever you are. But now you are going to be in danger. You know this. Do you want to go on with it?'

She looked at her watch. She said, 'It is half past four. I must go. Do not come with me to the car. Kiss me once and stay here. Do not worry about what you want done. I will do it well. It is either that or a stiletto in the back for this man.' She held out her arms. 'Come.'

Minutes later Bond heard the engine of the MG come to life. He waited until the sound had receded in the distance down the Western Coast Road, then he went to the Land Rover and climbed in and followed.

A mile down the coast, at the two white obelisks that marked the entrance to Palmyra, dust still hung in the driveway. Bond sneered at his impulse to drive in after her and stop her from going out to the yacht. What the hell was he thinking of? He drove on fast down the road to Old Fort Point, where the police watchers were housed in the garage of a deserted villa. They were there, one man reading a paperback in a canvas chair while the other sat before tripod binoculars that were trained on the *Disco* through a gap in the blinds of a side window. The khaki walkie-talkie set was beside them on the floor. Bond gave them the new briefing and got on the radio to the Police Commissioner and confirmed it to him. The Commissioner passed two messages to him from Leiter. One was to the effect that the visit to Palmyra had been negative except that a servant had said the girl's baggage had gone on board the *Disco* that afternoon. The boathouse was completely innocent. It contained a glass-bottomed boat and a pedallo. The pedallo would have made the tracks they had seen from the air. The second message said that the *Manta* was expected in twenty minutes. Would Bond meet Leiter at the Prince George Wharf, where she would dock.

The *Manta*, coming with infinite caution up-channel, had none of the greyhound elegance of the conventional submarine. She was blunt and thick and ugly. The bulbous metal cucumber, her rounded nose shrouded with tarpaulin to hide the secrets of her radar scanner from the Nassavians, held no suggestion of her speed, which Leiter said was around forty knots submerged. 'But they won't tell you that, James. That's Classified. I guess we're going to find that even the paper in the can is Classified when we go aboard. Watch out for these Navy guys. Nowadays they're so tight-lipped they think even a belch is a security risk.'

'What else do you know about her?'

'Well, we won't tell this to the captain, but of course in C.I.A. we had to be taught the basic things about these atom subs, so as we could brief agents on what to look for and recognize clues in their reports. She's one of the George Washington Class, about 4,000 tons, crew of around a hundred, cost about a hundred million dollars. Range, anything you want until the show runs out or until the nuclear reactor needs topping up–say every 100,000 miles or so. If she has the same armament as the George Washington, she'll have sixteen vertical launching tubes, two banks of eight, for the Polaris solid fuel missile. These have a range of around 1,200 miles. The crews call the tubes "the Sherwood Forest" because they're painted green and the missile compartment looks like rows of great big tree trunks. These Polaris jobs are fired from way down below the surface. The sub stops and holds dead steady. They have the ship's exact position at all times through radio fixes and star sights through a tricky affair called a star-tracker periscope. All this dope is fed into the missiles automatically. Then the chief gunner presses a button and a missile shoots up through the water by compressed air. When it breaks surface the solid fuel rockets ignite and take the missile the rest of the way. Hell of a weapon really when you come to think of it. Imagine these damned things shooting up out of the sea anywhere in the world and blowing some capital city to smithereens. We've got six of them already and we're going to have more. Good deterrent when you come to think of it. You don't know where they are or when. Not like bomber bases and firing pads and so on you can track down and put out of action with your first rocket wave.'

Bond commented drily, 'They'll find some way of spotting them. And presumably an atomic depth charge set deep would send a shock-wave through hundreds of miles of water and blow anything to pieces over a huge area. But has she got anything smaller than these missiles? If we're going to do a job on the *Disco* what are we going to use?'

'She's got six torpedo tubes up front and I dare say she's got some smaller stuff–machine-guns and so forth. The trouble's going to be to get the commander to fire them. He's not going to like firing on an unarmed civilian yacht on the order of a couple of plain-clothes guys, and one of them a Limey at that. Hope his orders from the Navy Department are as solid as mine and yours.'

The huge submarine bumped gently against the wharf. Lines were thrown and an aluminium gangplank was run ashore. There was a ragged cheer from the crowd of watchers being held back by a cordon of police. Leiter said, 'Well, here we go. And to one hell of a bad start. Not a hat between us to salute the quarter deck with. You curtsy, I'll bow.'

Chapter Twenty

Time for Decision

The interior of the submarine was incredibly roomy, and it was stairs and not a ladder that led down into the interior. There was no clutter, and the sparkling paintwork was in two-tone green. Powerlines painted in vivid colours provided a cheerful contrast to the almost hospital décor. Preceded by the officer of the watch, a young man of about twenty-eight, they went down two decks. The air (70° with 46% humidity, explained the officer) was beautifully cool. At the bottom of the stairs he turned left and knocked on a door that said 'Commander P. Pedersen, U.S.N.'

The captain looked about forty. He had a square, rather Scandinavian face with a black crew-cut just going grey. He had shrewd, humorous eyes but a dangerous mouth and jaw. He was sitting behind a neatly stacked metal desk smoking a pipe. There was an empty coffee cup in front of him and a signal pad on which he had just been writing. He got up and shook hands, waved them to two chairs in front of his desk and said to the officer of the watch, 'Coffee, please, Stanton. And have this sent, would you?' He tore the top sheet off the signal pad and handed it across. 'Most Immediate.'

He sat down. 'Well gentlemen. Welcome aboard. Commander Bond, it's a pleasure to have a member of the Royal Navy visit the ship. Ever been in subs before?'

'I have,' said Bond, 'but only as a supercargo. I was in intelligence–R.N.V.R. Special Branch. Strictly a chocolate sailor.'

The captain laughed. 'That's good! And you, Mr Leiter?'

'No, Captain. But I used to have one of my own. You operated it with a sort of rubber bulb and tube. Trouble was they'd never let me have enough depth of water in the bath to see what she could really do.'

'Sounds rather like the Navy Department. They'll never let me try this ship full out. Except once on trials. Every time you want to get going, the needle comes across a damn red line some interfering so-and-so has painted on the dial. Well, gentlemen,' the captain looked at Leiter, 'what's the score? Haven't had such a flood of Top Secret Most Immediates since Korea. I don't mind telling you, the last one was from the Chief of the Navy, Personal. Said I was to consider myself under your orders, or, on your death or incapacity, under Commander Bond's, until Admiral Carlson arrives at 1900 this evening. So what? What's cooking? All I know is that all signals have been prefixed Operation Thunderball. What is this operation?'

Bond had greatly taken to Commander Pedersen. He liked his ease and humour and, in general–the old navy phrase came back to him–the cut of his jib. Now he watched the stolid good-humoured face as Leiter told his story down to the departure of Largo's amphibian at 1.30 and the instructions Bond had given to Domino Vitali.

In the background to Leiter's voice there was a medley of soft noises–the high, constant whine of a generator overlaid by the muted background of canned music–the Ink Spots singing 'I love coffee, I love tea'. Occasionally the P.A. System above the captain's desk crackled and sang with operational double-talk–'Roberts to Chief of the Boat'–'Chief Engineer wants Oppenshaw'–'Team Blue to Compartment F'–and from somewhere came the suck and gurgle of a pumplike apparatus that sounded punctually every two minutes. It was like being inside the simple brain of a robot that worked by hydraulics and electrical impulses with a few promptings from its human masters.

After ten minutes, Commander Pedersen sat back. He reached for his pipe and began filling it absentmindedly. He said, 'Well, that's one hell of a story.' He smiled. 'And strangely enough, even if I hadn't had these signals from the Navy Department, I'd believe it. Always did think something like this would happen one of these days. Hell! I have to carry these missiles around, and I'm in command of a nuclear ship. But that doesn't mean that I'm not terrified by the whole business. Got a wife and two children, and that doesn't help either. These atomic weapons are just too damned dangerous. Why, any one of these little sandy cays around here could hold the whole of the United States to ransom–just with one of my missiles trained on Miami. And here am I, fellow called Peter Pedersen, age thirty-eight, maybe sane or maybe not, toting around sixteen of the things–enough to damn near wipe out England. However,' he puts his hands down on the desk in front of him, 'that's all by the way. Now we've got just one small piece of the problem on our hands–small, but as big as the world. So what are we to do? As I see it, the idea of you gentlemen is that this man Largo will be coming back any minute now in his plane after picking up the bombs from where he hid them. If he's got the bombs, and on what you've told me I'll go along with the probability that he has, this girl will give us the tip-off. Then we close in and arrest his ship or blow it out of the water. Right? But supposing he hasn't got the bombs on board, or for one reason or another we don't get the tip-off, what do we do then?'

Bond said quietly, 'We follow him, sit close on his tail, until the time limit, that's about twenty-four hours from now, is up. That's all we can do without causing one hell of a legal stink. When the time limit's up, we can hand the whole problem back to our governments and they can decide what to do with the *Disco* and the sunken plane and all the rest. By that time, some little man in a speedboat we've never heard of may have left one of the bombs off the coast of America, and Miami may have gone up in the air. Or there may be a big bang somewhere else in the world. There's been plenty of time to take those bombs off the plane and get them thousands of miles from here. Well, that'll be too bad and we'll have muffed it. But at this moment we're in the position of a detective watching a man he thinks is going to commit a murder. Doesn't even know for sure whether he's got a gun on him or not. There's nothing the detective can do but follow the man and wait until he actually pulls the gun out of his pocket and points it. Then, and only then, the detective can shoot the man or arrest him.' Bond turned to Leiter. 'Isn't that about it, Felix?'

'That's how it figures. And Captain, Commander Bond here and I are damn sure Largo's our man and that he'll be sailing for his target in no time at all. That's why we agreed to panic and ask you along. One gets you a hundred he'll be placing that bomb at night and tonight's the last night he's got. By the way, Captain, have you got steam up, or whatever the atom boys call it?'

'I have, and we can be under way in just about five minutes.' The captain shook his head. 'But there's one bit of bad news for you, gentlemen. I just can't figure how we're going to keep track of the *Disco*.'

'How's that? You've got the speed, haven't you?' Leiter caught himself pointing his steel hook threateningly at the captain, and hastily brought it down again to his lap.

The captain smiled. 'Guess so. Guess we could give her a good race on a straight course, but you gentlemen don't seem to have figured on the navigational hazards in this part of the ocean.' He pointed at the British Admiralty chart on the wall. 'Take a look at that. Ever seen a chart with so many figures on it? Looks like a spilled ants' nest. Those are soundings, gentlemen, and I can tell you that unless the *Disco* sticks to one of the deep-water channels–Tongue of the Ocean, North-West Providence Channel, or the North-East–we've had it, as Commander Bond would say. All the rest of that area'–he waved a hand–'may look the same blue colour on a map, but after your trip in that Grumman Goose you know darned well it isn't the same blue colour. Darned near the whole of that area is banks and shoal with only around three to ten fathoms over it. If I was quite crazy and looking for a nice cosy job ashore, I'd take the ship along surfaced in ten fathoms–if I could bribe the navigator and seal off the echo-sounder from crew members. But even if we got a long spell of ten fathoms on the chart, you got to remember that's an old chart, dates back to the days of sail, and these banks have been shifting for more than fifty years since it was drawn up. Then there's the tides that set directly on to and off the banks, and the coral niggerheads that won't show up on the echo-sounder until you hear the echo of them smashing up the hull or the screw.' The captain turned back to his desk. 'No, gentlemen. This Italian vessel was darned well chosen. With that hydrofoil device of hers, she probably doesn't draw more than a fathom. If she chooses to keep to the shallows, we just haven't got a chance. And that's flat.' The captain looked from one to another of them. 'Want me to call up the Navy Department and have Fort Lauderdale take over with those fighter bombers you've got on call–get them to do a shadowing job?'

The two men looked at each other. Bond said, 'She won't be showing lights. They'll have the hell of a job picking her up at night. What do you say, Felix? Maybe we'd better call them out even if it's only to keep some sort of a watch off the American coast. Then, if the Captain's willing, we'll take the North-West Channel–if the *Disco* sails, that is–and bank on the Bahamas Rocket Station being Target No. 1.'

Felix Leiter ran his left hand through the mop of straw-coloured hair. 'Goddammit,' he said angrily. 'Hell yes, I suppose so. We're looking fools enough already bringing the *Manta* on stage. What's a squadron of planes? Sure. We've just *got* to back our hunch that it's Largo and the *Disco*. Come on, let's get together with the Captain and whip off a signal that doesn't look too damned silly–copy to C.I.A. and to your Chief. How do you want it to go?'

'Admiralty for M, prefixed Operation Thunderball.' Bond wiped a hand down over his face. 'God, this is going to put the cat among the pigeons.' He looked up at the metal wall clock. 'Six. That'll be midnight in London. Popular time to get a signal like this.'

The P.A. System in the ceiling spoke more clearly. 'Watch Officer to Captain. Police officer with urgent message for Commander Bond.' The captain pressed a switch and spoke into a desk microphone. 'Bring him below. Prepare to cast off lines. All hands prepare for sailing.' The captain waited for the acknowledgment and released the switch. The captain smiled across at them. He said to Bond, 'What's the name of that girl? Domino? Well, Domino, say the good word.'

The door opened. A police corporal, his hat off, crashed to attention on the steel flooring and extended a stiff arm. Bond took the buff O.H.M.S. envelope and slit it open. He ran his eyes down the pencilled message signed by the Police Commissioner. Unemotionally he read out:

'PLANE RETURNED 1730 HOISTED INBOARD. DISCO SAILED AT 1755, FULL SPEED, COURSE NORTH WEST STOP GIRL DID NOT REPEAT NOT REAPPEAR ON DECK AFTER BOARDING.'

Bond borrowed a signal blank from the captain and wrote:

MANTA WILL ENDEAVOUR SHADOW VIA NORTHWEST PROVIDENCE CHANNEL STOP FIGHTER BOMBER SQUADRON FROM FORT LAUDERDALE WILL BE ASKED THROUGH NAVY DEPARTMENT TO COOPERATE WITHIN RADIUS OF TWO HUNDRED MILES OFF FLORIDA COAST STOP MANTA WILL KEEP CONTACT THROUGH WINDSOR FIELD AIR CONTROL STOP NAVY DEPARTMENT AND ADMIRALTY BEING INFORMED STOP PLEASE INFORM GOVERNOR ALSO ADMIRAL CARLSON AND BRIGADIER FAIRCHILD ON ARRIVAL.

Bond signed the message and passed it to the captain, who also signed, as did Leiter. Bond put the message in an envelope and gave it to the corporal, who wheeled smartly and clanked out in his heavy boots.

When the door was shut, the captain pressed down the switch on the intercom. He gave orders to sail, surfaced, course due north, at ten knots. Then he switched off. In the short silence, there was a flurry of background noise, piping of bosuns' whistles, a thin mechanical whine, and the sound of running feet. The submarine trembled slightly. The captain said quietly, 'Well, gentlemen, that's that. I'd like to have the goose a bit less wild and a bit more solid. But I'll be glad to chase her for you. Now then, that signal.'

With only half his mind on the wording of the signal, Bond sat and worried about the significance of the Commissioner's message and about Domino. It looked bad. It looked as if either the plane had not brought back the two bombs, or one of them, in which case the mobilization of the *Manta* and of the fighter bombers was a pretty meaningless precaution, hardly justified by the evidence. It could easily be that the crashed Vindicator and the missing bombs were the work of some entirely different group and that, while they chased the *Disco*, the field was being left clear for SPECTRE. But Bond's instincts refused to allow him to accept this possibility. As cover, the whole *Disco*-Largo set-up was one hundred per cent watertight. It could not be faulted in any respect. That in itself was enough to arouse Bond's suspicions. A plot of this magnitude and audacity could only have been conceived under faultless cover and down to the smallest detail. Largo could have just set off on his treasure hunt, and everything, down to the last-minute plane recce of the treasure location, to see if there were any fishing boats about for instance, fitted in with that possibility. Or he could be sailing to lay the bomb, adjust the time fuse for perhaps a few hours after the deadline to allow time for its recovery or destruction if England and America at the last moment agreed to pay the ransom, and get far enough away from the danger area to avoid the explosion and establish an alibi. But where was the bomb? Had it arrived on board in the plane and had Domino for some reason been unable to go up on deck to make her signal? Or was it going to be picked up en route to the target area? The westerly course from Nassau, heading perhaps for the North-West Light, through the Berry Island Channel, fitted both possibilities. The sunken plane lay westwards, south of the Biminis, and so did Miami and other possible targets on the American coast. Or, after passing through the channel, about fifty miles west of Nassau, the *Disco* could veer sharply northwards and, after another fifty miles of sailing through shoal water that would discourage pursuit, get back into the North-West Providence Channel and make straight for the Grand Bahamas and the missile station.

Bond, fretted with indecision and the fear that he and Leiter were making majestic fools of themselves, forced himself to face one certainty–he and Leiter and the *Manta* were engaged on a crazy gamble. If the bomb was on board, if the *Disco* veered north for the Grand Bahamas and the missile station, then, by racing up the North-West Channel, the *Manta* might intercept her in time.

But if this gamble came off, with all its possibilities of error, why hadn't Domino made her signal? What had happened to her?

Chapter Twenty-one

Very Softly, Very Slowly

The *Disco*, a dark torpedo leaving a deep, briefly creaming wake, hurtled across the indigo mirror of the sea. In the big stateroom there was silence save for the dull boom of the engines and the soft tinkle of a glass on the sideboard. Although, as a precaution, the storm shutters were battened down over the portholes, the only light inside came from a single port navigation lantern hung from the roof. The dim red light only just illuminated the faces of the twenty men sitting round the long table, and the red-and-black-shadowed features, contorting with the slight sway of the top light, gave the scene the appearance of a conspiracy in hell.

At the top of the table Largo, his face, though the cabin was air-conditioned, shining with sweat, began to speak. His voice was tense and hoarse with strain. 'I have to report that we are in a state of emergency. Half an hour ago, No. 17 found Miss Vitali in the well deck. She was standing fiddling with a camera. When No. 17 came upon her she lifted the camera and pretended to take a photograph of Palmyra, although the safety cap was over the lens. No. 17 was suspicious. He reported to me. I went below and took her to her cabin. She struggled with me. Her whole attitude aroused my suspicions. I was forced to subdue her by drastic measures. I took the camera and examined it.' Largo paused. He said quietly, 'The camera was a fake. It concealed a Geiger counter. The counter was, very naturally, registering over 500 milliroentgens. I brought her back to consciousness and questioned her. She refused to talk. In due course I shall force her to do so and then she will be eliminated. It was time to sail. I again rendered her unconscious and roped her securely to her bunk. I have now summoned this meeting to acquaint you of this occurrence, which I have already reported to No. 2.'

Largo was silent. A threatening, exasperated growl came from round the table. No. 14, one of the Germans, said through his teeth, 'And what, Mister No. 1, did No. 2 have to say about this?'

'He said we were to carry on. He said the whole world is full of Geiger counters looking for us. The secret services of the whole world have been mobilized against us. Some busybody in Nassau, the police probably, was perhaps ordered to have a radiation search made of all ships in harbour. Perhaps Miss Vitali was bribed to bring the counter on board. But No. 2 said that once we have placed the weapon in the target area there will be nothing to fear. I have had the radio operator listening for unusual traffic between Nassau and the Coast. The density is quite normal. If we were suspected, Nassau would be deluged with wireless traffic from London and Washington. But all is quiet. So the operation will proceed as planned. When we are well away from the area, we will dispose of the lead casing of the weapon. The lead casing will contain Miss Vitali.'

No. 14 persisted: 'But you will first obtain the truth from this woman? It is not pleasant for our future plans to think that we may be under suspicion.'

'Interrogation will begin as soon as the meeting is over. If you want my opinion, those two men who came on board yesterday–this Bond and the man Larkin–may be involved. They may be secret agents. The so-called Larkin had a camera. I did not look at it closely, but it was similar to that in the possession of Miss Vitali. I blame myself for not having been more careful with these two men. But their story was convincing. On our return to Nassau tomorrow morning, we shall have to be circumspect. Miss Vitali will have fallen overboard. I will work out the details of the story. There will be an inquest. This will be irritating but nothing more. Our witnesses will be unshakeable. It will be wise to use the coins as additional alibi for our whereabout tonight. No. 5, is the state of erosion of the coins satisfactory?'

No. 5, Kotze the physicist, said judiciously, 'It is no more than adequate. But they will pass examination, a cursory examination. They are authentic doubloons and Reals of the early seventeenth century. Sea water has no great effect on gold and silver. I have used a little acid to pit them. They will of course have to be handed to the coroner and declared as treasure trove. It would need a far greater expert than he or the court to pass judgment on them. There will be no compulsion to reveal the location of the treasure. We could perhaps give the depth of water–ten fathoms let us say, and an unspecified reef. I see no means by which our story could be upset. There is often very deep water outside reefs. Miss Vitali could have had trouble with her aqua-lung and could have been seen disappearing over the deep shelf where our echo-sounder gave the depth as a hundred fathoms. We did our best to dissuade her from taking part in the search. But she was an expert swimmer. The romance of the occasion was too much for her.' No. 5 opened his hands. 'There are often accidents of this nature. Many lives are lost in this way every year. A thorough search was instituted, but there were shark. The treasure hunt was broken off and we immediately returned to Nassau to report the tragedy.' No. 5 shook his head decisively. 'I see no reason to be dismayed by this occurrence. But I am in favour of a most rigorous interrogation.' No. 5 turned his head politely in Largo's direction. 'There are certain uses of electricity of which I have knowledge. The human body cannot resist them. If I can be of any service . . .?'

Largo's voice was equally polite. They might have been discussing remedies for a seasick passenger. 'Thank you. I have means of persuasion that I have found satisfactory in the past. But I shall certainly call upon you if the case is an obstinate one.' Largo looked down the table into the shadowed, ruby faces. 'And now we will quickly run through the final details.' He glanced down at his watch. 'It is midnight. There will be two hours' moonlight starting at three a.m. The first light of dawn will be shortly after five a.m. We thus have two hours for the operation. Our course will bring us in towards West End from the south. This is a normal entry to the islands, and even if our further progress towards the target area is noted by the missile station radar it will only be assumed that we are a yacht that has strayed slightly off course. We shall anchor at exactly three a.m. and the swimming party will leave for the half-mile swim to the laying point. The fifteen of you who will be taking part in this swim will, as arranged, swim in arrow formation, the Chariot and the sled with the missile in the centre. Formation must be strictly kept to avoid straying. The blue torch on my back should be an adequate beacon, but if any man gets lost, he returns to the ship. Is that understood? The first duty of the escort will be to watch for shark and barracuda. I will again remind you that the range of your guns is not much more than twenty feet and that fish must be hit in or behind the head. Any man who is about to fire must warn his neighbour, who will then stand by to give additional fire if required. However, one hit should be sufficient to kill if the curare is, as we have been informed, not affected by the passage through sea water. Above all,' Largo put his hands decisively down on the table before him, 'do not forget to remove the small protective sheath from the barb before firing.' Largo raised his hands. 'You will forgive me for repeating these points. We have had many exercises in similar conditions and I have confidence that all will be well. But the underwater terrain will be unfamiliar and the effect of the dexedrine pills–they will be issued to the swimming party after this meeting–will be to sensitize the nervous system as well as provide the extra stamina and encouragement. So we must all be prepared for the unexpected and know how to handle it. Are there any further questions?'

During the planning stages, months before in Paris, Blofeld had warned Largo that if trouble was caused by any members of his team it was to be expected from the two Russians, the ex-members of SMERSH, No. 10 and No. 11. 'Conspiracy,' Blofeld had said, 'is their lifeblood. Hand in hand with conspiracy walks suspicion. These two men will always be wondering if they are not the object of some subsidiary plot–to give them the most dangerous work, to make them fall-guys for the police, to kill them and steal their share of the profits. They will be inclined to inform against their colleagues and always to have reservations about the plans that are agreed upon. For them, the obvious plan, the right way to do a thing, will have been chosen for some ulterior reason which is being kept hidden from them. They will need constant reassurance that nothing is being kept hidden from them, but, once they have accepted their orders, they will carry them out meticulously and without regard for their personal safety. Such men, apart from their special talents, are worth having. But you will please remember what I have said and, should there be trouble, should they try and sow mistrust within the team, you must act quickly and with utter ruthlessness. The maggots of mistrust and disloyalty must not be allowed to get a hold in your team. They are the enemies within that can destroy even the most meticulous planning.'

Now No. 10, a once-famous SMERSH terrorist called Strelik, began talking. He was sitting two places away from Largo, on his left. He did not address Largo, but the meeting. He said, 'Comrades, I am thinking of the interesting matters recounted by No. 1, and I am telling myself that everything has been excellently arranged. I am also thinking that this operation will be a very fine one and that it will certainly not be necessary to explode the second weapon on Target No. 2. I have some documentations on these islands and I am learning from the *Yachtsman's*' (No. 10 had trouble with the word) '*Guide to the Bahamas* that there is a big new hotel within a few miles of our target site, also a scattered township. I am therefore estimating that the explosion of Weapon No. 1 will destroy perhaps two thousand persons. Two thousand persons is not very many in my country and their death, compared with the devastation of this important missile station, would not, in the Soviet Union, be considered of great importance. I am thinking that it will be otherwise in the West and that the destruction of these people and the rescuing of the survivors will be considered a grave matter that will act decisively towards immediate agreement with our terms and the saving of Target No. 2 from destruction. This being so, Comrades,' the full, flat voice gained a trace of animation, 'I am saying to myself that within as little as twenty-four hours our labours will have been completed and the great prize will be within our grasp. Now, Comrades,' the red and black shadows turned the taut little smile into a dark grimace, 'with so much money so near at hand, a most unworthy thought has come into my mind.' (Largo put his hand in his coat pocket and put up the safe on the little Colt ·25.) 'And I would not be performing my duty to my Russian comrade, No. 11, nor to the other members of our team, if I did not share this thought with you at the same time requesting forbearance for what may be unfounded suspicions.'

The meeting was very quiet, ominously so. These men had all been secret agents or conspirators. They recognized the smell of insurrection, the shadow of approaching disloyalty. What did No. 10 know? What was he going to divulge? Each man got ready to decide very quickly which way to jump when the cat was let out of the bag. Largo slipped the gun out of his pocket and held it along his thigh.

'There will come a moment,' continued No. 10, watching the faces of the men opposite for a quick gauge of their reactions, 'very shortly, when fifteen of us, leaving five members and six sub-agents on board this ship, will be out there,' waved a hand at the cabin wall, 'in the darkness, at least half an hour's swim from this ship. At that moment, Comrades,' the voice became sly, 'what a thing it would be if those remaining on board were to sail the ship away and leave us in the water.' There was a shifting and muttering round the table. No. 10 held up a hand. 'Ridiculous I am thinking, and so no doubt are you, Comrades. But we are men of a feather. We recognize the unworthy urges that can come upon even the best of friends and comrades when fortunes are at stake. And, Comrades, with fifteen of us gone, how much more of a fortune would there be for those remaining, with their story for No. 2 of a great fight with sharks in which we all succumbed?'

Largo said softly, 'And what is it you propose, No. 10?'

For the first time, No. 10 looked to his right. He could not see the expression in Largo's eye. He spoke at the great red and black mass of his face. The tone of his voice was obstinate. He said, 'I am proposing that one member of each national group should stay on board to safeguard the interests of the other members of his national group. That would reduce the swimming party to ten. In this way those who are undertaking this dangerous work would go about it with more enthusiasm knowing that no such happening as I have mentioned could come about.'

Largo's voice was polite, unemotional. He said, 'I have one very short and simple answer to your suggestion, No. 10.' The light glittered redly on the metal thumb that protruded from the big hand. The three bullets pumped so quickly into the face of the Russian that the three explosions, the three bright flashes, were almost one. No. 10 put up two feeble hands, palms forward, as if to catch any further bullets, gave a jerk forward with his stomach at the edge of the table and then crashed heavily backwards, in a splinter of chair wood, on to the floor.

Largo put the muzzle of the gun up to his nose and delicately sniffed at it, moving it to and fro under the nostrils as if it was some delicious vial of perfume. In silence, he looked slowly down one rank of faces and up the other. Finally he said softly, 'The meeting is now at an end. Will all members please return to their cabins and look for a last time to their equipment. Food will be ready from now on in the galley. One drink of alcohol will also be available for those who want it. I will detail two crew members to look after the late No. 10. Thank you.'

When Largo was alone he got to his feet, stretched, and gave a great cavernous yawn. Then he turned to the sideboard, opened a drawer and took out a box of Corona cigars. He chose one and, with a gesture of distaste, lit it. He then took the closed red rubber container that held the ice cubes and walked out of the door to the cabin of Domino Vitali.

He closed the door and locked it. Here also, a red riding light hung from the ceiling. Under it, on the double bunk, the girl lay offered like a starfish, her ankles and wrists strapped to the four corners of the ironwork below the mattress. Largo put the ice-box down on the chest of drawers and balanced the cigar carefully beside it so that the glowing tip would not spoil the varnish.

The girl watched him, her eyes glittering red points in the semi-darkness.

Largo said, 'My dear, I have had great enjoyment out of your body, much pleasure. In return, unless you tell me who gave you that machine to bring on board, I shall be forced to cause you great pain. It will be caused with these two simple instruments,' he held up the cigar and blew on the tip until it glowed brightly, 'this for heat, and these ice cubes for cold. Applied scientifically, as I shall apply them, they will have the inevitable effect of causing your voice, when it has stopped screaming, to speak, and speak the truth. Now then. Which is it to be?'

The girl's voice was deadly with hate. She said, 'You killed my brother and you will now kill me. Go on and enjoy yourself. You are already a piece of death yourself. When the rest of it comes, very soon, I pray God you will suffer a million times more than both of us.'

Largo's laugh was a short, harsh bark. He walked over to the edge of the bunk. He said, 'Very well, my dear. We must see what we can do with you, very softly and very, very slowly.'

He bent down and hooked his fingers in the neckline of her shirt and the join of the brassiere. Very slowly, but with great force, he tore downwards, the whole length of her. Then he threw aside the torn halves of material and exposed the whole gleaming length of her body. He examined it carefully and reflectively and then went to the chest of drawers and took the cigar and the bowl of ice cubes and came back and made himself comfortable on the edge of the bunk.

Then he took a puff at the cigar, knocked the ash off on to the floor and leant forward.

Chapter Twenty-two

The Shadower

In the attack centre of the *Manta* it was very quiet. Commander Pedersen, standing behind the man at the echo-sounder, occasionally made a comment over his shoulder to Bond and Leiter, who had been given canvas-backed chairs well away from the depth- and speed-gauges, which had been hooded so that they could only be read by the navigating team. These three men sat side by side on red leather, foam cushioned, aluminium seats, handling the rudder and the forward and aft diving planes as if they were pilots in an airliner. Now the captain left the echo-sounder and came over to Bond and Leiter. He smiled cheerfully. 'Thirty fathoms and the nearest cay is a mile to westwards. Now we've got a clear course all the way to Grand Bahama. And we're making good speed. If we keep it up, we've got about four hour's sailing. Be off Grand Bahama about an hour before first light. How about some food and a bit of sleep? There won't be anything on the radar for an hour–these Berry Islands'll fill the screen until we're clear of them. Then'll come the big question. When we clear them, shall we see that one of the smallest of the cays has broken loose and is sailing fast northwards on a parallel course to ours? If we see that on the screen, it'll be the *Disco*. If she's there, we'll submerge. You'll hear the alarm bells. But you can just roll over and have a bit more sleep. Nothing can happen until it's certain that she's in the target area. Then we'll have to think again.' The captain made for the stairway. 'Mind if I lead the way? Watch your head on the pipes. This is the one part of the ship where there isn't much clearance.'

They followed him down and along a passage to the mess hall, a well-lighted dining-room finished in cream with pastel pink and green panels. They took their places at the head of one of the Formica-top tables away from the other officers and men, who looked curiously at the two civilians. The captain waved a hand at the walls of the room. 'Bit of a change from the old battleship grey. You'd be surprised how many eggheads are involved in the design of these ships. Have to be, if you want to keep your crew happy when the ship's submerged for a month or more at a time. The trick-cyclists said we couldn't have just one colour, must have contrast everywhere or the men's eyes get sort of depressed. This hall's used for movies, closed-circuit television, cribbage tournaments, bingo, God knows what–anything to keep the men off duty from getting bored. And you notice there's no smell of cooking or engine smells. Electrostatic precipitators all over the ship that filter them off.' A steward came with menus. 'Now then, let's get down to it. I'm having the baked Virginia ham with red-eye gravy, apple-pie with ice cream, and iced coffee. And steward, don't go too easy on that red-eye.' He turned to Bond. 'Getting out of harbour always gives me an appetite. You know, it isn't the sea the captain hates, it's the land.'

Bond ordered poached eggs with rye toast and coffee. He was grateful for the captain's cheerful talk, but he himself had no appetite. There was a gnawing tension inside him which would only be released when the *Disco* was picked up on the radar and there would be a prospect of action. And lurking behind his concern about the whole operation was worry about the girl. Had he been right to trust her with so much of the truth? Had she betrayed him? Had she been caught? Was she alive? He drank down a glass of iced water, and listened to the captain explaining how the ice cubes and the water were distilled from the sea.

Finally Bond became impatient with the cheerful, even tone of the conversation. He said, 'Forgive me, Captain, but could I interrupt for a moment and clear my mind about what we're going to do if we're right about the *Disco* and if we come up with her off the Grand Bahama? I can't figure what the next step ought to be. I've got my own ideas, but were you thinking we'd try and go alongside and board her, or just blow her out of the water?'

The captain's grey eyes were quizzical. He said, 'I was kind of leaving all that to you fellers. The Navy Department says that I'm under your orders. I'm just the chauffeur. Supposing you tell me what you have in mind and I'll be glad to go along with anything you suggest so long as it doesn't endanger my ship–' he smiled–'too much, that is. In the last resort, if the Navy Department means what it says, and from your account of this operation it does, the safety of the ship will also have to go by the board. As I told you aloft in the attack centre, I got acknowledgment of our signal and full approval for our proposed course of action. That's all the clearance I need. Now then, you tell me.'

The food came. Bond pecked at his eggs and pushed them away. He lit a cigarette. He said, looking at Felix Leiter, 'Well, I don't know what you've worked out, Felix, but this is how I see the picture we may find around four o'clock in the morning, on the assumption, that is, that the *Disco* has been sailing north in shoal water under cover of the Berry Islands and that she'll then make for the Grand Bahama shore somewhere off the site of the missile station. Well now, on that assumption, I've had a good look at the charts and it seems to me that, if she's going to lay that bomb as close to the target as she can, she'll heave to and anchor about a mile off-shore in about ten fathoms and get the bomb another half-mile or so closer to the target, lay it in twelve feet of water or so, switch on the time mechanism and get the hell away. That's how I'd go about it. She'd be away by first light and there's plenty of yacht traffic around West End from what I can gather from the pilot. She'd show up on the station radar of course, but she'd be just another yacht. Assuming the bomb's set for the twelve hour's Largo's got before the time limit expires, he could be back in Nassau or twice as far away if he wanted in the time he's got. For my money, he'll go back to Nassau with his treasure-hunting story and wait for the next lot of orders from SPECTRE.' Bond paused. He avoided Leiter's eyes. 'That is, unless he's managed to get information out of the girl.'

Leiter said staunchly, 'Hell, I don't believe that girl would talk. She's a tough cookie. And supposing she did? He's only got to drop her overboard with some lead round her neck and say her aqualung failed on the treasure hunt, or some spiel of that sort. He'd go back to Nassau all right. That man's cover's as solid as J.P. Morgan and Company.'

The captain interrupted. 'Leaving all that aside, Commander Bond, and sticking to the operational angles, how do you suggest he's going to get that bomb out of the ship and right into the target area? I agree that according to the charts he can't get much closer in the yacht, and if he did he might be in trouble with the waterfront guard at the missile station. I see from my dope on the place that they've got some kind of a guard-boat for chasing away fishermen and suchlike when they're going to do a practice shoot.'

Bond said decisively, 'I'm sure that's the real purpose of the underwater compartment in the *Disco*. They've got one of those underwater sleds in there, and probably an electric torpedo to haul it. They'll load the bomb on the sled and take it in with a team of underwater swimmers, lay it and come back to the ship. Otherwise, why have all that underwater gear?'

The captain said slowly, 'You may be right, Commander. It makes sense. But so what do you want me to do about it?'

Bond looked the captain in the eye. 'There's only one moment to nail these people. If we show our hand too soon, the *Disco* can get the hell away–only a few hundred yards maybe, and dump the bombs in a hundred fathoms. The only time to get them, and the bomb, the first bomb anyway, is when that team has left the ship and is on its way to the laying point. We've got to get their underwater team with our underwater team. The second bomb, if it's aboard, doesn't matter. We can sink the ship with the second bomb inside her.'

The captain looked down at his plate. He arranged the knife and fork tidily together, straightened the dessert spoon and took the remains of his iced coffee and swirled the fragments of ice round so that they tinkled. He put the glass back on the table and looked up, first at Leiter then at Bond. He said thoughtfully, 'I guess what you say makes sense, Commander. We have plenty of oxygen rebreathers on board. We also have ten of the finest swimmers in the Nuclear Flotilla. But they'll only have knives to fight with. I'll have to ask for volunteers.' He paused. 'Who's going to lead them?'

Bond said, 'I'll do that. Skin-diving happens to be one of my hobbies. And I know what fish to look out for and which ones not to mind about. I'll brief your men about those things.'

Felix Leiter interrupted. He said obstinately, 'And don't think you're going to leave me behind eating Virginia ham. I put an extra foot-flipper on this,' he held up the shining hook, 'and I'll race you over half a mile any day, gammy leg and all. You'd be surprised the things one gets around to improvise when someone chews off one of your arms. Compensation it's called by the medics, in case you hadn't heard about it.'

The captain smiled. He got to his feet. 'Okay, okay. I'll leave you two heroes to fight it out while I have a word to the men over the speaker system. Then we'll have to get together with the charts and see that the gear's okay and suchlike. You fellers aren't going to get any sleep after all. I'll have a ration of battle pills issued to you. You're going to need them.' He raised a hand and went off down the mess hall.

Leiter turned to Bond. 'You goddam shyster. Thought you were going to leave your old pal behind, didn't you? God, the treachery of you Limeys! Perfidious Albion is right, all right.'

Bond laughed. 'How the hell was I to know you'd been in the hands of rehabilitators and therapists and so on? I never knew you took life so seriously. I suppose you've even found some way of petting with that damned meathook of yours.'

Leiter said darkly, 'You'd be surprised. Get a girl round the arm with this and you'd be amazed the effect it has on their good resolutions. Now then, let's get down to cases. What sort of formation are we going to swim in? Can we get some of those knives made into lances? How are we going to recognize our side from theirs underwater, and in semi-darkness at that? We've got to make this operation pretty solid. That Pedersen's a good guy. We don't want to get some of his men killed through some damn silly mistake of ours.'

The voice of the captain sounded over the communication system. 'Now hear this. This is your Captain speaking. It is possible that we may encounter hazards in the course of this operation. I will tell you how this may come about. This ship has been chosen by the Navy Department for an exercise that is tantamount to an operation of war. I will tell you the story, which will remain classified top secret until further orders. This is what has happened . . .'

Bond, asleep in one of the duty officers' bunks, was awakened by the alarm bell. The iron voice of the P.A. System said: 'Diving stations. Diving stations,' and almost at once his bunk tilted slightly and the distant whine of the engines altered pitch. Bond smiled grimly to himself. He slipped off the bunk and went along up to the attack centre. Felix Leiter was already there. The captain turned way from the plot. His face was tense. He said, 'It looks as if you were right, gentlemen. We've got her all right. About five miles ahead and two points to starboard. She's doing around thirty knots. No other ship could be holding that speed, or would be likely to. And she's showing no lights. Here, care to have a look through the scope? She's raising quite a wake and kicking up plenty of phosphorescence. No moon yet, but you'll see the white blur when your eyes get used to the dark.'

Bond bent to the rubber eye sockets. In a minute he had her, a white scut on the horizon of the soft, feathery swell. He stood back. 'What's her course?'

'Same as ours–western end of Grand Bahama. We'll go deeper now and put on a bit of speed. We've got her on the Sonar as well, so we shan't lose her. We'll get up parallel and close in a bit later. The met. report gives a light westerly breeze in the early hours. That'd be a help. Don't want it too calm when we unload the swimming party. The surface'll boil quite a bit as each man goes out. Here,' he turned to a powerful-looking man in white ducks, 'this is Petty Officer Fallon. He's in command of the swimming party, under your and Mr Leiter's orders of course. All the top swimmers volunteered. He's chosen nine of them. I've taken them off all duties. Maybe you gentlemen would like to get acquainted with your team. You'll want to discuss your routines. I guess discipline'll have to be pretty tight–recognition signals and so forth. Okay? The sergeant at arms is looking after the weapons.' He smiled. 'He's rustled up a dozen flick knives. Had some difficulty persuading the men to give them up, but he's done it. He's barbed them and sharpened them down almost to needles then fitted them into the tops of broom handles. Guess he'll make you sign an indent for the brooms or he'll have the supply officer on top of him when we get out of this. All right then. Be seeing you. Ask for anything you want.' He turned back to the plot.

Bond and Leiter followed Petty Officer Fallon along the lower deck to the engine room and then to the engine repair shop. On their way they passed through the reactor room. The reactor, the equivalent of a controlled atomic bomb, was an obscene knee-level bulge rising out of the thickly leaded deck. As they passed it, Leiter whispered to Bond, 'Liquid sodium Submarine Intermediate Reactor Mark B.' He grinned sourly and crossed himself.

Bond gave the thing a sideway kick with his shoe, 'Steam-age stuff. Our Navy's got the Mark C.'

The repair shop, a long low room equipped with various forms of precision machinery, presented a curious sight. At one end were grouped the nine swimmers clad only in bathing trunks, their fine bodies glowing with sunburn. At the other, two men in grey overalls, drab figures of the machine age, were working in semi-darkness with only pinpoints of bright light cast on the whirring lathes from which the knife blades threw small fountains of blue and orange sparks. Some of the swimmers already had their spears. After the introductions, Bond took one and examined it. It was a deadly weapon, the blade, sharpened to a stiletto and notched near the top into a barb, firmly wired into the top of a long stout stave. Bond thumbed the needle-sharp steel and touched the tip. Even a shark's skin would not stand up to that. But what would the enemy have? CO_2 guns for a certainty. Bond looked the smiling bronzed young men over. There were going to be casualties–perhaps many. Everything must be done to effect surprise. But those golden skins and his own and Leiter's paler skins would show at twenty feet in the moonlight–all right for the guns, but well out of range of the spears. Bond turned to Petty Officer Fallon: 'I suppose you don't have rubber suits on board?'

'Why sure, Commander. Have to, for escape in cold waters.' He smiled.

'We're not always sailing among the palm trees.'

'We'll all need them. And could you get white or yellow numbers, big ones, painted on their backs? Then we'll know more or less who's who.'

'Sure, sure.' He called to his men. 'Hey, Fonda and Johnson. Go along to the Quartermaster and draw rubber suits for the whole team. Bracken, get a pail of rubber solution paint from Stores. Paint numbers on the backs of the suits. A foot deep. From one to twelve. Get going.'

Later, with the gleaming black suits hanging like giant bat-skins along the wall, Bond called the team together. 'Men, we're going to have one hell of an underwater battle. There'll be casualties. Anyone care to change his mind?' The faces grinned back at him. 'All right then. Now, we'll be swimming at around ten feet for a quarter, perhaps half a mile. It'll be pretty light. The moon'll be up and the bottom's white sand with some seagrass. We'll take it easy and go in triangle formation with me, No. 1, leading followed by Mr Leiter here as No. 2, and Petty Officer Fallon as No. 3. Then we broaden out behind like a wedge of geese. All you have to do is follow the number in front of you and no one'll get lost. Watch out for isolated niggerheads. As far as I can gather from the chart there's no true reef, only broken clumps. It'll be getting on for early feeding time for the fish, so watch out for anything big. But leave it alone unless it gets too inquisitive. Then three of you take it on with the spears. But don't forget that it's most unlikely any fish will attack us. Close together we'll look like one hell of a big black fish to anyone else and I guess we'll be given a wide berth. Watch out for sea eggs on the coral and mind the tips of your spears. Hold them right up near the blade. Above all, keep quiet. We must try and get surprise on our side. The enemy's got CO_2 guns, range about twenty feet. But they're slow things to reload. If one's aimed at you, try and give a small target. Keep flat in the water. Don't put your feet down and give him a full-length target. As soon as he's fired, go for him like hell with your spear right out. One jab of those things in almost any part of the head or body and your man's had it. Wounded men will have to look after themselves. We can't spare stretcher bearers. If you're wounded, back out of the fight and get away to a coral clump and rest on it. Or make for the shore and shallow water. If you've got a spear in you, don't try and pull it out. Just hold it in the wound until someone gets to you. Petty Officer Fallon will have one of the ship's signal flares. He'll release that to the surface as soon as our attack begins and your Captain will at once surface and put out an escape dinghy with an armed party and the ship's surgeon. Now then, any questions?'

'What do we do as soon as we get out of the sub, sir?'

'Try and not make any fuss on the surface. Get down quickly to ten feet and take your place in the formation. We're likely to get help from a light breeze, but we're bound to create turbulence on the surface. Keep it down as much as you can.'

'What about signals underwater, sir. Suppose a mask goes wrong or something.'

'Thumbs down for any kind of emergency. Arm held straight out for a big fish. Thumbs up means "I understand" or "Coming to help you". That's all you'll need.' Bond smiled. 'If the feet go up, that's the signal that you've had it.'

The men laughed various kinds of laugh.

There came the sudden voice of the P.A. System. 'Swimming party to the escape hatch. I repeat, swimming party to the escape hatch. Don equipment. Don equipment. Commander Bond to the Attack Centre, please.'

The whine of the engines died to a moan and then was silent. There was a slight bump as the *Manta* hit bottom.

Chapter Twenty-three

Naked Warfare

Bond shot upwards out of the escape hatch in a blast of compressed air. Far above him the surface of the sea was a glittering plate of quicksilver bubbling and swirling with the small waves that Bond was glad to see had materialized. The balloon of air rushed on past him and he watched it hit the silver ceiling like a small bomb. There was a sharp pain in his ears. To get decompression he fought with his fins and slowed down until he hung suspended ten feet below the surface. Below him the long black shape of the *Manta* looked sinister and dangerous. He thought of the electric light blazing inside her and a hundred men going about their business. It gave him a creepy feeling. Now there came a great explosion from the escape hatch as if the *Manta* was firing at Bond and the black projectile of Leiter shot up at him through the burst of silver air-bubbles. Bond moved out of his path and swam on up to the surface. Cautiously he looked above the small flurry of the waves. The *Disco*, still blacked out, lay stopped less than a mile away to his left. There were no signs of activity on board. A mile to the north lay the long dark outline of Grand Bahama edged with the white of sand and small waves. There were small patches of broken white on the coral and niggerheads in the intervening water. Above the island, on top of the tall rocket gantries that showed as indistinct black skeletons, the red aircraft warning lights winked on and off. Bond got his bearings and quietly jack-knifed his body down below the surface. He stopped at about ten feet and, keeping his body pointed like a compass needle along the course he would have to follow, lay, paddling softly with his fins to keep position, and waited for the rest of his team.

Ten minutes before, Commander Pedersen's stolid calm had given way to controlled excitement. 'By gum, it's working out like you said it would!' he had said wonderingly when Bond came into the attack centre. 'They hove to just about ten minutes ago, and since then the Sonar keeps on picking up odd noises, underwater noises, just what one would expect if they were getting things mobilized in that underwater compartment of theirs. Nothing else to go on, but it's quite enough. I guess you and the boys had better get going. As soon as you're out of the way, I'm going to float up a surface antenna and get a signal off to Navy Department, give them a Sitrep and have the missile station warned to stand by to evacuate if things go wrong. Then I'm going to come up to twenty feet or so and have two tubes loaded and keep a periscope watch. I'm issuing Petty Officer Fallon with a second flare. I've told him to keep out of trouble as much as he can and be ready to let off the second flare if it looks as if things are going really bad for our side. Unlikely, but I can't take chances with things as they are. If that second flare comes up, I'm going to close in. Knock a piece or two off the *Disco* with the 4-inch and then board her. Then I'm going to be rough as hell until that bomb's been recovered and rendered safe.' The captain shook his head doubtfully. He ran his hand over the black iron filings of his crew-cut. 'This is one hell of a situation, Commander. We'll just have to play it by ear.' He held out his hand. 'Well. You'd better get going. Good luck. I hope my boys'll be a credit to the ship.' Bond felt a tap on his shoulder. It was Leiter. He grinned through his mask and jerked up a thumb. Bond took a quick look behind him. The men lay spread out in a rough wedge, their fins and hands working slowly as they marked time in the water. Bond nodded and got going, moving forward with a slow, even trudge, one hand at his side and the other holding his spear up the shaft against his chest. Behind him, the black wedge fanned out into formation and cruised forward like some giant delta-winged stingray on the prowl.

It was hot and sticky inside the black suit and the recirculating oxygen coming through the mouthpiece tasted of rubber, but Bond forgot the discomfort as he concentrated on keeping an even pace and a dead steady course on a prominent niggerhead with waves washing its head that he had chosen as a fix for his first contact with the shoal waters.

Far below, where the dancing moon shadows could not penetrate, the bottom was even white sand with an occasional dark patch that would be seagrass. All around there was nothing but the great pale luminous hall of the sea at night, a vast lonely mist through which, against his will and his intelligence, Bond expected at any moment the dark torpedo of a great fish to materialize, its eyes and senses questing towards the rippling shape of the black intruder. But there was nothing, and nothing came, and gradually the patches of seagrass became more distinct and ripples showed on the sandy bottom as it shelved slowly up from fifty to forty and then to thirty feet.

To reassure himself that all was well, Bond took a quick glance over his shoulder. Yes, they were all there, the oval panes of eleven gleaming masks with the fluttering fins kicking up behind them and the glint of the moonlight on the blades of the spears. Bond thought, By God, if only we can achieve surprise! What a terrifying ambush to meet coming at you through the shadows and shapes of the reef! His heart lifted momentarily at the thought, only to be checked by the deep gnawing of his hidden fears about the girl. Supposing she was part of the enemy team! Supposing he came face to face with her. Would he bring himself to do it–with the spear? But the whole idea was ridiculous. She was on board, safe. He would be seeing her again soon, as soon as this work was done.

A small coral clump showed up below and refocused his mind. Now he gazed watchfully ahead. There were more clumps, the ink splashes of sea eggs, crowds of small glittering reef fish, a small forest of sea fans that beckoned and waved with the ebb and flow like the hair of drowned women. Bond slowed and felt Leiter or Fallon bump into his fins. He made the slowing signal with his free hand. Now he crept carefully forward, looking for the silvery wash of the waves against the top of his navigation mark. Yes, it was there, away to the left. He was a good twenty feet off course. He swerved towards it, gave the halt signal and came slowly up under its protection. With infinite caution he raised his head through the sucking waves. He glanced first towards the *Disco*. Yes, she was still there, showing more plainly with the moon now full on her. No sign of life. Bond inched his gaze slowly across the intervening sea. Nothing. A flurry of wavelets down the mirrored pathway of the moon. Now Bond slid round to the other side of the coral head. Nothing but the broken waters of the shoal and, five or six hundred yards away, the clear coastline and the beach. Bond searched the clear channels for unusual turbulence in the water, for shapes, for anything moving. What was that? A hundred yards away, on the edge of a big patch, almost a lagoon, of clear water amongst the coral, a head, a pale head with the glitter of a mask across it, had broken the surface for an instant, taken a quick look round and immediately submerged.

Bond held his breath. He could feel his thrilled heart hammering against the inside of his rubber suit. Feeling stifled, he took the breathing tube from between his teeth and let his breath burst out of him. He quickly gulped in some mouthfuls of fresh air, got a good fix on the position, crammed the tube roughly between his lips and slid back and down.

Behind, the masks gazed blankly at him, waiting for a signal. Bond jerked up his thumb several times. Through the near masks he could see the answering flash of teeth. Bond shifted his grasp on the spear down to an attacking position and surged forward over the low coral.

Now it was only a question of speed and careful navigation among the occasional higher outcrops. Fish squirted out of his path and all the reef seemed to waken with the shock-wave of the twelve hastening bodies. Fifty yards on, Bond signalled to slow, to fan out in the attacking line. Then he crept on again, his eyes, aching and bloodshot with the strain, boring ahead through the jagged shapes amongst the pale mist. Yes! There was the glitter of white flesh, and there and there. Bond's arm made the hurling signal for the attack. He plunged forward, his spear held in front of him like a lance.

Bond's group came in from the flank. It was a mistake, as Bond quickly saw, for the SPECTRE team was still moving forward and at a speed that surprised Bond until he saw the small whirring propellers on the backs of the enemy. Largo's men were wearing compressed-air speed-packs, bulky cylinders strapped between the twin cylinders of their aqualungs, that operated small screws. Combined with the trudge of the fins, this gave them at least double normal swimming speed in open water, but here, amongst the broken coral, and slowed by the manœuvring of the sled preceded by the electric Chariot, the team was perhaps only a knot faster than Bond's group, now thrashing their way forward to an interception point that was rapidly escaping them. And there were the hell of a lot of the enemy. Bond stopped counting after twelve. And most of them carried CO_2 guns with extra spears in quivers strapped to their legs. The odds were bad. If only he could get within spear range before the alarm was given!

Thirty yards, twenty. Bond glanced behind him. There were six of his men almost at arm's length, the rest straggled out in a crooked line. Still the masks of Largo's men pointed forward. Still they hadn't seen the black shapes making for them through the coral. But now, when Bond was level with Largo's rearguard, the moon threw his shadow forward across a pale patch of sand and one man, then another, glanced quickly round. Bond got a foot against a lump of coral and, with this to give him impetus, flung himself forward. The man had no time to defend himself. Bond's spear caught him in the side and hurled him against the next man in line. Bond thrust and wrenched sickeningly. The man dropped his gun and bent double, clutching his side. Bond bored on into the mass of naked men now scattering in all directions, with their jet packs accelerated. Another man went down in front of him, clawing at his face. A chance thrust of Bond's had smashed the glass of his mask. He threshed his way up towards the surface, kicking Bond in the face as he went. A spear ripped into the rubber protecting Bond's stomach and Bond felt pain and wetness that might be blood or sea-water. He dodged another flash of metal and a gun butt him hit hard on the head, but with most of its force spent against the cushion of water. It knocked him silly and he clung for a moment to a niggerhead to get his bearings while the black tide of his men swept past him and individual fights filled the water with black puffs of blood.

The battleground had now shifted to a wide expanse of clear water fringed with broken coral. On the far side of this, Bond saw the grounded sled laden with something long and bulky with a rubber covering, the silver torpedo of the Chariot, and a close group of men that included the unmistakable, oversize figure of Largo. Bond melted back among the coral clumps, got close down to the sand and began to swim cautiously round the flank of the big clear pool. Almost immediately he had to stop. A squat figure was cowering in the shadows. His gun was raised and he was taking careful aim. It was at Leiter, in difficulties with one of Largo's men who had him by the throat while Leiter, the swim fin on his hook gone, clawed with the hook at the man's back. Bond gave two hard kicks of his flippers and hurled his spear from six feet, the light wood of the handle had no momentum, but the blade cut into the man's arm just as the bubbles of gas burst from the muzzle of the gun. His shot went wide, but he flashed around and thrust at Bond with the empty gun. Out of the corner of his eye Bond saw his spear floating slowly up towards the surface. He dived for the man's legs in a clumsy rugby tackle and clawed them off the ground. Then, as the gun muzzle hit him on the temple, he reached a desperate hand for the enemy's mask and ripped it off his face. That was enough. Bond swam aside and watched the man, blinded by the salt water, groping his way up towards the surface. Bond felt a nudge at his arm. It was Leiter, clutching at his oxygen tube. His face inside the mask was contorted. He made a feeble gesture upwards. Bond got the message. He seized Leiter round the waist and leaped for the surface fifteen feet up. As they broke through the silver ceiling, Leiter tore the broken tube from his mouth and gulped frantically for air. Bond held him through the paroxysm and then guided him to a clump of shallow coral and when Leiter pushed him angrily away and told him to get the hell back under and leave him alone, he put up a thumb and dived down again.

Now he kept well in the forest of coral and began again his stalk of Largo. Occasionally he caught glimpses of individual battles and once he passed under a man, one of his men from the *Manta*, staring down at him from the surface. But the face under the water, framed in its streaming hair, had no mask or oxygen tube, and the mouth gaped hideously in death. On the bottom, among the coral clumps, there were bits of wrack from the tide of battle–an oxygen pack, strips of black rubber, a complete aqualung and several spears from the CO2 guns. Bond picked up two of them. Now he was on the edge of the open lagoon of battle water. The sled, with its obscene rubber sausage, was still there, guarded by two of Largo's men with their guns at the ready. But there was no sign of Largo. Bond peered into the misty wall through which the moonlight, paler now, filtered down on to the ripples in the sand, their pretty patterns scuffed and churned by the feet of the combatants. Where the sand had been disturbed, reef fish were swarming to pick up minute fragments of algae and other fodder, like seagulls and rooks when the plough has passed. There was nothing else to be seen and there was no way for Bond to guess how the battle, dispersed into a dozen separate running fights, was going. What was happening on the surface? When Bond had taken Leiter up, the sea had been lit by the red flare. How soon would the rescue dinghy from the *Manta* be on the scene? Ought he to stay where he was and watch over the bomb?

With frightening suddenness, the decision was made for him. Out of the mists to Bond's right the gleaming torpedo shape of the electric Chariot shot into the arena. Largo sat astride it in the saddle. He was bent down behind the small perspex shield to get extra speed and his left hand held two of the *Manta* spears pointing forward while he controlled the single joystick with his right. As he appeared, the two guards dropped their guns on the sand and held up the coupling of the sled. Largo slowed down and drifted up to them. One man caught the rudder and wrestled to pull the Chariot backwards towards the couplings. They were going to get out! Largo was going to take the bomb back out through the reef and drop it in deep water or bury it! The same thing would be done with the second bomb in the *Disco*. With the evidence gone, Largo would say that he had been ambushed by rival treasure hunters. How was he to know they came from a United States submarine? His men had fought back with their shark guns, but only because they had been attacked first. Once again the treasure hunt cover would hide everything!

The men were still wrestling with the coupling. Largo was looking back anxiously. Bond measured the distance and flung himself forward with a great kick against the coral.

Largo turned in time to fling up an arm and parry Bond's stab with his right-hand spear and Bond's stab with the left rattled harmlessly off the aqualung cylinders on Largo's back. Bond drove on head first, his hands outstretched for the air tube in Largo's mouth. Largo's hands flashed to protect himself, dropping his two spears and jerking back the joystick he had been holding in his right. The Chariot surged forward away from the two guards and shot obliquely upwards towards the surface while the two bodies clung and struggled on its back.

It was impossible to fight scientifically. Both men tore vaguely at each other while their teeth clenched desperately on the rubber mouthpieces that were their lifelines, but Largo had a firm grip of the Chariot between his knees while Bond had to use one hand to hang on to Largo's equipment to prevent himself being thrown. Again and again Largo's elbow crashed into Bond's face while Bond dodged from side to side to take the blows on the mouth and not on the precious glass of his mask. At the same time Bond hammered with his free hand at his only target, Largo's kidneys, beneath the brown square of flesh that was all he could reach.

The Chariot broke surface fifty yards down the wide channel leading to the open sea and tore crazily on, its nose, tilted by Bond's weight over the tail, sticking at forty-five degrees out of the water. Now Bond was half in the wash and it would only be minutes before Largo managed to twist and get both hands to him. Bond made up his mind. He let go of Largo's aqualung and, clutching the stern of the torpedo between his legs, slid back until he felt the top of the rudder at his back. Now, if he could avoid the screw! He reached one hand down between his legs, got a firm grip of the rudder, and heaved himself backwards and off the machine. Now his face, inches away from the whirring propeller, was buffeted by the turbulence, but he dragged hard downwards and felt the stern coming with him. Soon the damned thing would be almost upright. Bond wrenched the blade of the rudder sideways in a right-angled turn and then, his arms almost torn out of their sockets by the strain, let go. Above and in front of him, as the torpedo veered right-handed, Largo's body, thrown by the sharp turn and the change of balance, crashed into the water, twisted quickly over and faced downwards, the mask searching for Bond.

Bond was beat, utterly defeated by exhaustion. Now there was nothing for him but to get away and somehow stay alive. The bomb was immobilized, the Chariot gone, careering in circles over the sea. Largo was finished. Bond summoned the remains of his strength and sluggishly dived down towards his last hope, a refuge among the coral.

Almost lazily, Largo, his strength unimpaired, came down after him, swimming in a giant, easy crawl. Bond swerved in among the coral heads. A white sand passage showed up and he followed it, then there was a fork. Bond, trusting to the small extra protection of his rubber suit, followed the narrower lane between the sharp clumps. But now a black shadow was above him, following him. Largo had not bothered to get into the channel. He was swimming above the coral, looking down, watching Bond, biding his time. Bond looked up. There was a gleam of teeth round the mouthpiece. Largo knew he had got him. Bond flexed his fingers to get more life into them. How could he hope to defeat those great hands, those hands that were machine-tools?

And now the narrow passage was widening. There was the glint of a sandy channel ahead. There was no room for Bond to turn round. He could only swim on into the open trap. Bond stopped and stood. It was the only thing to do. Largo had him like a rat in a trap. But at least Largo would have to come in and get him. Bond looked upwards. Yes, the great gleaming body, followed by its string of silver bubbles, was forging carefully on into the open water. Now, swiftly, like a pale seal, he dived down to the firm sand and stood facing Bond. Slowly he advanced between the walls of coral, the big hands held forward for the first hold. At ten paces he stopped. His eyes swivelled sideways to a coral clump. His right hand shot out at something and gave a quick yank. When the hand pulled back, it was writhing, writhing with eight more fingers. Largo held the baby octopus in front of him like a small, waving flower. His teeth drew away from the rubber mouthpiece and the clefts of a smile appeared in his cheeks. He put up one hand and significantly tapped his mask. Bond bent down and picked up a rock covered with seaweed. Largo was being melodramatic. A rock in Largo's mask would be more efficient than having an octopus slapped across his. Bond wasn't worried by the octopus. Only a day before he had been in company with a hundred of them. It was Largo's longer reach that worried him.

Largo took a pace forward and then another. Bond crouched, backing carefully, so as not to cut his rubber skin, into the narrow passage. Largo came on, slowly deliberately. In two more paces he would attack.

Bond caught a glint of movement out in the open behind Largo. Someone to the rescue? But the glint was white, not black. It was one of theirs!

Largo leaped forward.

Bond kicked off the coral and dived down for Largo's groin, the jagged rock in his hand. But Largo was ready. His knee came up hard against Bond's head and at the same time his right hand came swiftly down and clamped the small octopus across Bond's mask. Then from above, both his hands came down and got Bond by the neck, lifted him up like a child and held him at arm's length, pressing.

Bond could see nothing. Vaguely he felt the slimy tentacles groping over his face, getting a grip of the mouthpiece between his teeth, pulling. But the blood was roaring in his head and he knew he was gone.

Slowly he sank to his knees. But how, why was he sinking? What had happened to the hands at his throat? His eyes, squeezed tight in agony, opened and there was light. The octopus, now at his chest, let go and shot away among the coral. In front of him Largo, Largo with a spear sticking horribly through his neck, lay kicking feebly on the sand. Behind him and looking down at the body, stood a small, pale figure fitting another spear into an underwater gun. The long hair flowed round her head like a veil in the luminous sea.

Bond got slowly to his feet. He took a step forward. Suddenly he felt his knees beginning to give. A wave of blackness began to creep up over his vision. He leant against the coral, his mouth slackening round the oxygen tube. Water seeped into his mouth. No! he said to himself. No! Don't let that happen!

A hand took one of his. But Domino's eyes behind her mask were somewhere else. They were blank, lost. She was ill! What was the matter with her? Bond was suddenly awake again. His eyes took in the blood patches on her bathing dress, the angry red marks on her body between the scraps of bikini. They would both die, standing there, unless he did something about it. Slowly his leaden legs began to stir the black fins. they were moving up. It wasn't so difficult after all. And now, vaguely, her own fins were helping.

The two bodies reached the surface together and lay, face downwards, in the shallow troughs of the waves.

The oyster light of dawn slowly turned pink. It was going to be a beautiful day.

Chapter Twenty-four

'Take it easy, Mr Bond'

Felix Leiter came into the white, antiseptic room and closed the door conspiratorially behind him. He came and stood beside the bed where Bond lay on the edge of drugged sleep. 'How's it going, feller?'

'Not bad. Just doped.'

'Doctor said I wasn't to see you. But I thought you might care to hear the score. Okay?'

'Sure.' Bond struggled to concentrate. He didn't really care. All he could think about was the girl.

'Well, I'll make it quick. Doctor's just doing his rounds and I'll get hell if he finds me here. They've recovered both bombs, and Kotze–the physicist chap–is singing like a bird. Seems SPECTRE's a bunch of really big-time hoodlums–ex-operators of SMERSH, the Mafia, the Gestapo–all the big outfits. Headquarters in Paris. Top man's called Blofeld, but the bastard got away–or anyway they haven't caught up with him yet, according to C.I.A. Probably Largo's radio silence warned him. Must be quite a Mister Genius. Kotze says SPECTRE's banked millions of dollars since they got going five or six years ago. This job was going to be the final haul. We were right about Miami. It *was* going to be Target No. 2. Same sort of operation. They were going to plant the second bomb in the yacht basin.'

Bond smiled weakly. 'So now everybody's happy.'

'Oh sure. Except me. Haven't been able to get away from my damned radio until now. Valves were almost blowing. And there's a pile of cipher stuff from M just longing for you to get around to it. Thank God the top brass from C.I.A. and a team from your outfit are flying in this evening to take charge. Then we can hand over and watch our two Governments getting snarled up over the epilogue–what to tell the public, what to do with these SPECTRE guys, whether to make you a lord or a duke, how to persuade me to run for President–tricky little details like that. And then we'll damned well get away and have ourselves a ball some place. Maybe you'd care to take that girl along? Hell, she's the one that rates the medals! The guts! They cottoned on to her Geiger counter. God knows what that bastard Largo did to her. But she didn't sing–not a damned word! Then, when the team was under way, she somehow got herself out of the cabin porthole, with her gun and aqualung, and went to get him. Got him, and saved your life into the bargain! I swear I'll never call a girl a "frail" again–not an Italian girl anyway.' Leiter cocked an ear. He moved swiftly to the door. 'Hell, there's that damned medic gumshoeing down the corridor! Be seeing you, James.' He quickly turned the door handle, listened for a moment, and slipped out of the room.

Feebly, desperately, Bond called, 'Wait! Felix! Felix!' But the door had closed. Bond sank back and lay staring at the ceiling. Slowly anger boiled up inside him–and panic. Why in hell didn't someone tell him about the girl? What the hell did he care about all the rest? Was she all right? Where was she? Was she . . .

The door opened. Bond jerked himself upright. He shouted furiously at the white-coated figure. 'The girl. How is she? Quick! Tell me!'

Dr Stengel, the fashionable doctor of Nassau, was not only fashionable but a good doctor. He was one of the Jewish refugee doctors who, but for Hitler, would have been looking after some big hospital in a town the size of Düsseldorf. Instead, rich and grateful patients had built a modern clinic for him in Nassau where he treated the natives for shillings and the millionaires and their wives for ten guineas a visit. He was more used to handling overdoses of sleeping pills and the ailments of the rich and old than multiple abrasions, curare poisoning and odd wounds that looked more as if they belonged to the days of the pirates. But these were Government orders, and under the Official Secrets Act at that. Dr Stengel hadn't asked any questions about his patients, nor about the sixteen autopsies he had had to perform, six for Americans from the big submarine, and ten, including the corpse of the owner, from the fine yacht that had been in harbour for so long.

Now he said carefully, 'Miss Vitali will be all right. For the moment she is suffering from shock. She needs rest.'

'What else? What was the matter with her?'

'She had swum a long way. She was not in a condition to undertake such a physical strain.'

'Why not?'

The doctor moved towards the door. 'And now you too must rest. You have been through much. You will take one of those hypnotics once every six hours. Yes? And plenty of sleep. You will soon be on your feet again. But for some time you must take it easy, Mr Bond.'

Take it easy. You must take it easy, Mr Bond. Where had he heard those idiotic words before? Suddenly Bond was raging with fury. He lurched out of bed. In spite of the sudden giddiness, he staggered towards the doctor. He shook a fist in the urbane face–urbane because the doctor was used to the emotional storms of patients, and because he knew that in minutes the strong soporific would put Bond out for hours. 'Take it easy! God damn you! What do you know about taking it easy? Tell me what's the matter with that girl! Where is she? What's the number of her room?' Bond's hands fell limply to his sides. He said feebly, 'For God's sake tell me, Doctor. I, I need to know.'

Doctor Stengel said patiently, kindly, 'Someone has ill-treated her. She is suffering from burns–many burns. She is still in great pain. But,' he waved a reassuring hand, 'inside she is well. She is in the next room, in No. 4. You may see her, but only for a minute. Then she will sleep. And so will you. Yes?' He held open the door.

'Thank you. Thank you, Doctor.' Bond walked out of the room with faltering steps. His blasted legs were beginning to give again. The doctor watched him go to the door of No. 4, watched him open it and close it again behind him with the exaggerated care of a drunken man. The doctor went off along the corridor thinking: it won't do him any harm and it may do her some good. It is what she needs–some tenderness.

Inside the small room, the jalousies threw bands of light and shadow over the bed. Bond staggered over to the bed and knelt down beside it. The small head on the pillow turned towards him. A hand came out and grasped his hair, pulling his head closer to her. Her voice said huskily, 'You are to stay here. Do you understand? You are not to go away.'

When Bond didn't answer, she feebly shook his head to and fro. 'Do you hear me, James? Do you understand?' She felt Bond's body slipping to the floor. When she let go his hair, he slumped down on the rug beside her bed. She carefully shifted her position and looked down at him. He was already asleep with his head cradled on the inside of his forearm.

The girl watched the dark, rather cruel face for a moment. Then she gave a small sigh, pulled the pillow to the edge of the bed so that it was just above him, laid her head down so that she could see him whenever she wanted to, and closed her eyes.

ON HER MAJESTY'S SECRET SERVICE

ON HER MAJESTY'S SECRET SERVICE

For
Sable Basilisk Pursuivant
and Hilary Bray
who came to the aid of the party

Chapter One

Seascape with Figures

It was one of those Septembers when it seemed that the summer would never end.

The five-mile promenade of Royale-les-Eaux, backed by trim lawns emblazoned at intervals with tricolor beds of salvia, alyssum and lobelia, was bright with flags and, on the longest beach in the north of France, the gay bathing tents still marched prettily down to the tide-line in big, money-making battalions. Music, one of those lilting accordion waltzes, blared from the loudspeakers around the Olympic-size piscine and, from time to time, echoing above the music, a man's voice announced over the public address system that Philippe Bertrand, aged seven, was looking for his mother, that Yolande Lefèvre was waiting for her friends below the clock at the entrance, or that a Madame Dufours was demanded on the telephone. From the beach, particularly from the neighbourhood of the three playground enclosures–'Joie de Vivre', 'Hélio' and 'Azur'–came a twitter of children's cries that waxed and waned with the thrill of their games and, farther out, on the firm sand left by the now distant sea, the shrill whistle of the physical-fitness instructor marshalled his teenagers through the last course of the day.

It was one of those beautiful, naive seaside panoramas for which the Brittany and Picardy beaches have provided the setting–and inspired their recorders, Boudin, Tissot, Monet–ever since the birth of plages and bains de mer more than a hundred years ago.

To James Bond, sitting in one of the concrete shelters with his face to the setting sun, there was something poignant, ephemeral about it all. It reminded him almost too vividly of childhood–of the velvet feel of the hot powder sand, and the painful grit of wet sand between young toes when the time came for him to put his shoes and socks on, of the precious little pile of sea-shells and interesting wrack on the sill of his bedroom window ('No, we'll have to leave that behind, darling. It'll dirty up your trunk!'), of the small crabs scuttling away from the nervous fingers groping beneath the seaweed in the rock-pools, of the swimming and swimming and swimming through the dancing waves–always in those days, it seemed, lit with sunshine–and then the infuriating, inevitable 'time to come out'. It was all there, his own childhood, spread out before him to have another look at. What a long time ago they were, those spade-and-bucket days! How far he had come since the freckles and the Cadbury milk-chocolate Flakes and the fizzy lemonade! Impatiently Bond lit a cigarette, pulled his shoulders out of their slouch and slammed the mawkish memories back into their long-closed file. Today he was a grown-up, a man with years of dirty, dangerous memories–a spy. He was not sitting in this concrete hideout to sentimentalize about a pack of scrubby, smelly children on a beach scattered with bottle-tops and lolly-sticks and fringed by a sea thick with sun-oil and putrid with the main drains of Royale. He was here, he had chosen to be here, to spy. To spy on a woman.

The sun was getting lower. Already one could smell the September chill that all day had lain hidden beneath the heat. The cohorts of bathers were in quick retreat, striking their little camps and filtering up the steps and across the promenade into the shelter of the town where the lights were going up in the cafés. The announcer at the swimming-pool harried his customers: 'Allo! Allo! Fermeture en dix minutes! A dix-huit heures, fermeture de la piscine!' Silhouetted in the path of the setting sun, the two Bombard rescue-boats with flags bearing a blue cross on a yellow background were speeding northwards for their distant shelter up-river in the Vieux Port. The last of the gay, giraffe-like sand-yachts fled down the distant water-line towards its corral among the sand dunes, and the three agents cyclistes in charge of the car-parks pedalled away through the melting ranks of cars towards the police station in the centre of the town. In a matter of minutes the vast expanse of sand–the tide, still receding, was already a mile out–would be left to the seagulls that would soon be flocking in their hordes to forage for the scraps of food left by the picnickers. Then the orange ball of the sun would hiss down into the sea and the beach would, for a while, be entirely deserted, until, under cover of darkness, the prowling lovers would come to writhe briefly, grittily in the dark corners between the bathing-huts and the sea-wall.

On the beaten stretch of sand below where James Bond was sitting, two golden girls in exciting bikinis packed up the game of Jokari which they had been so provocatively playing, and raced each other up the steps towards Bond's shelter. They flaunted their bodies at him, paused and chattered to see if he would respond, and, when he didn't, linked arms and sauntered on towards the town, leaving Bond wondering why it was that French girls had more prominent navels than any others. Was it that French surgeons sought to add, even in this minute respect, to the future sex-appeal of girl babies?

And now, up and down the beach, the lifeguards gave a final blast on their horns to announce that they were going off duty, the music from the piscine stopped in mid-tune and the great expanse of sand was suddenly deserted.

But not quite! A hundred yards out, lying face downwards on a black and white striped bathing-wrap, on the private patch of firm sand where she had installed herself an hour before, the girl was still there, motionless, spread-eagled in direct line between James Bond and the setting sun that was now turning the left-behind pools and shallow rivulets into blood-red, meandering scrawls across the middle distance. Bond went on watching her–now in the silence and emptiness, with an ounce more tension. He was waiting for her to do something–for something, he didn't know what, to happen. It would be more true to say that he was watching *over* her. He had an instinct that she was in some sort of danger. Or was it just that there was the smell of danger in the air? He didn't know. He only knew that he mustn't leave her alone, particularly now that everyone else had gone.

James Bond was mistaken. Not everyone else had gone. Behind him, at the

Café de la Plage on the other side of the promenade, two men in raincoats and dark caps sat at a secluded table bordering the sidewalk. They had half-empty cups of coffee in front of them and they didn't talk. They sat and watched the blur on the frosted-glass partition of the shelter that was James Bond's head and shoulders. They also watched, but less intently, the distant white blur on the sand that was the girl. Their stillness, and their unseasonable clothes, would have made a disquieting impression on anyone who, in his turn, might have been watching them. But there was no such person, except their waiter who had simply put them in the category of 'bad news' and hoped they would soon be on their way.

When the lower rim of the orange sun touched the sea, it was almost as if a signal had sounded for the girl. She slowly got to her feet, ran both hands backwards through her hair and began to walk evenly, purposefully towards the sun and the far-away froth of the water-line over a mile away. It would be violet dusk by the time she reached the sea and one might have guessed that this was probably the last day of her holiday, her last bathe.

James Bond thought otherwise. He left his shelter, ran down the steps to the sand and began walking out after her at a fast pace. Behind him, across the promenade, the two men in raincoats also seemed to think otherwise. One of them briskly threw down some coins and they both got up and, walking strictly in step, crossed the promenade to the sand and, with a kind of urgent military precision, marched rapidly side by side in Bond's tracks.

Now the strange pattern of figures on the vast expanse of empty, blood-streaked sand was eerily conspicuous. Yet it was surely not one to be interfered with! The pattern had a nasty, a secret smell. The white girl, the bare-headed young man, the two squat, marching pursuers–it had something of a kind of deadly Grandmother's Steps about it. In the café, the waiter collected the coins and looked after the distant figures, still outlined by the last quarter of the orange sun. It smelt like police business–or the other thing. He would keep it to himself but remember it. He might get his name in the papers.

James Bond was rapidly catching up with the girl. Now he knew that he would get to her just as she reached the water-line. He began to wonder what he would say to her, how he would put it. He couldn't say, 'I had a hunch you were going to commit suicide so I came after you to stop you.' 'I was going for a walk on the beach and I thought I recognized you. Will you have a drink after your swim?' would be childish. He finally decided to say, 'Oh, Tracy!' and then, when she turned round, 'I was worried about you.' Which would at least be inoffensive and, for the matter of that, true.

The sea was now gunmetal below a primrose horizon. A small, westerly offshore breeze, drawing the hot land-air out to sea, had risen and was piling up wavelets that scrolled in whitely as far as the eye could see. Flocks of herring gulls lazily rose and settled again at the girl's approach, and the air was full of their mewing and of the endless lap-lap of the small waves. The soft indigo dusk added a touch of melancholy to the empty solitude of sand and sea, now so far away from the comforting bright lights and holiday bustle of 'La Reine de la Côte Opale', as Royale-les-Eaux had splendidly christened herself. Bond looked forward to getting the girl back to those bright lights. He watched the lithe golden figure in the white one-piece bathing-suit and wondered how soon she would be able to hear his voice above the noise of the gulls and the sea. Her pace had slowed a fraction as she approached the water-line and her head, with its bell of heavy fair hair to the shoulders, was slightly bowed, in thought perhaps, or tiredness.

Bond quickened his step until he was only ten paces behind her. 'Hey! Tracy!'

The girl didn't start or turn quickly round. Her steps faltered and stopped, and then, as a small wave creamed in and died at her feet, she turned slowly and stood squarely facing him. Her eyes, puffed and wet with tears, looked past him. Then they met his. She said dully, 'What is it? What do you want?'

'I was worried about you. What are you doing out here? What's the matter?'

The girl looked past him again. Her clenched right hand went up to her mouth. She said something, something Bond couldn't understand, from behind it. Then a voice, from very close behind Bond, said softly, silkily, 'Don't move or you get it back of the knee.'

Bond swirled round into a crouch, his gun hand inside his coat. The steady silver eyes of the two automatics sneered at him.

Bond slowly straightened himself. He dropped his hand to his side and the held breath came out between his teeth in a quiet hiss. The two dead-pan, professional faces told him even more than the two silver eyes of the guns. They held no tension, no excitement. The thin half-smiles were relaxed, contented. The eyes were not even wary. They were almost bored. Bond had looked into such faces many times before. This was routine. These men were killers–pro-killers.

Bond had no idea who these men were, who they worked for, what this was all about. On the theory that worry is a dividend paid to disaster before it is due, he consciously relaxed his muscles and emptied his mind of questions. He stood and waited.

'Position your hands behind your neck.' The silky, patient voice was from the south, from the Mediterranean. It fitted with the men's faces–tough-skinned, widely pored, yellow-brown. Marseillais perhaps, or Italians. The Mafia? The faces belonged to good secret police or tough crooks. Bond's mind ticked and whirred, selecting cards like an IBM machine. What enemies had he got in those areas? Might it be Blofeld? Had the hare turned upon the hound?

When the odds are hopeless, when all seems to be lost, then is the time to be calm, to make a show of authority–at least of indifference. Bond smiled into the eyes of the man who had spoken. 'I don't think your mother would like to know what you are doing this evening. You are a Catholic? So I will do as you ask.' The man's eyes glittered. Touché! Bond clasped his hands behind his head.

The man stood aside so as to have a clear field of fire while his Number Two removed Bond's Walther PPK from the soft leather holster inside his trouser belt and ran expert hands down his sides, down his arms to the wrists and down the inside of his thighs. Then Number Two stood back, pocketed the Walther and again took out his own gun.

Bond glanced over his shoulder. The girl had said nothing, expressed neither surprise nor alarm. Now she was standing with her back to the group, looking out to sea, apparently relaxed, unconcerned. What in God's name was it all about? Had she been used as a bait? But for whom? And now what? Was he to be executed, his body left lying to be rolled back inshore by the tide? It seemed the only solution. If it was a question of some kind of a deal, the four of them could not just walk back across the mile of sand to the town and say polite goodbyes on the promenade steps. No. This was the terminal point. Or was it? From the north, through the deep indigo dusk, came the fast, rattling hum of an outboard and, as Bond watched, the cream of a thick bow-wave showed and then the blunt outline of one of the Bombard rescue-craft, the flat-bottomed inflatable rubber boats with a single Johnson engine in the flattened stern. So they had been spotted! By the coastguards perhaps? And here was rescue! By God, he'd roast these two thugs when they got to the harbour police at the Vieux Port! But what story would he tell about the girl?

Bond turned back to face the men. At once he knew the worst. They had rolled their trousers up to the knees and were waiting, composedly, their shoes in one hand and their guns in the other. This was no rescue. It was just part of the ride. Oh well! Paying no attention to the men, Bond bent down, rolled up his trousers as they had done and, in the process of fumbling with his socks and shoes, palmed one of his heel knives and, half turning towards the boat that had now grounded in the shallows, transferred it to his right-hand trouser pocket.

No words were exchanged. The girl climbed aboard first, then Bond, and lastly the two men who helped the engine with a final shove on the stern. The boatman, who looked like any other French deep-sea fisherman, whirled the blunt nose of the Bombard round, changed gears to forward, and they were off northwards through the buffeting waves while the golden hair of the girl streamed back and softly whipped James Bond's cheek.

'Tracy. You're going to catch cold. Here. Take my coat.' Bond slipped his coat off. She held out a hand to help him put it on her. In the process her hand found his and pressed it. Now what the hell? Bond edged closer to her. He felt her body respond. Bond glanced at the two men. They sat hunched against the wind, their hands in their pockets, watchful, but somehow uninterested. Behind them the necklace of lights that was Royale receded swiftly until it was only a golden glow on the horizon. James Bond's right hand felt for the comforting knife in his pocket and ran his thumb across the razor-sharp blade.

While he wondered how and when he might have a chance to use it, the rest of his mind ran back over the previous twenty-four hours and panned them for the gold-dust of truth.

Chapter Two

Gran Turismo

Almost exactly twenty-four hours before, James Bond had been nursing his car, the old Continental Bentley–the 'R' type chassis with the big 6 engine and a 13:40 back-axle ratio–that he had now been driving for three years, along that fast but dull stretch of N.1 between Abbeville and Montreuil that takes the English tourist back to his country via Silver City Airways from Le Touquet or by ferry from Boulogne or Calais. He was hurrying safely, at between eighty and ninety, driving by the automatic pilot that is built in to all rally-class drivers, and his mind was totally occupied with drafting his letter of resignation from the Secret Service.

The letter, addressed 'Personal for M', had got to the following stage:

Sir,

I have the honour to request that you will accept my resignation from the Service, effective forthwith.

My reasons for this submission, which I put forward with much regret, are the following:

(1) My duties in the Service, until some twelve months ago, have been connected with the Double-O Section and you, Sir, have been kind enough, from time to time, to express your satisfaction with my performance of those duties, which I, for my part, have enjoyed. To my chagrin, [Bond had been pleased with this fine word] however, on the successful completion of Operation 'Thunderball', I received personal instructions from you to concentrate all my efforts, without a terminal date, [another felicitous phrase!] on the pursuit of Ernst Stavro Blofeld and on his apprehension, together with any members of SPECTRE–otherwise 'The Special Executive for Counter-Intelligence, Revenge and Extortion'–if that organization had been re-created since its destruction at the climax of Operation 'Thunderball'.

(2) I accepted the assignment with, if you will recall, reluctance. It seemed to me, and I so expressed myself at the time, that this was purely an investigatory matter which could well have been handled, using straightforward police methods, by other sections of the Service–local Stations, allied foreign secret services and Interpol. My objections were overruled, and for close on twelve months I have been engaged all over the world in routine detective work which, in the case of every scrap of rumour, every lead, has proved abortive. I have found no trace of this man nor of a revived SPECTRE, if such exists.

(3) My many appeals to be relieved of this wearisome and fruitless assignment, even when addressed to you personally, Sir, have been ignored or, on occasion, curtly dismissed, and my frequent animadversions [another good one!] to the effect that Blofeld is dead have been treated with a courtesy that I can only describe as scant. [Neat, that! Perhaps a bit too neat!]

(4) The above unhappy circumstances have recently achieved their climax in my undercover mission (Ref. Station R'S PX 437/007) to Palermo, in pursuit of a hare of quite outrageous falsity. This animal took the shape of one 'Blauenfelder', a perfectly respectable German citizen engaged in viniculture–specifically the grafting of Moselle grapes on to the Sicilian strains to enhance the sugar content of the latter which, for your passing information, [Steady on, old chap! Better redraft all this!] are inclined to sourness. My investigations into this individual brought me to the attention of the Mafia and my departure from Sicily was, to say the least, ignominious.

(5) Having regard, Sir, to the above and, specifically, to the continued misuse of the qualities, modest though they may be, that have

previously fitted me for the more arduous, and, to me, more rewarding, duties associated with the work of the Double-O Section, I beg leave to submit my resignation from the Service.

I am, Sir,

Your Obedient Servant,

007

Of course, reflected Bond, as he nursed the long bonnet of his car through a built-up S-bend, he would have to rewrite a lot of it. Some of it was a bit pompous and there were one or two cracks that would have to be ironed out or toned down. But that was the gist of what he would dictate to his secretary when he got back to the office the day after tomorrow. And if she burst into tears, to hell with her! He meant it. By God he did. He was fed to the teeth with chasing the ghost of Blofeld. And the same went for SPECTRE. The thing had been smashed. Even a man of Blofeld's genius, in the impossible event that he still existed, could never get a machine of that calibre running again.

It was then, on a ten-mile straight cut through a forest, that it happened. Triple wind-horns screamed their banshee discord in his ear, and a low, white two-seater, a Lancia Flaminia Zagato Spyder with its hood down, tore past him, cut in cheekily across his bonnet and pulled away, the sexy boom of its twin exhausts echoing back from the border of trees. And it was a girl driving, a girl with a shocking pink scarf tied round her hair, leaving a brief pink tail that the wind blew horizontal behind her.

If there was one thing that set James Bond really moving in life, with the exception of gun-play, it was being passed at speed by a pretty girl; and it was his experience that girls who drove competitively like that were always pretty–and exciting. The shock of the wind-horn's scream had automatically cut out 'George', emptied Bond's head of all other thought, and brought his car back under manual control. Now, with a tight-lipped smile, he stamped his foot into the floorboard, held the wheel firmly at a quarter to three, and went after her.

100, 110, 115, and he still wasn't gaining. Bond reached forward to the dashboard and flicked up a red switch. The thin high whine of machinery on the brink of torment tore at his eardrums and the Bentley gave an almost perceptible kick forward. 120, 125. He was definitely gaining. 50 yards, 40, 30! Now he could just see her eyes in her rear mirror. But the good road was running out. One of those exclamation marks that the French use to denote danger flashed by on his right. And now, over a rise, there was a church spire, the clustered houses of a small village at the bottom of a steepish hill, the snake sign of another S-bend. Both cars slowed down–90, 80, 70. Bond watched her tail-lights briefly blaze, saw her right hand reach down to the floor stick, almost simultaneously with his own, and change down. Then they were in the S-bend, on cobbles, and he had to brake as he enviously watched the way her de Dion axle married her rear wheels to the rough going, while his own live axle hopped and skittered as he wrenched at the wheel. And then it was the end of the village, and, with a brief wag of her tail as she came out of the S, she was off like a bat out of hell up the long straight rise and he had lost fifty yards.

And so the race went on, Bond gaining a little on the straights but losing it all to the famous Lancia road-holding through the villages–and, he had to admit, to her wonderful, nerveless driving. And now a big Michelin sign said 'Montreuil 5, Royale-les-Eaux 10, Le Touquet-Paris-Plage 15', and he wondered about her destination and debated with himself whether he shouldn't forget about Royale and the night he had promised himself at its famous casino and just follow where she went, wherever it was, and find out who this devil of a girl was.

The decision was taken out of his hands. Montreuil is a dangerous town with cobbled, twisting streets and much farm traffic. Bond was fifty yards behind her at the outskirts, but, with his big car, he couldn't follow her fast slalom through the hazards and, by the time he was out of the town and over the Étaples-Paris level-crossing, she had vanished. The left-hand turn for Royale came up. Was there a little dust hanging in the bend? Bond took the turn, somehow knowing that he was going to see her again.

He leaned forward and flicked down the red switch. The moan of the blower died away and there was silence in the car as he motored along, easing his tense muscles. He wondered if the supercharger had damaged the engine. Against the solemn warnings of Rolls-Royce, he had had fitted, by his pet expert at the Headquarters' motor pool, an Arnott supercharger controlled by a magnetic clutch. Rolls-Royce had said the crankshaft bearings wouldn't take the extra load and, when he confessed to them what he had done, they regretfully but firmly withdrew their guarantees and washed their hands of their bastardized child. This was the first time he had notched 125 and the rev. counter had hovered dangerously over the red line at 4500. But the temperature and oil were O.K. and there were no expensive noises. And, by God, it had been fun!

James Bond idled through the pretty approaches to Royale, though the young beeches and the heavy-scented pines, looking forward to the evening and remembering his other annual pilgrimages to this place and, particularly, the great battle across the baize he had had with Le Chiffre so many years ago. He had come a long way since then, dodged many bullets and much death and loved many girls, but there had been a drama and a poignancy about that particular adventure that every year drew him back to Royale and its casino and to the small granite cross in the little churchyard that simply said 'Vesper Lynd. R.I.P.'

And now what was the place holding for him on this beautiful September evening? A big win? A painful loss? A beautiful girl–that beautiful girl?

To think first of the game. This was the week-end of the 'clôture annuelle'. Tonight, this very Saturday night, the Casino Royale was holding its last night of the season. It was always a big event and there would be pilgrims even from Belgium and Holland, as well as the rich regulars from Paris and Lille. In addition, the 'Syndicat d'Initiative et des Bains de Mer de Royale' traditionally threw open its doors to all its local contractors and suppliers, and there was free champagne and a great groaning buffet to reward the town people for their work during the season. It was a tremendous carouse that rarely finished before breakfast time. The tables would be packed and there would be a very high game indeed.

Bond had one million francs of private capital–Old Francs, of course–about seven hundred pounds' worth. He always reckoned his private funds in Old Francs. It made him feel so rich. On the other hand, he made out his official expenses in New Francs because that made them look smaller–but probably not to the Chief Accountant at Headquarters! One million francs! For that evening he was a millionaire! Might he so remain by tomorrow morning!

And now he was coming into the Promenade des Anglais and there was the bastard Empire frontage of the Hotel Splendide. And there, by God, on the gravel sweep alongside its steps, stood the little white Lancia and, at this moment, a bagagiste, in a striped waistcoat and green apron, was carrying two Vuitton suitcases up the steps to the entrance!

So!

James Bond slid his car into the million-pound line of cars in the car park, told the same bagagiste, who was now taking rich, small stuff out of the Lancia, to bring up his bags, and went in to the reception-desk. The manager impressively took over from the clerk and greeted Bond with golden-toothed effusion, while making a mental note to earn a good mark with the Chef de Police by reporting Bond's arrival, so that the Chef could, in his turn, make a good mark with the Deuxième and the SDT by putting the news on the teleprinter to Paris.

Bond said, 'By the way, Monsieur Maurice. Who is the lady who has just driven up in the white Lancia? She is staying here?'

'Yes, indeed, Mon Commandant.' Bond received an extra two teeth in the enthusiastic smile. 'The lady is a good friend of the house. The father is a very big industrial from the South. She is La Comtesse Teresa di Vicenzo. Monsieur must surely have read of her in the papers. Madame la Comtesse is a lady–how shall I put it?'–the smile became secret, between men–'a lady, shall we say, who lives life to the full.'

'Ah, yes. Thank you. And how has the season been?'

The small talk continued as the manager personally took Bond up in the lift and showed him into one of the handsome grey and white Directoire rooms with the deep rose coverlet on the bed that Bond remembered so well. Then, with a final exchange of courtesies, James Bond was alone.

Bond was faintly disappointed. She sounded a bit grand for him, and he didn't happen to like girls, film stars for instance, who were in any way public property. He liked private girls, girls he could discover himself and make his own. Perhaps, he admitted, there was inverted snobbery in this. Perhaps, even less worthily, it was that the famous ones were less easy to get.

His two battered suitcases came and he unpacked leisurely and then ordered from Room Service a bottle of the Taittinger Blanc de Blancs that he had made his traditional drink at Royale. When the bottle, in its frosted silver bucket, came, he drank a quarter of it rather fast and then went into the bathroom and had an ice-cold shower and washed his hair with Pinaud Elixir, that prince among shampoos, to get the dust of the roads out of it. Then he slipped on his dark-blue tropical worsted trousers, white sea-island cotton shirt, socks and black casual shoes (he abhorred shoe-laces), and went and sat by the window and looked out across the promenade to the sea and wondered where he would have dinner and what he would choose to eat.

James Bond was not a gourmet. In England he lived on grilled soles, œufs cocotte and cold roast beef with potato salad. But when travelling abroad, generally by himself, meals were a welcome break in the day, something to look forward to, something to break the tension of fast driving, with its risks taken or avoided, the narrow squeaks, the permanent background of concern for the fitness of his machine. In fact, at this moment, after covering the long stretch from the Italian frontier at Ventimiglia in a comfortable three days (God knew there was no reason to hurry back to Headquarters!), he was fed to the teeth with the sucker-traps for gourmandizing tourists. The 'Hostelleries', the 'Vieilles Auberges', the 'Relais Fleuris'–he had had the lot. He had had their 'Bonnes Tables', and their 'Fines Bouteilles'. He had had their 'Spécialités du Chef'–generally a rich sauce of cream and wine and a few button mushrooms concealing poor quality meat or fish. He had had the whole lip-smacking ritual of winemanship and foodmanship and, incidentally, he had had quite enough of the Bisodol that went with it!

The French belly-religion had delivered its final kick at him the night before. Wishing to avoid Orléans, he had stopped south of this uninspiring city and had chosen a mock-Breton Auberge on the south bank of the Loire, despite its profusion of window-boxes and sham beams, ignoring the china cat pursuing the china bird across its gabled roof, because it was right on the edge of the Loire–perhaps Bond's favourite river in the world. He had stoically accepted the hammered copper warming pans, brass cooking utensils and other antique bogosities that cluttered the walls of the entrance hall, had left his bag in his room and had gone for an agreeable walk along the softly running, swallow-skimmed river. The dining-room, in which he was one of a small handful of tourists, had sounded the alarm. Above a fire-place of electric logs and over-polished fire-irons there had hung a coloured plaster escutcheon bearing the dread device: ICY DOULCE FRANCE. All the plates, of some hideous local ware, bore the jingle, irritatingly inscrutable, 'Jamais en Vain, Toujours en Vin', and the surly waiter, stale with 'fin de saison', had served him with the fly-walk of the Pâté Maison (sent back for a new slice) and a Poularde à la crème that was the only genuine antique in the place. Bond had moodily washed down this sleazy provender with a bottle of instant Pouilly-Fuissé and was finally insulted the next morning by a bill for the meal in excess of five pounds.

It was to efface all these dyspeptic memories that Bond now sat at his window, sipped his Taittinger and weighed up the pros and cons of the local eating places and wondered what dishes it would be best to gamble on. He finally chose one of his favourite restaurants in France, a modest establishment, unpromisingly placed exactly opposite the railway station of Étaples, rang up his old friend Monsieur Bécaud for a table and, two hours later, was motoring back to the Casino with Turbot poché, sauce mousseline, and half the best roast partridge he had eaten in his life, under his belt.

Greatly encouraged, and further stimulated by half a bottle of Mouton Rothschild '53 and a glass of ten-year-old Calvados with his three cups of coffee, he went cheerfully up the thronged steps of the Casino with the absolute certitude that this was going to be a night to remember.

Chapter Three

The Gambit of Shame

(The Bombard had now beaten round the dolefully clanging bell-buoy and was hammering slowly up the River Royale against the current. The gay lights of the little marina, haven of cross-channel yachtsmen, showed way up on the right bank, and it crossed Bond's mind to wait until they were slightly above it and then plunge his knife into the side and bottom of the rubber Bombard and swim for it. But he already heard in his mind the boom of the guns and heard the zwip and splash of the bullets round his head until, probably, there came the bright burst of light and the final flash of knowledge that he had at last had it. And anyway, how well could the girl swim, and in this current? Bond was now very cold. He leant closer against her and went back to remembering the night before and combing his memories for clues.)

After the long walk across the Salle d'Entrée, past the vitrines of Van Cleef, Lanvin, Hermès and the rest, there came the brief pause for identification at the long desk backed by the tiers of filing cabinets, the payment for the Carte d'Entrée pour les Salles de Jeux, the quick, comptometer survey of the physiognomiste at the entrance, the bow and flourish of the garishly uniformed huissier at the door, and James Bond was inside the belly of the handsome, scented machine.

He paused for a moment by the caisse, his nostrils flaring at the smell of the crowded, electric, elegant scene, then he walked slowly across to the top chemin de fer table beside the entrance to the luxuriously appointed bar, and caught the eye of Monsieur Pol, the Chef de Jeu of the high game. Monsieur Pol spoke to a huissier and Bond was shown to Number Seven, reserved by a counter from the huissier's pocket. The huissier gave a quick brush to the baize inside the line–that famous line that had been the bone of contention in the Tranby Croft case involving King Edward VII–polished an ash-tray and pulled out the chair for Bond. Bond sat down. The shoe was at the other end of the table, at Number Three. Cheerful and relaxed, Bond examined the faces of the other players while the Changeur changed his notes for a hundred thousand into ten blood-red counters of ten thousand each. Bond stacked them in a neat pile in front of him and watched the play which, he saw from the notice hanging between the green-shaded lights over the table, was for a minimum of one hundred New Francs, or ten thousand of the old. But he noted that the game was being opened by each banker for up to five hundred New Francs–serious money–say forty pounds as a starter.

The players were the usual international mixture–three Lille textile tycoons in over-padded dinner-jackets, a couple of heavy women in diamonds who might be Belgian, a rather Agatha Christie-style little Englishwoman who played quietly and successfully and might be a villa owner, two middle-aged Americans in dark suits who appeared cheerful and slightly drunk, probably down from Paris, and Bond. Watchers and casual punters were two-deep round the table. No girl!

The game was cold. The shoe went slowly round the table, each banker in turn going down on that dread third coup which, for some reason, is the sound barrier at chemin de fer which must be broken if you are to have a run. Each time, when it came to Bond's turn, he debated whether to bow to the pattern and pass his bank after the second coup. Each time, for nearly an hour of play, he obstinately told himself that the pattern would break, and why not with him? That the cards have no memory and that it was time for them to run. And each time, as did the other players, he went down on the third coup. The shoe came to an end. Bond left his money on the table and wandered off among the other tables, visiting the roulette, the trente et quarante and the baccarat table, to see if he could find the girl. When she had passed him that evening in the Lancia, he had only caught a glimpse of fair hair and of a pure, rather authoritative profile. But he knew that he would recognize her at once, if only by the cord of animal magnetism that had bound them together during the race. But there was no sign of her.

Bond went back to the table. The croupier was marshalling the six packs into the oblong block that would soon be slipped into the waiting shoe. Since Bond was beside him, the croupier offered him the neutral, plain red card to cut the pack with. Bond rubbed the card between his fingers and, with amused deliberation, slipped it as nearly half-way down the block of cards as he could estimate. The croupier smiled at him and at his deliberation, went through the legerdemain that would in due course bring the red stop card into the tongue of the shoe and stop the game just seven cards before the end of the shoe, packed the long block of cards into the shoe, slid in the metal tongue that held them prisoner and announced, loud and clear: 'Messieurs [the 'mesdames' are traditionally not mentioned; since Victorian days it has been assumed that ladies do not gamble], les jeux sont faits. Numéro six à la main.' The Chef de Jeu, on his throne behind the croupier, took up the cry, the huissiers shepherded distant stragglers back to their places, and the game began again.

James Bond confidently bancoed the Lille tycoon on his left, won, made up the cagnotte with a few small counters, and doubled the stake to two thousand New Francs–two hundred thousand of the old.

He won that, and the next. Now for the hurdle of the third coup and he was off to the races! He won it with a natural nine! Eight hundred thousand in the bank (as Bond reckoned it)! Again he won, with difficulty this time–his six against a five. Then he decided to play it safe and pile up some capital. Of the one million six, he asked for the six hundred to be put 'en garage', removed from the stake, leaving a bank of one million. Again he won. Now he put a million 'en garage'. Once more a bank of a million, and now he would have a fat cushion of one million six coming to him anyway! But it was getting difficult to make up his stake. The table was becoming wary of this dark Englishman who played so quietly, wary of the half-smile of certitude on his rather cruel mouth. Who was he? Where did he come from? What did he do? There was a murmur of excited speculation round the table. So far a run of six. Would the Englishman pocket his small fortune and pass the bank? Or would he continue to run it? Surely the cards must change! But James Bond's mind was made up. The cards have no memory in defeat. They also have no memory in victory. He ran the bank three more times, adding each time a million to his 'garage', and then the little old English lady, who had so far left the running to the others, stepped in and bancoed him at the tenth turn, and Bond smiled across at her, knowing that she was going to win. And she did, ignominiously, with a one against Bond's 'bûche'–three kings, making zero.

There was a sigh of relief round the table. The spell had been broken! And a whisper of envy as the heavy, mother-of-pearl plaques piled nearly a foot high, four million, six hundred thousand francs' worth, well over three thousand pounds, were shunted across to Bond with the flat of the croupier's spatula. Bond tossed a plaque for a hundred New Francs to the croupier, received the traditional 'Merci, monsieur! Pour le personnel!' and the game went on.

James Bond lit a cigarette and paid little attention as the shoe went shunting round the table away from him. He had made a packet, dammit! A bloody packet! Now he must be careful. Sit on it. But not too careful, not sit on all of it! This was a glorious evening. It was barely past midnight. He didn't want to go home yet. So be it! He would run his bank when it came to him, but do no bancoing of the others–absolutely none. The cards had got hot. His run had shown that. There would be other runs now, and he could easily burn his fingers chasing them.

Bond was right. When the shoe got to Number Five, to one of the Lille tycoons two places to the left of Bond, an ill-mannered, loud-mouthed player who smoked a cigar out of an amber-and-gold holder and who tore at the cards with heavily manicured, spatulate fingers and slapped them down like a German tarot player, he quickly got through the third coup and was off. Bond, in accordance with his plan, left him severely alone and now, at the sixth coup, the bank stood at twenty thousand New Francs–two million of the old, and the table had got wary again. Everyone was sitting on his money.

The croupier and the Chef de Jeu made their loud calls, 'Un banco de vingt mille! Faites vos jeux, messieurs. Il reste à compléter! Un banco de vingt mille!'

And then there she was! She had come from nowhere and was standing beside the croupier, and Bond had no time to take in more than golden arms, a beautiful golden face with brilliant blue eyes and shocking pink lips, some kind of a plain white dress, a bell of golden hair down to her shoulders, and then it came. 'Banco!'

Everyone looked at her and there was a moment's silence. And then 'Le banco est fait' from the croupier, and the monster from Lille (as Bond now saw him) was tearing the cards out of the shoe, and hers were on their way over to her on the croupier's spatula.

She bent down and there was a moment of discreet cleavage in the white V of her neckline.

'Une carte.'

Bond's heart sank. She certainly hadn't anything better than a five. The monster turned his up. Seven. And now he scrabbled out a card for her and flicked it contemptuously across. A simpering queen!

The croupier delicately faced her other two cards with the tip of his spatula. A four! She had lost!

Bond groaned inwardly and looked across to see how she had taken it.

What he saw was not reassuring. The girl was whispering urgently to the Chef de Jeu. He was shaking his head, sweat was beading on his cheeks. In the silence that had fallen round the table, the silence that licks its lips at the strong smell of scandal, which was now electric in the air, Bond heard the Chef de Jeu say firmly, 'Mais c'est impossible. Je regrette, madame. Il faut vous arranger à la caisse.'

And now that most awful of all whispers in a casino was running among the watchers and the players like a slithering reptile: 'Le coup du déshonneur! C'est le coup du déshonneur! Quelle honte! Quelle honte!'

Oh, my God! thought Bond. She's done it! She hasn't got the money! And for some reason she can't get any credit at the caisse!

The monster from Lille was making the most of the situation. He knew that the casino would pay in the case of a default. He sat back with lowered eyes, puffing at his cigar, the injured party.

But Bond knew of the stigma the girl would carry for the rest of her life. The Casinos of France are a strong trade union. They have to be. Tomorrow the telegrams would go out: 'Madame la Comtesse Teresa di Vicenzo, passport number X, is to be put on the black list.' That would be the end of her casino life in France, in Italy, probably also in Germany, Egypt and, today, England. It was like being declared a bad risk at Lloyd's or with the City security firm of Dun and Bradstreet. In American gambling circles, she might even have been liquidated. In Europe, for her, the fate would be almost as severe. In the circles in which, presumably, she moved, she would be bad news, unclean. The 'coup du déshonneur' simply wasn't done. It was social ostracism.

Not caring about the social ostracism, thinking only about the wonderful girl who had outdriven him, shown him her tail, between Abbeville and Montreuil, James Bond leant slightly forward. He tossed two of the precious pearly plaques into the centre of the table. He said, with a slightly bored, slightly puzzled intonation, 'Forgive me. Madame has forgotten that we agreed to play in partnership this evening.' And, not looking at the girl, but speaking with authority to the Chef de Jeu, 'I beg your pardon. My mind was elsewhere. Let the game continue.'

The tension round the table relaxed. Or rather it changed to another target, away from the girl. Was it true what this Englishman had said? But it must be! One does not pay two million francs for a girl. But previously there had been no relationship between them–so far as one could see. They had been at opposite sides of the table. No signs of complicity had been exchanged. And the girl? She had shown no emotion. She had looked at the man, once, with directness. Then she had quietly moved away from the table, towards the bar. There was certainly something odd here–something one did not understand. But the game was proceeding. The Chef de Jeu had surreptitiously wiped a handkerchief across his face. The croupier had raised his head, which, previously, had seemed to be bowed under some kind of emotional guillotine. And now the old pattern had re-established itself. 'La partie continue. Un banco de quarante mille!'

James Bond glanced down at the still formidable pile of counters between his curved, relaxed arms. It would be nice to get that two million francs back. It might be hours before a banco of equal size offered the chance. After all, he was playing with the casino's money! His profits represented 'found' money and, if he lost, he could still go away with a small profit–enough and to spare to pay for his night at Royale. And he had taken a dislike to the monster from Lille. It would be amusing to reverse the old fable–first to rescue the girl, then to slay the monster. And it was time for the man's run of luck to end. After all, the cards have no memory!

James Bond had not enough funds to take the whole banco, only half of it, what is known as 'avec la table', meaning that the other players could make up the remaining half if they wanted to. Bond, forgetting the conservative strategy he had sworn himself to only half an hour before, leant slightly forward and said, 'Avec la table,' and pushed twenty thousand New Francs over the line.

Money followed his on to the table. Was this not the Englishman with the green fingers? And Bond was pleased to note that the little old Agatha Christie Englishwoman supported him with ten thousand. That was a good omen! He looked at the banker, the man from Lille. His cigar had gone out in its holder and his lips, where they gripped the holder, were white. He was sweating profusely. He was debating whether to pass the hand and take his fat profits or have one more go. The sharp, pig-like eyes darted round the table, estimating if his four million was covered.

The croupier wanted to hurry the play. He said firmly, 'C'est plus que fait, monsieur.'

The man from Lille made up his mind. He gave the shoe a fat slap, wiped his hand on the baize and forced out a card. Then one for himself, another for Bond, the fourth for him. Bond did not reach across Number Six for the cards. He waited for them to be nudged towards him by the croupier. He raised them just off the table, slid them far enough apart between his hands to see the count, edged them together again and laid them softly face down again on the table. He had a five! That dubious jade on which one can either draw or not! The chances of improving your hand towards or away from a nine are equal. He said 'Non,' quietly, and looked across at the two anonymous pink backs of the cards in front of the banker. The man tore them up, disgustedly tossed them out on to the table. Two knaves. A 'bûche'! Zero!

Now there were only four cards that could beat Bond and only one, the five, that could equal him. Bond's heart thumped. The man scrabbled at the shoe, snatched out the card, faced it. A nine, the nine of diamonds! The curse of Scotland! The best!

It was a mere formality to turn over and reveal Bond's miserable five. But there was a groan round the table. 'Il fallait tirer,' said someone. But if he had, Bond would have drawn the nine and disimproved down to a four. It all depended on what the next card, its pink tongue now hiding its secret in the mouth of the shoe, might have been. Bond didn't wait to see. He smiled a thin, rueful smile round the table to apologize to his fellow losers, shovelled the rest of his chips into his coat pocket, tipped the huissier who had been so busy emptying his ash-tray over the hours of play, and slipped away from the table towards the bar, while the croupier triumphantly announced, 'Un banco de quatre-vingt mille francs! Faites vos jeux, messieurs! Un banco de quatre-vingt mille Nouveaux Francs.' To hell with it! thought Bond. Half an hour before he had had a small fortune in his pocket. Now, through a mixture of romantic quixotry and sheer folly he had lost it all. Well, he shrugged, he had asked for a night to remember. That was the first half of it. What would be the second?

The girl was sitting by herself, with half a bottle of Bollinger in front of her, staring moodily at nothing. She barely looked up when Bond slipped into the chair next to hers and said, 'Well, I'm afraid our syndicate lost again. I tried to get it back. I went "avec". I should have left that brute alone. I stood on a five and he had a "bûche" and then drew a nine.'

She said dully, 'You should have drawn on the five. I always do.' She reflected. 'But then you would have had a four. What was the next card?'

'I didn't wait to see. I came to look for you.'

She gave him a sideways, appraising glance. 'Why did you rescue me when I made the "coup du déshonneur"?'

Bond shrugged. 'Beautiful girl in distress. Besides, we made friends between Abbeville and Montreuil this evening. You drive like an angel.' He smiled. 'But I don't think you'd have passed me if I'd been paying attention. I was doing about ninety and not bothering to keep an eye on the mirror. And I was thinking of other things.'

The gambit succeeded. Vivacity came into her face and voice. 'Oh, yes. I'd have beaten you anyway. I'd have passed you in the villages. Besides'–there was an edge of bitterness in her voice–'I would always be able to beat you. You want to stay alive.'

Oh, lord! thought Bond. One of those! A girl with a wing, perhaps two wings, down. He chose to let the remark lie. The half-bottle of Krug he had ordered came. After the huissier had half filled the glass, Bond topped it to the brim. He held it towards her without exaggeration. 'My name is Bond, James Bond. Please stay alive, at any rate for tonight.' He drank the glass down at one long gulp and filled it again.

She looked at him gravely, considering him. Then she also drank. She said, 'My name is Tracy. That is short for all the names you were told at the reception in the hotel. Teresa was a saint. I am not a saint. The manager is perhaps a romantic. He told me of your inquiries. So shall we go now? I am not interested in conversation. And you have earned your reward.'

She rose abruptly. So did Bond, confused. 'No. I will go alone. You can come later. The number is 45. There, if you wish, you can make the most expensive piece of love of your life. It will have cost you four million francs. I hope it will be worth it.'

Chapter Four

All Cats are Grey

She was waiting in the big double bed, a single sheet pulled up to her chin. The fair hair was spread out like golden wings under the single reading light that was the only light in the room, and the blue eyes blazed with a fervour that, in other girls, in other beds, James Bond would have interpreted. But this one was in the grip of stresses he could not even guess at. He locked the door behind him and came over and sat on the edge of her bed and put one hand firmly on the little hill that was her left breast. 'Now listen, Tracy,' he began, meaning to ask at least one or two questions, find out something about this wonderful girl who did hysterical things like gambling without the money to meet her debts, driving like a potential suicide, hinting that she had had enough of life.

But the girl reached up a swift hand that smelt of Guerlain's 'Ode' and put it across his lips. 'I said "no conversation". Take off those clothes. Make love to me. You are handsome and strong. I want to remember what it can be like. Do anything you like. And tell me what you like and what you would like from me. Be rough with me. Treat me like the lowest whore in creation. Forget everything else. No questions. Take me.'

An hour later, James Bond slipped out of bed without waking her, dressed by the light of the promenade lights filtering between the curtains, and went back to his room.

He showered and got in between the cool, rough French sheets of his own bed and switched off his thinking about her. All he remembered, before sleep took him, was that she had said when it was all over, 'That was heaven, James. Will you please come back when you wake up. I must have it once more.' Then she had turned over on her side away from him and, without answering his last endearments, had gone to sleep–but not before he had heard that she was crying.

What the hell? All cats are grey in the dark.

True or false?

Bond slept.

At eight o'clock he woke her and it was the same glorious thing again. But this time he thought that she held him to her more tenderly, kissed him not only with passion but with affection. But, after, when they should have been making plans about the day, about where to have lunch, when to bathe, she was at first evasive and then, when he pressed her, childishly abusive.

'Get to hell away from me! Do you hear? You've had what you wanted. Now get out!'

'Wasn't it what you wanted too?'

'No. You're a lousy goddam lover. Get out!'

Bond recognized the edge of hysteria, at least of desperation. He dressed slowly, waiting for the tears to come, for the sheet that now covered her totally to shake with sobs. But the tears didn't come. That was bad! In some way this girl had come to the end of her tether, of too many tethers. Bond felt a wave of affection for her, a sweeping urge to protect her, to solve her problems, make her happy. With his hand on the door-knob he said softly, 'Tracy. Let me help you. You've got some troubles. That's not the end of the world. So have I. So has everyone else.'

The dull clichés fell into the silent, sun-barred room, like clinker in a grate.

'Go to hell!'

In the instant of opening and closing the door, Bond debated whether to bang it shut, to shake her out of her mood, or to close it softly. He closed it softly. Harshness would do no good with this girl. She had had it, somehow, somewhere–too much of it. He went off down the corridor, feeling, for the first time in his life, totally inadequate.

(The Bombard thrashed on up river. It had passed the marina and, with the narrowing banks, the current was stronger. The two thugs in the stern still kept their quiet eyes on Bond. In the bows, the girl still held her proud profile into the wind like the figure-head on a sailing ship. In Bond, the only warmth was in his contact with her back and his hand on the haft of his knife. Yet, in a curious way, he felt closer to her, far closer, than in the transports of the night before. Somehow he felt that she was as much a prisoner as he was. How? Why? Way ahead the lights of the Vieux Port, once close to the sea, but now left behind by some quirk of the Channel currents that had built up the approaches to the river, shone sparsely. Before many years they would go out and a new harbour, nearer the mouth of the river, would be built for the deep-sea trawlers that served Royale with their soles and lobsters and crabs and prawns. On this side of the lights were occasional gaunt jetties built out into the river by private yacht-owners. Behind them were villas that would have names like 'Rosalie', 'Toi et Moi', 'Nid Azur' and 'Nouvelle Vague'. James Bond nursed the knife and smelt the 'Ode' that came to him above the stink of mud and seaweed from the river banks. His teeth had never chattered before. Now they chattered. He stopped them and went back to his memories.)

Normally, breakfast was an important part of Bond's day, but today he had barely noticed what he was eating, hurried through the meal and sat gazing out of his window and across the promenade, chain-smoking and wondering about the girl. He knew nothing positive about her, not even her nationality. The Mediterranean was in her name, yet she was surely neither Italian nor Spanish. Her English was faultless and her clothes and the way she wore them were the products of expensive surroundings–perhaps a Swiss finishing school. She didn't smoke, seemed to drink only sparingly, and there was no sign of drug-taking. There had not even been sleeping pills beside the bed or in her bathroom. She could only be about twenty-five, yet she made love with the fervour and expertness of a girl who, in the American phrase, had 'gone the route'. She hadn't laughed once, had hardly smiled. She seemed in the grip of some deep melancholy, some form of spiritual accidie that made life, on her own admission, no longer worth living. And yet there were none of those signs that one associates with the hysteria of female neurotics–the unkempt hair and sloppy make-up, the atmosphere of disarray and chaos they create around them. On the contrary, she seemed to possess an ice-cold will, authority over herself and an exact idea of what she wanted and where she was going. And where was that? In Bond's book she had desperate intentions, most likely suicide, and last night had been the last fling.

He looked down at the little white car that was now not far from his in the parking lot. Somehow he must stick close to her, watch over her, at least until he was satisfied that his deadly conclusions were wrong. As a first step, he rang down to the concierge and ordered a drive-yourself Simca Aronde. Yes, it should be delivered at once and left in the parking lot. He would bring his international driving licence and green insurance card down to the concierge who would kindly complete the formalities.

Bond shaved and dressed and took the papers down and returned to his room. He stayed there, watching the entrance and the little white car until 4.30 in the afternoon. Then, at last, she appeared, in the black and white striped bathing-wrap, and Bond ran down the corridor to the lift. It was not difficult to follow her as she drove along the promenade, and left her car in one of the parking lots, and it was also no problem for the little anonymous 2CV Citroën that followed Bond.

And then had been set up the train of the watchers and the watched which was now drawing to its mysterious climax as the little Bombard thrashed its way up the River Royale under the stars.

What to make of it all? Had she been a witting or unwitting bait? Was this a kidnapping? If so, of one or of both? Was it blackmail? The revenge of a husband or another lover? Or was it to be murder?

Bond was still raking his mind for clues when the helmsman turned the Bombard in a wide curve across the current towards a battered, skeletal jetty that projected from the muddy bank into the stream. He pulled up under its lee, a powerful flashlight shone down on them out of the darkness, a rope clattered down and the boat was hauled to the foot of muddy wooden steps. One of the thugs climbed out first, followed by the girl, the white bottom of her bathing dress lascivious below Bond's coat, then Bond, then the second thug. Then the Bombard backed quickly away and continued up river, presumably, thought Bond, to its legitimate mooring in the Vieux Port.

There were two more men, of much the same build as the others, on the jetty. No words were spoken as, surrounded, the girl and Bond were escorted up the small dust road that led away from the jetty through the sand dunes. A hundred yards from the river, tucked away in a gully between tall dunes, there was a glimmer of light. When Bond got nearer he saw that it came from one of those giant corrugated aluminium transport-trucks that, behind an articulated driver's cabin, roar down the arterial routes of France belching diesel smoke and hissing angrily with their hydraulic brakes as they snake through the towns and villages. This one was a glinting, polished affair. It looked new, but might be just well cared for. As they approached, the man with the flashlight gave some signal, and an oblong of yellow light promptly blazed as the caravan-like door in the rear was thrown open. Bond fingered his knife. Were the odds in any way within reason? They were not. Before he climbed up the steps into the interior, he glanced down at the number-plate. The commercial licence said, 'Marseille-Rhône. M. Draco. Appareils Électriques. 397694.' So! One more riddle!

Inside it was, thank God, warm. A passage-way led between stacked rows of cartons marked with the famous names of television manufacturers. Dummies? There were also folded chairs and the signs of a disturbed game of cards. This was presumably used as the guard-room. Then, on both sides, the doors of cabins. Tracy was waiting at one of the doors. She held out his coat to him, said an expressionless 'Thank you' and closed the door after Bond had caught a brief glimpse of a luxurious interior. Bond took his time putting on his coat. The single man with the gun who was following him said impatiently, 'Allez!' Bond wondered whether to jump him. But, behind, the other three men stood watching. Bond contented himself with a mild 'Merde à vous!' and went ahead to the aluminium door that presumably sealed off the third and forward compartment in this strange vehicle. Behind this door lay the answer. It was probably one man – the leader. This might be the only chance. Bond's right hand was already grasping the hilt of his knife in his trouser pocket. Now he put out his left hand and, in one swirl of motion, leaped through, kicked the door shut behind him and crouched, the knife held for throwing.

Behind him he felt the guard throw himself at the door, but Bond had his back to it and it held. The man, ten feet away behind the desk, within easy range for the knife, called out something, an order, a cheerful, gay order in some language Bond had never heard. The pressure on the door ceased. The man smiled a wide, a charming smile that cracked his creased walnut of a face in two. He got to his feet and slowly raised his hands. 'I surrender. And I am now a much bigger target. But do not kill me, I beg of you. At least not until we have had a stiff whisky and soda and a talk. Then I will give you the choice again. O.K.?'

Bond rose to his full height. He smiled back. He couldn't help it. The man had such a delightful face, so lit with humour and mischief and magnetism that, at least in the man's present role, Bond could no more have killed him than he could have killed, well, Tracy.

There was a calendar hanging on the wall beside the man. Bond wanted to let off steam against something, anything. He said, 'September the sixteenth,' and jerked his right hand forward in the underhand throw. The knife flashed across the room, missed the man by about a yard, and stuck, quivering, half-way down the page of the calendar.

The man turned and looked inquisitively at the calendar. He laughed out loud. 'Actually the fifteenth. But quite respectable. I must set you against my men one of these days. And I might even bet on you. It would teach them a lesson.'

He came out from behind his desk, a smallish, middle-aged man with a brown, crinkled face. He was dressed in the sort of comfortable dark blue suit Bond himself wore. The chest and the arms bulged with muscle. Bond noticed the fullness of the cut of the coat under the arm-pits. Built for guns? The man held out a hand. It was warm and firm and dry. 'Marc-Ange Draco is my name. You have heard of it?'

'No.'

'Aha! But I have heard of yours. It is Commander James Bond. You have a decoration called the C.M.G. You are a member, an important member, of Her Majesty's Secret Service. You have been taken off your usual duties and you are on temporary assignment abroad.' The impish face creased with delight. 'Yes?'

James Bond, to cover his confusion, walked across to the calendar, verified that he had in fact pierced the fifteenth, pulled out the knife and slipped it back in his trouser pocket. He turned and said, 'What makes you think so?'

The man didn't answer. He said, 'Come. Come and sit down. I have much to talk to you about. But first the whisky and soda. Yes?' He indicated a comfortable armchair across the desk from his own, put in front of it a large silver box containing various kinds of cigarettes, and went to a metal filing cabinet against the wall and opened it. It contained no files. It was a complete and compact bar. With efficient, housekeeperly movements he took out a bottle of Pinchbottle Haig, another of I.W.Harper's Bourbon, two pint glasses that looked like Waterford, a bucket of ice cubes, a siphon of soda and a flagon of iced water. One by one he placed these on the desk between his chair and Bond's. Then, while Bond poured himself a stiff Bourbon and water with plenty of ice, he went and sat down across the desk from Bond, reached for the Haig and said, looking Bond very directly in the eye, 'I learned who you are from a good friend in the Deuxième in Paris. He is paid to give me such information when I want it. I learned it very early this morning. I am in the opposite camp to yourself–not directly opposite. Let us say at a tangent on the field.' He paused. He lifted his glass. He said with much seriousness, 'I am now going to establish confidence with you. By the only means. I am going once again to place my life in your hands.'

He drank. So did Bond. In the filing cabinet, in its ice-box, the hum of the generator broke in on what Bond suddenly knew was going to be an important moment of truth. He didn't know what the truth was going to be. He didn't think it was going to be bad. But he had an instinct that, somehow, perhaps because he had conceived respect and affection for this man, it was going to mean deep involvement for himself.

The generator stopped.

The eyes in the walnut face held his.

'I am the head of the Union Corse.'

Chapter Five

The Capu

The Union Corse! Now at least some of the mystery was explained. Bond looked across the desk into the brown eyes that were now shrewdly watching his reactions while his mind flicked through the file that bore the innocent title, 'The Union Corse', more deadly and perhaps even older than the Unione Siciliano, the Mafia. He knew that it controlled most organized crime throughout metropolitan France and her colonies–protection rackets, smuggling, prostitution and the suppression of rival gangs. Only a few months ago a certain Rossi had been shot dead in a bar in Nice. A year before that, a Jean Giudicelli had been liquidated after several previous attempts had failed. Both these men had been known pretenders to the throne of Capu–the ebullient, cheerful man who now sat so peacefully across the table from Bond. Then there was this mysterious business of Rommel's treasure, supposed to be hidden beneath the sea somewhere off Bastia. In 1948 a Czech diver called Fleigh, who had been in the Abwehr, and had got on the track of it, was warned off by the Union and then vanished off the face of the earth. Quite recently the body of a young French diver, André Mattei, was found riddled with bullets by the roadside near Bastia. He had foolishly boasted in the local bars that he knew the whereabouts of the treasure and had come to dive for it. Did Marc-Ange know the secret of this treasure? Had he been responsible for the killing of these two divers? The little village of Calenzana in the Balagne boasted of having produced more gangsters than any other village in Corsica and of being in consequence one of the most prosperous. The local mayor had held office for fifty-six years–the longest reigning mayor in France. Marc-Ange would surely be a son of that little community, know the secrets of that famous mayor, know, for instance, of that big American gangster who had just returned to discreet retirement in the village after a highly profitable career in the States.

It would be fun to drop some of these names casually in this quiet little room–fun to tell Marc-Ange that Bond knew of the old abandoned jetty called the Port of Crovani near the village of Galeria, and of the ancient silver mine called Argentella in the hills behind, whose maze of underground tunnels accommodates one of the great world junctions in the heroin traffic.

Yes, it would be fun to frighten his captor in exchange for the fright he had given Bond. But better keep this ammunition in reserve until more had been revealed! For the time being it was interesting to note that this was Marc-Ange Draco's travelling headquarters. His contact in the Deuxième Bureau would be an essential tip-off man. Bond and the girl had been 'sent for' for some purpose that was still to be announced. The 'borrowing' of the Bombard rescue-boat would have been a simple matter of finance in the right quarter, perhaps accompanied by a 'pot de vin' for the coastguards to look the other way. The guards were Corsicans. On reflection, that was anyway what they looked like. The whole operation was simple for an organization as powerful as the Union–as simple in France as it would have been for the Mafia in most of Italy. And now for more veils to be lifted! James Bond sipped his drink and watched the other man's face with respect. This was one of the great professionals of the world!

[How typical of Corsica, Bond thought, that their top bandit should bear the name of an angel! He remembered that two other famous Corsican gangsters had been called 'Gracieux' and 'Toussaint'–'All-Saints'.] Marc-Ange spoke. He spoke excellent but occasionally rather clumsy English, as if he had been well taught but had little occasion to use the language. He said, 'My dear Commander, everything I am going to discuss with you will please remain behind your Herkos Odonton. You know the expression? No?' The wide smile lit up his face. 'Then, if I may say so, your education was incomplete. It is from the classical Greek. It means literally "the hedge of the teeth". It was the Greek equivalent of your "top secret". Is that agreed?'

Bond shrugged. 'If you tell me secrets that affect my profession, I'm afraid I shall have to pass them on.'

'That I fully comprehend. What I wish to discuss is a personal matter. It concerns my daughter, Teresa.'

Good God! The plot was indeed thickening! Bond concealed his surprise. He said, 'Then I agree.' He smiled. '"Herkos Odonton" it is.'

'Thank you. You are a man to trust. You would have to be, in your profession, but I see it also in your face. Now then.' He lit a Caporal and sat back in his chair. He gazed at a point on the aluminium wall above Bond's head, only occasionally looking into Bond's eyes when he wished to emphasize a point. 'I was married once only, to an English girl, an English governess. She was a romantic. She had come to Corsica to look for bandits–' he smiled–'rather like some English women adventure into the desert to look for sheiks. She explained to me later that she must have been possessed by a subconscious desire to be raped. Well–' this time he didn't smile–'she found me in the mountains and she was raped–by me. The police were after me at the time, they have been for most of my life, and the girl was a grave encumbrance. But for some reason she refused to leave me. There was a wildness in her, a love of the unconventional, and, for God knows what reason, she liked the months of being chased from cave to cave, of getting food by robbery at night. She even learned to skin and cook a moufflon, those are our mountain sheep, and even eat the animal, which is tough as shoe leather and about as palatable. And in those crazy months, I came to love this girl and I smuggled her away from the island to Marseilles and married her.' He paused and looked at Bond. 'The result, my dear Commander, was Teresa, my only child.'

So, thought Bond. That explained the curious mixture the girl was–the kind of wild 'lady' that was so puzzling in her. What a complex of bloods and temperaments! Corsican English. No wonder he hadn't been able to define her nationality.

'My wife died ten years ago–' Marc-Ange held up his hand, not wanting sympathy–'and I had the girl's education finished in Switzerland. I was already rich and at that time I was elected Capu, that is chief, of the Union, and became infinitely richer–by means, my dear Commander, which you can guess but need not inquire into. The girl was–how do you say?–that charming expression, "the apple of my eye", and I gave her all she wanted. But she was a wild one, a wild bird, without a proper home, or, since I was always on the move, without proper supervision. Through her school in Switzerland, she entered the fast international set that one reads of in the newspapers–the South American millionaires, the Indian princelings, the Paris English and Americans, the playboys of Cannes and Gstaad. She was always getting in and out of scrapes and scandals, and when I remonstrated with her, cut off her allowance, she would commit some even grosser folly–to spite me, I suppose.' He paused and looked at Bond and now there was a terrible misery in the happy face. 'And yet all the while, behind her bravado, the mother's side of her blood was making her hate herself, despise herself more and more, and as I now see it, the worm of self-destruction had somehow got a hold inside her and, behind the wild, playgirl façade, was eating away what I can only describe as her soul.' He looked at Bond. 'You know that this can happen, my friend–to men and to women. They burn the heart out of themselves by living too greedily, and suddenly they examine their lives and see that they are worthless. They have had everything, eaten all the sweets of life at one great banquet, and there is nothing left. She made what I now see was a desperate attempt to get back on the rails, so to speak. She went off, without telling me, and married, perhaps with the idea of settling down. But the man, a worthless Italian called Vicenzo, Count Giulio di Vicenzo, took as much of her money as he could lay his hands on and deserted her, leaving her with a girl child. I purchased a divorce and bought a small château for my daughter in the Dordogne and installed her there, and for once, with the baby and a pretty garden to look after, she seemed almost at peace. And then, my friend, six months ago, the baby died–died of that most terrible of all children's ailments, spinal meningitis.'

There was silence in the little metal room. Bond thought of the girl a few yards away down the corridor. Yes. He had been near the truth. He had seen some of this tragic story in the calm desperation of the girl. She had indeed come to the end of the road!

Marc-Ange got slowly up from his chair and came round and poured out more whisky for himself and for Bond. He said, 'Forgive me. I am a poor host. But the telling of this story, which I have always kept locked up inside me, to another man, has been a great relief.' He put a hand on Bond's shoulder. 'You understand that?'

'Yes. I understand that. But she is a fine girl. She still has nearly all her life to live. Have you thought of psychoanalysis? Of her church? Is she a Catholic?'

'No. Her mother would not have it. She is Presbyterian. But wait while I finish the story.' He went back to his chair and sat down heavily. 'After the tragedy, she disappeared. She took her jewels and went off in that little car of hers, and I heard occasional news of her, selling the jewels and living furiously all over Europe, with her old set. Naturally I followed her, had her watched when I could, but she avoided all my attempts to meet her and talk to her. Then I heard from one of my agents that she had reserved a room here, at the Splendide, for last night, and I hurried down from Paris–' he waved a hand–'in this, because I had a presentiment of tragedy. You see, this was where we had spent the summers in her childhood and she had always loved it. She is a wonderful swimmer and she was almost literally in love with the sea. And, when I got the news, I suddenly had a dreadful memory, the memory of a day when she had been naughty and had been locked in her room all afternoon instead of going bathing. That night she had said to her mother, quite calmly, "You made me very unhappy keeping me away from the sea. One day, if I get really unhappy I shall swim out into the sea, down the path of the moon or the sun, and go on swimming until I sink. So there!" Her mother told me the story and we laughed over it together, at the childish tantrum. But now I suddenly remembered again the occasion and it seemed to me that the childish fantasy might well have stayed with her, locked away deep down, and that now, wanting to put an end to herself, she had resurrected it and was going to act on it. And so, my dear friend, I had her closely watched from the moment she arrived. Your gentlemanly conduct in the casino, for which–' he looked across at Bond–'I now deeply thank you, was reported to me, as of course were your later movements together.' He held up his hand as Bond shifted with embarrassment. 'There is nothing to be ashamed of, to apologize for, in what you did last night. A man is a man and, who knows?–but I shall come to that later. What you did, the way you behaved in general, may have been the beginning of some kind of therapy.'

Bond remembered how, in the Bombard, she had yielded when he had leaned against her. It had been a tiny reaction, but it had held more affection, more warmth, than all the physical ecstacies of the night. Now, suddenly he had an inkling of why he might be here, where the root of the mystery lay, and he gave an involuntary shudder, as if someone had walked over his grave.

Marc-Ange continued, 'So I put in my inquiry to my friend from the Deuxième, at six o'clock this morning. At eight o'clock he went to his office and to the central files and by nine o'clock he had reported to me fully about you–by radio. I have a high-powered station in this vehicle.' He smiled. 'And that is another of my secrets that I deliver into your hands. The report, if I may say so, was entirely to your credit, both as an officer in your Service, and, more important, as a man–a man, that is, in the terms that I understand the word. So I reflected. I reflected all through this morning. And, in the end, I gave orders that you were both to be brought to me here.' He made a throw-away gesture with his right hand. 'I need not tell you the details of my instructions. You yourself saw them in operation. You have been inconvenienced. I apologize. You have perhaps thought yourself in danger. Forgive me. I only trust that my men behaved with correctness, with finesse.'

Bond smiled. 'I am very glad to have met you. If the introduction had to be effected at the point of the two automatics, that will only make it all the more memorable. The whole affair was certainly executed with neatness and expedition.'

Marc-Ange's expression was rueful. 'Now you are being sarcastic. But believe me, my friend, drastic measures were necessary. I knew they were. He reached to the top drawer of his desk, took out a sheet of writing-paper and passed it over to Bond. 'And now, if you read that, you will agree with me. That letter was handed in to the concierge of the Splendide at 4.30 this afternoon for posting to me in Marseilles, when Teresa went out and you followed her. You suspected something? You also feared for her? Read it, please.'

Bond took the letter. he said, 'Yes. I was worried about her. She is a girl worth worrying about.' He held up the letter. It contained only a few words, written clearly, with decision.

> Dear Papa,
> I am sorry, but I have had enough. It is only sad because tonight I met a man who might have changed my mind. He is an Englishman called James Bond. Please find him and pay him 20,000 New Francs which I owe him. And thank him from me.
> This is nobody's fault but my own.
> Goodbye and forgive me.
> Tracy

Bond didn't look at the man who had received this letter. He slid it back to him across the desk. He took a deep drink of the whisky and reached for the bottle. He said, 'Yes, I see.'

'She likes to call herself Tracy. She thinks Teresa sounds too grand.'

'Yes.'

'Commander Bond.' There was now a terrible urgency in the man's voice–urgency, authority and appeal. 'My friend, you have heard the whole story and now you have seen the evidence. Will you help me? Will you help me save this girl? It is my only chance, that you will give her hope. That you will give her a reason to live. Will you?'

Bond kept his eyes on the desk in front of him. He dared not look up and see the expression on the man's face. So he had been right, right to fear that he was going to become involved in all this private trouble! He cursed under his breath. The idea appalled him. He was no Good Samaritan. He was no doctor for wounded birds. What she needed, he said fiercely to himself, was the psychiatrist's couch. All right, so she had taken a passing fancy to him and he to her. Now he was going to be asked, he knew it, to pick her up and carry her perhaps for the rest of her life, haunted by the knowledge, the unspoken blackmail, that, if he dropped her, it would almost certainly be to kill her. He said glumly, 'I do not see that I can help. What is it you have in mind?' He picked up his glass and looked into it. He drank, to give him courage to look across the desk into Marc-Ange's face.

The man's soft brown eyes glittered with tension. The creased dark skin round the mouth had sunk into deeper folds. He said, holding Bond's eyes, 'I wish you to pay court to my daughter and marry her. On the day of her marriage, I will give you a personal dowry of one million pounds in gold.'

James Bond exploded angrily. 'What you ask is utterly impossible. The girl is sick. What she needs is a psychiatrist. Not me. And I do not want to marry, not anyone. Nor do I want a million pounds. I have enough money for my needs. I have my profession.' (Is that true? What about that letter of resignation? Bond ignored the private voice.) 'You must understand all this.' Suddenly he could not bear the hurt in the man's face. He said, softly,

'She is a wonderful girl. I will do all I can for her. But only when she is well again. Then I would certainly like to see her again–very much. But, if she thinks so well of me, if you do, then she must first get well of her own accord. That is the only way. Any doctor would tell you so. She must go to some clinic, the best there is, in Switzerland probably, and bury her past. She must want to live again. Then, only then, would there be any point in our meeting again.' He pleaded with Marc-Ange. 'You do understand, don't you, Marc-Ange? I am a ruthless man. I admit it. And I have not got the patience to act as anyone's nurse, man or woman. Your idea of a cure might only drive her into deeper despair. You must see that I cannot take the responsibility, however much I am attracted by your daughter.' Bond ended lamely, 'Which I am.'

The man said resignedly, 'I understand you, my friend. And I will not importune you with further arguments. I will try and act in the way you suggest. But will you please do one further favour for me? It is now nine o'clock. Will you please take her out to dinner tonight? Talk to her as you please, but show her that she is wanted, that you have affection for her. Her car is here and her clothes. I have had them brought. If only you can persuade her that you would like to see her again, I think I may be able do the rest. Will you do this for me?'

Bond thought, God, what an evening! But he smiled with all the warmth he could summon. 'But of course. I would love to do that. But I am booked on the first morning flight from Le Touquet tomorrow morning. Will you be responsible for her from then?'

'Certainly, my friend. Of course I will do that.' Marc-Ange brusquely wiped a hand across his eyes. 'Forgive me. But you have given me hope at the end of a long night.' He straightened his shoulders and suddenly leaned across the desk and put his hands decisively down. 'I will not thank you. I cannot, but tell me, my dear friend, is there anything in this world that I can do for you, now at this moment? I have great resources, great knowledge, great power. They are all yours. Is there nothing I can do for you?'

Bond had a flash of inspiration. He smiled broadly. 'There is a piece of information I want. There is a man called Blofeld, Ernst Stavro Blofeld. You will have heard of him. I wish to know if he is alive and where he is to be found.'

Marc-Ange's face underwent a remarkable change. Now the bandit, cold, cruel, avenging, looked out through the eyes that had suddenly gone as hard as brown opals. 'Aha!' he said thoughtfully. 'The Blofeld. Yes, he is certainly alive. Only recently he suborned three of my men, bribed them away from the Union. He has done this to me before. Three of the members of the old SPECTRE were taken from the Union. Come, let us find out what we can.'

There was a single black telephone on the desk. He picked up the receiver and at once Bond heard the soft crackle of the operator responding. '*Dammi u commandu.*' Marc-Ange put the receiver back. 'I have asked for my local headquarters in Ajaccio. We will have them in five minutes. But I must speak fast. The police may know my frequency, though I change it every week. But the Corsican dialect helps.' The telephone burred. When Marc-Ange picked up the receiver, Bond could hear the zing and crackle he knew so well. Marc-Ange spoke, in a voice of rasping authority. '*Ecco u Capu. Avette nuttizie di Blofeld, Ernst Stavro? Duve sta?*' A voice crackled thinly.

'*Site sigura? Ma no ezzatu indirizzu?*' More crackle. '*Buon. Sara tutto.*'

Marc-Ange put back the receiver. He spread his hands apologetically. 'All we know is that he is in Switzerland. We have no exact address for him. Will that help? Surely your men there can find him–if the Swiss Sécurité will help. But they are difficult brutes when it comes to the privacy of a resident, particularly if he is rich.'

Bond's pulse had quickened with triumph. Got you, you bastard! He said enthusiastically, 'That's wonderful, Marc-Ange. The rest shouldn't be difficult. We have good friends in Switzerland.'

Marc-Ange smiled happily at Bond's reaction. He said seriously, 'But if things go wrong for you, on this case or in any other way, you will come at once to me. Yes?' He pulled open a drawer and handed a sheet of notepaper over to Bond. 'This is my open address. Telephone or cable to me, but put your request or your news in terms that would be used in connection with electrical appliances. A consignment of radios is faulty. You will meet my representative at such and such a place, on such and such a date. Yes? You understand these tricks, and anyway–' he smiled slyly–'I believe you are connected with an international export firm. "Universal Export", isn't it?'

Bond smiled. How did the old devil know these things? Should he warn Security? No. This man had become a friend. And anyway, all this was Herkos Odonton!

Marc-Ange said diffidently, 'And now may I bring in Teresa? She does not know what we have been discussing. Let us say it is about one of the South of France jewel robberies. You represent the insurance company. I have been making a private deal with you. You can manage that? Good.' He got up and came over to Bond and put his hand on Bond's shoulder. 'And thank you. Thank you for everything.' Then he went out of the door.

Oh my God! thought Bond. Now for my side of the bargain.

Chapter Six

Bond of Bond Street?

It was two months later, in London, and James Bond was driving lazily up from his Chelsea flat to his headquarters.

It was nine-thirty in the morning of yet another beautiful day of this beautiful year, but, in Hyde Park, the fragrance of burning leaves meant that winter was only just round the corner. Bond had nothing on his mind except the frustration of waiting for Station Z somehow to penetrate the reserves of the Swiss Sécurité and come up with the exact address of Blofeld. But their 'friends' in Zürich were continuing to prove obtuse, or, more probably, obstinate. There was no trace of any man, either tourist or resident, called Blofeld in the whole of Switzerland. Nor was there any evidence of the existence of a reborn SPECTRE on Swiss soil. Yes, they fully realized that Blofeld was still urgently 'wanted' by the governments of the NATO alliance. They had carefully filed all the circulars devoted to the apprehension of this man, and for the past year he had been constantly reconfirmed on their 'watch' lists at all frontier posts. They were very sorry, but unless the SIS could come up with further information or evidence about this man, they must assume that the SIS was acting on mistaken evidence. Station Z had asked for an examination of the secret lists at the banks, a search through those anonymous 'numbered' accounts which conceal the owners of most of the fugitive money in the world. This request had been peremptorily refused. Blofeld was certainly a very great criminal, but the Sécurité must point out that such information could only be legally obtained if the criminal in question was guilty of some crime committed on Federal soil and indictable under the Federal Code. It was true that this Blofeld had held up Britain and America to ransom by his illegal possession of atomic weapons. But this could not be considered a crime under the laws of Switzerland, and particularly not having regard to Article 47B of the banking laws. So that was that! The Holy Franc, and the funds which backed it, wherever they came from, must remain untouchable. Wir bitten höflichst um Entschuldigung!

Bond wondered if he should get in touch with Marc-Ange. So far, in his report, he had revealed only a lead into the Union Corse, whom he gave, corporately, as the source of his information. But he shied away from this course of action, which would surely have, as one consequence, the reopening with Marc-Ange of the case of Tracy. And that corner of his life, of his heart, he wanted to leave undisturbed for the time being. Their last evening together had passed quietly, almost as if they had been old friends, old lovers. Bond had said that Universal Export was sending him abroad for some time. They would certainly meet when he returned to Europe. The girl had accepted this arrangement. She herself had decided to go away for a rest. She had been doing too much. She had been on the verge of a nervous breakdown. She would wait for him. Perhaps they could go skiing together around Christmas time? Bond had been enthusiastic. That night, after a wonderful dinner at Bond's little restaurant, they had made love, happily, and this time without desperation, without tears. Bond was satisfied that the cure had really begun. He felt deeply protective towards her. But he knew that their relationship, and her equanimity, rested on a knife-edge which must not be disturbed.

It was at this moment in his reflections that the Syncraphone in his trouser pocket began to bleep. Bond accelerated out of the park and drew up beside the public telephone booth at Marble Arch. The Syncraphone had recently been introduced and was carried by all officers attached to Headquarters. It was a light plastic radio receiver about the size of a pocket watch. When an officer was somewhere in London, within a range of ten miles of Headquarters, he could be bleeped on the receiver. When this happened, it was his duty to go at once to the nearest telephone and contact his office. He was urgently needed.

Bond rang his exchange on the only outside number he was allowed to use, said '007 reporting,' and was at once put through to his secretary. She was a new one. Loelia Ponsonby had at last left to marry a dull, but worthy and rich member of the Baltic Exchange, and confined her contacts with her old job to rather yearning Christmas and birthday cards to the members of the Double-O Section. But the new one, Mary Goodnight, an ex-Wren with blue-black hair, blue eyes and 37-22-35, was a honey and there was a private five-pound sweep in the Section as to who would get her first. Bond had been lying equal favourite with the ex-Royal Marine Commando who was 006 but, since Tracy, had dropped out of the field and now regarded himself as a rank outsider, though he still, rather bitchily, flirted with her. Now he said to her, 'Good morning, Goodnight. What can I do for you? Is it war or peace?'

She giggled unprofessionally. 'It sounds fairly peaceful as peaceful as a hurry message from upstairs can be. You're to go at once to the College of Arms and ask for Griffon Or.'

'Or what?'

'Just Or. Oh, and he's Pursuivant as well, whatever that means. He's one of the Heralds. Apparently they've got some kind of a line on "Bedlam".'

'Bedlam' was the code name for the pursuit of Blofeld. Bond said respectfully, 'Have they indeed? Then I'd better get cracking. Goodbye, Goodnight.' He heard her giggle before he put the receiver down.

Now what the hell? Bond got back into his car, that had mercifully not yet attracted the police or the traffic wardens, and motored fast across London. This was a queer one. How the hell did the College of Arms, of which he knew very little except that they hunted up people's family trees, allotted coats of arms, and organized various royal ceremonies, get into the act?

The College of Arms is in Queen Victoria Street on the fringe of the City. It is a pleasant little Queen Anne backwater in ancient red brick with white sashed windows and a convenient cobbled courtyard, where Bond parked his car. There are horseshoe-shaped stone stairs leading up to an impressive entrance, over which, that day, there hung a banner showing a splendid heraldic beast, half animal and half bird, in gold against a pale blue background. Griffon, thought Bond. Made of Or. He went through the door into a large gloomy hall whose dark panelling was lined with the musty portraits of proud-looking gentlemen in ruffs and lace, and from whose cornice hung the banners of the Commonwealth. The porter, a kindly, soft-spoken man in a cherry-coloured uniform with brass buttons, asked Bond what he could do for him. Bond asked for the Griffon Or and confirmed that he had an appointment.

'Ah yes, sir,' said the porter mysteriously. 'Griffon Or is in waiting this week. That is why his banner is flying outside. This way please, sir.'

Bond followed the porter along a passage hung with gleaming coats of arms in carved wood, up a dank, cob-webby staircase and round a corner to a heavy door over which was written in gold 'Griffon Or Pursuivant' under a representation of the said golden griffon. The porter knocked, opened the door and announced Bond, and left him facing, across an unkempt study littered with books, papers and important-looking inscribed parchments, the top of a bald, round pink head fringed with grizzled curls. The room smelt like the crypt of a church. Bond walked down the narrow lane of carpet left between the piles of litter and stood beside the single chair that faced the man behind the books on the desk. He cleared his throat. The man looked up and the Pickwickian, pince-nez'd face broke into an absent smile. He got to his feet and made a little bow. 'Bond,' he said in a voice that creaked like the lid of an old chest. 'Commander James Bond. Now then, Bond, Bond, Bond. I think I've got you here.' He had kept his finger at the open page of a vast tome. He now sat down and Bond followed suit. 'Yes, yes, yes. Very interesting indeed. Very. But I fear I have to disappoint you, my dear sir. The title is extinct. Actually it's a baronetcy. Most desirable. But no doubt we can establish a relationship through a collateral branch. Now then–' he put his pince-nez very close to the page–'we have some ten different families of Bonds. The important one ended with Sir Thomas Bond, a most distinguished gentleman. He resided in Peckham. He had, alas, no issue–' the pince-nez gleamed encouragingly at Bond–'no legitimate issue that is. Of course in those days, ahem, morals were inclined to be laxer. Now if we could establish some connection with Peckham . . .'

'I have no connection with Peckham. Now, I . . .'

Griffon Or held up his hand. He said severely, 'Where did your parents come from, if I may ask? That, my dear fellow, is the first step in the chain. Then we can go back from there–Somerset House, parish records, old tombstones. No doubt, with a good old English name like yours, we will get somewhere in the end.'

'My father was a Scot and my mother was Swiss. But the point is . . .'

'Quite, quite. You are wondering about the cost of the research. That, my dear fellow, we can leave until later. But, now tell me. From whereabouts in Scotland did your father come? That is important. The Scottish records are of course less fully documented than those from the South. In those days I am forced to admit that our cousins across the border were little more than savages.' Griffon Or bobbed his head politely. He gave a fleeting and, to Bond's eye, rather false smile. 'Very pleasant savages, of course, very brave and all that. But, alas, very weak at keeping up their records. More useful with the sword than with the pen, if I may say so. But perhaps your grandparents and their forebears came from the South?'

'My father came from the Highlands, from near Glencoe. But look here . . .'

But Griffon Or was not to be diverted from the scent. He pulled another thick book towards him. His finger ran down the page of small print. 'Hum. Hum. Hum. Yes, yes. Not very encouraging, I fear. *Burke's General Armory* gives more than ten different families bearing your name. But, alas nothing in Scotland. Not that that means there is no Scottish branch. Now, perhaps you have other relatives living. So often in these matters there is some distant cousin . . .' Griffon Or reached into the pocket of the purple-flowered silk waistcoat that buttoned almost up to his neat bow tie, fished out a small silver snuff-box, offered it to Bond and then himself took two tremendous sniffs. He exploded twice into an ornate bandana handkerchief.

Bond took his opportunity. He leaned forward and said distinctly and forcibly, 'I didn't come here to talk about myself. It's about Blofeld.'

'What's that?' Griffon Or looked at him in astonishment. 'You are not interested in your line of descent?' He held up an admonishing finger. 'Do you realize, my dear fellow, that if we are successful, you may be able to claim direct–' he hesitated–'or at any rate collateral descent from an ancient baronetcy founded–' he went back to his first volume and peered at it–'in the year 1658! Does it not excite you that a possible ancestor of yours was responsible for the name of one of the most famous streets in the world–I refer of course to Bond Street? That was the Sir Thomas Bond, Baronet of Peckham in the County of Surrey, who, as you are no doubt aware, was Comptroller of the household of the Queen Mother, Henrietta Maria. The street was built in 1686 and its associations with famous British folk are, of course, well known. The first Duke of St Albans, son of Nell Gwynn, lived there, as did Laurence Sterne. Boswell's famous dinner party took place there, with Johnson, Reynolds, Goldsmith and Garrick being present. Dean Swift and Canning were residents at different times, and it is intriguing to recall that while Lord Nelson lived at number 141, Lady Hamilton lived at number 145. And this, my dear sir, is the great thoroughfare of which you bear the name! Do you still wish to establish no claim to this vastly distinguished connection? No?' The bushy eyebrows, raised in astonishment, were now lowered in further admonishment. 'This is the very warp and woof of history, my dear Commander Bond.' He reached for another volume that lay open on his desk and that he had obviously prepared for Bond's delectation. 'The coat of arms, for instance. Surely that must concern you, be at least of profound interest to your family, to your own children? Yes, here we are. "Argent on a chevron sable three bezants".' He held up the book so that Bond could see. 'A bezant is a golden ball, as I am sure you know. Three balls.'

Bond commented drily, 'That is certainly a valuable bonus–' the irony was lost on Griffon Or–'but I'm afraid I am still not interested. And I have no relatives and no children. Now about this man . . .'

Griffon Or broke in excitedly, 'And this charming motto of the line, "The World is not Enough". You do not wish to have the right to it?'

'It is an excellent motto which I shall certainly adopt, said Bond curtly. He looked pointedly at his watch. 'Now; I'm afraid we really must get down to business. I have to report back to my Ministry.'

Griffon Or Pursuivant looked genuinely affronted. 'And here is a name going back at least to Norman le Bond in 1180! A fine old English name, though one perhaps orginally of lowly origin. The *Dictionary of British Surnames* suggests that the meaning is clearly "husbandman, peasant, churl".' Was there an edge of malice in the Griffon's watery eye? He added with resignation, 'But, if you are not interested in your ancestry, in the womb of your family, then, my dear sir, in what can I be of service?'

At last! James Bond let out a sigh of relief. He said patiently, 'I came here to inquire about a certain Blofeld, Ernst Stavro Blofeld. It seems that your organization has some information about this man.'

Griffon Or's eyes were suddenly suspicious. 'But you represented yourself as a Commander James Bond. And now the name is Blofeld. How does this come about?'

Bond said icily, 'I am from the Ministry of Defence. Somewhere in this building is information about a man called Blofeld. Where can I find it?'

Griffon Or ran a puzzled hand round his halo of curls. 'Blofeld, is it? Well, well.' He looked accusingly at Bond. 'Forgive me, but you certainly have wasted plenty of my, of the College's, time, Commander Bond. It is a mystery to me why you did not mention this man's name before. Now let me see, Blofeld, Blofeld. Seem to recall that it came up at one of our Chapter meetings the other day. Now who had the case? Ah, yes.' He reached for a telephone among the nest of books and papers. 'Give me Sable Basilisk.'

Chapter Seven

The Hairy Heel of Achilles

James Bond's heart was still in his boots as he was conducted again through the musty corridors. Sable Basilisk indeed! What kind of a besotted old fogy would this be?

There came another heavy door with the name in gold and this time with a nightmare black monster, with a vicious beak, above it. But now Bond was shown into a light clean, pleasantly furnished room with attractive prints on the walls and meticulous order among its books. There was a faint smell of Turkish tobacco. A young man, a few years younger than Bond, got up and came across the room to meet him. He was rapier-slim, with a fine, thin, studious face that was saved from seriousness by wry lines at the edges of the mouth and an ironical glint in the level eyes.

'Commander Bond?' The handshake was brief and firm. 'I'd been expecting you. How did you get into the claws of our dear Griffon? He's a bit of an enthusiast, I'm afraid. We all are here, of course. But he's getting on. Nice chap, but he's a bit dedicated, if you know what I mean.'

It was indeed like a college, this place, reflected Bond. Much of the atmosphere one associates with the Senior Common Room at a University. No doubt Griffon Or mentally put down Sable Basilisk as a young dilettante who was too big for his boots. He said, 'He seemed very anxious to establish a connection between me and Bond Street. It took some time to persuade him that I'm perfectly content to be an ordinary Bond, which, by the way, he, rather churlishly I thought, said meant "a churl".'

Sable Basilisk laughed. He sat down behind his desk, pulled a file towards him, and gestured Bond to a chair beside him. 'Well, then. Let's get down to business. First of all–' he looked Bond very straight in the eye–'I gather, I guess that is, that this is an Intelligence matter of some kind. I did my national service with Intelligence in BAOR, so please don't worry about security. Secondly, we have in this building probably as many secrets as a government department–and nastier ones at that. One of our jobs is to suggest titles to people who've been ennobled in the Honours List. Sometimes we're asked to establish ownership to a title that has become lost or defunct. Snobbery and vanity positively sprawl through our files. Before my time, a certain gentleman who had come up from nowhere, made millions in some light industry or another, and had been given a peerage "for political and public services"–i.e., charities and the party funds–suggested that he should take the title of Lord Bentley Royal, after the village in Essex. We explained that the word Royal could not be used except by the reigning family, but, rather naughtily I fear, we said that "Lord Bentley Common" was vacant.' He smiled. 'See what I mean? If that got about, this man would become the laughing-stock of the country. Then sometimes we have to chase up lost fortunes. So-and-so thinks he's the rightful Duke of Blank and ought to have his money. His name happens to be Blank and his ancestors migrated to America or Australia or somewhere. So avarice and greed come to join snobbery and vanity in these rooms. Of course,' he added, putting the record straight, 'that's only the submerged tenth of our job. The rest is mostly official stuff for governments and embassies–problems of precedence and protocol, the Garter ceremonies and others. We've been doing it for around five hundred years so I suppose it's got its place in the scheme of things.'

'Of course it has,' said Bond staunchly. 'And certainly, so far as security is concerned, I'm sure we can be open with each other. Now this man Blofeld. Truth of the matter is he's probably the biggest crook in the world. Remember that Thunderball affair about a year ago? Only some of it leaked into the papers, but I can tell you that this Blofeld was at the bottom of it all. Now, how did you come to hear of him? Every detail, please. Everything about him is important.'

Sable Basilisk turned back to the first letter on the file. 'Yes,' he said thoughtfully, 'I thought this might be the same chap when I got a lot of urgent calls from the Foreign Office and the Ministry of Defence yesterday. Hadn't occurred to me before, I'm afraid, that this is a case where our secrets have to come second, or I'd have done something about it earlier. Now then, in June last, the tenth, we got this confidential letter from a firm of respectable Zürich solicitors, dated the day before. I'll read it out:

'Honoured Sirs,

'We have a valued client by the name of Ernst Stavro Blofeld. This gentleman styles himself Monsieur le Comte Balthazar de Bleuville in the belief that he is the rightful heir to this title which we understand to be extinct. His belief is based on stories he heard from his parents in childhood to the effect that his family fled France at the time of the Revolution, settled in Germany under the adopted name of Blofeld, assumed in order to evade the Revolutionary authorities and safeguard their fortune which they had sequestered in Augsburg, and subsequently, in the 1850's, migrated to Poland.

'Our client is now anxious to have these facts established in order legally to obtain right to the de Bleuville title supported by an Acte de Notoriété which would in due course receive the stamp of approval of the Ministère de la Justice in Paris.

'In the meantime, our client proposes to continue to adopt, albeit provisionally, the title of Comte de Bleuville together with the family arms which he informs us are "Argent four fusils in fesse gules" and the de Bleuville motto which, in English, is "For Hearth and Home".'

'That's a good one!' interjected Bond. Sable Basilisk smiled and continued:

'We understand that you, honoured Sirs, are the only body in the world who is capable of undertaking this research work and we have been instructed to get in touch with you *under the strictest conditions of confidence*, which, in view of the social aspects involved, we think we have the right to request.

'The financial standing of our client is impeccable and expense is no object in this matter. As a preliminary honorarium and upon acceptance of this commission, we propose a payment of one thousand pounds sterling to your account in such bank as you may designate.

'Awaiting the favour of an early reply, we remain, honoured sirs etc. etc., Gebrüder Gumpold-Moosbrugger, Advokaten, 16 bis, Bahnhofstrasse, Zürich.'

Sable Basilisk looked up. James Bond's eyes were glittering with excitement. Sable Basilisk smiled. 'We were even more interested than you seem to be. You see, to let you in on a secret, our salaries are extremely modest. So we all have private means which we supplement from fees received for special work like this. These fees rarely go above fifty guineas for a piece of pretty tough research and all the leg work at Somerset House and in parish records and graveyards that is usually involved in tracking a man's ancestry. So this looked like a real challenge for the College, and as I was "in waiting" the day the letter came in, sort of "officer of the watch", the job fell into my lap.'

Bond said urgently, 'So what happened? Have you kept the contact?'

'Oh yes, but rather tenuously, I'm afraid. Of course I wrote at once accepting the commission and agreeing to the vow of secrecy which–' he smiled–'you now force me to break presumably by invoking the Official Secrets Act. That is so, isn't it? I am acting under force majeure?'

'You are indeed,' said Bond emphatically.

Sable Basilisk made a careful note on the top paper in the file and continued. 'Of course the first thing I had to ask for was the man's birth certificate and, after a delay, I was told that it had been lost and that I was on no account to worry about it. The Count had in fact been born in Gdynia of a Polish father and a Greek mother–I have the names here–on May 28th, 1908. Could I not pursue my researches backwards from the de Bleuville end? I replied temporizing, but by this time I had indeed established from our library that there had been a family of de Bleuvilles, at least as lately as the seventeenth century, at a place called Blonville-sur-Mer, Calvados, and that their arms and motto were as claimed by Blofeld.' Sable Basilisk paused. 'this of course he must have known for himself. There would have been no purpose in inventing a family of de Bleuvilles and trying to stuff them down our throats. I told the lawyers of my discovery and, in my summer holidays–the North of France is more or less my private heraldic beat, so to speak, and very rich it is too in connections with England–I motored down there and sniffed around. But meanwhile I had, as a matter of routine, written to our Ambassador in Warsaw and asked him to contact our Consul in Gdynia and request him to employ a lawyer to make the simple researches with the Registrar and the various churches where Blofeld might have been baptized. The reply, early in September, was, but is no longer, surprising. The pages containing the record of Blofeld's birth had been neatly cut out. I kept this information to myself, that is to say I did not pass it on to the Swiss lawyers because I had been expressly instructed to make no inquiries in Poland. Meanwhile I had carried out similar inquiries through a lawyer in Augsburg. There, there was indeed a record of Blofelds, but of a profusion of them, for it is a fairly common German name, and in any case nothing to link any of them with the de Bleuvilles from Calvados. So I was stumped, but no more than I have been before, and I wrote a neutral report to the Swiss lawyers and said that I was continuing my researches. And there–' Sable Basilisk slapped the file shut–'until my telephone began ringing yesterday, presumably because someone in the Northern Department of the Foreign Office was checking the file copies from Warsaw and the name Blofeld rang a bell, and you appeared looking very impatient from the cave of my friend the Griffon, the case rests.'

Bond scratched his head thoughtfully. 'But the ball's still in play?'

'Oh yes, definitely.'

'Can you keep it in play? I take it you haven't got Blofeld's present address?' Sable Basilisk shook his head. 'Then would there be any conceivable excuse for an envoy from you?' Bond smiled. 'Me, for example, to be sent out from the College to have an interview with Blofeld–some tricky point that cannot be cleared up by correspondence, something that needs a personal inquiry from Blofeld?'

'Well, yes, there is in a way.' Sable Basilisk looked rather dubious. 'You see, in some families there is a strong physical characteristic that goes on inevitably from generation to generation. The Habsburg lip is a case in point. So is the tendency to haemophilia amongst descendants of the Bourbons. The hawk nose of the Medici is another. A certain royal family have minute, vestigial tails. The original maharajahs of Mysore were born with six fingers on each hand. I could go on indefinitely, but those are the most famous cases. Now, when I was scratching around in the crypt of the chapel at Blonville, having a look at the old Bleuville tombs, my flashlight, moving over the stone faces, picked out a curious fact that I tucked away in my mind but that your question has brought to the surface. None of the de Bleuvilles, as far as I could tell, and certainly not through a hundred and fifty years, had lobes to their ears.'

'Ah,' said Bond, running over in his mind the Identicast picture of Blofeld and the complete, printed physiognometry of the man in Records. 'So he shouldn't by rights have lobes to his ears. Or at any rate it would be a strong piece of evidence for his case if he hadn't?'

'That's right.'

'Well, he *has* got lobes,' said Bond, annoyed. 'Rather pronounced lobes as a matter of fact. Where does that get us?'

'To begin with, added to what I know anyway, that makes him probably not a de Bleuville. But after all–' Sable Basilisk looked sly–'there's no reason why he should know what physical characteristic we're looking for in this interview.'

'You think we could set one up?'

'Don't see why not. But–' Sable Basilisk was apologetic–'would you mind if I got clearance from Garter King of Arms? He's my boss, so to speak, under the Duke of Norfolk that is, the Earl Marshal, and I can't remember that we've ever been mixed up in this sort of cloak-and-dagger stuff before. Actually–' Sable Basilisk waved a deprecating hand–'we are, we have to be, damned meticulous. You do see that, don't you?'

'Naturally. And I'm sure there'd be no objection. But, even if Blofeld agreed to see me, how in hell could I play the part? This stuff is all double Dutch to me.' He smiled. 'I don't know the difference between a gule and a bezant and I've never been able to make out what a baronet is. What's my story to Blofeld? Who am I exactly?'

Sable Basilisk was getting enthusiastic. He said cheerfully, 'Oh that'll be all right. I'll coach you in all the dope about the de Bleuvilles. You can easily mug up a few popular books on heraldry. It's not difficult to be impressive on the subject. Very few people know anything about it.'

'Maybe. But this Blofeld is a pretty smart animal. He'll want the hell of a lot of credentials before he sees anyone but his lawyer and his banker. Who exactly am I?'

'You think Blofeld's smart because you've seen the smart side of him,' said Sable Basilisk sapiently. 'I've seen hundreds of smart people from the City, industry, politics–famous people I've been quite frightened to meet when they walked into this room. But when it comes to snobbery, to buying respectability so to speak, whether it's the title they're going to choose or just a coat of arms to hang over their fire-places in Surbiton, they dwindle and dwindle in front of you–' he made a downward motion over his desk with his hand–'until they're no bigger than homunculi. And the women are even worse. The idea of suddenly becoming a "lady" in their small community is so intoxicating that the way they bare their souls is positively obscene. It's as if–' Sable Basilisk furrowed his high, pale brow, seeking for a simile–'these fundamentally good citizens, these Smiths and Browns and Jones and–' he smiled across the desk–'Bonds, regarded the process of ennoblement as a sort of laying-on of hands, a way of ridding themselves of all the drabness of their lives, of all their, so to speak, essential meagreness, their basic inferiority. Don't worry about Blofeld. He has already swallowed the bait. He may be a tremendous gangster, and he must be from what I remember of the case. He may be tough and ruthless in his corner of human behaviour. But if he is trying to prove that he is the Comte de Bleuville, you can be sure of various things. He wants to change his name. That is obvious. He wants to become a new, a respectable personality. That is obvious too. But above all he wants to become a Count.' Sable Basilisk brought his hand flat down on his desk for emphasis. 'That, Mr Bond, is tremendously significant. He is a rich and successful man in his line of business–no matter what it is. He no longer admires the material things, riches and power. He is now 54, as I reckon it. He wants a new skin. I can assure you, Mr Bond, that he will receive you, if we play our cards right that is, as if he were consulting his doctor about–' Sable Basilisk's aristocratic face took on an expression of distaste–'as if he were consulting his doctor after contracting V.D.' Sable Basilisk's eyes were now compelling. He sat back in his chair and lit his first cigarette. The smell of Turkish tobacco drifted across to Bond. 'That's it,' he said with certitude. 'This man knows he is unclean, a social pariah. Which of course he is. Now he has thought up this way of buying himself a new identity. If you ask me, we must help the hair to grow and flourish on his heel of Achilles until it is so luxuriant that he trips on it.'

Chapter Eight

Fancy Cover

'And who the hell are *you* supposed to be?'

M more or less repeated Bond's question when, that evening, he looked up from the last page of the report that Bond had spent the afternoon dictating to Mary Goodnight. M's face was just outside the pool of yellow light cast by the green-shaded reading lamp on his desk, but Bond knew that the lined, sailor's face was reflecting, in varying degrees, scepticism, irritation and impatience. The 'hell' told him so. M rarely swore and when he did it was nearly always at stupidity. M obviously regarded Bond's plan as stupid, and now, away from the dedicated, minutely focused world of the Heralds, Bond wasn't sure that M wasn't right.

'I'm to be an emissary from the College of Arms, sir. This Basilisk chap recommended that I should have some kind of a title, the sort of rather highfalutin one that would impress a man with this kind of bee in his bonnet. And Blofeld's obviously got this bee or he wouldn't have revealed his existence, even to such a presumably secure and–er–sort of remote corner of the world as the College of Arms. I've put down there the arguments of this chap and they make a lot of sense to me. Snobbery's a real Achilles heel with people. Blofeld's obviously got the bug badly. I think we can get to him through it.'

'Well, I think it's all a pack of nonsense,' said M testily. (Not many years before, M had been awarded the K.C.M.G. for his services, and Miss Moneypenny, his desirable secretary, had revealed in a moment of candour to Bond that M had not replied to a single one of the notes and letters of congratulation. After a while he had refused even to read them and had told Miss Moneypenny not to show him any more but to throw them in the wastepaper basket.) 'All right then, what's this ridiculous title to be? And what happens next?'

If Bond had been able to blush, he would have blushed. He said, 'Er–well, sir, it seems there's a chap called Sir Hilary Bray. Friend of Sable Basilisk's. About my age and not unlike me to look at. His family came from some place in Normandy. Family tree as long as your arm. William the Conqueror and all that. And a coat of arms that looks like a mixture between a jigsaw puzzle and Piccadilly Circus at night. Well, Sable Basilisk says he can fix it with him. This man's got a good war record and sounds a reliable sort of chap. He lives in some remote glen in the Highlands, watching birds and climbing the hills with bare feet. Never sees a soul. No reason why anyone in Switzerland should have heard of him.' Bond's voice became defensive, stubborn. 'Well, sir, the idea is that I should be him. Rather fancy cover, but I think it makes sense.'

'Sir Hilary Bray, eh?' M tried to conceal his scorn. 'And then what do you do? Run around the Alps waving this famous banner of his?'

Bond said patiently, obstinately, refusing to be brow-beaten. 'First I'll get Passport Control to fix up a good passport. Then I mug up Bray's family tree until I'm word-perfect on the thing. Then I swot away at the rudiments of this heraldry business. Then, if Blofeld takes the bait, I go out to Switzerland with all the right books and suggest that I work out his de Bleuville pedigree with him.'

'Then what?'

'Then I try and winkle him out of Switzerland, get him over the frontier to somewhere where we can do a kidnap job on him, rather like the Israelis did with Eichmann. But I haven't worked out all the details yet, sir. Had to get your approval and then Sable Basilisk has got to make up a damned attractive fly and throw it over these Zürich solicitors.'

'Why not try putting pressure on the Zürich solicitors and winkle Blofeld's address out of them? Then we might think of doing some kind of a commando job.'

'You know the Swiss, sir. God knows what kind of a retainer these lawyers have from Blofeld. But it's bound to be millionaire size. We might eventually get the address, but they'd be bound to tip off Blofeld if only to lay their hands on their fees before he vamoosed. Money's the religion of Switzerland.'

'I don't need a lecture on the qualities of the Swiss, thank you, 007. At least they keep their trains clean and cope with the beatnik problem [two very rampant bees in M's bonnet!], but I daresay there's some truth in what you say. Oh, well.' M wearily pushed the file over to Bond. 'Take it away. It's a messy-looking bird's nest of a plan. But I suppose it had better go ahead.' M shook his head sceptically. 'Sir Hilary Bray! Oh, well, tell the Chief of Staff I approve. But reluctantly. Tell him you can have the facilities. Keep me informed.' M reached for the Cabinet telephone. His voice was deeply disgruntled. 'Suppose I'll have to tell the P.M. we've got a line on the chap. The kind of tangle it is, I'll keep to myself. That's all, 007.'

'Thank you, sir. Good night.' As Bond went across to the door he heard M say into the green receiver, 'M speaking. I want the Prime Minister personally, please.' He might have been asking for the mortuary. Bond went out and softly closed the door behind him.

So, as November blustered its way into December, James Bond went unwillingly back to school, swotting up heraldry at his desk instead of top-secret reports, picking up scraps of medieval French and English, steeping himself in fusty lore and myth, picking the brains of Sable Basilisk and occasionally learning interesting facts, such as that the founders of Gamages came from the de Gamaches in Normandy and that Walt Disney was remotely descended from the D'Isignys of the same part of France. But these were nuggets in a wasteland of archaisms, and when, one day, Mary Goodnight, in reply to some sally of his, addressed him as 'Sir Hilary' he nearly bit her head off.

Meanwhile the highly delicate correspondence between Sable Basilisk and the Gebrüder Moosbrugger proceeded haltingly and at a snail's pace. They, or rather Blofeld behind them, posed countless irritating but, Sable Basilisk admitted, erudite queries each one of which had to be countered with this or that degree of heraldic obfuscation. Then there were minute questions about this emissary, Sir Hilary Bray. Photographs were asked for, and, suitably doctored, were provided. His whole career since his schooldays had to be detailed and was sent down from Scotland with a highly amused covering note from the real man. To test the market, more funds were asked for by Sable Basilisk and, with encouraging promptitude, were forthcoming in the shape of a further thousand pounds. When the cheque arrived on December 15th Sable Basilisk telephoned Bond delightedly. 'We've got him,' he said. 'He's hooked!' And, sure enough, the next day came a letter from Zürich to say that their client agreed to a meeting with Sir Hilary. Would Sir Hilary please arrive at Zürich Central Airport by Swissair flight Number 105, due at Zürich at 1300 hours on December 21st. On Bond's prompting, Sable Basilisk wrote back that the date was not convenient to Sir Hilary owing to a prior engagement with the Canadian High Commissioner regarding a detail in the Arms of the Hudson's Bay Company. Sir Hilary could, however, manage the 22nd. By return came a cable agreeing and, to Bond, confirming that the fish had not only swallowed the hook but the line and sinker as well.

The last few days were spent in a flurry of meetings, with the Chief of Staff presiding, at Headquarters. The main decisions were that Bond should go to the meeting with Blofeld absolutely 'clean'. He would carry no weapons, no secret gear of any kind, and he would not be watched or followed by the Service in any way. He would communicate only with Sable Basilisk, getting across such information as he could by using heraldic double talk (Sable Basilisk had been cleared by M.I.5 immediately after Bond's first meeting with him), and Sable Basilisk, who vaguely thought that Bond was employed by the Ministry of Defence, would be given a cut-out at the Ministry who would be his go-between with the Service. This was all assuming that Bond managed to stay close to Blofeld for at least a matter of days. And that was to be his basic stratagem. It was essential to find out as much as possible about Blofeld, his activities and his associates, in order to proceed with planning the next step, his abduction from Switzerland. Physical action might not be necessary. Bond might be able to trick the man into a visit to Germany, as a result of a report which Sable Basilisk had prepared of certain Blofeld family documents at the Augsburg Zentral Archiv, which would need Blofeld's personal identification. Security precautions would include keeping Station Z completely in the dark about Bond's mission to Switzerland and a closure of the 'Bedlam' file at Headquarters which would be announced in the routine 'Orders of the Day'. Instead, a new codeword for the operation, known only to an essential handful of senior officers, would be issued. It would be 'CORONA'.

Finally, the personal dangers to Bond himself were discussed. There was total respect for Blofeld at Headquarters. Nobody questioned his abilities or his ruthlessness. If Bond's true identity somehow became known to Blofeld, Bond would of course instantly be liquidated. A more dangerous and likely event would be that, once Blofeld had probed Bond's heraldic gen to its rather shallow bottom and it had been proved that he was or was not the Comte de Bleuville, Sir Hilary Bray, his usefulness expended, might 'meet with an accident'. Bond would just have to face up to these hazards and watch out particularly for the latter. He, and Sable Basilisk behind him, would have to keep some tricks up their sleeves, tricks that would somehow make Sir Hilary Bray's continued existence important to Blofeld. In conclusion, the Chief of Staff said he considered the whole operation 'a lot of bezants' and that 'Bezants' would have been a better codeword than 'Corona'. However, he wished Bond the best of luck and said, cold-heartedly, that he would instruct the Technical Section to proceed forthwith with the devising of a consignment of explosive snowballs for Bond's protection.

It was on this cheery note that Bond, on the evening of December 21st, returned to his office for a last run-through of his documentation with Mary Goodnight.

He sat sideways to his desk, looking out over the triste winter twilight of Regent's Park under snow, while she sat opposite him and ran through the items: '*Burke's Extinct and Dormant Baronetage*, property of the College of Heralds. Stamped "Not to be removed from the Library". The printed *Visitations in the College of Arms*, stamped ditto. *Genealogist's Guide*, by G.W.Marshall, with Hatchard's receipted bill to Sable Basilisk inserted. *Burke's General Armory*, stamped "Property of the London Library", wrapped and franked December 10th. Passport in the name of Sir Hilary Bray, containing various recently-dated frontier stamps in and out of France, Germany and the Low Countries, fairly well used and dog-eared. One large file of correspondence with Augsburg and Zürich on College of Arms writing-paper and the writing-paper of the addressees. And that's the lot. You've fixed your laundry tags and so on?'

'Yes,' said Bond dully. 'I've fixed all that. And I've got two new suits with cuffs and double vents at the back and four buttons down the front. Also a gold watch and chain with the Bray seal. Quite the little baronet.' Bond turned and looked across the desk at Mary Goodnight. 'What do you think of this caper, Mary? Think it'll come off?'

'Well, it should do,' she said staunchly. 'With all the trouble that's been taken. But–' she hesitated–'I don't like you taking this man on without a gun.' She waved a hand at the pile on the floor. 'And all these stupid books about heraldry! It's just not *you*. You will take care, won't you?'

'Oh, I'll do that all right,' said Bond reassuringly. 'Now, be a good girl and get a radio taxi to the Universal Export entrance. And put all that junk inside it, would you? I'll be down in a minute. I'll be at the flat all this evening–' he smiled sourly–'packing my silk shirts with the crests on them.' He got up. 'So long, Mary. Or rather good night, Goodnight. And keep out of trouble till I get back.'

She said, 'You do that yourself.' She bent and picked up the books and papers from the floor and, keeping her face hidden from Bond, went to the door and kicked it shut behind her with her heel. A moment or two later she opened the door again. Her eyes were bright. 'I'm sorry, James. Good luck! And Happy Christmas!' She closed the door softly behind her.

Bond looked at the blank face of the Office of Works cream door. What a dear girl Mary was! But now there was Tracy. He would be near her in Switzerland. It was time to make contact again. He had been missing her, wondering about her. There had been three non-committal but cheerful postcards from the Clinique de l'Aube at Davos. Bond had made inquiries and had ascertained that this was run by a Professor Auguste Kommer, President of the Société Psychiatrique et Psychologique Suisse. Over the telephone, Sir James Molony, the nerve specialist by appointment to the Service, had told Bond that Kommer was one of the top men in the world at his job. Bond had written affectionately and encouragingly to Tracy and had

had the letters posted from America. He had said he would be home soon and would be in touch with her. Would he? And what would he do then? Bond had a luxurious moment feeling sorry for himself, for the miscellaneous burdens he was carrying alone. He then crushed out his cigarette and, banging doors behind him, got the hell out of his office and down in the lift to the discreet side-entrance that said 'Universal Export'.

The taxi was waiting. It was seven o'clock. As the taxi got under way, Bond made his plan for the evening. He would first do an extremely careful packing job of his single suitcase, the one that had no tricks to it, have two double vodkas and tonics with a dash of Angostura, eat a large dish of May's speciality–scrambled eggs fines herbes–have two more vodkas and tonics, and then, slightly drunk go to bed with half a grain of seconal.

Encouraged by the prospect of this cosy self-anaesthesia, Bond brusquely kicked his problems under the carpet of his consciousness.

Chapter Nine

Irma La not so Douce

The next day, at London Airport, James Bond, bowler hat, rolled umbrella, neatly folded *Times* and all, felt faintly ridiculous. He felt totally so when he was treated with the deference duc to his title and shown into the V.I.P. lounge before take-off. At the ticket desk, when he had been addressed as Sir Hilary, he had looked behind him to see who the girl was talking to. He really must pull himself together and damn well *be* Sir Hilary Bray!

Bond had a double brandy and ginger ale and stood aloof from the handful of other privileged passengers in the gracious lounge, trying to *feel* like a baronet. Then he remembered the real Sir Hilary Bray, perhaps now gralloching a hind with his bare hands somewhere up in the Glens. There was nothing of the baronet about him! He really must get rid of the inverted snobbery that, with its opposite, is ingrained in so many of the English! He must stop acting a part, being a stage nobleman! He would just be himself and, if he gave the appearance of being rather a rough-hewn baronet, the easy-going kind, well, that at least was like the real one up in Scotland. Bond threw down the *Times* that he had been carrying as an extra badge of Top Peopleship, picked up the *Daily Express*, and asked for another brandy and ginger ale.

Then, with its twin jets whispering far back of the first-class cabin, the Swissair Caravelle was airborne and Bond's mind was reaching forward to the rendezvous that had been so briefly detailed by the Zurich solicitors. Sir Hilary would be met at the airport by one of the Comte de Bleuville's secretaries. He would be seeing the Count that day or the next. Bond had a moment of panic. How should he address the man when he met him? Count? Monsieur le Comte? No, he would call him nothing–perhaps an occasional patronizing 'my dear sir' in context. What would Blofeld look like? Would he have changed his appearance much? Probably, or the fox wouldn't have kept ahead of the hounds so efficiently. Bond's excitement mounted as he consumed a delicious lunch served by a delicious stewardess, and the winter-brown chequerboard of France fled backwards distantly below. Now there was scattered snow and barren trees as they crossed the tiny hillocks of the Vosges, then permanent snow and ice-floes on the Rhine, a short stop at Basle, and then the black criss-cross of Zürich Airport and 'fasten your lap-straps' in three languages, and they were planing down, a slight bump, the roar of jet deflection, and then they were taxying up to the apron in front of the imposing, very European-looking buildings decked with the gay flags of the nations.

At the Swissair desk inside the door, a woman was standing beside the reception counter. As soon as Bond appeared in the entrance she came forward. 'Sair Hilary Bray?'

'Yes.'

'I am Fräulein Irma Bunt. Personal secretary to the Count. Good afternoon. I hope you had a happy flight.'

She looked like a very sunburned female wardress. She had a square, brutal face with hard yellow eyes. Her smile was an oblong hole without humour or welcome, and there were sunburn blisters at the left corner of her mouth which she licked from time to time with the tip of a pale tongue. Wisps of brownish grey hair, with a tight, neat bun at the back, showed from under a skiing hat with a yellow talc visor that had straps which met under her chin. Her strong, short body was dressed in unbecomingly tight vorlage trousers topped by a grey wind-jacket ornamented over the left breast with a large red G topped by a coronet. Irma La not so Douce, thought Bond. He said, 'Yes. It was very pleasant.'

'You have your baggage check? Will you follow me, please? And first your passport. This way.'

Bond followed her through the passport control and out into the customs hall. There were a few standers-by. Bond noticed her head nod casually. A man with a brief-case under his arm, hanging about, moved away. Bond studiously examined his baggage check. Beyond the scrap of cardboard, he noticed the man slip into one of the row of telephone booths in the main hall outside the customs area.

'You speak German?' The tongue flicked out and licked the blisters.

'No, I'm afraid not.'

'French perhaps?'

'A little. Enough for my work.'

'Ah, yes. That is important, yes?'

Bond's suitcase was unloaded off the trolley on to the barrier. The woman flashed some kind of a pass at the customs officer. It was very quickly done, but Bond caught a glimpse of her photograph and the heading 'Bundespolizei'. So! Blofeld had got the fix in!

The officer said deferentially, 'Bitte sehr,' and chalked his symbol in the colour of the day, yellow, on Bond's suitcase. A porter took it and they walked across to the entrance. When they came out on the steps, an anonymous black Mercedes 300 SE saloon pulled smartly out of the parking area and slid to a stop beside them. Next to the chauffeur sat the man who had gone to the telephone. Bond's suitcase was put in the boot and they moved off fast in the direction of Zürich. A few hundred yards down the wide road, the man beside the driver, who, Bond noticed, had been surreptitiously watching in the twin driving-mirror, said softly, 'Is' gut,' and the car turned right-handed up a side road which was marked 'Eingang Verboten! Mit Ausnahme von Eigentümer und Personell von Privatflugzeugen'.

Bond was amused as he ticked off the little precautions. It was obvious that he was still very much on probation.

The car came up with the hangars to the left of the main building, drove slowly between them and pulled up beside a bright orange Alouette helicopter, adapted by Sud Aviation for mountain rescue work. But this one had the red G with the coronet on its fuselage. So. He was going to be taken for a flight rather than a ride!

'You have travelled in one of these machines before? No? It is very pleasant. One obtains a fine view of the Alps.' Fräulein Bunt's eyes were blank with disinterest. They climbed up the aluminium ladder. 'Mind your head, please!' Bond's suitcase was handed up by the chauffeur.

It was a six-seater, luxurious in red leather. Above and in front of them under his Perspex canopy the pilot lifted a thumb. The ground staff pulled away the chocks and the big blades began to move. As they accelerated, the men on the ground drew away, shielding their faces against the whirling snow. There was a slight jolt and then they were climbing fast, and the crackle of radio from the control tower went silent.

Irma Bunt was across the passage-way from Bond. The extra man was in the rear, hidden behind the *Züricher Zeitung*. Bond leaned sideways and said loudly, against the rattle of the machine, 'Where are we heading for?'

She pretended not to hear. Bond repeated his question, shouting it.

'Into the Alps. Into the high Alps,' shouted the woman. She waved towards the window. 'It is very beautiful. You like the mountains, isn't it?'

'I love them,' shouted Bond. 'Just like Scotland.' He leaned back in his seat, lit a cigarette and looked out of the window. Yes, there was the Zürichersee to port. Their course was more or less east-south-east. They were flying at about 2,000 feet. And now there was the Wallensee. Bond, apparently uninterested, took the *Daily Express* out of his brief-case and turned to the sports pages. He read the paper from last page to first, meticulously, every now and then casting a bored glance out of the window. The big range to port would be the Rhätikon Alps. That would be the railway junction at Landquart below them. They held their course up the valley of the Prätigau. Would they keep on at Klosters or veer to starboard? Starboard it was. So! Up the Davos Valley! In a few minutes he would be flying over Tracy! A casual glance. Yes, there was Davos under its thin canopy of evening mist and smoke, while, above her, he was still in bright sunshine. At least she seemed to have had plenty of snow. Bond remembered the tremendous run down the Parsenn. Those had been the days! And now back on the old course again and giant peaks to right and left. This must be the Engadine. The Silvretta Group away to starboard, to port Piz Languard and, ahead, the Bernina range diving down, like a vast ski-jump, into Italy. That forest of lights away to starboard must be St Moritz! Now where? Bond buried himself in his paper. A slight veer to port. More lights. Pontresina? And now the radio began to crackle and the 'Seat belts' sign went up. Bond thought it time to express open interest. He gazed out. Below, the ground was mostly in darkness, but ahead the giant peaks were still golden in the dying sun. They were making straight for one of them, for a small plateau near its summit. There was a group of buildings from which golden wires swooped down into the darkness of the valley. A cable car, spangled in the sun, was creeping down. Now it had been swallowed up in the murk. The helicopter was still charging the side of the peak that towered above them. Now it was only a hundred feet up above the slope, coming in to the plateau and the buildings. The pilot's arms moved on his joy stick. The machine pitched a little and slowed. The rotor arms swung languidly and then accelerated as the machine hovered and settled. There came a slight bump as the inflated rubber 'floats' met the snow, a dying whirr from the rotor and they were there.

Where? Bond knew. They were in the Languard range, somewhere above Pontresina in the Engadine, and their altitude would be about 10,000 feet. He buttoned up his raincoat and prepared for the rasping dagger of the cold air on his lungs when the door was opened.

Irma Bunt gave her box-like smile. 'We have arrived,' she said unnecessarily.

The door, with a clatter of falling ice particles, was wrenched open. The last rays of the sun shone into the cabin. They caught the woman's yellow sun visor and shone through, turning her face Chinese. The eyes gave out a false blaze, like the glass eyes of a toy animal, under the light. 'Mind your head.' She bent low, her tight, squat behind inviting an enormous kick, and went down the ladder.

James Bond followed her, holding his breath against the searing impact of the Arctic, oxygenless air. There were one or two men standing around dressed like ski guides. They looked at Bond with curiosity, but there was no greeting. Bond went on across the hard-trodden snow in the wake of the woman, the extra man following with his suitcase. He heard the engine stutter and roar, and a blizzard of snow particles stung the right side of his face. Then the iron grasshopper rose into the air and rattled off into the dusk.

It was perhaps fifty yards from where the helicopter had landed to the group of buildings. Bond dawdled, getting preliminary bearings. Ahead was a long, low building, now ablaze with lights. To the right, and perhaps another fifty yards away, were the outlines of the typical modern cable railhead, a box-like structure, with a thick flat roof canted upwards from close to the ground. As Bond examined it, its lights went out. Presumably the last car had reached the valley and the line was closed for the night. To the right of this was a large, bogus-chalet type structure with a vast veranda, sparsely lit, that would be for the mass tourist trade–again a typical piece of high-Alpine architecture. Down to the left, beneath the slope of the plateau, lights shone from a fourth building that, except for its flat roof, was out of sight.

Bond was now only a few yards from the building that was obviously his destination. An oblong of yellow opened invitingly as the woman went in and held the door for him. The light illuminated a big sign with the red G surmounted by the coronet. It said GLORIA KLUB. 3605 METRES. PRIVAT! NUR FÜR MITGLIEDER. Below in smaller letters it said 'Alpenberghaus und Restaurant Piz Gloria', and the drooping index finger of the traditional hand pointed to the right, towards the building near the cable-head.

So! Piz Gloria! Bond walked into the inviting yellow oblong. The door, released by the woman, closed with a pneumatic hiss.

Inside it was deliciously warm, almost hot. They were in a small reception room, and a youngish man with a very pale crew-cut and shrewd eyes got to his feet from behind a desk, and made a slight bob in their direction. 'Sir Hilary is in Number Two.'

'Weiss schon,' said the woman curtly and, only just more politely, to Bond, 'Follow me, please.' She went through a facing door and down a thickly-piled, red-carpeted passage. The left-hand wall was only occasionally broken by windows interspersed with fine skiing and mountain photographs. On the right were at first the doors of the club rooms, marked Bar, Restaurant, and Toiletten. Bond was shown into Number Two. It was an extremely comfortable, chintzy room in the American motel style with a bathroom leading off. The broad picture window was now curtained, but Bond knew that it must offer a tremendous view over the valley to the Suvretta group above St Moritz. Bond threw his brief-case on the double bed and gratefully disposed of his bowler hat and umbrella. The extra man appeared with his suitcase, placed it on the luggage stand without looking at Bond and withdrew, closing the door behind him. The woman stayed where she was. 'This is to your satisfaction?' The yellow eyes were indifferent to his enthusiastic reply. She had more to say. 'That is good. Now perhaps I should explain some things, convey to you some laws of the club, isn't it?'

Bond lit a cigarette. 'That would certainly be helpful.' He put a politely interested expression on his face. 'Where are we, for instance?'

'In the Alps. In the high Alps,' said the woman vaguely. 'This Alp, Piz Gloria, is the property of the Count. Together with the Gemeinde, the local authorities, he constructed the Seilbahn. You have seen the cables, yes? This is the first year it is opened. It is very popular and brings in much money. There are some fine ski runs. The Gloria Abfahrt is already famous. There is also a bob-sleigh run that is much greater than the Cresta at St Moritz. You have heard of that? You ski perhaps? Or make the bob-sleigh?'

The yellow eyes were watchful. Bond thought he would continue to answer no to all questions. Instinct told him to. He said apologetically. 'I'm afraid not. Never got around to it, you know. Too much bound up with my books, perhaps.' He smiled ruefully, self-critically.

'Schade! That is a pity.' But the eyes registered satisfaction. 'These installations bring good income for the Count. That is important. It helps to support his life's work, the Institut.'

Bond raised his eyebrows a polite fraction.

'The Institut für physiologische Forschung. It is for scientific research. The Count is a leader in the field of allergies–you understand? This is like the hay fever, the unableness to eat shellfish, yes?'

'Oh really? Can't say I suffer from any myself.'

'No? The laboratories are in a separate building. There the Count also lives. In this building, where we are, live the patients. He asks that you will not disturb them with too many questions. These treatments are very delicate. You understand?'

'Yes, of course. And when may I see the Count? I'm afraid I am a very busy man, Fräulein Bunt. There are matters awaiting my attention in London.' Bond spoke impressively. 'The new African States. Much work has to be done on their flags, the design of their currency, their stamps, their medals. We are very short-handed at the College. I hope the Count understands that his personal problem, interesting and important though it is, must take second place to the problems of Government.'

Bond had got through. Now she was all eagerness, reassurance. 'But of course, my dear Sair Hilary. The Count asks to be excused tonight, but he would much like to receive you at eleven o'clock tomorrow morning. That is suitable?'

'Certainly, certainly. That will give me time to marshal my documents, my books. Perhaps–' Bond waved to the small writing desk near the window–'I could have an extra table to lay these things out. I'm afraid–' Bond smiled deprecatingly–'we bookworms need a lot of space.'

'Of course, Sair Hilary. It will be done at once.' She moved to the door and pressed a bell-button. She gestured downwards, now definitely embarrassed. 'You will have noticed that there is no door handle on this side?' (Bond had done so. He said he hadn't.) 'You will ring when you wish to leave the room. Yes? It is on account of the patients. It is necessary that they have quiet. It is difficult to prevent them visiting each other for the sake of gossiping. It is for their good. You understand? Bed-time is at ten o'clock. But there is a night staff in case you should need any service. And the doors are of course not locked. You may re-enter your room at any time. Yes? We meet for cocktails in the bar at six. It is–how do you say?–the rest-pause of the day.' The box-like smile made its brief appearance. 'My girls are much looking forward to meeting you.'

The door opened. It was one of the men dressed as guides, a swarthy, bull-necked man with brown Mediterranean eyes. One of Marc-Ange's Corsican defectors? In rapid, bad French, the woman said that another table was desired. This was to be furnished during dinner. The man said 'Entendu.' She held the door before he could close it and he went off down the passage to the right. Guard's quarters at the end of the passage? Bond's mind went on clicking up the clues.

'Then that is all for the present, Sair Hilary? The post leaves at midday. We have radio telephone communications if you wish to use them. May I convey any message to the Count?'

'Please say that I look forward greatly to meeting him tomorrow. Until six o'clock then.' Bond suddenly wanted to be alone with his thoughts. He gestured towards his suitcase. 'I must get myself unpacked.'

'Of course, of course, Sair Hilary. Forgive me for detaining you.' And, on this gracious note, Irma Bunt closed the door, with its decisive click, behind her.

Bond stood still in the middle of the room. He let out his breath with a quiet hiss. What the hell of a kettle of fish! He would have liked to kick one of the dainty bits of furniture very hard indeed. But he had noticed that, of the four electric light prisms in the ceiling, one was a blank, protruding eyeball. Closed-circuit television? If so, what would be its range? Not much more than a wide circle covering the centre of the room. Microphones? Probably the whole expanse of ceiling was one. That was the war-time gimmick. He must, he simply must assume that he was under constant supervision.

James Bond, his thoughts racing, proceeded to unpack, take a shower and make himself presentable for 'my girls'.

Chapter Ten

Ten Gorgeous Girls

It was one of those leather-padded bars, bogus-masculine, and still, because of its newness, smelling like the inside of a new motor-car. It was made to look like a Tyrolean Stube by a big stone fire-place with a roaring log fire and cartwheel chandeliers with red-stemmed electric 'candles'. There were many wrought-iron gimmicks–wall-light brackets, ashtrays, table lamps–and the bar itself was 'gay' with small flags and miniature liqueur bottles. Attractive zither music tripped out from a hidden loud-speaker. It was not, Bond decided, a place to get seriously drunk in.

When he closed the leather-padded, brass-studded door behind him, there was a moment's hush, then a mounting of decibels to hide the covert glances, the swift summing-up. Bond got a fleeting impression of one of the most beautiful groups of girls he had ever seen, when Irma Bunt, hideous in some kind of home-made, homespun 'après-ski', in which orange and black predominated, waddled out from among the galaxy and took him in charge. 'Sair Hilary.' She grasped his hand with a dry, monkey grip. 'How delightful, isn't it? Come please, and meet my girls.'

It was tremendously hot in the room and Bond felt the sweat bead on his forehead as he was led from table to table and shook this cool, this warm, this languid hand. Names like Ruby, Violet, Pearl, Anne, Elizabeth, Beryl, sounded in his ears, but all he saw was a sea of beautiful, sunburned faces and a succession of splendid, sweatered young bosoms. It was like being at home to the Tiller or the Bluebell Girls. At last he got to the seat that had been kept for him, between Irma Bunt and a gorgeous, bosomy blonde with large blue eyes. He sat down, overcome. The barman hovered. Bond pulled himself together. 'Whisky and soda, please,' he said, and heard his voice from far away. He took some time lighting a cigarette while sham, stage conversation broke out among the four tables in the semicircular embrasure that must, during the day, be the great lookout point. Ten girls and Irma. All English. No surnames. No other man. Girls in their twenties. Working girls probably. Sort of air-hostess type. Excited at having a man amongst them–a personable man and a baronet to boot–if that was what one did to a baronet. Pleased with his private joke, Bond turned to the blonde. 'I'm terribly sorry, but I didn't catch your name.'

'I'm Ruby.' The voice was friendly but refined. 'It must be quite an ordeal being the only chap–amongst all us girls, I mean.'

'Well, it was rather a surprise. But a very pleasant one. It's going to be difficult getting all your names right.' He lowered his voice conspiratorially. 'Be an angel and run through the field, so to speak.'

Bond's drink came and he was glad to find it strong. He took a long but discreet pull at it. He had noticed that the girls were drinking Colas and squashes with a sprinkling of feminine cocktails–Orange Blossoms,

Daiquiris. Ruby was one of the ones with a Daiquiri. It was apparently O.K. to drink, but he would be careful to show a gentlemanly moderation.

Ruby seemed pleased to be able to break the ice. 'Well, I'll start on your right. That's Miss Bunt, the sort of matron, so to speak. You've met her. Then, in the violet camelot sweater, well, that's Violet of course. Then at the next table. The one in the green and gold Pucci shirt is Anne and next to her in green is Pearl. She's my sort of best friend here.' And so it went on, from one glorious golden girl to the next. Bond heard scraps of their conversation. 'Fritz says I'm not getting enough Vorlage. My skis keep on running away from me.' 'It's the same with me–' a giggle–'my sit-upon's black and blue.' 'The Count says I'm getting on very well. Won't it be awful when we have to go?' 'I wonder how Polly's doing? She's been out a month now.' 'I think Skol's the only stuff for sunburn. All those oils and creams are nothing but frying-fat.' And so on–mostly the chatter you would expect from a group of cheerful, healthy girls learning to ski, except for the occasional rather awed reference to the Count and the covert glances at Irma Bunt and Bond to make sure that they were behaving properly, not making too much noise.

While Ruby continued her discreet roll-call, Bond tried to fix the names to the faces and otherwise add to his comprehension of this lovely but bizarre group locked up on top of a very high Alp indeed. The girls all seemed to share a certain basic, girl-guidish simplicity of manners and language, the sort of girls who, in an English pub, you would find sitting demurely with a boy friend sipping a Babycham, puffing rather clumsily at a cigarette and occasionally saying 'pardon'. Good girls, girls who, if you made a pass at them, would say, 'Please don't spoil it all', 'Men only want one thing' or, huffily, 'Please take your hand away'. And there were traces of many accents, accents from all over Britain–the broad vowels of Lancashire, the lilt of Wales, the burr of Scotland, the adenoids of refined Cockney.

Yours truly foxed, concluded Bond as Ruby finished with 'And that's Beryl in the pearls and twin-set. Now do you think you've got us all straight?'

Bond looked into the round blue eyes that now held a spark of animation. 'Frankly no. And I feel like one of those comic film stars who get snarled up in a girls' school. You know. Sort of St Trinian's.'

She giggled. (Bond was to discover that she was a chronic giggler. She was too 'dainty' to open her lovely lips and laugh. He was also to find that she couldn't sneeze like a human, but let out a muffled, demure squeak into her scrap of lace handkerchief, and that she took very small mouthfuls at meals and barely masticated with the tips of her teeth before swallowing with hardly a ripple of her throat. She had been 'well brought up'.) 'Oh, but we're not at all like St Trinian's. Those awful girls! How could you ever say such a thing!'

'Just a thought,' said Bond airily. 'Now then, how about another drink?'

'Oh, thenks awfully.'

Bond turned to Fräulein Bunt. 'And you, Miss Bunt?'

'Thank you, Sair Hilary. An apple-juice, if you please.'

Violet, the fourth at their table, said demurely that she wouldn't have another Coke. 'They give me wind,' she explained.

'Oh Violet!' Ruby's sense of the proprieties was outraged. 'How can you say such a thing!'

'Well, anyway, they do,' said Violet obstinately. 'They make me hiccup.

No harm in saying that, is there?'

Good old Manchester, thought Bond. He got up and went to the bar, wondering how he was going to plough on through this and other evenings. He ordered the drinks and had a brain-wave. He would break the ice! By hook or by crook he would become the life and soul of the party! He asked for a tumbler and that its rim should be dipped in water. Then he picked up a paper cocktail napkin and went back to the table. He sat down. 'Now,' he said as eyes goggled at him, 'if we were paying for our drinks, I'll show you how we'd decide who should pay. I learned this in the Army.' He placed the tumbler in the middle of the table, opened the paper napkin and spread the centre tightly over the top so that it clung to the moist edge of the glass. He took his small change out of his pocket, selected a five-centime piece and dropped it gently on to the centre of the stretched tissue. 'Now then,' he announced, remembering that the last time he had played this game had been in the dirtiest bar in Singapore. 'Who else smokes? We need three others with lighted cigarettes.' Violet was the only one at their table. Irma clapped her hands with authority. 'Elizabeth, Beryl, come over here. And come and watch, girls, Sair Hilary is making the joke game.' The girls clustered round, chattering happily at the diversion. 'What's he doing?' 'What's going to happen?' 'How do you play?'

'Now then,' said Bond, feeling like the games director on a cruise ship, 'this is for who pays for the drinks. One by one, you take a puff at your cigarette, knock off the ash, like this, and touch the top of the paper with the lighted end–just enough to burn a tiny hole, like this.' The paper sparkled briefly. 'Now Violet, then Elizabeth, then Beryl. The point is, the paper gets like a sort of cobweb with the coin just supported in the middle. The person who burns the last hole and makes the coin drop has to pay for the drinks. See? Now then, Violet.'

There were squeaks of excitement. 'What a lovely game!' 'Oh Beryl, look out!' Lovely heads craned over Bond. Lovely hair brushed his cheek. Quickly the three girls got the trick of very delicately touching a space that would not collapse the cobweb until Bond, who considered himself an expert at the game, decided to be chivalrous and purposely burned a vital strand. With the chink of the coin falling into the glass there was a burst of excited laughter and applause.

'So, you see, girls.' It was as if Irma Bunt had invented the game. 'Sair Hilary pays, isn't it? A most delightful pastime. And now–' she looked at her mannish wristwatch–'we must finish our drinks. It is five minutes to supper time.'

There were cries of 'Oh, one more game, Miss Bunt!' But Bond Politely rose with his whisky in his hand. 'We will play again tomorrow. I hope it's not going to start you all off smoking. I'm sure it was invented by the tobacco companies!'

There was laughter. But the girls stood admiringly round Bond. What a sport he was! And they had all expected a stuffed shirt! Bond felt justifiably proud of himself. The ice had been broken. He had got them all minutely on his side. Now they were all chums together. From now on he would be able to get to talk to them without frightening them. Feeling reasonably pleased with his gambit, he followed the tight pants of Irma Bunt into the dining-room next door.

It was seven-thirty. Bond suddenly felt exhausted, exhausted with the prospect of boredom, exhausted with playing the most difficult role of his career, exhausted with the enigma of Blofeld and the Piz Gloria. What in hell was the bastard up to? He sat down on the right of Irma Bunt in the same placing as for drinks, with Ruby on his right and Violet, dark, demure, self-effacing, opposite him, and glumly opened his napkin. Blofeld had certainly spent money on his eyrie. Their three tables, in a remote corner by the long, curved, curtained window, occupied only a fraction of the space in the big, low, luxuriously appointed, mock-German baroque room, ornate with candelabra suspended from the stomachs of flying cherubs, festooned with heavy gilt plaster-work, solemnized by the dark portraits of anonymous noblemen. Blofeld must be pretty certain he was here to stay. What was the investment? Certainly not less than a million sterling, even assuming a fat mortgage from Swiss banks on the cost of the cable railway. To lease an alp, put up a cable railway on mortgage, with the engineers and the local district council participating–that, Bond knew, was one of the latest havens for fugitive funds. If you were successful, if you and the council could bribe or bully the local farmers to allow right-of-way through their pastures, cut swaths through the tree-line for the cable pylons and the ski-runs, the rest was publicity and amenities for the public to eat their sandwiches. Add to that the snob-appeal of a posh, heavily restricted club such as Bond imagined this, during the daytime, to be, the coroneted G, and the mystique of a research institute run by a Count, and you were off to the races. Skiing today, Bond had read, was the most widely practised sport in the world. It sounded unlikely, but then one reckoned the others largely by spectators. Skiers were participants, and bigger spenders on equipment than in other sports. Clothes, boots, skis, bindings and now the whole 'après-ski' routine which took care of the day from four o'clock, when the sun went, onwards, were a tremendous industry. If you could lay your hands on a good alp, which Blofeld had somehow managed to do, you really had it good. Mortgages paid off–snow was the joker, but in the Engadine, at this height, you would be all right for that–in three or four years, and then jam for ever! One certainly had to hand it to him!

It was time to make the going again! Resignedly, Bond turned to Fräulein Bunt. 'Fräulein Bunt. Please explain to me. What is the difference between a piz and an alp and a berg?'

The yellow eyes gleamed with academic enthusiasm. 'Ah, Sair Hilary, but that is an interesting question. It had not occurred to me before. Now let me see.' She gazed into the middle distance. 'A piz, that is only a local name in this department of Switzerland for a peak. An alp, that one would think would be smaller than a berg–a hill, perhaps, or an upland pasture, as compared with a mountain. But that is not so. These–' she waved her hand–'are all alps and yet they are great mountains. It is the same in Austria, certainly in the Tyrol. But in Germany, in Bavaria for instance, which is my home land, there it is all bergs. No Sair Hilary–' the box-like smile was switched on and off–'I cannot help you. But why do you ask?'

'In my profession,' said Bond prosily, 'the exact meaning of words is vital. Now, before we met for cocktails, it amused me to look up your surname, Bunt, in my books of reference. What I found, Fräulein, was most interesting. Bunt, it seems, is German for "gay", "happy". In England, the name has almost certainly been corrupted into Bounty, perhaps even into Brontë, because the grandfather of the famous literary family by that name had in fact changed his name from the less aristocratic name of Brunty. Now this is most interesting.' (Bond knew that it wasn't, that this was all hocus-pocus, but he thought it would do no harm to stretch his heraldic muscles.) 'Can you remember if your ancestors had any connection with England? There is the Dukedom of Bronte, you see, which Nelson assumed. It would be interesting to establish a connection.'

The penny dropped! A duchess! Irma Bunt, hooked, went off into a dreary chronicle of her forebears, including proudly, distant relationship with a Graf von Bunt. Bond listened politely, prodding her back to the immediate past. She gave the name of her father and mother. Bond filed them away. He now had enough to find out in due course exactly who Irma Bunt was. What a splendid trap snobbery was! How right Sable Basilisk had been! There is a snob in all of us and only through snobbery could Bond have discovered who the parents of this woman were.

Bond finally calmed down the woman's momentary fever, and the head waiter, who had been politely hovering, presented giant menus covered in violet ink. There was everything from caviar down to Double Mokka au whisky irlandais. There were also many 'spécialités Gloria'–Poulet Gloria, Homard Gloria, Tournedos Gloria and so on. Bond, despite his forswearing of spécialités, decided to give the chicken a chance. He said so and was surprised by the enthusiasm with which Ruby greeted his choice. 'Oh, how right you are, Sir Hilary! I adore chicken too. I absolutely dote on it. Can I have that too, please, Miss Bunt?'

There was such surprising fervour in her voice that Bond watched Irma Bunt's face. What was that matronly gleam in her eye as she gave her approval? It was more than approval for a good appetite among her charges. There was enthusiasm, even triumph there. Odd! And it happened again when Violet stipulated plenty of potatoes with her tournedos. 'I simply love potatoes,' she explained to Bond, her eyes shining. 'Don't you?'

'They're fine,' agreed Bond, 'When you're taking plenty of exercise, that is.'

'Oh, they're just darling,' enthused Violet. 'Aren't they, Miss Bunt?'

'Very good indeed, my dear. Very good for you too. And Fritz, I will just have the mixed salad with some cottage cheese.' She gave the caricature of a simper. 'Alas–' she spoke to Bond–'I have to watch my figure. These young things take plenty of exercise, while I must stay in my office and do the paper-work, isn't it?'

At the next table Bond heard the girl with the Scottish burr, her voice full of saliva, ask that her Aberdeen Angus steak should be cooked very rare indeed. 'Guid and bluidy,' she emphasized.

What was this? wondered Bond. A gathering of beautiful ogresses? Or was this a day off from some rigorous diet? He felt completely clueless, out of his depth. Well, he would just go on digging. He turned to Ruby. 'You see what I mean about surnames. Fräulein Bunt may even have distant claim to an English title. Now what's yours, for instance? I'll see what I can make of it.'

Fräulein Bunt broke in sharply. 'No surnames here, Sair Hilary. It is a rule of the house. We use only first names for the girls. It is part of the Count's treatment. It is bound up with a change, a transference of identity, to help the cure. You understand?'

'No, I'm afraid that's way out of my depth,' said Bond cheerfully.

'No doubt the Count will explain some of these matters to you tomorrow.

He has special theories. One day the world will be startled when he reveals his methods.'

'I'm sure,' said Bond politely. 'Well now—' he searched for a subject that would leave his mind free to roam on its own. 'Tell me about your skiing. How are you getting on? Don't do it myself, I'm afraid. Perhaps I shall pick up some tips watching your classes.'

It was an adequate ball which went bouncing on between Ruby and Violet, and Bond kept it in play while their food came and proved delicious. Poulet Gloria was spatchcocked, with a mustard-and-cream sauce. The girls fell silent over their dishes, consuming them with polite but concentrated greed. There was a similar pause in the chatter at the other tables. Bond made conversation about the décor of the room and this gave him a chance to have a good look at the waiters. There were twelve of them in sight. It was not difficult to sum them up as three Corsicans, three Germans, three vaguely Balkan faces, Turks, Bulgars or Yugoslavs, and three obvious Slavs. There would probably be three Frenchmen in the kitchen. Was this the old pattern of SPECTRE? The well-tried communist-cell pattern of three men from each of the great gangster and secret-service organizations in Europe? Were the three Slavs ex-Smersh men? The whole lot of them looked tough enough, had that quiet smell of the pro. The man at the airport was one of them. Bond recognized others as the reception steward and the man who had come to his room about the table. He heard the girls calling them Fritz, Joseph, Ivan, Achmed. And some of them were ski-guides during the day. Well, it was a nice little set-up if Bond was right.

Bond excused himself after dinner on the grounds of work. He went to his room and laid out his books and papers on the desk and on the extra table that had been provided. He bent over them studiously while his mind reviewed the day.

At ten o'clock he heard the good-nights of the girls down the corridor and the click of the doors shutting. He undressed, turned the thermostat on the wall down from eighty-five to sixty, switched off the light and lay on his back for a while staring up into the darkness. Then he gave an authentic sigh of exhaustion for the microphones, if any, and turned over on his side and went to sleep.

Later, much later, he was awakened by a very soft murmuring that seemed to come from somewhere under the floor, but very, very far away. He identified it as a minute, spidery whispering that went on and on. But he could not make out any words and he finally put it down to the central-heating pipes, turned over and went to sleep again.

Chapter Eleven

Death for Breakfast

James Bond awoke to a scream. It was a terrible, masculine scream out of hell. It fractionally held its first high, piercing note and then rapidly diminished as if the man had jumped off a cliff. It came from the right, from somewhere near the cable station perhaps. Even in Bond's room, muffled by the double windows, it was terrifying enough. Outside it must have been shattering.

Bond jumped up and pulled back the curtains, not knowing what scene of panic, of running men, would meet his eyes. But the only man in sight was one of the guides, walking slowly, stolidly up the beaten snow-path from the cable station to the club. The spacious wooden veranda that stretched from the wall of the club out over the slope of the mountain was empty, but tables had been laid for breakfast and the upholstered chaises-longue for the sunbathers had already been drawn up in their meticulous, colourful rows. The sun was blazing down out of a crystal sky. Bond looked at his watch. It was eight o'clock. Work began early in this place! People died early. For that had undoubtedly been the death-scream. He turned back into his room and rang the bell.

It was one of the three men Bond had suspected of being Russians. Bond became the officer and gentleman. 'What is your name?'

'Peter, sir.'

'Piotr?' Bond longed to say. 'And how are all my old friends from SMERSH?' He didn't. He said, 'What was that scream?'

'Pliss?' The granite-grey eyes were careful.

'A man screamed just now. From over by the cable station. What was it?'

'It seems there has been an accident, sir. You wish for breakfast?' He produced a large menu from under his arm and held it out clumsily.

'What sort of an accident?'

'It seems that one of the guides has fallen.'

How could this man have known that, only minutes after the scream? 'Is he badly hurt?'

'Is possible, sir.' The eyes, surely trained in investigation, held Bond's blandly. 'You wish for breakfast?' The menu was once again nudged forward.

Bond said, with sufficient concern, 'Well, I hope the poor chap's all right.' He took the menu and ordered. 'Let me know if you hear what happened.'

'There will no doubt be an announcement if the matter is serious. Thank you, sir.' The man withdrew.

It was the scream that triggered Bond into deciding that, above all things, he must keep fit. He suddenly felt that, despite all the mystery and its demand for solution, there would come a moment when he would need all his muscle. Reluctantly he proceeded to a quarter of an hour of knee-bends and press-ups and deep-breathing chest-expansions–exercises of the skiing muscles. He guessed that he might have to get away from this place. But quick!

He took a shower and shaved. Breakfast was brought by Peter. 'Any more news about this poor guide?'

'I have heard no more, sir. It concerns the outdoor staff. I work inside the club.'

Bond decided to play it down. 'He must have slipped and broken an ankle. Poor chap! Thank you, Peter.'

'Thank you, sir.' Did the granite eyes contain a sneer?

James Bond put his breakfast on the desk and, with some difficulty, managed to prise open the double window. He removed the small bolster that lay along the sill between the panes to keep out draughts, and blew away the accumulated dust and small fly-corpses. The cold, savourless air of high altitudes rushed into the room and Bond went to the thermostat and put it up to 90 as a counter-attack. While, his head below the level of the sill, he ate a spare continental breakfast, he heard the chatter of the girls assembling outside on the terrace. The voices were high with excitement and debate. Bond could hear every word.

'I really don't think Sarah should have told on him.'

'But he came in in the dark and started mucking her about.'

'You mean actually *interfering* with her?'

'So she says. If I'd been her, I'd have done the same. And he's such a beast of a man.'

'*Was*, you mean. Which one was it, anyway?'

'One of the Yugos. Bertil.'

'Oh, I know. Yes, he was pretty horrible. He had such dreadful teeth.'

'You oughtn't to say such things of the dead.'

'How do you know he's dead? What happened to him, anyway?'

'He was one of the two you see spraying the start of the bob-run. You see them with hoses every morning. It's to get it good and icy so they'll go faster. Fritz told me he somehow slipped, lost his balance or something. And that was that. He just went off down the run like a sort of human bob-sleigh.'

'Elizabeth! How can you be so heartless about it!'

'Well, that's what happened. You asked.'

'But couldn't he save himself?'

'Don't be idiotic. It's sheet ice, a mile of it. And the bobs get up to sixty miles an hour. He hadn't got a prayer.'

'But didn't he fly off at one of the bends?'

'Fritz said he went all the way to the bottom. Crashed into the timing hut. But Fritz says he must have been dead in the first hundred yards or so.'

'Oh, here's Franz. Franz, can I have scrambled eggs and coffee? And tell them to make the scrambled eggs runny like I always have them.'

'Yes, miss. And you, miss?' The waiter took the orders and Bond heard his boots creak off across the boards. The sententious girl was being sententious again. 'Well, all I can say is it must have been some kind of punishment for what he tried to do to Sarah. You always get paid off for doing wrong.'

'Don't be ridiculous. God would never punish you as severely as that.' The conversation followed this new hare off into a maze of infantile morality and the Scriptures.

Bond lit a cigarette and sat back, gazing thoughtfully at the sky. No, the the girl was right. God wouldn't mete out such a punishment. But Blofeld would. Had there been one of those Blofeld meetings at which, before the full body of men, the crime and the verdict had been announced? Had this Bertil been taken out and dropped on to the bob-run? Or had his companion been quietly dealt the card of death, told to give the sinner the trip or the light push that was probably all that had been needed? More likely. The quality of the scream had been of sudden, fully realized terror as the man fell, scrabbled at the ice with his finger-nails and boots, and then, as he gathered speed down the polished blue gully, the blinding horror of the truth. And what a death! Bond had once gone down the Cresta, from 'Top', to prove to himself that he dared. Helmeted, masked against the blast of air, padded with leather and foam rubber, that had still been sixty seconds of naked fear. Even now he could remember how his limbs had shaken when he rose stiffly from the flimsy little skeleton bob at the end of the run-out. And that had been a bare three-quarters of a mile. This man, or the flayed remains of him, had done over a mile. Had he gone down head or feet first? Had his body started tumbling? Had he tried, while consciousness remained, to brake himself over the edge of one of the early, scientifically banked bends with the unspiked toe of this boot or that . . . ? No. After the first few yards, he would already have been going too fast for any rational thought or action. God, what a death! A typical Blofeld death, a typical SPECTRE revenge for the supreme crime of disobedience. That was the way to keep discipline in the ranks! So, concluded Bond as he cleared the tray away and got down to his books, SPECTRE walks again! But down what road this time?

At ten minutes to eleven, Irma Bunt came for him. After an exchange of affabilities, Bond gathered up an armful of books and papers and followed her round the back of the club building and along a narrow, well-trodden path past a sign that said PRIVAT. EINTRITT VERBOTEN.

The rest of the building, whose outlines Bond had seen the night before, came into view. It was an undistinguished but powerfully built one-storey affair made of local granite blocks, with a flat cement roof from which, at the far end, protruded a small, professional-looking radio mast which, Bond assumed, had given the pilot his landing instructions on the previous night and which would also serve as the ears and mouth of Blofeld. The building was on the very edge of the plateau and below the final peak of Piz Gloria, but out of avalanche danger. Beneath it the mountain sloped sharply away until it disappeared over a cliff. Far below again was the tree line and the Bernina valley leading up to Pontresina, the glint of a railway track and the tiny caterpillar of a long goods train of the Rhätische Bahn, on its way, presumably, over the Bernina Pass into Italy.

The door to the building gave the usual pneumatic hiss, and the central corridor was more or less a duplicate of the one at the club, but here there were doors on both sides and no pictures. It was dead quiet and there was no hint of what went on behind the doors. Bond put the question.

'Laboratories,' said Irma Bunt vaguely. 'All laboratories. And of course the lecture-room. Then the Count's private quarters. He lives with his work, Sair Hilary.'

'Good show.'

They came to the end of the corridor. Irma Bunt knocked on the facing door.

'Herein!'

James Bond was tremendously excited as he stepped over the threshold and heard the door sigh shut behind him. He knew what not to expect, the original Blofeld, last year's model–about twenty stone, tall, pale, bland face with black crew-cut, black eyes with the whites showing all round, like Mussolini's, ugly thin mouth, long pointed hands and feet–but he had no idea what alterations had been contrived on the envelope that contained the man.

But Monsieur le Comte de Bleuville, who now rose from the chaise-longue on the small private veranda and came in out of the sun into the penumbra of the study, his hands outstretched in welcome, was surely not even a distant relative of the man on the files!

Bond's heart sank. This man was tallish, yes, and, all right, his hands and naked feet were long and thin. But there the resemblance ended. The Count had longish, carefully-tended, almost dandified hair that was a fine silvery white. His ears, that should have been close to his head, stuck out slightly and, where they should have had heavy lobes, had none. The body that should have weighed twenty stone, now naked save for a black woollen slip, was not more than twelve stone, and there were no signs of the sagging flesh that comes from middle-aged weight-reduction. The mouth was full and friendly, with a pleasant, up-turned, but perhaps rather unwavering smile. The forehead was serrated with wrinkles above a nose that, while the files said it should be short and squat, was aquiline and, round the right nostril, eaten away, poor chap, by what looked like the badge of tertiary syphilis. The eyes? Well, there might be something there if one could see them, but they were only rather frightening dark-green pools. The Count wore, presumably against the truly dangerous sun at these altitudes, dark-green tinted contact lenses.

Bond unloaded his books on to a conveniently empty table and took the warm, dry hand.

'My dear Sir Hilary. This is indeed a pleasure.' Blofeld's voice had been said to be sombre and even. This voice was light and full of animation.

Bond said to himself, furiously, by God this has *got* to be Blofeld! He said, 'I'm so sorry I couldn't come on the 21st. There's a lot going on at the moment.'

'Ah yes. So Fräulein Bunt told me. These new African States. They must indeed present a problem. Now, shall we settle down here–' he waved towards his desk–'or shall we go outside? You see–' he gestured at his brown body–'I am a heliotrope, a sun-worshipper. So much so that I have had to have these lenses devised for me. Otherwise, the ultra-violet rays, at this altitude . . .' He left the phrase unfinished.

'I haven't seen that kind of lens before. After all, I can leave the books here and fetch them if we need them for reference. I have the case pretty clear in my mind. And–' Bond smiled chummily–'it would be nice to go back to the fogs with something of a sunburn.'

Bond had equipped himself at Lillywhites with clothing he thought would be both appropriate and sensible. He had avoided the modern elasticized vorlage trousers and had chosen the more comfortable but old-fashioned type of ski-trouser in a smooth cloth. Above these he wore an aged black wind-cheater that he used for golf, over his usual white sea-island cotton shirt. He had wisely reinforced this outfit with long and ugly cotton and wool pants and vests. He had conspicuously brand-new ski-boots with powerful ankle-straps. He said. 'Then I'd better take off my sweater.' He did so and followed the Count out on to the veranda.

The Count lay back again in his upholstered aluminium chaise-longue. Bond drew up a light chair made of similar materials. He placed it also facing the sun, but at an angle so that he could watch the Count's face.

'And now,' said the Comte de Bleuville, 'what have you got to tell me that necessitated this personal visit?' He turned his fixed smile on Bond. The dark-green glass eyes were unfathomable. 'Not of course that the visit is not most welcome, most welcome. Now then, Sir Hilary.'

Bond had been well trained in two responses to this obvious first question. The first was for the event that the Count had lobes to his ears. The second, if he had not. He now, in measured, serious tones, launched himself into Number Two.

'My dear Count–' the form of address seemed dictated by the silvery hair, by the charm of the Count's manners–'there are occasions in the work of the College when research and paper work are simply not enough. We have, as you know, come to a difficult passage in our work on your case. I refer of course to the hiatus between the disappearance of the de Bleuville line around the time of the French Revolution and the emergence of the Blofeld family, or families, in the neighbourhood of Augsburg. And–' Bond paused impressively–'in the latter context I may later have a proposal that I hope will find favour with you. But what I am coming to is this. You have already expended serious funds on our work, and it would not have been fair to suggest that the researches should go forward unless there was a substantial ray of hope in the sky. The possibility of such a ray existed, but it was of such a nature that it definitely demanded a physical confrontation.'

'Is that so? And for what purpose, may I inquire?'

James Bond recited Sable Basilisk's examples of the Habsburg lip, the royal tail and the others. He then leaned forward in his chair for emphasis. 'And such a physical peculiarity exists in connection with the de Bleuvilles. You did not know this?'

'I was not aware of it. No. What is it?'

'I have good news for you, Count.' Bond smiled his congratulations. 'All the de Bleuville effigies or portraits that we have been able to trace have been distinctive in one vital respect, in one inherited characteristic. It appears that the family had no lobes to their ears!'

The Count's hands went up to his ears and felt them. Was he acting?

'I see,' he said slowly. 'Yes, I see.' He reflected. 'And you had to see this for yourself? My word, or a photograph, would not have been sufficient?'

Bond looked embarrassed. 'I am sorry, Count. But that was the ruling of Garter King of Arms. I am only a junior free-lance research worker for one of the Pursuivants. He in turn takes his orders in these matters from above. I hope you will appreciate that the College has to be extremely strict in cases concerned with a most ancient and honourable title such as the one in question.'

The dark pools aimed themselves at Bond like the muzzles of guns. 'Now that you have seen what you came to see, you regard the title as still in question?'

This was the worst hurdle. 'What I have seen certainly allows me to recommend that the work should continue, Count. And I would say that our chances of success have greatly multiplied. I have brought out the materials for a first sketch of the Line of Descent, and that, in a matter of days, I could lay before you. But alas, as I have said, there are still many gaps, and it is most important for me to satisfy Sable Basilisk particularly about the stages of your family's migration from Augsburg to Gdynia. It would be of the greatest help if I might question you closely about your parentage in the male line. Even details about your father and grandfather would be of the greatest assistance. And then, of course, it would be of the utmost importance if you could spare a day to accompany me to Augsburg to see if the handwriting of these Blofeld families in the Archives, their Christian names and other family details, awaken any memories or connections in your mind. The rest would then remain with us at the College. I could spare no more than a week on this work. But I am at your disposal if you wish it.'

The Count got to his feet. Bond followed suit. He walked casually over to the railing and admired the view. Would this bedraggled fly be taken? Bond now desperately hoped so. During the interview he had come to one certain conclusion. There was not a single one of the peculiarities in the Count's appearance that could not have been achieved by good acting and by the most refined facial and stomach surgery applied to the original Blofeld. Only the eyes could not have been tampered with. And the eyes were obscured.

'You think that with patient work, even with the inclusion of a few question marks where the connecting links are obscure, I would achieve an Acte de Notoriété that would satisfy the Minister of Justice in Paris?'

'Most certainly,' lied Bond. 'With the authority of the College in support.'

The fixed smile widened minutely. 'That would give me much satisfaction, Sir Hilary. I *am* the Comte de Bleuville. I am certain of it in my heart, in my veins.' There was real fervour in the voice. 'But I am determined that my title shall be officially recognized. You will be most welcome to remain as my guest and I shall be constantly at your disposal to help with your researches.'

Bond said politely, but with a hint of weariness, of resignation, 'All right, Count. And thank you. I will go and make a start straight away.'

Chapter Twelve

Two Near Misses

Bond was shown out of the building by a man in a white coat with the conventional white gauze of the laboratory worker over the lower half of his face. Bond attempted no conversation. He was now well inside the fortress, but he would have to continue to walk on tiptoe and be damned careful where he put his feet!

He returned to his room and got out one of the giant sheets of squared paper with which he had been furnished. He sat down at his table and wrote firmly at the top centre of the paper 'Guillaume de Bleuville, 1207–1243'. Now there were five hundred years of de Bleuvilles, with their wives and children, to be copied down from his books and notes. That would fill up an impressive number of pages with impeccable fact. He could certainly spread that chore over three days, interspersed with more tricky work–gassing with Blofeld about the Blofeld end of the story. Fortunately there were some English Blofields he could throw in as make-weight. And some Bluefields and Blumfields. He could start some pretty hares running in those directions! And, in between these idiotic activities, he would ferret and ferret away at the mystery of what in hell the new Blofeld, the new SPECTRE, were up to!

One thing was certain, they had already been through his belongings. Before going for his interview. Bond had gone into the bathroom, away from that seemingly watchful hole in the ceiling, and had painfully pulled out half a dozen of his hairs. These, while he had selected the books he needed to take with him, he had dispersed inconspicuously among his other papers and in his passport. The hairs were all gone. Someone had been through all his books. He got up and went to the chest of drawers, ostensibly for a handkerchief. Yes, the careful patterns in which he had laid out his things had all been minutely disturbed. Unemotionally he went back to his work, thanking heaven he had travelled as 'clean' as a whistle! But by God he'd have to keep his cover solid! He didn't at all like the thought of that one-way trip down the bob-run!

Bond got as far as 1350 and then the noise from the veranda became too distracting. Anyway, he had done a respectable stint, almost to the bottom of the giant page. He would go out and do a little very discreet exploring. He wanted to get his bearings, or rather confirm them, and this would be a perfectly reasonable activity for a newcomer. He had left his door into the passage ajar. He went out and along to the reception lounge, where the man in the plum coat was busy entering the names of the morning's visitors in a book. Bond's greeting was politely answered. There was a ski-room and workshop to the left of the exit. Bond wandered in. One of the Balkan types was at the work-bench, screwing a new binding on to a ski. He looked up and went on with his work while Bond gazed with seeming curiosity at the ranks of skis standing along the wall. Things had changed since his day. The bindings were quite different and designed, it seemed, to keep the heel dead flat on the ski. And there were new safety releases. Many of the skis were of metal and the ski-sticks were fibre-glass lances that looked to Bond extremely dangerous in the event of a bad fall. Bond wandered over to the work-bench and feigned interest in what the man was doing. In fact he had seen something that excited him very much–an untidy pile of lengths of thin plastic strip for the boot to rest on in the binding, so that, on the shiny surface, snow would not ball under the sole. Bond leaned over the work-bench, resting on his right elbow, and commented on the precision of the man's work. The man grunted and concentrated all the more closely to avoid further conversation. Bond's left hand slid under his leaning arm, secured one of the strips and slid it up his sleeve. He made a further inane comment, which was not answered, and strolled out of the ski-room.

(When the man in the workshop heard the front door hiss shut, he turned to the pile of plastic strips and counted them carefully twice. Then he went out to the man in the plum-coloured coat and spoke to him in German. The man nodded and picked up the telephone receiver and dialled O. The workman went stolidly back to his ski-room.)

As Bond strolled along the path that led to the cable station, he transferred the plastic strip from his sleeve to his trouser pocket, feeling pleased with himself. He had at least provided himself with one tool–the traditional burglar's tool for opening the Yale-type locks that secured the doors.

Away from the club house, to which only a thin trickle of smart-looking people were making their way, he got into the usual mountain-top crowd–people swarming out of the cable-head, skiers wobbling or schussing down the easy nursery slopes on the plateau, little groups marshalled under individual teachers and guides from the valley. The terrace of the public restaurant was already crowded with the under-privileged who hadn't got the money or the connections to join the club. He walked below it on the well-trampled snow and stood amongst the skiers at the top of the first plunging schuss of the Gloria run. A large notice-board, crowned with the G and the coronet, announced GLORIA ABFAHRT! Then below, ROT–FREIE FAHRT. GELB–FREIE FAHRT. SCHWARZ–GESPERRT, meaning that the red and yellow runs were open but the black closed, presumably because of avalanche danger. Below this again was a painted metal map of the three runs. Bond had a good look at it, reflecting that it might be wise to commit to memory the red, which was presumably the easiest and most popular. There were red, yellow and black marker flags on the map, and Bond could see the actual flags fluttering way down the mountain until the runs, studded with tiny moving figures, disappeared to the left, round the shoulder of the mountain and under the cable railway. The red seemed to continue to zigzag under the cable and between the few high pylons until it met the tree line. Then there was a short stretch of wood-running until the final easy schuss across the undulating lower meadows to the bottom cable-head, beyond which lay the main railway line and then the Pontresina-Samaden road. Bond tried to get it all fixed in his mind. Then he watched some of the starts. These varied between the arrow-like dive of the Kannonen, the stars, who took the terrific schuss dead straight in a low crouch with their sticks jauntily tucked under their arm-pits, the average amateur who braked perhaps three or four times on his way down, and the terrified novice who, with stuck-out behind, stemmed his way down, his skis angled and edged like a snow-plough, with occasional straight runs diagonally across the polished slope–dashing little sprints that usually ended in a mild crash as he ran off the flattened surface into the thick powder snow that edged the wide, beaten piste.

The scene was the same as a thousand others Bond had witnessed when, as a teen-ager, he learned his skiing in the old Hannes Schneider School at St Anton in the Arlberg. He had got pretty good and had won his golden K, but the style in those days was rudimentary compared with what he was now witnessing from the occasional expert who zoomed down and away from beside him. Today the metal skis seemed to run faster and truer than the old steel-edged hickory. There was less shoulder-work and the art of Wedeln, a gentle waggling of the hips, was a revelation. Would it be as effective in deep new snow as it was on the well-beaten piste? Bond was doubtful, but he was envious of it. It was so much more graceful than the old Arlberg crouch. Bond wondered how he would fare on this terrific run. He would certainly not dare to take the first schuss straight. He would brake at least twice, perhaps there and there. And his legs would be trembling before he had been going for five minutes. His knees and ankles and wrists would be giving out. He *must* get on with his exercises!

Bond, excited, left the scene and followed arrows that pointed to the GLORIA EXPRESS BOB-RUN. It lay on the other side of the cable station. There was a small wooden hut, the starter's hut, with telephone-wires connected to the station, and, beneath the cable station, a little 'garage' that housed the bob-sleighs and one-man skeleton-bobs. A chain, with a notice on it saying ABFAHRTEN TÄGLICH 0900–1100, was stretched across the wide mouth of the gulch of blue ice that curved away to the left and then disappeared over the shoulder. Here again was a metal map showing the zigzag course of the run down into the valley. In deference to the English traditions at the sport, outstanding curves and hazards were marked with names such as 'Dead Man's Leap', 'Whizz-Bang Straight', 'Battling S', 'Hell's Delight', 'The Boneshaker', and the finishing straight down 'Paradise Alley'. Bond visualized the scene that morning, heard again that heart-rending scream. Yes, that death certainly had the old Blofeld touch!

'Sair Hilary! Sair Hilary!'

Startled out of his thoughts, Bond turned. Fräulein Irma Bunt, her short arms akimbo, was standing on the path to the club.

'Lunch time! Lunch!'

'Coming,' Bond called back, and strolled up the slope towards her. He noted that, even in that hundred yards, his breathing was shallow and his limbs were heavy. This blasted height! He really must get into training!

He came up with her. She looked surly. He said that he was sorry, he had not noticed the time. She said nothing. The yellow eyes surveyed him with active dislike before she turned her back and led the way along the path.

Bond looked back over the morning. What had he done? Had he made a mistake? Well, he just might have. Better re-insure! As they came through the entrance into the reception lounge, Bond said casually, 'Oh, by the way, Fräulein Bunt, I was in the ski-room just now.'

She halted. Bond noticed that the head of the receptionist bent a fraction lower over his visitors' book.

'Yes?'

Bond took the length of plastic out of his pocket, 'I found just what I wanted.' He stitched a smile of innocent pleasure on his face. 'Like an idiot I forgot to bring a ruler with me. And there were these things on the work-bench. Just right. So I borrowed one. I hope that was all right. Of course I'll leave it behind when I go. But for these family trees, you know–' Bond sketched a series of descending straight lines in the air–'one has to get them on the right levels. I hope you don't mind.' He smiled charmingly. 'I was going to confess the next time I saw you.'

Irma Bunt veiled her eyes. 'It is of no consequence. In future, anything you need you will perhaps ring for, isn't it? The Count wishes you to have every facility. Now–' she gestured–'if you will perhaps go out on the terrace. You will be shown to our table. I will be with you in a moment.'

Bond went through the restaurant door. Several of the interior tables were occupied by those who had had enough sun. He went across the room and out through the now open french windows. The man Fritz, who appeared to be the maître d'hôtel, came towards him through the crowded tables. His eyes too were cold with hostility. He held up a menu. 'Please to follow me.'

Bond followed him to the table up against the railing. Ruby and Violet were already there. Bond felt almost light-hearted with relief at having clean hands again. By God, he must pay attention, take care! This time he had got away with it. And he still had the strip of plastic! Had he sounded innocent enough, stupid enough? He sat down and ordered a double medium dry-vodka Martini, on the rocks, with lemon peel, and edged his foot up against Ruby's.

She didn't withdraw hers. She smiled. Violet smiled. They all started talking at once. It was suddenly a beautiful day.

Fräulein Bunt appeared and took her place. She was gracious again. 'I am so pleased to hear that you will be staying with us for a whole week, Sair Hilary. You enjoyed your interview with the Count? Is he not an interesting man?'

'Very interesting. Unfortunately our talk was too short and we discussed only my own subject. I was longing to ask him about his research work. I hope he didn't think me very rude.'

Irma Bunt's face closed perceptibly. 'I am sure not. The Count does not often like to discuss his work. In these specialized scientific fields, you understand, there is much jealousy and, I am sorry to say, much intellectual thieving.' The box-like smile. 'I do not of course refer to yourself, my dear Sair Hilary, but to scientists less scrupulous than the Count, to spies from the chemical companies. That is why we keep ourselves very much to ourselves in our little Eagle's Nest up here. We have total privacy. Even the police in the valley are most co-operative in safeguarding us from intruders. They appreciate what the Count is doing.'

'The study of allergies?'

'Just so.' The maître d'hôtel was standing by her side. His feet came together with a perceptible click. Menus were handed round and Bond's drink came. He took a long pull at it and ordered Oeufs Gloria and a green salad. Chicken again for Ruby, cold cuts 'with stacks of potatoes' for Violet. Irma Bunt ordered her usual cottage cheese and salad.

'Don't you girls eat anything but chicken and poatoes? Is this something to do with your allergies?'

Ruby began, 'Well, yes, in a way. Somehow I've come to simply love . . .'

Irma Bunt broke in sharply. 'Now then, Ruby. No discussion of treatments, you remember? Not even with our good friend Sair Hilary.' She waved a hand towards the crowded tables around them. 'A most interesting crowd, do you not find, Sair Hilary? Everybody who is anybody. We have quite taken the international set away from Gstaad and St Moritz. That is your Duke of Marlborough over there with such a gay party of young things. And near by that is Mr Whitney and Lady Daphne Straight. Is she not chic? They are both wonderful skiers. And that beautiful girl with the long fair hair at the big table, that is Ursula Andress, the film star. What a wonderful tan she has! And Sir George Dunbar, he always has the most enchanting companions.' The box-like smile. 'Why, we only need the Aga Khan and perhaps your Duke of Kent and we would have everybody, but everybody. Is it not sensational for the first season?'

Bond said it was. The lunch came. Bond's eggs were delicious–chopped hard-boiled eggs, with a cream and cheese sauce laced with English mustard (English mustard seemed to be the clue to the Gloria specialities) gratinés in a copper dish. Bond commented on the excellence of the cooking.

'Thank you,' said Irma Bunt. 'We have three expert Frenchmen in the kitchen. Men are very good at cooking, is it not?'

Bond felt rather than saw a man approaching their table. He came to Bond. He was a military-looking man, of about Bond's age, and he had a puzzled expression on his face. He bowed slightly to the ladies and said to Bond, 'Excuse me, but I saw your name in the visitors' book. It is Hilary Bray, isn't it?'

Bond's heart sank. This situation had always been a possibility and he had prepared a fumbling counter to it. But this was the worst possible moment with that damned woman watching and listening!

Bond said, 'Yes, it is,' with heartiness.

'*Sir* Hilary Bray?' The pleasant face was even more puzzled.

Bond got to his feet and stood with his back to his table, to Irma Bunt. 'That's right.' He took out his handkerchief and blew his nose to obscure the next question, which might be fatal.

'In the Lovat Scouts during the war?'

'Ah,' said Bond. He looked worried, lowered his voice appropriately. 'You're thinking of my first cousin. From Ben Trilleachan. Died six months ago, poor chap. I inherited the title.'

'Oh, lord!' The man's puzzlement cleared. Grief took its place. 'Sorry to hear that. Great pal of mine in the war. Funny! I didn't see anything about it in *The Times*. Always read the "Births, Marriages and Deaths". What was it?'

Bond felt the sweat running down under his arms. 'Fell off one of those bloody mountains of his. Broke his neck.'

'My God! Poor chap! But he was always fooling around the tops by himself. I must write to Jenny at once.' He held out his hand. 'Well, sorry to have butted in. Thought this was a funny place to find old Hilary. Well, so long, and sorry again.' He moved off between the tables. Out of the corner of his eye, Bond saw him rejoin a very English-looking table of men and, obviously, wives, to whom he began talking animatedly.

Bond sat down, reached for his drink and drained it and went back to his eggs. The woman's eyes were on him. He felt the sweat running down his face. He took out his handkerchief and mopped at it. 'Gosh, it's hot out here in the sun! That was some pal of my first cousin's. My cousin had the same name. Collateral branch. Died not long ago, poor chap.' He frowned sadly. 'Didn't know this man from Adam. Nice-looking fellow.' Bond looked bravely across the table. 'Do you know any of his party, Fräulein Bunt?'

Without looking at the party, Fräulein Bunt said shortly, 'No, I do not know everyone who comes here.' The yellow eyes were still inquisitive, holding his. 'But it was a curious coincidence. Were you very alike, you and your cousin?'

'Oh, absolutely,' said Bond, gushing. 'Spit image. Often used to get taken for each other.' He looked across at the English group. Thank God they were picking up their things and going. They didn't look particularly smart or prosperous. Probably staying at Pontresina or under the ex-officers' scheme at St Moritz. Typical English skiing party. With any luck they were just doing the big runs in the neighbourhood one by one. Bond reviewed the way the conversation had gone while coffee came and he made cheerful small talk with Ruby, whose foot was again clamped against his, about her skiing progress that morning.

Well, he decided, the woman couldn't have heard much of it with all the clatter and chatter from the surrounding tables. But it had been a narrow squeak, a damned narrow squeak. The second of the day!

So much for walking on tiptoe inside the enemy lines!

Not good enough! Definitely not good enough!

Chapter Thirteen

Princess Ruby?

My dear Sable Basilisk,

I arrived safely–by helicopter, if you please!–at this beautiful place called Piz Gloria, 10,000 feet up somewhere in the Engadine. Most comfortable with an excellent male staff of several nationalities and a most efficient secretary to the Count named Fräulein Irma Bunt who tells me that she comes from Munich.

I had a most profitable interview with the Count this morning as a result of which he wishes me to stay on for a week to complete the first draft of his genealogical tree. I do hope you can spare me for so long. I warned the Count that we had much work to do on the new Commonwealth States. He himself, though busily engaged on what sounds like very public-spirited research work on allergies and their cause (he has ten English girls here as his patients), has agreed to see me daily in the hope that together we may be able to bridge the gap between the migration of the de Bleuvilles from France and their subsequent transference, as Blofelds, from Augsburg to Gdynia. I have suggested to him that we conclude the work with a quick visit to Augsburg for the purposes you and I discussed, but he has not yet given me his decision.

Please tell my cousin Jenny Bray that she may be hearing from a friend of her late husband who apparently served with him in the Lovat Scouts. He came up to me at lunch today and took me for the other Hilary! Quite a coincidence!

Working conditions are excellent. We have complete privacy here, secure from the madding world of skiers, and very sensibly the girls are confined to their rooms after ten at night to put them out of the temptation of roaming and gossiping. They seem a very nice lot, from all over the United Kingdom, but rather on the dumb side!

Now for my most interesting item. The Count has *not* got lobes to his ears! Isn't that good news! He also is of a most distinguished appearance and bearing with a fine head of silvery hair and a charming smile. His slim figure also indicates noble extraction. Unfortunately he has to wear dark-green contact lenses because of weak eyes and the strength of the sunshine at this height, and his aquiline nose is blemished by a deformed nostril which I would have thought could easily have been put right by facial surgery. He speaks impeccable English with a gay lilt to his voice and I am sure that we will get on very well.

Now to get down to business. It would be most helpful if you would get in touch with the old printers of the Almanach de Gotha and see if they can help us over our gaps in the lineage. They may have some traces. Cable anything helpful. With the new evidence of the ear-lobes I am quite confident that the connection exists.

That's all for now.

Yours ever,
Hilary Bray

P.S. Don't tell my mother, or she will be worried for my safety among the eternal snows! But we had a nasty accident here this morning. One of the staff, a Yugoslav it seems, slipped on the bob-run and went the whole way to the bottom! Terrible business. He's apparently being buried in Pontresina tomorrow. Do you think we ought to send some kind of a wreath? H.B.

Bond read the letter several times. Yes, that would give the officers in charge of Operation 'Corona' plenty to bite on. Particularly the hint that they should get the dead man's name from the registrar in Pontresina. And he had covered up a bit on the Bray mix-up when the letter, as Bond was sure it would be, was steamed open and photostated before dispatch. They might of course just destroy it. To prevent this, the bit of bogosity about the Almanach de Gotha would be a clincher. This source of heraldic knowledge hadn't been mentioned before. It would surely excite the interest of Blofeld.

Bond rang the bell, handed out the letter for dispatch, and got back to his work, which consisted initially of going into the bathroom with the strip of plastic and his scissors in his pocket and snipping two inch-wide strips off the end. These would be enough for the purposes he and, he hoped, Ruby would put them to. Then, using the first joint of his thumb as a rough guide, he marked off the remaining eighteen inches into inch measures, to support his lie about the ruler, and went back to his desk and to the next hundred years of the de Bleuvilles.

At about five o'clock the light got so bad that Bond got up from his table and stretched, preparatory to going over to the light-switch near the door. He took a last look out of the window before he closed it. The veranda was completely deserted and the foam rubber cushions for the reclining-chairs had already been taken in. From the direction of the cable-head there still came the whine of machinery that had been part of the background noises to the day. Yesterday the railway had closed at about five, and it must be time for the last pair of gondolas to complete their two-way journey and settle in their respective stations for the night. Bond closed the double windows, walked across to the thermostat and put it down to seventy. He was just about to reach for the light-switch when there came a very soft tapping at the door.

Bond kept his voice low. 'Come in!'

The door opened and quickly closed to within an inch of the lock. It was Ruby. She put her fingers to her lips and gestured towards the bathroom. Bond, highly intrigued, followed her in and shut the door. Then he turned on the light. She was blushing. She whispered imploringly, 'Oh, please forgive me, Sir Hilary. But I did so want to talk to you for a second.'

'That's fine, Ruby. But why the bathroom?'

'Oh, didn't you know? No, I suppose you wouldn't. It's supposed to be a secret, but of course I can tell you. You won't let on, will you?'

'No, of course not.'

'Well, all the rooms have microphones in them. I don't know where. But sometimes we girls have got together in each other's rooms, just for a gossip, you know, and Miss Bunt has always known. We think they've got some sort of television too.' She giggled. 'We always undress in the bathroom. It's just a sort of feeling. As if one was being watched the whole time. I suppose its something to do with the treatment.'

'Yes, I expect so.'

'The point is, Sir Hilary, I was tremendously excited by what you were saying at lunch today, about Miss Bunt perhaps being a duchess. I mean, is that really possible?'

'Oh yes,' said Bond airily.

'I was so disappointed at not being able to tell you my surname. You see, you see–' her eyes were wide with excitement–'it's Windsor!'

'Gosh,' said Bond, 'that's interesting!'

'I knew you'd say that. You see, there's always been talk in my family that we're distantly connected with the Royal Family!'

'I can quite understand that.' Bond's voice was thoughtful, judicious. 'I'd like to be able to do some work on that. What were your parents' names? I must have them first.'

'George Albert Windsor and Mary Potts. Does that mean anything?'

'Well, of course, the Albert's significant.' Bond felt a cur. 'You see, there was the Prince Consort to Queen Victoria. He was Albert.'

'Oh golly!' Ruby's knuckles went up to her mouth.

'But of course all this needs a lot of working on. Where do you come from in England? Where were you born?'

'In Lancashire. Morecambe Bay, where the shrimps come from. But a lot of poultry too. You know.'

'So that's why you love chicken so much.'

'Oh, no.' She seemed surprised by the remark. 'That's just the point. You see, I was allergic to chickens. I simply couldn't bear them–all those feathers, the stupid pecking, the mess and the smell. I loathed them. Even eating chicken brought me out in a sort of rash. It was awful, and of course my parents were mad at me, they being poultry farmers in quite a big way and me being supposed to help clean out the batteries–you know, those modern mass-produced chicken places. And then one day I saw this advertisement in the paper, in the *Poultry Farmer's Gazette*. It said that anyone suffering from chicken allergy–then followed a long Latin name–could apply for a course of re . . . of re . . . for a cure in a Swiss institute doing research work on the thing. All found and ten pounds a week pocket-money. Rather like those people who go and act as rabbits in that place that's trying to find a cure for colds.'

'I know,' said Bond encouragingly.

'So I applied and my fare was paid down to London and I met Miss Bunt and she put me through some sort of exam.' She giggled. 'Heaven only knows how I passed it, as I failed by G.C.E. twice. But she said I was just what the Institute wanted and I came out here about two months ago. It's not bad. They're terribly strict. But the Count has absolutely cured my trouble. I simply love chickens now.' Her eyes became suddenly rapt. 'I think they're just the most beautiful, wonderful birds in the world.'

'Well, that's a jolly good show,' said Bond, totally mystified. 'Now about your name. I'll get to work on it right away. But how are we going to talk? You all seem to be pretty carefully organized. How can I see you by yourself? The only place is my room or yours.'

'You mean *at night*?' The big blue eyes were wide with fright, excitement, maidenly appraisal.

'Yes, it's the only way.' Bond took a bold step towards her and kissed her full on the mouth. He put his arms round her clumsily. 'And you know I think you're terribly attractive.'

'Oh, Sir Hilary!'

But she didn't recoil. She just stood there like a great lovely doll, passive, slightly calculating, wanting to be a princess. 'But how would you get out of here? They're terribly strict. A guard goes up and down the passage every so often. Of course–' the eyes were calculating–'it's true that I'm next door to you, in Number Three actually. If only we had some way of getting out.'

Bond took one of the inch strips of plastic out of his pocket and showed it to her. 'I knew you were somewhere close to me. Instinct, I suppose. [Cad!] I learned a thing or two in the Army. You can get out of these sort of doors by slipping this in the door crack in front of the lock and pushing. It slips the latch. Here, take this, I've got another. But hide it away. And promise not to tell anyone.'

'Ooh! You are a one! But of course I promise. But do you think there's any hope–about the Windsors, I mean?' Now she put her arms round his neck, round the witch-doctor's neck, and the big blue orbs gazed appealingly into his.

'You definitely mustn't rely on it,' said Bond firmly, trying to get back an ounce of his self-respect. 'But I'll have a quick look now in my books. Not much time before drinks. Anyway, we'll see.' He gave her another long and, he admitted to himself, extremely splendid kiss, to which she responded with an animalism that slightly salved his conscience. 'Now then, baby.' His right hand ran down her back to the curve of her behind, to which he gave an encouraging and hastening pat. 'We've got to get you out of here.'

His bedroom was dark. They listened at the door like two children playing hide-and-seek. The building was in silence. He inched open the door. He gave the behind an extra pat and she was gone.

Bond paused for a moment. Then he switched on the light. The innocent room smiled at him. Bond went to his table and reached for the *Dictionary of British Surnames*. Windsor, Windsor, Windsor. Here we are! Now then! As he bent over the small print, an important reflection seared his spy's mind like a shooting star. All right. So sexual perversions, and sex itself, were a main security risk. So was greed for money. But what about status? What about that most insidious of vices, snobbery?

Six o'clock came. Bond had a nagging headache, brought on by hours of poring over small-print reference books and aggravated by the lack of oxygen at the high altitude. He needed a drink, three drinks. He had a quick shower and smartened himself up, rang his bell for the 'warder' and went along to the bar. Only a few of the girls were already there. Violet sat alone at the bar and Bond joined her. She seemed pleased to see him. She was drinking a Daiquiri. Bond ordered another and, for himself, a double Bourbon on the rocks. He took a deep pull at it and put the squat glass down.

'By God, I needed that! I've been working like a slave all day while you've been waltzing about the ski-slopes in the sun!'

'Have I indeed!' A slight Irish brogue came out with the indignation. 'Two lectures this morning, frightfully boring, and I had to catch up with my reading most of this afternoon. I'm way behind with it.'

'What sort of reading?'

'Oh, sort of agricultural stuff.' The dark eyes watched him carefully. 'We're not supposed to talk about our cures, you know.'

'Oh, well,' said Bond cheerfully, 'then let's talk about something else. Where do you come from?'

'Ireland. The South. Near Shannon.'

Bond had a shot in the dark. 'All that potato country.'

'Yes, that's right. I used to hate them. Nothing but potatoes to eat and potato crops to talk about. Now I'm longing to get back. Funny, isn't it?'

'Your family'll be pleased.'

'You can say that again! And my boy friend! He's on the wholesale side. I said I wouldn't marry anyone who had anything to do with the damned, dirty, ugly things. He's going to get a shock all right . . .'

'How's that?'

'All I've learned about how to improve the crop. The latest scientific ways, chemicals and so on.' She put her hand up to her mouth. She glanced swiftly round the room, at the bartender. To see if anyone had heard this innocent stuff? She put on a hostess smile. 'Now you tell me what you've been working on, Sir Hilary.'

'Oh, just some heraldic stuff for the Count. Like I was talking about at lunch. I'm afraid you'd find it frightfully dry stuff.'

'Oh no, I wouldn't. I was terribly interested in what you were saying to Miss Bunt. You see–'she lowered her voice and spoke into her raised glass–'I'm an O'Neill. They used to be almost kings of Ireland. Do you think . . .' She had seen something over his shoulder. She went on smoothly, 'And I simply can't get my shoulders round enough. And when I try to I simply over-balance.'

''Fraid I don't know anything about skiing,' said Bond loudly.

Irma Bunt appeared in the mirror over the bar. 'Ah, Sair Hilary.' She inspected his face. 'But yes, you are already getting a little of the sunburn, isn't it? Come! Let us go and sit down. I see poor Miss Ruby over there all by herself.'

They followed her meekly. Bond was amused by the little undercurrent of rule-breaking that went on among the girls–the typical resistance pattern to strict discipline and the governessy ways of this hideous matron. He must be careful how he handled it, useful though it was proving. It wouldn't do to get these girls too much 'on his side'. But, if only because the Count didn't want him to know them, he must somehow ferret away at their surnames and addresses. Ferret! That was the word! Ruby would be his ferret. Bond sat down beside her, the back of his hand casually brushing against her shoulder.

More drinks were ordered. The Bourbon was beginning to uncoil Bond's tensions. His headache, instead of occupying his whole head, had localized itself behind the right temple. He said gaily, 'Shall we play the game again?'

There was a chorus of approval. The glass and paper napkins were brought from the bar and now more of the girls joined in. Bond handed round cigarettes and the girls puffed vigorously, occasionally choking over the smoke. Even Irma Bunt seemed infected by the laughter and squeals of excitement as the cobweb of paper became more and more tenuous. 'Careful! Gently, Elizabeth! Ayee! But now you have done it! And there was still this little corner that was safe!'

Bond was next to her. Now he sat back and suggested that the girls should have a game among themselves. He turned to Fräulein Bunt. 'By the way, if I can find the time, it crossed my mind that it might be fun to go down in the cable car and pay a visit to the valley. I gathered from talk among the crowds today that St Moritz is the other side of the valley. I've never been there. I'd love to see it.'

'Alas, my dear Sair Hilary, but that is against the rules of the house. Guests here, and the staff too, have no access to the Seilbahn. That is only for the tourists. Here we keep ourselves to ourselves. We are–how shall I say?–a little dedicated community. We observe the rules almost of a monastery. It is better so, isn't it? Thus we can pursue our researches in peace.'

'Oh, I quite see that.' Bond's smile was understanding, friendly. 'But I hardly count myself as a patient here, really. Couldn't an exception be made in my case?'

'I think that would be a mistake, Sair Hilary. And surely you will need all the time you have to complete your duties for the Count. No–' it was an order–'I am afraid, with many apologies, that what you ask is out of the question.' She glanced at her watch and clapped her hands. 'And now, girls,' she called, 'it is time for the supper. Come along! Come along!'

It had only been a try-on, to see what form the negative answer would take. But, as Bond followed her into the dining-room, it was quite an effort to restrain his right shoe from giving Irma Bunt a really tremendous kick in her tight, bulging behind.

Chapter Fourteen

Sweet Dreams–Sweet Nightmare!

It was eleven o'clock and the place was as quiet as the grave. Bond, with due respect for the eye in the ceiling, went through the motions of going to the bathroom and then climbing into bed and switching off his light. He gave it ten minutes, then got quietly out of bed and pulled on his trousers and shirt. Working by touch, he slipped the end of the inch of plastic into the door crack, found the lock and pressed gently. The edge of the plastic caught the curve of the lock and slid it back. Bond now only had to push gently and the door was open. He listened, his ears pricked like an animal's. Then he carefully put his head out. The empty corridor yawned at him. Bond slipped out of the door, closed it softly, took the few steps along to Number Three and gently turned the handle. It was dark inside but there was a stirring in the bed. Now to avoid the click of the shutting door! Bond took his bit of plastic and got it against the lock, holding it in the mortice. Then he inched the door shut, at the same time gently withdrawing the plastic. The lock slid noiselessly into place.

There came a whisper from the bed. 'Is that you?'

'Yes, darling.' Bond slid out of his clothes and, assuming the same geography as in his own room, walked gingerly over to the bed and sat down on its edge.

A hand came out of the darkness and touched him. 'Ooh, you've got nothing on!'

Bond caught the hand and reached along it. 'Nor have you,' he whispered. 'That's how it should be.'

Gingerly he lay down on the bed and put his head beside hers on the pillow. He noticed with a pang of pleasure that she had left room for him. He kissed her, at first softly and then with fierceness. Her body stirred. Her mouth yielded to his and when his left hand began its exploration she put her arms round him. 'I'm catching cold.' Bond followed the lie by pulling the single sheet away from under him and then covering them both with it. The warmth and softness of her splendid body were now all his. Bond lay against her. He drew the fingernails of his left hand softly down her flat stomach. The velvety skin fluttered. She gave a small groan and reached down for his hand and held it. 'You do love me a little bit?'

That awful question! Bond whispered, 'I think you're the most adorable, beautiful girl. I wish I'd met you before.'

The stale, insincere words seemed to be enough. She removed her restraining hand.

Her hair smelt of new-mown summer grass, her mouth of Pepsodent and her body of Mennen's Baby Powder. A small night wind rose up outside and moaned round the building, giving an extra sweetness, an extra warmth, even a certain friendship to what was no more than an act of physical passion. There was real pleasure in what they did to each other, and in the end, when it was over and they lay quietly in each other's arms, Bond knew, and knew that the girl knew, that they had done nothing wrong, done no harm to each other.

After a while Bond whispered into her hair, 'Ruby!'

'Mmmm.'

'About your name. About the Windsors. I'm afraid there's not much hope.'

'Oh, well, I never really believed. You know these old family stories.'

'Anyway, I haven't got enough books here. When I get back I'll dig into it properly. Promise. It'll be a question of starting with your family and going back–church and town records and so forth. I'll have it done properly and send it to you. Great slab of parchment with a lot of snazzy print. Heavy black italics with coloured letters to start each line. Although it mayn't get you anywhere, it might be nice to have.'

'You mean like old documents in museums?'

'That's right.'

'That'd be nice.'

There was silence in the little room. Her breathing became regular. Bond thought: how extraordinary! Here on top of this mountain, a death's run away from the nearest hamlet in the valley, in this little room were peace, silence, warmth, happiness–many of the ingredients of love. It was like making love in a balloon. Which nineteenth-century rake had it been who had recorded a bet in a London club that he would make love to a woman in a balloon?

Bond was on the edge of sleep. He let himself slide down the soft, easy slope. Here it was wonderful. It would be just as easy for him to get back to his room in the early hours. He softly eased his right arm from under the sleeping girl, took a lazy glance at his left wrist. The big luminous numerals said midnight.

Bond had hardly turned over on his right side, up against the soft flanks of the sleeping girl, when, from underneath the pillow, under the floor, deep in the bowels of the building, there came the peremptory ringing of a deep-toned, melodious electric bell. The girl stirred. She said sleepily, 'Oh, damn!'

'What is it?'

'Oh, it's only the treatment. I suppose it's midnight?'

'Yes.'

'Don't pay any attention. It's only for me. Just go to sleep.'

Bond kissed her between the shoulder-blades but said nothing.

Now the bell had stopped. In its place there started up a droning whine, rather like the noise of a very fast electric fan, with, behind it, the steady, unvarying tick-pause-tock, tick-pause-tock of some kind of metronome. The combination of the two sounds was wonderfully soothing. It compelled attention, but only just on the fringe of consciousness–like the night-noises of childhood, the slow tick of the nursery clock combined with the sound of the sea or the wind outside. And now a voice, the Count's voice, came over the distant wire or tape that Bond assumed was the mechanical source of all this. The voice was pitched in a low, singsong murmur, caressing yet authoritative, and every word was distinct. 'You are going to sleep.' The voice fell on the word 'sleep'. 'You are tired and your limbs feel like lead.' Again the falling cadence on the last word. 'Your arms feel as heavy as lead. Your breathing is quite even. Your breathing is as regular as a child's. Your eyes are closed and the eyelids are heavy as lead. You are becoming tireder and tireder. Your whole body is becoming tired and heavy as lead. You are warm and comfortable. You are slipping, slipping down into sleep. Your bed is as soft and downy as a nest. You are as soft and sleepy as a chicken in a nest. A dear little chicken, fluffy and cuddly.' There came the sound of a sweet cooing and clucking, the gentle brushing together of wings, the dozy murmuring of mother hens with their chicks. It went on for perhaps a full minute. Then the voice came back. 'The little darlings are going to sleep. They are like you, comfortable and sleepy in their nests. You love them dearly, dearly, dearly. You love all chickens. You would like to make pets of them all. You would like them to grow up beautiful and strong. You would like no harm to come to them. Soon you will be going back to your darling chickens. Soon you will be able to look after them again. Soon you will be able to help all the chickens of England. You will be able to improve the breed of chickens all over England. This will make you very, very happy. You will be doing so much good that it will make you very, very happy. But you will keep quiet about it. You will say nothing of your methods. They will be your own secret, your very own secret. People will try and find out your secret. But you will say nothing because they might try and take your secret away from you. And then you would not be able to make your darling chickens happy and healthy and strong. Thousands, millions of chickens made happier because of you. So you will say nothing and keep your secret. You will say nothing, nothing at all. You will remember what I say. You will remember what I say.' The murmuring voice was getting farther and farther away. The sweet cooing and clucking of chickens softly obscured the vanishing voice, then that too died away and there was only the electric whine and the tick-pause-tock of the metronome.

Ruby was deeply asleep. Bond reached out for her wrist and felt the pulse. It was plumb on beat with the metronome. And now that, and the whine of the machine, receded softly until all was dead silence again save for the soft moan of the night wind outside.

Bond let out a deep sigh. So now he had heard it all! He suddenly wanted to get back to his room and think. He slipped out from under the sheet, got to his clothes and put them on. He manipulated the lock without trouble. There was no movement, no sound, in the passage. He slipped back into Number Two and eased the door shut. Then he went into his bathroom, closed the door, switched on the light and sat down on the lavatory and put his head in his hands.

Deep hypnosis! That was what he had heard. The Hidden Persuader! The repetitive, singsong message injected into the brain while it was on the twilight edge of consciousness. Now, in Ruby's subconscious, the message would work on all by itself through the night, leaving her, after weeks of repetition, with an in-built mechanism of obedience to the voice that would be as deep, as compelling, as hunger.

But what in hell was the message all about? Surely it was a most harmless, even a praiseworthy message to instil in the simple mind of this country girl. She had been cured of her allergy and she would return home fully capable of helping with the family poultry business–more than that, enthusiastic, dedicated. Had the leopard changed his spots? Had the old lag become, in the corny, hackneyed tradition, a do-gooder? Bond simply couldn't believe it. What about all those high-powered security arrangements? What about the multi-racial staff that positively stank of SPECTRE? And what about the bob-run murder? Accident? So soon after the man's attempted rape of this Sarah girl? An impossible coincidence! Malignity must somewhere lie behind the benign, clinical front of this maddeningly innocent research outfit! But where? How in hell could he find out?

Bond, exhausted, got up and turned off the light in the bathroom and quietly got himself into bed. The mind whirred on for a sterile half-hour in the over-heated brain and then, mercifully, he went to sleep.

When, at nine o'clock, he awoke and threw open his windows, the sky was overcast with the heavy blank grey that meant snow. Over by the Berghaus, the Schneefinken and Schneevögel, the snow-finches and Alpine choughs, that lived on the crumbs and left-overs of the picnickers, were fluttering and swooping close round the building–a sure storm-warning. The wind had got up and was blowing in sharp, threatening gusts, and no whine of machinery came from the cable railway. The light aluminium gondolas would have too bad a time in winds of this strength, particularly over the last great swoop of cable that brought them a good quarter of a mile over the exposed shoulder beneath the plateau.

Bond shut the windows and rang for his breakfast. When it came there was a note from Fräulein Bunt on the tray. 'The Count will be pleased to receive you at eleven o'clock. I.B.'

Bond ate his breakfast and got down to his third page of de Bleuvilles. He had quite a chunk of work to show up, but this was easy stuff. The prospect of successfully bamboozling his way along the Blofeld part of the trail was not so encouraging. He would start boldly at the Gdynia end and work back–get the old rascal to talk about his youth and his parents. Old rascal? Well, dammit, whatever he had become since Operation 'Thunderball', there weren't two Ernst Stavro Blofelds in the world!

They met in the Count's study. 'Good morning, Sir Hilary. I hope you slept well? We are going to have snow.' The Count waved towards the window. 'It will be a good day for work. No distractions.'

Bond smiled a man-to-man smile. 'I certainly find those girls pretty distracting. But most charming. What's the matter with them, by the way? They all look healthy enough.'

The Count was off-hand. 'They suffer from allergies, Sir Hilary. Crippling allergies. In the agricultural field. They are country girls and their disabilities affect the possibility of their employment. I have devised a cure for such symptoms. I am glad to say that the signs are propitious. We are making much progress together.' The telephone by his side buzzed. 'Excuse me.' The Count picked up the receiver and listened. 'Ja. Machen Sie die Verbindung.' He paused. Bond politely studied the papers he had brought along. 'Zdies de Bleuville . . . Da . . . Da . . . Kharascho!' He put the receiver back. 'Forgive me. That was one of my research workers. He has been purchasing some materials for the laboratories. The cable railway is closed, but they are making a special trip up for him. Brave man. He will probably be very sick, poor fellow.' The green contact lenses hid any sympathy he may have felt. The fixed smile showed none. 'And now, my dear Sir Hilary, let us get on with our work.'

Bond laid out his big sheets on the desk and proudly ran his finger down through the generations. There was excitement and satisfaction in the Count's comments and questions. 'But this is tremendous, really tremendous, my dear fellow. And you say there is mention of a broken spear or a broken sword in the arms? Now when was that granted?'

Bond rattled off a lot of stuff about the Norman Conquest. The broken sword had probably been awarded as a result of some battle. More research in London would be needed to pin the occasion down. Finally Bond rolled up the sheets and got out his notebook. 'And now we must start working back from the other end, Count.' Bond became inquisitorial, authoritative. 'We have your birth date in Gdynia, May 28th, 1908. Yes?'

'Correct.'

'Your parents' names?'

'Ernst George Blofeld and Maria Stavro Michelopoulos.'

'Also born in Gdynia?'

'Yes.'

'Now your grandparents?'

'Ernst Stefan Blofeld and Elizabeth Lubomirskaya.'

'Hm, so the Ernst is something of a family Christian name?'

'It would seem so. My great-grandfather, he was also Ernst.'

'That is most important. You see, Count, among the Blofelds of Augsburg there are no less than two Ernsts!'

The Count's hands had been lying on the green blotting-pad on his desk, relaxed. Now, impulsively, they joined together and briefly writhed, showing white knuckles.

My God, you've got it bad! thought Bond.

'And that is important?'

'Very. Christian names run through families. We regard them as most significant clues. Now, can you remember any farther back? You have done well. We have covered three generations. With the dates I shall later ask you for, we have already got back to around 1850. Only another fifty years to go and we shall have arrived at Augsburg.'

'No.' It was almost a cry of pain. 'My great-great-grandfather. Of him I know nothing.' The hands writhed on the blotting-paper. 'Perhaps, perhaps. If it is a question of money. People, witnesses could be found.' The hands parted, held themselves out expansively. 'My dear Sir Hilary, you and I are men of the world. We understand each other. Extracts from archives, registry offices, the churches–these things, do they have to be completely authentic?'

Got you, you old fox! Bond said affably, with a hint of conspiracy, 'I don't quite understand what you mean, Count.'

The hands were now flat on the desk again, happy hands. Blofeld had recognized one of his kind. 'You are a hard-working man, Sir Hilary. You live modestly in this remote region of Scotland. Life could perhaps be made easier for you. There are perhaps material benefits you desire–motor-cars, a yacht, a pension. You have only to say the word, name a figure.' The dark-green orbs bored into Bond's modestly evasive eyes, holding them. 'Just a little co-operation. A visit here and there in Poland and Germany and France. Of course your expenses would be heavy. Let us say five hundred pounds a week. The technical matters, the documents and so forth. Those I can arrange. It would only require your supporting evidence. Yes? The Ministry of Justice in Paris, for them the word of the College of Arms is the word of God. Is that not so?'

It was too good to be true! But how to play it? Diffidently, Bond said, 'What you are suggesting, Count, is–er–not without interest. Of course–' Bond's smile was sufficiently expansive, sufficiently bland–'if the documents were convincing, so to speak solid, very solid, then it would be quite reasonable for me to authenticate them.' Bond put spaniel into his eyes, asking to be patted, to be told that everything would be all right, that he would be completely protected. 'You see what I mean?'

The Count began, with force, sincerity, 'You need have absolutely no . . .' when there was the noise of an approaching hubbub down the passage. The door burst open. A man, propelled from behind, lurched into the room and fell, writhing, to the floor.

Two of the guards came stiffly to attention behind him. They looked first at the Count and then, sideways, towards Bond, surprised to see him there.

The Count said sharply, 'Was ist denn los?'

Bond knew the answer and, momentarily, he died. Behind the snow and the blood on the face of the man on the floor, Bond recognized the face of a man he knew.

The blond hair, the nose broken boxing for the Navy, belonged to a friend of his in the Service. It was, unmistakably, Number 2 from Station Z in Zürich!

Chapter Fifteen

The Heat Increases

Yes, it was Shaun Campbell all right! Christ Almighty, what a mess! Station Z had especially been told nothing about Bond's mission. Campbell must have been following a lead of his own, probably trailing this Russian who had been 'buying supplies'. Typical of the sort of balls-up that over-security can produce!

The leading guard was talking in rapid, faulty German with a Slav accent. 'He was found in the open ski compartment at the back of the gondola. Much frozen, but he put up a strong resistance. He had to be subdued. He was no doubt following Captain Boris.' The man caught himself up. 'I mean, your guest from the valley, Herr Graf. He says he is an English tourist from Zürich. That he had got no money for the fare. He wanted to pay a visit up here. He was searched. He carried five hundred Swiss francs. No identity papers.' The man shrugged. 'He says his name is Campbell.'

At the sound of his name, the man on the ground stirred. He lifted his head and looked wildly round the room. He had been badly battered about the face and head with a pistol or a cosh. His control was shot to pieces. When his eyes lit on the familiar face of Bond, he looked astonished, then, as if a lifebuoy had been thrown to him, he said hoarsely, 'Thank God, James. Tell 'em it's me! Tell 'em I'm from Universal Export. In Zürich. You know! For God's sake, James! Tell 'em I'm O.K.' His head fell forward on the carpet.

The Count's head slowly turned towards Bond. The opaque green eyes caught the pale light from the window and glinted whitely. The tight, face-lifted smile was grotesquely horrible. 'You know this man, Sir Hilary?'

Bond shook his head sorrowfully. He knew he was pronouncing the death sentence on Campbell. 'Never seen him before in my life. Poor chap. He sounds a bit daft to me. Concussed, probably. Why not ship him down to a hospital in the valley? He looks in a pretty bad way.'

'And Universal Export?' The voice was silky. 'I seem to have heard that name before.'

'Well, *I* haven't,' said Bond indifferently. 'Never heard of it.' He reached in his pocket for his cigarettes, lit one with a dead steady hand.

The Count turned back to the guards. He said softly, 'Zur Befragungszelle.' He nodded his dismissal. The two guards bent down and hauled Campbell up by his armpits. The hanging head raised itself, gave one last terrible look of appeal at Bond. Then the man who was Bond's colleague was hustled out of the room and the door was closed softly behind his dragging feet.

To the interrogation cell! That could mean only one thing, under modern methods, total confession! How long would Campbell hold out for? How many hours had Bond got left?

'I have told them to take him to the sick-room. He will be well looked after.' The Count looked from the papers on his desk to Bond. 'I am afraid this unhappy intrusion has interfered with my train of thought, Sir Hilary. So perhaps you will forgive me for this morning?'

'Of course, of course. And, regarding your proposition, that we should work a little more closely together on your interests, I can assure you, Count, that I find it most interesting.' Bond smiled conspiratorially. 'I'm sure we could come to some satisfactory arrangement.'

'Yes? That is good.' The Count linked his hands behind his head and gazed for a moment at the ceiling and then, reflectively, back at Bond. He said casually, 'I suppose you would not be connected in any way with the British Secret Service, Sir Hilary?'

Bond laughed out loud. The laugh was a reflex, forced out of him by tension. 'Good God, no! Didn't even know we had one. Didn't all that sort of thing go out with the end of the war?' Bond chuckled to himself, fatuously amused. 'Can't quite see myself running about behind a false moustache. Not my line of country at all. Can't bear moustaches.'

The Count's unwavering smile did not seem to share Bond's amusement. He said coldly, 'Then please forget my question, Sir Hilary. The intrusion by this man has made me over-suspicious. I value my privacy up here, Sir Hilary. Scientific research can only be pursued in an atmosphere of peace.'

'I couldn't agree more.' Bond was effusive. He got to his feet and gathered up his papers from the desk. 'And now I must get on with my own research work. Just getting into the fourteenth century. I think I shall have some interesting data to show you tomorrow, Count.'

The Count got politely to his feet and Bond went out of the door and along the passage.

He loitered, listening for any sound. There was none, but half-way down the corridor one of the doors was ajar. A crack of blood-red light showed. Bond thought, I've probably had it anyway. In for a penny, in for a pound! He pushed the door open and stuck his head into the room. It was a long, low laboratory with a plastic-covered work-bench extending its whole length beneath the windows, which were shuttered. Dark red light, as in a film-developing chamber, came from neon strips above the cornice. The bench was littered with retorts and test-tubes, and there were line upon line of test-tubes and phials containing a cloudy liquid in racks against the far wall. Three men in white, with gauze pads over the bottoms of their faces and white surgical caps over their hair, were at work, absorbed. Bond took in the scene, a scene from a theatrical hell, withdrew his head and walked on down the corridor and out into what was now a driving snow-storm. He pulled the top of his sweater over his head and forced his way along the path to the blessed warmth of the club-house. Then he walked quickly to his room, closed the door, and went into the bathroom and sat down on his usual throne of reflection and wondered what in God's name to do.

Could he have saved Campbell? Well, he could have had a desperate shot at it. 'Oh, yes. I know this man. Perfectly respectable chap. We used to work for the same export firm, Universal, in London. You look in pretty bad shape, old boy. What the devil happened?' But it was just as well he hadn't tried. As cover, solid cover, Universal was 'brulé' with the pros. It had been in use too long. All the secret services in the world had penetrated it by now. Obviously Blofeld knew all about it. Any effort to save Campbell would simply have tied Bond in with him. There had been no alternative except to throw him to the wolves. If Campbell had a chance to get his wits back before they really started on him, he would know that Bond was there for some purpose, that his disavowal by Bond was desperately important to Bond, to the Service. How long would he have the strength to cover for Bond, retrieve his recognition of Bond? At most a few hours. But how many hours? That was the vital question. That and how long the storm would last. Bond couldn't possibly get away in this stuff. If it stopped, there might be a chance, a damned slim one, but better than the alternatives, of which, if and when Campbell talked, there was only one–death, probably a screaming death.

Bond surveyed his weapons. They were only his hands and feet, his Gillette razor and his wrist-watch, a heavy Rolex Oyster Perpetual on an expanding metal bracelet. Used properly, these could be turned into most effective knuckledusters. Bond got up, took the blade out of his Gillette and dropped the razor into his trouser pocket. He slipped the shaft between the first and second fingers of his left hand so that the blade-carrier rested flat along his knuckles. Yes, that was the way! Now was there anything, any evidence he should try and take with him? Yes, he must try and get more, if not all, of the girls' names and, if possible, addresses. For some reason he knew they were vital. For that he would have to use Ruby. His head full of plans for getting the information out of her, Bond went out of the bathroom and sat down at his desk and got on with a fresh page of de Bleuvilles. At least he must continue to show willing, if only to the recording eye in the ceiling.

It was about twelve-thirty when Bond heard his door-knob being softly turned. Ruby slipped in and, her finger to her lips, disappeared into his bathroom. Bond casually threw down his pen, got up and stretched and strolled over and went in after her.

Ruby's eyes were wide and frightened. 'You're in trouble,' she whispered urgently. 'What *have* you been doing?'

'Nothing,' said Bond innocently. 'What's up?'

'We've all been told that we mustn't talk to you unless Miss Bunt is there.' Her knuckles went distractedly up to her teeth. 'Do you think they know about *us*?'

'Couldn't possibly,' said Bond, radiating confidence. 'I think I know what it is.' (With so much obfuscation in the air, what did an extra, a reassuring, lie matter?) 'This morning the Count told me I was an upsetting influence here, that I was what he called "disruptive", interfering with your treatments. He asked me to keep myself more to myself. Honestly–' (how often that word came into a lie!)–'I'm sure that's all it is. Rather a pity really. Apart from you–I mean you're sort of special–I think all you girls are terribly sweet. I'd like to have helped you all.'

'How do you mean? Helped us?'

'Well, this business of surnames. I talked to Violet last night. She seemed awfully interested. I'm sure it would have amused all the others to have theirs done. Everyone's interested in where they came from. Rather like palmistry in a way.' Bond wondered how the College of Arms would have liked *that* one! He shrugged. 'Anyway, I've decided to get the hell away from here. I can't bear being shepherded and ordered about like this. Who the hell do they think I am? But I'll tell you what I'll do. If you can give me the names of the girls, as many as you know, I'll do a piece on each of them and post them when you all get back to England. How much longer have you got, by the way?'

'We're not told exactly, but the rumour is about another week. There's another batch of girls due about then. When we're slow at our work or get behind-hand with our reading, Miss Bunt says she hopes the next lot won't be so stupid. The old bitch! But Sir Hilary–' the blue eyes filled with concern–'how *are* you going to get away? You know we're practically prisoners up here.'

Bond was off-hand. 'Oh, I'll manage somehow. They can't hold *me* here against my will. But what about the names, Ruby? Don't you think it would give the girls a treat?'

'Oh, they'd love it. Of course I know all of them. We've found plenty of ways of exchanging secrets. But you won't be able to remember. Have you got anything to write down on?'

Bond tore off some strips of lavatory paper and took out a pencil. 'Fire away!'

She laughed. 'Well, you know me and Violet, then there's Elizabeth Mackinnon. She's from Aberdeen. Beryl Morgan from somewhere in Herefordshire. Pearl Tampion, Devonshire–by the way, all those simply loathed every kind of cattle. Now they live on steaks! Would you believe it? I must say the Count's a wonderful man.'

'Yes, indeed.'

'Then there's Anne Charter from Canterbury and Caresse Ventnor from the National Stud, wherever that is–fancy her working there and she came up in a rash all over whenever she went near a horse! Now all she does is dream of pony clubs and read every word she can get hold of about Pat Smythe! And Denise Robertson . . .'

The list went on until Bond had got the whole ten. He said, 'What about that Polly somebody who left in November?'

'Polly Tasker. She was from East Anglia. Don't remember where, but I can find out the address when I get back to England. Sir Hilary–' she put her arm round his neck–'I *am* going to see you again, aren't I?'

Bond held her tight and kissed her. 'Of course, Ruby. You can always get me at the College of Arms in Queen Victoria Street. Just send me a postcard when you get back. But for God's sake cut out the "Sir". You're my girl friend. Remember?'

'Oh, yes, I will–er–Hilary,' she said fervently. 'And you will be careful, getting away I mean. You're sure it's all right? Is there anything I can do to help?'

'No, darling. Just don't breathe a word of all this. It's a secret between us. Right?'

'Of course, darling.' She glanced at her watch. 'Oh lord! I must simply fly. Only ten minutes to lunch-time. Now, can you do your trick with the door? There shouldn't be anyone about. It's their lunch-time from twelve till one.'

Bond, out of any possible line of vision from the eye in the ceiling, did his trick with the door and she was gone with a last whispered goodbye.

Bond eased the door shut. He let out a deep sigh and went over to the window and peered out through the snow-heaped panes. It was thick as Hades outside and the fine powder snow on the veranda was whirling up in little ghosts as the wind tore at the building. Pray God it would let up by night-time! Now, what did he need in the way of equipment? Goggles and gloves were two items he might harvest over lunch. Bond went into the bathroom again and rubbed soap into his eyes. It stung like hell, but the blue-grey eyes emerged from the treatment realistically bloodshot. Satisfied, Bond rang for the 'warden' and went thoughtfully off to the restaurant.

Silence fell as he went through the swing doors, followed by a polite, brittle chatter. Eyes followed him discreetly as he crossed the room and the replies to his good-mornings were muted. Bond took his usual seat between Ruby and Fräulein Bunt. Apparently oblivious to her frosty greeting, he snapped his fingers for a waiter and ordered his double vodka dry Martini. He turned to Fräulein Bunt and smiled into the suspicious yellow eyes. 'Would you be very kind?'

'Yes, Sair Hilary. What is it?'

Bond gestured at his still watering eyes. 'I've got the Count's trouble. Sort of conjunctivitis, I suppose. The tremendous glare up here. Better today of course, but there's still a lot of reflection from the snow. And all this paper-work. Could you get me a pair of snow-goggles? I'll only need to borrow them for a day or two. Just till my eyes get used to the light. Don't usually have this sort of trouble.'

'Yes. That can be done. I will see that they are put in your room.' She summoned the head waiter and gave him the order in German. The man, looking at Bond with overt dislike, said, 'Sofort, gnädiges Fräulein,' and clicked his heels.

'And one more thing, if you will,' said Bond politely. 'A small flask of schnapps.' He turned to Fräulein Bunt. 'I find I am not sleeping well up here. Perhaps a nightcap would help. I always have one at home–generally whisky. But here I would prefer schnapps. When in Gloria, do as the Glorians do. Ha ha!'

Fräulein Bunt looked at him stonily. She said to the waiter curtly, 'In Ordnung!' The man took Bond's order at Paté Maison followed by Oeufs Gloria and the cheese tray (Bond thought he had better get some stuffing into him!), clicked his heels and went away. Was he one of those who had been at work in the interrogation room? Bond silently ground his teeth. By God, if it came to hitting any of these guards tonight, he was going to hit them damned hard, with everything he'd got! He felt Fräulein Bunt's eyes inquisitively on him. He untensed himself and began to make amiable conversation about the storm. How long would it last? What was the barometer doing?

Violet, guardedly but helpfully, said the guides thought it would clear up during the afternoon. The barometer was rising. She looked nervously at Fräulein Bunt to see if she had said too much to the pariah, and then, not reassured, went back to her two vast baked potatoes with poached eggs in them.

Bond's drink came. He swallowed it in two gulps and ordered another. He felt like making any gesture that would startle and outrage. He said, combatively, to Fräulein Bunt, 'And how is that poor chap who came up in the cable car this morning? He looked in terrible shape. I do hope he's up and about again.'

'He makes progress.'

'Oh! Who was that?' asked Ruby eagerly.

'It was an intruder.' Fräulein Bunt's eyes were hard with warning. 'It is not a subject for conversation.'

'Oh, but why not?' asked Bond innocently. 'After all, you can't get much excitement up here. Anything out of the ordinary should be a bit of a relief.'

She said nothing. Bond raised his eyebrows politely and then accepted the snub with a good grace. He asked if any newspapers came up. Or was there a radio bulletin like on board ship? Did they get any news from the outside world?

'No.'

Bond gave up the struggle and got on with his lunch. Ruby's foot crept up against his in sympathy with the man sent to Coventry. Bond gave it a gentle kick of warning and withdrew his. The girls at the other tables began to leave. Bond toyed with his cheese and coffee until Fräulein Bunt got to her feet and said, 'Come, girls.' Bond rose and sat down again. Now, except for the waiters clearing up, he was alone in the restaurant. That was what he wanted. He got up and strolled to the door. Outside, on pegs against the wall, the girls' outdoor coats and skiing gloves hung in an orderly row. The corridor was empty. Bond swept the largest pair of leather gauntlets he could see off the peg where they hung by their joining cord and stuffed them inside his sweater. Then he sauntered along to the reception room. It was empty. The door to the ski-room was open and the surly man was at his work-bench. Bond went in and made one-sided conversation about the weather. Then, under cover of desultory talk about whether the metal skis were not more dangerous than the old wooden ones, he wandered, his hands innocently in his pockets, round the numbered racks in which the skis stood against the wall. They were mostly the girls' skis. No good! The bindings would be too small for his boots. But, by the door, in unnumbered slots, stood the guides' skis. Bond's eyes narrowed to slits as he scanned them, measuring, estimating. Yes, the pair of metal Heads with the red V's painted on the black curved tips was the best bet. They were of the stiffer, Master's, category, designed for racing. Bond remembered reading somewhere that the Standard model was inclined to 'float' at speed. His choice had the Attenhofer Flex forward release with the Marker lateral release. Two transverse leather thongs wound round the ankle and buckled over the instep would, if he fell, which he was certain to do, ensure against losing a ski.

Bond made a quick guess at how much the bindings would need adjustment to fit his boots and went off down the corridor to his room.

Chapter Sixteen

Downhill Only

Now it was just a question of sitting out the hours. When would they have finished with Campbell? Quick, rough torture is rarely effective against a professional, apart from the likelihood of the man rapidly losing consciousness, becoming so punch-drunk that he is incoherent. The pro, if he is a tough man spiritually, can keep the 'game' alive for hours by minor admissions, by telling long, rambling tales and sticking to them. Such tales need verification. Blofeld would undoubtedly have his man in Zürich, would be able to contact him on his radio, get him to check this or that date or address, but that also would require time. Then, if it was proved that Campbell had told lies, they would have to begin again. So far as Bond and his identity were concerned, it all depended on Campbell's reading of why Bond was up at the Gloria Club. He must guess, because of Bond's curt disavowal of him, that it was something clandestine, something important. Would he have the wits to cover up Bond, the guts, against the electrical and mechanical devices they would surely use against him? He could say that, when he came to and saw Bond, in his semi-conscious state he had for a moment thought Bond was his brother, James Campbell. Some story like that. If he had the wits! If he had the guts! Had Campbell got a death pill, perhaps one of the buttons on his ski-jacket or trousers? Bond sharply put the thought away. He had been on the edge of wishing that Campbell had!

Well, he would be wise to assume that it was only a matter of hours and then they would come for him. They wouldn't do it until after lights-out. To do it before would cause too much talk among the girls. No, they would fetch him at night and the next day it would be put about that he had left by the first cable car down to the valley. Meanwhile he would be buried deep in a snow overcoat, or more likely deposited in a high crevasse in the near-by Piz Languard glacier, to come out at the bottom, fifty years later, out of his deep freeze, with multiple contusions but no identification marks–a nameless victim of 'les neiges éternelles'!

Yes, he must plan for that. Bond got up from the desk where he had been automatically scribbling down lists of fifteenth-century de Bleuvilles and opened the window. The snow had stopped and there was broken blue in the sky. It would be perfect powder snow, perhaps a foot of it, on the Gloria Run. Now to make everything ready!

There are hundreds of secret inks, but there was only one available to Bond, the oldest one in the world, his own urine. He went into the bathroom (what must the televising eye think of his digestive tracts?) with his pen, a clean nib, and his passport. Then he sat down and proceeded to transcribe, from the flimsy pieces of paper in his pocket on to a blank page of his passport, the names and approximate locations by county of the girls. The page showed nothing. Held in front of a flame, the writing would come up brown. He slipped the passport into his hip-pocket. Next he took the gloves from under his sweater, tried them on and found them an adequate but tight fit, took the top off the lavatory cistern and laid the gloves along the arm of the stop-cock.

What else? It was going to be fiendishly cold at the start, but his body would soon be drenched in sweat. He would just have to make do with the ski-clothes he possessed, the gloves, the goggles that had been placed on his table, and the flat glass flask of schnapps that he would carry in one of his side pockets and not, in case of a fall, in his hip-pocket. Extra covering for his face? Bond thought of using one of his warm vests and cutting eye-holes in it. But it would surely slip and perhaps blind him. He had some dark-red silk bandanna handkerchiefs. He would tie one tight over his face below the goggles and discard it if it interfered with his breathing. So! That was the lot!

There was nothing else he could do or insure against. The rest was up to the Fates. Bond relaxed his thoughts and went out and back to his desk. He sat down and bent to his paper-work and tried not to listen to the hastening tick of the Rolex on his wrist, tried to fix in his mind the rough geography of the Gloria Run he had inadequately learned from the metal map. It was too late now to go and have another look at it. He must stay put and continue to play the toothless tiger!

Dinner was as ghastly as lunch. Bond concentrated on getting plenty of whisky and food under his belt. He made urbane conversation and pretended he didn't notice the chill in the air. Then he gave Ruby's foot one warm press under the table, excused himself on the grounds of work, and strode with dignity out of the room.

He had changed for dinner and he was relieved to find his ski-clothes in the half-tidy heap in which he had left them. He went, with utter normalcy, about his work–sharpened pencils, laid out his books, bent to the squared paper: 'Simon de Bleuville, 1510–1570. Alphonse de Bleuville, 1546–1580, married 1571 Mariette d'Escourt, and had issue, Jean, Françoise, Pierre'. Thank God he would soon be released from all this blether!

9.15, 9.30, 9.45, 10! Bond felt the excitement ball up inside him like a cat's fur. He found that his hands were wet. He wiped them down the sides of his trousers. He got up and stretched. He went into the bathroom and made appropriate noises, retrieved the gloves and laid them on the bathroom floor just inside the door. Then, naked, he came back into the room and got into bed and switched off the light. He regularized his breathing and, in ten minutes, began to snore softly. He gave it another ten, then slid out of bed and, with infinite precaution, dressed himself in ski-clothes. He softly retrieved his gloves from the bathroom, put on the goggles so that they rested in his hair above the forehead, tied the dark-red handkerchief tightly across his nose, schnapps into pocket, passport into hip-pocket and, finally, Gillette through the fingers of the left hand and the Rolex transferred to his right, the bracelet clasped in the palm of his hand and round the fingers so that the face of the watch lay across his middle knuckles

James Bond paused and ran over his equipment. The ski-gloves, their cord drawn through his sweater and down the sleeves, hung from his wrists. They would be a hindrance until he was outside. Nothing to be done about that. The rest was all right. He was set! He bent to the door, manipulated the lock with the plastic and, praying that the television eye had been closed down and would not see the light shining in from the passage, listened briefly and slipped out.

There was, as usual, light from the reception room to his left. Bond crept along, inched round the door jamb. Yes! The guard was there, bent over something that looked like a time sheet. The neck was offered. Bond dropped the Gillette in his pocket and stiffened the fingers of his left hand into the old Commando cutting edge. He took the two steps into the room and crashed the hand down on the back of the offered neck. The man's face hit the table top with a thud, bounced up and half turned towards Bond. Bond's right flashed out and the face of the Rolex disintegrated against the man's jaw. The body slid sluggishly off its chair on to the carpet and lay still, its legs untidy as if in sleep. The eyes fluttered and stared, unseeing, upwards. Bond went round the desk and bent down. There was no heartbeat. Bond straightened himself. It was the man he had seen coming back alone from the bob-run on his first morning, when Bertil had met with his accident. So! Rough justice!

The telephone on the desk buzzed like a trapped wasp. Bond looked at it. He picked up the receiver and spoke through the handkerchief across his mouth. 'Ja?'

'Alles in Ordnung?'

'Ja.'

'Also hör zu! Wir kommen für den Engländer in zehn Minuten. Verstanden?'

'Is' recht.'

'Also, aufpassen. Ja?'

'Zu Befehl!'

At the other end the receiver went down. The sweat was beading on Bond's face. Thank God he had answered! So they were coming for him in ten minutes! There was a bunch of keys on the desk. Bond snatched them up and ran to the front door. After three misfits, he had the right one. He tried the door. It was now only held by its air-pressure device. Bond leaped for the ski-room. Unlocked! He went in and, by the light from the reception room, found his skis. There were sticks beside them. Carefully he lifted everything out of its wooden slot and strode to the main door and opened it. He laid the skis and sticks softly down in the snow, turned back to the door, locked it from the outside and threw the keys far away into the snow.

The three-quarter moon burned down with an almost dazzling fire and the snow crystals scintillated back at it like a carpet of diamond dust. Now minutes would have to be wasted getting the bindings absolutely right. James Bond kicked one boot into the groove of the Marker toe-hold and knelt down, feeling for the steel cable that went behind his heel. It was too short. Coolly, unhurriedly, he adjusted the regulating screw on the forward latch and tried again. This time it was all right. He pressed down on the safety latch and felt it lock his boot into the toe-hold. Next, the safety thong round the top of his boot that would keep the ski prisoner if the latch sprung, which it would do with a fall. His fingers were beginning to freeze. The tip of the thong refused to find its buckle! A full minute wasted! Got it! And now the same job on the other ski. At last Bond stood up, slipped the gloves over his aching fingers, picked up the lance-like sticks and pushed himself off along the faint ridge that showed the outlines of yesterday's well trodden path. It felt all right! He pulled the goggles down over his eyes and now the vast snowscape was a silvery green as if he was swimming under sunny water. The skis hissed smoothly through the powder snow. Bond tried to get up more speed down the gentle slope by langlaufing, the sliding, forward stride of the first Norwegian skiers. But it didn't work. The heels of his boots felt nailed to the skis. He punted himself forward as fast as he could with his sticks. God, what a trail he must be leaving–like a tram-line! As soon as they get the front door open, they would be after him. Their fastest guide would certainly catch him easily unless he got a good start! Every minute, every second was a bonus. He passed between the black outlines of the cable head and the Berghaus. There was the starting point of the Gloria Run, the metal notices beside it hatted with snow! Bond didn't pause. He went straight for it and over the edge.

The first vertical drop had a spine-chilling bliss to it. Bond got down into his old Arlberg crouch, his hands forward of his boots, and just let himself go. His skis were an ugly six inches apart. The Kannonen he had watched had gone down with their boots locked together, as if on a single ski. But this was no time for style, even if he had been capable of it! Above all he must stay upright!

Bond's speed was now frightening. But the deep cushion of cold, light powder snow gave him the confidence to try a parallel swing. Minimum of shoulder turn needed at this speed–weight on to the left ski–and he came round and held it as the right-hand edges of his skis bit against the slope, throwing up a shower of moon-lit snow crystals. Danger was momentarily forgotten in the joy of speed, technique, and mastery of the snow. Bond straightened up and almost dived into his next turn, this time to the left, leaving a broad S on the virgin mountain behind him. Now he could afford to schuss the rest down to the hard left-hand turn round the shoulder. He pointed his skis down and felt real rapture as, like a black bullet on the giant slope, he zoomed down the 45-degree drop. Now for the left-hand corner. There was the group of three flags, black, red and yellow, hanging limply, their colours confused by the moonlight! He would have to stop there and take a recce over the next lap. There was a slight upward slope short of the big turn. Bond took it at speed, felt his skis leave the ground at the crest of it, jabbed into the snow with his left stick as an extra lever and threw his skis and his right shoulder and hips round to the left. He landed in a spray of snow, at a dead halt. He was delighted with himself! A Sprung-Christiana is a showy and not an easy turn at speed. He wished his old teacher, Fuchs, had been there to see that one!

He was now on the shoulder of the mountain. High overhead the silver strands of the cable railway plunged downwards in one great swoop towards the distant black line of the trees, where the moonlight glinted on a spidery pylon. Bond remembered that there now followed a series of great zigs and zags more or less beneath the cables. With the piste unobscured, it would have been easy, but the new snow made every descent look desirable. Bond jerked up his goggles to see if he could spot a flag. Yes, there was one away down to the left. He would do some S turns down the next slope and then make for it.

As he pulled down his goggles and gripped his sticks, two things happened. First there came a deep boom from high up the mountain, and a speck of flame, that wobbled in its flight, soared into the sky above him. There was a pause at the top of its parabola, a sharp crack and a blazing magnesium flare on a parachute began its wandering descent, wiping out the black shadows in the hollows, turning everything into a hideous daylight. Another and another sprayed out across the sky, lighting every cranny over the mountain side.

And, at the same time, the cables high above Bond's head began to sing! They were sending the cable car down after him!

Bond cursed into the sodden folds of his silk handkerchief and got going. The next thing would be a man after him–probably a man with a gun!

He took the second lap more carefully than the first, got across to the second flag, turned at it and made back across the plunging slope for the series of linked S's under the cables. How fast did these bloody gondolas go? Ten, fifteen, twenty miles an hour? This was the latest type. It would be the fastest. Hadn't he read somewhere that the one between Arosa and the

Weisshorn did 25? Even as he got into his first S, the tune of the singing cable above him momentarily changed and then went back to its usual whine. That was the gondola passing the first pylon! Bond's knees, the Achilles heel of all skiers, were beginning to ache. He cut his S's narrower, snaking down faster, but now feeling the rutted tracks of the piste under his skis at every turn. Was that a flag away over to the left? The magnesium flares were swaying lower, almost directly over him. Yes. It looked all right. Two more S turns and he would do a traverse schuss to it!

Something landed with a tremendous crack amidst a fountain of snow to his right! Another to his left! They had a grenade-thrower up front in the cable car! A bracket! Would the next one be dead on? Almost before the thought flashed through his mind, there came a tremendous explosion just ahead of him and he was hurled forward and sideways in a catherine wheel of sticks and skis.

Bond got gingerly to his feet, gasping and spitting snow. One of his bindings had opened. His trembling fingers found the forward latch and banged it tight again. Another sharp crack, but wide by twenty yards. He must get away from the line of fire from the blasted railway! Feverishly he thought, the left-hand flag! I must do the traverse now. He took a vague bearing across the precipitous slope and flung himself down it.

Chapter Seventeen

Bloody Snow

It was tricky, undulating ground. The magnesium flares had sailed lower and there were ugly patches of black shadow, any of which might have been a small ravine. Bond had to check at all of them and each time the sharp Christie reminded him of his legs and ankles. But he got across without a fall and pulled up at the flag, panting. He looked back. The gondola had stopped. They had telephone communication with the top and bottom stations, but why had it stopped? As if to answer, blue flames fluttered gaily from the forward cabin. But Bond heard no bullets. The gondola would be swaying on its cable. But then, high up above him, from somewhere near the first flags on the shoulder, came more rapid fire, from two points, and the snow kicked up daintily around him. So the guides had finally got after him! His fall would have cost him minutes. How much lead had he got? Certainly less than ten minutes. A bullet whanged into one of his skis and sang off down the mountain. Bond took a last gulp of breath and got going again, still left-handed, away from the cable railway, towards the next flag, a distant dot on the edge of the shadow thrown by the great Matterhorn-shaped peak of Piz Gloria, which knifed up into the spangled sky in dreadful majesty.

It looked as if the run was going to take him dangerously close to the skirts of the peak. Something was nagging at his mind, a tiny memory. What was it? It was something unpleasant. Yes, by God! The last flag! It had been black. He was on the Black Run, the one closed because of avalanche danger!

God! Well, he'd had it now. No time to try and get back on the Red Run. And anyway the Red had a long stretch close to the cables. He'd just have to chance it. And what a time to chance it, just after a heavy fall of new snow, and with all these detonations to loosen up the stuff! When there was danger of an avalanche, guides forbade even speech! Well, to hell with it! Bond zoomed on across the great unmarked slope, got to the next flag, spotted the next, away down the mountain side towards the tree line. Too steep to schuss! He would just have to do it in S's.

And then the bastards chose to fire off three more flares followed by a stream of miscellaneous rockets that burst prettily among the stars. Of course! Bright idea! This was for the sake of watchers in the valley who might be inquisitive about the mysterious explosions high up the mountain. They were having a party up there, celebrating something. What fun these rich folk had, to be sure! And then Bond remembered. But of course! It was Christmas Eve! God rest ye merry gentlemen, let nothing ye dismay! Bond's skis hissed an accompaniment as he zigzagged fast down the beautiful snow slope. White Christmas! Well, he'd certainly got himself that!

But then, from high up above him, he heard that most dreaded of all sounds in the high Alps, that rending, booming crack! The Last Trump! Avalanche!

The ground shook violently under Bond's skis and the swelling rumble came down to him like the noise of express trains roaring through a hundred tunnels. God Almighty, now he really had had it! What was the rule? Point the skis straight downhill! Try and race it! Bond pointed his skis down towards the tree line, got down in his ugly crouch and shot, his skis screaming, into white space.

Keep forward, you bastard! Get your hands way in front of you! The wind of his speed was building up into a great wall in front of him, trying to knock him off balance. Behind him the giant roar of the mountain seemed to be gaining. Other, smaller cracks sounded high up among the crags. The whole bloody mountain was on the move! If he beat the gigantic mass of hurtling snow to the tree line, what comfort would he find there? Certainly no protection until he was deep in the wood. The avalanche would snap perhaps the first hundred yards of firs down like match-sticks. Bond used his brain and veered slightly left-handed. The opening, the glade cut for the Black Run, would surely be somewhere below the last flag he had been aiming for. If it wasn't, he was a dead duck!

Now the wild schuss was coming to an end. The trees were rushing towards him. Was there a break in the bloody black line of them? Yes! But more to the left. Bond veered, dropping his speed, gratefully, but with his ears strained to gauge the range of the thunder behind and above him. It couldn't be far from him. The shudder in the ground had greatly increased and a lot of the stuff would also find the hole through the trees, funnel itself in and pursue him even there! Yes! There was the flag! Bond hurtled into a right-hand Christie just as, to his left, he heard the first trees come crashing down with the noise of a hundred monster crackers being pulled–Christmas crackers! Bond flung himself straight down the wide white glade between the trees. But he could hear that he was losing! The crashing of the trees was coming closer. The first froth of the white tide couldn't be far behind his heels! What did one do when the avalanche hit? There was only one rule. Get your hands to your boots and grip your ankles. Then, if you were buried, there was some hope of undoing your skis, being able, perhaps, to burrow your way to the surface–if you knew in your tomb where the surface lay! If you couldn't go down like a ball, you would end up immovable, a buried tangle of sticks and skis at all angles. Thank God the opening at the end of the glade, the shimmer of the last, easily sloping fields before the finish, was showing up! The crackling roar behind him was getting louder! How high would the wall of snow be? Fifty feet? A hundred? Bond reached the end of the glade and hurled himself into a right-hand Christie. It was his last hope, to get below the wide belt of trees and pray that the avalanche wouldn't mow down the lot of them. To stay in the path of the roaring monster at his heels would be suicide!

The Christie came off, but Bond's right ski snarled a root or a sapling and he felt himself flying through space. He landed with a crash and lay gasping, all the wind knocked out of him. Now he was done for! Not even enough strength to get his hands to his ankles! A tremendous buffet of wind hit him and a small snowstorm covered him. The ground shook wildly and a deep crashing roar filled his ears. And then it had passed him and given way to a slow, heavy rumble. Bond brushed the snow out of his eyes and got unsteadily to his feet, both skis loose, his goggles gone. Only a cricket pitch away, a great torrent of snow, perhaps twenty feet high, was majestically pouring out of the wood and down into the meadows. Its much higher, tumbling snout, tossing huge crags of broken snow around it, was already a hundred yards ahead and still going fast. But, where Bond stood, it was now silent and peaceful except for the machine-gun-fire crackling of the trees as they went down in the wood that had finally protected him. The crackling was getting nearer! No time to hang about! But Bond took off one sodden glove and dug into his trouser pocket. If ever he needed a drink it was now! He tilted the little flask down his throat, emptied it and threw the bottle away. Happy Christmas! he said to himself, and bent to his bindings.

He got to his feet and, rather light-headed but with the wonderful glow of the Enzian in his stomach, started on the last mile of finishing schuss across the meadows to the right, away from the still hurtling river of snow. Blast! There was a fence across the bottom of the meadows! He would have to take the normal outlet for the runs beside the cable station. It looked all right. There was no sign of the gondola, but he could now hear the song of the cables. Had the downcoming car reversed back up to Piz Gloria, assuming him to have been killed by the avalanche? There was a large black saloon car in the forecourt to the cable station, and lights on in the station, but otherwise no sign of life. Well, it was his only way to get off the run and on to the road that was his objective. Bond schussed easily downwards, resting his limbs, getting his breath back.

The sharp crack of a heavy-calibre pistol and the phut as the bullet hit the snow beside him pulled him together. He jinked sideways and glanced quickly up to the right, where the shot had come from. The gun blazed again. A man on skis was coming fast after him. One of the guides! Of course! He would have taken the Red Run. Had the other followed Bond on the Black? Bond hoped so, gave a deep sigh of anger and put on all the speed he could, crouching low and jinking occasionally to spoil the man's aim. The single shots kept on coming. It was going to be a narrow shave who got to the end of the run first!

Bond studied the finishing point that was now coming at him fast. There was a wide break in the fence to let the skiers through, a large parking place in front of the cable station and then the low embankment that protected the main line of the Rhätische Bahn up to Pontresina and the Bernina Pass. On the other side of the rails the railway embankment dropped into the road from Pontresina to Samaden, the junction for St Moritz, perhaps two miles down the valley.

Another shot kicked up the snow in front of him. That was six that had gone. With any luck the man's pistol was empty. But that wouldn't help much. There was no stuffing left in Bond for a fight.

Now a great blaze of light showed coming up the railway line, and, before it was hidden by the cable station, Bond identified an express and could just hear the thudding of its electro-diesels. By God, it would just about be passing the cable station as he wanted to get across the track! Could he make it–take a run at the low embankment and clear it and the lines before the train got there? It was his only hope! Bond dug in with his sticks to get on extra speed. Hell! A man had got out of the black car and was crouching, aiming at him. Bond jinked and jinked again as fire bloomed from the man's hand. But now Bond was on top of him. He thrust hard with the rapier point of a ski-stick and felt it go through clothing. The man gave a scream and went down. The guide, now only yards behind, yelled something. The great yellow eye of the diesel glared down the tracks, and Bond caught a sideways glimpse of a huge red snow-fan below the headlight that was fountaining the new snow to right and left of the engine in two white wings. Now! He flashed across the parking place, heading straight at the mound of the embankment and, as he hit, dug both his sticks in to get his skis off the ground, and hurled himself forward into the air. There was a brief glimpse of steel rails below, a tremendous thudding in his ears and a ferocious blast, only yards away, from the train's siren. Then he crashed on to the icy road, tried to stop, failed and fetched up in an almighty skid against the hard snow wall on the other side. As he did so, there came a terrible scream from behind him, a loud splintering of wood and the screech of the train's brakes being applied.

At the same time, the spray from the snow-fan, that had now reached Bond, turned pink!

Bond wiped some of it off his face and looked at it. His stomach turned. God! The man had tried to follow him, had been too late or had missed his jump, and had been caught by the murderous blades of the snow-fan! Mincemeat! Bond dug a handful of snow off the bank and wiped it over his face and hair. He rubbed more of it down his sweater. He suddenly realized that people were pulling down the windows in the brilliantly-lit train above him. Others had got down on the line. Bond pulled himself together and punted off down the black ice of the road. Shouts followed him–the angry bawls of Swiss citizens. Bond edged his skis a little against the camber of the road and kept going. Ahead of him, down the black gulch of the road, in his mind's eye, the huge red propeller whirred, sucking him into its steel whirlpool. Bond, close to delirium, slithered on towards its bloody, beckoning vortex.

Bond, a grey-faced, lunging automaton, somehow stayed upright on the two miles of treacherous Langlauf down the gentle slope to Samaden. Once a passing car, its snow-chains clattering, forced him into the bank. He leaned against the comforting soft snow for a moment, the breath sobbing in his throat. Then he drove himself on again. He had got so far, done so well! Only a few more hundred yards to the lights of the darling, straggling little paradise of people and shelter! The slender campanile of the village church was floodlit and there was a great warm lake of light on the left of the twinkling group of houses. The strains of a waltz came over the still, frozen air. The skating-rink! A Christmas Eve skaters' ball. That was the place for him! Crowds! Gaiety! Confusion! Somewhere to lose himself from the double hunt that would now be on–by SPECTRE and the Swiss police, the cops and the robbers hand in hand!

Bond's skis hit a pile of horse's dung from some merrymaker's sleigh. He lurched drunkenly into the snow wall of the road and righted himself, cursing feebly. Come on! Pull yourself together! Look respectable! Well, you needn't look *too* respectable. After all, it's Christmas Eve. Here were the first houses. The noise of accordion music, deliciously nostalgic, came from a Gasthaus with a beautiful iron sign over its door. Now there was a twisty, uphill bit–the road to St Moritz. Bond shuffled up it, placing his sticks carefully. He ran a hand through his matted hair and pulled the sweat-soaked handkerchief down to his neck, tucking the ends into his shirt collar. The music lilted down towards him from the great pool of light over the skating-rink. Bond pulled himself a little more upright. There were a lot of cars drawn up, skis stuck in mounds of snow, luges and toboggans, festoons of paper streamers, a big notice in three languages across the entrance: 'Grand Christmas Eve Ball! Fancy Dress! Entrance 2 Francs! Bring all your friends! Hooray!'

Bond dug in his sticks and bent down to unlatch his skis. He fell over sideways. If only he could just lie there, go to sleep on the hard, trodden snow that felt like swansdown! He gave a small groan and heaved himself gingerly into a crouch. The bindings were frozen solid, caked, like his boots, with ice. He got one of his sticks and hacked feebly at the metal and tried again. At last the latches sprang and the thongs were off. Where to put the bloody things, hide their brilliant red markings? He lugged them down the trodden path towards the entrance, gay with fairy lights, shoved the skis and the sticks under a big saloon car, and staggered on. The man at the ticket-table was as drunk as Bond seemed. He looked up blearily: 'Zwo Franken. Two francs. Deux francs.' The routine incantation was slurred into one portmanteau word. Bond held on to the table, put down the coins and got his ticket. The man's eyes focused. 'The fancy dress, the travesti, it is obligatoire.' He reached into a box by his side and threw a black and white domino-mask on the table. 'One franc.' He gave a lop-sided smile. 'Now you are the gangster, the spy. Yes?'

'Yeah, that's right.' Bond paid and put on the mask. He reluctantly let go of the table and wove through the entrance. There were raised tiers of wooden benches round the big square rink. Thank God for a chance to sit down! There was an empty seat on the aisle in the bottom row at rink level. Bond stumbled down the wooden steps and fell into it. He righted himself, said 'Sorry,' and put his head in his hands. The girl beside him, part of a group of harlequins, Wild Westerners and pirates, drew her spangled skirt away, whispered something to her neighbour. Bond didn't care. They wouldn't throw him out on a night like this. Through the loudspeakers the violins sobbed into 'The Skaters' Waltz'. Above them the voice of the M.C. called, 'Last dance, ladies and gentlemen. And then all out on to the rink and join hands for the grand finale. Only ten minutes to go to midnight! Last dance, ladies and gentlemen. Last dance!' There was a rattle of applause. People laughed excitedly.

God in Heaven! thought Bond feebly. Now this! Won't anybody leave me alone? He fell asleep.

Hours later he felt his shoulder being shaken. 'On to the rink, sir. Please. All on to the rink for the grand finale. Only a minute to go.' A man in purple and gold uniform was standing beside him, looking down impatiently.

'Go away,' said Bond dully. Then some inner voice told him not to make a scene, not to be conspicuous. He struggled to his feet, made the few steps to the rink, somehow stood upright. His head lowered, like a wounded bull, he looked to left and right, saw a gap in the human chain round the rink and slid gingerly towards it. A hand was held out to him and he grasped it thankfully. One the other side someone else was trying to get hold of his free hand. And then there came a diversion. From right across the rink, a girl in a short black skating-skirt topped by a shocking-pink fur-lined parka, sped like an arrow across the ice and came to a crash-stop in front of Bond. Bond felt the ice particles hit his legs. He looked up. It was a face he recognized–those brilliant blue eyes, the look of authority now subdued beneath golden sunburn and a brilliant smile of excitement. Who in hell?

The girl slipped in beside him, seized his right hand in her left, joined up on her right. 'James–' it was a thrilling whisper–'oh, James. It's me! Tracy! What's the matter with you? Where have you come from?'

'Tracy,' said Bond dully. 'Tracy. Hold on to me. I'm in bad shape. Tell you later.'

Then Auld Lang Syne began and everyone swung linked hands in unison to the music.

Chapter Eighteen

Fork Left for Hell!

Bond had no idea how he managed to stay upright, but at last it was over and everyone cheered and broke up into pairs and groups.

Tracy got her arm under his. Bond pulled himself together. He said hoarsely, 'Mix with the crowd, Tracy. Got to get away from here. People after me.' A sudden hope came to him. 'Got your car?'

'Yes, darling. Everything'll be all right. Just hang on to me. Are people waiting for you outside?'

'Could be. Watch out for a big black Mercedes. There may be shooting. Better stay away from me. I can make it. Where's the car?'

'Down the road to the right. But don't be silly. Here, I've got an idea. You get into this parka.' She ran the zip down and stripped it off 'It'll be a tight fit. Here, put your arm into this sleeve.'

'But you'll get cold.'

'Do as I tell you. I've got a sweater and plenty on underneath. Now the other arm. That's right.' She pulled up the zip. 'Darling James, you look sweet.'

The fur of the parka smelt of Guerlain's 'Ode'. It took Bond back to Royale. What a girl! The thought of her, of having an ally, of not being on his own, of being away from that bloody mountain, revived Bond. He held her hand and followed her through the crowd that was now steaming towards the exit. This was going to be a bad moment! Whether or not that cable car had come on down the mountain, by now Blofeld would have had time to get one down full of SPECTRE men. Bond had been seen from the train, would be known to have made for Samaden. By now they would have covered the railway station. They would expect him to try and hide in a crowd. Perhaps the drunken man at the entrance had remembered him. If that saloon moved off and revealed the red-arrowed skis, it would be a cert. Bond let go the girl's hand and slipped the shattered Rolex back over the knuckles of his right hand. He had gathered enough strength, mostly from the girl, to have one more bash at them!

She looked at him. 'What are you doing?'

He took her hand again. 'Nothing.'

They were getting near the exit. Bond peered through the slits in his mask. Yes, by God! Two of the thugs were standing beside the ticket man watching the throng with deadly concentration. On the far side of the road stood the black Mercedes, petrol vapour curling up from its exhaust. No escape. There was only bluff. Bond put his arm round Tracy's neck and whispered, 'Kiss me all the way past the ticket-table. They're there, but I think we can make it.'

She flung an arm over his shoulder and drew him to her. 'How did you know that that's what I've been waiting for?' Her lips crushed down sideways on his and, in a tide of laughing, singing people, they were through and on the street.

They turned, still linked, down the road. Yes! There was the darling little white car!

And then the horn on the Mercedes began sounding urgently. Bond's gait, or perhaps his old-fashioned ski-trousers, had given him away to the man in the car!

'Quick, darling!' said Bond urgently.

The girl threw herself in under the wheel, pressed the starter and the car was moving as Bond scrambled in through the opposite door. Bond looked back. Through the rear window he could see the two men standing in the road. They would not shoot with so many witnesses about. Now they ran to the Mercedes. Thank God it was pointing up the hill towards St Moritz! And then Tracy had done a controlled skid round the S bend in the village and they were on the main road that Bond had staggered down half an hour before.

It would be five minutes at least before the Mercedes could turn and get after them. The girl was going like hell, but there was traffic on the road–tinkling sleighs full of fur-wrapped merrymakers on their way back to Pontresina, an occasional car, its snow-chains rattling. She drove on her brakes and her horn, the same triple wind-horn that sounded the high discord Bond remembered so well. Bond said, 'You're an angel, Tracy. But take it easy. We don't want to end up in the ditch.'

The girl glanced sideways at him and laughed with pleasure. 'That sounds as if you were feeling better. But I cannot see you. Now you can take off that silly mask and my parka. In a minute the heat will come on and you will be roasted. And I would like to see you as I remember you. But you are pleased with me?'

Life was beginning to come back into Bond. It was so wonderful to be in this little car with this marvellous girl. The memory of the dreadful mountain, of all that he had been through, was receding. Now there was hope again, after so much dread and despair. He could feel the tensions uncoiling in his stomach. He said, 'I'll tell you if I'm pleased when we get to Zürich. Can you make it? It's a hell of a way to spend Christmas.' He wound down the window and threw the domino-mask out, stripped off the parka and draped it over her shoulders. The big sign for the main road down into the valley came up. He said, 'Left here, Tracy. Filisur and then Coire.'

She took the turning, in Bond's estimation, dangerously fast. She went into a skid that Bond swore was going to be uncontrolled. But, even on the black ice of the road, she got out of it and motored blithely on. Bond said, 'For God's sake, Tracy! How in hell did you manage that? You haven't even got chains on.'

She laughed, pleased at the awe in his voice. 'Dunlop Rally studs on all the tyres. They're only supposed to be for Rally drivers, but I managed to wangle a set out of them. Don't worry. Just sit back and enjoy the drive.'

There was something entirely new in the girl's voice, a lilt and happiness that had certainly not been there at Royale. Bond turned and looked at her carefully for the first time. Yes, she was somehow a new woman, radiating health and a kind of inner glow. The tumbled fair hair glittered with vitality and the half-open, beautiful lips seemed always to be on the verge of a smile.

'Satisfied?'

'You look absolutely wonderful. But now for God's sake tell me how you happened to be at Samaden. It was a bloody miracle. It saved my life.'

'All right. But then you tell. I've never seen a man look so dead on his feet. I couldn't believe my eyes. I thought you must be plastered.' She gave him a quick glance. 'You still look pretty bad. Here–' she leant forward to the dashboard–'I'll switch on the blower. Get you properly warmed up.' She paused. 'Well, my bit of the story's quite simple really. Papa rang me up one day from Marseilles to find out how I was. He asked if I had seen you and seemed very annoyed when he heard I hadn't. He practically ordered me to go and find you.' She glanced at him. 'He's quite taken to you, you know. Anyway he said he had found out the address of a certain man you were looking for. He said he was sure that by now you would have found out that address too. He said that, knowing you, I would find you somewhere close to this address. It was the Piz Gloria Club. He told me if I found you to tell you to watch your step, to look after yourself.' She laughed. 'How right he was! Well, so I left Davos, which had really put me on my feet again, like you said it would, and I came up to Samaden the day before yesterday. The Seilbahn wasn't running yesterday, so I was going to come up today to look for you. It was all as simple as that. Now you tell.'

They had been keeping up a good speed down the sloping, winding road into the valley. Bond turned to look through the rear window. He swore under his breath. Perhaps a mile behind, twin lights were coming after them. The girl said, 'I know. I've been watching in the mirror. I'm afraid they're gaining a little. Must be a good driver who knows the road. Probably got snow-chains. But I think I can hold them. Now go on. What have you been up to?'

Bond gave her a garbled version. There was a big gangster up the mountain, living under a false name. He was wanted by the police in England. Bond was vaguely connected with the police, with the Ministry of Defence. (She snorted, 'Don't try and fool me. I know you're in the Secret Service. Papa told me so.' Bond said curtly, 'Well, Papa's talking through his hat.' She laughed knowingly.) Anyway, Bond continued, he had been sent out to make sure this was the man they wanted. He had found out that he was. But the man had become suspicious of Bond and Bond had had to get out quickly. He gave her a graphic account of the moonlit nightmare of the mountain, of the avalanche, of the man who had been killed by the train, of how he had got to Samaden, dead beat, and had tried to hide in the crowd on the skating-rink. 'And then,' he ended lamely, 'you turned up like a beautiful angel on skates, and here we are.'

She thought the story over for a minute. Then she said calmly, 'And now, my darling James, just tell me how many of them you killed. And tell me the truth.'

'Why?'

'I'm just curious.'

'You promise to keep this between you and me?'

She said enigmatically, 'Of course. Everything's between you and me from now on.'

'Well, there was the main guard at the so-called Club. That had to be done or I'd be dead myself by now. Then I suppose one got caught by the avalanche. Then, at the bottom, one of them shot at me and I had to spear him with my ski-stick–self-defence. I don't know how badly he's hurt. And then there was the man killed by the train. He'd fired six shots at me. And anyway it was his own fault. Let's say three and a half got themselves killed one way or another.'

'How many are left?'

'What are you getting at?'

'I just want to know. Trust me.'

'Well, I think there were about fifteen up there all told. So that leaves eleven and a half–plus the big man.'

'And there are three in the car behind? Would they kill us if they caught us?'

'I'm afraid so. I haven't got any weapons. I'm sorry, Tracy, but I'm afraid you wouldn't have much chance either, being a witness and a sort of accomplice of mine. These people think I'm pretty bad news for them.'

'And you are?'

'Yes. From now on, I'm the worst.'

'Well, I've got pretty bad news for you. They're gaining on us and I've only got a couple of gallons left in the tank. We'll have to stop in Filisur. There won't be a garage open and it'll mean waking someone up. Can't hope to do it under ten minutes and they'll have us. You'll have to think u[illegible] something clever.'

There was a ravine and an S turn over a bridge. They were coming ou[illegible] the first curve over the bridge. Lights blazed at them from across the rav[illegible] There was half a mile between the two cars, but the range across the r[illegible] was perhaps only three hundred yards. Bond wasn't surprised to s[illegible] familiar blue flames flutter from the front of the car. Chips of granite from the overhang splattered down on the bonnet of the car. Then they were into the second half of the S bend and out of sight of their pursuers.

Now came a stretch of reconstruction work where there had been a landslide. There were big warning notices: 'Achtung! Baustelle! Vorsichtig Fahren!' The broken road hugged the mountain side on the right. On the left was rickety fencing and then a precipice falling hundreds of feet down into a gorge with an ice-floed river. In the middle of the bad stretch, a huge red wooden arrow pointed right to a narrow track across a temporary bridge. Bond suddenly shouted 'Stop!'

Tracy pulled up, her front wheels on the bridge. Bond tore open the door. 'Get on! Wait for me round the next corner. It's the only chance.'

Good girl! She got going without a word. Bond ran back the few yards to the big red arrow. It was held in the forks of two upright poles. Bond wrenched it off, swung it round so that it pointed to the left, towards the flimsy fence that closed off the yards of old road leading to the collapsed bridge. Bond tore at the fence, pulling the stakes out, flattening it. Glare showed round the corner behind him. He leaped across the temporary road into the shadow of the mountain, flattened himself against it, waited, holding his breath.

The Mercedes was coming faster than it should over the bumpy track, its chains clattering inside the mud-guards. It made straight for the black opening to which the arrow now pointed. Bond caught a glimpse of white, strained faces and then the desperate scream of brakes as the driver saw the abyss in front of him. The car seemed almost to stop, but its front wheels must have been over the edge. It balanced for a moment on its iron belly and then slowly, slowly toppled and there was a first appalling crash as it hit the rubble beneath the old bridge. Then another crash and another. Bond ran forward past the lying arrow and looked down. Now the car was flying upside-down through the air. It hit again and a fountain of sparks flashed from a rock ledge. Then, somersaulting, and with its lights somehow still blazing, it smashed on down into the gorge. It hit a last outcrop that knocked it sideways and, spinning laterally, but now with its lights out and only the glint of the moon on metal, it took the last great plunge into the iced-up river. A deep rumble echoed up from the gorge and there was the patter of rocks and stones following the wreckage. And then all was peaceful, moonlit silence.

Bond let out his breath in a quiet hiss between his clenched teeth. Then, mechanically, he straightened things out again, put up the remains of the fence, lifted the arrow and put it back facing to the right. Then he wiped his sweating hands down the side of his trousers and walked unsteadily down the road and round the next corner.

The little white car was there, pulled in to the side, with its lights out. Bond got in and slumped into his seat. Tracy said nothing but got the car going. The lights of Filisur appeared, warm and yellow in the valley below. She reached out a hand and held his tightly. 'You've had enough for one day. Go to sleep. I'll get you to Zürich. Please do what I say.'

Bond said nothing. He pressed her hand weakly, leaned his head against door jamb and was instantly asleep.

e was out for the count.

Chapter Nineteen

Love for Breakfast

In the grey dawn, Zürich airport was depressing and almost deserted, but, blessedly, there was a Swissair Caravelle, delayed by fog at London Airport, waiting to take off for London. Bond parked Tracy in the restaurant and, regretfully forsaking the smell of coffee and fried eggs, went and bought himself a ticket, had his passport stamped by a sleepy official (he had half expected to be stopped, but wasn't), and went to a telephone booth and shut himself in. He looked up Universal Export in the telephone book, and read underneath, as he had hoped, 'Hauptvertreter Alexander Muir. Privat Wohnung' and the number. Bond glanced through the glass window at the clock in the departure hall. Six o'clock. Well, Muir would just have to take it.

He rang the number and, after minutes, a sleepy voice said, 'Ja! Hier Muir.'

Bond said 'Sorry, 410, but this is 007. I'm calling from the airport. This is bloody urgent so I'll have to take a chance on your line being bugged. Got a paper and pencil?'

The voice at the other end had grown brisker. 'Hang on, 007. Yes, got it. Go ahead.'

'First of all I've got some bad news. Your Number Two has had it. Almost for sure. Can't give you any details over this line, but I'm off to London in about an hour–Swissair Flight 110–and I'll signal the dope back straight away. Could you put that on the teleprinter? Right. Now I'm guessing that in the next day or so a party of ten girls, British, will be coming here by helicopter from the Engadine. Yellow Sud Aviation Alouette. I'll be teleprinting their names back from London some time today. My bet is they'll be flying to England, probably on different flights and perhaps to Prestwick and Gatwick as well as London Airport, if you've any planes using those airports. Anyway, I guess they'll be dispersed. Now, I think it may be very important to tell London their flight numbers and E.T.A. Rather a big job, but I'll get you authority in a few hours to use men from Berne and Geneva to lend a hand. Got it? Right. Now I'm pretty certain you're blown. Remember the old Operation Bedlam that's just been cancelled? Well, it's him and he's got radio and he'll probably have guessed I'd be contacting you this morning. Just take a look out of the window and see if there's any sign of watchers. He's certainly got his men in Zürich.'

'Christ what a shambles!' The voice at the other end was tight wit tension. 'Hang on.' There was a pause. Bond could visualize Muir, whom didn't know except as a number, going over to the window, caref drawing aside the curtain. Muir came back on the wire. 'Looks damn li There's a black Porsche across the road. Two men in it. I'll get my frie the Sécurité to chase them away.'

Bond said, 'Be careful how you go about it. My guess is that our got a pretty good fix in with the police. Anyway, put all this on the telex to M personally, would you? Ciphered of course. And tell him if I get back in one piece I must see him today, with 501 [the Chief Scientific Officer to the Service] and if possible with someone in the same line of business from the Ministry of Agriculture and Fisheries. Sounds daft, but there it is. It's going to upset their paper hats and Christmas pudding, but I can't help that. Can you manage all that? Good lad. Any questions?'

'Sure I oughtn't to come out to the airport and get some more about my Number Two? He was tailing one of Redland's men. Chap's been buying some pretty odd stuff from the local rep. of Badische Anilin. Number Two thought it seemed damned fishy. Didn't tell what the stuff was. Just thought he'd better see where it was being delivered to.'

'I thought it must be some kind of a spiel like that. No. You stay away from me. I'm hot as a pistol, going to be hotter later in the day when they find a certain Mercedes at the bottom of a precipice. I'll get off the line now. Sorry to have wrecked your Christmas. 'Bye.'

Bond put down the receiver and went up to the restaurant. Tracy had been watching the door. Her face lit up when she saw him. He sat down very close to her and took her hand, a typical airport farewell couple. He ordered plenty of scrambled eggs and coffee. 'It's all right Tracy. I've fixed everything at my end. But now about you. That car of yours is going to be bad news. There'll be people who'll have seen you drive away with the Mercedes on your tail. There always are, even at midnight on Christmas Eve. And the big man on top of the mountain has got his men down here too. You'd better finish your breakfast and get the hell over the frontier. Which is the nearest?'

'Schaffhausen or Konstanz, I suppose, but–' she pleaded–'James, do I have to leave you now? It's been so long waiting for you. And I *have* done well, haven't I? Why do you want to punish me?' Tears, that would never have been there in the Royale days, sparkled in her eyes. She wiped them angrily away with the back of her hand.

Bond suddenly thought, Hell! I'll never find another girl like this one. She's got everything I've ever looked for in a woman. She's beautiful, in bed and out. She's adventurous, brave, resourceful. She's exciting always. She seems to love me. She'd let me go on with my life. She's a lone girl, not cluttered up with friends, relations, belongings. Above all, she needs me. It'll be someone for me to look after. I'm fed up with all these untidy, casual affairs that leave me with a bad conscience. I wouldn't mind having children. I've got no social background into which she would or wouldn't fit. We're two of a pair, really. Why not make it for always?

Bond found his voice saying those words that he had never said in his life before, never expected to say.

'Tracy. I love you. Will you marry me?'

She turned very pale. She looked at him wonderingly. Her lips trembled. You mean that?'

'Yes, I mean it. With all my heart.'

She took her hand away from his and put her face in her hands. When she [illegible]oved them she was smiling. 'I'm sorry, James. It's so much what I've [illegible] dreaming of. It came as a shock. But yes. Yes, of course I'll marry you. [illegible] won't be silly about it. I won't make a scene. Just kiss me once and I'll [illegible]g.' She looked seriously at him, at every detail of his face. Then she leaned forward and they kissed.

She got up briskly. 'I suppose I've got to get used to doing what you say. I'll drive to Munich. To the Vier Jahreszeiten. It's my favourite hotel in the world. I'll wait for you there. They know me. They'll take me in without any luggage. Everything's at Samaden. I'll just have to send out for a toothbrush and stay in bed for two days until I can go out and get some things. You'll telephone me? Talk to me? When can we get married? I must tell Papa. He'll be terribly excited.'

'Let's get married in Munich. At the consulate. I've got a kind of diplomatic immunity. I can get the papers through quickly. Then we can be married again in an English church, or Scottish rather. That's where I come from. I'll call you up tonight and tomorrow. I'll get to you just as soon as I can. I've got to finish this business first.'

'You promise you won't get hurt?'

Bond smiled. 'I wouldn't think of it. For once I'll run away if someone starts shooting.'

'All right then.' She looked at him carefully again. 'It's time you took off that red handkerchief. I suppose you realize it's bitten to ribbons. Give it to me. I'll mend it.'

Bond undid the red bandanna from around his neck. It was a dark, sweat-soaked rag. And she was right. Two corners of it were in shreds. He must have got them between his teeth and chewed on them when the going was bad down the mountain. He couldn't remember having done so. He gave it to her.

She took it and, without looking back, walked straight out of the restaurant and down the stairs towards the exit.

Bond sat down. His breakfast came and he began eating mechanically. What had he done? What in hell had he done? But the only answer was a feeling of tremendous warmth and relief and excitement. James and Tracy Bond! Commander and Mrs Bond! How utterly, utterly extraordinary!

The voice of the Tannoy said, 'Attention, please. Passengers on Swissair Flight Number 110 for London, please assemble at gate number 2. Swissair Flight Number 110 for London. Passengers to gate Number 2, please .'

Bond stubbed out his cigarette, gave a quick glance round their trysting-place to fix its banality in his mind, and walked to the door, leaving the fragments of his old life torn up amidst the debris of an airport breakfast.

Chapter Twenty

M en Pantoufles

Bond slept in the plane and was visited by a terrible nightmare. It was the hallway of a very grand town-house, an embassy perhaps, and a wide staircase led up under a spangled chandelier to where the butler was standing at the door of the drawing-room, from which came the murmur of a large crowd of guests. Tracy, in oyster satin, was on his arm. She was loaded with jewels and her golden hair had been piled up grandly into one of those fancy arrangements you see in smart hairdressers' advertisements. On top of the pile was a diamond tiara that glittered gorgeously. Bond was dressed in tails (where in hell had he got *those* from?), and the wing collar stuck into his neck below the chin. He was wearing his medals, and his order as C.M.G., on its blue and scarlet ribbon, hung below his white tie. Tracy was chattering, gaily, excitedly, looking forward to the grand evening. Bond was cursing the prospect before him and wishing he was playing a tough game of bridge for high stakes at Blades. They got to the top of the stairs and Bond gave his name.

'Commander and Mrs James Bond!' It was the stentorian bellow of a toast-master. Bond got the impression that a sudden hush fell over the elegant crowd in the gilt and white drawing-room.

He followed Tracy through the double doors. There was a gush of French from Tracy as she exchanged those empty 'Mayfair' kisses, that end up wide of the kissers' ears, with her hostess. Tracy drew Bond forward. 'And this is James. Doesn't he look sweet with that beautiful medal round his neck? Just like the old De Reszke cigarette advertisements!'

'Fasten your seat belts, please, and extinguish your cigarettes.'

Bond awoke, sweating. God Almighty! What had he done? But no! It wouldn't be like that! Definitely not. He would still have his tough, exciting life, but now there would be Tracy to come home to. Would there be room in his flat at Chelsea? Perhaps he could rent the floor above. And what about May, his Scottish treasure? That would be tricky. He must somehow persuade her to stay.

The Caravelle hit the runway and there came the roar of jet deflection, and then they were trundling over the tarmac in a light drizzle. Bond suddenly realized that he had no luggage, that he could go straight to Passport Control and then out and back to his flat to change out of these ridiculous skiing clothes that stank of sweat. Would there be a car from the pool for him? There was, with Miss Mary Goodnight sitting beside the driver.

'My God, Mary, this is a hell of a way to spend your Christmas! This is far beyond the line of duty. Anyway, get in the back and tell me why you're not stirring the plum pudding or going to church or something.'

She climbed into the back seat and he followed. She said, 'You don't seem to know much about Christmas. You make plum puddings at least two months before and let them sort of settle and mature. And church isn't till eleven.' She glanced at him. 'Actually I came to see how you were. I gather you've been in trouble again. You certainly look pretty ghastly. Don't you own a comb? And you haven't shaved. You look like a pirate. And–'she wrinkled her nose–'when did you last have a bath? I wonder they let you out of the airport. You ought to be in quarantine.'

Bond laughed. 'Winter sports are very strenuous–all that snowballing and tobogganing. Matter of fact, I was at a Christmas Eve fancy-dress party last night. Kept me up till all hours.'

'In those great clod-hopping boots? I don't believe you.'

'Well, sucks to you! It was on a skating-rink. But seriously, Mary, tell me the score. Why this V.I.P. treatment?'

'M. You're to check with H.Q. first and then go down to lunch with him at Quarterdeck. Then, after lunch, he's having these men you wanted brought down for a conference. Everything top priority. So I thought I'd better stand by too. As you're wrecking so many other people's Christmases, I thought I might as well throw mine on the slag-heap with the others. Actually, if you want to know, I was only having lunch with an aunt. And I loathe turkey and plum pudding. Anyway, I just didn't want to miss the fun and when the duty officer got on to me about an hour ago and told me there was a major flap, I asked him to tell the car to pick me up on the way to the airport.'

Bond said seriously, 'Well, you're a damned good girl. As a matter of fact it's going to be the hell of a rush getting down the bare bones of a report. And I've got something for the lab to do. Will there be someone there?'

'Of course there will. You know M insists on a skeleton staff in every Section, Christmas Day or not. But seriously, James. Have you been in trouble? You really do look awful.'

'Oh, somewhat. You'll get the photo as I dictate.' The car drew up outside Bond's flat. 'Now be an angel and stir up May while I clean myself up and get out of these bloody clothes. Get her to brew me plenty of black coffee and to pour two jiggers of our best brandy into the pot. You ask May for what you like. She might even have some plum pudding. Now then, it's nine-thirty. Be a good girl and call the Duty Officer and say O.K. to M's orders and that we'll be along by ten-thirty. And get him to ask the lab to stand by in half an hour.' Bond took his passport out of his hip pocket. 'Then give this to the driver and ask him to get the hell over and give it to the Duty Officer personally. Tell the D.O.–' Bond turned down the corner of a page–'to tell the lab that the ink used is–er–home-made. All it needs is expose to heat. They'll understand. Got that? Good girl. Now come on and we'll get May going.' Bond went up the steps and rang two shorts and a long on the bell.

When Bond got to his desk a few minutes after ten-thirty, feeling back to nine-tenths human, he found a folder on his desk with the red star in the top right corner that meant Top Secret. It contained his passport and a dozen copies of blown-up photostats of its page 21. The list of girls' names was faint but legible. There was also a note marked 'personal'. Bond opened it. He laughed. It just said, 'The ink showed traces of an excess of uric acid. This is often due to a super-abundancy of alcohol in the blood-stream. You have been warned!' There was no signature. So the Christmas spirit had permeated even into the solemn crevices of one of the most secret Sections in the building. Bond crumpled the paper and then, thinking of Mary Goodnight's susceptibilities, more prudently burned it with his lighter.

She came in and sat down with her shorthand book. Bond said, 'Now this is only a first draft, Mary, and it's got to be fast. So don't mind about the mistakes. M'll understand. We've got about an hour and a half if I'm to get down to Windsor by lunch-time. Think you can manage it? All right then, here goes. "Top Secret. Personal to M. As instructed, on December 22nd I arrived at Zürich Central Airport at 1330 by Swissair to make first contact in connection with Operation 'Corona'. . ." '

Bond turned sideways to his secretary and, as he talked, looked out acros the bare trees in Regent's Park, remembering every minute of the last thr days–the sharp, empty smell of the air and the snow, the dark green pool Blofeld's eyes, the crunch as the edge of his left hand, still bruised, thuc down across the offered neck of the guard. And then all the rest until T whom, without mention of romance, he left in his report on her way

Vier Jahreszeiten in Munich. Then the report was finished and the muted clack of Mary's typewriter came from behind the closed door. He would ring Tracy up that night when he got back to his flat. He could already hear her laughing voice at the other end of the wire. The nightmare in the plane was forgotten. Now there was only the happy, secret looking-forward to the days to come. Bond lost himself in his plans–how to get the days off, how to get the necessary papers, where to have the service in Scotland. Then he pulled himself together, picked up the photostat containing the girls' names and went up to the Communications Centre to get on the teleprinter to Station Z.

M would have preferred to live by the sea, near Plymouth perhaps or Bristol–anywhere where he could see the stuff whenever he wanted to and could listen to it at night. As it was, and since he had to be within easy call of London, he had chosen the next best thing to water, trees, and had found a small Regency manor-house on the edge of Windsor Forest. This was on Crown Lands, and Bond had always suspected that an ounce of 'Grace and Favour' had found its way into M's lease. The head of the Secret Service earned £5,000 a year, with the use of an ancient Rolls Royce and driver thrown in. M's naval pay (as a Vice-Admiral on the retired list) would add perhaps another £1,500. After taxes, he would have about £4,000 to spend. His London life would probably take at least half of that. Only if his rent and rates came to no more than £500, would he be able to keep a house in the country, and a beautiful small Regency house at that.

These thoughts ran again through Bond's mind as he swung the clapper of the brass ship's-bell of some former H.M.S. *Repulse*, the last of whose line, a battle-cruiser, had been M's final sea-going appointment. Hammond, M's Chief Petty Officer in that ship, who had followed M into retirement, greeted Bond as an old friend, and he was shown into M's study.

M had one of the stock bachelor's hobbies. He painted in water-colour. He painted only the wild orchids of England, in the meticulous but uninspired fashion of the naturalists of the nineteenth century. He was now at his painting-table up against the window, his broad back hunched over his drawing-board, with, in front of him, an extremely dim little flower in a tooth-glass full of water. When Bond came in and closed the door, M gave the flower one last piercingly inquisitive glance. He got to his feet with obvious reluctance. But he gave Bond one of his rare smiles and said, 'Afternoon, James.' (He had the sailor's meticulous observance of the exact midday.) 'Happy Christmas and all that. Take a chair.' M himself went behind his desk and sat down. He was about to come on duty. Bond automatically took his traditional place across the desk from his Chief.

M began to fill a pipe. 'What the devil's the name of that fat American detective who's always fiddling about with orchids, those obscene hybrids from Venezuela and so forth? Then he comes sweating out of his orchid house, eats a gigantic meal of some foreign muck and solves the murder. What's he called?'

'Nero Wolfe, sir. They're written by a chap called Rex Stout. I like them.'

'They're readable,' condescended M. 'But I was thinking of the orchid ff in them. How in hell can a man like those disgusting flowers? Why, 're damned near animals, and their colours, all those pinks and mauves he blotchy yellow tongues, are positively hideous! Now that–' M waved at the meagre little bloom in the toothglass–'that's the real thing. That's an Autumn Lady's Tresses–*spiranthes spiralis*, not that I care particularly. Flowers in England as late as October and should be under the ground by now. But I got this forced-late specimen from a man I know–assistant to a chap called Summerhayes who's the orchid king at Kew. My friend's experimenting with cultures of a fungus which oddly enough is a parasite on a lot of orchids, but, at the same time, gets eaten by the orchids and acts as its staple diet. Mycorhiza it's called.' M gave another of his rare smiles. 'But you needn't write it down. Just wanted to take a leaf out of this fellow Nero Wolfe's book. However–' M brushed the topic aside–'can't expect you to get excited about these things. Now then.' He settled back. 'What the devil have you been up to?' The grey eyes regarded Bond keenly. 'Looks as if you haven't been getting much sleep. Pretty gay these winter sport places, they tell me.'

Bond smiled. He reached into his inside pocket and took out the pinned sheets of paper. 'This one provided plenty of miscellaneous entertainment, sir. Perhaps you'd like to have a look at my report first. 'Fraid it's only a draft. There wasn't much time. But I can fill in anything that isn't clear.'

M reached across for the papers, adjusted his spectacles, and began reading.

Soft rain scratched at the windows. A big log fell in the grate. The silence was soft and comfortable. Bond looked round the walls at M's treasured collection of naval prints. Everywhere there were mountainous seas, crashing cannon, bellying sails, tattered battle pennants–the fury of ancient engagements, the memories of ancient enemies, the French, the Dutch, the Spaniards, even the Americans. All gone, all friends now with one another. Not a sign of the enemies of today. Who was backing Blofeld, for instance, in the inscrutable conspiracy in which he was now certainly engaged? The Russians? The Chinese? Or was it an independent job, as Thunderball had been? And what was the conspiracy? What was the job for the protection of which six or seven of Blofeld's men had died within less than a week? Would M read anything into the evidence? Would the experts who were coming that afternoon? Bond lifted his left wrist. Remembered that he no longer had a watch. *That* he would certainly be allowed on expenses. He would get another one as soon as the shops opened after Boxing Day. Another Rolex? Probably. They were on the heavy side, but they worked. And at least you could see the time in the dark with those big phosphorus numerals. Somewhere in the hall, a clock struck the half-hour. 1.30. Twelve hours before, he must have just set up the trap that killed the three men in the Mercedes. Self-defence, but the hell of a way to celebrate Christmas!

M threw the papers down on his desk. His pipe had gone out and he now slowly lit it again. He tossed the spent match accurately over his shoulder into the fire. He put his hands flat on the desk and said–and there was an unusual kindness in his voice–'Well, you were pretty lucky to get out of that one, James. Didn't know you could ski.'

'I only just managed to stay upright, Sir. Wouldn't like to try it again.'

'No. And I see you say you can't come to any conclusions about w[illegible] Blofeld is up to?'

'That's right, sir. Haven't got a clue.'

'Well, nor have I. I just don't understand any part of it. Perh[illegible] professors'll help us out this afternoon. But you're obviously right[illegible]

SPECTRE all over again. By the way, your tip about Pontresina was a good one. He was a Bulgar. Can't remember his name, but Interpol turned him up for us. Plastic explosives expert. Worked for K.G.B. in Turkey. If it's true that the U.2 that fellow Powers was piloting was brought down by delayed charges and not by rockets, it may be this man was implicated. He was on the list of suspects. Then he turned free-lance. Went into business on his own. That's probably when SPECTRE picked him up. We were doubtful about your identification of Blofeld. The Pontresina lead helped a lot. You're absolutely sure of him, are you? He certainly seems to have done a good job on his face and stomach. Better set him up on the Identicast when you get back this evening. We'll have a look at him and get the views of the medical gentry.'

'I think it must be him, sir. I was really getting the authentic smell of him on the last day–yesterday, that is. It seems a long time ago already.'

'You were lucky to run into this girl. Who is she? Some old flame of yours?' M's mouth turned down at the corners.

'More or less, sir. She came into my report on the first news we got that Blofeld was in Switzerland. Daughter of this man Draco, head of the Union Corse. Her mother was an English governess.'

'Hm. Interesting breeding. Now then. Time for lunch. I told Hammond we weren't to be disturbed.' M got up and pressed the bell by the fire-place. ''Fraid we've got to go through the turkey and plum pudding routine. Mrs Hammond's been brooding over her pots and pans for weeks. Damned sentimental rubbish.'

Hammond appeared at the door, and Bond followed M through and into the small dining-room beyond the hall whose walls glittered with M's other hobby, the evolution of the naval cutlass. They sat down. M said, with mock ferocity, to Hammond, 'All right, Chief Petty Officer Hammond. Do your worst.' And then, with real vehemence, 'What in hell are those things doing here?' He pointed at the centre of the table.

'Crackers, sir,' said Hammond stolidly. 'Mrs Hammond thought that seeing as you have company . . .'

'Throw them out. Give 'em to the schoolchildren. I'll go so far with Mrs Hammond, but I'm damned if I'm going to have my dining-room turned into a nursery.'

Hammond smiled. He said, 'Aye, aye, sir,' gathered up the shimmering crackers and departed.

Bond was aching for a drink. He got a small glass of very old Marsala and most of a bottle of very bad Algerian wine.

M treated his two glasses as if they had been Château Lafitte. 'Good old "Infuriator". Staple drink for the fleet in the Mediteranean. Got real guts to it. I remember an old shipmate of mine, McLachlan, my Chief Gunnery Officer at the time, betting he could get down six bottles of the stuff. Damn fool. Measured his length on the wardroom floor after only three. Drink up, James! Drink up!'

At last the plum pudding arrived, flaming traditionally. Mrs Hammond ad implanted several cheap silver gew-gaws in it and M nearly broke a oth on the miniature horseshoe. Bond got the bachelor's button. He ught of Tracy. It should have been the ring!

Chapter Twenty-one

The Man from Ag. and Fish.

They had coffee in M's study and smoked the thin black cheroots of which M allowed himself two a day. Bond burnt his tongue on his. M continued with his stories about the Navy which Bond could listen to all day–stories of battles, tornadoes, bizarre happenings, narrow shaves, courts martial, eccentric officers, neatly-worded signals, as when Admiral Somerville, commanding the battleship *Queen Elizabeth*, had passed the liner *Queen Elizabeth* in mid-Atlantic and had signalled the one word 'SNAP'! Perhaps it was all just the stuff of boys' adventure books, but it was all true and it was about a great navy that was no more and a great breed of officers and seamen that would never be seen again.

It was three o'clock. A car's wheels scrunched on the gravel outside. Dusk was already creeping into the room. M got up and switched on the lights and Bond arranged two more chairs up against the desk. M said, 'That'll be 501. You'll have come across him. Head of the Scientific Research Section. And a man called Franklin from the Ministry of Agriculture. 501 says he's the top on his subject–Pest Control. Don't know why Ag. and Fish. chose to send him in particular, but the Minister told me they've got a bit of trouble on their hands, wouldn't tell even me what it is, and they think you may have run into something pretty big. We'll let them have a look at your report and see what they make of it. All right?'

'Yes, sir.'

The door opened and the two men came in.

Number 501 of the Secret Service, whose name Bond remembered was Leathers, was a big-boned, rangy man with the stoop and thick spectacles of the stage scientist. He had a pleasant, vague smile and no deference, but only politeness, towards M. He was appropriately dressed in shaggy tweeds and his knitted woollen tie didn't cover his collar stud. The other man was small and brisk and keen-looking, with darting, amused eyes. As became a senior representative of a Ministry who had received his orders from his Minister in person and who knew nothing of Secret Services, he had put on a neat dark-blue pin-stripe and a stiff white collar. His black shoes gleamed efficiently. So did the leather of his fat brief-case. His greeting was reserved, neutral. He wasn't quite sure where he was or what this was all about. He was going to smell his way carefully in this business, be wary of what he said and how far he committed his Ministry. Of such, Bond reflected, is 'Government'.

When the appropriate greetings and apologies for disturbed Christmas had been made, and they were in their chairs, M said, 'Mr Franklin, if yo forgive my saying so, everything you are going to see and hear in this roo subject to the Official Secrets Act. You will no doubt be in possessi many secret matters affecting your own Ministry. I would be grateful would respect those of the Ministry of Defence. May I ask you to discuss what you are about to hear only with your Minister personally?'

Mr Franklin made a little bow of acquiescence. 'My Minister has already instructed me accordingly. My particular duties in the Ministry have accustomed me to handling Top Secret matters. You need have no reservations in what you tell me. Now then–' the amused eyes rested on each of the other three in turn–'perhaps you can tell me what this is all about. I know practically nothing except that a man on top of an alp is making efforts to improve our agriculture and livestock. Very decent of him. So why are we treating him as if he had stolen atomic secrets?'

'He did once, as a matter of fact,' said M drily. 'I think the best course would be for you and Mr Leathers to read the report of my representative here. It contains code numbers and other obscure references which need not concern you. The story tells itself without them.' M handed Bond's report to 501. 'Most of this will be new to you also. Perhaps you would like to read a page at a time and then pass them on to Mr Franklin.'

A long silence fell in the room. Bond looked at his finger-nails and listened to the rain on the window panes and the soft noises of the fire. M sat hunched up, apparently in a doze. Across the table the sheets of paper rustled slowly. Bond lit a cigarette. The rasp of his Ronson caused M's eyes to open lazily and then close again. 501 passed across the last page and sat back. Franklin finished his reading, shuffled the pages together and staked them neatly in front of him. He looked at Bond and smiled. 'You're lucky to be here.'

Bond smiled back but said nothing.

M turned to 501. 'Well?'

501 took off his thick spectacles and polished them on a none too clean handkerchief. 'I don't get the object of the exercise, sir. It seems perfectly above-board–praiseworthy, in fact, if we didn't know what we do know about Blofeld. Technically, what he has done is this. He has obtained ten, or rather eleven, counting the one that's left the place, suitable subjects for deep hypnosis. These are all simple girls from the country. It is significant that the one called Ruby had failed her G.C.E. twice. They seem to suffer, and there's no reason to believe that they don't, from certain fairly common forms of allergy. We don't know the origins of their allergies and these are immaterial. They are probably psychosomatic–the adverse reaction to birds is a very common one, as is the one brought on by cattle. The reactions to crops and plants are less common. Blofeld appears to be attempting cures of these allergies by hypnosis, and not only cures, but a pronounced affinity with the cause of the allergy in place of the previous repulsion. In the case of Ruby, for instance, she is told, in the words of the report, to "love" chickens, to wish to "improve their breed" and so forth. The mechanical means of the cure are, in practice, simple. In the twilight stage, on the edge of sleep–the sharp ringing of the bell would waken those who were already asleep–the use of the metronome exactly on the pulse-beat, and the distant whirring noise, are both common hypnotic aids. The singsong, authoritative murmur is the usual voice of the hypnotist. We have no knowledge of what lectures these girls attended or what reading they did, but we can assume that these were merely additional means to influence the mind in the path desired by Blofeld. Now, there is plenty of medical evidence for the efficacy of hypnosis. There are well-authenticated cases of the successful treatment by means of such stubborn disabilities as warts, certain types of asthma,

bed-wetting, stammering, and even alcoholism, drug-taking and homosexual tendencies. Although the British Medical Association frowns officially on the practitioners of hypnosis, you would be surprised, sir, to know how many doctors themselves, as a last resort, particularly in cases of alcoholism, have private treatment from qualified hypnotists. But this is by the way. All I can contribute to this discussion is that Blofeld's ideas are not new and that they can be completely efficacious.'

M nodded, 'Thank you, Mr Leathers. Now would you like to be unscientific and hazard any wild guesses that would contribute in any way to what you have told us?' M smiled briefly. 'You will not be quoted, I can assure you.'

501 ran a worried hand through his hair. 'Well, sir, it may be nonsense, but a train of thought came to me as I read the report. This is a very expensive set-up of Blofeld's. Whether his intentions are benign or malignant, and I must say that I think we can accept them as being malignant, who is paying for all this? How did he fall upon this particular field of research and find the finance for it? Well, sir, this may sound fanciful, looking for burglars under the bed, so to speak, but the leaders in this field, ever since Pavlov and his salivating dogs, have been the Russians. If you recall, sir, at the time of the first human orbiting of the earth by the Russians, I put in a report on the physiology of the astronaut Yuri Gagarin. I drew attention to the simple nature of this man, his equable temperament when faced with his hysterical welcome in London. This equability never failed him and, if you will remember, we kept him under discreet observation throughout his visit and on his subsequent tours abroad, at the request of the Atomic Energy authorities. That bland, smiling face, sir, those wide-apart, innocent eyes, the extreme psychological simplicity of the man, all added up, as I said in my report, to the perfect subject for hypnosis, and I hazarded the guess that, in the extremely complicated movements required of him in his space capsule, Gagarin was operating throughout in a state of deep hypnosis. All right, sir–' 501 made a throw-away gesture of his hand–'my conclusions were officially regarded as fanciful. But, since you ask, I now repeat them, and I throw out the suggestion that the Power behind Blofeld in all this may well be the Russians.' He turned to Bond. 'Was there any sign of Russian inspiration or guidance at this Gloria place? Any Russians anywhere in the offing?'

'Well, there was this man, Captain Boris. I never saw him, but he was certainly a Russian. Otherwise nothing I can think of except the three SPECTRE men who I'd guess were ex-Smersh. But they seemed definitely staff men, what the Americans would call "mechanics".'

501 shrugged. He said to M, 'Well, I'm afraid that's all I can contribute, sir. But, if you come to the conclusion that this is dirty business, for my money, this Captain Boris was either the paymaster or supervisor of the scheme and Blofeld the independent operator. It would fit in with the free-lance character of the old SPECTRE–an independent gang working f[illegible] whoever was willing to pay them.'

'Perhaps you've got something there, Mr Leathers.' said M reflecti[illegible] 'But what the devil's the object of the exercise?' He returned to Fra[illegible] 'Well now, Mr Franklin, what do *you* think of all this?'

The man from Ag. and Fish. had lit a small, highly polished pipe [illegible] it between his teeth and reached down for his brief-case and took [illegible] papers. From among them he extracted a black and white outline map of Britain and Eire and smoothed it down across the desk. The map was dotted with symbols, forests of them here, blank spaces there. He said, 'This is a map showing the total agricultural and livestock resources of Britain and Eire, leaving out grassland and timber. Now, at my first sight of the report, I admit I was completely confused. As Mr Leathers said, these experiments seem perfectly harmless–more than that, to use his word, praiseworthy. But–' Franklin smiled–'you gentlemen are concerned with searching for the dark side of the moon. I adjusted my mind accordingly. The result was that I am filled with a very deep and terrible suspicion. Perhaps these black thoughts have entered my mind by a process of osmosis with the present company's way of looking at the world–' he looked deprecatingly at M–'but I also have one piece of evidence which may be decisive. Excuse me, but there was one sheet of paper missing from the report–the list of the girls and their addresses. Is that available?'

Bond took the photostat out of his inside pocket. 'Sorry. I didn't want to clutter up the report too much.' He slipped it across the table to Franklin.

Franklin ran his eyes down it. Then he said, and there was awe in his voice, 'I've got it! I do believe I've got it!' He sat back heavily in his chair as if he couldn't believe what he had seen.

The three men watched him tensely, believing him, because of what was written on his face–waiting for it.

Franklin took a red pencil out of his breast pocket and leaned over the map. Glancing from time to time at the list, he made a series of red circles at seemingly unrelated points across Britain and Eire, but Bond noticed that they covered the areas where the forests of symbols were at their densest. As he made the circles he commented, 'Aberdeen–Aberdeen Angus, Devon–Red Poll, Lancashire–poultry, Kent–fruit, Shannon–potatoes, until ten red circles stood out on the map. Finally he poised his pencil over East Anglia and made a big cross. He looked up, said 'Turkeys,' and threw his pencil down.

In the silence that followed, M said, rather testily, 'Well, Mr Franklin, what have you in mind?'

The man from Ag. and Fish. had no intention of being pushed about by someone, however grand and hush-hush, from another Ministry. He bent and dug again into his brief-case. He came up with several papers. He selected one, a newspaper cutting. He said, 'I don't expect you gentlemen have time to read much of the agricultural news in the paper, but this is from the *Daily Telegraph* of early December. I won't read it all. It's from their agricultural correspondent, good man by the name of Thomas. These are the headlines: "CONCERN OVER TURKEYS. FLOCKS RAVAGED BY FOWL PEST". Then it goes on: "Supplies of turkeys to the Christmas market may be hit by recent fowl pest outbreaks which have resulted in large numbers of birds being slaughtered . . ." and farther down, "Figures vailable show that 218,000 birds have been slaughtered . . . last year, total pplies for the Christmas market were estimated at between 3,700,000 and 0,000 birds, so much will depend now on the extent of further fowl pest eaks."'

Franklin put the cutting down. He said seriously, 'That news was only f the iceberg. We managed to keep later details out of the press. But I ou this, gentlemen. Within the past four weeks or so we have slaughtered three million turkeys. And that's only the beginning of it. Fowl pest is running wild in East Anglia and there are signs of it in Suffolk and Hampshire, where a lot of turkey-raising goes on. What you ate at lunch today was almost certainly a foreign bird. We allowed the import of two million from America to cover this position up.'

M said sourly, 'Well, so far as I'm concerned, I don't care if I never eat another turkey again. However, I see you've had quite a problem on your hands. But to get back to our case. Where do we go from turkeys?'

Franklin was not amused. He said, 'We have one clue. All the birds that died first were exhibited at the National Poultry Show at Olympia early this month. Olympia had been cleared and cleaned out for the next exhibition before we had reached that conclusion, and we could find no trace on the premises of the virus–Fowl Pest is a virus, by the way, highly infectious, with a mortality of one hundred per cent. Now then–' he held up a stout white pamphlet with the insignia of the United States on it–'how much do you gentlemen know about Biological Warfare?'

Leathers said, 'We were indirectly concerned in the fringes of the subject during the war. But in the end neither side used it. Around 1944 the Americans had a plan for destroying the whole of the Japanese rice crop by the use of aerial sprays. But, as I recall, Roosevelt vetoed the idea.'

'Right,' said Franklin. 'Dead right. But the subject is still very much alive. And very much so in my Ministry. We happen to be the most highly agriculturalized country in the world. We had to make ourselves so during the war to keep ourselves from starvation. So, in theory, we would be an ideal target for an attack of this kind.' He slowly brought his hands down on the table for emphasis. 'I don't think it would be too much to say, gentlemen, that if such an attack could be launched, and it can only be countered by slaughtering the poultry and animals and burning the crops, we would be a bankrupt country within a matter of months. We would literally be down on our knees, begging for bread!'

'Never thought of that,' said M reflectively, 'but it seems to make sense.'

'Now this,' continued Franklin, holding up the pamphlet, 'is the latest thinking on the subject by our friends in America. It also covers Chemical and Radiological Warfare, but we're not concerned with those–CW, BW and RW they call them. It's a United States Senate paper, Number 58991, dated August 29th, 1960, prepared by "The Subcommittee on Disarmament of the Committee of Foreign Relations". My Ministry goes along with the general findings on BW, with the reservation that America is a vast country and we are a very small and tightly-packed one. BW would hit us a thousand times harder that it would hit the States. May I read you a few extracts?'

M positively loathed the problems of other Ministries. In the end, on the Intelligence side, they all ended upon his plate. Bond, amused, watched him summon an expression of polite interest. 'Go ahead, Mr Franklin.'

Chapter Twenty-two

Something called 'BW'

Franklin began reading in an even, expository tone of voice, frequently stopping to explain a point or when he skipped irrelevant passages.

'This section,' he said, 'is headed "Biological Warfare Weapons and Defense". This is how it goes on:

'"Biological Warfare,' he read, 'is often referred to as bacteriological, bacterial, or germ warfare but it is preferred over those terms because it includes all micro-organisms, insects and other pests, and toxic products of plant and animal life. The Army lists five groups of BW agents, including certain chemical compounds used to inhibit or destroy plant growth:

Micro-organisms (bacteria, viruses, rickettsiae, fungi, protozoa.)
Toxins (microbial, animal, plant.)
Vectors of disease (arthropods (insects and acarids), birds and animals.)
Pests (of animals and crops.)
Chemical anti-crop compounds (plant-growth inhibitors, herbicides, defoliants.)

'"Biological Warfare agents, like Chemical Warfare agents, vary in lethality, making it possible to select an agent best suited to accomplish the objective desired, whether it be temporary incapacity with little after-effects or serious illness and many deaths. There are some important differences between BW and CW other than their scientific classifications. BW agents have an incubation period of days, sometimes weeks–' (Franklin looked up. 'See what I mean about Olympia?')–'which produces a lag in their action while CW weapons usually bring reactions within a few seconds to a few hours. CW agents are easier to detect than BW agents, and identification of the latter could often be too late to permit effective counter-measures.' (Franklin again looked significantly at his audience) '. . . BW agents theoretically are more dangerous, weight for weight, than CW agents, though this advantage may be cancelled because of loss of virulence by BW agents under exposure."'

Franklin paused. His finger went down the page. 'Then it goes on to talk about anti-personnel BW agents like anthrax, typhus, smallpox, botulism and so on. Yes–' his finger stopped–'here we are. "Anti-animal BW agents which might be used to incapacitate or destroy domestic animals are

Bacteria: Anthrax, three closely related species of brucella, and glanders.
Viruses: Foot-and-mouth disease, rinderpest, Rift Valley fever, vesicular stomatitis, vesicular exanthema, hog cholera, African swine

fever, fowl plague, Newcastle disease, and equine encephalomyelitis."'

Franklin looked up apologetically. 'Sorry about all this jaw-breaking stuff, but there's not much more of it. Then it goes on to "Anti-crop BW agents", which they say would be used as economic weapons, as I personally think is the case with the Blofeld scheme, and they mention a whole list including potato blight, cereal stem disease, crown rust of oats, curly top disease of sugar beets, block rot of crucifers and potato ring rot, and insects such as the Colorado beetle and something called "the Giant African Land-snail", which I somehow don't think we need worry about. Then they talk about "chemical anti-crop agents", but I don't think we need worry about those either as they'd have to be sprayed from an aeroplane, though, for what it's worth, they're damned lethal. Now, this is more to the point.' Franklin's finger halted on the page. '"The nature of BW agents makes them very adaptable for covert or undercover operations. The fact that these agents are so concentrated, cannot be detected by physical senses, and have a delayed casualty effect, would enable an operator quietly to introduce effective amounts into building ventilation systems, food and water supplies, and other places where they would be spread rapidly through contact with a heavily concentrated population."' Franklin paused. 'And that means us. You see what I mean about livestock shows and so on? After the show, the virus gets carried off all over the country by the exhibits.' He went back to his pamphlet. 'And here it goes on, "A significant factor is that the possible area of effective coverage is generally greater with BW than with CW agents. tests have been made which show that coverage measured in the thousands of square miles is quite feasible with biological agents."' Franklin tapped the paper in front of him. 'How about that, gentlemen? We talk about the new poison gases, the nerve gases the Germans invented in the war. We march and counter-march about radiation and the atom bomb. "Thousands of square miles" it says here. A Committee of the United States Senate says it. How many thousands of square miles are there in the United Kingdom and Eire, gentlemen?' The eyes, urgent and holding humour no longer, looked almost scornfully into the faces of these three top officers of the Secret Service. 'I'll tell you. There are only something over one hundred thousand square miles of this little atoll of ours, including the little atoll of all Ireland.' His eyes retained their fire. 'And let me just give you a last quote and then perhaps–' the eyes regained some of their humour–'you'll realize why I'm getting so steamed up on this Day of Goodwill to all Men. Look here, what it says under "Defensive Measures". It says, "Defense against BW warfare is greatly complicated by the difficulties involved in detection of BW agents, a situation which is almost unique as to these weapons."' (Franklin looked up and now he smiled. 'Bad English. Perhaps we might improve on "as to".) "They cannot be detected by sight, smell, or any other physical sense. So far no means have been devised for their quick detection and identification."'

Franklin threw the pamphlet on to the desk. Suddenly he gave a big, embracing smile. He reached for his little polished pipe and began filling it 'All right, gentlemen. The prosecution rests.'

Franklin had had his day, a Christmas he would never forget.

M said, 'Thank you, Mr Franklin. Am I right in thinking that conclude that this man Blofeld is mounting Biological Warfare against this country?'

'Yes.' Franklin was definite. 'I am.'

'And how do you work that out? It seems to me he's doing exactly the opposite–or rather it would if I didn't know something about the man. Anyway, what are your deductions?'

Franklin reached over and pointed to the red cross he had made over East Anglia. 'That was my first clue. The girl, Polly Tasker, who left this Gloria place over a month ago, came from somewhere round here where you'll see from the symbols that there's the greatest concentration of turkey farmers. She suffered from an allergy against turkeys. She came back inspired to improve the breed. Within a week of her return, we have the biggest outbreak of fowl pest affecting turkeys in the history of England.'

Leathers suddenly slapped his thigh. 'By God, I think you've got it, Franklin! Go on!'

'Now–' Franklin turned to Bond–'when this officer took a look into the laboratory up there he saw rack upon rack of test-tubes containing what he describes as "a cloudy liquid". How would it be if those were viruses, Fowl Pest, anthrax, God knows what all? The report mentions that the laboratory was lit with a dim red light. That would be correct. Virus cultures suffer from exposure to bright light. And how would it be if before this Polly girl left she was given an aerosol spray of the right stuff and told that this was some kind of turkey elixir–a tonic to make them grow fatter and healthier. Remember that stuff about "improving the breed" in the hypnosis talk? And suppose she was told to go to Olympia for the Show, perhaps even take a job for the meeting as a cleaner or something, and just casually spray this aerosol here and there among the prize birds. It wouldn't be bigger than one of those shaving-soap bombs. That'd be quite enough. She'd been told to keep it secret, that it was patent stuff. Perhaps even that she'd be given shares in the company if the tonic proved the success this man Blofeld claimed it would. It'd be quite easy to do so. She'd just wander round the cages–perhaps she was even given a special purse to carry the thing in–lean up against the wire and psst! the job would be done. Easy as falling off a log. All right, if you'll go along with me so far, she was probably told to do the job on one of the last two days of the show, so that the effects wouldn't be seen too soon. Then, at the end of the show, all the prize birds are dispersed back to their owners all over England. And that's that! And–' he paused–'mark you, that *was* that. Three million birds dead and still dying all over the place, and a great chunk of foreign currency coughed up by the Treasury to replace them.'

Leathers, his face red with excitement, butted in. He swept his hand over the map. 'And the other girls! All from the danger spots. All from the areas of greatest concentration. Local shows taking place all the time–cattle, poultry, even potatoes–Colorado beetle for that crop, I suppose, Swine Fever for the pigs. Golly!' There was reverence in Leathers's voice. 'And it's so damned simple! All you'd need would be to keep the viruses at the right temperature for a while. They'd be instructed in that, the little darlings. And all the time they'd be sure they were being saints! Marvellous. I really must hand it to the man.'

M's face was thunderous with the fury of his indecision. He turned to Bond. He barked, 'What do you think?'

'I'm afraid it fits, sir. The whole way along the line. We know the man. It fits him too. Right up his street. And it doesn't even matter who's paying him. He can pay himself, make a fortune. All he has to do is go a bear of sterling or Gilt-Edged. If Mr Franklin's right, and that Senate paper's pretty solid backing for him, our currency'll literally go through the floor–and the country with it.'

M got to his feet. He said, 'All right, gentlemen. Mr Franklin, will you tell your Minister what you've heard? It'll be up to him to tell the P.M. and the Cabinet as he thinks fit. I'll get on with the preventive measures, first of all through Sir Ronald Vallance of the C.I.D. We must pick up this Polly woman and get the others as they come into the country. They'll be gently treated. It's not their fault. Then we'll have to think what to do with Mister Blofeld.' He turned to Bond. 'Stay behind, would you?'

Goodbyes were said and M rang for Hammond to see the other two out. He then rang again. 'Tea, please, Hammond.' He turned to Bond. 'Or rather have a whisky and soda?'

'Whisky, please, sir,' said Bond with infinite relief.

'Rot-gut,' commented M. He walked over to the window and looked out at the darkness and rain.

Bond drew Franklin's map towards him and studied it. He reflected that he was learning quite a lot on this case–about other people's businesses, other people's secrets, from the innards of the College of Arms to the innards of Ag. and Fish. Odd how this gigantic, many-branched tree had grown from one tiny seed in September–a girl calling banco in a casino and not having the money to pay. And what about Bond's letter of resignation? That looked pretty silly now. He was up to his ears, as deeply as ever in his life before, in his old profession. And now a big mopping-up job would have to be done. And he would have to do it, or at any rate lead it, organize it. And Bond knew exactly what he was going to put to M when the tea and whisky came. Only *he* could do the cleaning up. It was written in his stars!

Hammond came in with the tray and withdrew. M came back to his desk, gruffly told Bond to pour himself a whisky, and himself took a vast cup, as big as a baby's chamber-pot, of black tea without sugar or milk, and put it in front of him.

At length he said moodily, 'This is a dirty business, James. But I'm afraid it makes sense. Better do something about it, I suppose.' He reached for the red telephone with scrambler attachment that stood beside the black one on his desk and picked up the receiver. It was a direct line to that very private switchboard in Whitehall to which perhaps fifty people in all Britain have access. 'Put me on to Sir Ronald Vallance, would you? Home number, I suppose.' He reached out and took a deep gulp at his cup of tea and put the cup back on its saucer. Then, 'That you, Vallance? M here. Sorry to disturb your afternoon nap.' There was an audible explosion at the other end of the line! M smiled. 'Reading a report on teen-age prostitution? I'm ashamed of you. On Christmas Day too. Well, scramble, would you?' M pressed down the large black button on the side of the cradle. 'Right? Now I'm afraid this is top priority. Remember Blofeld and the Thunderball case? Well, he's up t[illegible] his tricks again. Too long to explain now. You'll get my side of the report [illegible] the morning. And Ag. and Fish. are mixed up in it. Yes, of all people. M[illegible] called Franklin is your contact. One of their top pest-control men. Only [illegible] and his Minister. So would your chaps report to him, copy to me? I'm [illegible] dealing with the foreign side. Your friend 007's got the ball. Yes, same[illegible]

He can fill you in with any extra detail you may need on the foreign angles. Now, the point is this. Even though it's Christmas and all that, could your chaps try at once and lay their hands on a certain girl, Polly Tasker, aged about 25, who lives in East Anglia? Yes, I know it's a hell of a big area, but she'll probably come from a respectable lower-middle-class family connected with turkey farming. Certainly find the family in the telephone book. Can't give you any description, but she's just been spending several weeks in Switzerland. Got back the last week in November. Don't be ridiculous! Of course you can manage it. And when you find her, take her into custody for importing Fowl Pest into the country. Yes, that's right.' M spelt it out. 'The stuff that's been killing all our turkeys.' M muttered 'Thank God!' away from the receiver. 'No, I didn't say anything. Now, be kind to the girl. She didn't know what she was doing. And tell the parents it'll be all right. If you need a formal charge, you'll have to get one out of Franklin. Then tell Franklin when you've got her and he'll come down and ask her one or two simple questions. When he's got the answers, you can let her go. Right? But we've *got* to find that girl. You'll see why all right when you've read the report. Now then, next assignment. There are ten girls of much the same type as this Polly Tasker who'll probably be flying from Zürich to England and Eire any day from tomorrow on. Each one has got to be held by the Customs at the port or airport of entry. 007 has a list of their names and fairly good descriptions. My people in Zürich may or may not be able to give us warning of their arrival. Is that all right? Yes, 007 will bring the list to Scotland Yard this evening. No, I can't tell you what it's all about. Too long a story. But have you ever heard of Biological Warfare? That's right. Anthrax and so on. Well, this is it. Yes. Blofeld again. I know. That's what I'm just going to talk to 007 about. Well now, Vallance, have you got all that? Fine.' M listened. He smiled grimly. 'And a Happy Christmas to *you*.'

He put the receiver back and the scrambler button automatically clicked to OFF. He looked across at Bond. He said, with a hint of weariness, 'Well, that's taken care of this end. Vallance said it was about time we had this fellow Blofeld in the bag. I agree. And that's *our* job. And I don't for a moment think we're going to get any help from the Swiss. Even if we were to, they'd trample all over the case with their big boots for weeks before we saw any action. By that time the man would be in Peking or somewhere, cooking up something else.' M looked straight at Bond. 'Any ideas?'

It had come, as Bond knew it would. He took a deep pull at his whisky and put the glass carefully down. He began talking, urgently, persuasively. As he expounded his plan, M's face sank deeper and deeper in gloom, and, when Bond concluded with 'And that's the only way I can see, sir. All I need is two weeks' leave of absence. I could put in a letter of resignation if it would help,' M turned in his chair and gazed deep into the dying flames of the log fire.

Bond sat quietly, waiting for the verdict. He hoped it would be yes, but he also hoped it would be no. That damned mountain! He never wanted to see the bloody thing again!

M turned back. The grey eyes were fierce. 'All right, 007. Go ahead. I n't go to the P.M. about it. He'd refuse. But for God's sake bring it off. I 't mind being sacked, but we don't want to get the Government mixed n another U.2 fiasco. Right?'

nderstand, sir. And I can have the two weeks' leave?'

.'

Chapter Twenty-three

Gauloises and Garlic

With the Walther PPK in its leather holster warm against his stomach and his own name in his passport, James Bond looked out of the window at the English Channel sliding away beneath the belly of the Caravelle and felt more like his old, his pre-Sir Hilary Bray, self.

He glanced at the new Rolex on his wrist–the shops were still shut and he had had to blarney it out of Q Branch–and guessed they would be on time, 6 p.m. at Marseilles. It had been the hell of a rush to get off. He had worked until late in the night at H.Q. and all that morning, setting up the Identicast of Blofeld, checking details with Ronnie Vallance, fixing up the private, the Munich side of his life, chattering on the teleprinter to Station Z, even remembering to tell Mary Goodnight to get on to Sable Basilisk after the holiday and ask him to please do some kind of job on the surnames of the ten girls and please to have the family tree of Ruby Windsor embellished with gold capitals.

At midnight he had called Tracy in Munich and heard her darling, excited voice. 'I've got the tooth-brush, James,' she had said, 'and a pile of books. Tomorrow I'm going to go up the Zugspitze and sit in the sun so as to look pretty for you. Guess what I had for dinner tonight in my room! Krebsschwänze mit Dilltunke. That's crayfish tails with rice and a cream and dill sauce. And Rehrücken mit Sahne. That's saddle of roebuck with a smitane sauce. I bet it was better than what you had.'

'I had two ham sandwiches with stacks of mustard and half a pint of Harper's Bourbon on the rocks. The bourbon was better than the ham. Now listen, Tracy, and stop blowing down the telephone.'

'I was only sighing with love.'

'Well, you must have got a Force Five sigh. Now listen. I'm posting my birth certificate to you tomorrow with a covering letter to the British Consul saying I want to get married to you as soon as possible. Look, you're going up to Force Ten! For God's sake pay attention. It'll take a few days, I'm afraid. They have to post the banns or something. He'll tell you all about it. Now, you must quickly get your birth certificate and give it to him, too. Oh, you have, have you?' Bond laughed. 'So much the better. Then we're all set. I've got three days or so of work to do and I'm going down to see your father tomorrow and ask for you hand, both of them, and the feet and all the rest, in marriage. No, you're to stay where you are. This is men's talk. Will he be awake? I'm going to ring him up now. Good. Well, now you go off to sleep or you'll be too tired to say "Yes" when the time comes.'

They had not wanted to let go of each other's voices, but finally the last good-night, the last kiss, had been exchanged, and Bond called the Marseilles number of Appareils Électriques Draco, and Marc-Ange's voice, almost as excited as Tracy's, was on the line. Bond dampened down the raptures about the 'fiançailles' and said, 'Now listen, Marc-Ange. I want you to give me a wedding present.'

'Anything, my dear James. Anything I possess.' He laughed. 'And perhaps certain things of which I could take possession. What is it you would like?'

'I'll tell you tomorrow evening. I'm booked on the afternoon Air France to Marseilles. Will you have someone meet me? And it's business, I'm afraid. So could you have your other directors present for a little meeting? We shall need all our brains. It is about our sales organization in Switzerland. Something drastic needs to be done about it.'

'Aha!' There was full understanding in the voice. 'Yes, it is indeed a bad spot on our sales map. I will certainly have my colleagues available. And I assure you, my dear James, that anything that can be done will be done. And of course you will be met. I shall perhaps not be there in person–it is very cold out these winter evenings. But I shall see that you are properly looked after. Good night, my dear fellow. Good night.'

The line had gone dead. The old fox! Had he thought Bond might commit an indiscretion, or had he got fitted to his telephone a 'bug-meter', the delicate instrument that measures the resonance on the line and warns of listening-in?

The winter sun spread a last orange glow over the thick overcast 10,000 feet below the softly whistling plane and switched itself off for the night.

Bond dozed, reflecting that he must somehow, and pretty soon, find a way of catching up on his sleep.

There was a stage-type Marseilles taxi-driver to meet Bond–the archetype of all Mariuses, with the face of a pirate and the razor-sharp badinage of the lower French music-halls. He was apparently known and enjoyed by everyone at the airport, and Bond was whisked through the formalities in a barrage of wisecracks about 'le milord anglais', which made Marius, for his name turned out in fact to be Marius, the centre of attraction and Bond merely his butt, the dim-witted English tourist. But, once in the taxi, Marius made curt, friendly apologies over his shoulder. 'I ask your pardon for my bad manners.' His French had suddenly purified itself of all patois. It also smelt like acetylene gas. 'I was told to extract you from the airport with the least possible limelight directed upon you. I know all those 'flics' and douaniers. They all know me. If I had not been myself, the cab-driver they know as Marius, if I had shown deference, eyes, inquisitive eyes, would have been upon you, mon Commandant. I did what I thought best. You forgive me?'

'Of course I do, Marius. But you shouldn't have been so funny. You nearly made me laugh. That would have been fatal.'

'You understand our talk here?'

'Enough of it.'

'So!' There was a pause. Then Marius said, 'Alas, since Waterloo, one can never underestimate the English.'

Bond said, seriously, 'The same date applied to the French. It was a near thing.' This was getting too gallant. Bond said, 'Now tell me, is the bouillabaisse chez Guido always as good?'

'It is passable,' said Marius. 'But this is a dish that is dead, gone. There is no more true bouillabaisse, because there is no more fish in the

Mediterranean. For the bouillabaisse, you must have the rascasse, the tender flesh of the scorpion fish. Today they just use hunks of morue. The saffron and the garlic, they are always the same. But you could eat pieces of a woman soaked in those and it would be good. Go to any of the little places down by the harbour. Eat the plat du jour and drink the vin du Cassis that they give you. It will fill your stomach as well as it fills the fishermen's. The toilette will be filthy. What does that matter? You are a man. You can walk up the Canebière and do it at the Noailles for nothing after lunch.'

They were now weaving expertly through the traffic down the famous Canebière and Marius needed all his breath to insult the other drivers. Bond could smell the sea. The accordions were playing in the cafés. He remembered old times in this most criminal and tough of all French towns. He reflected that it was rather fun, this time, being on the side of the devil.

At the bottom of the Canebière, where it crosses the Rue de Rome, Marius turned right and then left into the Rue St Ferréol, only a long stone's throw from the Quai des Belges and the Vieux Port. The lights from the harbour's entrance briefly winked at them and then the taxi drew up at a hideous, but very new apartment house with a broad vitrine on the ground floor, which announced in furious neon 'Appareils Électriques Draco'. The well-lit interior of the store contained what you would expect–television sets, radios, gramophones, electric irons, fans and so forth. Marius very quickly carried Bond's suitcase across the pavement and through the swing doors beside the vitrine. The close-carpeted hallway was more luxurious than Bond had expected. A man came out of the porter's lodge beside the lift and wordlessly took the suitcase. Marius turned to Bond, gave him a smile and a wink and a bone-crushing handshake, said curtly, 'A la prochaine,' and hurried out. The porter stood beside the open door of the lift. Bond noticed the bulge under his right arm and, out of curiosity, brushed against the man as he entered the lift. Yes, and something big too, a real stopper. The man gave Bond a bored look, as much as to say, 'Clever? Eh?' and pressed the top button. The porter's twin, or very nearly his twin–dark, chunky, brown-eyed, fit–was waiting at the top floor. He took Bond's suitcase and led the way down a corridor, close-carpeted and with wall brackets in good taste. He opened a door. It was an extremely comfortable bedroom with a bathroom leading off. Bond imagined that the big picture window, now curtained, would have a superb view of the harbour. The man put down his suitcase and said, 'Monsieur Draco est immédiatement à votre disposition.'

Bond thought it time to make some show of independence. He said firmly, 'Un moment, je vous en prie,' and went into the bathroom and cleaned himself up–amused to notice that the soap was that most English of soaps, Pears Transparent, and that there was a bottle of Mr Trumper's 'Eucris' beside the very masculine brush and comb by Kent. Marc-Ange was indeed making his English guest feel at home!

Bond took his time, then went out and followed the man to the end door. The man opened it without knocking and closed it behind Bond. Marc-Ange, his creased walnut face split by his great golden-toothed smile, got up from his desk (Bond was getting tired of desks!) trotted across the broad room, threw his arms round Bond's neck and kissed him squarely on both cheeks. Bond suppressed his recoil and gave a reassuring pat to Marc-Ange's broad back. Marc-Ange stood away and laughed. 'All right! I swear never to do it again. It is once and for ever. Yes? But it had to come out–fro the Latin temperament, isn't it? You forgive me? Good. Then come and take a drink–' he waved at a loaded sideboard–'and sit down and tell me what I can do for you. I swear not to talk about Teresa until you have finished with your business. But tell me–' the brown eyes pleaded–'it is all right between you? You have not changed your mind?'

Bond smiled. 'Of course not, Marc-Ange. And everything is arranged. We will be married within the week. At the Consulate in Munich. I have two weeks' leave. I thought we might spend the honeymoon in Kitzbühel. I love that place. So does she. You will come to the wedding?'

'Come to the wedding!' Marc-Ange exploded. 'You will have a time keeping me away from Kitzbühel. Now then–' he waved at the sideboard–'take your drink while I compose myself. I must stop being happy and be clever instead. My two best men, my organizers if you like, are waiting. I wanted to have you for a moment to myself.'

Bond poured himself a stiff Jack Daniel's sourmash bourbon on the rocks and added some water. He walked over to the desk and took the right-hand of the three chairs that had been arranged in a semicircle facing the 'Capu'. 'I wanted that too, Marc-Ange. Because there are some things I must tell you which affect my country. I have been granted leave to tell them to you, but they must remain, as you put it, behind the Herkos Odonton–behind the hedge of your teeth. Is that all right?'

Marc-Ange lifted his right hand and crossed his heart, slowly, deliberately, with his forefinger. His face was now deadly serious, almost cruelly implacable. He leaned forward and rested his forearms on the desk. 'Continue.'

Bond told him the whole story, not even omitting his passage with Ruby. He had developed much love, and total respect, for this man. He couldn't say why. It was partly animal magnetism and partly that Marc-Ange had so opened his heart to Bond, so completely trusted him with his own innermost secrets.

Marc-Ange's face remained impassive throughout. Only his quick, animal eyes flickered continually across Bond's face. When Bond had finished, Marc-Ange sat back. He reached for a blue packet of Gauloises, fixed one in the corner of his mouth and talked through the blue clouds of smoke that puffed continuously out through his lips, as if somewhere inside him there was a small steam-engine. 'Yes, it is indeed a dirty business. It must be finished with, destroyed, and the man too. My dear James–' the voice was sombre–'I am a criminal, a great criminal. I run houses, chains of prostitutes, I smuggle, I sell protection, whenever I can, I steal from the very rich. I break many laws and I have often had to kill in the process. Perhaps one day, perhaps very soon, I shall reform. But it is difficult to step down from being Capu of the Union. Without the protection of my men, my life would not be worth much. However, we shall see. But this Blofeld, he is too bad, too disgusting. You have come to ask the Union to make war on him, to destroy him. You need not answer. I know it is so. This is something that cannot be done officially. Your Chief is correct. You would get nowhere with the Swiss. You wish me and my men to do the job.' He smiled suddenly. 'That is the wedding present you talked of. Yes?'

'That's right, Marc-Ange. But I'll do my bit. I'll be there too. I want this man for myself.'

Marc-Ange looked at him thoughtfully. 'That I do not like. And you know why I do not like it.' He said mildly, 'You are a bloody fool, James. You are already lucky to be alive.' He shrugged. 'But I am wasting my breath. You started on a long road after this man. And you want to come to the end of it. Is that right?'

'That's right. I don't want someone else to shoot my fox.'

'O.K., O.K. We bring in the others, yes? They will not need to know the reason why. My orders are my orders. But we all need to know *how* we are to bring this about. I have some ideas. I think it can be done and swiftly done. But it must also be well done, cleanly done. There must be no untidiness about this thing.'

Marc-Ange picked up his telephone and spoke into it. A minute later the door opened and two men came in and, with hardly a glance at Bond, took the other two chairs.

Marc-Ange nodded at the one next to Bond, a great ox of a man with the splayed ears and broken nose of a boxer or wrestler. 'This is Ché-Ché–Ché-Ché le Persuadeur. And–' Marc-Ange smiled grimly–'he is very adept at persuading.'

Bond got a glimpse of two hard yellow-brown eyes that looked at him quickly, reluctantly, and then went back to the Capu. 'Plaisir.'

'And this is Toussaint, otherwise known as "Le Pouff". He is our expert with le plastique. We shall need plenty of plastique.'

'We shall indeed,' said Bond, 'with pretty quick time-pencils.'

Toussaint leaned forward to show himself. He was thin and grey-skinned, with an almost fine Phoenician profile pitted with smallpox. Bond guessed that he was on heroin, but not as a mainliner. He gave Bond a brief, conspiratorial smile. 'Plaisir.' He sat back.

'And this–' Marc-Ange gestured at Bond–'is my friend. My absolute friend. He is simply "Le Commandant". And now to business.' He had been speaking in French, but he now broke into rapid Corsican which, apart from a few Italian and French roots, was incomprehensible to Bond. At one period he drew a large-scale map of Switzerland out of a drawer of his desk, spread it out, searched with his finger and pointed to a spot in the centre of the Engadine. The two men craned forward, examined the map carefully and then sat back. Ché-Ché said something which contained the word Strasbourg and Marc-Ange nodded enthusiastically. He turned to Bond and handed him a large sheet of paper and a pencil. 'Be a good chap and get to work on this, would you? A map of the Gloria buildings, with approximate sizes and distances from each other. Later we will do a complete maquette in plasticine so that there is no confusion. Every man will have his job to do–' he smiled–'like the commandos in the war. Yes?'

Bond bent to his task while the others talked. The telephone rang. Marc-Ange picked it up. He jotted down a few words and rang off. He turned to Bond, his eyes momentarily suspicious. 'It is a telegram for me from London signed Universal. It says, "The birds have assembled in the town and all fly tomorrow." What is this, my friend?'

Bond kicked himself for his forgetfulness. 'I'm sorry, Marc-Ange. I meant to tell you you might get a signal like that. It means that the girls are in Zürich and are flying to England tomorrow. It is very good news. It was important to have them out of the way.'

'Ah, good! Very good indeed! That is fine news. And you were quite righ not to have the telegram addressed to you. You are not supposed to be he or to know me at all. It is better so.' He fired some more Corsican at the two men. They nodded their understanding.

After that, the meeting soon broke up. Marc-Ange examined Bond's handiwork and passed it over to Toussaint. The man glanced at the sketch and folded it as if it were a valuable share-certificate. With short bows in Bond's direction, the two men left the room.

Marc-Ange sat back with a sigh of satisfaction. 'It goes well,' he said. 'The whole team will receive good danger money. And they love a good rough fight. And they are pleased that I am coming to lead them.' He laughed slyly. 'They are less certain of you, my dear James. They say you will get in the way. I had to tell them that you could outshoot and outfight the lot of them. When I say something like that, they have to believe me. I have never let them down yet. I hope I am right?'

'Please don't try me,' said Bond. 'I've never taken on a Corsican and I don't want to start now.'

Marc-Ange was delighted. 'You might win with guns. But not in close combat. They are pigs, my men. Great pigs. The greatest. I am taking five of the best. With you and me that is seven. How many did you say there are on the mountain?'

'About eight. And the big one.'

'Ah yes, the big one,' said Marc-Ange reflectively. 'That is one that must not get away.' He got up. 'And now, my friend, I have ordered dinner, a good dinner, to be served us up here. And then we will go to bed stinking of garlic and, perhaps, just a little bit drunk. Yes?'

From his heart Bond said, 'I can't think of anything better.'

Chapter Twenty-four

Blood-Lift

The next day, after lunch, Bond made his way by plane and train to the Hotel Maison Rouge at Strasbourg, his breath bearing him close company like some noisome, captive pet.

He was totally exhilarated by his hours with Marc-Ange in Marseilles and by the prospects before him–the job that was to be done and, at the end of it, Tracy.

The morning had been an endless series of conferences round the model of Piz Gloria and its buildings that had been put up in the night. New faces came, received their orders in a torrent of dialect, and disappeared–rough, murderous faces, bandits' faces, but all bearing one common expression, devotion to their Capu. Bond was vastly impressed by the authority and incisiveness of Marc-Ange as he dealt with each problem, each contingency, from the obtaining of a helicopter down to the pensions that would be paid to the families of the dead. Marc-Ange hadn't liked the helicopter business. He had explained to Bond, 'You see, my friend, there is only one source for this machine, the O.A.S., the French secret army of the right wing. It happens that they are under an obligation to me, a heavy one, and that is the way I would have it. I do not like being mixed up in politics. I like the country where I operate to be orderly, peaceful. I do not like revolutions. They make chaos everywhere. Today, I never know when an operation of my own is not going to be interfered with by some damned emergency concerning Algerian terrorists, the rounding up of some nest of these blasted O.A.S. And road blocks! House to house searches! They are the bane of my existence. My men can hardly move without falling over a nest of flies or S.D.T. spies–that, as I'm sure you know, is the latest of the French Secret Services. They are getting as bad as the Russians with their constant changes of initials. It is the Section Défense Territoire. It comes under the Ministry of the Interior and I am finding it most troublesome and difficult to penetrate. Not like the good old Deuxième. It makes life for the peace-loving very difficult. But I naturally have my men in the O.A.S. and I happen to know that the O.A.S. has a military helicopter, stolen from the French Army, hidden away at a château on the Rhine not far from Strasbourg. The château belongs to some crazy fascist count. He is one of those Frenchmen who cannot live without conspiring against something. So now he has put all his money and property behind this General Salan. His château is remote. He poses as an inventor. His farm people are not surprised that there is some kind of flying machine kept in an isolated barn with mechanics to tend it–O.A.S. mechanics, bien entendu. And now, early this morning, I have spoken on my radio to the right man and I have the machine on loan for twenty-four hours with the best pilot in their secret air force. He is already on his way to the place to make his preparations, fuel and so on. But it is unfortunate. Before, these people were in my debt. Now I am in theirs.' He shrugged. 'What matter? I will soon have them under my thumb again. Half the police and Customs officers in France are Corsicans. It is an important laissez-passer for the Union Corse. You understand?'

At the Maison Rouge, a fine room had been booked for Bond. He was greeted with exaggerated courtesy tinged with reserve. Where didn't the freemasonry of the Union operate? Bond, obedient to the traditions of the town, made a simple dinner off the finest foie gras, pink and succulent, and half a bottle of champagne, and retired gratefully to bed. He spent the next morning in his room, changed into his ski clothes and sent out for a pair of snow-goggles and thin leather gloves, sufficient to give some protection to his hands but close-fitting enough for the handling of his gun. He took the magazine out of his gun, pumped out the single round in the chamber and practised shooting himself in the wardrobe mirror with the gloves on until he was satisfied. Then he reloaded and got the fitting of the stitched pigskin holster comfortable inside the waist-band of his trousers. He had his bill sent up and paid it, and ordered his suitcase to be forwarded on to Tracy at the Vier Jahreszeiten. Then he sent for the day's papers and sat in front of the window, watching the traffic in the street and forgetting what he read.

When, at exactly midday, the telephone rang, he went straight down and out to the grey Peugeot 403 he had been told to expect. The driver was Ché-Ché. He acknowledged Bond's greeting curtly and, in silence, they drove for an hour across the uninteresting countryside, finally turning left off a secondary road into a muddy lane that meandered through thick forest. In due course there was the ill-kept stone wall of a large property and ther vast broken-down iron gateway leading into a park. On the unweeded driveway were the recent tracks of vehicles. They followed these past the dilapidated façade of a once-imposing château, on through the forest to where the trees gave way to fields. On the edge of the trees was a large barn in good repair. They stopped outside and Ché-Ché sounded three shorts on his horn. A small door in the wide double doors of the barn opened and Marc-Ange came out. He greeted Bond cheerfully. 'Come along in, my friend. You are just in time for some good Strasbourg sausage and a passable Riquewihr. Rather thin and bitter. I would have christened it "Château Pis-de-Chat", but it serves to quench the thirst.'

Inside it was almost like a film set. Lights blazed down on the ungainly shape of the Army helicopter and from somewhere came the cough of a small generator. The place seemed to be full of people. Bond recognized the faces of the Union men. The others were, he assumed, the local mechanics. Two men on ladders were busily engaged painting red crosses on white backgrounds on the black-painted fuselage of the machine, and the paint of the recognition letters, FL-BGS, presumably civilian and false, still glittered wetly. Bond was introduced to the pilot, a bright-eyed, fair-haired young man in overalls called Georges. 'You will be sitting beside him,' explained Marc-Ange. 'He is a good navigator, but he doesn't know the last stretch up the valley and he has never heard of Piz Gloria. You had better go over the maps with him after some food. The general route is Basle-Zürich.' He laughed cheerfully. He said in French, 'We are going to have some interesting conversation with the Swiss Air Defences, isn't it, Georges?'

Georges didn't smile. He said briefly, 'I think we can fool them,' and went about his business.

Bond accepted a foot of garlic sausage, a hunk of bread and a bottle of the 'Pis-de-Chat', and sat on an upturned packing-case while Marc-Ange went back to supervising the loading of the 'stores'–Schmeisser sub-machine guns and six-inch square packets in red oilcloth.

In due course, Marc-Ange lined up his team, including Bond, and carried out a quick inspection of side-arms, which, in the case of the Union men, included well-used flick-knives. The men, as well as Marc-Ange, were clothed in brand-new ski clothes of grey cloth. Marc-Ange handed to all of them armlets in black cloth bearing the neatly stitched words 'Bundesalpenpolizei'. When Marc-Ange gave Bond his, he commented. 'There is no such force as the "Federal Police of the Alps". But I doubt if our SPECTRE friends will know that. At least the armbands will make an important first impression.'

Marc-Ange looked at his watch. He turned and called out in French, 'Two forty-five. All ready? Then let us roll!'

The farm tractor attached to the wheel-base of the helicopter started up, the gates of the barn were thrown wide and the great metal insect moved slowly out on to the grassland under the pale winter sun. The tractor was uncoupled and the pilot, followed by Bond, climbed up the little aluminium ladder and then into the raised cockpit and strapped themselves in. The others followed into the ten-seat cabin, the ladder was pulled up and the door banged and locked. On the ground, the mechanics lifted their thumbs and the pilot bent to his controls. He pressed the starter and, after a first indecisive cough, the engine fired healthily and the great blades began to turn. The pilot glanced back at the whirring tail-rotor. He waited while the needle on the rotor speed-indicator crept up to 200, then he released the wheel-brakes and pulled up slowly on the pitch-lever. The helicopter trembled, unwilling to leave the earth, but then came a slight jerk and they were up and climbing rapidly above the trees. The pilot retracted his wheels above the inflated snow-floats, gave the machine left rudder, pushed forward the joystick, and they were off.

Almost at once they were over the Rhine and Basle lay ahead under a thick canopy of chimney-smoke. They reached two thousand feet and the pilot held it, skirting the town to the north. Now there came a crackle of static over Bond's ear-phones and Swiss Air Control, in thick Schwyzerdütch, asked them politely to identify themselves. The pilot made no reply and the question was repeated with more urgency. The pilot said in French, 'I don't understand you.' There was a pause, then a French voice again queried them. The pilot said, 'Repeat yourself more clearly.' The voice did so. The pilot said, 'Helicopter of the Red Cross flying blood plasma to Italy.' The radio went dead. Bond could imagine the scene in the control room somewhere down below–the arguing voices, the doubtful faces. Another voice, with more authority to it, spoke in French. 'What is your destination?' 'Wait,' said the pilot. 'I have it here. A moment please.' After minutes he said, 'Swiss Air Control?' 'Yes, yes.' 'FL-BGS reporting. My destination is Ospedale Santa Monica at Bellinzona.' The radio again went dead, only to come to life five minutes later. 'FL-BGS, FL-BGS.' 'Yes,' said the pilot. 'We have no record of your identification symbol. Please explain.' 'Your registration manual must be out of date. The aircraft was commissioned only one month ago.' Another long pause. Now Zürich lay ahead and the silver boomerang of the Zürichersee. Now Zürich Airport came on the air. They must have been listening to Swiss Air Control. 'FL-BGS, FL-BGS.' 'Yes, yes. What is it now?' 'You have infringed the Civil Airlines Channel. Land and report to Flying Control. I repeat. Land and report.' The pilot became indignant. 'What do you mean "land and report"? Have you no comprehension of human suffering? This is a mercy flight carrying blood plasma of a rare category. It is to save the life of an illustrious Italian scientist at Bellinzona. Have you no hearts down there? You tell me to "land and report" when a life is at stake? Do you wish to be responsible for murder?' This Gallic outburst gave them peace until they had passed the Zürichersee. Bond chuckled. He gave a thumbs-up sign to the pilot. But then Federal Air Control at Berne came on the air and a deep, resonant voice said, 'FL-BGS, FL-BGS. Who gave you clearance? I repeat. Who gave you clearance for your flight?' 'You did.' Bond smiled into his mouthpiece. The Big Lie! There was nothing like it. Now the Alps were ahead of them–those blasted Alps, looking beautiful and dangerous in the evening sun. Soon they would be in the shelter of the valleys, off the radar screens. But records had been hastily checked in Berne and the sombre voice came over to them again. The voice must have realized that the long debate would have been heard at every airport and by most pilots flying over Switzerland that evening. It was extremely polite, but firm. 'FL-BGS, we have no record at Federal Air Control of your proposed flight. I regret but you are transgressing Swiss air-space. Unless you can give further authority for your flight, kindly return to Zürich and report to Flying Control.'

The helicopter rocked. There was a flash of silver and a Dassault Mirage with Swiss markings flashed by not a hundred yards away, turned, leaving a trail of black vapour from the slow-burning of its fuel at this low altitude, and headed straight back at them, swerving off to port only at the last moment. The helicopter gave another lurch. The pilot spoke angrily into his mouthpiece. 'Federal Air Control. This is FL-BGS. For further information contact International Red Cross at Geneva. I am just a pilot. I am not a "rond de cuir", a chairborne flyer. If you have lost the papers, that is not my fault. I repeat check with Geneva. And, in the meantime, kindly call off the whole of the Swiss Air Force which is at present trying to make my passengers air-sick.' The voice came back, but now more faintly, because of the mountains. 'Who are your passengers?' The pilot played his trump card. 'Representatives of the world's press. They have been listening to all this nonsense coming from the home of the famous International Red Cross. I wish you happy reading of your newspapers at breakfast-time tomorrow, gentlemen. And now, a little peace, yes? And please record in your log-books that I am not, repeat, not, the Soviet Air Force invading Switzerland.'

There was silence. The Dassault Mirage had disappeared. They were climbing up the valley and were already past Davos. The gold-tipped needles of the glittering mountains seemed to be closing in on them from right and left. Ahead were the great peaks. Bond looked at his watch. Barely another ten minutes to go.

He turned and glanced down the hatch. The faces of Marc-Ange and of the others looked up at him, tense and livid under the setting sun that poured in through the windows, their eyes glinting redly.

Bond held up his thumb encouragingly. He spread out his ten fingers in their thin leather gloves.

Marc-Ange nodded. There was a shifting of the bodies in their seats. Bond turned back and gazed ahead, looking for the soaring peak that he loathed and feared.

Chapter Twenty-five

Hell's Delight, etc.

Yes! There was the bloody place! Now only the peak was golden. The plateau and the buildings were in indigo shadow, soon to be lit by the full moon.

Bond pointed. The helicopter wasn't liking the altitude. At 10,000 feet it rotors were finding it hard to get a grip of the thin air and the pilot was struggling to keep it at maximum revs. As he turned to port, in towards the face of the mountain, his radio crackled sharply and a harsh voice said, in German and then in French, 'Landing forbidden. This is private property. I repeat, landing forbidden!' The pilot reached up to the cockpit roof and switched off the radio. He had studied his landing-point on the plateau on the mock-up. He got to it, hovered and gently came down. The helicopter bounced once on its rubber floats and settled. Already there was a group of men waiting for them. Eight men. Bond recognized some of them. They all had their hands in their pockets or in their wind-jackets. The engine coughed to a stop and the rotors swung round briefly in neutral and halted. Bond heard the bang of the door being opened behind him and the rattle of the men piling down the ladder. The two groups lined up facing each other. Marc-Ange said, with authority, 'This is the Federal Police Alpine Patrol. There was trouble up here on Christmas Eve. We have come to investigate.'

Fritz, the 'head waiter', said angrily, 'The local police have already been here. They have made their report. All is in order. Please leave at once. What is the Federal Police Alpine Patrol? I have never heard of it.'

The pilot nudged Bond and pointed over to the left, to the building that housed the Count and the laboratories. A man, clumsy in bob-sleigh helmet and padding, was running down the path towards the cable station. He would be out of sight of the men on the ground. Bond said 'Blast!' and scrambled out of his seat and into the cabin. He leaned out of the door and shouted, 'The Big One. He's getting away!'

As Bond jumped, one of the SPECTRE men shouted, 'Der Engländer. Der Spion!' And then, as Bond started running away to the right, weaving and dodging, all hell broke loose. There came the boom of heavy automatics as the SPECTRE team got off their first rounds, and bullets, tracer, flashed past Bond with the noise of humming-birds' wings. Then came the answering roar of the Schmeissers and Bond was left alone.

Now he was round the corner of the club, and, a hundred yards down the slope, the man in the crash helmet had torn open the door of the 'garage' for the bob-sleighs in the foundations of the cable station. He emerged carrying a one-man skeleton bob. Holding it in front of him as a shield, he fired a burst from a heavy automatic at Bond and again the humming-birds whirred past. Bond knelt and, steadying his gun with two hands, fired three rounds with his Walther, but the man was now running the few yards to the glistening ice-mouth of the Gloria Express bob-run. Bond got a glimpse of the profile under the moon. Yes, it was Blofeld all right! Even as Bond ran on down the slope, the man had flung himself down on his skeleton and had disappeared as if swallowed up by the glistening landscape. Bond got to the 'garage'. Damn, they were all six-men or two-men models! No, there was one skeleton at the back! Bond hauled it out. No time to see if the runners were straight, the steering-arm shifting easily! He ran to the start and hurled himself under the protecting chain in a mad forward dive that landed him half on and half off his skeleton. He straightened himself and shifted his body well forward on the flimsy little aluminium platform and gripped the steering-arm, keeping his elbows well in to his sides. He was already going like hell down the dark-blue gutter! He tried braking with the toes of both his boots. Damned little difference! What came first on the blasted run? There was this lateral straight across the shoulder of the mountain, then a big banked curve. He was into it now! Bond kept his right shoulder down and inched right on the steering-arm. Even so, he went perilously near the top edge of the bank before he dived down into the dark gully again. What came next on that metal map? Why in hell hadn't he studied it more carefully? He got his answer! It looked like a straight, but the shadows camouflaged a sharp dip. Bond left the ground and flew. The crash of his landing almost knocked the wind out of his body. He frantically dug his toes into the ice, managed to get down from perhaps fifty m.p.h. to forty. Well, well! So that was 'Dead Man's Leap'. What in hell was the next bit of murder? 'Whizz-Bang Straight'! And by God it was!–200 yards when he must have been doing around seventy. He remembered that on the finishing straight of the Cresta the stars got up to over eighty. No doubt something like that was still to come! But now, flashing towards him, in silver and black, came an S-bend–'Battling S'. The toes of Bond's boots slid maddeningly on the black ice. Under his nose he could see the parallel tracks of Blofeld's runners and, between them, the grooves of his toe-spikes. The old fox! As soon as he heard the helicopter, he must have got himself fixed for his only escape route. But at this speed Bond must surely be catching up with him! For God's sake look out! Here comes the S! There was nothing he could do about it. He swayed his body as best he could, felt the searing crash of one elbow against one wall, was hurled across into the opposite one and was then spewed out into the straight again. God Almighty, but it hurt! He could feel the cold wind on both elbows. The cloth had gone! Then so had the skin! Bond clenched his teeth. And he was only half-way down, if that! But then, ahead, flashing through a patch of moonlight, was the other body, Blofeld! Bond took a chance, heaved himself up on one hand and reached down for his gun. The wind tried to tear him off the bob, but he had the gun. He opened his mouth wide and gripped the gun between his teeth, flexed the ice-caked leather on his right hand. Then he got the gun in his right hand, lifted his toes off the ice and went like hell. But now the man had disappeared into the shadows and a giant bank reared up ahead. This would be 'Hell's Delight'! Oh well, if he could make this, there would be another straight and he could begin shooting. Bond dug his toes in, got a glimpse of an ice-wall ahead and to the left, and in a flash was climbing it, straight up! God, in a split second he would be over the edge! Bond hammered in his right boot and lurched his body to the right, tearing at the steering-arm. Reluctantly the sliver of aluminium answered and Bond, inches from the top of the wall, found himself swooping down into blackness and then out again on to a moonlit straight. Only fifty yards ahead was the flying figure, with chips of ice fountaining up from the braking spikes on his boots. Bond held his breath and got off two shots. He thought they were good ones, but now the man had gone into shadow again. But Bond was gaining, gaining. His lips drew back from his teeth in an almost animal snarl. You bastard! You're a dead duck! You can't stop or fire back. I'm coming after you like lightning! Soon I shall only be ten, five yards behind you. Then you'll have had it!

But the shadows concealed another hazard, long traverse waves in the ice–'The Bone-shaker'! Bond crashed from one to the next, felt his boots being almost torn from his feet as he tried to brake, nearly lost his gun, felt his stomach flatten against his spine with each shattering impact, felt his rib cage almost cracking. But then it was over and Bond sucked in air through his clenched teeth. Now for a length of straight! But what was that ahead on the track? It was something black, something the size of a big lemon that was bouncing along gaily like a child's rubber ball. Had Blofeld, now only about thirty yards ahead, dropped something, a bit of his equipment? *Had he*? The realization came to Bond in a surge of terror that almost made him vomit. He ground his toes into the ice. No effect! He was gaining on the gaily bouncing thing. Flashing down on it. On the grenade!

Bond, sick in the stomach, lifted his toes and let himself go. What setting had Blofeld put on it? How long had he held it with the pin out? The only hope was to pray to God and race it!

The next thing Bond knew was that the whole track had blown up in his face and that he and his skeleton bob were flying through the air. He landed in soft snow, with the skeleton on tip of him and passed out like a light.

Later, Bond was to estimate that he lay there only a matter of minutes. It was a tremendous explosion from the mountain above him that brought him staggering to his feet, up to his belly in snow. He looked vaguely up to where it had come from. It must have been the club building going up, because now there was the glare of flames and a tower of smoke that rose towards the moon. There came the echoing crack of another explosion and Blofeld's block disintegrated, great chunks of it crashing down the mountain side, turning themselves into giant snowballs that bounded off down towards the tree-line. By God, they'll start another avalanche! thought Bond vaguely. Then he realized that it didn't matter this time, he was away to the right, almost underneath the cable railway. And now the station went up and Bond stared fascinated as the great wires, their tension released, came hissing and snaking down the mountain towards him. There was nothing he could do about it but stand and watch. If they cut him down, they cut him down. But they lashed past in the snow, wrapped themselves briefly round the tall pylon above the tree-line, tore it away in a metallic crackling, and disappeared over the edge of the shoulder.

Bond laughed weakly with pleasure and began feeling himself for damage. His torn elbows he already knew about, but his forehead hurt like hell. He felt it gingerly, then scooped up a handful of snow and held it against the wound. The blood showed black in the moonlight. He ached all over, but there didn't seem to be anything broken. He bent dazedly to the twisted remains of the skeleton. The steering-arm had gone, had probably saved his head, and both runners were bent. There were a lot of rattles from the rivets, but perhaps the damned thing would run. It had bloody well got to! There was no other way for Bond to get down the mountain! His gun? Gone to hell, of course. Wearily Bond heaved himself over the wall of the track and slid carefully down, clutching the remains of his skeleton. As soon as he got to the bottom of the gutter, everything began to slip downwards, but he managed to haul himself on to the bob and get shakily going. In fact, the bent runners were a blessing and the bob scraped slowly down, leaving great furrows in the ice. There were more turns, more hazards, but, at a bare ten miles an hour, they were child's play and soon Bond was through the tree-line and into 'Paradise Alley', the finishing straight, where he slowly came to a halt. He left the skeleton where it stopped and scrambled over the low ice-wall. Here the snow was beaten hard by spectators' feet and he stumbled slowly along, nursing his aches and occasionally dabbing at his head with handfuls of snow. What would he find at the bottom, by the cable station? If it was Blofeld, Bond would be a dead duck! but there were no lights on in the station into which the cables now trailed limply along the ground. By God, that had been an expensive bang! But what of Marc-Ange and his merry men, and the helicopter?

As if to answer him, he heard the clatter of its engine high up in the mountains and in a moment the ungainly black shape crossed the moon and disappeared down the valley. Bond smiled to himself. They were going to have a tough time arguing themselves across Swiss air space this time! But Marc-Ange had thought out an alternative route over Germany. That would also not be fun. They would have to argue the toss with NATO! Well, if a

Marseillais couldn't blarney his way across two hundred miles, nobody could!

And now, up the road from Samaden that Bond knew so well, came the iron hee-haw warning of the local fire-engine. The blinking red light on its cabin roof was perhaps a mile away. Bond, carefully approaching the corner of the darkened cable station, prepared his story. He crept up to the wall of the building and looked round. Nobody! No trace except fresh tyre-marks outside the entrance door. Blofeld must have telephoned his man down here before he started and used him and his car for the getaway. Which way had he gone? Bond walked out on to the road. The tracks turned left. Blofeld would be at the Bernina Pass or over it by now, on his way down into Italy and away. It might still have been possible to have him held at the frontier by alerting the fire-brigade, whose light now held Bond in their beam. No! That would be idiotic. How had Bond got this knowledge unless he himself had been up at Piz Gloria that night? No, he must just play the part of the stupidest tourist in the Engadine!

The shining red vehicle pulled up in front of the cable station and the warning klaxons ran down with an iron groan. Men jumped to the ground. Some went into the station while others stood gazing up at the Piz Gloria, where a dull red glow still showed. A man in a peaked cap, presumably the captain of the team, came up to Bond and saluted. He fired off a torrent of Schwyzerdütch. Bond shook his head. The man tried French. Bond again showed incomprehension. Another man with fragmentary English was called over. 'What is it that is happening?' he asked.

Bond shook his head dazedly. 'I don't know. I was walking down from Pontresina to Samaden. I came on a day excursion from Zürich and missed my bus. I was going to take a train from Samaden. Then I saw these explosions up the mountain–' he waved vaguely–'and I walked up there past the station to see better, and the next thing I knew was a bang on the head and being dragged along a path.' He indicated his bleeding head and the raw elbows that protruded from his torn sleeves. 'It must have been the broken cable. It must have hit me and dragged me with it. Have you got a Red Cross outfit with you?'

'Yes, yes.' The man called over to the group, and one of his colleagues wearing a Red Cross brassard on his arm fetched his black box from the vehicle and came over. He clucked his tongue over Bond's injuries and, while his interrogator told Bond's story to the Captain, bade Bond follow him into the toilette in the station. There, by the light of a torch, he washed Bond's wounds, applied quantities of iodine that stung like hell and then strapped wide strips of Elastoplast over the damage, Bond looked at his face in the mirror. He laughed. Hell of a bridegroom he was going to make! The Red Cross man cluck-clucked in sympathy, produced a flask of brandy out of his box and offered it to Bond. Bond gratefully took a long swig. The interpreter came in. 'There is nothing we can do here. It will need a helicopter from the mountain rescue team. We must go back to Samaden and report. You wish to come?'

'I certainly do,' said Bond enthusiastically, and, with many politenesses and no question of why he should attempt the icy walk to Samaden in the dark instead of taking a taxi, he was borne comfortably to Samaden and dropped off, with the warmest gestures of goodwill and sympathy, at the railway station.

By the rattling Personenzug to Coire and then by express to Zurich, Bond got to the door of the flat of Head of Station Z in the Bahnhofstrasse at two in the morning. He had had some sleep in the train but he was almost out on his feet, and his whole body felt as if it had been beaten with wooden truncheons. He leaned wearily against the bell ticketed 'Muir' until a tousled man in pyjamas came and opened the door and held it on the chain. 'Um Gottes Willen! Was ist denn los?' he inquired angrily. The English accent came through. Bond said, 'It's me that's "los". It's 007 again, I'm afraid.'

'Good God, man, come in, come in!' Muir opened the door and looked quickly up and down the empty street. 'Anyone after you?'

'Shouldn't think so,' said Bond thickly, coming gratefully into the warmth of the entrance hall. Head of Z closed the door and locked it. He turned and looked at Bond. 'Christ, old boy, what in hell's been happening to you? You look as if you'd been through a mangle. Here, come in and have a drink.' He led the way into a comfortable sitting-room. He gestured at the sideboard. 'Help yourself. I'll just tell Phyllis not to worry–unless you'd like her to have a look at the damage. She's quite a hand at that sort of thing.'

'No, it's all right, thanks. A drink'll fix me. Nice and warm in here. I never want to see a patch of snow again as long as I live.'

Muir went out and Bond heard a quick confabulation across the passage. Muir came back. 'Phyllis is fixing the spare room. She'll put some fresh dressings and stuff out in the bathroom. Now then–' he poured himself a thin whisky and soda to keep Bond company and sat down opposite him–'tell me what you can.'

Bond said, 'I'm terribly sorry, but I can't tell you much. The same business as the other day. Next chapter. I promise you'd do better to know nothing about it. I wouldn't have come here only I've got to get a signal off to M, personal, triple X cipher to be deciphered by recipient only. Would you be a good chap and put it on the printer?'

'Of course.' Muir looked at his watch. 'Two-thirty a.m. Hell of a time to wake the old man up. But that's your business. Here, come into the cockpit, so to speak.' He walked across to the book-lined wall, took out a book and fiddled. There was a click and a small door swung open. 'Mind your head,' said Muir. 'Old disused lavatory. Just the right size. Gets a bit stuffy when there's a lot of traffic coming or going, but that can't be helped. We can afford to leave the door open.' He bent down to a safe on the floor, worked the combination and brought out what looked like a portable typewriter. He set it on the shelf next to the bulky teleprinter, sat down and clacked off the prefix and routing instructions, winding a small handle at the side of the machine at the end of each word. 'O.K Fire away!'

Bond leaned up against the wall. He had toyed with various formulas on his journey down to Samaden. It had to be something that would get through accurately to M and yet keep Muir in the dark, keep his hands clean. Bond said, 'All right. Make it this, would you? REDOUBT PROPERLY FIXED STOP DETAILS LACKING AS EYE WENT SOLO AFTER THE OWNER WHO GREATLY REGRET GOT AWAY AND PROBABLY ITALICIZED BY NOW STOP FORWARDING FULL REPORT FROM STATION M THEN GRATEFULLY ACCEPTING TEN DAYS LEAVE SIGNED 007.'

Muir repeated the signal and then began putting it, in the five-figure groups that had come off the Triple X machine, on to the teleprinter.

Bond watched the message go, the end of another chapter of his duties, as

Marc-Ange had put it, 'On Her Majesty's Secret Service'. What would Her Majesty think of this string of crimes committed in her name? God, it was stuffy in the little room! Bond felt the cold sweat break out on his forehead. He put his hand up to his face, muttered something indistinctly about 'that bloody mountain' and gracefully crumpled to the floor.

Chapter Twenty-six

Happiness without a Shadow?

Tracy gazed at him wide-eyed when she met him outside Passport Control at Munich Airport, but she waited until they were inside the little Lancia before she burst into tears. 'What have they been doing to you?' she said through her sobs. 'What have they been doing to you now?'

Bond took her in his arms. 'It's all right, Tracy. I promise you. These are only cuts and bruises, like a bad ski-fall. Now don't be a goose. They could happen to anyone.' He smoothed back her hair and took out his handkerchief and dabbed at her eyes.

She took the handkerchief from him and laughed through her tears. 'Now you've ruined my eye-black. And I put it on so carefully for you.' She took out her pocket mirror and carefully wiped away the smudges. She said, 'It's so silly. But I knew you were up to no good. As soon as you said you were going off for a few days to clean up something instead of coming to me. I knew you were going to get into more trouble. And now Marc-Ange has telephoned and asked me if I've seen you. He was very mysterious and sounded worried. And when I said I hadn't he just rang off. And now there's this story in the papers about Piz Gloria. And you were so guarded on the telephone this morning. And from Zürich. I knew it all tied up.' She put back her mirror and pressed the self-starter. 'All right. I won't ask questions. And I'm sorry I cried.' She added fiercely, 'But you *are* such an idiot! You don't seem to think it matters to *anyone*. The way you go on playing Red Indians. It's so–so selfish.'

Bond reached out and pressed her hand on the wheel. He hated 'scenes'. But it was true what she said. He hadn't thought of her, only of the job. It never crossed his mind that anybody really cared about him. A shake of the head from his friends when he went, a few careful lines in the obituary columns of *The Times*, a momentary pang in a few girls' hearts. But now, in three days' time, he would no longer be alone. He would be a half of two people. There wouldn't only be May and Mary Goodnight who would tut-tut over him when he came back from some job as a hospital case. Now, if he got himself killed, there would be Tracy who would at any rate partially die with him.

The little car wove expertly through the traffic. Bond said, 'I'm sorry, Tracy. It was something that had to be done. You know how it is. I just couldn't back out of it. I really wouldn't have been happy here, like I am now, if I'd shirked it. You do see that, don't you?'

She reached out and touched his cheek. 'I wouldn't love you if you weren't a pirate. I expect it's in the blood. I'll get used to it. Don't change. I don't want to draw your teeth like women do with their men. I want to live with *you*, not with somebody else. But don't mind if I howl like a dog every now and then. Or rather like a bitch. It's only love.' She gave him a fleeting smile. '*Die Welt*, with the story in it, is behind the seat on the floor.'

Bond laughed at her mind-reading. 'Damn you, Tracy.' He reached for the paper. He had been aching to see what it said, how much had come out.

There it was, down the central gutter between the first lead, inevitably on Berlin, and the second, equally inevitably, on the miracle of the latest German export figures. All it said, 'from our correspondent', date-lined St Moritz, was 'MYSTERIOUS EXPLOSIONS ON PIZ GLORIA. Cable Railway to Millionaires' Resort Destroyed.' And then a few lines repeating the content of the headings and saying that the police would investigate by helicopter at first light in the morning. The next headline caught Bond's eye: 'IN ENGLAND, POLIO SCARE'. And then, date-lined the day before from London, a brief Reuter dispatch: 'The nine girls held at various British airports on suspicion of having had contact with a possible polio carrier at Zürich Airport, also an English girl, are still being held in quarantine. A Ministry of Health representative said that this was purely a routine precaution. A tenth girl, the origin of the scare, a Miss Violet O'Neill, is under observation at Shannon Hospital. She is a native of Eire.'

Bond smiled to himself. When they were pushed the British could do this sort of thing supremely well. How much co-ordination had this brief report required? To begin with, M. Then the C.I.D., M.I.5, Ag. and Fish., H.M. Customs, Passport Control, the Ministry of Health and the Government of Eire. All had contributed, and with tremendous speed and efficiency. And the end product, put out to the world, had been through the Press Association to Reuter. Bond tossed the paper over his shoulder and watched the Kaiser Yellow buildings of what had once been one of the most beautiful towns in Europe, now slowly being rebuilt in the same old Kaiser Yellow, file by in their post war drabness. So the case is closed, the assignment over!

But still The Big One had got away!

They got to the hotel at about three o'clock. There was a message for Tracy to call Marc-Ange at the Maison Rouge at Strasbourg. They went up to her room and got through. Tracy, said. 'Here he is, Papa, and almost in one piece.' She handed the receiver to Bond.

Marc-Ange said, 'Did you get him?'

'No, damn it. He's in Italy now. At least I think he is. That was the way he went. How did you get on? It looked fine from down below.'

'Satisfactory. All accounted for.'

'Gone?'

'Yes. Gone for good. There was no trace of your man from Zürich. I lost two. Our friend had left a surprise in his filing-cabinet. That accounted for Ché-Ché. Another one wasn't quick enough. That is all. The trip back was entertaining. I will give you the details tomorrow. I shall travel tonight in my sleeping-car. You know?'

'Yes. By the way, what about the girl friend, Irma?'

'There was no sign of her. Just as well. It would have been difficult to send her away like the others.'

'Yes. Well, thanks, Marc-Ange. And the news from England is also good.

See you tomorrow.'

Bond put down the receiver. Tracy had discreetly retired to the bathroom and locked the door. She now called, 'Can I come out?'

'Two minutes, darling.' Bond got on to Station M. His call was expected. He arranged to visit the Head of Station, a man he knew slightly called Lieutenant-Commander Savage, in an hour's time. He released Tracy and they made plans for the evening, then he went along to his room.

His suitcase had been unpacked and there was a bowl of crocuses beside his bed. Bond smiled, picked up the bowl and placed it firmly on the window-sill. Then he had a quick shower, complicated by having to keep his dressings dry, changed out of his stinking ski clothes into the warmer of the two dark-blue suits he had brought with him, sat down at the writing-desk and jotted down the headings of what he would have to put on the teleprinter to M. Then he put on his dark-blue raincoat and went down into the street and along to the Odeons Platz.

(If he had not been thinking of other things, he might have noticed the woman on the other side of the street, a squat, toad-like figure in a frowsty dark-green Loden cloak, who gave a start of surprise when she saw him sauntering along, hustled across the street through the traffic, and got on his tail. She was expert at what she was doing, and, when he went into the newish apartment house on the Odeons Platz, she didn't go near the door to verify the address, but waited on the far side of the square until he came out. Then she tailed him back to the Vier Jahreszeiten, took a taxi back to her flat and put in a long-distance call to the Metropole Hotel on Lake Como.)

Bond went up to his room. On the writing-desk an impressive array of dressing and medicaments had been laid out. He got on to Tracy and said, 'What the hell is this? Have you got a pass-key or something?'

She laughed. 'The maid on this floor has become a friend. She understands people who are in love. Which is more than you do. What do you mean by moving those flowers?'

'They're lovely. I thought they looked prettier by the window and they will get some sun there. Now I'll make a deal. If you'll come along and change my dressings, I'll take you down and buy you a drink. Just one. And three for me. That's the right ratio between men and women. All right?'

'Wilco.' Her receiver went down.

It hurt like hell and Bond couldn't prevent the tears of pain from squeezing out of his eyes. She kissed them away. She looked pale at what she had seen. 'You're sure you oughtn't to see a doctor?'

'I'm just seeing one. You did it beautifully. What worries me is how we're going to make love. In the proper fashion, elbows are rather important for the man.'

'Then we'll do it in an improper fashion. But not tonight, or tomorrow. Only when we're married. Till then I am going to pretend I'm a virgin.' She looked at him seriously. 'I wish I was, James. I am in a way, you know. People can make love without loving.'

'Drinks,' said Bond firmly. 'We've got all the time in the world to talk about love.'

'You *are* a pig,' she said indignantly. 'We've got so much to talk about and all you think about is drink.'

Bond laughed. He put an arm gingerly round her neck and kissed her long and passionately. He broke away. 'There, that's just the beginning of my conversation. We'll go on with the duller bits in the bar. Then we'll have a wonderful dinner in Walterspiel's and talk about rings and whether we'll sleep in twin beds or one, and whether I've got enough sheets and pillows for two, and other exciting things to do with being married.'

And it was in that way that the evening passed and Bond's head reeled with all the practical feminine problems she raised, in high seriousness, but he was surprised to find that all this nest-building gave him a curious pleasure, a feeling that he had at last come to rest and that life would now be fuller, have more meaning, for having someone to share it with. Togetherness! What a curiously valid cliché it was!

The next day was occupied with hilarious meals with Marc-Ange, whose giant trailer had come during the night to take up most of the parking space behind the hotel, and with searching the antique shops for an engagement and a wedding ring. The latter was easy, the traditional plain gold band, but Tracy couldn't make up her mind about the engagement ring and finally dispatched Bond to find something he liked himself while she had her last fitting for her 'going-away' dress. Bond hired a taxi, and he and the taxi-man, who had been a Luftwaffe pilot during the war and was proud of it, tore round the town together until, at an antique shop near the Nymphenburg Palace, Bond found what he wanted–a baroque ring in white gold with two diamond hands clasped. It was graceful and simple and the taxi-man was also in favour, so the deal was done and the two men went off to celebrate at the Franziskaner Keller, where they ate mounds of Weisswurst and drank four steins of beer each and swore they wouldn't ever fight each other again. Then, happy with his last bachelor party, Bond returned tipsily to the hotel, avoiding being embraced by the taxi-man and went straight up to Tracy's room and put the ring on her finger.

She burst into tears, sobbing that it was the most beautiful ring in the world, but when he took her in his arms she began to giggle. 'Oh, James, you are bad. You stink like a pig of beer and sausages. Where *have* you been?'

When Bond told her, she laughed at the picture he painted of his last fling and then paraded happily up and down the room, making exaggeratedly gracious gestures with her hand to show off the ring and for the diamonds to catch the light. Then the telephone rang and it was Marc-Ange saying that he wanted to talk to Bond in the bar, and would Tracy kindly keep out of the way for half an hour?

Bond went down and, after careful consideration, decided that schnapps would go with his beer and ordered a double Steinhäger. Marc-Ange's face was serious. 'Now listen, James. We have not had a proper talk. It is very wrong. I am about to become your father-in-law and I insist. Many months ago, I made you a serious offer. You declined it. But now you have accepted it. What is the name of your bank?'

Bond said angrily, 'Shut up, Marc-Ange. If you think I'll accept a million pounds from you or from anyone else you're mistaken. I don't want my life to be ruined. Too much money is the worst curse you can lay on anyone's head. I have enough. Tracy has enough. It will be fun saving up to buy something we want but can't quite afford. That is the only kind of money to have–not quite enough.'

Marc-Ange said furiously, 'You have been drinking. You are drunk. You don't understand what you are saying. What I am giving you is only a fifth of my fortune. You understand? It means nothing to me. Tracy is used to having whatever she wants. I wish it to remain so. She is my only child. You cannot possibly keep her on a Civil Servant's pay. You have got to accept!'

'If you give me any money, I swear I will pass it on to charity. You want to give your money away to a dogs' home? All right. Go ahead!'

'But James–' Marc-Ange was now pleading–'what will you accept from me? Then a trust fund for any children you may have. Yes?'

'Even worse. If we have children, I will not have this noose hung round their heads. I didn't have any money and I haven't needed it. I've loved winning money gambling because that is found money, money that comes out of the air like a great surprise. If I'd inherited money, I'd have gone the way of all those playboy friends of Tracy's you complained about so much. No, Marc-Ange.' Bond drained his Steinhäger decisively. 'It's no good.'

Marc-Ange looked as if he would burst into tears. Bond relented. He said, 'It's very kind of you, Marc-Ange, and I appreciate it from the heart. I'll tell you what. If I swear to come to you if either of us ever needs help, will that do? There may be illnesses and things. Perhaps it would be nice if we had a cottage in the country somewhere. We may need help if we have children. Now. How about that? Is it a bargain?'

Marc-Ange turned doubtful, dogs' eyes on Bond. 'You promise? You would not cheat me of helping you, adding to your happinesss when you allow me to?'

Bond reached over and took Marc-Ange's right hand and pressed it. 'My word on it. Now come on, pull yourself together. Here comes Tracy. She'll think we've been having a fight.'

'So we have,' said Marc-Ange gloomily. 'And it is the first fight I have ever lost.'

Chapter Twenty-seven

All the Time in the World

'I do.'

James Bond said the words at ten-thirty in the morning of a crystal-clear New Year's Day in the British Consul General's drawing-room.

And he meant them.

The Consul General had proved himself, as British Consuls so often do, to be a man of efficiency and a man with a heart. It was a holiday for him and, as he confessed, he should have been recovering from a New Year's Eve hangover. And he had shaved many days off the formal period of notice, but that, he explained, he had occasionally, and improperly, risked in his career if there were exceptional circumstances such as the imminent death of either party. 'You both look healthy enough,' he had said when they first visited him together, 'but that's a nasty cut on your head, Commander Bond, and the Countess is perhaps looking a little pale. And I have taken the precaution of obtaining special dispensation from the Foreign Secretary, which I may say, to my surprise, was immediately forthcoming. So let's make it New Year's Day. And come to my home. My wife is hopelessly sentimental about these occasional jobs I have to do, and I know she'd love to meet you both.'

The papers were signed, and Head of Station M, who had agreed to act as Bond's best man and who was secretly longing to write a sensational note to the head of his London Section about all this, produced a handful of confetti and threw most of it over Marc-Ange, who had turned up in a 'cylindre' and a full suit of very French tails with, surprisingly, two rows of medals of which the last, to Bond's astonishment, was the King's Medal for foreign resistance-fighters.

'I will tell you all about it one day, my dear James,' he had said in answer to Bond's admiring inquiry. 'It was tremendous fun. I had myself what the Americans call "a ball". And–' his voice sank to a whisper and he put one finger along his brown, sensitive nose–'I confess that I profited by the occasion to lay my hands on the secret funds of a certain section of the Abwehr. But Herkos Odonton, my dear James! Herkos Odonton! Medals are so often just the badges of good luck. If I am a hero, it is for things for which no medals are awarded. And–' he drew lines with his fingers across his chest–'there is hardly room on the breast of this "frac", which, by the way, is by courtesy of the excellent Galeries Barbès in Marseilles, for all that I am due under that heading.'

The farewells were said and Bond submitted himself, he swore for the last time, to Marc-Ange's embraces and they went down the steps to the waiting Lancia. Someone, Bond suspected the Consul's wife, had tied white ribbons from the corners of the wind-screen to the grill of the radiator, and there was a small group of bystanders, passers-by, who had stopped, as they do all over the world, to see who it was, what they looked like.

The Consul General shook Bond by the hand. 'I'm afraid we haven't managed to keep this as private as you'd have liked. A woman reporter came on from the *Münchener Illustrierte* this morning. Wouldn't say who she was. Gossip-writer, I suppose. I had to give her the bare facts. She particularly wanted to know the time of the ceremony, if you can call it that, so that they could send a camera-man along. At least you've been spared that. All still tight, I suppose. Well, so long and the best of luck.'

Tracy, who had elected to 'go away' in a dark-grey Tyroler outfit with the traditional dark-green trimmings and stag's-horn buttons, threw her saucy mountaineer's hat with its gay chamois' beard cockade into the back seat, climbed in and pressed the starter. The engine purred and then roared softly as she went through the gears down the empty street. They both waved one hand out of a window and Bond, looking back, saw Marc-Ange's 'cylindre' whirling up into the air. There was a small flutter of answering hands from the pavement and then they were round the corner and away.

When they found the Autobahn exit for Salzburg and Kufstein, Bond said, 'Be an angel and pull in to the side, Tracy. I've got two things to do.'

She pulled in on to the grass verge. The brown grass of winter showed through the thin snow. Bond reached for her and took her in his arms. He kissed her tenderly. 'That's the first thing, and I just wanted to say that I'll look after you, Tracy. Will you mind being looked after?'

She held him away from her and looked at him. She smiled. Her eyes were introspective. 'That's what it means being Mr and Mrs, doesn't it? They don't say Mrs and Mr. But *you* need looking after too. Let's just look after each other.'

'All right. But I'd rather have my job than yours. Now. I simply must get out and take down those ribbons. I can't stand looking like a coronation. D'you mind?'

She laughed. 'You like being anonymous. I want everyone to cheer as we go by. I know you're going to have this car sprayed grey or black as soon as you get a chance. That's all right. But nothing's going to stop me wearing you like a flag from now on. Will you sometimes feel like wearing me like a flag?'

'On all holidays and feast days.' Bond got out and removed the ribbons. He looked up at the cloudless sky. The sun felt warm on his face. He said, 'Do you think we'd be too cold if we took the roof down?'

'No, let's. We can only see half the world with it up. And it's a lovely drive from here to Kitzbühel. We can always put it up again if we want to.'

Bond unscrewed the two butterfly nuts and folded the canvas top back behind the seats. He had a look up and down the Autobahn. There was plenty of traffic. At the big Shell station on the roundabout they had just passed, his eye was caught by a bright-red open Maserati being tanked up. Fast job. And a typical sporty couple, a man and a woman in the driving-seat–white dust-coats and linen helmets buttoned under the chin. Big dark-green talc goggles that obscured most of the rest of the faces. Usual German speedsters' uniform. Too far away to see if they were good-looking enough for the car, but the silhouette of the woman wasn't promising. Bond got in beside Tracy and they set off again down the beautifully landscaped road.

They didn't talk much. Tracy kept at about eighty and there was wind-roar. That was the trouble about open cars. Bond glanced at his watch. 11.45. They would get to Kufstein at about one. There was a splendid Gasthaus up the winding streets towards the great castle. Here was a tiny lane of pleasure, full of the heart-plucking whine of zither music and the gentle melancholy of Tyrolean yodellers. It was here that the German tourist traditionally stopped after his day's outing into cheap Austria, just outside the German frontier, for a last giant meal of Austrian food and wine. Bond put his mouth up close to Tracy's ear and told her about it and about the other attraction at Kufstein–the most imaginative war memorial, for the 1914–18 war, ever devised. Punctually at midday every day, the windows of the castle are thrown open and a voluntary is played on the great organ inside. It can be heard for kilometres down the valley between the giant mountain ranges for which Kufstein provides the gateway. 'But we shall miss it. It's coming up for twelve now.'

'Never mind,' said Tracy, 'I'll make do with the zithers while you guzzle your beer and schnapps.' She turned in to the right-hand fork leading to the underpass for Kufstein, and they were at once through Rosenheim and the great white peaks were immediately ahead.

The traffic was much sparser now and there were kilometres where theirs was the only car on the road that arrowed away between white meadows and larch copses, towards the glittering barrier where blood had been shed between warring armies for centuries. Bond glanced behind him. Miles away down the great highway was a speck of red. The Maserati? They certainly hadn't got much competitive spirit if they couldn't catch the Lancia at eighty! No good having a car like that if you didn't drive it so as to lose all other traffic in your mirror. Perhaps he was doing them an injustice. Perhaps they too only wanted to motor quietly along and enjoy the day.

Ten minutes later, Tracy said, 'There's a red car coming up fast behind. Do you want me to lose him?'

'No,' said Bond. 'Let him go. We've got all the time in the world.'

Now he could hear the rasping whine of the eight cylinders. He leaned over to the left and jerked a laconic thumb forwards, waving the Maserati past.

The whine changed to a shattering roar. The wind-screen of the Lancia disappeared as if hit by a monster fist. Bond caught a glimpse of a taut, snarling mouth under a syphilitic nose, the flash-eliminator of some automatic gun being withdrawn, and then the red car was past and the Lancia was going like hell off the verge across a stretch of snow and smashing a path through a young copse. Then Bond's head crashed into the wind-screen frame and he was out.

When he came to, a man in the khaki uniform of the Autobahn Patrol was shaking him. The young face was stark with horror. 'Was ist denn geschehen? Was ist denn Geschehen?'

Bond turned towards Tracy. She was lying forward with her face buried in the ruins of the steering-wheel. Her pink handkerchief had come off and the bell of golden hair hung down and hid her face. Bond put his arm round her shoulders, across which the dark patches had begun to flower.

He pressed her against him. He looked up at the young man and smiled his reassurance.

'It's all right,' he said in a clear voice as if explaining something to a child. 'It's quite all right. She's having a rest. We'll be going on soon. There's no hurry. You see–'Bond's head sank down against hers and he whispered into her hair–'you see, we've got all the time in the world.'

The young patrolman took a last scared look at the motionless couple, hurried over to his motor cycle, picked up the hand-microphone and began talking urgently to the rescue headquarters.